Glencoe Life Science
Features and Benefits

S0-BBZ-542

		Pages
Dynamic Instructional Strategies	... **present clear and comprehensive coverage of middle school science.**	
	■ Each engaging chapter opener includes a *Launch Lab* and *Foldables*™.	5
	■ *National Geographic Visualizing* features illustrate important concepts in middle school science.	48–49
A Strong Reading Strand	... **encourages active reading and learning for students of all reading levels. In the *Student Edition*:**	
	■ **as you read** gives students a preview of learning objectives and vocabulary for each section;	66
	■ *Reading Checks* help students check their reading comprehension; and	125
	■ *Caption questions* ask students to interpret visuals.	165
	■ *Reading Essentials, An Interactive Student Textbook* is designed to help struggling readers comprehend core content. It is written at a reading level of about two to three grades below the *Student Edition*.	194
Meeting the Needs of All Students	... **facilitates understanding of science concepts for students of all learning levels. In the *Teacher Wraparound Edition*:**	
	■ *Differentiated Instruction* strategies help meet the needs of students with learning disabilities and physical challenges, or create opportunities to enrich and extend students' learning;	218
	■ *Daily Intervention* provides intervention strategies for struggling students; and	245
	■ *Identifying Misconceptions* helps uncover and address common science misconceptions.	282
	■ The *English/Spanish Glossary*, also in the *Student Edition*, helps English-language learners comprehend science terms.	854–893
Extensive Standardized Test Practice	... **gives students the opportunity to practice for state and national exams.**	
	■ Each chapter ends with a variety of standardized test practice questions, including *Multiple Choice, Short Response/Grid In*, and *Open Ended*.	356–357
A Variety of Labs	... **gets students excited about being involved in science. The *Student Edition* provides:**	
	■ *MiniLABs,* traditional labs, and *Design Your Own, Model and Invent,* and *Use the Internet* labs; and	372, 379, 384
	■ *Extra Try at Home Labs* provide opportunities for students to practice their science skills at home with adult supervision using materials from the kitchen, junk drawer, or backyard.	814–827
	■ *Virtual Labs* CD-ROM contains an interactive virtual lab for each chapter.	405
	■ *Video Labs* (VHS) reinforce lab techniques and safety skills, offer troubleshooting tips, and give expected outcomes.	438
	■ The *Science Lab Manual, Probeware Lab Manual,* and *Science Inquiry Lab Manual* provide additional opportunities to practice laboratory techniques.	
Multi-Level Review	... **presents multiple opportunities for all students to review and master content.**	
	■ Each section ends with a review that contains a *Summary* of the section's major concepts and a *Self Check* that has questions to assess student learning and practice math or science skills.	461
	■ The *Study Guide* at the end of each chapter can preview, review, summarize, and visualize the chapter's main ideas.	505
	■ *Study Guide* and *Reinforcement* help students grasp core content.	
Teacher Resources	... **provide innovative strategies to help new and experienced teachers.**	
	■ *Chapter Resources Fast File* ™ contains important reproducible masters.	510B
	■ Section Focus, Assessment, and Teaching transparencies accompany each chapter.	510C
	■ *Performance Assessment in the Science Classroom* has assessment guidelines, strategies, sample rubrics, and more.	
Online Resources	... **enrich the learning experience with the click of a mouse.**	
	■ For prescreened Web links, standardized test practice, self-check quizzes, chapter tests, *Vocabulary PuzzleMaker*, extra math practice, science career information, current science news, and *WebQuest* interactive projects, visit **life.msscience.com**.	
	■ The complete interactive *Student Edition* is available at The *McGraw-Hill Learning Network* Web site, **mhln.com**.	
Technology	... **provides timesaving products to help teachers creatively engage their students.**	
	■ *MindJogger Videoquizzes* (VHS & DVD) provide a game-show style interactive quiz for each chapter.	
	■ Easy to edit *Interactive Chalkboard* Microsoft® PowerPoint® presentations include step-by-step lessons, an image bank, chapter and section review questions, standardized test practice, and transparencies.	
	■ *ExamView® Pro Testmaker* CD-ROM in English or Spanish allows you to customize assessments.	
	■ *TeacherWorks* CD-ROM is your all-in-one resource center that helps you plan and organize lessons.	
	■ *StudentWorks* CD-ROM solves the heavy backpack problem.	

SAFETY SYMBOLS

SAFETY SYMBOLS	HAZARD	EXAMPLES	PRECAUTION	REMEDY
DISPOSAL	Special disposal procedures need to be followed.	certain chemicals, living organisms	Do not dispose of these materials in the sink or trash can.	Dispose of wastes as directed by your teacher.
BIOLOGICAL	Organisms or other biological materials that might be harmful to humans	bacteria, fungi, blood, unpreserved tissues, plant materials	Avoid skin contact with these materials. Wear mask or gloves.	Notify your teacher if you suspect contact with material. Wash hands thoroughly.
EXTREME TEMPERATURE	Objects that can burn skin by being too cold or too hot	boiling liquids, hot plates, dry ice, liquid nitrogen	Use proper protection when handling.	Go to your teacher for first aid.
SHARP OBJECT	Use of tools or glassware that can easily puncture or slice skin	razor blades, pins, scalpels, pointed tools, dissecting probes, broken glass	Practice common-sense behavior and follow guidelines for use of the tool.	Go to your teacher for first aid.
FUME	Possible danger to respiratory tract from fumes	ammonia, acetone, nail polish remover, heated sulfur, moth balls	Make sure there is good ventilation. Never smell fumes directly. Wear a mask.	Leave foul area and notify your teacher immediately.
ELECTRICAL	Possible danger from electrical shock or burn	improper grounding, liquid spills, short circuits, exposed wires	Double-check setup with teacher. Check condition of wires and apparatus.	Do not attempt to fix electrical problems. Notify your teacher immediately.
IRRITANT	Substances that can irritate the skin or mucous membranes of the respiratory tract	pollen, moth balls, steel wool, fiberglass, potassium permanganate	Wear dust mask and gloves. Practice extra care when handling these materials.	Go to your teacher for first aid.
CHEMICAL	Chemicals can react with and destroy tissue and other materials	bleaches such as hydrogen peroxide; acids such as sulfuric acid, hydrochloric acid; bases such as ammonia, sodium hydroxide	Wear goggles, gloves, and an apron.	Immediately flush the affected area with water and notify your teacher.
TOXIC	Substance may be poisonous if touched, inhaled, or swallowed.	mercury, many metal compounds, iodine, poinsettia plant parts	Follow your teacher's instructions.	Always wash hands thoroughly after use. Go to your teacher for first aid.
FLAMMABLE	Flammable chemicals may be ignited by open flame, spark, or exposed heat.	alcohol, kerosene, potassium permanganate	Avoid open flames and heat when using flammable chemicals.	Notify your teacher immediately. Use fire safety equipment if applicable.
OPEN FLAME	Open flame in use, may cause fire.	hair, clothing, paper, synthetic materials	Tie back hair and loose clothing. Follow teacher's instruction on lighting and extinguishing flames.	Notify your teacher immediately. Use fire safety equipment if applicable.

 Eye Safety Proper eye protection should be worn at all times by anyone performing or observing science activities.

 Clothing Protection This symbol appears when substances could stain or burn clothing.

 Animal Safety This symbol appears when safety of animals and students must be ensured.

 Handwashing After the lab, wash hands with soap and water before removing goggles.

Teacher Wraparound Edition

Glencoe Science

Life Science

NATIONAL GEOGRAPHIC

life.msscience.com

Glencoe

New York, New York   Columbus, Ohio   Chicago, Illinois   Peoria, Illinois   Woodland Hills, California

Glencoe Science

Life Science

About the Cover Photo: The Indo-Chinese tigers found in Thailand are very similar to Bengal tigers, but are slightly smaller and darker with shorter, narrower stripes. In Thailand, there are less than 600 in the wild. Their habitat is remote forests that are commonly hilly and mountainous.

 **Glencoe**

The **McGraw·Hill** Companies

Send all inquiries to:
Glencoe/McGraw-Hill
8787 Orion Place
Columbus, OH 43240-4027

ISBN 0-07-861702-2 (Student Edition)
ISBN 0-07-861703-0 (Teacher Wraparound Edition)

Printed in the United States of America.

4 5 6 7 8 9 10 027/043 09 08 07 06

Authors

NATIONAL GEOGRAPHIC
Education Division
Washington, D.C.

Lucy Daniel, EdD
Teacher/Consultant
Rutherford County Schools
Rutherfordton, NC

Peter Rillero, PhD
Associate Professor of
Science Education
Arizona State University West
Phoenix, AZ

Alton Biggs
Retired Biology Teacher
Allen High School
Allen, TX

Edward Ortleb
Science Consultant
St. Louis, MO

Dinah Zike
Educational Consultant
Dinah-Might Activities, Inc.
San Antonio, TX

Science Consultants

CONTENT

Sandra K. Enger, PhD
Associate Director,
Associate Professor
UAH Institute for Science Education
Huntsville, AL

Michael A. Hoggarth, PhD
Department of Life and Earth
Sciences
Otterbein College
Westerville, OH

Jerome A. Jackson, PhD
Whitaker Eminent Scholar in Science
Program Director
Center for Science, Mathematics,
and Technology Education
Florida Gulf Coast University
Fort Meyers, FL

Connie Rizzo, MD, PhD
Depatment of Science/Math
Marymount Manhattan College
New York, NY

Dominic Salinas, PhD
Middle School Science Supervisor
Caddo Parish Schools
Shreveport, LA

Series Consultants

MATH

READING

Michael Hopper, DEng
Manager of Aircraft Certification
L-3 Communications
Greenville, TX

Teri Willard, EdD
Mathematics Curriculum Writer
Belgrade, MT

Elizabeth Babich
Special Education Teacher
Mashpee Public Schools
Mashpee, MA

Barry Barto
Special Education Teacher
John F. Kennedy Elementary
Manistee, MI

Carol A. Senf, PhD
School of Literature,
Communication, and Culture
Georgia Institute of Technology
Atlanta, GA

Rachel Swaters-Kissinger
Science Teacher
John Boise Middle School
Warsaw, MO

SAFETY

Aileen Duc, PhD
Science 8 Teacher
Hendrick Middle School, Plano ISD
Plano, TX

Sandra West, PhD
Department of Biology
Texas State University-San Marcos
San Marcos, TX

ACTIVITY TESTERS

Nerma Coats Henderson
Pickerington Lakeview Jr. High
School
Pickerington, OH

Mary Helen Mariscal-Cholka
William D. Slider Middle School
El Paso, TX

**Science Kit and Boreal
Laboratories**
Tonawanda, NY

Series Reviewers

Deidre Adams
West Vigo Middle School
West Terre Haute, IN

Sharla Adams
IPC Teacher
Allen High School
Allen, TX

Maureen Barrett
Thomas E. Harrington Middle
School
Mt. Laurel, NJ

John Barry
Seeger Jr.-Sr. High School
West Lebanon, IN

Desiree Bishop
Environmental Studies Center
Mobile County Public Schools
Mobile, AL

William Blair
Retired Teacher
J. Marshall Middle School
Billerica, MA

Tom Bright
Concord High School
Charlotte, NC

Lois Burdette
Green Bank Elementary-Middle
School
Green Bank, WV

Marcia Chackan
Pine Crest School
Boca Raton, FL

Obioma Chukwu
J.H. Rose High School
Greenville, NC

Karen Curry
East Wake Middle School
Raleigh, NC

Inga Dainton
Merrilville High School
Merrilville, IN

Joanne Davis
Murphy High School
Murphy, NC

Robin Dillon
Hanover Central High School
Cedar Lake, IN

Anthony J. DiSipio, Jr.
8th Grade Science
Octorana Middle School
Atglen, PA

Annette D'Urso Garcia
Kearney Middle School
Commerce City, CO

Dwight Dutton
East Chapel Hill High School
Chapel Hill, NC

Carolyn Elliott
South Iredell High School
Statesville, NC

Sueanne Esposito
Tipton High School
Tipton, IN

Sandra Everhart
Dauphin/Enterprise Jr. High Schools
Enterprise, AL

Mary Ferneau
Westview Middle School
Goose Creek, SC

Cory Fish
Burkholder Middle School
Henderson, NV

Teacher Advisory Board

The Teacher Advisory Board gave the editorial staff and design team feedback on the content and design of the Student Edition. They provided valuable input in the development of the 2005 edition of *Glencoe Life Science.*

John Gonzales
Challenger Middle School
Tucson, AZ

Rachel Shively
Aptakisic Jr. High School
Buffalo Grove, IL

Roger Pratt
Manistique High School
Manistique, MI

Kirtina Hile
Northmor Jr. High/High School
Galion, OH

Marie Renner
Diley Middle School
Pickerington, OH

Nelson Farrier
Hamlin Middle School
Springfield, OR

Jeff Remington
Palmyra Middle School
Palmyra, PA

Erin Peters
Williamsburg Middle School
Arlington, VA

Rubidel Peoples
Meacham Middle School
Fort Worth, TX

Kristi Ramsey
Navasota Jr. High School
Navasota, TX

Student Advisory Board

The Student Advisory Board gave the editorial staff and design team feedback on the design of the Student Edition. We thank these students for their hard work and creative suggestions in making a more friendly edition of 2005 *Glencoe Life Science.*

Jack Andrews
Reynoldsburg Jr. High School
Reynoldsburg, OH

Peter Arnold
Hastings Middle School
Upper Arlington, OH

Emily Barbe
Perry Middle School
Worthington, OH

Kirsty Bateman
Hilliard Heritage Middle School
Hilliard, OH

Andre Brown
Spanish Emersion Academy
Columbus, OH

Chris Dundon
Heritage Middle School
Westerville, OH

Ryan Manafee
Monroe Middle School
Columbus, OH

Addison Owen
Davis Middle School
Dublin, OH

Teriana Patrick
Eastmoor Middle School
Columbus, OH

Ashley Ruz
Karrer Middle School
Dublin, OH

The Glencoe middle school science Student Advisory Board taking a timeout at COSI, a science museum in Columbus, Ohio.

Teacher Handbook

Table of Contents

Dynamic Instruction

The consistent instructional strategies in each chapter strengthen students' learning—from the beginning of each chapter where students see "Chapter Preview," to the end where they have a chance to test the knowledge they have acquired and prepare for the next lesson.

Dinah Zike's Foldables™ let students create interactive study guides.

Launch Lab gives students an opportunity to explore new ideas at the beginning of the chapter.

Chapter Preview at the beginning of each chapter introduces the main concepts.

Science Journal promotes writing and critical-thinking skills.

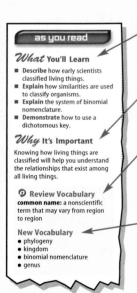

What You'll Learn at the beginning of each section introduces the main concepts.

Why It's Important provides an answer to "Why do we have to learn this?"

Review Vocabulary reviews a term that helps students better understand section content.

New Vocabulary highlights new terms students will learn in the section.

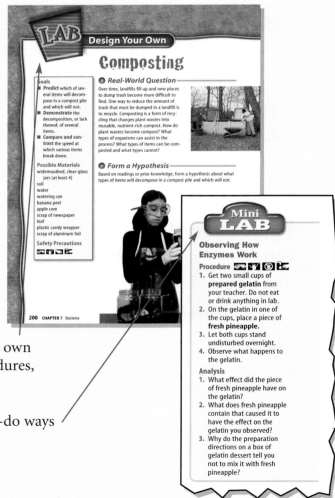

Labs Whether students are designing their own experiments or following well-tested procedures, they'll learn and practice science processes.

MiniLABS offer students quick and easy-to-do ways to clarify concepts and reinforce skills.

Multi-Level Review and Assessment

Each chapter provides five pages of review and testing to help you evaluate students' knowledge and ability to apply science concepts.

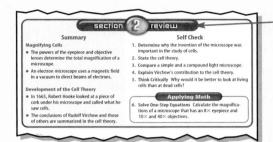

Section Review
- Summary pinpoints important concepts in the section
- Skill-based questions promote critical thinking skills.

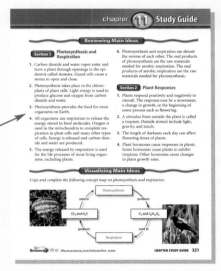

Study Guide
- Main idea summary of each section
- Concept mapping activity to help students visualize the main ideas

Chapter Review
- Using Vocabulary
- Checking Concepts
- Thinking Critically
- Performance Activities
- Applying Math

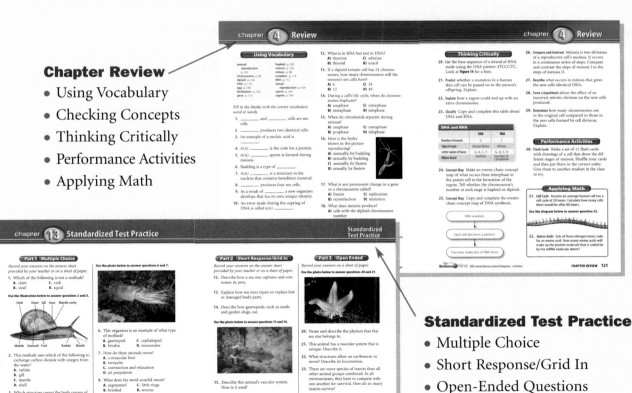

Standardized Test Practice
- Multiple Choice
- Short Response/Grid In
- Open-Ended Questions

Time-Saving Teacher Resources

Glencoe Science provides an extensive array of support materials and resources designed to help you create and customize your science course quickly and easily.

FAST FILE Chapter Resources

For each chapter, Chapter Resources contain key reproducible masters along with additional teaching strategies, teacher support, and answer keys.

Reproducible Student Resources include:

- Worksheets for all MiniLABs and Labs
- *Directed Reading for Content Mastery* (in English and Spanish), *Reinforcement* and *Enrichment* worksheets for each chapter
- *Section Focus, Teaching,* and *Assessment Transparencies* masters
- Chapter Review and Chapter Test masters

Teacher Support and Planning includes:

- Additional student preparation materials for each chapter
- Spanish Resources provide translations of all objectives, vocabulary, and main ideas
- Answer keys and teaching strategies

Teacher Wraparound Edition

The *Teacher Wraparound Edition* is your key to the teaching resources available. In addition to teaching strategies and suggestions, the *Teacher Wraparound Edition* provides a guide for all print and software materials available for each lesson.

Transparencies

- Section Focus Transparency
- Assessment Transparency
- Teaching Transparency
- Transparency masters and worksheets

Exam*View*® Pro Testmaker CD-ROM

- Create, edit, and customize tests
- Create multiple versions of tests
- Translate tests from English to Spanish and vice versa
- Build tests aligned with state standards

Video Labs

- Step-by-step lab procedures for selected *Student Edition* labs
- Lab safety skills
- Teacher support
- Troubleshooting advice

Technology Support

This CD-ROM is your all-in-one resource center. Personalize a lesson plan, access resources from the *Teacher Wraparound Edition,* connect to the Internet, or make a to-do list. These are only a few of the many features that can assist you in the planning and organizing of your lessons.

Includes:

- A calendar feature
- Access to all program blackline masters
- Standards correlations and more

This CD-ROM is a valuable resource for students to access content online and use online resources to continue learning chapter concepts.

🎧 Guided Reading Audio Program has been updated to StudentWorks Plus™

Includes:

- Complete *Student Edition* on CD-ROM
- Links to online activities and resources
- Access to all student worksheets

INTERACTIVE CHALKBOARD
with Image Bank

This CD-ROM brings Microsoft® Powerpoint® presentations right to your door. With the large number of graphics provided, students can use a visual approach to learning chapter content.

Includes:

- A pre-made presentation for every chapter
- Image bank and interactive graphics
- Animations and audio clips
- All new section and chapter questions
- Standardized test practice
- Transparencies
- Foldables™ directions
- Links to life.msscience.com

💿 Virtual Labs CD-ROM Program

The Virtual Labs CD-ROM contains a collection of labs that allow students to complete labs that are too dangerous, too expensive, or take too long to complete in a classroom laboratory.

life.msscience.com

For students:

- Prescreened Internet sites (Web links) that correlate to text chapters
- Interactive activities that review chapter concepts
- Internet Labs where students can share data with each other
- Access to *Student Edition* online
- Interactive self-check quizzes for each chapter section as well as the entire chapter

For teachers:

- *WebQuest* activities
- Teacher Forum for teachers to share activities and ideas

 **Learning Network** mhln.com

mhln.com is an online teaching and learning space for teachers, students, and parents.

- For students, mhln.com provides an interactive online textbook. This means a lighter student backpack.
- For teachers, mhln.com provides a customizable online learning space for posting assignments, web-based instruction, student resources, and a class calendar.
- For parents, mhln.com provides tools to help their child succeed in school. Parents have instant access to their child's progress and daily assignments.

Help Your Students with Reading and Writing

Glencoe Science increases science literacy, improves reading comprehension, and deepens students' understanding of ideas and concepts. The reading strategies are active, constructive, and engaging.

In the Student Edition

Reading Checks stimulate quick recall and keep students focused on the main idea.

Caption Questions offer a visual approach to learning. Students are asked to recall what they have read by interpreting the visual.

> **Figure 4** The cell plate shown in this plant cell appears when the cytoplasm is being divided.
> **Identify** *the next phase of mitosis.*

Science Journals provide opportunities to write responses to questions that require critical thinking, to conduct research and write about it, or to practice creative writing skills.

Skill Words such as *compare and contrast, describe, explain,* and *state* are included in the Self Check at the end of each section, in the goals of each Lab, and in the chapter reviews.

Technology Support

Vocabulary PuzzleMaker allows you to create crossword puzzles, jumble puzzles, or word searches in minutes to review chapter vocabulary. The puzzles can be printed or played on the computer screen.

Guided Reading Audio Program (available on MP3-formatted CD-ROMs) provides a comprehensive overview in Spanish and English for auditory learners, students with reading difficulties, and English-language learners (ELL).

In the Teacher Edition

Project CRISS™ (**C**reating **I**ndependence through **S**tudent-Owned **S**trategies) strategies are highlighted in the Unit Openers where an activity is supplied that relates to unit content. For more information about Project CRISS™, visit **www.projectcriss.com**.

Use Science Words features encourage students to look up biology terms. Use these as a pre-reading activity, or have students keep a vocabulary journal.

> **Use Science Words**
> **Word Usage** The distinction between distance and displacement can be confusing. Have students use each of these words correctly in a sentence. Possible response: When I go to school and then back home, my displacement is zero, even though the distance from home to school is 2 km.

Additional Science Journal writing activities promote writing and critical thinking skills and extend the Student Edition journaling activity.

Active Reading Strategies utilize a variety of learning styles, and encourage cooperative learning and intrapersonal reflection on chapter content.

Additional Teacher Resources

Reading Essentials provides summaries of each section of the textbook, focusing on the most important scientific concepts.

Reading and Writing in the Science Classroom provides teachers with effective strategies for building students' skills in reading and writing about science.

Making Concept Maps and Charts

Bubble Map Students brainstorm and organize words in clusters to describe concepts.

Flow Chart Students logically analyze and draw a sequence of events.

Cause-and-Effect Chart Students visually represent the causes and effects of an event or process.

Supporting-Idea Chart Students make a concept map to analyze relationships between a whole and its parts.

Network-Tree Concept Map Students show a hierarchy and use branching procedures.

Events-Chain Concept Map Students order steps or stages in a linear procedure.

Cycle Concept Map Students show how a series of events interact.

Spider Concept Map Students use for brainstorming and grouping nonrelated terms to a central idea.

Using the Science Journal

Double-Reference Journal Students read and record ideas.

Metacognition Students analyze what and how they have learned.

Learning Journal Students create notes and reflect on the content.

Problem-Solution Journal Students analyze problems and suggest workable solutions.

Speculation About Effects/Prediction Journal Students examine events and speculate about their possible long-term effects.

Synthesis Journal Students reflect on a project, a paper, or a performance task and plan how to apply what they have learned to their own lives.

Reflective Journal Students identify what they learned in an activity and record responses.

Quickwrites Students use spontaneous writing to discover what they already know.

Collaborative Learning Strategies

Pair of Pairs Partners respond to a question and compare their response to other pairs and to the class.

Write-Draw-Discuss Students write about and draw a picture of a concept, then share it with the class.

Active Reading

Learning Reading Have students divide a sheet of paper in half. Have them record research notes, lecture notes, and vocabulary terms related to the laws of motion in the left column. Tell them to use the right column to respond, interpret, question, and analyze left-column entries. L2 **Intrapersonal**

Four-Corner Discussion The class works in four groups to debate a complex issue.

Jigsaw Students work in groups to become experts on a portion of text and share what they've learned with the class.

Buddy Interviews Students interview one another to find out what strategies they use to learn the text.

Reciprocal Teaching Students take turns reading a section of text, retelling it in their own words, then asking questions about it.

News Summary Students are given several minutes to summarize, retell, or analyze an activity for a "TV" audience.

ReQuest The teacher reads aloud an article or story. Student pairs then construct discussion questions and review the content.

Reading and Writing

Foldables™

Foldables™ are easy-to-make, three-dimensional, interactive graphic organizers that students create out of simple sheets of paper. These unique hands-on tools for studying and reviewing were created exclusively for Glencoe by education specialist Dinah Zike.

Research Behind Foldables™

According to research (Bransford, 1979; Corno, 1994), study strategies help students understand, organize, remember and apply new information presented in science textbooks. Some study strategies include concept mapping, highlighting, outlining, note taking, summarizing, and underlining (Peverly, Brobst, Graham & Shaw, 2003). Glencoe Science offers Dinah Zike's Foldables™ Study Organizers as an organizational tool and study guide for students.

Build Prereading Skills

- Encourages students to prepare for what they will be learning
- Gives students an opportunity to recall what they already know about a subject

Encourage Active Reading and Writing

- Practices basic reading and writing skills
- Develops skills in finding and reporting main ideas
- Organizes information
- Reviews key vocabulary terms

Summarize Content for Review

- Creates a comprehensive, interactive snapshot of the chapter
- Provides preparation support for chapter, unit, and end-of-course exams, as well as standardized tests

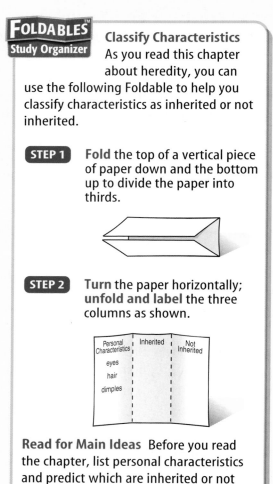

FOLDABLES™ Study Organizer

Classify Characteristics As you read this chapter about heredity, you can use the following Foldable to help you classify characteristics as inherited or not inherited.

STEP 1 **Fold** the top of a vertical piece of paper down and the bottom up to divide the paper into thirds.

STEP 2 **Turn** the paper horizontally; **unfold and label** the three columns as shown.

Personal Characteristics | Inherited | Not Inherited
eyes
hair
dimples

Read for Main Ideas Before you read the chapter, list personal characteristics and predict which are inherited or not inherited. As you read the chapter, check and change your list.

Dinah Zike's *Teaching Science with Foldables*™

- Comprehensive presentations of Foldables™ instructions
- More ideas on how to incorporate Foldables™ into your lessons
- Easy-to-read folding instruction pages in color

Course Planning Guide

Glencoe Science programs provide a complete selection of core concepts that can be presented in a way that meets the needs of all your students. As the teacher, you are in the best position to design a science course that sets the pace at which the content is covered and determines what material should be given the most emphasis. To assist you in planning the course, the following Course Planning Guide is provided.

The chart shown below offers general suggestions for pacing your students through the book. Pacing for both standard class periods and block schedule class periods is given. The total number of days in each level of pacing is the typical 180-day school year and 90-day semester.

Chapter	Single-Class (180 days)	Block (90 days)
1	8	4
2	7	3.5
3	7	3.5
4	7	3.5
5	7	3.5
6	7	3.5
7	5	2.5
8	7	3.5
9	7	3.5
10	7	3.5
11	5	2.5
12	7	3.5
13	9	4.5
14	9	4.5
15	5	2.5
16	5	2.5
17	7	3.5
18	5	2.5
19	7	3.5
20	5	2.5
21	5	2.5
22	7	3.5
23	7	3.5
24	7	3.5
25	7	3.5
26	7	3.5
27	7	3.5

Assessment

Glencoe Science offers the Glencoe Assessment Advantage, a system designed to give you all the tools you need to prepare your students for success in any testing situation.

In the Student Edition

Section Review, Applying Skills, and **Applying Math** questions appear in every chapter.

Chapter Review questions help you evaluate students' knowledge and ability to apply science concepts.

Standardized Test Practice questions at the end of each chapter provide students with additional opportunities to practice their test-taking skills.

In the Teacher Wraparound Edition

Assessments located throughout the *Teacher Wraparound Edition* provide methods for assessing students' comprehension with Performance, Process, and Content exercises.

Teacher Classroom Resources

Performance Assessment in the Science Classroom
- Guidelines for assessing the performance of a task
- Reproducible activities for evaluating students
- Sample rubrics and checklists

Fast File Chapter Resources provides six pages of assessment for every chapter including *Testing Concepts, Applying Concepts,* and *Writing Skills.*

Technology Support

MindJogger Videoquizzes are interactive video quizzes set in game show format. Each is designed for the full range of student learning styles.

ExamView® Pro Testmaker CD-ROM for Windows® and Macintosh® provides an easy way to create, edit, and customize your tests. Select your own test items by objective from two different levels of difficulty, or write and edit your own. Translate tests from English to Spanish and vice versa.

Rubrics

The following rubrics are sample scoring devices for short response and open-ended questions.

Short Response

Points	Description
2	The student demonstrates a thorough understanding of the science of the task. The response may contain minor flaws that do not detract from the demonstration of a thorough understanding.
1	The student has provided a response that is only partially correct.
0	The student has provided a completely incorrect solution or no response at all.

Open Ended

Points	Description
4	The student demonstrates a thorough understanding of the science of the task. The response may contain minor flaws that do not detract from the demonstration of a thorough understanding.
3	The student demonstrates an understanding of the science of the task. The response is essentially correct and demonstrates an essential but less than thorough understanding of the science.
2	The student demonstrates only a partial understanding of the science of the task. Although the student may have used the correct approach to a solution or may have provided a correct solution, the work lacks an essential understanding of the underlying science concepts.
1	The student demonstrates a very limited understanding of the science of the task. The response is incomplete and exhibits many flaws.
0	The student provides a completely incorrect solution or no response at all.

Assessment

Educational Partnerships

NATIONAL GEOGRAPHIC

Some topics in the chapter either require or benefit from a larger, more detailed visual explanation. The National Geographic Society has created *Visualizing* features that call out an important concept from the chapter and illustrate it in a way that will inform, excite, and motivate your students.

TIME magazine brings science topics and history together to further explain the chapter's main ideas and show how science relates to real life.

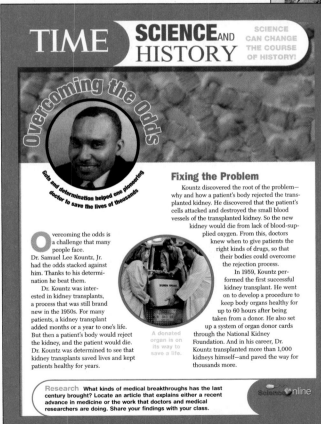

Differentiated Instruction

Teaching Strategies

Following each suggested assessment and activity, ability levels are supplied to accommodate all students.

- **LS** Multiple Learning Styles logos are used throughout the text to indicate strategies that address different learning styles.
- **L1** Level 1 activities should be appropriate for students with learning difficulties.
- **L2** Level 2 activities should be within the ability range of all students.
- **L3** Level 3 activities are designed for above-average students.
- **ELL** English-Language Learners activities should be within the ability range of English-Language Learners or students who speak English as a second language (ESL).
- **COOP LEARN** Cooperative Learning activities are designed for small group work.
- **PBL** Problem-Based Learning activities apply real-world situations to learning.
- **P** Portfolio strategies represent student products that can be placed into a best-work portfolio.

Identifying Misconceptions

These short, diagnostic, and perscriptive lessons target common science misconceptions.

Necessary Metals Students may think it strange that metals are needed by the body. Explain that the metals calcium, potassium, and sodium, for example, help transmit electrical signals within the nervous system.

Multiple Learning Styles

Look for these italicized designations under various activities to help you target your lessons to each student's preferred learning style.

- *Kinesthetic* learners learn through touch, movement, and manipulating objects.
- *Visual-Spatial* learners think in terms of images, illustrations, and models.
- *Interpersonal* learners understand and work well with other people.
- *Intrapersonal* learners can analyze their own strengths and weaknesses and may prefer to work on their own.
- *Linguistic* learners write clearly and easily understand the written word.
- *Logical-Mathematical* learners understand numbers easily and have highly-developed reasoning skills.

Daily Interventions

Found at the end of each chapter section, this feature is designed to intercept students who are struggling and prescribe a system to help them get back on track. Reteach provides reinforcement of the section's concepts through visual activities.

DAILY INTERVENTION

Shaky Construction Have students use information from this section to make a time line that shows major Earth events during the mesozoic and Cenozoic Eras. Some students might want to add small sketches at various places along the timeline, illustrating the events. **LS** **Linguistics**

Differentiated Instruction

These activities present various teaching strategies designed to help you meet the special needs of students with learning disabilities, physical challenges, visual impairment, and hearing impairment. Challenge activities provide opportunities for students who excel to engage in activities and research projects that extend the chapter's concepts. English-language learners in the classroom will also find exercises that bridge the gap between language barriers and the chapter content.

Differentiated Instruction

English-Language Learners Have students make flashcards with the name of a gland on one side and the hormone it produces on the other. Student pairs can quiz each other using the flashcards.

Cultural Diversity

These readings provide insights into the unique ways in which people of different ethnicities and cultural heritage have approached science. The intent of these features is to build awareness and appreciation for the global community in which we live.

Cultural Diversity

Tsunami! Tsunamis occur in many areas around the world and have been reported since ancient times. One of the earliest record tsunamis struck Syria around 2,000 B.C. Thera, one of the Cyclades Islands in the Mediterranean, may be the remnant of a volcano that erupted—causing tsunamis that ended the Minoan civilization on Crete. Tsunami is a Japanese word for "harbor wave." Many have struck the Japanese shore. Because Japan is an island nation, the threat of tsunamis is a national safety concer. Today, by using expected tsunami characteristics, the Japan Meteorological Agency can forecast tsunami heights for the Japanese coastline. This provides residents with the knowledge necessary to move a safe distance away from the shore.

Inquiry-Based Science

The call for more inquiry-based science by the *National Science Education Standards* has been met by Glencoe Science.

Glencoe Science recognizes the importance of conducting inquiry-based science activities in the classroom. The process of doing inquiry models actual science practice, encouraging problem-solving strategies and developing critical thinking skills. Inquiry gets students actively involved in the learning process by allowing them to determine materials, procedures, or the topics and questions they want to investigate.

Inquiry can range from a very structured activity for those students who need more guidance to a more open-ended approach where students lead the investigations. Glencoe Science recognizes that the inquiry activities suggested will not look the same in every classroom. We encourage teachers to modify the suggested activities in a manner that best supports your students.

Glencoe also provides teachers with Alternative Inquiry Labs, teaching strategies or suggestions for making existing labs more inquiry-based.

Alternative Inquiry Lab

Extend the Experience To make this Lab an Inquiry Lab, have students examine the magnetic field around the motor, using a compass or iron fillings. Test the armature and rotor before final assembly, as it will be difficult to fit the compass inside the motor. Encourage students to make various adaptations to the motor. Ask them to figure out how to make the motor spin the other way, spin faster, and spin slower. How could the motor be turned into a generator? How could they make the motor consume less power? Finally, students might research how these issues are handled by industry or other questions they find interesting.

Research-Based Learning Strategies

Glencoe Science incorporates the most current and applicable educational research on science learning and follows recommendations from the American Association for the Advancement of Science and the National Science Teachers Association. The following research-based strategies can be found throughout the text.

Learning Strategies

The following research-based strategies can be found throughout the text:

- **Using Prior Knowledge** Glencoe Science encourages students to use their prior knowledge to learn information because this adds relevance to the material. Students are referred back to other parts of the text or to their own real-life experiences.

- **Practicing Important Tasks** By offering students an opportunity to practice important tasks using a variety of labs and activities in the *Student Edition, Teacher Wraparound Edition,* ancillaries and technology, Glencoe Science makes learning fun and relevant for students.

- **Using Visuals to Communicate, Organize, and Reinforce Learning** High-quality art and photos throughout the text communicate concepts more efficiently and reinforce learning, while allowing students to organize information.

White Paper

The Glencoe Science White Paper outlines the educational strategies on which this program was based. This document provides specific examples from the *Student Edition, Teacher Wraparound Edition,* ancillary program, and technology resources, highlighting extensive use of educationally sound strategies that help students learn science.

- **Motivating Students to Achieve** Active strategies and real-world experiences motivate students to achieve. Throughout Glencoe's programs, students are encouraged to apply their knowledge in ways that will motivate them to learn.

- **Developing Decoding and Reading Comprehension Strategies** Throughout the text, students are supplied with caption questions, reading checks, and other strategies to aid in comprehension.

- **Using Study Strategies** Through the use of highlighting, outlining, note-taking, summarizing, and other such strategies, students can monitor their own progress and organize information more effectively, thereby increasing their scientific literacy. These strategies are found throughout the text and ancillaries.

The use of these strategies within Glencoe Science will help teachers to achieve the goals set forth by the *National Science Education Standards.*

Glencoe Life Science, Earth Science, and Introduction to Physical Science

Field Research and Testing

Feedback from students, teachers, curriculum supervisors, department chairpersons, parents, learning specialists, and science content experts was invaluable in the development of this program. The following pre-publication and post-publication research was conducted.

Prior to Publication

- Detailed classroom teacher and curriculum supervisor **surveys** were conducted by independently contracted researchers.
- A **nationwide panel** of science teachers, curriculum supervisors, and department chairpersons provided countless hours of feedback and assistance throughout program development.
- A wide range of **educator and content reviewers** provided in-depth reviews of and suggestions for manuscripts and pre-publication versions of the program.
- **Face-to-face interviews** with science teachers provided insight into teachers' day-to-day challenges.

After Publication

- Field tests were conducted in which student and teachers used a pre-publication manuscript in the classroom.
- Follow-up interviews, observations, and surveys of Glencoe Science users provide ongoing opportunities for program develop ment and verification of program success.

Field-Test Results

- Field-test research indicates that test scores increased among students using Glencoe Science programs.
- Nine out of ten students earned higher scores after using Glencoe programs.
- Scores improved among both male and female students.
- Scores improved among both minority and non-minority students.
- Overall, the gap between the average pre-test score and a perfect score closed by 33 percent. Stated differently, on average, **scores increased 77 percent after students used the Glencoe program.**

KS Studios

National Education Standards

Correlation of *Glencoe Life Science* to the National Science Education Standards.

Science Standard	Chapter and Section
(UCP) Unifying Concepts and Processes	
1. Systems, order, and organization	1-1, 1-2, 1-3, 1-4, 2-1, 2-2, 2-3, 3-1, 3-2, 3-3, 4-1, 4-2, 4-3, 5-1, 5-2, 5-3, 6-1, 6-2, 6-3, 7-1, 8-1, 8-2, 10-1, 10-2, 10-3, 11-1, 11-2, 12-1, 13-1, 13-2, 13-3, 13-4, 14-1, 14-2, 14-3, 14-4, 15-1, 15-2, 16-1, 16-2, 17-1, 17-2, 17-3, 18-1, 18-2, 19-1, 19-2, 19-3, 20-1, 20-2, 21-1, 21-2, 22-1, 22-2, 22-3, 24-1, 24-2, 24-3, 25-1, 25-2, 26-1, 26-2, 26-3
2. Evidence, models, and explanation	1-1, 2-2, 1-3, 1-4, 2-1, 2-2, 2-3, 3-1, 3-2, 3-3, 4-1, 4-2, 4-3, 5-1, 5-2, 5-3, 6-1, 6-2, 6-3, 7-1, 8-1, 8-2, 9-3, 10-1, 10-2, 10-3, 11-1, 11-2, 12-1, 12-2, 12-3, 13-1, 13-2, 13-4, 14-1, 14-2, 14-3, 14-4, 15-1, 15-2, 16-1, 16-2, 17-1, 17-2, 17-3, 18-1, 19-1, 19-2, 19-3, 20-1, 20-2, 21-1, 21-2, 22-1, 22-2, 22-3, 23-1, 23-2, 23-3, 24-1, 24-2, 24-3, 25-1, 25-2, 26-1, 26-2, 26-3, 27-1, 27-2, 27-3
3. Change, constancy, and measurement	1-1, 1-2, 1-3, 1-4, 2-1, 2-2, 3-1, 3-2, 3-3, 4-3, 5-1, 5-2, 5-3, 6-1, 6-2, 6-3, 8-1, 8-2, 10-1, 10-2, 11-1, 11-2, 12-1, 13-1, 13-2, 13-4, 14-1, 14-2, 14-3, 14-4, 15-1, 15-2, 16-1, 16-2, 17-1, 17-2, 17-3, 19-1, 19-2, 19-3, 20-1, 20-2, 21-1, 21-2, 22-1, 22-2, 22-3, 24-1, 24-2, 24-3, 25-1, 25-2, 26-1, 26-2, 26-3, 27-1, 27-2, 27-3
4. Evolution and equilibrium	4-3, 5-2, 5-3, 6-1, 6-2, 6-3, 8-1, 14-1, 14-2, 14-3, 14-4, 15-1, 16-1, 16-2, 19-3, 24-2, 24-3, 25-1, 26-1
5. Form and function	1-1, 1-2, 1-3, 1-4, 2-1, 2-2, 2-3, 3-1, 3-2, 3-3, 4-3, 5-1, 5-2, 5-3, 6-1, 6-2, 6-3, 7-1, 7-2, 8-1, 8-2, 9-1, 9-2, 9-3, 10-1, 10-2, 10-3, 11-1, 11-2, 12-1, 12-2, 12-3, 13-1, 13-2, 13-3, 13-4, 14-2, 14-3, 14-4, 15-1, 15-2, 17-1, 17-2, 17-3, 19-1, 19-2, 19-3, 20-1, 20-2, 21-1, 21-2, 22-1, 22-2, 22-3, 23-1, 23-2, 23-3, 24-2, 24-3, 25-2, 26-1, 26-2, 26-3
(A) Science as Inquiry	
1. Abilities necessary to do scientific inquiry	1-1, 1-2, 1-3, 1-4, 2-1, 2-2, 2-3, 3-1, 3-2, 3-3, 4-1, 4-2, 4-3, 5-1, 5-2, 5-3, 6-2, 6-3, 7-1, 7-2, 8-1, 8-2, 9-1, 9-2, 9-3, 10-1, 10-2, 10-3, 11-1, 11-2, 12-1, 12-2, 12-3, 13-1, 13-2, 13-3, 13-4, 14-1, 14-2, 14-3, 14-4, 15-1, 15-2, 16-1, 16-2, 17-1, 17-2, 17-3, 18-1, 18-2, 19-1, 19-2, 19-3, 20-1, 20-2, 21-1, 21-2, 22-1, 22-2, 22-3, 23-1, 23-2, 23-3, 24-1, 24-2, 24-3, 25-1, 25-2, 26-1, 26-2, 26-3, 27-1, 27-2, 27-3
2. Understandings about scientific inquiry	1-1, 1-2, 1-3, 1-4, 2-1, 2-2, 2-3, 3-1, 3-2, 4-1, 4-3, 5-1, 5-2, 5-3, 6-1, 6-2, 6-3, 7-1, 8-1, 8-2, 9-1, 10-1, 10-2, 10-3, 11-1, 11-2, 12-2, 12-3, 13-1, 13-2, 13-3, 13-4, 14-1, 14-2, 14-3, 14-4, 15-1, 15-2, 16-1, 16-2, 17-1, 17-2, 17-3, 18-1, 18-2, 19-1, 19-2, 19-3, 20-1, 20-2, 21-1, 21-2, 22-1, 22-2, 22-3, 23-1, 23-3, 24-1, 24-2, 24-3, 25-1, 25-2, 26-1, 26-2, 26-3, 27-1, 27-2, 27-3
(B) Physical Science	
1. Properties and changes of properties in matter	3-1, 18-2
2. Motions and forces	17-2, 22-3
3. Transfer of energy	17-2, 18-1, 18-2, 25-1, 25-2, 25-3
(C) Life Science	
1. Structure and function in living systems	1-2, 1-3, 2-1, 2-2, 2-3, 3-1, 3-2, 3-3, 4-1, 4-2, 4-3, 5-1, 5-2, 5-3, 6-1, 6-3, 7-1, 8-1, 9-1, 9-2, 9-3, 10-1, 10-2, 10-3, 11-1, 11-2, 12-1, 12-2, 12-3, 13-1, 13-2, 13-3, 13-4, 14-1, 14-2, 14-3, 14-4, 15-1, 17-1, 17-2, 17-3, 18-1, 18-2, 19-1, 19-2, 19-3, 20-1, 20-2, 21-1, 21-2, 22-1, 22-2, 22-3, 23-1, 23-2, 23-3, 24-2, 24-3, 25-2, 25-3, 26-1, 26-2, 26-3
2. Reproduction and heredity	1-2, 2-3, 4-1, 4-2, 4-3, 5-1, 5-2, 5-3, 7-1, 8-1, 9-1, 9-2, 9-3, 10-1, 10-2, 10-3, 12-2, 13-1, 13-2, 13-3, 13-4, 14-1, 14-2, 14-3, 14-4, 15-1, 16-2, 17-1, 17-2, 17-3, 22-1, 22-2, 23-1, 23-2, 23-3, 24-1, 24-2, 24-3
3. Regulation and behavior	1-2, 2-1, 3-2, 4-1, 4-2, 4-3, 7-1, 7-2, 8-1, 9-1, 9-2, 9-3, 11-1, 11-2, 12-1, 12-2, 12-3, 13-1, 13-2, 13-3, 13-4, 14-1, 14-2, 15-1, 16-1, 17-2, 17-3, 18-1, 18-2, 19-1, 19-2, 19-3, 20-1, 20-2, 21-1, 21-2, 22-1, 22-2, 22-3, 23-1, 23-2, 23-3, 24-2, 25-2, 26-1, 26-2, 26-3
4. Populations and ecosystems	6-1, 7-1, 7-2, 8-1, 9-1, 9-2, 9-3, 10-3, 12-2, 12-3, 15-1, 16-2, 24-2, 24-3, 25-1, 25-2, 26-1, 26-2, 26-3
5. Diversity and adaptations of organisms	1-4, 2-3, 4-2, 6-1, 6-3, 7-1, 7-2, 8-1, 9-1, 9-2, 9-3, 10-1, 10-2, 10-3, 11-2, 12-1, 12-2, 12-3, 13-2, 13-3, 13-4, 14-1, 14-2, 14-3, 14-4, 15-1, 16-1, 16-2, 17-1, 17-2, 17-3, 18-1, 18-2, 19-1, 19-2, 19-3, 21-1, 21-2, 22-1, 22-2, 22-3, 23-1, 23-2, 23-3, 24-2, 24-3, 25-2, 25-3, 26-3
(D) Earth and Space Science	
1. Structure of the Earth system	25-1, 25-2, 25-3
2. Earth's history	6-2
3. Earth in the solar system	25-1

Science Standard	Chapter and Section
(E) Science and Technology	
1. Abilities of technological design	7-2
2. Understandings about science and technology	7-2
(F) Science in Personal and Social Perspectives	
1. Personal health	5-2, 6-2, 7-2, 8-2, 14-2, 15-2, 17-1, 17-2, 17-3, 18-1, 18-2, 21-1, 23-1, 23-2, 23-3
2. Populations, resources, and environments	2-3, 10-3, 26-3, 27-1, 27-2, 27-3
3. Natural hazards	5-3, 21-1, 23-3, 24-2, 24-3
4. Risks and benefits	7-2, 13-3, 14-4, 23-2
5. Science and technology in society	5-3, 7-2, 14-4, 23-2, 23-3
(G) History and Nature of Science	
1. Science as a human endeavor	3-3, 5-2, 6-1, 6-3, 9-2, 17-3, 18-2, 19-3, 23-3
2. Nature of science	1-1, 3-3, 5-1, 6-1, 6-2, 6-3, 9-2, 10-3, 12-1, 17-3, 18-2, 23-1, 23-3
3. History of science	1-3, 1-4, 2-2, 2-3, 3-3, 5-1, 6-1, 6-3, 9-2, 10-3, 16-2, 19-3, 20-2

How Glencoe Science Aligns with the National Science Education Standards

The correlations at the left show the close alignment between Glencoe Science and the grade-appropriate standards. Glencoe Science allows students to discover concepts within each of the content standards and gives students opportunities to make connections among the science disciplines. Hands-on activities and inquiry-based lessons reinforce the science processes emphasized in the standards.

How Glencoe Science Aligns with the NCTM Standards for Grades 6–8

Throughout Glencoe Science, each Applying Math activity provides students with the opportunity to practice and apply some of the mathematical concepts and applications described in the NCTM Standards. These activities serve to reinforce mathematical skills in real-life situations, thus preparing students to meet their needs in an ever-changing world.

Correlation of *Glencoe Life Science* to NCTM Standards Grades 6–8

Math Standard	Page
1. Number and Operations	33, 44, 72, 91, 121, 131, 149, 179, 235, 290, 297, 313, 323, 347, 355, 374, 389, 404, 451, 477, 487, 507, 535, 563, 609, 617, 623, 677, 707, 716, 735, 756, 797
2. Algebra	33, 44, 91, 179, 235, 290, 297, 347, 374, 609, 716, 756, 797
3. Geometry	44, 487, 839, 840, 841
4. Measurement	33, 44, 61, 535, 716, 756
5. Data Analysis and Probability	33, 91, 131, 149, 179, 205, 235, 267, 297, 313, 323, 389, 423, 451, 477, 507, 535, 563, 589, 617, 677, 716, 735, 797
6. Problem Solving	44, 91, 121, 205, 267, 347, 355, 423, 535, 609, 677, 707, 716, 735, 765
7. Reasoning and Proof	404, 707
8. Communication	310, 501, 643
9. Connections	33, 44, 61, 72, 91, 121, 131, 149, 179, 205, 235, 290, 297, 313, 323, 347, 374, 355, 389, 451, 477, 535, 563, 609, 617, 623, 716, 735, 756, 797
10. Representation	131, 716

Learning in the Laboratory

In the Student Edition

Working in the lab is perhaps the most exciting part of science. Labs and MiniLABs give your students the hands-on opportunity to create, investigate, and explore science. Students will learn new material, while having fun.

Traditional Labs provide guided inquiry as students hypothesize, plan investigations, and collect and analyze data.

Design Your Own Labs challenge students to design their own experiments that will provide answers to lab problems.

Model and Invent Labs allow students to create a model or invent a product that can demonstrate scientific concepts.

Use the Internet Labs help students share and retrieve data from others around the country and world, by posting data they have collected on life.msscience.com. These activities show students the possible range of data, importance of collecting large amounts of data, and data analysis.

MiniLABs and **Applying Science** activities are a quick way for students to practice specific process skills as they learn science concepts. Many of them can be classroom demonstrations or homework assignments.

Extra Try at Home Labs reinforce chapter content while providing students more opportunities to practice laboratory techniques. They are written for performance at home, but can be used in the classroom.

In the Teacher Wraparound Edition

Quick Demos allow students to visualize biology concepts.

Inquiry Labs in each chapter can be used to support inquiry-based science or as alternatives to traditional labs.

Alternative Inquiry Labs offer a strategy to make many of the student labs more open-ended and inquiry-based. These labs can be used as explorations or as extensions before or after completion of the Student Edition lab.

Technology Support

Virtual Labs CD-ROM includes a collection of interactive activities involving major chapter themes that allow students to understand science concepts in a virtual setting. These labs provide a way to conduct experiments without classroom time, cost, and safety constraints.

Video Labs show students step-by-step lab procedures while emphasizing important lab safety skills. The lab videos also include teacher support, troubleshooting advice, and expected outcomes.

Additional Resources

Laboratory Activities offer a variety of traditional laboratory experiences that reinforce the science principles in the text. The *Teacher Wraparound Edition* provides full support.

Probeware Labs present activities for students to explore scientific concepts using a probeware data collection system. These hand-held systems provide a fast and simple way to collect, view, and analyze data in the classroom or during a field investigation. Integrating technology in the classroom is made simple with step-by-step instructions for setting up and using probeware.

Science Inquiry Lab Manual gives students the opportunity to become increasingly independent in stating hypotheses, designing and performing experiments, and collecting and analyzing data.

Safety in the Laboratory

All activities are designed to minimize dangers in the laboratory. Careful laboratory planning and management by both the instructor and the student are essential to a safe laboratory experience. **Local, state, and federal laboratory safety laws and regulations must be strictly followed.** The information provided here is one of the many resources to which you can refer for information about laboratory safety.

Classroom and Laboratory Preparation

1. Label and store chemicals properly and securely. See p. 20T.
2. Store equipment properly and securely and other thing.
   a. Clean and dry all equipment before storing.
   b. Protect electronic equipment and microscopes from dust, humidity, and extreme temperatures.
   c. Number, catalog, and organize equipment.
3. Ensure adequate work space for each student.
4. Ensure adequate classroom and storeroom ventilation.
5. Explain and post safety and evacuation guidelines along with expectations of conduct.
6. Ensure that all safety equipment is functioning properly and is clearly visible.
7. Provide hot plates as a heat source whenever possible. If gas burners are used, know where the central gas supply shutoff valve is located.
8. Ensure that each workstation has a GFCI-protected electrical source.
9. Provide safety goggles consistent with ANSI Standard Z87.1 for each student, including students who wear corrective lenses.

First Day of Class (with students)

1. Distribute and discuss safety rules, safety symbols, and first aid guidelines. Have students to review safety symbols and guidelines.
2. Review safe use of equipment and chemicals.
3. Review use and location of safety equipment.
4. Discuss safe disposal of materials and laboratory cleanup policy.
5. Discuss proper laboratory attitude and conduct.
6. Document students' understanding of the preceding points. Have students sign a safety contract and return it.

Before Each MiniLAB or Lab

1. Perform each investigation yourself before assigning it.
2. Arrange the lab in such a way that equipment and supplies are clearly labeled and easily accessible.
3. Have available only equipment and supplies needed to complete the assigned investigation.
4. Review the procedure with students, emphasizing any caution statements or safety symbols that appear.
5. Be sure all students know the proper procedures to follow if an accident should occur.
6. Provide containers for disposing of chemicals, waste products, and biological specimens. Disposal methods should meet local guidelines.

During the MiniLAB or Lab

1. Make sure the lab is clean and free of clutter.
2. Insist that students wear goggles and aprons.
3. Never allow a student to work alone in the lab.
4. Never allow students to use a cutting device with more than one edge.
5. Students should not point the open end of a heated test tube toward anyone.
6. Remove broken glassware or frayed cords from use. Also clean up any spills immediately. Dilute solutions with water before removing.
7. Be sure all glassware that is to be heated is of a heat-treated type that will not shatter.
8. Remind students that hot glassware looks cool.
9. Prohibit eating and drinking in the lab.

After the MiniLAB or Lab

1. Be sure that the lab is clean.
2. Be certain that students have returned all equipment and disposed of broken glassware and chemicals properly.
3. Be sure that all hot plates and electrical connections are off.
4. Insist that each student wash his or her hands when lab work is completed.

Chemical Storage and Disposal

General Guidelines

Be sure to store all chemicals properly. The following are guidelines commonly used. Your school, city, county, or state may have additional requirements for handling chemicals. It is the responsibility of each teacher to become informed of the rules or guidelines in effect in his or her area.

1. Separate chemicals by reaction type. Strong acids should be stored together. Likewise, strong bases should be stored together and should be separated from acids. Oxidants should be stored away from easily oxidized materials, and so on.

2. Be sure all chemicals are stored in labeled containers indicating contents, concentration, source, date purchased (or prepared), any precautions for handling and storage, and expiration date.

3. Dispose of any outdated or waste chemicals properly according to accepted disposal procedures.

4. Do not store chemicals above eye level.

5. Wood shelving is preferable to metal. All shelving should be firmly attached to the wall and should have anti-roll edges.

6. Store only those chemicals that you plan to use.

7. Hazardous chemicals require special storage containers and conditions. Be sure to know which chemicals those are and the accepted practices for your area. Some substances must be stored outside the building.

8. When working with chemicals or preparing solutions, observe the same general safety precautions that you would expect from students. These include wearing an apron and goggles. Wear gloves and use the fume hood when necessary. Students will want to do as you do whether they admit it or not.

9. If you are a new teacher in a particular laboratory, it is your responsibility to survey the chemicals stored there to be sure they are stored properly. If not, they should be disposed of. Consult the rules and laws in your area concerning which chemicals can be kept in your classroom. For disposal, consult up-to-date disposal information from state and federal governments.

Disposal of Chemicals

Local, state, and federal laws regulate the proper disposal of chemicals. These laws should be consulted before chemical disposal is attempted. Although many substances encountered in the science classroom can be flushed down the drain with plenty of water, it is not safe to assume that this is always true. Teachers who use chemicals should consult the following book from the National Research Council:

Prudent Practices in the Laboratory. Washington, DC: National Academy Press, 1995. This book is useful and was revised in 1995. Current laws in your area would, of course, supersede the information in this book.

DISCLAIMER

Glencoe Publishing Company makes no claims to the completeness of this discussion of laboratory safety and chemical storage. The material presented is not all-inclusive, nor does it address all of the hazards associated with handling, storing, and disposing of chemicals, or with laboratory management.

Clement Mok/PictureQuest

Preparation of Solutions

It is important to use safe laboratory techniques when handling all chemicals. Always check the MSDS (Material Safety Data Sheet) for each chemical before using it in the classroom. Many substances might appear harmless, but might be toxic, corrosive, or very reactive. Chemicals should never be ingested. Use proper techniques to smell any chemical, wear safety goggles and an apron in the laboratory, and observe the following precautions.

1. **Dilution of Acids and Bases** When diluting acids with water, always add the acids to the water. Never add water to acids. When sulfuric acid and sodium hydroxide are added to water, a large amount of thermal energy is released. Use extra care when handling these substances.

2. **Poisonous and Corrosive Liquids or Vapors** Use a fume hood if possible. Examples include hydrochloric acid, acetic acid, nitric acid, and ammonium hydroxide.

3. **Poisonous and Corrosive to Eyes, Lungs, and Skin** Examples include acids, bases, silver nitrate, iodine, and potassium permanganate.

Bromthymol blue: Add 0.5 g bromthymol blue powder to 500 mL distilled water to make a BTB stock solution. Dilute 40 mL BTB stock solution to 2 L with distilled water. Solution should be bright blue. If not, add one drop of NaOH at a time, swirling to mix. Check color.

Hydrochloric acid (HCL) solution: To make a 5% solution, add 13.6 mL concentrated HCl to 73 mL water while stirring. To make a $0.1M$ solution, add 1 mL concentrated hydrochloric acid to 100 mL water while stirring.

Iodine solution/Iodine stain: Dilute 1 part Lugol's solution with 15 parts water.

Lugol's solution: Dissolve 10 g potassium iodide in 100 mL distilled water. Then add and dissolve 5 g iodine. Store in dark bottle. Keeps indefinitely.

Phenolphthalein indicator: From a drug store, buy a package of any laxative that contains phenolphthalein. To make 1% solution, mash 4 tablets and pour the powder into 10 mL of rubbing alcohol. Let mixture soak for 15 minutes. Pour liquid into and store in a dropper bottle.

Potassium permanganate: For a $0.01M$ solution of potassium permanganate, dissolve 0.15 g $KMnO_4$ in 100 mL water.

Red cabbage concentrate: Put 5 leaves of red cabbage in a pot. Add 1 L of water, bring to a boil, and simmer until water turns a deep purple. Pour liquid through a strainer or piece of cheesecloth into a storage bottle. Keep refrigerated.

Salt solution: For a 3.5% salt (NaCl) solution that simulates the concentration of ocean water, dissolve 35 g of salt (NaCl) in 965 mL of water. For a 1% solution (weak), dissolve 1 g of salt (NaCl) in 99 mL of water. For a 6% solution, dissolve 6 g of salt (NaCl) in 94 mL of water.

Silver nitrate solution: To make a 10% solution, put 5 g of silver nitrate in 50 mL of distilled water.

Sugar solution: Add 1 tablespoon of sugar to 1 cup of warm water in a deep jar or flask. Stir to dissolve.

Sodium hydroxide (dilute): To make a 1% solution, dissolve 1 g NaOH in 99 mL of water.

Equipment and Materials List

These easy-to-use tables of equipment and consumable materials can help you prepare for your science classes for the year. Refer to the Chapter Organizer in front of each chapter for a list of equipment and materials used for each laboratory activity in the chapter.

Nonconsumables			
Material	**Launch Lab Chapter**	**MiniLAB Chapter Section**	**Lab Chapter Section**
aquarium			14-4
triple-beam or pan balance		1-1	3-2, 18-1, 18-2, 25-3
basin, plastic or aluminum-foil baking pan	27		
beaker(s)	27	7-2	14-4, 18-2, 27-3
bicycle pump			20-2
binoculars			26-2
book		13-4, 17-2	
bowl		14-2, 18-2, 19-1, 20-1	24-3
button		10-3	
colored markers or pencils			5-3, 6-1, 11-2, 13-4, 16-3, 19-3, 25-1
compass			26-2
container or jar		2-1, 9-2, 9-3, 13-3, 14-3, 25-1, 26-3	1-4, 3-2, 7-2, 8-2, 11-2, 13-4, 25-1
cooking pot			23-3
cookware, black			27-3
coverslip			2-1, 2-3, 8-1, 8-2, 10-2, 11-1
coverslip(s)			2-3, 8-1, 8-2
culture containers (with tops)			24-3
cup		20-2	
dissecting needle			10-2
dissecting tray			20-2
dropper(s)	22	19-2	2-1, 2-3, 8-1, 10-2, 18-1, 19-3
field guide to fungi or club fungi			8-2
field guides			26-2
fishnet, small			14-4
flashlight		2-1	16-2
footprint diagram			15-2
forceps			2-1, 10-2, 11-1
fruit fly culture kit			24-3
funnel		20-2	
glass plate		23-2	
glass, clear		2-2	23-3
globe or world map	19, 25		
gloves			23-2
graduated cylinder			10-3, 18-1, 25-1
graduated cylinder, 10-mL			19-3
lamp (100 W lightbulb)			27-2
magazine picture of a piece of furniture		1-4	
magnifying lens	2, 8, 13	8-1, 17-3, 26-3	1-4, 1-4, 6-3, 8-2, 10-2, 20-2, 24-3, 26-2
marbles		20-1	
meterstick or ruler		5-2, 7-1, 21-1	1-4, 6-3, 17-3, 21-2, 25-1
microscope(s)			2-1, 2-3, 4-1, 7-1, 8-2, 10-2, 11-1
microscope slide(s)			2-1, 2-3, 8-1, 8-2, 10-2, 11-1
mortar and pestle			18-2
net		26-3	
notebook			26-2
pencil with eraser			10-2, 22-2, 22-3, 23-2, 26-2
pencil, glass-marking			18-1
penny		23-1	
petri dishes, plastic			2-3
photos of foods and landscapes		16-1	
photos of *Oscillatoria* and *Nostoc*			7-1
plant pots		24-2	

Material	Launch Lab Chapter	MiniLAB Chapter Section	Lab Chapter Section
plant trays or plastic cups			10-3
plate	7, 22		
rubber	14		
safety goggles	21		
scalpel			20-2
scissors		10-1	3-3, 16-2, 17-3, 20-2, 27-3
shoe box with lid			16-2
sink		26-2	
sponge, dry		1-1	
spoon			3-2, 23-3
sports bottle			20-2
spray bottle	27		
stereomicroscope			2-3
stirrer			13-3, 18-1
stirring rod			3-3, 14-4, 18-2
stopwatch			18-2, 27-3
table		17-2	
tape measure			22-3, 26-2
test tube(s)			3-3, 18-1
test-tube rack			3-3, 18-1
thermometer(s)			10-3, 14-1, 14-4, 18-2, 26-2, 27-2, 27-3
timer			16-2
tuning fork	14		
watch or clock (with second hand)			19-1, 27-2
Consumables			
alcohol, rubbing			23-2
ammonia, household, clear			23-3
apple (core, peels, fresh, rotting)			7-2, 13-4, 23-2
art supplies			8-2
bag, plastic, self-sealing	4, 11	15-1, 17-3	23-2
baking soda	22		23-3
balloon		14-2	
banana		11-2, 13-3	7-2, 13-4, 24-3
beads			6-1
beans (dried, red, white)		7-2	5-1
bottles, clear, 1-L, plastic, soft-drink			27-2
boxes, cardboard			27-3
bromothymol blue solution			3-3
candy wrapper, plastic			7-2
cardboard			6-1
cardboard tube		20-1	
carrot sticks	3		
cheese		18-1	
cheesecloth		9-2, 13-3	
clay, modeling			6-1, 20-2
cloth			14-1
cloth, cotton		15-1, 18-2	
coat hangers, wire			27-3
coffee filter			23-3
cookie, chocolate-chip		27-1	
corn syrup, light			3-2
cornstarch			18-1
cotton ball	23		23-2
cracked corn	15		
crayons			6-1
cup, plastic or paper, 8-oz			25-3
dishwashing liquid		25-1	
egg, unshelled			3-2
fiberfill			14-1
filter paper	22	20-2	
food coloring		3-2, 9-3	19-3
food flavoring, peppermint	23		
fruit and seeds from one species			6-3
fruits (cubed, whole)		18-1, 24-2	
gauze		19-2	

Material	Launch Lab Chapter	MiniLAB Chapter Section	Lab Chapter Section
gelatin, prepared		3-1	
gelatin, unflavored		2-1	
gloves, disposable			20-2
glue			6-1, 27-3
grapes	10		
graph paper			6-3, 22-3, 26-2
gravel	15	20-2	
grocery bag, brown		18-1	
ground beef, uncooked			13-3
houseplant fertilizer		25-2	
humus			13-4
hydrogen peroxide		23-2	
ice water		15-1	14-4
index card		21-2	
iodine, 2% tincture			18-1
kiwi fruit skin			13-4
labels			1-4, 23-2
leaf			7-2
lemon juice			23-3
lettuce			11-1, 24-3
liquid bandage solution		19-2	
liver or meat, raw			24-3
meat		18-1	
milk, low-fat			19-3
moss	27		
mushrooms		8-2	
newspaper		2-2	7-2, 17-3, 23-2
newspaper, classified ads from	6		
nuts	15		
onion, green		9-3	
orange juice			23-3
orange peel(s)			13-4, 24-3
paper (black, white, construction, unlined)	6, 12, 21	4-3, 6-1, 8-2, 11-1	5-3, 13-4, 16-2, 20-2, 22-2
paper bag(s)		11-2	5-1
paper cups, small			19-3
paper strip(s)		21-2	
paper towel(s)	4		11-2, 16-2, 23-2, 25-3
paper towel roll or other tube			20-2
peanuts		18-1	
perfume or air freshener		16-2	
petroleum jelly		15-1	
pH indicator paper		27-2	
pineapple, fresh		3-1	
plastic sheets, clear			27-3
plastic wrap			27-2
plate, paper		27-1	
pond sediment or debris		26-3	
poster board		26-2	5-3, 16-3, 27-2
potato chips		18-1	
pretzels		18-1	
rainwater		27-2	
red cabbage			23-3
rubber band(s)			13-4, 27-2
salt	3, 22		10-3
salt solution (strong, weak)			1-4, 11-1
sand, moist	27		
sandpaper			23-2
seeds (bean, sunflower, mustard, radish)	4, 15	27-2	10-3, 11-2
sequins			6-1
slide of an onion root tip			4-1
soap			23-2
sock, old	15		
soil, garden		10-1, 25-1	7-2
soil, potting	27	24-2	10-3, 13-4, 25-3, 27-2
sponge, synthetic	7		
spoon, small, plastic			1-4

Material	Launch Lab Chapter	MiniLAB Chapter Section	Lab Chapter Section
string or yarn		7-1	27-3
styling gel	7		
sugar cubes			18-2
sugar granules			18-2
tap water, aged			3-3
tape	18	11-1, 21-2	6-3, 13-4, 16-2, 17-3, 27-2, 27-3
toothpick(s)		21-2, 27-1	12-2
vegetable shortening		15-1	
vegetables		18-1	
vinegar	22		
vinegar, white			23-3
water, aquarium			14-4
water, carbonated			3-3
water		2-2, 3-2	18-2
water, distilled		7-2, 27-2	1-4, 2-3, 3-2
water, from pond or stream			24-3
watermelon rind			13-4
weighing paper			18-1, 18-2
wire screen		20-2	

Biologicals

Material	Launch Lab Chapter	MiniLAB Chapter Section	Lab Chapter Section
Amoeba culture			8-1
animal kidney, large			20-2
arborvitae branch			9-3
brine shrimp eggs			1-4
cedar branch			9-3
clam's shell	13		
coleus or other houseplant		10-1	
crayfish			13-3
Daphnia or brine shrimp			12-2
Douglas fir branch			9-3
earthworms			13-4, 16-2
Elodea plant			2-1
Elodea sprigs			3-3
Euglena culture			8-1
ferns with gametophytes and sporophytes			10-2
fir branch			9-3
frog		14-3	
fruit flies			24-3
goldfish			14-4
grass clippings or green leaves			25-1
guppies			24-3
hemlock branch			9-3
houseplant (small)	11, 26	11-1	
human cheek cells			2-1
hydra culture			12-2
juniper branch			9-3
liver, small piece			12-3
liverworts, live			10-2
mosses, live			10-2
mushroom	8		
organisms		26-3	
Paramecium culture			8-1
Physarum polycephaalum specimen, live	8-1		
pine branch			9-3
planarian(s)		12-3	12-3, 24-3
redwood branch			9-3
seeds, packaged			1-4
slide of a tapeworm			12-3
slides of *Anabaena*			7-1
slides of *Gloeocapsa*			7-1
slides of slime mold			8-1
sod	24		
Sphagnum moss		9-2	
Spirogyra culture			8-1
spruce branch			9-3
yeast, dry		23-2	

Suppliers

Equipment Suppliers

American Science & Surplus
P.O. Box 1030
Skokie, IL 60076
(847) 647-0011
www.sciplus.com

Bio-Rad Laboratories
2000 Alfred Nobel Dr.
Life Science Group
Hercules, CA 94547
(800) 424-6723
www.bio-rad.com

Carolina Biological Supply Co.
2700 York Road
Burlington, NC 27215
(800) 334-5551
www.carolina.com

Chem Scientific, LLC
1250 Washington St.
Norwood, MA 02062
(888) 527-5827
www.chemscientific.com

Edmund Scientific Company
60 Pearce Ave.
Tonawanda, NY 14150
(800) 728-6999
www.edmundscientific.com

Fisher Science Education
Educational Materials Division
4500 Turnberry Dr.
Hanover Park, IL 60133
(800) 955-1177
www.fisheredu.com

Flinn Scientific
P.O. Box 219
770 N. Raddant Rd.
Batavia, IL 60510
(800) 452-1261
www.flinnsci.com

Frey Scientific, Div. of Beckley Cardy
P.O. Box 8101
Mansfield, OH 44901
(800) 225-FREY (3739)
www.freyscientific.com

Nasco Science
901 Janesville Avenue
P.O. Box 901
Fort Atkinson, WI 53538-0901
(800) 558-9595
www.enasco.com

Nebraska Scientific
3823 Leavenworth St.
Omaha, NE 68105-1180
(800) 228-7117
nebraskascientific.com

PASCO Scientific
10101 Foothills Blvd.
Roseville, CA 95747
(800) 772-8700
www.pasco.com

Sargent-Welch/VWR Scientific Products
P.O. Box 5229
Buffalo Grove, IL 60089-5229
(800) SAR-GENT 727-4368
www.SargentWelch.com

Science Kit and Boreal Laboratories
777 East Park Dr.
P.O. Box 5003
Tonawanda, NY 14150
(800) 828-7777
www.sciencekit.com

Ward's Natural Science Est.
5100 W. Henrietta Road
P.O. Box 92912
Rochester, NY 14692-9012
(800) 962-2660
www.wardsci.com

Audiovisual Distributors

Bullfrog Films
P.O. Box 149
Oley, PA 19547
(800) 543-FROG (3764)
www.bullfrogfilms.com

Coronet/MTI Film & Video
2349 Chaffee Dr.
St. Louis, MO 63146
(800) 221-1274
www.phoenixlearninggroup.com

Discovery Channel School
1 Discovery Place
Silver Springs, MD 20910
(240) 662-2000
www.discoveryschool.com

Films for the Humanities and Sciences
P.O. Box 2053
Princeton, NJ 08543
(800) 257-5126
www.films.com

Flinn Scientific
P.O. Box 219
770 N. Raddant Rd.
Batavia, IL 60510
(800) 452-1261
www.flinnsci.com

Frey Scientific, Div. of Beckley Cardy
P.O. Box 8101
Mansfield, OH 44901
(800) 225-FREY (3739)
www.freyscientific.com

Media Design Associates
1731 15th St.
Suite 220
Boulder, CO 80302
(866) 546-9151
www.indra.com

National Geographic Society Educational Services
1145 17th Street, N.W.
Washington, DC 20036-4688
(800) 647-5463
www.nationalgeographic.com

Scholastic, Inc.
557 Broadway
New York, NY 10012-3999
(800) 246-2986
www.scholastic.com

Videodiscovery Inc.
920 N. 34th St.
Seattle, WA 98103
(800) 548-3472
www.videodiscovery.com

Software Distributors

Boreal Laboratories, Ltd.
399 Vansickle Rd.
St. Catharines, Ontario,
L2S 3T4
Canada
(800) 387-9393
boreal.com

Educational Activities, Inc.
1937 Grand Ave.
P.O. Box 87
Baldwin, NY 11510
(800) 645-3739
www.edact.com

IBM Education
1133 Westchester Ave.
White Plains, NY 10604
(800) 426-4968
www.solutions.ibm.com/k12

J. Weston Walch, Publisher
40 Walch Dr.
P.O. Box 658
Portland, ME 04104-0658
(800) 341-6094
www.walch.com

Scholastic, Inc.
557 Broadway
New York, NY 10012-3999
(800) 246-2986
www.scholastic.com

Sunburst Technology, Inc.
1550 Executive Drive
Elgin, IL 60123
(888) 492-8817
www.SUNBURST.com

Suppliers

Contents In Brief

HOW TO...
Use Your Science Book

Why do I need my science book?

Have you ever been in class and not understood all of what was presented? Or, you understood everything in class, but at home, got stuck on how to answer a question? Maybe you just wondered when you were ever going to use this stuff?

These next few pages are designed to help you understand everything your science book can be used for . . . besides a paperweight!

Before You Read

- **Chapter Opener** Science is occurring all around you, and the opening photo of each chapter will preview the science you will be learning about. The **Chapter Preview** will give you an idea of what you will be learning about, and you can try the **Launch Lab** to help get your brain headed in the right direction. The **Foldables** exercise is a fun way to keep you organized.

- **Section Opener** Chapters are divided into two to four sections. The **As You Read** in the margin of the first page of each section will let you know what is most important in the section. It is divided into four parts. **What You'll Learn** will tell you the major topics you will be covering. **Why It's Important** will remind you why you are studying this in the first place! The **Review Vocabulary** word is a word you already know, either from your science studies or your prior knowledge. The **New Vocabulary** words are words that you need to learn to understand this section. These words will be in **boldfaced** print and highlighted in the section. Make a note to yourself to recognize these words as you are reading the section.

Glencoe Science

Life Science

NATIONAL GEOGRAPHIC

As You Read

- **Headings** Each section has a title in large red letters, and is further divided into blue titles and small red titles at the beginnings of some paragraphs. To help you study, make an outline of the headings and subheadings.

- **Margins** In the margins of your text, you will find many helpful resources. The **Science Online** exercises and **Integrate** activities help you explore the topics you are studying. **MiniLabs** reinforce the science concepts you have learned.

- **Building Skills** You also will find an **Applying Math** or **Applying Science** activity in each chapter. This gives you extra practice using your new knowledge, and helps prepare you for standardized tests.

- **Student Resources** At the end of the book you will find **Student Resources** to help you throughout your studies. These include **Science, Technology,** and **Math Skill Handbooks,** an **English/Spanish Glossary,** and an **Index.** Also, use your **Foldables** as a resource. It will help you organize information, and review before a test.

- **In Class** Remember, you can always ask your teacher to explain anything you don't understand.

FOLDABLES™
Study Organizer

Science Vocabulary Make the following Foldable to help you understand the vocabulary terms in this chapter.

STEP 1 Fold a vertical sheet of notebook paper from side to side.

STEP 2 Cut along every third line of only the top layer to form tabs.

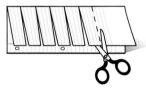

STEP 3 Label each tab with a vocabulary word from the chapter.

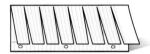

Build Vocabulary As you read the chapter, list the vocabulary words on the tabs. As you learn the definitions, write them under the tab for each vocabulary word.

Look For...

FOLDABLES™

At the beginning of every section.

In Lab

Working in the laboratory is one of the best ways to understand the concepts you are studying. Your book will be your guide through your laboratory experiences, and help you begin to think like a scientist. In it, you not only will find the steps necessary to follow the investigations, but you also will find helpful tips to make the most of your time.

- Each lab provides you with a **Real-World Question** to remind you that science is something you use every day, not just in class. This may lead to many more questions about how things happen in your world.

- Remember, experiments do not always produce the result you expect. Scientists have made many discoveries based on investigations with unexpected results. You can try the experiment again to make sure your results were accurate, or perhaps form a new hypothesis to test.

- Keeping a **Science Journal** is how scientists keep accurate records of observations and data. In your journal, you also can write any questions that may arise during your investigation. This is a great method of reminding yourself to find the answers later.

Look For...
- **Launch Labs** start every chapter.
- **MiniLabs** in the margin of each chapter.
- **Two Full-Period Labs** in every chapter.
- **EXTRA Try at Home Labs** at the end of your book.
- the **Web site** with laboratory demonstrations.

Before a Test

Admit it! You don't like to take tests! However, there *are* ways to review that make them less painful. Your book will help you be more successful taking tests if you use the resources provided to you.

- Review all of the **New Vocabulary** words and be sure you understand their definitions.

- Review the notes you've taken on your **Foldables,** in class, and in lab. Write down any question that you still need answered.

- Review the **Summaries** and **Self Check questions** at the end of each section.

- Study the concepts presented in the chapter by reading the **Study Guide** and answering the questions in the **Chapter Review.**

Look For...

- **Reading Checks** and **caption questions** throughout the text.
- the **summaries** and **self check questions** at the end of each section.
- the **Study Guide** and **Review** at the end of each chapter.
- the **Standardized Test Practice** after each chapter.

Let's Get Started

To help you find the information you need quickly, use the Scavenger Hunt below to learn where things are located in Chapter 1.

1. What is the title of this chapter?

2. What will you learn in Section 1?

3. Sometimes you may ask, "Why am I learning this?" State a reason why the concepts from Section 2 are important.

4. What is the main topic presented in Section 2?

5. How many reading checks are in Section 1?

6. What is the Web address where you can find extra information?

7. What is the main heading above the sixth paragraph in Section 2?

8. There is an integration with another subject mentioned in one of the margins of the chapter. What subject is it?

9. List the new vocabulary words presented in Section 2.

10. List the safety symbols presented in the first Lab.

11. Where would you find a Self Check to be sure you understand the section?

12. Suppose you're doing the Self Check and you have a question about concept mapping. Where could you find help?

13. On what pages are the Chapter Study Guide and Chapter Review?

14. Look in the Table of Contents to find out on which page Section 2 of the chapter begins.

15. You complete the Chapter Review to study for your chapter test. Where could you find another quiz for more practice?

Life's Structure and Function—2

In each chapter, look for these opportunities for review and assessment:
• Reading Checks
• Caption Questions
• Section Review
• Chapter Study Guide
• Chapter Review
• Standardized Test Practice
• Online practice at life.msscience.com

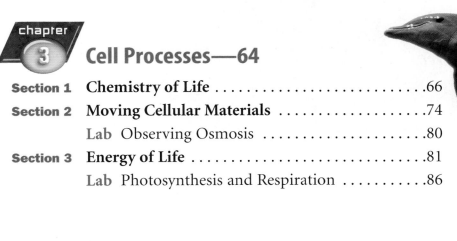

Contents

 **From Bacteria to Plants—182**

In each chapter, look for these opportunities for review and assessment:
- Reading Checks
- Caption Questions
- Section Review
- Chapter Study Guide
- Chapter Review
- Standardized Test Practice
- Online practice at life.msscience.com

Contents

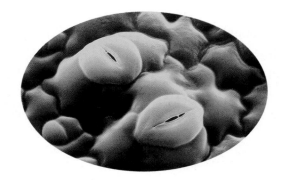

Animal Diversity—326

In each chapter, look for these opportunities for review and assessment:
- Reading Checks
- Caption Questions
- Section Review
- Chapter Study Guide
- Chapter Review
- Standardized Test Practice
- Online practice at life.msscience.com

Contents

Contents

Contents

Human Body Systems—480

In each chapter, look for these opportunities for review and assessment:
- **Reading Checks**
- **Caption Questions**
- **Section Review**
- **Chapter Study Guide**
- **Chapter Review**
- **Standardized Test Practice**
- **Online practice at life.msscience.com**

Contents

In each chapter, look for these opportunities for review and assessment:

- **Reading Checks**
- **Caption Questions**
- **Section Review**
- **Chapter Study Guide**
- **Chapter Review**
- **Standardized Test Practice**
- **Online practice at life.msscience.com**

Student Resources—800

Cross-Curricular Readings

Content Details

TIME SCIENCE AND Society

TIME SCIENCE AND HISTORY

Oops! Accidents in SCIENCE

Science and Language Arts

SCIENCE Stats

LABS

 available as a video lab

Launch LAB

Mini LAB

Content Details

Mini LAB Try at Home

LABS

 available as a video lab

One-Page Labs

Content Details

Content Details

Activities

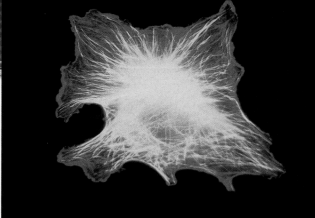

Content Details

Astronomy: 21, 429, 606, 685
Career: 83, 97, 137, 228, 303, 497, 634, 717, 755
Chemistry: 15, 109, 338, 465, 466, 499, 598, 633, 779
Earth Science: 21, 164, 167, 190, 288, 363, 569, 598, 718, 727, 750, 758
Environment: 142, 247, 284, 529, 669
Health: 77, 199, 217, 255, 402, 457, 782
History: 242, 278, 417, 466, 554, 595, 699
Language Arts: 158, 331
Physics: 42, 73, 312, 363, 403, 545, 640
Social Studies: 17, 196, 373, 431, 491, 519, 605, 658, 773

8, 15, 23, 53, 54, 70, 84, 113, 115, 127, 135, 156, 165, 189, 197, 214, 223, 248, 259, 274, 282, 306, 316, 334, 340, 368, 382, 409, 413, 432, 441, 459, 468, 486, 491, 514, 526, 547, 551, 571, 574, 599, 601, 609, 629, 637, 654, 663, 686, 692, 717, 725, 741, 757, 780, 790

Standardized Test Practice

34–35, 62–63, 92–93, 122–123, 150–151, 180–181, 206–207, 236–237, 268–269, 298–299, 324–325, 356–357, 390–391, 424–425, 452–453, 478–479, 508–509, 536–537, 564–565, 590–591, 618–619, 648–649, 678–679, 708–709, 736–737, 766–767, 798–799

Unit Contents

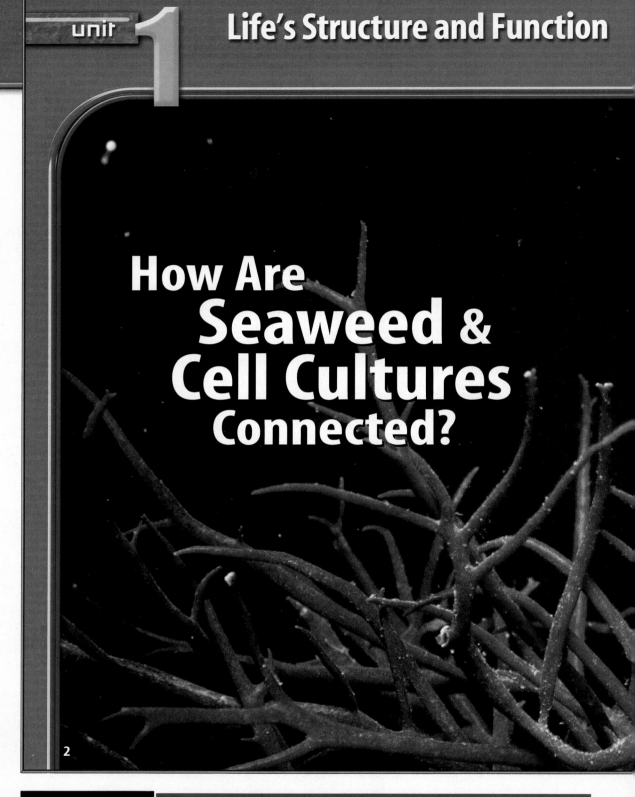

How Are Seaweed & Cell Cultures Connected?

2

 *New Research on Cells* is an investigation of current cell research and an exploration into the roles that cells play in our bodies. After answering a set of questions designed to guide student learning, students will write a summary paragraph, using a style suited for posting on a Web site.

PROJECT
CRISSsm

Study Skills

Discussion The Think-Pair-Share strategy ensures active participation of all students. Given the parts of the cell, have students brainstorm ideas about the appearance and function of each cell part on their own. Then have pairs discuss their notes and ideas before returning to share with the whole class.

In the 1800s, many biologists were interested in studying one-celled microorganisms. But to study them, the researchers needed to grow, or culture, large numbers of these cells. And to culture them properly, they needed a solid substance on which the cells could grow. One scientist tried using nutrient-enriched gelatin, but the gelatin had drawbacks. It melted at relatively low temperatures—and some microorganisms digested it. Fannie Eilshemius Hesse came up with a better option. She had been solidifying her homemade jellies using a substance called agar, which is derived from red seaweed (such as the one seen in the background here). It turned out that nutrient-enriched agar worked perfectly as a substance on which to culture cells. On the two types of agar in the dishes below, so many cells have grown that, together, they form dots and lines.

unit ⚡ projects

Visit life.msscience.com/unit_project to find project ideas and resources.
Projects include:
- **Career** Brainstorm a list of questions for a health professional about cell reproduction, or bacteria and virus resistance to drugs.
- **Technology** Design both a chart and a graph that present information on cell reproduction rates during specific time intervals.
- **Model** Construct a thumb flip book that models mitosis. Complete a second book for meiosis to analyze and compare the two processes.

WebQuest *New Research on Cells* is a Web-based investigation of current research involving different types of cells, and why their structures vary according to their location.

unit ⚡ projects

Careers Have students brainstorm a list of questions they might ask a pharmacist, nurse, pathologist, veterinarian, medical researcher, or other health-care professional. Questions might focus on bacteria or virus reproduction, adaptation of cells to their environment, or drug immunity or resistance. Students might explore homeopathic remedies, historical medicines and treatments, Native American treatments, or medicines and procedures of the future. Acquired information can be displayed in a Venn diagram.

Technology Have students imagine that a cell is placed in a dish of nutrient-enriched agar. Twenty minutes later, the virtual cell would have divided to form two cells. Assuming that the cells continue to divide every 20 minutes, how many cells would be in the dish an hour after the first division? Two hours after the first division? Using a computer graphing program, have students illustrate the pattern of cell reproduction with the correct number of cells at 20-minute intervals.

Model Have students design a small flip book of approximately 40 pages to demonstrate mitosis. Original illustrations clearly should show the four phases of cell division. Students may produce a second book on meiosis that allows for the comparison of the two processes.

Additional Resources For more information, resources, and assessment rubrics, visit
life.msscience.com/unit_project

NATIONAL GEOGRAPHIC How Are Seaweed & Cell Cultures Connected?

Agar, a gelatinlike product, is made primarily from red seaweeds. It is used in cosmetics, medicines, dentistry, and as a clarifying agent in brewing and wine making. It also is used as a thickening agent in ice cream, pastries, desserts, and salad dressings.

It was in 1883 that Frau Hess developed this medium for culturing cells. Unlike gelatin, agar can be liquefied by only a few microorganisms and is not a food source, thus it allows better control of the nutrient content of the medium.

Section/Objectives	Standards		Labs/Features
Chapter Opener	**National**	**State/Local**	**Launch Lab:** Classify Organisms, p. 5 **Foldables,** p. 5
	See pp. 16T–17T for a Key to Standards.		
Section 1 What is science? ⏱ 2 sessions 🧊 1 block 1. **Apply** scientific methods to problem solving. 2. **Demonstrate** how to measure using scientific units.	National Content Standards: UCP.1–UCP.3, UCP.5, A.1, A.2, G.2		**Science Online,** p. 8 **MiniLAB:** Analyzing Data, p. 9 **Applying Science:** Does temperature affect the rate of bacterial reproduction?, p. 11
Section 2 Living Things ⏱ 2 sessions 🧊 1 block 3. **Distinguish** between living and nonliving things. 4. **Identify** what living things need to survive.	National Content Standards: UCP.1–UCP.3, UCP.5, A.1, A.2, C.1–C.3		**Science Online,** p. 15 **Integrate Social Studies,** p. 17
Section 3 Where does life come from? ⏱ 1 session 🧊 0.5-block 5. **Describe** experiments about spontaneous generation. 6. **Explain** how scientific methods led to the idea of biogenesis.	National Content Standards: UCP.1–UCP.3, UCP.5, A.1, A.2, C.1, G.3		**Visualizing the Origins of Life,** p. 20 **Integrate Earth Science,** p. 21
Section 4 How are living things classified? ⏱ 3 sessions 🧊 1.5 block 7. **Describe** how early scientists classified living things. 8. **Explain** how similarities are used to classify organisms. 9. **Explain** the system of binomial nomenclature. 10. **Demonstrate** how to use a dichotomous key.	National Content Standards: UCP.1–UCP.3, UCP.5, A.1, A.2, C.5, G.3		**MiniLAB:** Communicating Ideas, p. 25 **Lab:** Classifying Seeds, p. 27 **Lab:** Using Scientific Methods, p. 28 **Science and Society:** Monkey Business, p. 30

Lab Materials	Reproducible Resources	Section Assessment	Technology
Launch Lab: insect collection	**Chapter FAST FILE Resources** Foldables Worksheet, p. 15 Directed Reading Overview, p. 17 Note-taking Worksheets, pp. 33–35	GLENCOE'S ASSESSMENT ADVANTAGE	**Teacher Works** includes: • Interactive Teacher Edition • Lesson Planner with calendar • Access to all program blacklines • Correlations to standards • Web links
MiniLAB: pan balance, dry sponge, water, Science Journal	**Chapter FAST FILE Resources** Transparency Activity, p. 44 MiniLAB, p. 3 Enrichment, p. 29 Reinforcement, p. 25 Lab Activity, pp. 9–10 Directed Reading, p. 18	**Portfolio** Science Journal, p. 7 **Performance** MiniLAB, p. 9 Applying Science, p. 11 Applying Skills, p. 13 **Content** Section Review, p. 13	Section Focus Transparency Virtual Labs CD-ROM Guided Reading Audio Program Interactive Chalkboard CD-ROM Video Lab
	Chapter FAST FILE Resources Transparency Activity, p. 45 Enrichment, p. 30 Reinforcement, p. 26 Directed Reading, p. 18	**Portfolio** Curriculum Connection, p. 16 **Performance** Applying Skills, p. 18 **Content** Section Review, p. 18	Section Focus Transparency Virtual Labs CD-ROM Guided Reading Audio Program Interactive Chalkboard CD-ROM
Need materials? Contact Science Kit at 1-800-828-7777 or www.sciencekit.com on the Internet.	**Chapter FAST FILE Resources** Transparency Activity, p. 46 Enrichment, p. 31 Reinforcement, p. 27 Directed Reading, p. 19	**Portfolio** Reteach, p. 21 **Performance** Applying Skills, p. 21 **Content** Section Review, p. 21	Section Focus Transparency Virtual Labs CD-ROM Guided Reading Audio Program Interactive Chalkboard CD-ROM
MiniLAB: magazine picture of a piece of furniture **Lab:** packets of seeds (10 different kinds), metric ruler, magnifying lens **Lab:** 3 500-mL, wide-mouthed containers; brine shrimp eggs; small, plastic spoon; distilled water; weak salt solution; strong salt solution; 3 labels; magnifying lens	**Chapter FAST FILE Resources** Transparency Activity, p. 47 MiniLAB, p. 4 Enrichment, p. 32 Reinforcement, p. 28 Directed Reading, pp. 19, 20 Transparency Activity, pp. 49–50 Lab Activity, pp. 11–13 Lab Worksheets, pp. 5–6, 7–8	**Portfolio** Assessment, p. 26 **Performance** MiniLAB, p. 25 Applying Skills, p. 26 **Content** Section Review, p. 26	Section Focus Transparency Teaching Transparency Virtual Labs CD-ROM Guided Reading Audio Program Interactive Chalkboard CD-ROM

End of Chapter Assessment

GLENCOE'S ASSESSMENT ADVANTAGE

Blackline Masters	Technology	Professional Series
Chapter FAST FILE Resources Chapter Review, pp. 37–38 Chapter Tests, pp. 39–42 **Standardized Test Practice,** pp. 7–10	MindJogger Videoquiz Virtual Labs CD-ROM ExamView® Pro Testmaker TeacherWorks CD-ROM Interactive Chalkboard CD-ROM	**Performance Assessment in the Science Classroom (PASC)**

Transparencies

Section Focus

Section Focus Transparency 1 — Do the chimpanzees ever study Dr. Goodall?

Jane Goodall, a zoologist from England, researches chimpanzees in Gombe Stream National Park. She has described and reported many aspects of chimpanzees, including hunting, tool use, and social behaviors.

1. How was Dr. Goodall able to discover so many chimpanzee behaviors?
2. How does studying an animal in a laboratory compare with studying an animal in its natural habitat?

L2

Section Focus Transparency 2 — Most Enlightening

Have you ever seen a house plant growing toward the window? Most plants grow toward the light. This bending is caused by a plant hormone that makes plant cells stretch and grow in the direction of the light source.

1. Why do plants need light?
2. What would happen if you gave the pot a half turn?
3. What does this plant need to live?

L2

Section Focus Transparency 3 — How About a Field Trip?

Is there life on other planets? If there is, it probably doesn't resemble the aliens we see in the movies. Some scientists believe that Europa, one of Jupiter's moons (pictured in the center of the image below), is a candidate for supporting extraterrestrial life.

1. What general resources are needed to sustain life on Earth?
2. Is it possible that other planets or moons in our galaxy might have the resources to support life? Explain.

L2

This is a representation of key blackline masters available in the Teacher Classroom Resources. See Resource Manager boxes within the chapter for additional information.

Key to Teaching Strategies

The following designations will help you decide which activities are appropriate for your students.

L1 Level 1 activities should be appropriate for students with learning difficulties.

L2 Level 2 activities should be within the ability range of all students.

L3 Level 3 activities are designed for above-average students.

ELL ELL activities should be within the ability range of English-Language Learners.

COOP LEARN Cooperative Learning activities are designed for small group work.

LS Multiple Learning Styles logos, as described on page 12T, are used throughout to indicate strategies that address different learning styles.

P These strategies represent student products that can be placed into a best-work portfolio.

PBL Problem-Based Learning activities apply real-world situations to learning.

Assessment

Assessment Transparency — Exploring and Classifying Life

Directions: Carefully review the table and answer the following questions.

Fruit and Vegetable Seed Germination Rate					
Type of seed	Number of seeds	Amount of water added (mL)	Number of seeds germinating		
			Day 3	Day 5	Day 7
Orange	10	50	0	0	1
Lemon	10	50	0	1	1
Cucumber	10	50	6	7	7
Onion	10	50	7	9	10

1. Which hypothesis was probably being tested?
   A Less than 25 percent of vegetable seeds will germinate.
   B Seeds prefer to grow in soil versus sand.
   C Vegetable seeds germinate faster than fruit seeds.
   D A period of one week is required before seeds will germinate.
2. Which of the following would improve an experiment to compare the rate of seed germination?
   F using more types of seeds
   G measuring the length of the plants
   H adding 100mL of water to each seed
   J conducting the experiment for a shorter time
3. Which factor would have the LEAST effect on the results?
   A the amount of light to which the seeds were exposed
   B the amount of soil used for the seeds
   C the color of the pots used
   D the depth the seeds were planted in the soil

L2

Teaching

Teaching Transparency — Modern Classification

Kingdom — Animalia
Phylum — Chordata
Class — Mammalia
Order — Cetacea
Family — Delphinidae
Genus — Tursiops
Species — Tursiops truncatus

L2

Hands-on Activities

Student Text Lab Worksheet

Activity — Classifying Seeds

Lab Preview
Directions: Answer the questions before you begin the Activity.
1. Why should seeds that are meant for planting not be tasted or eaten?

2. What is one feature of a seed that might be used for classifying seeds?

Scientists use classification systems to show how organisms are related. How do they determine what features to use to classify organisms? In this activity, you will observe seeds and use their features to classify them.

What You'll Investigate
How can the features of seeds be used to develop a key to identify the seed?

Materials
packets of seeds (10 different kinds)
hand lens
metric ruler

Goals
• **Observe** the seeds and notice their features.
• **Classify** seeds using these features.

Safety Precautions
Do not eat any seeds or put them in your mouth. Some may have been treated with chemicals.

Procedure
1. Record the features of each seed in the table below.
2. Use the features to develop a key.
3. Exchange keys with another group. Can you use their key to identify seeds?

Features	Type of Seed
Color	
Length (mm)	
Shape	
Texture	

L2

Laboratory Activities

Laboratory Activity 1 — Scientific Methods

When scientists are asked questions, they may not know the answers. They think of the possible answers, called hypotheses, and experiment to find the correct answers. Using the results of the experiment, they may need to form another hypothesis and test it. This way of solving a problem is called scientific methods.

Strategy
You will predict whether or not red cabbage juice will remain red when chemicals are added to it.
You will test your prediction with an experiment.
You will observe what happens and record your observations.
You will draw conclusions based on your observations.

Materials
apron   labels   chemical X (vinegar)
goggles   3 droppers   chemical Y (ammonia)
4 test tubes (18 × 150 mm) graduated cylinder (25 mL.) chemical Z (baking soda solution)
test tube rack   40 mL red cabbage juice

Procedure
1. In the space below, predict what will happen to the red cabbage juice when chemicals X, Y and Z are added to it.

2. Label four test tubes 1, 2, 3, and 4.
3. Add 10 mL of red cabbage juice to each test tube. CAUTION: Do not spill chemicals X, Y, or Z on clothes or skin. Rinse with water if spilled.
4. Add 10 drops of chemical X to test tube 1.
5. Add 10 drops of chemical Y to test tube 2.
6. Add 10 drops of chemical Z to test tube 3.
7. Do not add anything to test tube 4. This is the control. The control is part of the experiment that is not tested.
8. Record your observations in Table 1.

Data and Observations
Table 1

Test tube	Substance added	Color
1		
2		
3		
4		

L2

Resource Manager

Meeting Different Ability Levels

Content Outline

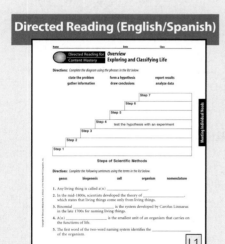

L2

Reinforcement

L2

Enrichment

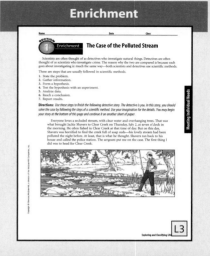

L3

Directed Reading (English/Spanish)

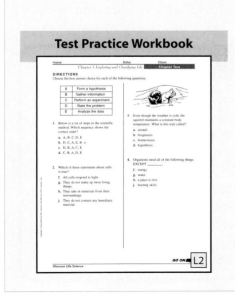

L1

Study Guide

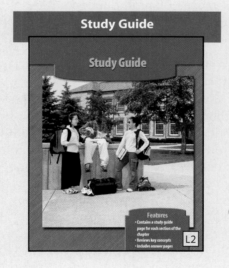

Study Guide

Features
• Contains a study guide page for each section of the chapter
• Reviews key concepts
• Includes answer pages

L2

Reading Essentials

Reading Essentials for Glencoe Science
An Interactive Student Workbook

Features
• Condensed core content
• Actively involves students in reading
• Reinforces key vocabulary

L1

Assessment

Test Practice Workbook

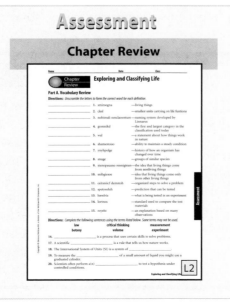

L2

Chapter Review

L2

Chapter Tests

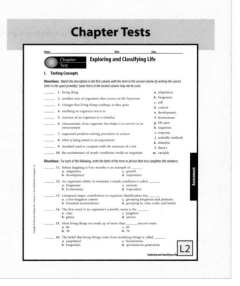

L2

Science Content Background

section 2 Living Things

Living Versus Nonliving

Living organisms consist of highly organized systems that interact and are dependent upon one another. Living systems require a constant source of energy. All living organisms have metabolic processes by which the energy in carbohydrates is released for use. All living organisms respond to their environment in adaptive ways, including physiological responses as well as behaviors. Living organisms also have a means of reproduction, growth, and development.

section 4 How are living things classified?

Modern Classification

This textbook uses a combination of phenetics and cladistics to classify organisms. Phenetics is based on particular features. Cladistics uses shared, derived characteristics to classify organisms. By comparing DNA nucleotide sequences between species and by measuring the amount of bonding between DNA from different species, taxonomists infer the degree of similarity between organisms. Scientists hypothesize that organisms with similar proteins are closely related. A comparison of the amino acid sequences between species' proteins provides objective, quantitative data for taxonomists because the structure of proteins is genetically determined.

Domains

Most taxonomists currently divide the six-kingdom system into groups called domains. The three domains are Eubacteria, Archaea, and Eukarya. The domains Eubacteria and Archaea contain Kingdom Eubacteria and Kingdom Archaebacteria, respectively.

Kingdom Eubacteria and Kingdom Archaebacteria differ. Eubacteria have muramic acid in their cell walls, but archaebacteria do not. The RNA sequences of the two groups also differ.

Domain Eukarya contains four kingdoms—Kingdom Protista, Kingdom Fungi, Kingdom Plantae, and Kingdom Animalia.

Scientific Names

A system of classification avoids ambiguity among species, reflects the phylogeny (evolutionary history) of organisms, and provides clues about the organism's habits and possible features shared with similar organisms. The second word of a scientific name is called the specific epithet, usually an adjective that describes the organism, indicates the organism's place of origin, or is a Latinized surname to honor someone. Subspecies have two specific epithets.

chapter content resources

Internet Resources

For additional content background, visit **life.msscience.com** to:
- access your book online
- find references to related articles in popular science magazines
- access Web links with related content background
- access current events with science journal topics

Print Resources

The Science of Life: Projects and Principles for Beginning Biologists, by Frank G. Bottone, Chicago Review Press, 2001

The Origins of Life, by Roy A. Gallant, Marshall Cavendish, 2000

Carl Linnaeus: Father of Classification, by Margaret Jean Anderson, Enslow Publishers, 1997

National Audubon Society First Field Guide: Reptiles, by John L. Behler, Scholastic Inc., 1999

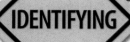 **Misconceptions**

Find Out What Students Think

Students may think that . . .

All things that move are alive.
Students generally define "living" according to the characteristics of large animals. Hence they associate "living" with movement. Students often do not consider plants and fungi to be alive because they do not appear to move, but may classify rivers or clouds as living because they do move. Students may add other mammalian characteristics to their definitions of life such as eating, breathing, or the presence of a heartbeat.

Clouding the concept further is the confusion between "nonliving" and "dead." Students may classify both a dead animal and a rock as "nonliving" objects, even though they classify animals in general as alive.

Discussion
Place a rock, a houseplant, and a living animal (such as a caged hamster or a volunteer student) in view of the class. Ask students if they think any of the three items are alive. As students respond, ask them why they think the item is or is not alive. From this, generate a list of characteristics that students believe belong to all living organisms. Students will probably recognize that the animal is alive. Some will understand that the plant is alive, but have difficulty explaining why. Most will know that the rock is not alive.

Promote Understanding

Activity
Have the students read **Section 2** in this chapter, then review the list they generated in the discussion suggestion above. Ask the students if they want to change anything on the list.

Next, place a candle in full view of the class and light it. Ask students if they think the flame is alive. Then do the following:

- Blow gently on the flame to show that it responds.

- Light another candle or a match from the flame to show that the flame can reproduce.

- Point out that the wax of the candle is being consumed, showing that the flame uses energy.

Remind students that many nonliving things have some characteristics of living things.

- Ask the class what characteristics the candle flame lacks. Students should recognize that the flame is not highly organized, it is not made up of organic molecules, and it contains no cells. L2

Assess
After completing the chapter, see *Identifying Misconceptions* in the Study Guide at the end of the chapter.

Chapter Vocabulary

Science Journal Students' answers will vary. Characteristics might include method of movement, shape of body, and what they eat.

INTERACTIVE CHALKBOARD with Image Bank

PowerPoint® Presentations

This CD-ROM is an editable Microsoft® PowerPoint® presentation that includes:

- a pre-made presentation for every chapter
- interactive graphics
- animations
- audio clips
- image bank
- all new section and chapter questions
- Standardized Test Practice
- transparencies
- pre-lab questions for all labs
- Foldables directions
- links to life.msscience.com

Exploring and Classifying Life

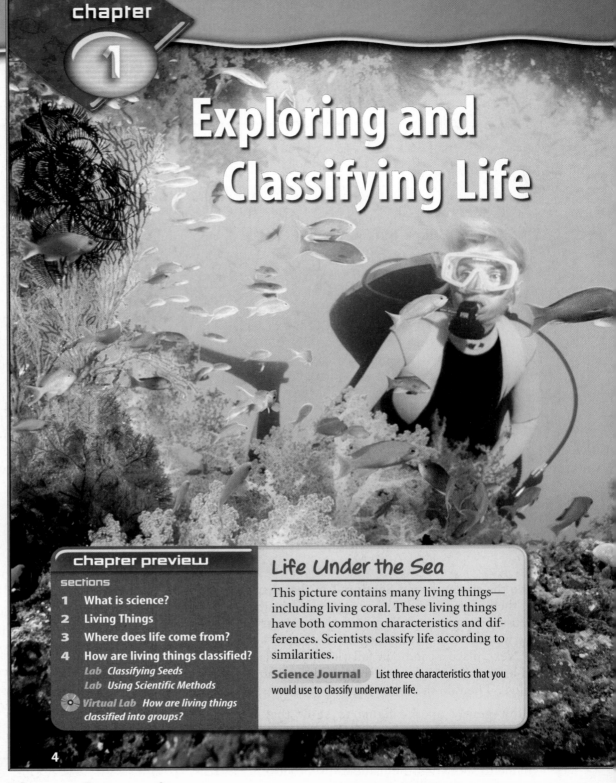

chapter preview

sections

1 **What is science?**

2 **Living Things**

3 **Where does life come from?**

4 **How are living things classified?**
    Lab Classifying Seeds
    Lab Using Scientific Methods
    Virtual Lab **How are living things classified into groups?**

4

Life Under the Sea

This picture contains many living things—including living coral. These living things have both common characteristics and differences. Scientists classify life according to similarities.

Science Journal List three characteristics that you would use to classify underwater life.

Theme Connection

Systems and Interactions Scientists have devised systems for classifying organisms. These systems use an organism's traits, which have changed over time often as a result of natural selection as organisms interact with the environment.

About the Photo

Diversity of Life The diver is surrounded by a wide variety of living organisms. Some are easily recognizable as living, while others may look more like nonliving rocks. While all the organisms, including the diver, share characteristics that classify them as living, those that are more closely classified share the most characteristics.

Start-Up Activities

Classify Organisms

Life scientists discover, describe, and name hundreds of organisms every year. How do they decide if a certain plant belongs to the iris or orchid family of flowering plants, or if an insect is more like a grasshopper or a beetle?

1. Observe the organisms on the opposite page or in an insect collection in your class.
2. Decide which feature could be used to separate the organisms into two groups, then sort the organisms into the two groups.
3. Continue to make new groups using different features until each organism is in a category by itself.
4. **Think Critically** How do you think scientists classify living things? List your ideas in your Science Journal.

Preview this chapter's content and activities at
life.msscience.com

 Vocabulary Make the following Foldable to help you understand the vocabulary terms in this chapter.

STEP 1 Fold a vertical sheet of notebook paper from side to side.

STEP 2 Cut along every third line of only the top layer to form tabs.

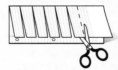

STEP 3 Label each tab.

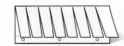

Build Vocabulary As you read the chapter, write the vocabulary words on the tabs. As you learn the definitions, write them under the tab for each vocabulary word.

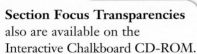
What is science?

Bellringer

INTERACTIVE CHALKBOARD
PowerPoint® Presentations

Section Focus Transparencies also are available on the Interactive Chalkboard CD-ROM.

L2 ELL

SECTION 1
Section Focus Transparency
Do the chimpanzees ever study Dr. Goodall?

Jane Goodall, a zoologist from England, researches chimpanzees in Gombe Stream National Park. She has described and reported many aspects of chimpanzees, including hunting, tool use, and social behaviors.

1. How was Dr. Goodall able to discover so many chimpanzee behaviors?
2. How does studying an animal in a laboratory compare with studying an animal in its natural habitat?

Exploring and Classifying Life

Tie to Prior Knowledge

Daily Decisions Students use problem-solving skills daily. Discuss how they solve everyday problems, such as deciding what outfit to wear or how to manage homework with extra-curricular activities. Relate solving everyday problems to scientific methods.

Text Question Answer

bacteria

---

as you read

What You'll Learn
- **Apply** scientific methods to problem solving.
- **Demonstrate** how to measure using scientific units.

Why It's Important
Learning to use scientific methods will help you solve ordinary problems in your life.

Review Vocabulary
experiment: using controlled conditions to test a prediction

New Vocabulary
- scientific methods
- hypothesis
- control
- variable
- theory
- law

The Work of Science

Movies and popcorn seem to go together. So before you and your friends watch a movie, sometimes you pop some corn in a microwave oven. When the popping stops, you take out the bag and open it carefully. You smell the mouthwatering, freshly popped corn and avoid hot steam that escapes from the bag. What makes the popcorn pop? How do microwaves work and make things hot? By the way, what are microwaves anyway?

Asking questions like these is one way scientists find out about anything in the world and the universe. Science is often described as an organized way of studying things and finding answers to questions.

Types of Science Many types of science exist. Each is given a name to describe what is being studied. For example, energy and matter have a relationship. That's a topic for physics. A physicist could answer most questions about microwaves.

On the other hand, a life scientist might study any of the millions of different animals, plants, and other living things on Earth. Look at the objects in **Figure 1.** What do they look like to you? A life scientist could tell you that some of the objects are living plants and some are just rocks. Life scientists who study plants are botanists, and those who study animals are zoologists. What do you suppose a bacteriologist studies?

Figure 1 Examine the picture carefully. Some of these objects are actually *Lithops* plants. They commonly are called stone plants and are native to deserts in South Africa.

6 CHAPTER 1

Critical Thinking

Whether or not you become a trained scientist, you are going to solve problems all your life. You probably solve many problems every day when you sort out ideas about what will or won't work. Suppose your CD player stops playing music. To figure out what happened, you have to think about it. That's called critical thinking, and it's the way you use skills to solve problems.

If you know that the CD player does not run on batteries and must be plugged in to work, that's the first thing you check to solve the problem. You check and the player is plugged in so you eliminate that possible solution. You separate important information from unimportant information—that's a skill. Could there be something wrong with the first outlet? You plug the player into a different outlet, and your CD starts playing. You now know that it's the first outlet that doesn't work. Identifying the problem is another skill you have.

Solving Problems

Scientists use the same types of skills that you do to solve problems and answer questions. Although scientists don't always find the answers to their questions, they always use critical thinking in their search. Besides critical thinking, solving a problem requires organization. In science, this organization often takes the form of a series of procedures called **scientific methods. Figure 2** shows one way that scientific methods might be used to solve a problem.

State the Problem Suppose a veterinary technician wanted to find out whether different types of cat litter cause irritation to cats' skin. What would she do first? The technician begins by observing something she cannot explain. A pet owner brings his four cats to the clinic to be boarded while he travels. He leaves his cell phone number so he can be contacted if any problems arise. When they first arrive, the four cats seem healthy. The next day however, the technician notices that two of the cats are scratching and chewing at their skin. By the third day, these same two cats have bare patches of skin with red sores. The technician decides that something in the cats' surroundings or their food might be irritating their skin.

Figure 2 The series of procedures shown below is one way to use scientific methods to solve a problem.

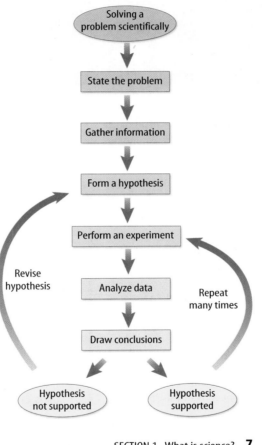

Activity

Life Scientists Divide the class into small groups. Ask: What do you think life scientists do? Where might they work? Allow time for groups to discuss the questions and record their responses. Have each group use their results to write a Help Wanted advertisement seeking a life scientist. Ask groups to present their advertisements to the class.
L2 COOP LEARN **IS Interpersonal**

IDENTIFYING Misconceptions

Science for Everybody Science is often thought of as a discipline out of reach of most people. Many believe that only well-educated or specially trained people can practice science. Explain that science is a process of understanding and that anyone can use the methods of science in daily life.

Visual Learning

Figure 2 Are all the steps shown here always followed in the exact same sequence? No; if a hypothesis is not supported, the scientist starts over by forming a new hypothesis. Sometimes, only a few of the steps are used.

Science Journal

Critical-Thinking Log Ask students to keep in their journals a log of instances in which they used critical thinking to solve problems. Logs should note the date, problem, and solution. At the end of one week, have students share their logs with classmates. Guide students in recognizing that critical thinking is a life skill. L2 **IS Interpersonal** P

Quick Demo

Testing a Hypothesis

Materials 2-L clear container, pond water

Estimated Time 20 minutes

Procedure Fill the container with pond water and place it in a well-lighted area. Have students write a hypothesis about how the water will appear in ten days. Collect the hypotheses and in ten days, have students check their hypotheses against the conditions in the jar.

Fun Fact

Scientists use computer models to study how cloud cover affects Earth's climate.

Caption Answer

Figure 3 Accept any reasonable answers. Possible answers include: an observatory, space station, rain forest, or underwater.

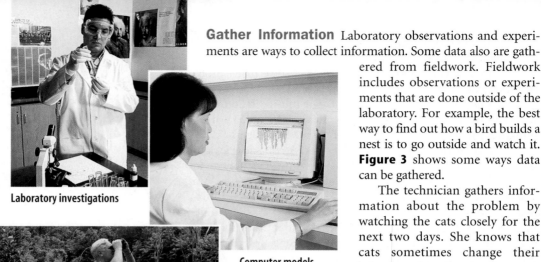

Laboratory investigations

Computer models

Fieldwork

Figure 3 Observations can be made in many different settings. **List** *three other places where scientific observations can be made.*

Topic: Controlled Experiments

Visit life.msscience.com for Web links to information about how scientists use controlled experiments.

Activity List the problem, hypothesis, and how the hypothesis was tested for a recently performed controlled experiment.

Gather Information Laboratory observations and experiments are ways to collect information. Some data also are gathered from fieldwork. Fieldwork includes observations or experiments that are done outside of the laboratory. For example, the best way to find out how a bird builds a nest is to go outside and watch it. **Figure 3** shows some ways data can be gathered.

The technician gathers information about the problem by watching the cats closely for the next two days. She knows that cats sometimes change their behavior when they are in a new place. She wants to see if the behavior of the cats with the skin sores seems different from that of the other two cats. Other than the scratching and chewing at their skin, all four cats' behavior seems to be the same.

The technician calls the owner and tells him about the problem. She asks him what brand of cat food he feeds his cats. Because his brand is the same one used at the clinic, she decides that food is not the cause of the skin irritation. She decides that the cats probably are reacting to something in their surroundings. There are many things in the clinic that the cats might react to. How does she decide what it is?

During her observations she notices that the cats seem to scratch and chew themselves most after using their litter boxes. The cat litter used by the clinic contains a deodorant. The technician calls the owner and finds out that the cat litter he buys does not contain a deodorant.

Form a Hypothesis Based on this information, the next thing the veterinary technician does is form a hypothesis. A **hypothesis** is a prediction that can be tested. After discussing her observations with the clinic veterinarian, she hypothesizes that something in the cat litter is irritating the cats' skin.

Test the Hypothesis with an Experiment The technician gets the owner's permission to test her hypothesis by performing an experiment. In an experiment, the hypothesis is tested using controlled conditions. The technician reads the labels on two brands of cat litter and finds that the ingredients of each are the same except that one contains a deodorant.

8 CHAPTER 1 Exploring and Classifying Life

LAB DEMONSTRATION

Purpose to compare observations and inferences

Materials one red apple

Alternate Materials one purple grape for each student pair

Preparation Wash the fruit.

Procedure Have students record visual observations of the fruit and then classify the following statements as observations or inferences. 1. The apple's covering is red. 2. The apple is edible. 3. There are seeds inside the apple.

Expected Outcome 1 is an observation; 2 and 3 are inferences.

Assessment

How are observations and inferences different? Observations are information gathered through the senses. Inferences result from past observations. L2

Controls The technician separates the cats with sores from the other two cats. She puts each of the cats with sores in a cage by itself. One cat is called the experimental cat. This cat is given a litter box containing the cat litter without deodorant. The other cat is given a litter box that contains cat litter with deodorant. The cat with deodorant cat litter is the control.

A **control** is the standard to which the outcome of a test is compared. At the end of the experiment, the control cat will be compared with the experimental cat. Whether or not the cat litter contains deodorant is the variable. A **variable** is something in an experiment that can change. An experiment should have only one variable. Other than the difference in the cat litter, the technician treats both cats the same.

✓ Reading Check *How many variables should an experiment have?*

Analyze Data The veterinary technician observes both cats for one week. During this time, she collects data on how often and when the cats scratch or chew, as shown in **Figure 4.** These data are recorded in a journal. The data show that the control cat scratches and chews more often than the experimental cat does. The sores on the skin of the experimental cat begin to heal, but those on the control cat do not.

Draw Conclusions The technician then draws the conclusion—a logical answer to a question based on data and observation—that the deodorant in the cat litter probably irritated the skin of the two cats. To accept or reject the hypothesis is the next step. In this case, the technician accepts the hypothesis. If she had rejected it, new experiments would have been necessary.

Although the technician decides to accept her hypothesis, she realizes that to be surer of her results she should continue her experiment. She should switch the experimental cat with the control cat to see what the results are a second time. If she did this, the healed cat might develop new sores. She makes an ethical decision and chooses not to continue the experiment. Ethical decisions, like this one, are important in deciding what science should be done.

Mini LAB

Analyzing Data

Procedure
1. Obtain a **pan balance.** Follow your teacher's instructions for using it.
2. Record all data in your **Science Journal.**
3. Measure and record the mass of a **dry sponge.**
4. Soak this sponge in **water.** Measure and record its mass.
5. Calculate how much water your sponge absorbed.
6. Combine the class data and calculate the average amount of water absorbed.

Analysis
What other information about the sponges might be important when analyzing the data from the entire class?

Figure 4 Collecting and analyzing data is part of scientific methods.

Discussion
Observation First Is it possible to form a hypothesis without first making observations? Explain. No; a hypothesis is formed from observations. L2

Answer one

Mini LAB

Purpose to obtain data using a pan balance L1 IS **Logical-Mathematical**

Materials pan balance, sponge, water, Science Journal

Teaching Strategies
• Demonstrate the use of a balance.
• Review techniques for transporting a balance: be sure all riders are back to the zero point; place one hand under the balance and the other hand on the beam's support to carry the balance.

Analysis
Accept all reasonable answers. Students may suggest that the size of the sponges or how long each was soaked in water would affect results.

Assessment
Performance Have students use a meterstick to measure the length and width of their lab tables. Ask them to explain how they decided which units of measure to use. Use **Performance Assessment in the Science Classroom,** p. 97.

Teacher FYI

Galileo One of the first scientists credited with using the scientific method was Galileo. In his investigation of falling objects, the steps he used were (1) observation, (2) hypothesis, (3) mathematical analysis or deduction from hypothesis, (4) experimental test, and (5) revision of hypothesis.

Curriculum Connection

Language Arts Have students research a major discovery in life science and the person who made the discovery. Possible research subjects include Francesco Redi, William Harvey, Alexander Fleming, Barbara McClintock, and George Washington Carver. Have students use their findings to write newspaper articles describing their discoveries. L2 IS **Linguistic**

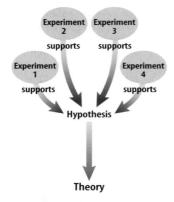

Figure 5 If data collected from several experiments over a period of time all support the hypothesis, it finally can be called a theory.

Report Results When using scientific methods, it is important to share information. The veterinary technician calls the cats' owner and tells him the results of her experiment. She tells him she has stopped using the deodorant cat litter.

The technician also writes a story for the clinic's newsletter that describes her experiment and shares her conclusions. She reports the limits of her experiment and explains that her results are not final. In science it is important to explain how an experiment can be made better if it is done again.

Developing Theories

After scientists report the results of experiments supporting their hypotheses, the results can be used to propose a scientific theory. When you watch a magician do a trick you might decide you have an idea or "theory" about how the trick works. Is your idea just a hunch or a scientific theory? A scientific **theory** is an explanation of things or events based on scientific knowledge that is the result of many observations and experiments. It is not a guess or someone's opinion. Many scientists repeat the experiment. If the results always support the hypothesis, the hypothesis can be called a theory, as shown in **Figure 5.**

✔ Reading Check *What is a theory based on?*

A theory usually explains many hypotheses. For example, an important theory in life sciences is the cell theory. Scientists made observations of cells and experimented for more than 100 years before enough information was collected to propose a theory. Hypotheses about cells in plants and animals are combined in the cell theory.

A valid theory raises many new questions. Data or information from new experiments might change conclusions and theories can change. Later in this chapter you will read about the theory of spontaneous generation and how this theory changed as scientists used experiments to study new hypotheses.

Laws A scientific **law** is a statement about how things work in nature that seems to be true all the time. Although laws can be modified as more information becomes known, they are less likely to change than theories. Laws tell you what will happen under certain conditions but do not necessarily explain why it happened. For example, in life science you might learn about laws of heredity. These laws explain how genes are inherited but do not explain how genes work. Due to the great variety of living things, laws that describe them are few. It is unlikely that a law about how all cells work will ever be developed.

✔ Active Reading

Learning Journal In this strategy, students analyze their own learning processes. Have students fold a paper in half. On the left, have them record what they have learned about a topic. On the right, have them record the page number of the text and any illustrations that helped them learn it. Have students write a Learning Journal about scientific methods. L2

Cultural Diversity

Development of Cell Theory One theory in life science that has been widely accepted by scientists is the cell theory. The cell theory originated through the work of English scientist Robert Hooke in 1665. Almost two hundred years later, the works of three German scientists—Matthias Schleiden, Theodor Schwann, and Rudolph Virchow—were incorporated to form the modern cell theory.

Scientific Methods Help Answer Questions You can use scientific methods to answer all sorts of questions. Your questions may be as simple as "Where did I leave my house key?" or as complex as "Will global warming cause the polar ice caps to melt?" You probably have had to find the answer to the first question. Someday you might try to find the answer to the second question. Using these scientific methods does not guarantee that you will get an answer. Often scientific methods just lead to more questions and more experiments. That's what science is about—continuing to look for the best answers to your questions.

Applying Science

Does temperature affect the rate of bacterial reproduction?

Some bacteria make you sick. Other bacteria, however, are used to produce foods like cheese and yogurt. Understanding how quickly bacteria reproduce can help you avoid harmful bacteria and use helpful bacteria. It's important to know things that affect how quickly bacteria reproduce. How do you think temperature will affect the rate of bacterial reproduction? A student makes the hypothesis that bacteria will reproduce more quickly as the temperature increases.

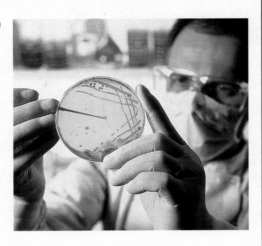

Identifying the Problem

The table below lists the reproduction-doubling rates at specific temperatures for one type of bacteria. A rate of 2.0 means that the number of bacteria doubled two times that hour (e.g., 100 to 200 to 400).

Bacterial Reproductive Rates	
Temperature (°C)	**Doubling Rate per Hour**
20.5	2.0
30.5	3.0
36.0	2.5
39.2	1.2

Look at the table. What conclusions can you draw from the data?

Solving the Problem

1. Do the data in the table support the student's hypothesis?
2. How would you write a hypothesis about the relationship between bacterial reproduction and temperature?
3. Make a list of other factors that might have influenced the results in the table.
4. Are you satisfied with these data? List other things that you wish you knew.
5. Describe an experiment that would help you test these other ideas.

The label of this juice bottle shows you that it contains 473 mL of juice.

Figure 6 Your food often is measured in metric units. Nutritional information on the label is listed in grams or milligrams.

Measuring with Scientific Units

An important part of most scientific investigations is making accurate measurements. Think about things you use every day that are measured. Ingredients in your hamburger, hot dog, potato chips, or soft drink are measured in units such as grams and milliliters, as shown in **Figure 6.** The water you drink, the gas you use, and the electricity needed for a CD player are measured, too.

Reading Check
Why is it important to make accurate measurements?

In your classroom or laboratory this year, you will use the same standard system of measurement scientists use to communicate and understand each other's research and results. This system is called the International System of Units, or SI. For example, you may need to calculate the distance a bird flies in kilometers. Perhaps you will be asked to measure the amount of air your lungs can hold in liters or the mass of an automobile in kilograms. Some of the SI units are shown in **Table 1.**

Table 1 Common SI Measurements			
Measurement	**Unit**	**Symbol**	**Equal to**
Length	1 millimeter	mm	0.001 (1/1,000) m
	1 centimeter	cm	0.01 (1/100) m
	1 meter	m	100 cm
	1 kilometer	km	1,000 m
Volume	1 milliliter	mL	0.001 (1/1,000) L
	1 liter	L	1,000 mL
Mass	1 gram	g	1,000 mg
	1 kilogram	kg	1,000 g
	1 tonne	t	1,000 kg = 1 metric ton

12 CHAPTER 1 Exploring and Classifying Life

Safety First

Doing science is usually much more interesting than just reading about it. Some of the scientific equipment that you will use in your classroom or laboratory is the same as what scientists use. Laboratory safety is important. In many states, a student can participate in a laboratory class only when wearing proper eye protection. Don't forget to wash your hands after handling materials. Following safety rules, as shown in **Figure 7,** will protect you and others from injury during your lab experiences. Symbols used throughout your text will alert you to situations that require special attention. Some of these symbols are shown below. A description of each symbol is in the Safety Symbols chart at the front of this book.

Figure 7 Proper eye protection should be worn whenever you see this safety symbol.
Predict *what might happen if you do not wear eye protection in the lab.*

3 Assess

DAILY INTERVENTION

Check for Understanding
Intrapersonal Have students make a set of flash cards they can use to review important terms from this section. [L1]

Reteach
Scientific Methods Divide the class into groups. Give each student in a group a slip of paper labeled with a step of a scientific method. After all the papers have been distributed, have students arrange themselves in a line that shows the order in which the steps are often carried out. Have groups compare their results and discuss why each group may not necessarily have the steps in the same order. [L2]

✓ Assessment

Portfolio Safety is just as important at home as it is in the laboratory. For each safety symbol in the chart at the front of the book, have students write one safety rule to follow at home in the kitchen, bathroom, or outdoors. Use **Performance Assessment in the Science Classroom,** p. 157. [L1]

Summary

The Work of Science
● Science is an organized way of studying things and finding answers to questions.

Solving Problems and Developing Theories
● Scientific methods are procedures used to solve problems and answer questions.
● A theory is an explanation based on many scientific observations.

Measuring with Scientific Units
● Scientists use the SI system for measurements.

Safety First
● Follow safety rules in the lab.

Self Check

1. **Describe** scientific methods.
2. **Infer** why it is important to test only one variable at a time during an experiment.
3. **Identify** the SI unit you would use to measure the width of your classroom.
4. **Compare and contrast** a theory with a hypothesis.
5. **Think Critically** Can the veterinary technician in this section be sure that deodorant caused the cats' skin problems? How could she improve her experiment?

Applying Skills

6. **Write a paper** that explains what the veterinary technician discovered from her experiment.

---

section 1 review

1. State the problem, gather information, form a hypothesis, experiment to test the hypothesis, analyze data, and draw conclusions.
2. so the scientist can understand which condition caused the results
3. meters
4. theory—an explanation based on many observations; hypothesis—

a testable prediction
5. Possible answer: Both cats may not be allergic to the same thing. She could repeat the experiment, this time giving the other cat non-deodorized litter. If the skin problem clears up, she has likely identified the problem.

6. The paper should include observations that led to stating the problem, how she gathered the information to form the hypothesis, how she experimented to test the hypothesis, analyzed the data, drew conclusions, and reported the results.

Living Things

as you read

What **You'll Learn**
- **Distinguish** between living and nonliving things.
- **Identify** what living things need to survive.

Why **It's Important**
All living things, including you, have many of the same traits.

Review Vocabulary
raw materials: substances needed by organisms to make other necessary substances

New Vocabulary
- organism
- cell
- homeostasis

What are living things like?

What does it mean to be alive? If you walked down your street after a thunderstorm, you'd probably see earthworms on the sidewalk, birds flying, clouds moving across the sky, and puddles of water. You'd see living and nonliving things that are alike in some ways. For example, birds and clouds move. Earthworms and water feel wet when they are touched. Yet, clouds and water are nonliving things, and birds and earthworms are living things. Any living thing is called an **organism.**

Organisms vary in size from the microscopic bacteria in mud puddles to gigantic oak trees and are found just about everywhere. They have different behaviors and food needs. In spite of these differences, all organisms have similar traits. These traits determine what it means to be alive.

Living Things Are Organized If you were to look at almost any part of an organism, like a plant leaf or your skin, under a microscope, you would see that it is made up of small units called cells. A **cell** is the smallest unit of an organism that carries on the functions of life. Some organisms are composed of just one cell while others are composed of many cells. Cells take in materials from their surroundings and use them in complex ways. Each cell has an orderly structure and contains hereditary material. The hereditary material contains instructions for cellular organization and function. **Figure 8** shows some organisms that are made of many cells. All the things that these organisms can do are possible because of what their cells can do.

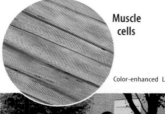

Muscle cells

Color-enhanced LM Magnification: 106×

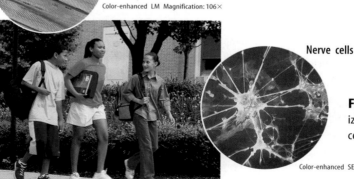

Nerve cells

Figure 8 Your body is organized into many different types of cells. Two types are shown here.

Color-enhanced SEM Magnification: 2500×

Living Things Respond Living things interact with their surroundings. Watch your cat when you use your electric can opener. Does your cat come running to find out what's happening even when you're not opening a can of cat food? The cat in **Figure 9** ran in response to a stimulus—the sound of the can opener. Anything that causes some change in an organism is a stimulus (plural, *stimuli*). The reaction to a stimulus is a response. Often that response results in movement, such as when the cat runs toward the sound of the can opener. To carry on its daily activity and to survive, an organism must respond to stimuli.

Living things also respond to stimuli that occur inside them. For example, water or food levels in organisms' cells can increase or decrease. The organisms then make internal changes to keep the right amounts of water and food in their cells. Their temperature also must be within a certain range. An organism's ability to keep the proper conditions inside no matter what is going on outside the organism is called **homeostasis.** Homeostasis is a trait of all living things.

Reading Check *What are some internal stimuli living things respond to?*

Figure 9 Some cats respond to a food stimulus even when they are not hungry.
Infer *why a cat comes running when it hears a can opener.*

Living Things Use Energy Staying organized and carrying on activities like homeostasis require energy. The energy used by most organisms comes either directly or indirectly from the Sun. Plants and some other organisms use the Sun's energy and the raw materials carbon dioxide and water to make food. You and most other organisms can't use the energy of sunlight directly. Instead, you take in and use food as a source of energy. You get food by eating plants or other organisms that ate plants. Most organisms, including plants, also must take in oxygen in order to release the energy of foods.

Some bacteria live at the bottom of the oceans and in other areas where sunlight cannot reach. They can't use the Sun's energy to produce food. Instead, the bacteria use energy stored in some chemical compounds and the raw material carbon dioxide to make food. Unlike most other organisms, many of these bacteria do not need oxygen to release the energy that is found in their food.

Topic: Homeostasis
Visit life.msscience.com for Web links to information about homeostasis.

Activity Describe the external stimuli and the corresponding internal changes for three different situations.

SECTION 2 Living Things **15**

Fun Fact

Some bacteria can use petroleum as a food source. These bacteria have been used to help clean up oil spills.

Seed Development How does an acorn grow and develop? An acorn sprouts and produces roots, stems, and leaves that continue to grow for years. As it grows, it takes in substances from the air and soil and changes those substances into living cells. It continues to add new cells and tissues to replace those that wear out. L2

IDENTIFYING Misconceptions

Nonliving Movement Students may think that all things that move are alive. Refer to page F at the beginning of this chapter for teaching strategies that address this misconception.

Teacher FYI

Energy Uses Nonliving things use energy just as living things do. Windmills, solar calculators, solar panels, and thunderclouds all use energy from their environments and change it into different forms. However, living things take in energy from their environments and use it for specialized purposes such as growth, development, and reproduction.

Figure 10 Complete development of an organism can take a few days or several years. The pictures below show the development of a dog, a human, a pea plant, and a butterfly.

Living Things Grow and Develop When a puppy is born, it might be small enough to hold in one hand. After the same dog is fully grown, you might not be able to hold it at all. How does this happen? The puppy grows by taking in raw materials, like milk from its female parent, and making more cells. Growth of many-celled organisms, such as the puppy, is mostly due to an increase in the number of cells. In one-celled organisms, growth is due to an increase in the size of the cell.

Organisms change as they grow. Puppies can't see or walk when they are born. In eight or nine days, their eyes open, and their legs become strong enough to hold them up. All of the changes that take place during the life of an organism are called development. **Figure 10** shows how four different organisms changed as they grew.

The length of time an organism is expected to live is its life span. Adult dogs can live for 20 years and a cat for 25 years. Some organisms have a short life span. Mayflies live only one day, but a land tortoise can live for more than 180 years. Some bristlecone pine trees have been alive for more than 4,600 years. Your life span is about 80 years.

Science Journal

Characteristics of Living Things Have students choose an animal that they have observed. In their Science Journals, have them write an essay explaining how their observations show that the animal is a living organism. L1 LS **Linguistic**

Curriculum Connection

Math Have students obtain data that illustrates how they have changed as they have grown older. Ask them to research their heights at three different ages. (If this information is not available at home, have students obtain the data from their school records.) Then have students work in pairs to measure their current heights. Ask students to present their results as bar graphs. L2 LS **Logical-Mathematical** P

Figure 11 Living things reproduce themselves in many different ways. A *Paramecium* reproduces by dividing into two. Beetles, like most insects, reproduce by laying eggs. Every spore released by the puffballs can grow into a new fungus.

Beetle

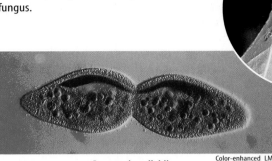
Paramecium dividing
Color-enhanced LM
Magnification: 400×

Puffballs

Living Things Reproduce Cats, dogs, alligators, fish, birds, bees, and trees eventually reproduce. They make more of their own kind. Some bacteria reproduce every 20 minutes while it might take a pine tree two years to produce seeds. **Figure 11** shows some ways organisms reproduce.

Without reproduction, living things would not exist to replace those individuals that die. An individual cat can live its entire life without reproducing. However, if cats never reproduced, all cats soon would disappear.

✓ **Reading Check** *Why is reproduction important?*

What do living things need?

What do you need to live? Do you have any needs that are different from those of other living things? To survive, all living things need a place to live and raw materials. The raw materials that they require and the exact place where they live can vary.

A Place to Live The environment limits where organisms can live. Not many kinds of organisms can live in extremely hot or extremely cold environments. Most cannot live at the bottom of the ocean or on the tops of mountains. All organisms also need living space in their surroundings. For example, thousands of penguins build their nests on an island. When the island becomes too crowded, the penguins fight for space and some may not find space to build nests. An organism's surroundings must provide for all of its needs.

INTEGRATE Social Studies

Social Development Human infants quickly develop their first year of life. Research to find out how infants interact socially at different stages of development. Make a chart that shows changes from birth to one year old.

Caption Answer

Figure 12 Plants take in water through their roots.

Figure 12 You and a corn plant each take in and give off about 2 L of water in a day. Most of the water you take in is from water you drink or from foods you eat. **Infer** *where plants get water to transport materials.*

Raw Materials Water is important for all living things. Plants and animals take in and give off large amounts of water each day, as shown in **Figure 12.** Organisms use homeostasis to balance the amounts of water lost with the amounts taken in. Most organisms are composed of more than 50 percent water. You are made of 60 to 70 percent water. Organisms use water for many things. For example, blood, which is about 90 percent water, transports digested food and wastes in animals. Plants have a watery sap that transports materials between roots and leaves.

Living things are made up of substances such as proteins, fats, and sugars. Animals take in most of these substances from the foods they eat. Plants and some bacteria make them using raw materials from their surroundings. These important substances are used over and over again. When organisms die, substances in their bodies are broken down and released into the soil or air. The substances can then be used again by other living organisms. Some of the substances in your body might once have been part of a butterfly or an apple tree.

At the beginning of this section, you learned that things such as clouds, sidewalks, and puddles of water are not living things. Now do you understand why? Clouds, sidewalks, and water do not reproduce, use energy, or have other traits of living things.

section 2 review

Summary

What are living things like?

- A cell is the smallest unit of an organism that carries on the functions of life.
- Anything that causes some change in an organism is a stimulus.
- Organisms use energy to stay organized and perform activities like homeostasis.
- All of the changes that take place during an organism's life are called development.

What do living things need?

- Living things need a place to live, water, and food.

Self Check

1. **Identify** the source of energy for most organisms.
2. **List** five traits that most organisms have.
3. **Infer** why you would expect to see cells if you looked at a section of a mushroom cap under a microscope.
4. **Determine** what most organisms need to survive.
5. **Think Critically** Why is homeostasis important to organisms?

Applying Skills

6. **Use a Database** Use references to find the life span of ten animals. Use your computer to make a database. Then, graph the life spans from shortest to longest.

Sciencenline life.msscience.com/self_check_quiz

section 2 review

1. the Sun
2. Living things are organized, respond, take in and use energy, grow and develop, and reproduce.
3. All living things are made of cells.
4. Organisms need raw materials and a place to live.
5. Without homeostasis—the maintaining of proper conditions inside an organism regardless of external conditions—the organism would die.
6. Life spans will vary in different references. Sample data (in years): humans: 76; horses: 30; cows: 24; dogs: 15; cats: 12; turtles: 125; elephants: 60; penguins: 23; shrews: 1; snakes: 11; spiders: 3

Where does life come from?

Life Comes from Life

You've probably seen a fish tank, like the one in **Figure 13,** that is full of algae. How did the algae get there? Before the seventeenth century, some people thought that insects and fish came from mud, that earthworms fell from the sky when it rained, and that mice came from grain. These were logical conclusions at that time, based on repeated personal experiences. The idea that living things come from nonliving things is known as **spontaneous generation.** This idea became a theory that was accepted for several hundred years. When scientists began to use controlled experiments to test this theory, the theory changed.

Reading Check *Why did the theory of spontaneous generation change?*

Spontaneous Generation and Biogenesis From the late seventeenth century through the middle of the eighteenth century, experiments were done to test the theory of spontaneous generation. Although these experiments showed that spontaneous generation did not occur in most cases, they did not disprove it entirely.

It was not until the mid-1800s that the work of Louis Pasteur, a French chemist, provided enough evidence to disprove the theory of spontaneous generation. It was replaced with **biogenesis** (bi oh JE nuh suss), which is the theory that living things come only from other living things.

as you read

What **You'll Learn**
- **Describe** experiments about spontaneous generation.
- **Explain** how scientific methods led to the idea of biogenesis.

Why **It's Important**
You can use scientific methods to try to find out about events that happened long ago or just last week. You can even use them to predict how something will behave in the future.

🔍 **Review Vocabulary**
contaminate: to make impure by coming into contact with an unwanted substance

New Vocabulary
- spontaneous generation
- biogenesis

Figure 13 The sides of this tank were clean and the water was clear when the aquarium was set up. Algal cells, which were not visible on plants and fish, reproduced in the tank. So many algal cells are present now that the water is cloudy.

SECTION 3 Where does life come from? **19**

Visualizing the Origins of Life

Have students examine the pictures and read the captions. Then ask the following questions.

What are the similarities of Spallanzani's and Redi's work? Students should note that both Spallanzani and Redi did experiments that questioned the idea of spontaneous generation.

What must have been present in the neck of the S-necked flasks used by Pasteur in his experiments? The necks of the S-neck flasks must have contained microorganisms, which contaminated the broth when the flask was tilted.

Activity

Matching Game Students should work in small groups to create and play a matching game based on the scientists in the this feature and their work. In the game, points should be awarded for correctly matching a scientist with his work. Have students explain the rules of their game to the class.

Fun Fact

A seventeenth-century recipe for mice called for sweaty underwear and wheat to be placed in an open container for 21 days.

Visual Learning

Figure 14 Have students create a poster showing the progression of scientific thought on life origins, as evidenced by the experiments in this feature.

Figure 14

For centuries scientists have theorized about the origins of life. As shown on this timeline, some examined spontaneous generation—the idea that nonliving material can produce life. More recently, scientists have proposed theories about the origins of life on Earth by testing hypotheses about conditions on early Earth.

1668 Francesco Redi put decaying meat in some jars, then covered half of them. When fly maggots appeared only on the uncovered meat (see below, left), Redi concluded that they had hatched from fly eggs and had not come from the meat.

John Needham heated broth in sealed flasks. When **1745** the broth became cloudy with microorganisms, he mistakenly concluded that they developed spontaneously from the broth.

Lazzaro Spallanzani boiled **1768** broth in sealed flasks for a longer time than Needham did. Only the ones he opened became cloudy with contamination.

Not contaminated   Contaminated

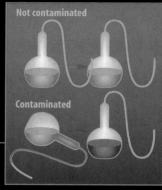

Not contaminated

Contaminated

1859 Louis Pasteur disproved spontaneous generation by boiling broth in S-necked flasks that were open to the air. The broth became cloudy (see above, bottom right) only when a flask was tilted and the broth was exposed to dust in the S-neck.

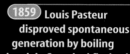

Gases of Earth's early atmosphere

Electric current

Oceanlike mixture forms

Cools

Materials in present-day cells

1924 Alexander Oparin hypothesized that energy from the Sun, lightning, and Earth's heat triggered chemical reactions early in Earth's history. The newly-formed molecules washed into Earth's ancient oceans and became a part of what is often called the primordial soup.

Stanley Miller and Harold Urey sent electric currents **1953** through a mixture of gases like those thought to be in Earth's early atmosphere. When the gases cooled, they condensed to form an oceanlike liquid that contained materials such as amino acids, found in present-day cells.

20 CHAPTER 1 Exploring and Classifying Life

Differentiated Instruction

Challenge Have students research world events that occurred in the years the experiments shown in this feature took place. Students can construct an expanded time line showing these events, and share their findings with the class. L3

Hearing Impaired Have students pantomime the work of one of the scientists who studied life's origins. Other students must guess which scientist is being represented.

Life's Origins

If living things can come only from other living things, how did life on Earth begin? Some scientists hypothesize that about 5 billion years ago, Earth's solar system was a whirling mass of gas and dust. They hypothesize that the Sun and planets were formed from this mass. It is estimated that Earth is about 4.6 billion years old. Rocks found in Australia that are more than 3.5 billion years old contain fossils of once-living organisms. Where did these living organisms come from?

Oparin's Hypothesis In 1924, a Russian scientist named Alexander I. Oparin suggested that Earth's early atmosphere had no oxygen but was made up of the gases ammonia, hydrogen, methane, and water vapor. Oparin hypothesized that these gases could have combined to form the more complex compounds found in living things.

Using gases and conditions that Oparin described, American scientists Stanley L. Miller and Harold Urey set up an experiment to test Oparin's hypothesis in 1953. Although the Miller-Urey experiment showed that chemicals found in living things could be produced, it did not prove that life began in this way.

For many centuries, scientists have tried to find the origins of life, as shown in **Figure 14.** Although questions about spontaneous generation have been answered, some scientists still are investigating ideas about life's origins.

Oceans Scientists hypothesize that Earth's oceans originally formed when water vapor was released into the atmosphere from many volcanic eruptions. Once it cooled, rain fell and filled Earth's lowland areas. Identify five lowland areas on Earth that are now filled with water. Record your answer in your Science Journal.

Oceans Students may list five of Earth's oceans and seas.

Career Explore the jobs of oceanographers and what they might study.

Teacher FYI

Oparin's Theory When Oparin first presented his hypotheses on the origins of life, they received negative responses. It was only after continued retesting that his ideas began to be accepted.

---

section 3 review

Summary

Life Comes from Life

- Spontaneous generation is the idea that living things come from nonliving things.
- The work of Louis Pasteur in 1859 disproved the theory of spontaneous generation.
- Biogenesis is the theory that living things come only from other living things.

Life's Origins

- Alexander I. Oparin hypothesized about the origin of life.
- The Miller-Urey experiment did not prove that Oparin's hypothesis was correct.

Self Check

1. **Compare and contrast** spontaneous generation with biogenesis.
2. **Describe** three controlled experiments that helped disprove the theory of spontaneous generation and led to the theory of biogenesis.
3. **Summarize** the results of the Miller-Urey experiment.
4. **Think Critically** How do you think life on Earth began?

Applying Skills

5. **Draw Conclusions** Where could the organisms have come from in the 1768 broth experiment described in **Figure 14?**

---

section 3 review

1. spontaneous generation: living things come from nonliving matter; biogenesis: living things come only from other living things of the same kind
2. Students should describe the experiments performed by Redi, Pasteur, and Spallanzani.
3. Miller and Urey passed electricity through gasses as suggested by Oparin's hypothesis and produced chemicals found in living things.
4. Students' answers will vary. Accept all reasonable responses.
5. The organisms could have come from the air.

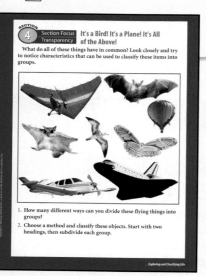
How are living things classified?

as you read

What You'll Learn
- **Describe** how early scientists classified living things.
- **Explain** how similarities are used to classify organisms.
- **Explain** the system of binomial nomenclature.
- **Demonstrate** how to use a dichotomous key.

Why It's Important
Knowing how living things are classified will help you understand the relationships that exist among all living things.

Review Vocabulary
common name: a nonscientific term that may vary from region to region

New Vocabulary
- phylogeny
- kingdom
- binomial nomenclature
- genus

Classification

If you go to a library to find a book about the life of Louis Pasteur, where do you look? Do you look for it among the mystery or sports books? You expect to find a book about Pasteur's life with other biography books. Libraries group similar types of books together. When you place similar items together, you classify them. Organisms also are classified into groups.

History of Classification When did people begin to group similar organisms together? Early classifications included grouping plants that were used in medicines. Animals were often classified by human traits such as courageous—for lions—or wise—for owls.

More than 2,000 years ago, a Greek named Aristotle observed living things. He decided that any organism could be classified as either a plant or an animal. Then he broke these two groups into smaller groups. For example, animal categories included hair or no hair, four legs or fewer legs, and blood or no blood. **Figure 15** shows some of the organisms Aristotle would have grouped together. For hundreds of years after Aristotle, no one way of classifying was accepted by everyone.

Figure 15 Using Aristotle's classification system, all animals without hair would be grouped together.
List other animals without hair that Aristotle would have put in this group.

Section 4 Resource Manager

Chapter FAST FILE Resources
Transparency Activity, pp. 47, 49–50
Directed Reading for Content Mastery, pp. 19, 20
Enrichment, p. 32
Reinforcement, p. 28

MiniLAB, p. 4
Lab Worksheets, pp. 5–6, 7–8
Lab Activity, pp. 11–13
Lab Management and Safety, p. 65

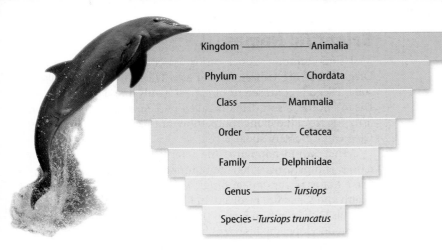

Kingdom ———— Animalia

Phylum ———— Chordata

Class ———— Mammalia

Order ———— Cetacea

Family ——— Delphinidae

Genus ———— *Tursiops*

Species – *Tursiops truncatus*

Figure 16 The classification of the bottle-nosed dolphin shows that it is in the order Cetacea. This order includes whales and porpoises.

Linnaeus In the late eighteenth century, Carolus Linnaeus, a Swedish naturalist, developed a new system of grouping organisms. His classification system was based on looking for organisms with similar structures. For example, plants that had similar flower structure were grouped together. Linnaeus's system eventually was accepted and used by most other scientists.

Modern Classification Like Linnaeus, modern scientists use similarities in structure to classify organisms. They also use similarities in both external and internal features. Specific characteristics at the cellular level, such as the number of chromosomes, can be used to infer the degree of relatedness among organisms. In addition, scientists study fossils, hereditary information, and early stages of development. They use all of this information to determine an organism's phylogeny. **Phylogeny** (fi LAH juh nee) is the evolutionary history of an organism, or how it has changed over time. Today, it is the basis for the classification of many organisms.

> **Reading Check** *What information would a scientist use to determine an organism's phylogeny?*

Six Kingdoms A classification system commonly used today groups organisms into six kingdoms. A **kingdom** is the first and largest category. Organisms are placed into kingdoms based on various characteristics. Kingdoms can be divided into smaller groups. The smallest classification category is a species. Organisms that belong to the same species can mate and produce fertile offspring. To understand how an organism is classified, look at the classification of the bottle-nosed dolphin in **Figure 16.** Some scientists propose that before organisms are grouped into kingdoms, they should be placed in larger groups called domains. One proposed system groups all organisms into three domains.

Science Online

Topic: Domains
Visit life.msscience.com for Web links to information about domains.

Activity List all the domains and give examples of organisms that are grouped in each domain.

Inquiry Lab

Classifying with Bones

Question While excavating for a new building, the skeleton of a large animal is found. How could scientists determine the classification of this animal?

Possible Materials photos of skeletons of mammoth, elephant, dinosaurs, and other large animals; real or model skeletons of smaller animals; books concerning fossils and animal structure

Estimated Time 1 class session

Teaching Strategies

• Students can look at photos of animal skeletons and determine how to use them to gain information about classification.

• Students can compare photos of mammoth and elephant skeletons and note similarities.

• Students can hypothesize what animals would have similar skeletons and then use pictures or bones of the animals to collect data; they can research to find out what scientists think.

• A trip to a museum may be planned to look at skeletons of larger animals. [L2]

For additional inquiry activities, see *Science Inquiry Labs.*

> **Reading Check**

Answer similar structures, fossils, hereditary information, and early stages of development

Fun Fact

Amber is the hardened resin of some trees. Some amber contains fossils of insects that became trapped in the resin.

Differentiated Instruction

English-Language Learners Have students listen to a variety of songs and determine how the songs might be classified into different categories. [L2]

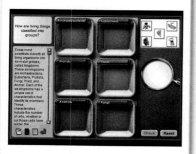

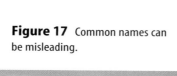

Figure 17 Common names can be misleading.

Sea lions are more closely related to seals than to lions. **Identify** *another misleading common name.*

Jellyfish are neither fish nor jelly.

Scientific Names

Using common names can cause confusion. Suppose that Diego is visiting Jamaal. Jamaal asks Diego if he would like a soda. Diego is confused until Jamaal hands him a soft drink. At Diego's house, a soft drink is called pop. Jamaal's grandmother, listening from the living room, thought that Jamaal was offering Diego an ice-cream soda.

What would happen if life scientists used only common names of organisms when they communicated with other scientists? Many misunderstandings would occur, and sometimes health and safety are involved. In **Figure 17,** you see examples of animals with common names that can be misleading. A naming system developed by Linnaeus helped solve this problem. It gave each species a unique, two-word scientific name.

Binomial Nomenclature The two-word naming system that Linnaeus used to name the various species is called **binomial nomenclature** (bi NOH mee ul • NOH mun klay chur). It is the system used by modern scientists to name organisms. The first word of the two-word name identifies the genus of the organism. A **genus** is a group of similar species. The second word of the name might tell you something about the organism—what it looks like, where it is found, or who discovered it.

In this system, the tree species commonly known as red maple has been given the name *Acer rubrum.* The maple genus is *Acer.* The word *rubrum* is Latin for red, which is the color of a red maple's leaves in the fall. The scientific name of another maple is *Acer saccharum.* The Latin word for sugar is *saccharum.* In the spring, the sap of this tree is sweet.

Uses of Scientific Names

Two-word scientific names are used for four reasons. First, they help avoid mistakes. Both of the lizards shown in **Figure 18** have the name *iguana*. Using binomial nomenclature, the green iguana is named *Iguana iguana*. Someone who studied this *iguana*, shown in the left photo, would not be confused by information he or she read about *Dispsosaurus dorsalis*, the desert iguana, shown in the right photo. Second, organisms with similar evolutionary histories are classified together. Because of this, you know that organisms in the same genus are related. Third, scientific names give descriptive information about the species, like the maples mentioned earlier. Fourth, scientific names allow information about organisms to be organized easily and efficiently. Such information may be found in a book or a pamphlet that lists related organisms and gives their scientific names.

✓ Reading Check *What are four functions of scientific names?*

Tools for Identifying Organisms

Tools used to identify organisms include field guides and dichotomous (di KAH tuh mus) keys. Using these tools is one way you and scientists solve problems scientifically.

Many different field guides are available. You will find some field guides at the back of this book. Most have descriptions and illustrations of organisms and information about where each organism lives. You can identify species from around the world using the appropriate field guide.

Mini LAB

Communicating Ideas

Procedure
1. Find a **magazine picture of a piece of furniture** that can be used as a place to sit and to lie down.
2. Show the picture to ten people and ask them to tell you what word they use for this piece of furniture.
3. Keep a record of the answers in your **Science Journal.**

Analysis
1. In your Science Journal, infer how using common names can be confusing.
2. How do scientific names make communication among scientists easier?

Try at Home

Mini LAB

Purpose Students ask people to give them the name of a common piece of furniture seen in a photo.
L2 IS **Visual-Spatial**

Materials photo from magazine

Teaching Strategy Review how to collect and record data.

Analysis
1. More than one name might be used for the same object.
2. Each organism has a specific, unique name.

Assessment

Oral To further assess students' abilities to identify characteristic features, ask them to list traits of other common objects. L2

Try at Home

✓ Reading Check

Answer to avoid mistakes, classify organisms with similar evolutionary histories together, give descriptive information about a species, help organize information about species

Make a Model

Object Dichotomy Have students list the characteristics of several related objects such as shoes, animals, or foods. Then have students use their lists to make a model dichotomous key. L1

Visual Learning

Figure 18 What traits do the desert iguana and green iguana share? clawed toes, scaly skin L2

Differentiated Instruction

Challenge Challenge students to identify an organism from its scientific name. Use *Musca domestica* (housefly), *Equus zebra* (zebra), and *Camelus dromedarius* (dromedary camel). Have students find other scientific names to present to their classmates. L3 IS

Using Keys Pass out taxonomic keys or field guides. Ask students to describe how these tools are used. Have them use the keys to identify a particular organism. Note that students may try to skip steps in keys. Point out that skipping steps often leads to the wrong identification. [L2]

Text Question Answer

Microtus pinetorum

3 Assess

DAILY INTERVENTION

Check for Understanding

Auditory-Musical Have students write a poem that demonstrates their understanding of binomial nomenclature and scientific names. [L2]

Reteach

Classification Develop understanding of modern classification by asking students to name the lowest taxonomic category for the organisms described. Ask: Which level contains a spider plant? species Which level contains all willow trees? genus Which level contains all plants? kingdom [L2]

☑ Assessment

Performance Have students make a concept map to show how an address is like a classification system. The first step should be Country—United States. Use **Performance Assessment in the Science Classroom**, p. 161. [L2] [P]

Dichotomous Keys A dichotomous key is a detailed list of identifying characteristics that includes scientific names. Dichotomous keys are arranged in steps with two descriptive statements at each step. If you learn how to use a dichotomous key, you can identify and name a species.

Did you know many types of mice exist? You can use **Table 2** to find out what type of mouse is pictured to the left. Start by choosing between the first pair of descriptions. The mouse has hair on its tail, so you go to 2. The ears of the mouse are small, so you go on to 3. The tail of the mouse is less that 25 mm. What is the name of this mouse according to the key?

Table 2 Key to Some Mice of North America

1. Tail hair	**a.** no hair on tail; scales show plainly; house mouse, *Mus musculus* **b.** hair on tail, go to 2
2. Ear size	**a.** ears small and nearly hidden in fur, go to 3 **b.** ears large and not hidden in fur, go to 4
3. Tail length	**a.** less than 25 mm; woodland vole, *Microtus pinetorum* **b.** more than 25 mm; prairie vole, *Microtus ochrogaster*
4. Tail coloration	**a.** sharply bicolor, white beneath and dark above; deer mouse, *Peromyscus maniculatus* **b.** darker above than below but not sharply bicolor; white-footed mouse, *Peromyscus leucopus*

section 4 review

Summary

Classification
- Organisms are classified into groups based on their similarities.
- Scientists today classify organisms into six kingdoms.
- Species is the smallest classification category.

Scientific Names
- Binomial nomenclature is the two-word naming system that gives organisms their scientific names.

Tools for Identifying Organisms
- Field guides and dichotomous keys are used to identify organisms.

Self Check

1. **State** Aristotle's and Linnaeus' contributions to classifying living things.
2. **Identify** a specific characteristic used to classify organisms.
3. **Describe** what each of the two words identifies in binomial nomenclature.
4. **Think Critically** Would you expect a field guide to have common names as well as scientific names? Why or why not?

Applying Skills

5. **Classify** Create a dichotomous key that identifies types of cars.

 Science Online life.msscience.com/self_check_quiz

---

section 4 review

1. Aristotle—two kingdoms: plants and animals; Linnaeus—binomial nomenclature
2. Students' answers will vary. Accept all reasonable responses.
3. first word is the genus and second word tells something about the organism
4. Yes. Field guides are also used by non-scientists.
5. Students' keys will vary and may divide cars by color, make, size, or other variable characteristics.

Classifying Seeds

BENCH TESTED

Scientists use classification systems to show how organisms are related. How do they determine which features to use to classify organisms? In this lab, you will observe seeds and use their features to classify them.

◉ Real-World Question

How can the features of seeds be used to develop a key to identify the seed?

Goals
■ **Observe** the seeds and notice their features.
■ **Classify** seeds using these features.

Materials
packets of seeds (10 different kinds)
magnifying lens
metric ruler

Safety Precautions

WARNING: *Some seeds may have been treated with chemicals. Do not put them in your mouth.*

◉ Procedure

1. Copy the following data table in your Science Journal and record the features of each seed. Your table will have a column for each different type of seed you observe.

Seed Data			
Feature	Type of Seed		
	corn	kidney bean	wheat
Color	yellow	dark brown	light brown
Length (mm)	10	17	5
Shape	triangle	oval	oval
Texture	smooth	smooth	smooth

2. Use the features to develop a key.
3. Exchange keys with another group. Can you use their key to identify seeds?

◉ Conclude and Apply

1. **Determine** how different seeds can be classified.
2. **Explain** how you would classify a seed you had not seen before using your data table.
3. **Explain** why it is an advantage for scientists to use a standardized system to classify organisms. What observations did you make to support your answer?

𝒞ommunicating Your Data

Compare your conclusions with those of other students in your class. **For more help, refer to the** Science Skill Handbook.

𝒞ommunicating Your Data

Comparisons may or may not result in agreement. If one group can use another group's key, the second group was successful.

✓ Assessment

Performance Give students photocopies of ten different leaves. Have them devise and describe a classification system for the leaves. Use **Performance Assessment in the Science Classroom,** p. 121.

◉ Real-World Question

Purpose Students observe seed features and then classify the seeds. L2 IS **Kinesthetic**

Process Skills observe and infer, classify, form operational definitions, communicate, make and use tables, compare and contrast

Time Required 45 minutes

◉ Procedure

Alternate Materials Any objects may be used, but biological specimens should be used if possible.

Safety Precautions Use only edible seeds, not seeds that have been treated for planting.

Teaching Strategy Prepare packets of ten different kinds of easily classified seeds, such as black-eyed peas, squash, beans (lima, kidney, pinto, black), green peas, popcorn, seed corn, and sunflower.

◉ Conclude and Apply

1. color, shape, size, texture, how they are attached to the plant
2. You would use the data table to categorize identifying characteristics of seeds.
3. Different classification systems could result in confusion. Answers should be based on the observation that students classified the same seeds in different ways.

◉ Real-World Question

Purpose Design and carry out an experiment using scientific methods to infer why brine shrimp live in salty waters. L2

COOP LEARN IŠ **Interpersonal**

Process Skills observe and infer, compare and contrast, recognize cause and effect, interpret data, hypothesize, communicate, make and use tables, make and use graphs, design an experiment, separate and control variables, measure in SI

Time Required 50 minutes on Day 1, 5 minutes a day for 3 days, 30 minutes to summarize

Materials Purchase brine shrimp eggs from a pet store or a biological supply house. Do not place too many brine shrimp eggs in each container. Brine shrimp are orange-colored and swim with a jerking motion. To maintain the brine shrimp, add a pinch of yeast to the container two or three times a week.

Safety Precautions Students should use care when working with live animals.

◉ Form a Hypothesis

Possible Hypothesis Brine shrimp will best grow in a strong salt solution since they naturally live in salty lakes.

◉ Test Your Hypothesis

Possible Procedures The same amount of brine shrimp eggs can be added to the three solutions and observed.

Design Your Own

USING SCIENTIFIC METHODS

Goals
- **Design** and carry out an experiment using scientific methods to infer why brine shrimp live in the ocean.
- **Observe** the jars for one week and notice whether the brine shrimp eggs hatch.

Possible Materials
500-mL, widemouthed containers (3)
brine shrimp eggs
small, plastic spoon
distilled water (500 mL)
weak salt solution (500 mL)
strong salt solution (500 mL)
labels (3)
magnifying lens

Safety Precautions

WARNING: *Protect eyes and clothing. Be careful when working with live organisms.*

◉ Real-World Question

Brine shrimp are relatives of lobsters, crabs, crayfish, and the shrimp eaten by humans. They are often raised as a live food source in aquariums. In nature, they live in the oceans where fish feed on them. They can hatch from eggs that have been stored in a dry condition for many years. How can you use scientific methods to determine whether salt affects the hatching and growth of brine shrimp?

Brine shrimp

◉ Form a Hypothesis

Based on your observations, form a hypothesis to explain how salt affects the hatching and growth of brine shrimp.

◉ Test Your Hypothesis

Make a Plan

1. As a group, agree upon the hypothesis and decide how you will test it. Identify what results will confirm the hypothesis.

28 CHAPTER 1 Exploring and Classifying Life

Alternative Inquiry Lab

Environmental Change Have students investigate how other environmental conditions, like temperature and light, might affect the development and growth of brine shrimp. Allow students to prepare variable salt solutions. Since brine shrimp are an important food for birds, have students hypothesize how changing salinity levels might affect both shrimp and bird populations. L2

2. **List** steps that you need to test your hypothesis. Be specific. Describe exactly what you will do at each step.

3. **List** your materials.

4. **Prepare** a data table in your Science Journal to record your data.

5. Read over your entire experiment to make sure that all planned steps are in logical order.

6. **Identify** any constants, variables, and controls of the experiment.

Follow Your Plan

1. Make sure your teacher approves your plan before you start.

2. Carry out the experiment as planned by your group.

3. While doing the experiment, record any observations and complete the data table in your Science Journal.

4. Use a bar graph to plot your results.

◉ Analyze Your Data

1. **Describe** the contents of each jar after one week.

2. **Identify** your control in this experiment.

3. **Identify** your variable in this experiment.

◉ Conclude and Apply

1. **Explain** whether or not the results support your hypothesis.

2. **Predict** the effect that increasing the amount of salt in the water would have on the brine shrimp eggs.

3. **Compare** your results with those of other groups.

Communicating Your Data

Prepare a set of instructions on how to hatch brine shrimp to use to feed fish. Include diagrams and a step-by-step procedure.

Communicating Your Data

Instructions should include information on the amount of salt to add to the water, light conditions, and so on. Students can use word-processing software programs to write their instructions.

☑ Assessment

Performance Have students design an experiment to determine how ocean currents affect brine shrimp. Use **Performance Assessment in the Science Classroom,** p. 95.

Teaching Strategies

Prepare the solutions as follows:

- Dechlorinated water: Allow tap water to stand for 48 hours.
- Weak salt solution: Add 20 mL non-iodized salt to 4 L dechlorinated water. Stir until dissolved.
- Strong salt solution: Add 75 mL non-iodized salt to 4 L dechlorinated water. Stir until dissolved.

Expected Outcome Results likely will reflect that the brine shrimp grew best in the strong salt solution.

◉ Analyze Your Data

Answers to Questions

1. There were no shrimp in the distilled water or weak salt solution. There were many shrimp in the strong salt solution.

2. The dechlorinated water without salt was the control.

3. The amount of salt in the water was the variable.

Error Analysis Have students compare their results and their hypotheses and explain any differences.

◉ Conclude and Apply

1. Answers will be determined by students' hypotheses.

2. Answers will vary. Some may predict that more brine shrimp will hatch.

3. Results will vary.

Content Background

The rain forests of the world are home to fifty percent of all species of plants and animals. Some insect species evolve and become extinct without ever having been seen alive by humans. Most rain forest species live in the forest canopy between 18 to 46 meters (60–150 ft) above the ground. While observing wildlife in the canopy is extremely difficult, the need for extensive study is pressing as logging and slash and burn agriculture destroys more forest habitat.

One method being attempted to halt uncontrolled agriculture is the development of programs that preserve wild areas by attracting tourists, or ecotourism. Building an economy based on service industries can relieve pressure to clear more land for farming. One version of ecotourism is the canopy tour ranging from climbing harnesses to walkways and aerial tramways. A benefit of these tours is that canopy research can be conducted from these structures.

Discussion

Invisible Species What features of the rain forest cause a large number species to remain unknown? Possible answer: The difficulty of travel and the remoteness of some areas make observation points difficult to get to. The fact that most of the species live in the canopy further complicates surveys. L2

Investigate the Issue

Numbers of Species Direct students to research the estimated number of plant and animal species worldwide and chart their distribution on a map using colored pins. How many species are in the rain forests? How will deforestation affect these species? L2

Acari marmoset

Manicore marmoset

Monkey BUSINESS

In 2000, a scientist from Brazil's Amazon National Research Institute came across two squirrel-sized monkeys in a remote and isolated corner of the rain forest, about 2,575 km from Rio de Janeiro.

It turns out that the monkeys had never been seen before, or even known to exist.

Acari marmoset

The new species were spotted by a scientist who named them after two nearby rivers the Manicore and the Acari, where the animals were discovered. Both animals are marmosets, which is a type of monkey found only in Central and South America. Marmosets have claws instead of nails, live in trees, and use their extraordinarily long tail like an extra arm or leg. Small and light, both marmosets measure about 23 cm in length with a 38 cm tail, and weigh no more than 0.4 kg.

The Manicore marmoset has a silvery-white upper body, a light-gray cap on its head, a yellow-orange underbody, and a black tail.

The Acari marmoset's upper body is snowy white, its gray back sports a stripe running to the knee, and its black tail flashes a bright-orange tip.

Amazin' Amazon

The Amazon Basin is a treasure trove of unique species. The Amazon River is Earth's largest body of freshwater, with 1,100 smaller tributaries. And more than half of the world's plant and animal species live in its rain forest ecosystems.

Research and Report Working in small groups, find out more about the Amazon rain forest. Which plants and animals live there? What products come from the rain forest? How does what happens in the Amazon rain forest affect you? Prepare a multimedia presentation.

Science Online
For more information, visit life.msscience.com/time

Research and Report As an extension, have students discuss the pros and cons of ecotourism in light of their research of current rain forest uses and conditions.

Resources for Teachers and Students

Rain Forests of the World: Water, Fire, Earth, Air, by Art Wolfe and Sir Ghillean Prance, New York: Crown Publishers, 1998

Amazonia: the Land, the Wildlife, the River, the People, by Afonso Capelas, Firefly Books, 2003

Reviewing Main Ideas

Section 1 What is science?

1. Scientists use problem-solving methods to investigate observations about living and nonliving things.

2. Scientists use SI measurements to gather measurable data.

3. Safe laboratory practices help you learn more about science.

Section 2 Living Things

1. Organisms are made of cells, use energy, reproduce, respond, grow, and develop.

2. Organisms need energy, water, food, and a place to live.

Section 3 Where does life come from?

1. Controlled experiments finally disproved the theory of spontaneous generation.

2. Pasteur's experiment proved biogenesis.

Section 4 How are living things classified?

1. Classification is the grouping of ideas, information, or objects based on their similar characteristics.

2. Scientists today use phylogeny to group organisms into six kingdoms.

3. All organisms are given a two-word scientific name using binomial nomenclature.

Visualizing Main Ideas

Copy and complete this events-chain concept map that shows the order in which you might use a scientific method. Use these terms: analyze data, perform an experiment, *and* form a hypothesis.

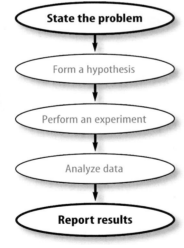

State the problem
↓
Form a hypothesis
↓
Perform an experiment
↓
Analyze data
↓
Report results

 life.msscience.com/interactive_tutor

CHAPTER STUDY GUIDE 31

Reviewing Main Ideas

Summary statements can be used by students to review the major concepts of the chapter.

Visualizing Main Ideas

See student page.

Visit life.msscience.com
/self_check_quiz
/interactive_tutor
/vocabulary_puzzlemaker
/chapter_review
/standardized_test

Assessment Transparency

For additional assessment questions, use the *Assessment Transparency* located in the transparency book.

Assessment

Assessment Transparency — Exploring and Classifying Life

Directions: *Carefully review the table and answer the following questions.*

Fruit and Vegetable Seed Germination Rate

Type of seed	Number of seeds	Amount of water added (mL)	Number of seeds germinating Day 3	Day 5	Day 7
Orange	10	50	0	0	1
Lemon	10	50	0	1	1
Cucumber	10	50	6	7	7
Onion	10	50	7	9	10

1. Which hypothesis was probably being tested?
   A Less than 25 percent of vegetable seeds will germinate.
   B Seeds prefer to grow in soil versus sand.
   C Vegetable seeds germinate faster than fruit seeds.
   D A period of one week is required before seeds will germinate.

2. Which of the following would improve an experiment to compare the rate of seed germination?
   F using more types of seeds
   G measuring the length of the plants
   H adding 100mL of water to each seed
   J conducting the experiment for a shorter time

3. Which factor would have the LEAST effect on the results?
   A the amount of light to which the seeds were exposed
   B the amount of soil used for the seeds
   C the color of the pots used
   D the depth the seeds were planted in the soil

Exploring and Classifying Life

◆ **Identifying Misconceptions**

Assess

Activity Have students record whether items in several pictures are living or nonliving and their reason. Have students share ideas and generate a list of characteristics that they think describe living things. Compare this list to the list in **Section 2** and ask the class if they would like to make any changes in their list.

Expected Outcome Most students should be forming a more sophisticated definition that includes characteristics from the text. L2

chapter 1 Review

Using Vocabulary

1. variable—condition tested; control—standard used to compare with outcome of the test

2. theory—explanation of things or events based on many observations; law—a statement about how things work in nature

3. The theory of spontaneous generation (living things come from non-living things) was replaced with the theory of biogenesis (living things come only from other living things).

4. Phylogeny is the evolutionary history of an organism; binomial nomenclature is a naming system based on phylogeny.

5. A cell is the smallest unit of an organism that carries out the functions of life. All organisms are made of cells.

6. Phylogeny is the basis for placing organisms into kingdoms.

7. Forming a hypothesis is an important part of solving a problem with scientific methods.

8. Homeostasis—keeping proper internal conditions no matter what external conditions are—is a trait of all organisms.

9. A genus is a subgroup of a kingdom.

10. If the results of repeated experiments always support the same hypothesis, the hypothesis may be called a theory.

Checking Concepts

11. D	16. D
12. D	17. A
13. A	18. B
14. D	19. D
15. C	20. B

chapter 1 Review

Using Vocabulary

binomial nomenclature p. 24
biogenesis p. 19
cell p. 14
control p. 9
genus p. 24
homeostasis p. 15
hypothesis p. 8
kingdom p. 23
law p. 10
organism p. 14
phylogeny p. 23
scientific methods p. 7
spontaneous generation p. 19
theory p. 10
variable p. 9

Explain the differences in the vocabulary words in each pair below. Then explain how they are related.

1. control—variable

2. law—theory

3. biogenesis—spontaneous generation

4. binomial nomenclature—phylogeny

5. organism—cell

6. kingdom—phylogeny

7. hypothesis—scientific methods

8. organism—homeostasis

9. kingdom—genus

10. theory—hypothesis

Checking Concepts

Choose the word or phrase that best answers the question.

11. What category of organisms can mate and produce fertile offspring?
    A) family
    C) genus
    B) class
    D) species

12. What is the closest relative of *Canis lupus?*
    A) *Quercus alba*
    C) *Felis tigris*
    B) *Equus zebra*
    D) *Canis familiaris*

13. What is the source of energy for plants?
    A) the Sun
    C) water
    B) carbon dioxide
    D) oxygen

14. What makes up more than 50 percent of all living things?
    A) oxygen
    C) minerals
    B) carbon dioxide
    D) water

15. Who finally disproved the theory of spontaneous generation?
    A) Oparin
    C) Pasteur
    B) Aristotle
    D) Miller

16. What gas do some scientists think was missing from Earth's early atmosphere?
    A) ammonia
    C) methane
    B) hydrogen
    D) oxygen

17. What is the length of time called that an organism is expected to live?
    A) life span
    C) homeostasis
    B) stimulus
    D) theory

18. What is the part of an experiment that can be changed called?
    A) conclusion
    C) control
    B) variable
    D) data

19. What does the first word in a two-word name of an organism identify?
    A) kingdom
    C) phylum
    B) species
    D) genus

Use the photo below to answer question 20.

20. What SI unit is used to measure the volume of soda shown above?
    A) meter
    C) gram
    B) liter
    D) degree

 Science Online life.msscience.com/vocabulary_puzzlemaker

Use the ExamView® Pro Testmaker CD-ROM to:
- create multiple versions of tests
- create modified tests with one mouse click for inclusion students
- edit existing questions and add your own questions
- build tests aligned with state standards using built-in State Curriculum Tags
- change English tests to Spanish with one mouse click and vice versa

Thinking Critically

21. Predict what *Lathyrus odoratus*, the scientific name for a sweet pea plant, tells you about one of its characteristics.

Use the photo below to answer question 22.

22. Determine what problem-solving techniques this scientist would use to find how dolphins learn.

Use the graph below to answer question 23.

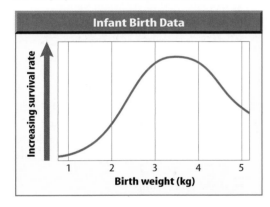

Infant Birth Data

Increasing survival rate

Birth weight (kg)

23. Interpret Data Do the data in the graph above support the hypothesis that babies with a birth weight of 2.5 kg have the best chance of survival? Explain.

24. List advantages of using SI units.

25. Form a Hypothesis A lima bean plant is placed under green light, another is placed under red light, and a third under blue light. Their growth is measured for four weeks to determine which light is best for plant growth. What are the variables in this experiment? State a hypothesis for this experiment.

Performance Activities

26. Bulletin Board Interview people in your community whose jobs require a knowledge of life science. Make a Life Science Careers bulletin board. Summarize each person's job and what he or she had to study to prepare for that job.

Applying Math

27. Body Temperature Normal human body temperature is 98.6°F. What is this temperature in degrees Celsius? Use the following expression, $5/9(°F-32)$, to find degrees Celsius.

Use the graph below to answer question 28.

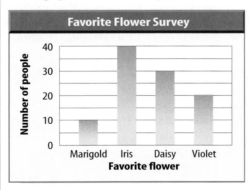

Favorite Flower Survey

Number of people

Marigold Iris Daisy Violet
Favorite flower

28. Favorite Flower The graph above shows how many people selected a certain type of flower as their favorite. According to the graph, what percentage of the people picked daisy as their favorite?

Thinking Critically

21. The name *odoratus* tells you that the sweet pea probably has an odor.

22. critical thinking including scientific methods of observation, forming hypotheses, performing experiments, and analyzing data

23. No. The graph indicates that a birth weight of 3.5 kg is best for survival.

24. Scientists can compare and repeat experiments; they have a common tool for measurement.

25. The colors of light used are variables. A possible hypothesis is that plants will grow better under some colors of light than under other colors.

Performance Activities

26. Careers could include farmers, produce clerks, florists, veterinary technicians, health care workers, and teachers. Use **Performance Assessment in the Science Classroom,** p. 131.

Applying Math

National Math Standards
1, 2, 4, 5, 9

27. $5/9(98.6-32) = 37°C$

28. 30 people out of the 100 surveyed chose the daisy or $30/100 = 0.3 = 30\%$

Answer Sheet A practice answer sheet can be found at life.msscience.com/answer_sheet.

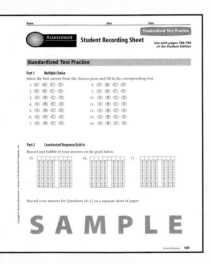

S A M P L E

Part 1 | Multiple Choice

1. C	6. C
2. B	7. A
3. B	8. A
4. C	9. D
5. B	10. A

Part 1 | Multiple Choice

Record your answers on the answer sheet provided by your teacher or on a sheet of paper.

1. A prediction that can be tested is a
   A. conclusion.   **C.** hypothesis.
   B. variable.   **D.** theory.

2. Which of the following units would a scientist likely use when measuring the length of a mouse's tail?
   A. kilometers   **C.** grams
   B. millimeters   **D.** milliliters

Use the illustrations below to answer questions 3 and 4.

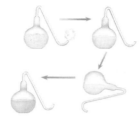

3. What scientist used the flasks pictured above to support the theory of biogenesis?
   A. John Needham   **C.** Lazzaro Spallanzani
   B. Louis Pasteur   **D.** Francesco Redi

4. Why did only the broth in the flask that was tilted become cloudy and contaminated?
   A. The broth was not boiled.
   B. Flies contaminated the broth.
   C. The broth was exposed to dust in the neck of the flask.
   D. Decaying meat caused the broth to be contaminated.

Test-Taking Tip

Practice Skills Remember that test-taking skills can improve with practice. If possible, take at least one practice test and familiarize yourself with the test format and instructions.

Use the photos below to answer questions 5 and 6.

5. The dog pictured above has increased in size. How did most of this size increase take place?
   A. an increase in cell size
   B. an increase in the number of cells
   C. an increase in cell water
   D. an increase in cell energy

6. What characteristic of life is illustrated by the change in the dog?
   A. reproduction
   B. homeostasis
   C. growth and development
   D. response to stimulus

7. What gas must most organisms take in to release the energy of foods?
   A. oxygen   **C.** water vapor
   B. carbon dioxide   **D.** hydrogen

8. What characteristic of living things is represented by a puffball releasing millions of spores?
   A. reproduction   **C.** organization
   B. development   **D.** use of energy

9. When using scientific methods to solve a problem, which of the following is a scientist most likely to do after forming a hypothesis?
   A. analyze data
   B. draw conclusions
   C. state a problem
   D. perform an experiment

10. What are the smallest units that make up your body called?
   A. cells   **C.** muscles
   B. organisms   **D.** fibers

Part 2 | Short Response/Grid In

11. They use energy stored in chemical compounds.

12. process of homeostasis

13. The theory would state that earthworms come from other earthworms not from the rain or sky.

14. similarities in structure, study of fossils, study of hereditary information, or study of early stages of development

15. the hypothesis that plants grow toward light

16. Remove the boxes over the plants.

Part 2 | Short Response/Grid In

Record your answers on the answer sheet provided by your teacher or on a sheet of paper.

11. From where do bacteria that live in areas where there is no sunlight obtain energy?

12. Organisms take in and give off large amounts of water each day. What process do they use to balance the amount of water lost with the amount taken in?

13. After a rain storm, earthworms may be seen crawling on the sidewalk or road. How would the theory of spontaneous generation explain the origin of the worms?

14. List three things modern scientists study when they classify organisms.

Use the illustrations below to answer questions 15 and 16.

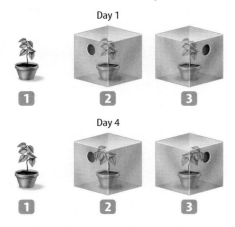

Day 1

1   2   3

Day 4

1   2   3

15. A science class set up the experiment above to study the response of plants to the stimulus of light. What hypothesis is likely being tested by this experiment?

16. After day 4, Fatima wanted to find out how plant 2 and plant 3 would grow in normal light. What did she have to do to find out?

Part 3 | Open Ended

Record your answers on a sheet of paper.

17. Describe several different ways scientists gather information. Which of these ways would likely be used to collect data about which foods wild alligators eat in Florida?

18. Some scientists think that lightning may have caused chemicals in the Earth's early atmosphere to combine to begin the origin of life. Explain how the experiment of Miller and Urey does not prove this hypothesis.

Use the photo below to answer questions 19 and 20.

19. Both of these living things use energy. Describe the difference between the source of energy for each. In what similar ways would each of these organisms use energy?

20. How are the needs of the two organisms alike? Explain why the plant is raw material for the beetle. When the beetle dies, how could it be raw material for the plant?

21. Explain stimulus and response. How is response to a stimulus related to homeostasis?

22. What information would you need to write a field guide used to identify garden plants? What other information would you need if the guide included a dichotomous key?

23. Explain the difference between a kingdom and a species in the classification system commonly used.

21. The cause of any change in an organism is a stimulus. Reaction to a stimulus is a response. Living things respond to internal and external stimuli. Keeping proper internal conditions is homeostasis.

22. You would need to collect information describing each plant, pictures of each plant, and information about where each plant grows. A dichotomous key would include scientific names of each plant and detailed identifying characteristics.

23. A kingdom is the first and largest of seven classification categories. One system includes six kingdoms. A species is the smallest category. Every type of living thing is a separate species.

Rubrics

For more help evaluating open-ended assessment questions, see the rubric on p. 10T.

Part 3 | Open Ended

17. Information may be gathered in the laboratory, from field work, or by computer models. Fieldwork would be the best way to study the alligator's diet.

18. Using an electric current and a mixture of gasses, chemicals found in present-day cells were produced.

However, the experiment did not produce living things.

19. Plants use the Sun's energy. Since the beetles eat plants for energy they also indirectly use the Sun. Both use energy for organization and homeostasis.

20. Both need an environment with proper conditions and the raw materials water and oxygen. Plants need carbon dioxide and soil minerals. The beetles need plants for food. Dead beetles will be broken down into substances in the soil which plants use as raw materials.

chapter 2 Organizer

Section/Objectives	Standards		Labs/Features
Chapter Opener	**National**	**State/Local**	**Launch Lab:** Magnifying Cells, p. 37 **Foldables,** p. 37
	See pp. 16T–17T for a Key to Standards.		A data-collection lab using Probeware technology can be found in the **Probeware Lab Manual,** pp. 1–4
Section 1 Cell Structure ⏱ 2 sessions 📦 1 block 1. **Identify** names and functions of each part of a cell. 2. **Explain** how important a nucleus is in a cell. 3. **Compare** tissues, organs, and organ systems.	National Content Standards: UCP.1–UCP.3, UCP.5, A.1, A.2, C.1, C.3		**MiniLAB:** Modeling Cytoplasm, p. 40 **Integrate Environment,** p. 44 **Applying Math:** Cell Ratio, p. 44 **Lab:** Comparing Cells, p. 46
Section 2 Viewing Cells ⏱ 2 sessions 📦 1 block 4. **Compare** the differences between the compound light microscope and the electron microscope. 5. **Summarize** the discoveries that led to the development of the cell theory.	National Content Standards: UCP.1–UCP.3, UCP.5, A.1, A.2, C.1, G.3		**Visualizing Microscopes,** p. 48 **MiniLAB:** Observing Magnified Objects, p. 52 **Integrate Career,** p. 50
Section 3 Viruses ⏱ 3 sessions 📦 1.5 blocks 6. **Explain** how a virus makes copies of itself. 7. **Identify** the benefits of vaccines. 8. **Investigate** some uses of viruses.	National Content Standards: UCP.1, UCP.2, UCP.5, A.1, A.2, C.1, C.2, C.5, F.2, G.3		**Science Online,** p. 53 **Science Online,** p. 54 **Lab:** Comparing Light Microscopes, p. 56 **Science and History:** Cobb Against Cancer, p. 58

Glencoe Exclusive!
Teacher Works™
All-In-One Planner and Resource Center

Lab Materials	Reproducible Resources	Section Assessment	Technology
Launch Lab: hand lens, metric ruler	**Chapter *FAST FILE* Resources** Foldables Worksheet, p. 17 Directed Reading Overview, p. 19 Note-taking Worksheets, pp. 33–35	GLENCOE'S ASSESSMENT ADVANTAGE	**Teacher Works includes:** • Interactive Teacher Edition • Lesson Planner with calendar • Access to all program blacklines • Correlations to standards • Web links
MiniLAB: water, clear container, unflavored gelatin, flashlight, stirring rod **Lab:** microscope, microscope slide, coverslip, forceps, tap water, dropper, *Elodea* plant, prepared slide of human cheek cells	**Chapter *FAST FILE* Resources** Transparency Activity, p. 44 MiniLAB, p. 3 Enrichment, p. 30 Reinforcement, p. 27 Directed Reading, p. 20 Transparency Activity, pp. 47–48 Lab Worksheet, pp. 5–6 **Mathematics Skill Activities,** p. 5	Portfolio Visual Learning, p. 41 Performance MiniLAB, p. 41 Applying Math, p. 44 Applying Skills, p. 45 Content Section Review, p. 45	Section Focus Transparency Teaching Transparency Virtual Labs CD-ROM Guided Reading Audio Program Interactive Chalkboard CD-ROM Video Lab
MiniLAB: newspaper, clear empty glass, clear empty glass bowl, water, magnifying lens *Need materials?* Contact Science Kit at 1-800-828-7777 or www.sciencekit.com on the Internet.	**Chapter *FAST FILE* Resources** Transparency Activity, p. 45 MiniLAB, p. 4 Enrichment, p. 31 Reinforcement, p. 28 Directed Reading, p. 20 Lab Activity, pp. 9–12, 13–16	Portfolio Assessment, p. 51 Performance MiniLAB, p. 50 Applying Math, p. 51 Content Section Review, p. 51	Section Focus Transparency Virtual Labs CD-ROM Guided Reading Audio Program Interactive Chalkboard CD-ROM
Lab: compound light microscope, stereomicroscope, 8 classroom items to view, microscope slides and coverslips, plastic petri dishes, distilled water, dropper	**Chapter *FAST FILE* Resources** Transparency Activity, p. 46 Enrichment, p. 32 Reinforcement, p. 29 Directed Reading, pp. 21, 22 Lab Worksheet, pp. 7–8 **Lab Management and Safety,** p. 58 **Reading and Writing Skill Activities,** p. 31	Performance Applying Skills, p. 55 Content Section Review, p. 55	Section Focus Transparency Virtual Labs CD-ROM Guided Reading Audio Program Interactive Chalkboard CD-ROM Probeware Lab

End of Chapter Assessment

GLENCOE'S ASSESSMENT ADVANTAGE

Blackline Masters	Technology	Professional Series
Chapter *FAST FILE* Resources Chapter Review, pp. 37–38 Chapter Tests, pp. 39–42 **Standardized Test Practice,** pp. 11–14	MindJogger Videoquiz Virtual Labs CD-ROM Exam*View®* Pro Testmaker TeacherWorks CD-ROM Interactive Chalkboard CD-ROM	**Performance Assessment in the Science Classroom (PASC)**

Transparencies

Section Focus

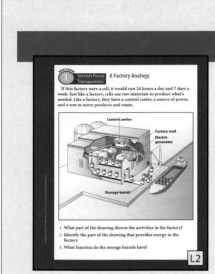

Section Focus Transparency 1 — A Factory Analogy

If this factory were a cell, it would run 24 hours a day and 7 days a week. Just like a factory, cells use raw materials to produce what's needed. Like a factory, they have a control center, a source of power, and a way to move products and waste.

Control center
Factory wall
Electric generator
Storage barrel

1. What part of the drawing directs the activities in the factory?
2. Identify the part of the drawing that provides energy to the factory.
3. What function do the storage barrels have?

L2

Section Focus Transparency 2 — At Home in the Salt

The Dead Sea has very high salt concentrations, and people have used it as a salt resource since ancient times. But is the Dead Sea really dead? The concentration of salt is too high for most living things, but bacteria like the ones below are able to live in its waters.

1. Why might ancient people have thought the Dead Sea was totally without life?
2. What tool would you use to show there really is life in the Dead Sea?
3. Do you think the living thing pictured is simple or complex? Defend your answer.

L2

Section Focus Transparency 3 — Thanks for Sharing!

Sneezing is an involuntary action that aids the body by clearing congestion within the nose. But sneezing also spreads germs, including cold and influenza viruses.

1. What are your symptoms when you catch a cold?
2. What can you do to limit the spread of viruses?

L2

This is a representation of key blackline masters available in the Teacher Classroom Resources. See Resource Manager boxes within the chapter for additional information.

Key to Teaching Strategies

The following designations will help you decide which activities are appropriate for your students.

L1 Level 1 activities should be appropriate for students with learning difficulties.

L2 Level 2 activities should be within the ability range of all students.

L3 Level 3 activities are designed for above-average students.

ELL ELL activities should be within the ability range of English-Language Learners.

COOP LEARN Cooperative Learning activities are designed for small group work.

LS Multiple Learning Styles logos, as described on page 12T, are used throughout to indicate strategies that address different learning styles.

P These strategies represent student products that can be placed into a best-work portfolio.

PBL Problem-Based Learning activities apply real-world situations to learning.

Assessment

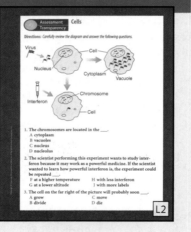

Assessment Transparency — Cells

Directions: Carefully review the diagram and answer the following questions.

Virus — Cell
Nucleus — Cytoplasm — Vacuole
Interferon — Chromosome — Cell

1. The chromosomes are located in the ___.
   A cytoplasm
   B vacuoles
   C nucleus
   D nucleolus
2. The scientist performing this experiment wants to study interferon because it may work as a powerful medicine. If the scientist wanted to learn how powerful interferon is, the experiment could be repeated ___.
   F at a higher temperature   H with less interferon
   G at a lower altitude   J with more labels
3. The cell on the far right of the picture will probably soon ___.
   A grow   C move
   B divide   D die

L2

Teaching

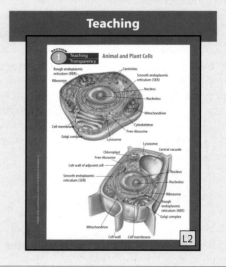

Teaching Transparency 1 — Animal and Plant Cells

Rough endoplasmic reticulum (RER), Ribosome, Cell membrane, Golgi complex, Centrioles, Smooth endoplasmic reticulum (SER), Nucleus, Nucleolus, Mitochondrion, Cytoskeleton, Free ribosome, Lysosome, Chloroplast, Free ribosome, Central vacuole, Cell wall of adjacent cell, Smooth endoplasmic reticulum (SER), Nucleus, Nucleolus, Ribosome, Rough endoplasmic reticulum (RER), Golgi complex, Mitochondrion, Cell wall, Cell membrane

L2

Hands-on Activities

Student Text Lab Worksheet

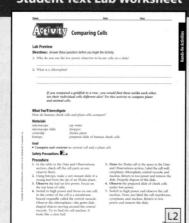

Activity — Comparing Cells

Lab Preview
Directions: Answer these questions before you begin the Activity.
1. Why do you use the low power objective to locate cells on a slide?

2. What is a chloroplast?

If you compared a goldfish to a rose, you would find them unlike each other. Are their individual cells different also? Try this activity to compare plant and animal cells.

What You'll Investigate
How do human cheek cells and plant cells compare?

Materials
microscope
microscope slide
coverslip
forceps
tap water
dropper
Elodea plant
prepared slide of human cheek cells

Goal
• Compare and contrast an animal cell and a plant cell.

Safety Precautions

Procedure
1. In the table in the Data and Observations section, check off the cell parts as you observe them.
2. Using forceps, make a wet-mount slide of a young leaf from the tip of an *Elodea* plant.
3. Observe the leaf on low power. Focus on the top layer of cells.
4. Switch to high power and focus on one cell. In the center of the cell is a membrane-bound organelle called the central vacuole. Observe the chloroplasts—the green disk-shaped objects moving around the central vacuole. Try to find the cell nucleus. It looks like a clear ball.
5. Draw the *Elodea* cell in the space in the Data and Observations section. Label the cell wall, cytoplasm, chloroplasts, central vacuole, and nucleus. Return to low power and remove the slide. Properly dispose of this slide.
6. Observe the prepared slide of cheek cells under low power.
7. Switch to high power and observe the cell nucleus. Draw and label the cell membrane, cytoplasm, and nucleus. Return to low power and remove the slide.

L2

Laboratory Activities

Laboratory Activity 1 — The Microscope

A microscope is a scientific tool used to see very small objects. Objects you cannot see with your eyes alone can be seen using a microscope. In this experiment you will look at a small letter *e* cut from a magazine, some thread, and a strand of hair.

Strategy
You will learn the names of microscope parts.
You will learn how to use a microscope.
You will learn to prepare objects for viewing under a microscope.
You will examine several objects under a microscope.
You will determine how the lens system of a microscope changes the position of an object being viewed.

Materials
microscope   coverslip   water   nylon thread
scissors   dropper   strands of hair   wool thread
magazine

Procedure
Part A—Using the Microscope
1. Study Figure 1. Identify the parts of your microscope so that you will understand the directions for this activity.
2. Cut out a small letter *e* from a magazine and place the letter on a microscope slide. CAUTION: *Use care when handling sharp objects.* Put a small drop of water on the letter and place a coverslip over the water and the letter.
3. Place the slide on the microscope stage. Move the slide to center the letter *e* over the hole in the stage. Use the stage clips to hold the slide in place.
4. Turn on the light if your microscope has one. If it does not, adjust the mirror so that the light is reflected through the eyepiece. Do not use direct sunlight as a light source. It can damage eyes.

Figure 1
Eyepiece, Revolving nosepiece, Low power objective, High power objective, Stage, Diaphragm, Coarse adjustment, Fine adjustment, Stage clips, Arm, Base, Mirror, Light, Arm

L2

Resource Manager

Meeting Different Ability Levels

Content Outline
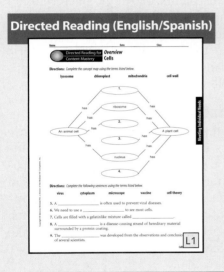

Reinforcement

Enrichment

Directed Reading (English/Spanish)
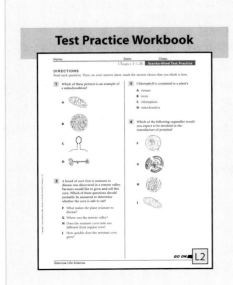

Study Guide
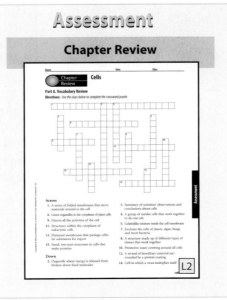

Reading Essentials
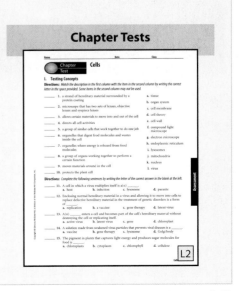

Assessment

Test Practice Workbook

Chapter Review

Chapter Tests

Science Content Background

section 1

Cell Structure
Common Cell Traits

The two kinds of cells are prokaryotes and eukaryotes. Each type is surrounded by a cell membrane and contains cytoplasm, DNA, and ribosomes. Prokaryotes have a relatively uniform cytoplasm that is not divided into separate compartments by interior membranes. The ribosomes of prokaryotes are different from those of eukaryotes. Prokaryotic DNA is a single molecule and is found floating freely in the cell's cytoplasm. The nucleus is the organelle that contains the eukaryotic cell's many molecules of DNA. All prokaryotic cells are one-celled organisms. Eukaryotic cells make up all multicellular organisms and some one-celled organisms.

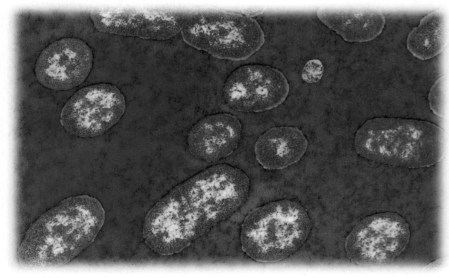

Dwight R. Kuhn/DRK Photo

Cell Wall

Although structurally they resemble plant cell walls, the walls of fungi cells are chemically quite different. Some contain cellulose, but most fungal cell walls are made up of chitin, a polysaccharide that also is found in the exoskeletons of insects. Just like cellulose in plants, the chitin is laid down in bundles of fibers that make the fungal cell walls tough and able to support the fungal body.

Bacterial cell walls are different from those found in either plants or fungi. Bacterial cell walls are composed in large part of a compound called peptidoglycan. Various other substances coat and bind to the cell wall. Other bacteria have an outer membrane that surrounds the peptidoglycan cell wall.

Cell Organization

The cytoskeleton, found only in eukaryotic cells, anchors cell organelles. This "scaffolding" cannot be seen with a normal light microscope but stands out clearly when special fluorescent dyes are used on the cell. Three different kinds of protein fibers—microfilaments, microtubules, and intermediate fibers—make up the cytoskeleton.

Teacher to Teacher
Steve Federman, 6th Grade Teacher
Loveland Middle School
Loveland, Ohio

"I reinforce the concepts of cell structures and functions by having students create a cell from a light colored flavored gelatin mixed with unflavored gelatin (6-oz. package will make 5 cells). Pour into a small cup or petri dish. Students then use items such as cake sprinkles for ribosomes, hot tamale candies for mitochondria, a gumball for the nucleus, and so on."

Steve Federman

---

section 2 Viewing Cells

Magnifying Cells

Microscopes enlarge the image of an object and show its details. The change of an object's apparent size is magnification. The power to show details is resolution. The resolution power of light microscopes is limited by the wavelengths of visible light. Unless the wavelength of light can pass between two objects, the objects are seen as one unit, not two. The electron microscope allows for greater resolution because it uses a beam of electrons to generate an image of the specimen. Because they move in waves that have extremely short wavelengths, electron waves can easily pass through microscopic spaces that visible light cannot enter.

Development of the Cell Theory

The cell theory is sometimes called the cell doctrine. Those scientists who use the term *cell doctrine* want to make it clear that extensive data support the cell theory and that it is universally accepted by biologists.

chapter content resources

Internet Resources
For additional content background, visit
life.msscience.com to:
- access your book online
- find references to related articles in popular science magazines
- access Web links with related content background
- access current events with science journal topics

Print Resources
Cells (The Kidhaven Science Library), by Jeanne Duprau, Kidhaven, 2001
Science Experiments with a Microscope, by Shar Levine and Leslie Johnstone, Sterling Publications, 2002
Influenza and Other Viruses (Perspectives on Disease and Illness), by Judy Monroe, Lifematters Press, 2001

Telegraph Colour Library/FPG International

section 3 Viruses

Living or Not?

To a biologist, living organisms are cellular and are able to grow and reproduce independently. The smallest organisms that satisfy these criteria are bacteria. Viruses do not meet most criteria for being a living organism.

Viruses are segments of DNA or RNA wrapped in a protein coat. A membranous envelope surrounds many animal viruses. The lipids of the envelope are taken from the host cell, but the proteins are coded by the virus's genetic material. Viruses cannot reproduce on their own but multiply only within host cells using the cellular machinery of the host cell. The host cells often are destroyed when viruses multiply. For the host organism, infection by a virus may have a minor effect like a cold or may be devastating like AIDS. Several types of cancer, including some skin and cervical cancers, are now known to be caused by viruses. Viruses continue to have a major impact on the living world.

Chapter Vocabulary

Science Journal Student responses will vary, but may include how they became a scientist, how can cancer be treated, and when will there be a cure for cancer.

INTERACTIVE CHALKBOARD with Image Bank

PowerPoint® Presentations

This CD-ROM is an editable Microsoft® PowerPoint® presentation that includes:

- a pre-made presentation for every chapter
- interactive graphics
- animations
- audio clips
- image bank
- all new section and chapter questions
- Standardized Test Practice
- transparencies
- pre-lab questions for all labs
- Foldables directions
- links to life.msscience.com

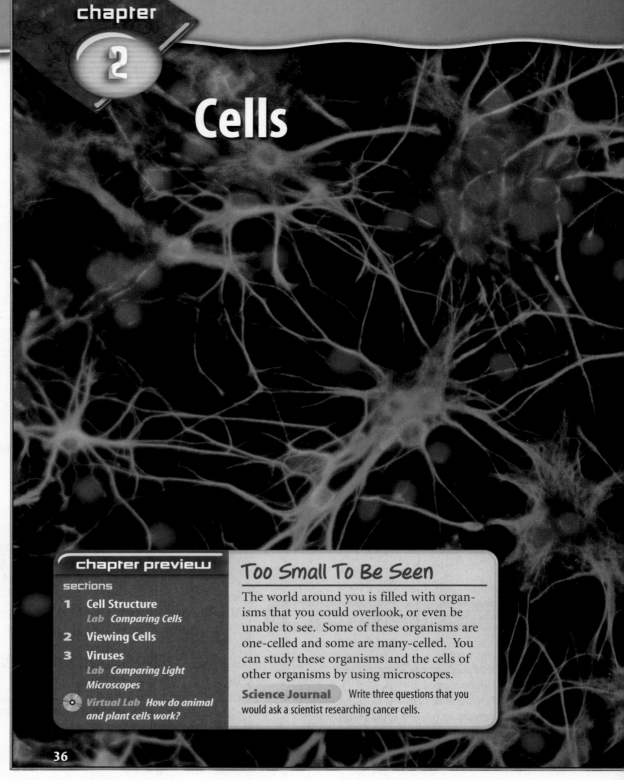

Cells

chapter preview

sections

1 Cell Structure
Lab Comparing Cells

2 Viewing Cells

3 Viruses
Lab Comparing Light Microscopes

Virtual Lab How do animal and plant cells work?

Too Small To Be Seen

The world around you is filled with organisms that you could overlook, or even be unable to see. Some of these organisms are one-celled and some are many-celled. You can study these organisms and the cells of other organisms by using microscopes.

Science Journal Write three questions that you would ask a scientist researching cancer cells.

36

Theme Connection

Scale and Structure All organisms are made up of cells, which are the basic unit organisms. Cells are made up of many types of smaller structures, or organelles. This idea wasn't conceived of until the invention of the microscope.

About the Photo

Brain Cells These are brain cells from the cortex of a mammalian brain. Astrocytes are star-shaped cells that might play a role in the storage of information. A technique called immunofluorescence was used to stain the cells shown here. Fluorescent dyes are attached to antibodies that recognize specific molecules in the cells. Under ultraviolet light, the dye fluoresces. Each cell's cytoplasm appears green, and each astrocyte's nucleus and other neighboring cells appear blue.

Start-Up Activities

Magnifying Cells

If you look around your classroom, you can see many things of all sizes. Using a magnifying lens, you can see more details. You might examine a speck of dust and discover that it is a living or dead insect. In the following lab, use a magnifying lens to search for the smallest thing you can find in the classroom.

1. Obtain a magnifying lens from your teacher. Note its power (the number followed by ×, shown somewhere on the lens frame or handle).
2. Using the magnifying lens, look around the room for the smallest object that you can find.
3. Measure the size of the image as you see it with the magnifying lens. To estimate the real size of the object, divide that number by the power. For example, if it looks 2 cm long and the power is 10×, the real length is about 0.2 cm.
4. **Think Critically** Write a paragraph that describes what you observed. Did the details become clearer? Explain.

Cells Make the following Foldable to help you illustrate the main parts of cells.

STEP 1 Fold a vertical sheet of paper in half from top to bottom.

STEP 2 Fold in half from side to side with the fold at the top.

STEP 3 Unfold the paper once. Cut only the fold of the top flap to make two tabs.

STEP 4 Turn the paper vertically and write on the front tabs as shown.

Plant Cell

Animal Cell

Illustrate and Label As you read the chapter, draw and identify the parts of plant and animal cells under the appropriate tab.

Preview this chapter's content and activities at life.msscience.com

Launch LAB

Purpose Students will use a magnifying lens to study very small objects. Students will calculate the actual size of the object from a measured size seen through the magnifying lens. L2

Preparation Obtain magnifying lenses and make sure the power is clearly visible on each one.

Materials magnifying lenses, rulers

Teaching Strategy Have some very small objects, such as grains of sand, salt, sugar, etc., available for students to study with their magnifying lenses.

Think Critically
Details of small objects will become larger and clearer when seen through a magnifying lens.

Assessment
Oral Have students describe aloud additional features of small objects, such as sand, salt, sugar, dust particles, etc., that they can observe through a magnifying lens. Use **Performance Assessment in the Science Classroom**, p. 89. L2

 Dinah Zike Study Fold

Student preparation materials for this Foldable are available in the Chapter *FAST FILE* Resources.

Probeware Labs

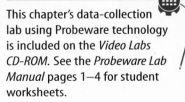

This chapter's data-collection lab using Probeware technology is included on the *Video Labs CD-ROM.* See the *Probeware Lab Manual* pages 1–4 for student worksheets.

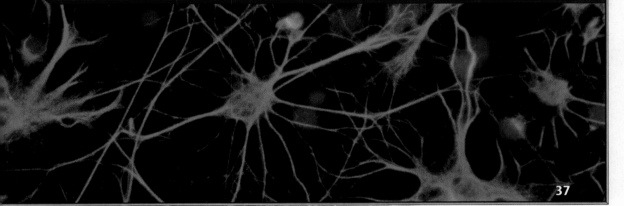

Cell Structure

Bellringer

Section Focus Transparencies also are available on the Interactive Chalkboard CD-ROM.

L2 ELL

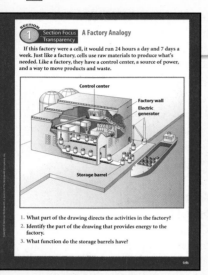

Section Focus Transparency A Factory Analogy

If this factory were a cell, it would run 24 hours a day and 7 days a week. Just like a factory, cells use raw materials to produce what's needed. Like a factory, they have a control center, a source of power, and a way to move products and waste.

Control center
Factory wall
Electric generator
Storage barrel

1. What part of the drawing directs the activities in the factory?
2. Identify the part of the drawing that provides energy to the factory.
3. What function do the storage barrels have?

Tie to Prior Knowledge

Body Systems Ask students what body systems they need to live. Write their responses on the board or overhead projector. Use this list to help students understand that the functions of life are carried out in the cell.

L2

as you read

What You'll Learn

- **Identify** names and functions of each part of a cell.
- **Explain** how important a nucleus is in a cell.
- **Compare** tissues, organs, and organ systems.

Why It's Important

If you know how organelles function, it's easier to understand how cells survive.

🔍 Review Vocabulary

photosynthesis: process by which most plants, some protists, and many types of bacteria make their own food

New Vocabulary

- cell membrane
- cytoplasm
- cell wall
- organelle
- nucleus
- chloroplast
- mitochondrion
- ribosome
- endoplasmic reticulum
- Golgi body
- tissue
- organ

Common Cell Traits

Living cells are dynamic and have several things in common. A cell is the smallest unit that is capable of performing life functions. All cells have an outer covering called a **cell membrane.** Inside every cell is a gelatinlike material called **cytoplasm** (SI tuh pla zum). In the cytoplasm of every cell is hereditary material that controls the life of the cell.

Comparing Cells Cells come in many sizes. A nerve cell in your leg could be a meter long. A human egg cell is no bigger than the dot on this *i*. A human red blood cell is about one-tenth the size of a human egg cell. A bacterium is even smaller—8,000 of the smallest bacteria can fit inside one of your red blood cells.

A cell's shape might tell you something about its function. The nerve cell in **Figure 1** has many fine extensions that send and receive impulses to and from other cells. Though a nerve cell cannot change shape, muscle cells and some blood cells can. In plant stems, some cells are long and hollow and have openings at their ends. These cells carry food and water throughout the plant.

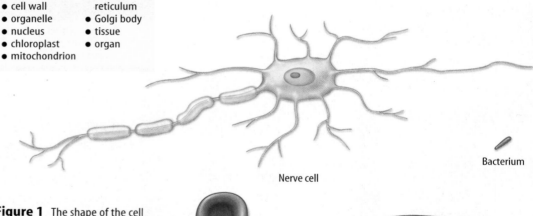

Bacterium

Nerve cell

Figure 1 The shape of the cell can tell you something about its function. These cells are drawn 700 times their actual size.

Red blood cell

Muscle cell

Section 1 Resource Manager

Chapter *FAST FILE* Resources

Transparency Activity, pp. 44, 47–48

Directed Reading for Content Mastery, pp. 19, 20

Note-taking Worksheets, pp. 33–35

MiniLAB, p. 3

Enrichment, p. 30

Lab Worksheet, pp. 5–6

Reinforcement, p. 27

Life Science Critical Thinking/Problem Solving, p. 1

Mathematics Skill Activities, p. 5

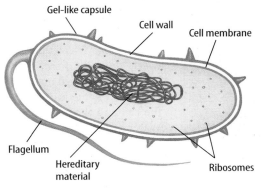

Gel-like capsule
Cell wall
Cell membrane
Flagellum
Hereditary material
Ribosomes

Prokaryotic cell

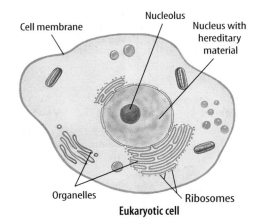

Cell membrane
Nucleolus
Nucleus with hereditary material
Organelles
Ribosomes

Eukaryotic cell

Cell Types

Cell Types Scientists have found that cells can be separated into two groups. One group has no membrane-bound structures inside the cell and the other group does, as shown in **Figure 2.** Cells without membrane-bound structures are called prokaryotic (proh KAYR ee yah tihk) cells. Cells with membrane-bound structures are called eukaryotic (yew KAYR ee yah tihk) cells.

✔ Reading Check *Into what two groups can cells be separated?*

Cell Organization

Each cell in your body has a specific function. You might compare a cell to a busy delicatessen that is open 24 hours every day. Raw materials for the sandwiches are brought in often. Some food is eaten in the store, and some customers take their food with them. Sometimes food is prepared ahead of time for quick sale. Wastes are put into trash bags for removal or recycling. Similarly, your cells are taking in nutrients, secreting and storing chemicals, and breaking down substances 24 hours every day.

Cell Wall Just like a deli that is located inside the walls of a building, some cells are enclosed in a cell wall. The cells of plants, algae, fungi, and most bacteria are enclosed in a cell wall. **Cell walls** are tough, rigid outer coverings that protect the cell and give it shape.

A plant cell wall, as shown in **Figure 3,** mostly is made up of a carbohydrate called cellulose. The long, threadlike fibers of cellulose form a thick mesh that allows water and dissolved materials to pass through it. Cell walls also can contain pectin, which is used in jam and jelly, and lignin, which is a compound that makes cell walls rigid. Plant cells responsible for support have a lot of lignin in their walls.

Figure 2 Examine these drawings of cells. Prokaryotic cells are only found in one-celled organisms, such as bacteria. Protists, fungi, plants, and animals are made of eukaryotic cells.
Describe *differences you see between them.*

Figure 3 The protective cell wall of a plant cell is outside the cell membrane.

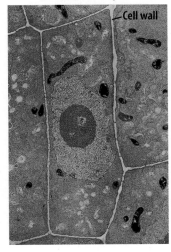

Color-enhanced TEM Magnification: 9000×

Cell wall

Fun Fact

Creatures 20–150 nanometers in length were found living in sandstone from the Australian seabed. They are smaller than any other known living organism. They contain DNA and distinct cell membranes.

Curriculum Connection

Health Cellulose, found in all plant cell walls, is not digestible by humans. However, it provides fiber, which is important because it helps in the elimination of wastes. Have students make a list of foods that contain fiber. Lists should include fruits, grains, and leafy vegetables. L2

Discussion

Damaged Cells What would happen if the nucleus of a cell were damaged? The cell would no longer function correctly because the nucleus controls all the cell's activities.

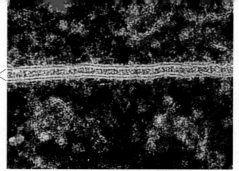

Figure 4 A cell membrane is made up of a double layer of fatlike molecules.

Cell membranes

Color-enhanced TEM Magnification: 125000×

Stained LM Magnification: 700×

Figure 5 Cytoskeleton, a network of fibers in the cytoplasm, gives cells structure and helps them maintain shape.

Modeling Cytoplasm

Procedure
1. Add 100 mL of **water** to a **clear container.**
2. Add **unflavored gelatin** and stir.
3. Shine a **flashlight** through the solution.

Analysis
1. Describe what you see.
2. How does a model help you understand what cytoplasm might be like?

Cell Membrane The protective layer around all cells is the cell membrane, as shown in **Figure 4.** If cells have cell walls, the cell membrane is inside of it. The cell membrane regulates interactions between the cell and the environment. Water is able to move freely into and out of the cell through the cell membrane. Food particles and some molecules enter and waste products leave through the cell membrane.

Cytoplasm Cells are filled with a gelatinlike substance called cytoplasm that constantly flows inside the cell membrane. Many important chemical reactions occur within the cytoplasm.

Throughout the cytoplasm is a framework called the cytoskeleton, which helps the cell maintain or change its shape. Cytoskeletons enable some cells to move. An amoeba, for example, moves by stretching and contracting its cytoskeleton. The cytoskeleton is made up of thin, hollow tubes of protein and thin, solid protein fibers, as shown in **Figure 5.** Proteins are organic molecules made up of amino acids.

✓ **Reading Check** *What is the function of the cytoskeleton?*

Most of a cell's life processes occur in the cytoplasm. Within the cytoplasm of eukaryotic cells are structures called **organelles.** Some organelles process energy and others manufacture substances needed by the cell or other cells. Certain organelles move materials, while others act as storage sites. Most organelles are surrounded by membranes. The nucleus is usually the largest organelle in a cell.

Nucleus The nucleus is like the deli manager who directs the store's daily operations and passes on information to employees. The **nucleus,** shown in **Figure 6,** directs all cell activities and is separated from the cytoplasm by a membrane. Materials enter and leave the nucleus through openings in the membrane. The nucleus contains the instructions for everything the cell does. These instructions are found on long, threadlike, hereditary material made of DNA. DNA is the chemical that contains the code for the cell's structure and activities. During cell division, the hereditary material coils tightly around proteins to form structures called chromosomes. A structure called a nucleolus also is found in the nucleus.

40 CHAPTER 2 Cells

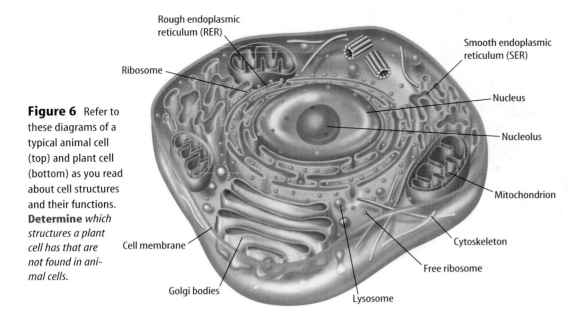

Figure 6 Refer to these diagrams of a typical animal cell (top) and plant cell (bottom) as you read about cell structures and their functions. **Determine** which structures a plant cell has that are not found in animal cells.

Rough endoplasmic reticulum (RER)

Ribosome

Smooth endoplasmic reticulum (SER)

Nucleus

Nucleolus

Mitochondrion

Cell membrane

Cytoskeleton

Golgi bodies

Free ribosome

Lysosome

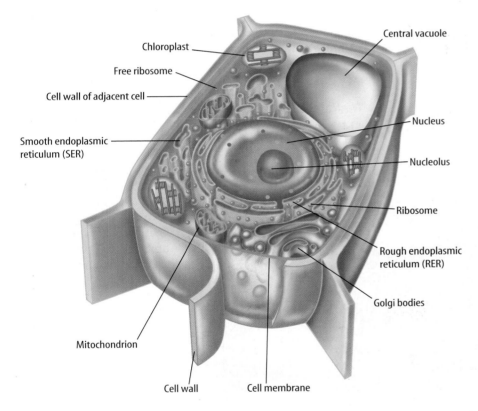

Chloroplast

Free ribosome

Cell wall of adjacent cell

Smooth endoplasmic reticulum (SER)

Central vacuole

Nucleus

Nucleolus

Ribosome

Rough endoplasmic reticulum (RER)

Golgi bodies

Mitochondrion

Cell wall

Cell membrane

Organelle Functions Point out that just as each part of a car engine performs a different function to enable the car to run, each organelle performs a different function in the cell.

Use Science Words

Word Origin Greek and Latin words are used in naming cell parts. Have students make a list of cell parts and use a dictionary to find the origins of the words and their meanings. L2 LS **Linguistic**

IDENTIFYING
Misconceptions

Water in Cells Students may think that cells are solid. Explain that almost 80 percent of a cell is water. The water is enclosed in a membrane that allows certain materials to enter and leave.

Caption Answer

Figure 6 cell wall, central vacuole, chloroplast

Virtual Labs

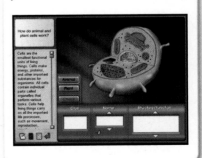

Cells How do animal and plant cells work?

Visual Learning

Figure 6 Have students create a network tree concept map comparing and contrasting plant and animal cells. Diagrams should make clear which organelles appear in both cells and which are specific to only one type of cell. L2 LS **Visual-Spatial** P

Differentiated Instruction

Challenge Have students do research on the cylindrical organelles in animal cells that are called centrioles. Have students discuss the function of these organelles. How many centrioles are contained within a cell? What is their function in mitosis and meiosis? Students can draw what they learn and share their findings. L3

Teacher FYI

Mitochondria A liver cell has hundreds of mitochondria, which makes up about 25% of the cell's volume. The high number of mitochondria reflects the high level of energy a liver cell requires.

IDENTIFYING Misconceptions

Plant Mitochondria Students may think that because plant cells carry out photosynthesis, they do not have mitochondria. Explain that plants also carry out cellular respiration.

Discussion

Cell Color What color are most cells? Most cells are colorless. Photographs of cells are usually color-enhanced; prepared slides of cells are usually stained so cell parts are visible.

Text Question Answer

Mitochondria provide energy, and active cells would be more in need of energy than inactive cells.

Caption Answer

Figure 8 Possible answer: muscle cells

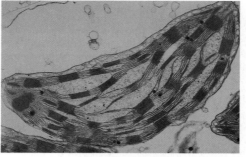

Figure 7 Chloroplasts are organelles that use light energy to make sugar from carbon dioxide and water.

Color-enhanced TEM Magnification: 37000×

Figure 8 Mitochondria are known as the powerhouses of the cell because they release energy that is needed by the cell from food.
Name *the cell types that might contain many mitochondria.*

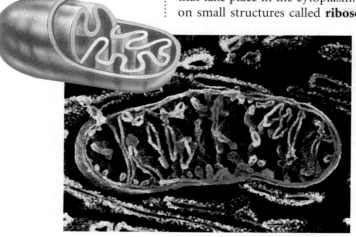

Color-enhanced SEM Magnification: 48000×

INTEGRATE Physics

Energy-Processing Organelles Cells require a continuous supply of energy to process food, make new substances, eliminate wastes, and communicate with each other. In plant cells, food is made in green organelles in the cytoplasm called **chloroplasts** (KLOR uh plasts), as shown in **Figure 7.** Chloroplasts contain the green pigment chlorophyll, which gives many leaves and stems their green color. Chlorophyll captures light energy that is used to make a sugar called glucose. Glucose molecules store the captured light energy as chemical energy. Many cells, including animal cells, do not have chloroplasts for making food. They must get food from their environment.

The energy in food is stored until it is released by the mitochondria. **Mitochondria** (mi tuh KAHN dree uh) (singular, *mitochondrion*), such as the one shown in **Figure 8,** are organelles where energy is released from breaking down food into carbon dioxide and water. Just as the gas or electric company supplies fuel for the deli, a mitochondrion releases energy for use by the cell. Some types of cells, such as muscle cells, are more active than other cells. These cells have large numbers of mitochondria. Why would active cells have more or larger mitochondria?

Manufacturing Organelles One substance that takes part in nearly every cell activity is protein. Proteins are part of cell membranes. Other proteins are needed for chemical reactions that take place in the cytoplasm. Cells make their own proteins on small structures called **ribosomes.** Even though ribosomes are considered organelles, they are not membrane bound. Some ribosomes float freely in the cytoplasm; others are attached to the endoplasmic reticulum. Ribosomes are made in the nucleolus and move out into the cytoplasm. Ribosomes receive directions from the hereditary material in the nucleus on how, when, and in what order to make specific proteins.

42 CHAPTER 2 Cells

Cultural Diversity

Cell Function Ernest Everett Just, an African American biologist in the early 1900s, studied cells and how they function. His research showed that all parts of the cell influence its activities, not just the nucleus, as scientists then believed. This idea changed scientific opinion concerning the basis of life. Discuss how Just's research is important to the study of cells today.

Differentiated Instruction

Learning Disabled Provide pairs of students with an unlabeled drawing of an animal cell. Have students print small stick-on labels and place them appropriately on the drawing. The labels can be folded to conceal the words and removed as the students learn the cell structures, then replaced for review. L1

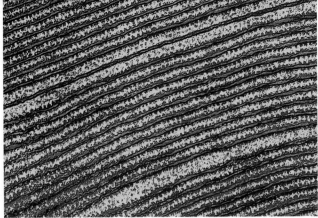

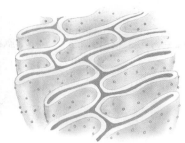

Figure 9 Endoplasmic reticulum (ER) is a complex series of membranes in the cytoplasm of the cell.
Infer *what smooth ER would look like.*

Color-enhanced TEM Magnification: 65000×

Caption Answer
Figure 9 Smooth ER looks the same as rough ER, only without ribosomes attached to it.

Processing, Transporting, and Storing Organelles

The **endoplasmic reticulum** (en duh PLAZ mihk • rih TIHK yuh lum) or ER, as shown in **Figure 9,** extends from the nucleus to the cell membrane. It is a series of folded membranes in which materials can be processed and moved around inside of the cell. The ER takes up a lot of space in some cells.

The endoplasmic reticulum may be "rough" or "smooth." ER that has no attached ribosomes is called smooth endoplasmic reticulum. This type of ER processes other cellular substances such as lipids that store energy. Ribosomes are attached to areas on the rough ER. There they carry out their job of making proteins that are moved out of the cell or used within the cell.

✔ **Reading Check** *What is the difference between rough ER and smooth ER?*

After proteins are made in a cell, they are transferred to another type of cell organelle called the Golgi (GAWL jee) bodies. The **Golgi bodies,** as shown ion **Figure 10,** are stacked, flattened membranes. The Golgi bodies sort proteins and other cellular substances and package them into membrane-bound structures called vesicles. The vesicles deliver cellular substances to areas inside the cell. They also carry cellular substances to the cell membrane where they are released to the outside of the cell.

Just as a deli has refrigerators for temporary storage of some of its foods and ingredients, cells have membrane-bound spaces called vacuoles for the temporary storage of materials. A vacuole can store water, waste products, food, and other cellular materials. In plant cells, the vacuole may make up most of the cell's volume.

Figure 10 The Golgi body packages materials and moves them to the outside of the cell.
Explain *why materials are removed from the cell.*

Color-enhanced TEM Magnification: 28000×

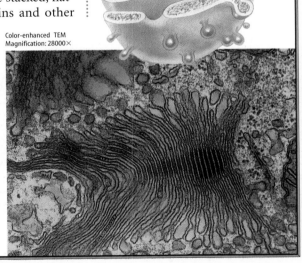

Make a Model
Cell Cutaway Have students make a cutaway model of a eukaryotic cell, using a clear plastic bag for the cell membrane, gelatin for cytoplasm, kidney beans for mitochondria, small seeds for ribosomes, noodles for ER and Golgi bodies, a lemon for the nucleus, and peppercorns for lysosomes. Sealed plastic bags full of water can be used for vacuoles. To make a model of a plant cell, green peas can be used for chloroplasts, and licorice for cell walls. [L2] [LS] **Kinesthetic**

✔ **Reading Check**

Answer Rough endoplasmic reticulum has ribosomes attached to it and makes proteins; smooth ER has no ribosomes and processes cellular substances.

Caption Answer
Figure 10 Materials are removed from a cell because they are waste products of the cell, or are to be used in other parts of the organism.

Activity
Cell Magnification Have students study a cell under increasing magnifications. A microprojector or photos can be used if microscopes are not available. Have them describe the cells at each magnification. Students can make drawings based on their descriptions. [L2]

Recycling Posters will vary.

Research Have students research the different methods that are used in recycling. Methods could include those for paper, plastic, aluminum, steel, and glass. Students' research should also include what products are made from recycled material and the benefits of recycling. Information from students' research can be included on their promotional poster. L2

Applying Math

National Math Standards
Correlation to Mathematics Objectives
1, 2, 4, 6, 9

Answers to Practice Problems

1. $A = 2 \text{ cm} \times 2 \text{ cm} \times 6 = 24 \text{ cm}^2$
$V = 2 \text{ cm} \times 2 \text{ cm} \times 2 \text{ cm}$
$= 8 \text{ cm}^3$
$R = 24 \text{ cm}^2/8 \text{ cm}^3 = 3 \text{ cm}^2/\text{cm}^3$
As the size of the cube decreases, the ratio increases.

2. $A = 2(4 \text{ cm} \times 4 \text{ cm}) + 4(4 \text{ cm} \times 8 \text{ cm}) = 160 \text{ cm}^2$
$V = 4 \text{ cm} \times 4 \text{ cm} \times 8 \text{ cm}$
$= 128 \text{ cm}^3$
$R = 160 \text{ cm}^2/128 \text{ cm}^3$
$= 1.25 \text{ cm}^2/\text{cm}^3$
The ratio decreases.

Recycling Just like a cell, you can recycle materials. Paper, plastics, aluminum, and glass are materials that can be recycled into usable items. Make a promotional poster to encourage others to recycle.

Recycling Organelles Active cells break down and recycle substances. Organelles called lysosomes (LI suh sohmz) contain digestive chemicals that help break down food molecules, cell wastes, and worn-out cell parts. In a healthy cell, chemicals are released into vacuoles only when needed. The lysosome's membrane prevents the digestive chemicals inside from leaking into the cytoplasm and destroying the cell. When a cell dies, a lysosome's membrane disintegrates. This releases digestive chemicals that allow the quick breakdown of the cell's contents.

✔ **Reading Check** *What is the function of the lysosome's membrane?*

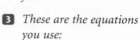 **Calculate a Ratio**

CELL RATIO Assume that a cell is like a cube with six equal sides. Find the ratio of surface area to volume for a cube that is 4 cm high.

4 cm
4 cm   4 cm

Solution

1 *This is what you know:* A cube has 6 equal sides of 4 cm × 4 cm.

2 *This is what you need to find out:* What is the ratio (R) of surface area to volume for the cube?

3 *These are the equations you use:*
- surface area (A) = width × length × 6
- volume (V) = length × width × height
- R = A/V

4 *This is the procedure you need to use:*
- Substitute in known values and solve the equations
$A = 4 \text{ cm} \times 4 \text{ cm} \times 6 = 96 \text{ cm}^2$
$V = 4 \text{ cm} \times 4 \text{ cm} \times 4 \text{ cm} = 64 \text{ cm}^3$
$R = 96 \text{ cm}^2/64 \text{ cm}^3 = 1.5 \text{ cm}^2/\text{cm}^3$

5 *Check your answer:* Multiply the ratio by the volume. Did you calculate the surface area?

Practice Problems

1. Calculate the ratio of surface area to volume for a cube that is 2 cm high. What happens to this ratio as the size of the cube decreases?

2. If a 4-cm cube doubled just one of its dimensions, what would happen to the ratio of surface area to volume?

 For more practice, visit
life.msscience.com/
math_practice

✔ **Active Reading**

ReQuest To improve listening skills, have students listen carefully as you read an interesting article or story aloud. After the reading, have students construct discussion questions. Have students participate in a ReQuest with the chapter feature or another interesting article related to cell structure or function. L2

From Cell to Organism

Many one-celled organisms perform all their life functions by themselves. Cells in a many-celled organism, however, do not work alone. Each cell carries on its own life functions while depending in some way on other cells in the organism.

In **Figure 11,** you can see cardiac muscle cells grouped together to form a tissue. A **tissue** is a group of similar cells that work together to do one job. Each cell in a tissue does its part to keep the tissue alive.

Tissues are organized into organs. An **organ** is a structure made up of two or more different types of tissues that work together. Your heart is an organ made up of cardiac muscle tissue, nerve tissue, and blood tissues. The cardiac muscle tissue contracts, making the heart pump. The nerve tissue brings messages that tell the heart how fast to beat. The blood tissue is carried from the heart to other organs of the body.

 **Reading Check** *What types of tissues make up your heart?*

A group of organs working together to perform a certain function is an organ system. Your heart, arteries, veins, and capillaries make up your cardiovascular system. In a many-celled organism, several systems work together in order to perform life functions efficiently. Your nervous, circulatory, respiratory, muscular, and other systems work together to keep you alive.

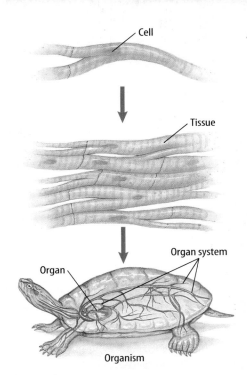

Figure 11 In a many-celled organism, cells are organized into tissues, tissues into organs, organs into systems, and systems into an organism.

Reading Check

Answer cardiac muscle tissue, nerve tissue, and blood tissue

3 Assess

DAILY INTERVENTION

Check for Understanding
Visual-Kinesthetic Have students make a bulletin board showing unlabeled parts of an animal cell. As students review each cell part, have a student place a label by it on the bulletin board. L2

Reteach
Cell Differences What are the differences between plant and animal cells? Most plant cells contain chloroplasts and cell walls; animal cells do not. What is the difference between a prokaryotic and eukaryotic cell? Eukaryotic cells have membrane-bound structures; prokaryotic cells do not. L2

---

section 1 review

Summary

Common Cell Traits
- All cells have an outer covering called a cell membrane.
- Cells can be classified as prokaryotic or eukaryotic.

Cell Organization
- Each cell in your body has a specific function.
- Most of a cell's life processes occur in the cytoplasm.

From Cell to Organism
- In a many-celled organism, several systems work together to perform life functions.

Self Check

1. **Explain** why the nucleus is important in the life of a cell.
2. **Determine** why digestive enzymes in a cell are enclosed in a membrane-bound organelle.
3. **Discuss** how cells, tissues, organs, and organ systems are related.
4. **Think Critically** How is the cell of a one-celled organism different from the cells in many-celled organisms?

Applying Skills

5. **Interpret Scientific Illustrations** Examine **Figure 6.** Make a list of differences and similarities between the animal cell and the plant cell.

Science Online life.msscience.com/self_check_quiz

---

section 1 review

1. It directs the activities of the cell and stores hereditary information.
2. It prevents the digestive chemicals inside from destroying the cell.

3. Organ systems are made of organs, which are made of tissues. Tissues are made of cells.
4. one-celled—performs all life functions; multicellular—cells depend on each other

5. Plant cells have chloroplasts and cell walls which animal cells do not have. Unlike plant cells, animal cells have centrioles.

Assessment

Process To further assess students' abilities to compare and contrast different cell types, have them write statements in their Science Journals comparing animal and plant cells. Use **Performance Assessment in the Science Classroom,** p. 175. L2

Real-World Question

Purpose Students identify and compare the parts of a plant and animal cell. L2 ELL LS **Visual-Spatial**

Process Skills observe, identify, infer, diagram, compare and contrast, classify

Time Required 45 minutes

Procedure

Alternate Materials If *Elodea* is unavailable, the thin, newest leaves of a coleus plant or similar houseplant.

Safety Precautions Caution students to use extreme care when working with a microscope and microscope slides.

Teaching Strategies

• Have students work in pairs. One student obtains and sets up the microscope while the other prepares the wet mount and obtains the cheek-cell slide. Both observe the slides and record data.

• Have students clean slides and coverslips after use.

Troubleshooting To see movement of cytoplasm, use only leaves from the tips of *Elodea*. Help students focus so they will see cell layers. Students may not be able to see the nucleus. Many students may mistake the chloroplast for the cells.

Conclude and Apply

1. The *Elodea* cell is rectangular; the cheek cell is oval.
2. Only plant cells have a cell wall and chloroplasts.

Comparing Cells

If you compared a goldfish to a rose, you would find them unlike each other. Are their individual cells different also?

Real-World Question

How do human cheek cells and plant cells compare?

Goals

■ **Compare and contrast** an animal cell and a plant cell.

Materials

microscope	dropper
microscope slide	*Elodea* plant
coverslip	prepared slide of human
forceps	cheek cells
tap water	

Safety Precautions

Procedure

1. Copy the data table in your Science Journal. Check off the cell parts as you observe them.

Cell Observations		
Cell Part	**Cheek**	***Elodea***
Cytoplasm	✔	✔
Nucleus	✔	✔
Chloroplasts		✔
Cell wall		✔
Cell membrane	✔	✔

2. Using forceps, make a wet-mount slide of a young leaf from the tip of an *Elodea* plant.

3. **Observe** the leaf on low power. Focus on the top layer of cells.

4. Switch to high power and focus on one cell. In the center of the cell is a membrane-bound organelle called the central vacuole. Observe the chloroplasts—the green, disk-shaped objects moving around the central vacuole. Try to find the cell nucleus. It looks like a clear ball.

5. **Draw** the *Elodea* cell. Label the cell wall, cytoplasm, chloroplasts, central vacuole, and nucleus. Return to low power and remove the slide. Properly dispose of the slide.

6. **Observe** the prepared slide of cheek cells under low power.

7. Switch to high power and observe the cell nucleus. Draw and label the cell membrane, cytoplasm, and nucleus. Return to low power and remove the slide.

Conclude and Apply

1. **Compare and contrast** the shapes of the cheek cell and the *Elodea* cell.

2. **Draw conclusions** about the differences between plant and animal cells.

Communicating Your Data

Draw the two kinds of cells on one sheet of paper. Use a green pencil to label the organelles found only in plants, a red pencil to label the organelles found only in animals, and a blue pencil to label the organelles found in both. **For more help, refer to the** Science Skill Handbook.

☑ Assessment

Performance To further assess students' abilities to compare plant and animal cells, have them examine cells from lettuce leaves and other types of animal cells on prepared slides. Use **Performance Assessment in the Science Classroom,** p. 97. L2

Communicating Your Data

Chloroplasts and cell walls should be labeled in green on the plant cell. No organelles are labeled red. Cytoplasm, nuclei, and cell membranes should be labeled in blue on plant and animal cells. L2

Viewing Cells

Magnifying Cells

The number of living things in your environment that you can't see is much greater than the number that you can see. Many of the things that you cannot see are only one cell in size. To see most cells, you need to use a microscope.

Trying to see separate cells in a leaf, like the ones in **Figure 12,** is like trying to see individual photos in a photo mosaic picture that is on the wall across the room. As you walk toward the wall, it becomes easier to see the individual photos. When you get right up to the wall, you can see details of each small photo. A microscope has one or more lenses that enlarge the image of an object as though you are walking closer to it. Seen through these lenses, the leaf appears much closer to you, and you can see the individual cells that carry on life processes.

Early Microscopes In the late 1500s, the first microscope was made by a Dutch maker of reading glasses. He put two magnifying glasses together in a tube and got an image that was larger than the image that was made by either lens alone.

In the mid 1600s, Antonie van Leeuwenhoek, a Dutch fabric merchant, made a simple microscope with a tiny glass bead for a lens, as shown in **Figure 13.** With it, he reported seeing things in pond water that no one had ever imagined. His microscope could magnify up to 270 times. Another way to say this is that his microscope could make the image of an object 270 times larger than its actual size. Today you would say his lens had a power of 270×. Early compound microscopes were crude by today's standards. The lenses would make an image larger, but it wasn't always sharp or clear.

as you read

What You'll Learn

- **Compare** the differences between the compound light microscope and the electron microscope.
- **Summarize** the discoveries that led to the development of the cell theory.

Why It's Important

Humans are like other living things because they are made of cells.

🔍 **Review Vocabulary**
magnify: to increase the size of something

New Vocabulary
- cell theory

Figure 12 Individual cells become visible when a plant leaf is viewed using a microscope with enough magnifying power.

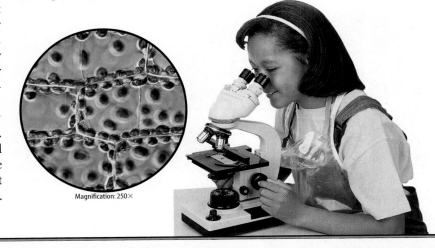
Magnification: 250×

Bellringer

Section Focus Transparencies also are available on the Interactive Chalkboard CD-ROM.
L2 ELL

SECTION 2 Section Focus Transparency — **At Home in the Salt**

The Dead Sea has very high salt concentrations, and people have used it as a salt resource since ancient times. But is the Dead Sea really dead? The concentration of salt is too high for most living things, but bacteria like the ones below are able to live in its waters.

1. Why might ancient people have thought the Dead Sea was totally without life?
2. What tool would you use to show there really is life in the Dead Sea?
3. Do you think the living thing pictured is simple or complex? Defend your answer.

Tie to Prior Knowledge

Magnification Students may have used magnifying glasses and binoculars. Explain that a microscope magnifies in the same way.

Section 2 Resource Manager

Chapter FAST FILE Resources
Transparency Activity, p. 45
Directed Reading for Content Mastery, p. 20
Enrichment, p. 31
Lab Activity, pp. 9–12, 13–16
MiniLAB, p. 4

Reinforcement, p. 28

Visualizing Microscopes

Have students examine the pictures and read the captions. Then ask the following questions.

What are the similarities and differences between a fluorescence microscope and a phase-contrast microscope? Possible answers: Both microscopes magnify up to 1500×. With the fluorescence microscope, the specimen must be stained and can be viewed through the scope directly. With the phase-contrast microscope, the specimen is not stained and can only be viewed on a monitor or in a photograph. Phase-contrast microscopes are good for viewing living things.

Compare and contrast the features of a TEM and an SEM. Possible answers: Both microscopes use electrons to help produce the magnified image. Also, with both microscopes the specimen can only be viewed on a monitor or in a photograph. In a TEM the electrons go through the specimen and the magnification is up to 1,000,000×. With an SEM, the electrons sweep over the surface of the specimen and a three-dimensional image is produced. The magnification of an SEM is only up to 200,000×.

Activity

Microscope Types Have students identify the type of microscope(s) they use in science class. Then have students view different slides under the microscope (e.g. onion slices, hair, sliver from a grass blade, color-comics section of the newspaper). Have students draw what they observe. If possible, use several types of microscopes and a magnifying glass and have students compare how the same slide looks under each one. Ask students to list the similarities and differences between them, and hypothesize what accounts for these differences. L2

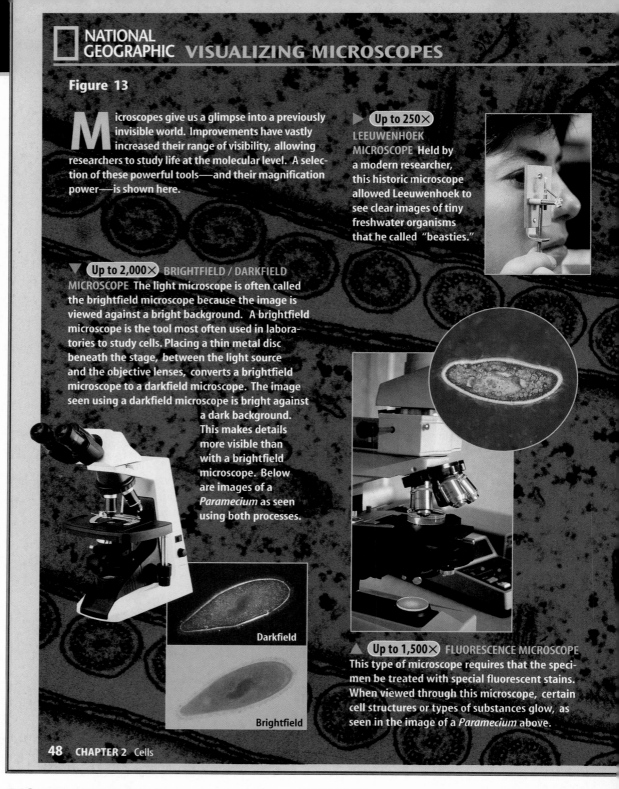

NATIONAL GEOGRAPHIC VISUALIZING MICROSCOPES

Figure 13

Microscopes give us a glimpse into a previously invisible world. Improvements have vastly increased their range of visibility, allowing researchers to study life at the molecular level. A selection of these powerful tools—and their magnification power—is shown here.

Up to 250×
LEEUWENHOEK MICROSCOPE Held by a modern researcher, this historic microscope allowed Leeuwenhoek to see clear images of tiny freshwater organisms that he called "beasties."

Up to 2,000× BRIGHTFIELD / DARKFIELD MICROSCOPE The light microscope is often called the brightfield microscope because the image is viewed against a bright background. A brightfield microscope is the tool most often used in laboratories to study cells. Placing a thin metal disc beneath the stage, between the light source and the objective lenses, converts a brightfield microscope to a darkfield microscope. The image seen using a darkfield microscope is bright against a dark background. This makes details more visible than with a brightfield microscope. Below are images of a *Paramecium* as seen using both processes.

Darkfield

Brightfield

Up to 1,500× FLUORESCENCE MICROSCOPE This type of microscope requires that the specimen be treated with special fluorescent stains. When viewed through this microscope, certain cell structures or types of substances glow, as seen in the image of a *Paramecium* above.

Science Journal

Magnification Have students make a time line showing discoveries made with the light microscope, beginning with Robert Hooke (1665) identifying and drawing cells. L2

Teacher FYI

Artifacts Any phenomenon that occurs as a result of the fixing or staining procedure used to prepare a specimen to be viewed on a slide is called an artifact. An artifact is not a feature of the living organism. Sometimes an artifact can be a simple air bubble; other times the procedure can change the shape of a particular feature.

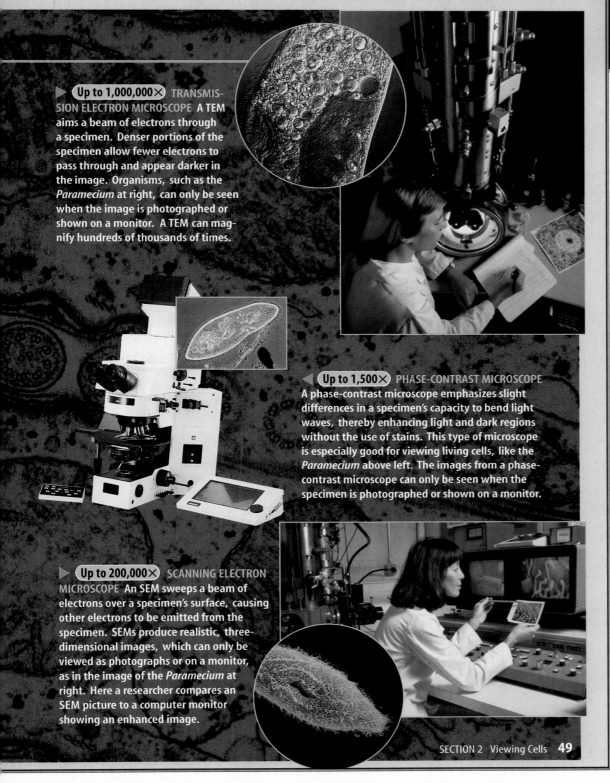

▶ **Up to 1,000,000×** TRANSMIS-SION ELECTRON MICROSCOPE A TEM aims a beam of electrons through a specimen. Denser portions of the specimen allow fewer electrons to pass through and appear darker in the image. Organisms, such as the *Paramecium* at right, can only be seen when the image is photographed or shown on a monitor. A TEM can magnify hundreds of thousands of times.

◀ **Up to 1,500×** PHASE-CONTRAST MICROSCOPE A phase-contrast microscope emphasizes slight differences in a specimen's capacity to bend light waves, thereby enhancing light and dark regions without the use of stains. This type of microscope is especially good for viewing living cells, like the *Paramecium* above left. The images from a phase-contrast microscope can only be seen when the specimen is photographed or shown on a monitor.

▶ **Up to 200,000×** SCANNING ELECTRON MICROSCOPE An SEM sweeps a beam of electrons over a specimen's surface, causing other electrons to be emitted from the specimen. SEMs produce realistic, three-dimensional images, which can only be viewed as photographs or on a monitor, as in the image of the *Paramecium* at right. Here a researcher compares an SEM picture to a computer monitor showing an enhanced image.

SECTION 2 Viewing Cells **49**

Visualizing Microscopes

Content Background

Microscopes are used by many different types of scientists, including biologists, microbiologists, botanists, geologists, and epidemiologists. In 1665, Robert Hooke was the first person to see cells through a microscope of his creation. The idea of cell theory—that all living things are made of cells—was borne from his discovery. Although Hooke could see the individual cells clearly, he did not stain any of his specimens; therefore, he would not have been able to see other single-celled organisms such as bacteria. It was Antoni van Leeuwenhoek who first examined living organisms through a simple microscope in the late seventeenth century. He found organisms in the rain-water he collected, as well as in the scrapings he took from the surface of his teeth.

Differentiated Instruction

English-Language Learners Have students work in pairs to create an advertisement for a microscope. Students should discuss all of the parts of a microscope in their advertisement. The advertisement should also include all of the parts of a cell that can be visualized using the microscope. L2

Visual Learning

Figure 13 Have students make a chart comparing and contrasting the different types of microscopes in this figure. They should include information on lenses and the uses of each. L2
LS **Visual-Spatial**

2 Teach

Mini LAB

Purpose Students discover objects that can be used to magnify. [L2] [ELL] [LS] **Kinesthetic**

Materials clear drinking glass, clear glass bowl, water, magnifying lens, newspaper pages

Teaching Strategy Try this lab with the glasses students will use. Determine beforehand the amount of water that will be needed.

Analysis
Each of the objects magnifies the newsprint.

Assessment

Performance Cover newsprint with clear plastic wrap. Place a drop of water on the plastic wrap. Have students explain what they see and why. The words appear magnified because the water drop acts like a convex lens. Use **Performance Assessment in the Science Classroom**, p. 89.

INTEGRATE Career

Cell Biologist The field of cell biology is very diverse. Many techniques require the use of different microscopes. As students research the drugs that cell biologists are studying, also have them identify techniques that require microscopes, and the types of microscopes that cell biologists use.

Mini LAB

Observing Magnified Objects

Procedure
1. Look at a **newspaper** through the curved side and through the flat bottom of an **empty, clear glass.**
2. Look at the newspaper through a **clear glass bowl filled with water** and then with a **magnifying lens.**

Analysis
In your Science Journal, compare how well you can see the newspaper through each of the objects.

Try at Home

INTEGRATE Career

Cell Biologist Microscopes are important tools for cell biologists as they research diseases. In your Science Journal, make a list of diseases for which you think cell biologists are trying to find effective drugs.

Modern Microscopes Scientists use a variety of microscopes to study organisms, cells, and cell parts that are too small to be seen with the human eye. Depending on how many lenses a microscope contains, it is called simple or compound. A simple microscope is similar to a magnifying lens. It has only one lens. A microscope's lens makes an enlarged image of an object and directs light toward your eye. The change in apparent size produced by a microscope is called magnification. Microscopes vary in powers of magnification. Some microscopes can make images of individual atoms.

The microscope you probably will use to study life science is a compound light microscope, similar to the one in the Reference Handbook at the back of this book. The compound light microscope has two sets of lenses—eyepiece lenses and objective lenses. The eyepiece lenses are mounted in one or two tubelike structures. Images of objects viewed through two eyepieces, or stereomicroscopes, are three-dimensional. Images of objects viewed through one eyepiece are not. Compound light microscopes usually have two to four movable objective lenses.

Magnification The powers of the eyepiece and objective lenses determine the total magnifications of a microscope. If the eyepiece lens has a power of 10× and the objective lens has a power of 43×, then the total magnification is 430× (10× times 43×). Some compound microscopes, like those in **Figure 13,** have more powerful lenses that can magnify an object up to 2,000 times its original size.

Electron Microscopes Things that are too small to be seen with other microscopes can be viewed with an electron microscope. Instead of using lenses to direct beams of light, an electron microscope uses a magnetic field in a vacuum to direct beams of electrons. Some electron microscopes can magnify images up to one million times. Electron microscope images must be photographed or electronically produced.

Several kinds of electron microscopes have been invented, as shown in **Figure 13.** Scanning electron microscopes (SEM) produce a realistic, three-dimensional image. Only the surface of the specimen can be observed using an SEM. Transmission electron microscopes (TEM) produce a two-dimensional image of a thinly-sliced specimen. Details of cell parts can be examined using a TEM. Scanning tunneling microscopes (STM) are able to show the arrangement of atoms on the surface of a molecule. A metal probe is placed near the surface of the specimen and electrons flow from the tip. The hills and valleys of the specimen's surface are mapped.

50 CHAPTER 2 Cells

Curriculum Connection

Art Discuss the use of art in science before the camera was invented. Photocopy a picture of Hooke's drawing of cells for each student. Ask them to compare it with the photographs of cells throughout the chapter and write in their Science Journals their opinions of the advantages and disadvantages of using artwork and photography. [L2] [LS] **Linguistic and Visual-Spatial**

Differentiated Instruction

Challenge Have students research the Italian scientist who discover the Golgi body. Their research should include how this discovery was made possible and why this organelle was not seriously studied until the 1950s. Students can use references to find electron micrographs of the Golgi body to learn about it in greater depth. Students can write a biographical report on Camillo Golgi and the Golgi body. [L3]

Cell Theory

During the seventeenth century, scientists used their new invention, the microscope, to explore the newly discovered microscopic world. They examined drops of blood, scrapings from their own teeth, and other small things. Cells weren't discovered until the microscope was improved. In 1665, Robert Hooke cut a thin slice of cork and looked at it under his microscope. To Hooke, the cork seemed to be made up of empty little boxes, which he named cells.

In the 1830s, Matthias Schleiden used a microscope to study plants and concluded that all plants are made of cells. Theodor Schwann, after observing different animal cells, concluded that all animals are made up of cells. Eventually, they combined their ideas and became convinced that all living things are made of cells.

Several years later, Rudolf Virchow hypothesized that cells divide to form new cells. Virchow proposed that every cell came from a cell that already existed. His observations and conclusions and those of others are summarized in the **cell theory,** as described in **Table 1.**

Reading Check *Who first concluded that all animals are made of cells?*

Table 1 The Cell Theory	
All organisms are made up of one or more cells.	An organism can be one cell or many cells like most plants and animals.
The cell is the basic unit of organization in organisms.	Even in complex organisms, the cell is the basic unit of structure and function.
All cells come from cells.	Most cells can divide to form two new, identical cells.

---

section 2 review

Summary

Magnifying Cells

- The powers of the eyepiece and objective lenses determine the total magnification of a microscope.
- An electron microscope uses a magnetic field in a vacuum to direct beams of electrons.

Development of the Cell Theory

- In 1665, Robert Hooke looked at a piece of cork under his microscope and called what he saw cells.
- The conclusions of Rudolf Virchow and those of others are summarized in the cell theory.

Self Check

1. **Determine** why the invention of the microscope was important in the study of cells.
2. **State** the cell theory.
3. **Compare** a simple and a compound light microscope.
4. **Explain** Virchow's contribution to the cell theory.
5. **Think Critically** Why would it be better to look at living cells than at dead cells?

Applying Math

6. **Solve One-Step Equations** Calculate the magnifications of a microscope that has an $8\times$ eyepiece and $10\times$ and $40\times$ objectives.

---

section 2 review

1. Microscopes made cells visible, which established them as a scientific fact. This led to the understanding that all living things are made of cells.
2. All organisms are made of one or more cells. The cell is the basic unit of organization in organisms. All cells come from other cells.
3. A simple light microscope has one lens. A compound light microscope has two or more lenses.
4. Virchow proposed that every cell came from a cell that already existed.
5. Possible answer: some cell parts disintegrate when the cell dies.
6. The low-power magnification is $80\times = (8 \times 10)$ and the high-power magnification is $320\times = (8 \times 40)$.

1 Motivate

Bellringer

Section Focus Transparencies also are available on the Interactive Chalkboard CD-ROM.

L2 **ELL**

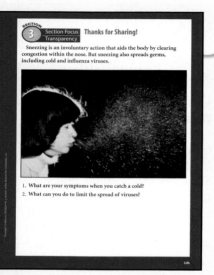

Tie to Prior Knowledge

Viral Symptoms Most students will be familiar with at least one viral disease (chicken pox, cold sores, the common cold). Have them list its symptoms on the board.

---

section 3 Viruses

as you read

What You'll Learn
- **Explain** how a virus makes copies of itself.
- **Identify** the benefits of vaccines.
- **Investigate** some uses of viruses.

Why It's Important
Viruses infect nearly all organisms, usually affecting them negatively yet sometimes affecting them positively.

Review Vocabulary
disease: a condition that results from the disruption in function of one or more of an organism's normal processes

New Vocabulary
- virus
- host cell

What are viruses?

Cold sores, measles, chicken pox, colds, the flu, and AIDS are diseases caused by nonliving particles called viruses. A **virus** is a strand of hereditary material surrounded by a protein coating. Viruses don't have a nucleus or other organelles. They also lack a cell membrane. Viruses, as shown in **Figure 14,** have a variety of shapes. Because they are too small to be seen with a light microscope, they were discovered only after the electron microscope was invented. Before that time, scientists only hypothesized about viruses.

How do viruses multiply?

All viruses can do is make copies of themselves. However, they can't do that without the help of a living cell called a **host cell.** Crystalized forms of some viruses can be stored for years. Then, if they enter an organism, they can multiply quickly.

Once a virus is inside of a host cell, the virus can act in two ways. It can either be active or it can become latent, which is an inactive stage.

Figure 14 Viruses come in a variety of shapes.

Color-enhanced TEM Magnification: 160000×

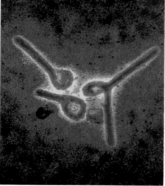

Filoviruses do not have uniform shapes. Some of these *Ebola* viruses have a loop at one end.

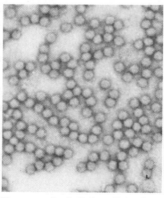

The potato leafroll virus, *Polervirus,* damages potato crops worldwide.

Color-enhanced SEM Magnification: 140000×

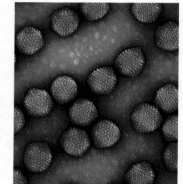

This is just one of the many adenoviruses that can cause the common cold.

52 CHAPTER 2 Cells

Section 3 Resource Manager

Chapter *Fast File* Resources
Transparency Activity, p. 46
Directed Reading for Content Mastery, pp. 21, 22
Enrichment, p. 32
Reinforcement, p. 29
Lab Worksheet, pp. 7–8

Reading and Writing Skill Activities, p. 31
Home and Community Involvement, p. 26
Lab Management and Safety, p. 58

52 CHAPTER 2 Cells

Figure 15 An active virus multiplies and destroys the host cell.

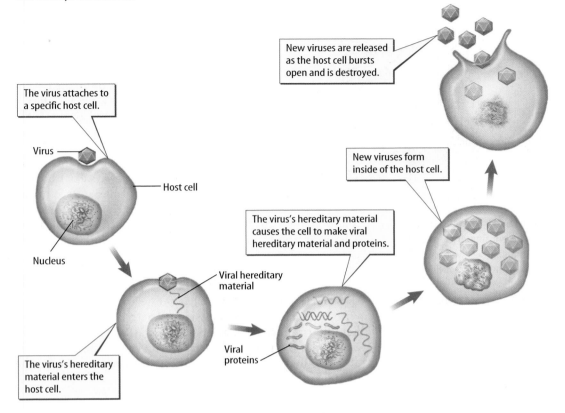

New viruses are released as the host cell bursts open and is destroyed.

The virus attaches to a specific host cell.

Virus

Host cell

Nucleus

The virus's hereditary material enters the host cell.

Viral hereditary material

Viral proteins

The virus's hereditary material causes the cell to make viral hereditary material and proteins.

New viruses form inside of the host cell.

Active Viruses When a virus enters a cell and is active, it causes the host cell to make new viruses. This process destroys the host cell. Follow the steps in **Figure 15** to see one way that an active virus functions inside a cell.

Latent Viruses Some viruses can be latent. That means that after the virus enters a cell, its hereditary material can become part of the cell's hereditary material. It does not immediately make new viruses or destroy the cell. As the host cell reproduces, the viral DNA is copied. A virus can be latent for many years. Then, at any time, certain conditions, either inside or outside your body, can activate the virus.

If you have had a cold sore on your lip, a latent virus in your body has become active. The cold sore is a sign that the virus is active and destroying cells in your lip. When the cold sore disappears, the virus has become latent again. The virus is still in your body's cells, but it is hiding and doing no apparent harm.

Science Online

Topic: Virus Reactivation
Visit life.msscience.com for Web links to information about viruses.

Activity In your Science Journal, list five stimuli that might activate a latent virus.

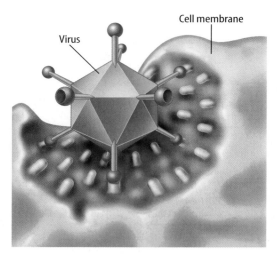

Virus — Cell membrane

Figure 16 Viruses and the attachment sites of the host cell must match exactly. That's why most viruses infect only one kind of host cell.
Identify *diseases caused by viruses.*

Science Online

Topic: Filoviruses
Visit life.msscience.com for Web links to information about the virus family *Filoviridae*.

Activity Make a table that displays the virus name, location, and year of the initial outbreaks associated with the *Filoviridae* family.

How do viruses affect organisms?

Viruses attack animals, plants, fungi, protists, and all prokaryotes. Some viruses can infect only specific kinds of cells. For instance, many viruses, such as the potato leafroll virus, are limited to one host species or to one type of tissue within that species. A few viruses affect a broad range of hosts. An example of this is the rabies virus. Rabies can infect humans and many other animal hosts.

A virus cannot move by itself, but it can reach a host's body in several ways. For example, it can be carried onto a plant's surface by the wind or it can be inhaled by an animal. In a viral infection, the virus first attaches to the surface of the host cell. The virus and the place where it attaches must fit together exactly, as shown in **Figure 16.** Because of this, most viruses attack only one kind of host cell.

Viruses that infect bacteria are called bacteriophages (bak TIHR ee uh fay jihz). They differ from other kinds of viruses in the way that they enter bacteria and release their hereditary material. Bacteriophages attach to a bacterium and inject their hereditary material. The entire cycle takes about 20 min, and each virus-infected cell releases an average of 100 viruses.

Fighting Viruses

Vaccines are used to prevent disease. A vaccine is made from weakened virus particles that can't cause disease anymore. Vaccines have been made to prevent many diseases, including measles, mumps, smallpox, chicken pox, polio, and rabies.

✔ Reading Check *What is a vaccine?*

The First Vaccine Edward Jenner is credited with developing the first vaccine in 1796. He developed a vaccine for smallpox, a disease that was still feared in the early twentieth century. Jenner noticed that people who got a disease called cowpox didn't get smallpox. He prepared a vaccine from the sores of people who had cowpox. When injected into healthy people, the cowpox vaccine protected them from smallpox. Jenner didn't know he was fighting a virus. At that time, no one understood what caused disease or how the body fought disease.

Treating Viral Diseases Antibiotics treat bacterial infections but are not effective against viral diseases. One way your body can stop viral infections is by making interferons. Interferons are proteins that are produced rapidly by virus-infected cells and move to noninfected cells in the host. They cause the noninfected cells to produce protective substances.

Antiviral drugs can be given to infected patients to help fight a virus. A few drugs show some effectiveness against viruses but some have limited use because of their adverse side effects.

Preventing Viral Diseases Public health measures for preventing viral diseases include vaccinating people, improving sanitary conditions, quarantining patients, and controlling animals that spread disease. For example, annual rabies vaccinations of pets and farm animals protect them and humans from infection. To control the spread of rabies in wild animals such as coyotes and wolves, wildlife workers place bait containing an oral rabies vaccine, as shown in **Figure 17,** where wild animals will find it.

Research with Viruses

You might think viruses are always harmful. However, through research, scientists are discovering helpful uses for some viruses. One use, called gene therapy, substitutes normal hereditary material for a cell's defective hereditary material. The normal material is enclosed in viruses that "infect" targeted cells. The new hereditary material enters the cells and replaces the defective hereditary material. Using gene therapy, scientists hope to help people with genetic disorders and find a cure for cancer.

Figure 17 This oral rabies bait is being prepared for an aerial drop by the Texas Department of Health as part of their Oral Rabies Vaccination Program. This five-year program has prevented the expansion of rabies into Texas.

Teacher FYI

Virus Invasion Even though bacteriophages typically inject their DNA into the host cell, not all viruses invade a host cell in this way. Many animal viruses enter the host cell through endocytosis, the binding of the virus to the cell membrane. Once inside the host cell, the virus sheds its protein coat and either undergoes replication or becomes part of the host's DNA.

Use Science Words

Word Meaning Have students look up the terms *lysis*, *virion*, and *virology*. Have them write a paragraph about the relevance of each to the study of viruses. L2
IS **Linguistic**

3 Assess

DAILY INTERVENTION

Check for Understanding

Visual-Kinesthetic Have students make a puzzle that shows the steps of viral infection and replication. Students can exchange puzzles to test each other's knowledge of the information. L2

Reteach

Viruses Have students write a paragraph that describes the differences between active and latent viruses. L1 IS **Linguistic**

✓ Assessment

Oral How does a virus invade a cell? The virus's hereditary material enters the cell, which becomes infected and eventually replicates the virus.

---

section 3 review

Summary

What are viruses?
- A virus is a strand of hereditary material surrounded by a protein coating.

How do viruses multiply?
- An active virus immediately destroys the host cell but a latent virus does not.

Fighting Viruses and Research with Viruses
- Antiviral drugs can be given to infected patients to help fight a virus.
- Scientists are discovering helpful uses for some viruses.

Self Check

1. **Describe** how viruses multiply.
2. **Explain** how vaccines are beneficial.
3. **Determine** how some viruses might be helpful.
4. **Discuss** how viral diseases might be prevented.
5. **Think Critically** Explain why a doctor might not give you any medication if you have a viral disease.

Applying Skills

6. **Concept Map** Make an events-chain concept map to show what happens when a latent virus becomes active.

---

section 3 review

1. An active virus enters a cell and causes the host cell to make new viruses. When a latent virus enters a cell, its DNA is copied as the host cell reproduces. Under certain conditions, the body can activate the virus.
2. Vaccines, when properly administered, help prevent many viral infections.
3. They may be used to transfer normal DNA into a cell.
4. vaccinating people, improving sanitary conditions, quarantining patients, and controlling animals that spread disease
5. No medications cure a viral disease.
6. Maps should show the following: latent virus enters cell; virus becomes part of cell's DNA; cell divides; virus reproduces as part of cell division; virus becomes active; virus forms new virus particles; cell is destroyed.

Real-World Question

Purpose Students will design an experiment to compare uses of stereomicroscopes and compound light microscopes.

L2 COOP LEARN
Logical-Mathematical

Process Skills observe, identify, recognize and use spatial relationships, classify, communicate

Time Required 15 minutes to plan and 45 minutes to do the experiment

Safety Precautions Caution students to use care when working with microscope slides and coverslips.

Form a Hypothesis

Possible Hypothesis Students may hypothesize that large items can be viewed with the stereomicroscope and small objects can be viewed with the compound light microscope.

Test Your Hypothesis

Possible Procedures Separate items into two groups: those that can be viewed with the stereomicroscope, and those that can be viewed with the light microscope.

Teaching Strategies
• Demonstrate how to make a wet-mount.
• If microscopes have mirrors, explain how to use them.

Design Your Own

Comparing Light Microscopes

Goals
■ **Learn** how to correctly use a stereomicroscope and a compound light microscope.
■ **Compare** the uses of the stereomicroscope and compound light microscope.

Possible Materials
compound light microscope
stereomicroscope
items from the classroom—include some living or once-living items (8)
microscope slides and coverslips
plastic petri dishes
distilled water
dropper

Safety Precautions
⬡ ☣ ✋ 🔥 ⬡

Real-World Question

You're a technician in a police forensic laboratory. You use a stereomicroscope and a compound light microscope in the laboratory. A detective just returned from a crime scene with bags of evidence. You must examine each piece of evidence under a microscope. How do you decide which microscope is the best tool to use? Will all of the evidence that you've collected be viewable through both microscopes?

Form a Hypothesis

Compare the items to be examined under the microscopes. Form a hypothesis to predict which microscope will be used for each item and explain why.

Alternative Inquiry Lab

Comparing Light Microscopes To make this Lab an Inquiry Lab, tell students that they are forensics technicians. They are leading a crime scene investigation, and they need to determine the best way to examine the evidence. Have them determine what sorts of evidence would be collected at a crime scene. They also should evaluate which type of microscope would be used with each piece

of evidence to help with their examination. Which microscope works best to view a piece of clothing? For examining blood samples, hair, or clothing fibers, which microscope(s) could be used? This can include predicting what types of microscopes could be used by forensics technicians and what types would work best for different life science experiments.

◉ Test Your Hypothesis

Make a Plan

1. As a group, decide how you will test your hypothesis.
2. **Describe** how you will carry out this experiment using a series of specific steps. Make sure the steps are in a logical order. Remember that you must place an item in the bottom of a plastic petri dish to examine it under the stereomicroscope and you must make a wet mount of any item to be examined under the compound light microscope. For more help, see the Reference Handbook.
3. If you need a data table or an observation table, design one in your Science Journal.

Follow Your Plan

1. Make sure your teacher approves the objects you'll examine, your plan, and your data table before you start.
2. Carry out the experiment.
3. While doing the experiment, record your observations and complete the data table.

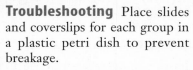

◉ Analyze Your Data

1. **Compare** the items you examined with those of your classmates.
2. **Classify** the eight items you observed based on this experiment.

◉ Conclude and Apply

1. **Infer** which microscope a scientist might use to examine a blood sample, fibers, and live snails.
2. **List** five careers that require people to use a stereomicroscope. List five careers that require people to use a compound light microscope. Enter the lists in your Science Journal.
3. **Infer** how the images would differ if you examined an item under a compound light microscope and a stereomicroscope.
4. **Determine** which microscope is better for looking at large, or possibly live, items.

Communicating Your Data

In your Science Journal, **write** a short description of an imaginary crime scene and the evidence found there. Sort the evidence into two lists—items to be examined under a stereomicroscope and items to be examined under a compound light microscope. **For more help, refer to the Science Skill Handbook.**

LAB **57**

Communicating Your Data

Items small enough to fit under a coverslip should be examined with a compound light microscope; larger items should be examined with a stereomicroscope.

☑ Assessment

Performance To further assess students' understanding of the differences in microscopes, provide other items and have students demonstrate how to use the appropriate microscope to view each item. Use **Performance Assessment in the Science Classroom,** p. 97. L2

Troubleshooting Place slides and coverslips for each group in a plastic petri dish to prevent breakage.

Expected Outcome The stereomicroscope is used for items that are too large to fit under a coverslip on a slide. The compound light microscope reveals greater detail. Students should note that the image produced by the compound light microscope is upside down and reversed left to right.

◉ Analyze Your Data

Answers to Questions

1. Answers will vary.
2. Large items should be classified together, and items small enough to fit on a slide should be grouped together.

Error Analysis Have students compare their results and their hypotheses and explain why differences occurred.

◉ Conclude and Apply

1. A scientist might use a stereomicroscope to examine live snails and a compound light microscope to examine blood and fibers.
2. Answers will vary, but may include lab technicians, forensic scientists, and cell biologists for the compound light microscope and surgeons, botanists, entomologists, geologists, and gemologists for the stereomicroscope.
3. The image under the compound light microscope will be magnified more, show greater detail, be upside down, and reversed left to right.
4. stereomicroscope

Content Background

Jewel Plummer Cobb hoped to discover if there was a particular drug or combination of drugs which would be effective in destroying specific types of cancer. She would also need to determine whether these drugs would also destroy healthy tissues. Cobb exposed cells from both cancerous and non-cancerous tissues to chemotherapy drugs.

Her results demonstrated that some drugs could stop the uncontrolled growth of certain types of cancer cells. Although normal cells were also harmed, they never showed the dramatic destruction produced in some cancer cells.

Discussion

Experimental Results Using Cobb's research as an example, discuss the value of experiments even if the results do not meet the researcher's specific goals. Possible answer: Science is a continuing process of discovery. Cobb's work is a necessary first step to new approaches to treatment like Levy's.

Historical Significance

The structure and function of DNA were not discovered until 1953. Cobb's research began shortly thereafter, long before the role of genes in the development of cancer was understood. Research like Cobb's leads to questions about how certain drugs can stop the unchecked growth of tumors. In combination with an increasing understanding of how genes work, these results allow scientists to refine the methods of administering treatments and to target the development of drugs specifically aimed at preventing the replication of DNA, a process that all cells require.

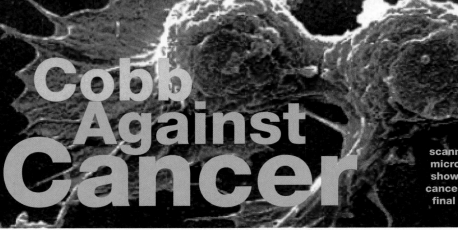

TIME SCIENCE AND HISTORY

SCIENCE CAN CHANGE THE COURSE OF HISTORY!

Cobb Against Cancer

This colored scanning electron micrograph (SEM) shows two breast cancer cells in the final stage of cell division.

Jewel Plummer Cobb is a cell biologist who did important background research on the use of drugs against cancer in the 1950s. She removed cells from cancerous tumors and cultured them in the lab. Then, in a controlled study, she tried a series of different drugs against batches of the same cells. Her goal was to find the right drug to cure each patient's particular cancer. Cobb never met that goal, but her research laid the groundwork for modern chemotherapy—the use of chemicals to treat cancer.

Jewel Cobb also influenced science in another way. She was a role model, especially in her role as dean or president of several universities. Cobb promoted equal opportunity for students of all backgrounds, especially in the sciences.

Light Up a Cure

Vancouver, British Columbia 2000. While Cobb herself was only able to infer what was going on inside a cell from its reactions to various drugs, her work has helped others go further. Building on Cobb's work, Professor Julia Levy and her research team at the University of British Columbia actually go inside cells, and even organelles, to work against cancer. One technique they are pioneering is the use of light to guide cancer drugs to the right cells. First, the patient is given a chemotherapy drug that reacts to light. Then, a fiber optic tube is inserted into the tumor. Finally, laser light is passed through the tube, which activates the light-sensitive drug—but only in the tumor itself. This will hopefully provide a technique to keep healthy cells healthy while killing sick cells.

Write Report on Cobb's experiments on cancer cells. What were her dependent and independent variables? What would she have used as a control? What sources of error did she have to guard against? Answer the same questions about Levy's work.

Science online

For more information, visit life.msscience.com/time

Write Levy and Cobb were both targeting cancer cells and working to avoid harming normal cells. In both studies, the control group would be normal human cells that were exposed to the chemotherapeutic drugs. The independent variables were the specific drugs administered to the cells. The dependent variables were the response of the cells to the treatment.

Resources for Teachers and Students

Advancing Current Treatments for Cancer, by Samuel Hellman and Everett E. Vokes, Scientific American, September 2000

How Cancer Arises, by Robert A. Weinberg, Scientific American, September 2001

Reviewing Main Ideas

Section 1 Cell Structure

1. Prokaryotic and eukaryotic are the two cell types.

2. The DNA in the nucleus controls cell functions.

3. Organelles such as mitochondria and chloroplasts process energy.

4. Most many-celled organisms are organized into tissues, organs, and organ systems.

Section 2 Viewing Cells

1. A simple microscope has just one lens. A compound light microscope has an eyepiece and objective lenses.

2. To calculate the magnification of a microscope, multiply the power of the eyepiece by the power of the objective lens.

3. According to the cell theory, the cell is the basic unit of life. Organisms are made of one or more cells, and all cells come from other cells.

Section 3 Viruses

1. A virus is a structure containing hereditary material surrounded by a protein coating.

2. A virus can make copies of itself only when it is inside a living host cell.

Reviewing Main Ideas

Summary statements can be used by students to review the major concepts of the chapter.

Visualizing Main Ideas

See student page.

Science online

Visit life.msscience.com
/self_check_quiz
/interactive_tutor
/vocabulary_puzzlemaker
/chapter_review
/standardized_test

Assessment Transparency

For additional assessment questions, use the *Assessment Transparency* located in the transparency book.

Visualizing Main Ideas

Copy and complete the following concept map of the basic units of life.

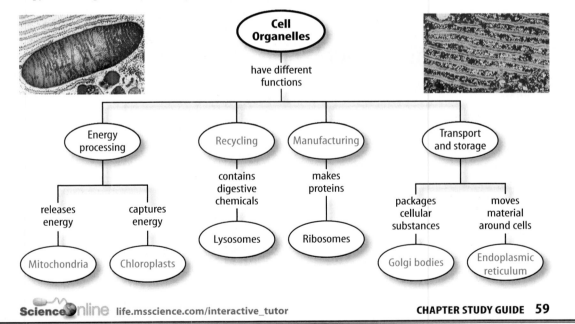

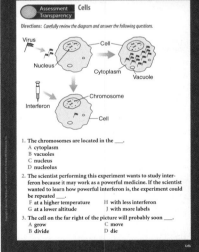

Using Vocabulary

1. tissue

2. chloroplast, ER, Golgi body, mitochondrion, nucleus, organelle, ribosome, or virus

3. chloroplast, ER, Golgi body, nucleus, or ribosome

4. cell membrane or cytoplasm

5. mitochondrion

6. cell theory

7. cytoplasm, nucleus, or virus

8. cell membrane or cell wall

9. host cell

10. organ or tissue

Checking Concepts

11. B   15. C

12. D   16. C

13. B   17. A

14. A   18. A

Thinking Critically

19. Once a virus infects a cell, it uses the cell to produce more viruses. No drugs will kill viruses.

20. Answers may vary, but a stereomicroscope would enable you to view a large specimen as well as to look closely at the mold.

21. The plant cell would die or become dependent on other cells to provide its food.

Using Vocabulary

cell membrane p. 38
cell theory p. 51
cell wall p. 39
chloroplast p. 42
cytoplasm p. 38
endoplasmic
  reticulum p. 43
Golgi body p. 43

host cell p. 52
mitochondrion p. 42
nucleus p. 40
organ p. 45
organelle p. 40
ribosome p. 42
tissue p. 45
virus p. 52

Using the vocabulary words, give an example of each of the following.

1. found in every organ

2. smaller than one cell

3. a plant-cell organelle

4. part of every cell

5. powerhouse of a cell

6. used by biologists

7. contains hereditary material

8. a structure that surrounds the cell

9. can be damaged by a virus

10. made up of cells

Checking Concepts

Choose the word or phrase that best answers the question.

11. What structure allows only certain things to pass in and out of the cell?
    A) cytoplasm   C) ribosomes
    B) cell membrane   D) Golgi body

12. What is the organelle to the right?
    A) nucleus
    B) cytoplasm
    C) Golgi body
    D) endoplasmic reticulum

Use the illustration below to answer question 13.

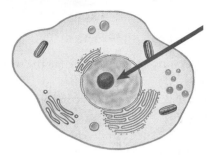

13. In the figure above, what is the function of the structure that the arrow is pointing to?
    A) recycles old cell parts
    B) controls cell activities
    C) protection
    D) releases energy

14. Which scientist gave the name *cells* to structures he viewed?
    A) Hooke   C) Schleiden
    B) Schwann   D) Virchow

15. Which of the following is a viral disease?
    A) tuberculosis   C) smallpox
    B) anthrax   D) tetanus

16. Which microscope can magnify up to a million times?
    A) compound light microscope
    B) stereomicroscope
    C) transmission electron microscope
    D) atomic force microscope

17. Which of the following is part of a bacterial cell?
    A) a cell wall   C) mitochondria
    B) lysosomes   D) a nucleus

18. Which of the following do groups of different tissues form?
    A) organ   C) organ system
    B) organelle   D) organism

Science  nline life.msscience.com/vocabulary_puzzlemaker

Use the Exam*View*® Pro Testmaker CD-ROM to:

• create multiple versions of tests

• create modified tests with one mouse click for inclusion students

• edit existing questions and add your own questions

• build tests aligned with state standards using built-in State Curriculum Tags

• change English tests to Spanish with one mouse click and vice versa

Thinking Critically

19. Infer why it is difficult to treat a viral disease.

20. Explain which type of microscope would be best to view a piece of moldy bread.

21. Predict what would happen to a plant cell that suddenly lost its chloroplasts.

22. Predict what would happen if the animal cell shown to the right didn't have ribosomes.

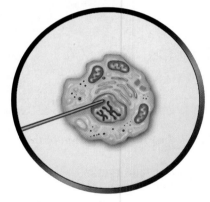

23. Determine how you would decide whether an unknown cell was an animal cell, a plant cell, or a bacterial cell.

24. Concept Map Make an events-chain concept map of the following from simple to complex: *small intestine, circular muscle cell, human,* and *digestive system*.

25. Interpret Scientific Illustrations Use the illustrations in **Figure 1** to describe how the shape of a cell is related to its function.

Use the table below to answer question 26.

Cell Structures

Structure	Prokaryotic Cell	Eukaryotic Cell
Cell membrane	Yes	Yes
Cytoplasm	Yes	Yes
Nucleus	No	Yes
Endoplasmic reticulum	No	Yes
Golgi bodies	No	Yes

26. Compare and Contrast Copy and complete the table above.

27. Make a Model Make and illustrate a time line about the development of the cell theory. Begin with the development of the microscope and end with Virchow. Include the contributions of Leeuwenhoek, Hooke, Schleiden, and Schwann.

Performance Activities

28. Model Use materials that resemble cell parts or represent their functions to make a model of a plant cell or an animal cell. Include a cell-parts key.

29. Poster Make a poster about the history of vaccinations. Contact your local Health Department for current information.

Applying Math

Use the illustration below to answer question 30.

30. Cell Width If the pointer shown above with the cell is 10 micrometers (μm) in length, then about how wide is this cell?
  A) 20 μm   **C)** 5 μm
  B) 10 μm   **D)** 0.1 μm

31. Magnification Calculate the magnification of a microscope with a 20× eyepiece and a 40× objective.

Thinking Critically

22. No proteins could be made, and the animal cell would die.

23. If there is a cell wall and chloroplasts, it is a plant cell. A cell with no chloroplasts or cell wall is an animal cell. If no membrane-bound organelles are present, it is a bacterial cell.

24. circular muscle cell, small intestine, digestive system, human

25. Answers will vary but should relate each shape to a function of the cell, such as the elongated shape of the nerve cell and its function in transmitting impulses.

26. See student page.

27. The time line should have equal divisions of time and cover from the late 1500s to the late 1800s. Include these dates: late 1500s, microscope invented; late 1600s, Leeuwenhoek improves microscope; 1665, Hooke uses the word *cell*; 1830s, Schleiden discovers plants are made of cells; mid 1800s, Schwann discovers animals are made of cells; mid 1800s, Virchow concludes that all cells come from cells.

Performance Activities

28. Model should include cell parts and a key to identify them. Use **PASC**, p. 123.

29. Posters should correctly show the history of vaccinations. Use **PASC**, p. 145.

Applying Math

National Math Standards
4, 9

30. B

31. the magnification would be 800×

✓ Assessment   Resources

📁 **Reproducible Masters**

Chapter *Fast File* Resources
  Chapter Review, pp. 37–38
  Chapter Tests, pp. 39–42
  Assessment Transparency Activity, p. 49

Glencoe Science Web site
  Chapter Review Test
  Standardized Test Practice

Glencoe Technology
  🖋 Assessment Transparency
  🔵 Exam*View*® Pro Testmaker
  📺 MindJogger Videoquiz
  🔵 Interactive Chalkboard

FAST FILE

Answer Sheet A practice answer sheet can be found at life.msscience.com/answer_sheet.

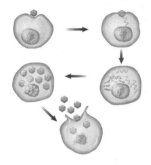

S A M P L E

Part 1 Multiple Choice

1. B	6. C
2. A	7. D
3. C	8. D
4. A	9. A
5. D	

Part 2 Short Response

10. Cell walls are outer coverings for the cell that are tough, rigid and provide cell shape found in plants, fungi and bacteria. The cell membrane is a protective layer around the cell that regulates the movement of water, food and other particles into and out of the cell.

11. by digesting it with the enzymes present in the lysosome or vacuole

12. The body produces interferons which is a protective protein, when it is infected by a virus. This protein is rapidly transported to neighboring cells to help protect them against infection. Other ways to

Part 1 Multiple Choice

Record your answers on the answer sheet provided by your teacher or on a sheet of paper.

1. What do a bacterial cell, a plant cell, and a nerve cell have in common?
   A. cell wall and nucleus
   B. cytoplasm and cell membrane
   C. endoplasmic reticulum
   D. flagella

2. Which of the following is not a function of an organelle?
   A. tough outer coating
   B. energy producers
   C. chemical producers
   D. chemical storage

Use the images below to answer question 3.

 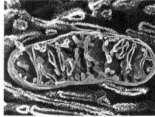

3. What is the primary function of this organelle?
   A. capturing light energy
   B. directing cell processes
   C. releasing energy stored in food
   D. making proteins

4. Which organelles receive the directions from the DNA in the nucleus about which proteins to make?
   A. ribosomes
   B. endoplasmic reticulum
   C. Golgi bodies
   D. cell wall

5. Why is a virus not considered a living cell?
   A. It has a cell wall.
   B. It has hereditary material.
   C. It has no organelles.
   D. It cannot multiply.

Use the illustration below to answer questions 6 and 7.

6. What does the diagram above represent?
   A. cell reproduction
   B. bacterial reproduction
   C. active virus multiplication
   D. vaccination

7. What does the largest circular structure represent?
   A. a host cell   C. a vacuole
   B. a ribosome   D. the nucleus

8. Where do most of a cell's life processes occur?
   A. nucleus   C. organ
   B. cell wall   D. cytoplasm

9. A group of similar cells that work together is a(n)
   A. tissue.   C. organ system.
   B. organ.   D. organism.

Test-Taking Tip

Read Carefully Read each question carefully for full understanding.

protect against viral infection are anti-viral medication, vaccines, improved sanitary conditions (washing hands), isolating sick individuals and controlling animals that spread the disease.

13. in the cell wall; The fibers form a thick mesh to support the cell and let water and other materials pass through it.

14.

Organelle	Function
(nucleus)	directs all cellular activities
Mitochondria	(releases energy stored in food)
(chloroplasts)	captures light energy to make glucose
Ribosomes	(where proteins are made)

15. The Golgi bodies sort proteins and other substances and package them into vesicles to be delivered to other parts of the cell or released out of the cell just like how items are packaged and shipped in a plant.

16. Viruses need a host cell to make copies of themselves.

17. an example might be the cardiovascular system; heart, arteries, veins, and capillaries

Part 2 | Short Response/Grid In

Record your answers on the answer sheet provided by your teacher or on a sheet of paper.

10. Compare and contrast the cell wall and the cell membrane.

11. How would a cell destroy or breakdown a harmful chemical which entered the cytoplasm?

12. How does your body stop viral infections? What are other ways of protection against viral infections?

13. Where is cellulose found in a cell and what is its function?

Use the following table to answer question 14.

Organelle	Function
	Directs all cellular activities
Mitochondria	
	Captures light energy to make glucose
Ribosomes	

14. Copy and complete the table above with the appropriate information.

15. How are Golgi bodies similar to a packaging plant?

16. Why does a virus need a host cell?

17. Give an example of an organ system and list the organs in it.

18. Compare and contrast the energy processing organelles.

19. Describe the structure of viruses.

20. How do ribosomes differ from other cell structures found in the cytoplasm?

21. What kind of microscope uses a series of lenses to magnify?

Part 3 | Open Ended

Record your answers on a sheet of paper.

22. Name three different types of microscopes and give uses for each.

23. Some viruses, like the common cold, only make the host organism sick, but other viruses, like *Ebola,* are deadly to the host organism. Which of these strategies is more effective for replication and transmission of the virus to new host organisms? Which type of virus would be easier to study and develop a vaccine against?

24. Discuss the importance of the cytoplasm.

25. Explain how Hooke, Schleiden, and Schwann contributed to the cell theory.

Use the illustration below to answer question 26.

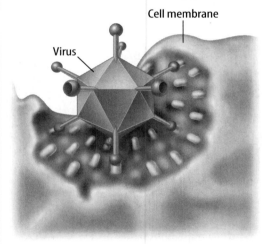

Cell membrane

Virus

26. What interaction is taking place in the illustration above? What are two possible outcomes of this interaction?

27. Describe how the first vaccine was developed.

 life.msscience.com/standardized_test

23. The common cold is more effective for replication and transmission of the virus because the host is still alive to carry the virus around. *Ebola* kills the host before there is a lot of chance for replication and transmission to the next host. The common cold would be easier to study because there are many sources and it only makes the individual sick. However, there is no vaccine for the common cold because there are so many types of viruses.

24. Many important chemical reactions take place in the cytoplasm. The cytoplasm contains the framework cytoskeleton which supports the organelles and maintains the shape of the cell. Eukaryotic cells have organelles in the cytoplasm.

25. Hooke coined the term *cells* by observing cork cells. Schleiden observed plant cells and stated that all plants were made up of cells. Schwann observed animal cells and stated that animals were made up of cells.

26. A virus is attaching to a host cell at the cell surface. If the virus and the cell match, the virus will infect the cell and replicate. If the virus and the cell do not match, there will be no infection.

27. Edward Jenner notice people who got the disease cowpox did not get smallpox. Injecting cowpox protected people from getting smallpox.

Rubrics

For more help evaluating openended assessment questions, see the rubic on p. 10T.

18. Chloroplasts and mitochondria are both energy-processing organelles. Chloroplasts use light energy to make sugar from carbon dioxide and water. Mitochondria release energy from the breakdown of food into carbon dioxide and water.

19. A strand of hereditary material is surrounded by a protein coating; there is no nucleus or other organelles; viruses lack a cell membrane.

20. They are not membrane bound; some float freely, and others are attached to the endoplasmic reticulum.

21. a compound microscope

Part 3 | Open Ended

22. simple microscope has one lens— to view objects such as the surface of a leaf; compound microscope has two lenses to produce 3-D images—to view plant or animal cells; scanning or transmission electron microscope—to view specimens such as the organelles of a cell

Section/Objectives	Standards		Labs/Features
Chapter Opener	**National**	**State/Local**	**Launch Lab:** Why does water enter and leave plant cells?, p. 65 **Foldables,** p. 65
	See pp. 16T–17T for a Key to Standards.		
Section 1 Chemistry of Life ⏱ 2 sessions 🧊 1 block 1. **List** the differences among atoms, elements, molecules, and compounds. 2. **Explain** the relationship between chemistry and life science. 3. **Discuss** how organic compounds are different from inorganic compounds.	National Content Standards: UCP.1, UCP.2, UCP.3, UCP.5, A.1, A.2, B.1, C.1		**Science Online,** p. 70 **MiniLAB:** Observing How Enzymes Work, p. 71 **Applying Math:** Calculating the Importance of Water, p. 72
Section 2 Moving Cellular Materials ⏱ 2 sessions 🧊 1 block 4. **Describe** the function of a selectively permeable membrane. 5. **Explain** how the processes of diffusion and osmosis move molecules in living cells. 6. **Explain** how passive transport and active transport differ	National Content Standards: UCP.1, UCP.2, UCP.3, UCP.5, A.1, A.2, C.1, C.3		**MiniLAB:** Observing Diffusion, p. 75 **Integrate Health,** p. 77 **Visualizing Cell Membrane Transport,** p. 79 **Lab:** Observing Osmosis, p. 80
Section 3 Energy for Life ⏱ 3 sessions 🧊 1.5 blocks 7. **List** the differences between producers and consumers. 8. **Explain** how the processes of photosynthesis and respiration store and release energy. 9. **Describe** how cells get energy from glucose through fermentation.	National Content Standards: UCP.1, UCP.2, UCP.3, UCP.5, A.1, C.1, G.1, G.2, G.3		**Integrate Career,** p. 83 **Science Online,** p. 84 **Lab:** Photosynthesis and Respiration, p. 86 **Science and Language Arts:** from "Tulip," p. 88

Lab Materials	Reproducible Resources	Section Assessment	Technology
Launch Lab: bowl (2), label, water (500 mL), salt (15 g), carrot sticks (6), watch or clock, beaker (250mL), stirrer	**Chapter FAST FILE Resources** Foldables Worksheet, p. 15 Directed Reading Overview, p. 17 Note-taking Worksheets, pp. 31–33	GLENCOE'S ASSESSMENT ADVANTAGE	**TeacherWorks includes:** • Interactive Teacher Edition • Lesson Planner with calendar • Access to all program blacklines • Correlations to standards • Web links
MiniLAB: 2 small cups of prepared gelatin, fresh pineapple pieces *Need materials?* Contact Science Kit at 1-800-828-7777 or www.sciencekit.com on the Internet.	**Chapter FAST FILE Resources** Transparency Activity, p. 42 MiniLAB, p. 3 Enrichment, p. 28 Reinforcement, p. 25 Directed Reading, p. 18 Transparency Activity, pp. 45–46 **Cultural Diversity,** p. 65	**Portfolio** Science Journal, p. 70 **Performance** MiniLAB, p. 71 Applying Math, p. 72 Applying Skills, p. 73 **Content** Section Review, p. 73	Section Focus Transparency Teaching Transparency Virtual Labs CD-ROM Guided Reading Audio Program Interactive Chalkboard CD-ROM
MiniLAB: clean glasses (2 of equal size), labels, very warm water, cold water, food coloring, dropper, clock, marker or wax pencil **Lab:** unshelled egg, balance, spoon, distilled water (250 mL), light corn syrup (250 mL), 500-mL container	**Chapter FAST FILE Resources** Transparency Activity, p. 43 MiniLAB, p. 4 Enrichment, p. 29 Reinforcement, p. 26 Directed Reading, p. 18 Lab Activity, pp. 9–10 Lab Worksheet, pp. 5–6 **Home and Community Involvement,** p. 47	**Portfolio** Visual Learning, p. 79 **Performance** MiniLAB, p. 75 Applying Skills, p. 78 **Content** Section Review, p. 78	Section Focus Transparency Virtual Labs CD-ROM Guided Reading Audio Program Interactive Chalkboard CD-ROM Video Lab
Lab: 16-mm test tubes (3), 150-mm test tubes with stoppers (4), test-tube rack, stirring rod, scissors, carbonated water (5 mL), bromthymol blue solution in dropper bottle, aged tap water (20 mL), sprig of *Elodea*	**Chapter FAST FILE Resources** Transparency Activity, p. 44 Enrichment, p. 30 Reinforcement, p. 27 Directed Reading, pp. 19, 20 Lab Activity, pp. 11–14 Lab Worksheet, pp. 7–8 **Lab Management and Safety,** p. 63	**Portfolio** Visual Learning, p. 85 **Performance** Applying Math, p. 85 **Content** Section Review, p. 85	Section Focus Transparency Virtual Labs CD-ROM Guided Reading Audio Program Interactive Chalkboard CD-ROM

End of Chapter Assessment

GLENCOE'S ASSESSMENT ADVANTAGE

Blackline Masters	Technology	Professional Series
Chapter FAST FILE Resources Chapter Review, pp. 35–36 Chapter Tests, pp. 37–40 **Standardized Test Practice,** pp. 15–18	MindJogger Videoquiz Virtual Labs CD-ROM ExamView® Pro Testmaker TeacherWorks CD-ROM Interactive Chalkboard CD-ROM	**Performance Assessment in the Science Classroom (PASC)**

Transparencies

Section Focus

This is a representation of key blackline masters available in the Teacher Classroom Resources. See Resource Manager boxes within the chapter for additional information.

Assessment

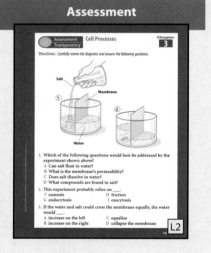

Teaching

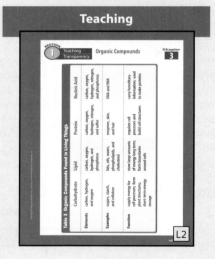

Key to Teaching Strategies

The following designations will help you decide which activities are appropriate for your students.

L1 Level 1 activities should be appropriate for students with learning difficulties.

L2 Level 2 activities should be within the ability range of all students.

L3 Level 3 activities are designed for above-average students.

ELL ELL activities should be within the ability range of English-Language Learners.

COOP LEARN Cooperative Learning activities are designed for small group work.

LS Multiple Learning Styles logos, as described on page 12T, are used throughout to indicate strategies that address different learning styles.

P These strategies represent student products that can be placed into a best-work portfolio.

PBL Problem-Based Learning activities apply real-world situations to learning.

Hands-on Activities

Student Text Lab Worksheet

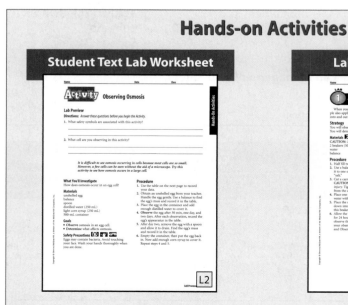

Laboratory Activities

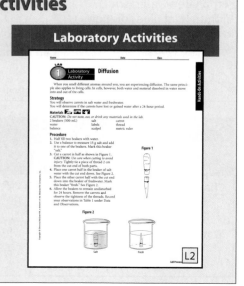

Meeting Different Ability Levels

Content Outline

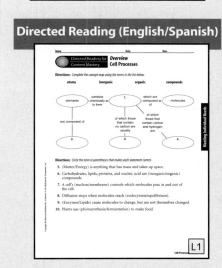

Note-taking Worksheet — Cell Processes

Section 1 — Chemistry of Life

L2

Reinforcement

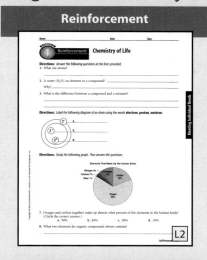

Reinforcement — Chemistry of Life

L2

Enrichment

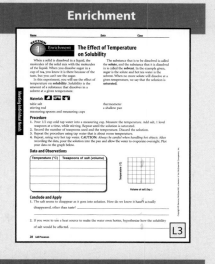

Enrichment — The Effect of Temperature on Solubility

L3

Directed Reading (English/Spanish)

Directed Reading for Content Mastery — Overview — Cell Processes

L1

Study Guide

Study Guide

Features
- Contains a study guide page for each section of the chapter
- Reviews key concepts
- Includes answer pages

L2

Reading Essentials

Reading Essentials for Glencoe Science — An Interactive Student Workbook

Features
- Condensed core content
- Actively involves students in reading
- Reinforces key vocabulary

L1

Assessment

Test Practice Workbook

Chapter 3 Cell Processes — Standardized Test Practice

GO ON L2

Chapter Review

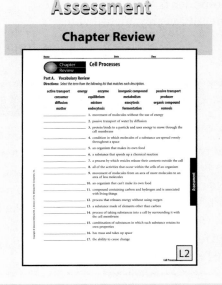

Chapter Review — Cell Processes

Part A. Vocabulary Review

L2

Chapter Tests

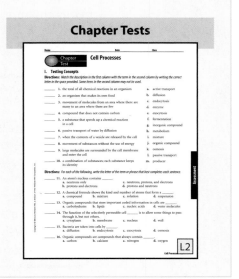

Chapter Test — Cell Processes

I. Testing Concepts

L2

Science Content Background

section 1 — Chemistry of Life
The Nature of Matter

Democritus, an ancient Greek philosopher, proposed that atoms were small, solid spheres. Until recently, it was thought that negatively-charged electrons orbited the positively-charged nucleus in specific paths. Quantum mechanics provide us with the current model of a positively-charged nucleus surrounded by a region in which the electrons move. The location of the electrons depends on each electron's energy level.

Compounds and Mixtures

Compounds are formed when two or more elements combine by a chemical reaction. Molecular components form when atoms share electrons. Ionic compounds form when negative and positive ions join. Organic compounds all contain carbon atoms and most are produced within living organisms. However, organic compounds such as plastics and synthetic fibers are made from organic substances such as petroleum. Inorganic compounds usually are made from elements other than carbon. Water is the most important inorganic compound.

Most things in nature are mixtures of elements. Components of homogeneous mixtures, such as solutions, cannot be distinguished from one another. The components of a heterogeneous mixture are generally visibly identifiable.

section 2 — Moving Cellular Materials
Maintaining Balance

The cell membrane regulates what enters and leaves a cell. The path taken through a membrane depends on the substance's size, shape, and electrical charge. A cell must maintain its internal concentrations of substances such as water, glucose, and other nutrients and eliminate waste products.

Transport

Passive transport—transport without the input of energy—depends on temperature. One form of passive transport, called diffusion, occurs when molecules move from an area where their concentration is greater into an area where they are less concentrated. Osmosis is the diffusion of water into or out of a cell. Active transport, transport with energy input, requires transport proteins.

section 3 — Energy for Life
Photosynthesis, Respiration, and Fermentation

During photosynthesis, plants and other producers convert light energy to chemical energy and make carbohydrates (food). During respiration, the food is broken down and the released energy can be used by the producer, other producers, and consumers. When there is a shortage of oxygen, fermentation is a process some cells can use to release energy from glucose.

---

chapter content resources

Internet Resources
For additional content background, visit
life.msscience.com to:
- access your book online
- find references to related articles in popular science magazines
- access Web links with related content background
- access current events with science journal topics

Print Resources
Cells and Systems (Life Processes), by Holly Wallace and Anita Ganeri, Heinemann Library, 2001

Atoms and Molecules, by Phil Roxbee Cox, E D C Publications, 1993

Illustrated Dictionary of Science, by Corinne Stockley, Usborne Books, 2000

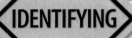

IDENTIFYING > Misconceptions

Find Out What Students Think

Students may think that . . .

Plants do not use oxygen and do not release carbon dioxide.
Students may not understand the complementary nature of photosynthesis and respiration, especially with respect to exchange of gases.

Demonstration
Ask students to give the relationship among producers, consumers, oxygen, and carbon dioxide. Summarize students' responses on the board. If students do not respond that plants also give off carbon dioxide, let that understanding come from the activities below.

Promote Understanding

Activity 1
WARNING: *Remind students not to suck on the straw.*

Prepare a 0.1% solution of bromthymol blue.

- Have students blow through a straw into the bromthymol blue solution. The solution should turn yellow as the carbon dioxide dissolves forming carbonic acid.

- Have students add drops of dilute ammonium hydroxide so that the solution again turns blue. Explain that the bromthymol blue is an indicator that turns yellow in an acidic solution and blue in a neutral or alkaline solution.

- Ask students what gas is given off in the process of respiration. (carbon dioxide) Explain that the carbon dioxide blown into the solution dissolves and makes the solution slightly acidic. Point out that adding the ammonium hydroxide made the solution slightly basic. L2

Activity 2
Acidify a large test tube of bromthymol blue by adding carbonated water to the solution. Add a sprig of *Elodea* to the tube.

- Put the test tube in sunlight or under a bright light. The solution should begin to turn blue in 30 to 45 minutes. Have students record results.

- Also, have students put a sprig of *Elodea* in a test tube of bromthymol blue solution that is slightly alkaline and blue. Place the tube in a dark area. Within 24 hours the solution should change to a pale yellow as the plant respires and releases carbon dioxide. Again have students record their results. L2

Discussion

- Ask why the bromthymol blue solution turned blue in the light. Ask students what evidence supports their answer. Explicitly reinforce the fact the carbon dioxide was absorbed by the plant and used in the process of photosynthesis.

- Ask students whether they think carbon dioxide was given off by the *Elodea* kept in the dark. Light-independent photosynthesis and respiration occur in the dark, so less carbon dioxide is used and released. Stress that their results indicate that plants give off carbon dioxide during respiration. Point out that all living things must carry out some form of respiration.

Assess

After completing the chapter, see *Identifying Misconceptions* in the Study Guide at the end of the chapter.

Chapter Vocabulary

mixture, p. 69
organic compound, p. 70
enzyme, p. 71
inorganic compound, p. 71
passive transport, p. 74
diffusion, p. 75
equilibrium, p. 75
osmosis, p. 76
active transport, p. 77
endocytosis, p. 78
exocytosis, p. 78
metabolism, p. 81
photosynthesis, p. 82
respiration, p. 83
fermentation, p. 84

Science Journal Student responses will vary, but may include "from the Sun" and "from the ground."

INTERACTIVE CHALKBOARD
with Image Bank

PowerPoint® Presentations

This CD-ROM is an editable Microsoft® PowerPoint® presentation that includes:
- a pre-made presentation for every chapter
- interactive graphics
- animations
- audio clips
- image bank
- all new section and chapter questions
- Standardized Test Practice
- transparencies
- pre-lab questions for all labs
- Foldables directions
- links to life.msscience.com

Cell Processes

chapter preview

sections

1 Chemistry of Life

2 Moving Cellular Material
   Lab Observing Osmosis

3 Energy for Life
   Lab Photosynthesis and Respiration

   Virtual Lab Under what conditions do cells gain or lose water?

The Science of Gardening

Growing a garden is hard work for both you and the plants. Like you, plants need water and food for energy. How plants get food and water is different from you. Understanding how living things get the energy they need to survive will make a garden seem like much more than just plants and dirt.

Science Journal Describe two ways in which you think plants get food for energy.

Theme Connection

Stability and Change Living things function as a result of chemical reactions in cells. The equilibrium maintained by cells results from their selectively permeable membranes. This is critical to the life of cells and the organism as a whole.

About the Photo

A Growing Garden Growing a bountiful garden requires sunlight, soil, and lots of water. Each plant in a garden, however, has individual requirements. The amount of sunlight, nutrients required, and amount of water needed have to be considered for all the types of plants.

Start-Up Activities

Why does water enter and leave plant cells?

If you forget to water a plant, it will wilt. After you water the plant, it probably will straighten up and look healthier. In the following lab, find out how water causes a plant to wilt and straighten.

1. Label a small bowl *Salt Water.* Pour 250 mL of water into the bowl. Then add 15 g of salt to the water and stir.

2. Pour 250 mL of water into another small bowl.

3. Place two carrot sticks into each bowl. Also, place two carrot sticks on the lab table.

4. After 30 min, remove the carrot sticks from the bowls and keep them next to the bowl they came from. Examine all six carrot sticks, then describe them in your Science Journal.

5. **Think Critically** Write a paragraph in your Science Journal that describes what would happen if you moved the carrot sticks from the plain water to the lab table, the ones from the salt water into the plain water, and the ones from the lab table into the salt water for 30 min. Now move the carrot sticks as described and write the results in your Science Journal.

FOLDABLES™ Study Organizer

How Living Things Survive Make the following vocabulary Foldable to help you understand the chemistry of living things and how energy is obtained for life.

STEP 1 Fold a vertical sheet of notebook paper from side to side.

STEP 2 Cut along every third line of only the top layer to form tabs.

Build Vocabulary As you read this chapter, list the vocabulary words about cell processes on the tabs. As you learn the definitions, write them under the tab for each vocabulary word. Write a sentence about one of the cell processes using the vocabulary word on the tab.

Preview this chapter's content and activities at
life.msscience.com

Purpose Use the Launch Lab to show students that water moves into and out of carrot cells. Explain that the materials moving into and out of cells are atoms, molecules, and compounds. [L1]

LS Visual-Spatial

Preparation Purchase carrots for the lab. Peel and cut the carrots into sticks.

Materials salt, 250-mL beaker, 2 bowls, stirrer, 6 thin carrot sticks, water, label, watch or clock

Teaching Strategy Provide students with water at room temperature so the salt will dissolve more readily.

Think Critically

The carrot sticks in salt water and on the lab table were limp because water moved out of them. The carrot sticks in plain water were crisp because water moved into the cells that had less water. Students should predict that these conditions are reversible, depending on the relative amount of water inside and outside the carrot's cells. [L1]

Assessment

Oral Why does a wilted plant become rigid again after it has been watered? The water diffuses into the plant's cells.

 Dinah Zike Study Fold

Student preparation materials for this Foldable are available in the Chapter *FAST FILE* Resources.

Chemistry of Life

1 Motivate

Bellringer

Section Focus Transparencies also are available on the Interactive Chalkboard CD-ROM.

SECTION 1 Section Focus Transparency — **Chemicals for Life** — Chapter 3

Every living thing is made of compounds containing carbon and hydrogen. We consume many of these compounds for energy. However, some compounds that we consume do not contain the elements carbon and hydrogen. These compounds are also necessary for life.

1. Of the objects above, which come from living things?
2. Which objects do not contain substances that were once alive?
3. Name three substances that your body needs to survive that do not come from living things.

Cell Processes

Tie to Prior Knowledge

Food Labels Bring in labels from foods and cleaning products. Have students use the periodic table at the back of the book to determine what elements are in the compounds contained in these products. [L2]

as you read

What You'll Learn

- **List** the differences among atoms, elements, molecules, and compounds.
- **Explain** the relationship between chemistry and life science.
- **Discuss** how organic compounds are different from inorganic compounds.

Why It's Important

You grow because of chemical reactions in your body.

Review Vocabulary

cell: the smallest unit of a living thing that can perform the functions of life

New Vocabulary

- mixture
- organic compound
- enzyme
- inorganic compound

The Nature of Matter

Think about everything that surrounds you—chairs, books, clothing, other students, and air. What are all these things made up of? You're right if you answer "matter and energy." Matter is anything that has mass and takes up space. Energy is anything that brings about change. Everything in your environment, including you, is made of matter. Energy can hold matter together or break it apart. For example, the food you eat is matter that is held together by chemical energy. When food is cooked, energy in the form of heat can break some of the bonds holding the matter in food together.

Atoms Whether it is solid, liquid, or gas, matter is made of atoms. **Figure 1** shows a model of an oxygen atom. At the center of an atom is a nucleus that contains protons and neutrons. Although they have nearly equal masses, a proton has a positive charge and a neutron has no charge. Outside the nucleus are electrons, each of which has a negative charge. It takes about 1,837 electrons to equal the mass of one proton. Electrons are important because they are the part of the atom that is involved in chemical reactions. Look at **Figure 1** again and you will see that an atom is mostly empty space. Energy holds the parts of an atom together.

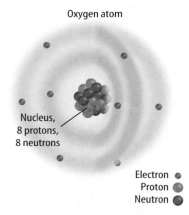

Oxygen atom

Nucleus, 8 protons, 8 neutrons

Electron
Proton
Neutron

Figure 1 An oxygen atom model shows the placement of electrons, protons, and neutrons.

Section 1 Resource Manager

Chapter *FAST FILE* Resources

Transparency Activity, p. 42

Directed Reading for Content Mastery, pp. 17, 18

Note-taking Worksheets, pp. 31–33

Enrichment, p. 28

MiniLAB, p. 3

Reinforcement, p. 25

Table 1 Elements in the Human Body		
Symbol	Element	Percent
O	Oxygen	65.0
C	Carbon	18.5
H	Hydrogen	9.5
N	Nitrogen	3.2
Ca	Calcium	1.5
P	Phosphorus	1.0
K	Potassium	0.4
S	Sulfur	0.3
Na	Sodium	0.2
Cl	Chlorine	0.2
Mg	Magnesium	0.1
	Other elements	0.1

Oxygen 65.0%

Carbon 18.5%

Hydrogen 9.5%

Nitrogen 3.2%

Calcium 1.5%

Phosphorus 1.0%
Other elements 1.3%

Elements When something is made up of only one kind of atom, it is called an element. An element can't be broken down into a simpler form by chemical reactions. The element oxygen is made up of only oxygen atoms, and hydrogen is made up of only hydrogen atoms. Scientists have given each element its own one- or two-letter symbol.

All elements are arranged in a chart known as the periodic table of elements. You can find this table at the back of this book. The table provides information about each element including its mass, how many protons it has, and its symbol.

Everything is made up of elements. Most things, including all living things, are made up of a combination of elements. Few things exist as pure elements. **Table 1** lists elements that are in the human body. What two elements make up most of your body?

Six of the elements listed in the table are important because they make up about 99 percent of living matter. The symbols for these elements are S, P, O, N, C, and H. Use **Table 1** to find the names of these elements.

Reading Check *What types of things are made up of elements?*

Teacher FYI

Element Names Elements are often given names by their discoverers. An element's name may reflect a property of the element. For example, chlorine, a greenish gas, comes from the Greek word *chloros*, which means "green." Some elements, such as ytterbium—discovered in Ytterby, Sweden—are named for the place where they were discovered. Other elements are named to honor someone. Einsteinium is named in honor of Albert Einstein, fermium for Enrico Fermi, and curium for Marie and Pierre Curie.

Activity

Elements Song Play Tom Lehrer's *Elements Song*, which lists the elements. Have students listen to see how many elements they recognize. L2

Fun Fact

The symbols of many elements are derived from the first one or two letters of the Greek, Latin, or English name of the elements. Scientists worldwide use these symbols.

Text Question Answer

oxygen and carbon

Reading Check

Answer Everything is made up of elements or a combination of elements.

Differentiated Instruction

Visually Impaired To help visually impaired students understand the structure of an atom, make a model of an atom. Outline the nucleus and energy levels by gluing yarn to cardboard. Use marshmallows for protons, gumdrops for neutrons, and red hots for electrons. Have students feel the model to compare the sizes of the different parts. L1 **Kinesthetic**

Figure 2 The words *atoms*, *molecules*, and *compounds* are used to describe substances.
Explain *how these terms are related to each other.*

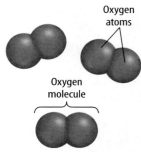

A Some elements, like oxygen, occur as molecules. These molecules contain atoms of the same element bonded together.

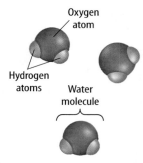

B Compounds also are composed of molecules. Molecules of compounds contain atoms of two or more different elements bonded together, as shown by these water molecules.

Compounds and Molecules

Suppose you make a pitcher of lemonade using a powdered mix and water. The water and the lemonade mix, which is mostly sugar, contain the elements oxygen and hydrogen. Yet, in one, they are part of a nearly tasteless liquid—water. In the other they are part of a sweet solid—sugar. How can the same elements be part of two materials that are so different? Water and sugar are compounds. Compounds are made up of two or more elements in exact proportions. For example, pure water, whether one milliliter of it or one million liters, is always made up of hydrogen atoms bonded to oxygen atoms in a ratio of two hydrogen atoms to one oxygen atom. Compounds have properties different from the elements they are made of. There are two types of compounds—molecular compounds and ionic compounds.

Molecular Compounds The smallest part of a molecular compound is a molecule. A molecule is a group of atoms held together by the energy of chemical bonds, as shown in **Figure 2.** When chemical reactions occur, chemical bonds break, atoms are rearranged, and new bonds form. The molecules produced are different from those that began the chemical reaction.

Molecular compounds form when different atoms share their outermost electrons. For example, two atoms of hydrogen each can share one electron on one atom of oxygen to form one molecule of water, as shown in **Figure 2B.** Water does not have the same properties as oxygen and hydrogen. Under normal conditions on Earth, oxygen and hydrogen are gases. Yet, water can be a liquid, a solid, or a gas. When hydrogen and oxygen combine, changes occur and a new substance forms.

Ions Atoms also combine because they've become positively or negatively charged. Atoms are usually neutral—they have no overall electric charge. When an atom loses an electron, it has more protons than electrons, so it becomes positively charged. When an atom gains an electron, it has more electrons than protons, so it becomes negatively charged. Electrically charged atoms—positive or negative—are called ions.

68 **CHAPTER 3** Cell Processes

Differentiated Instruction

Hearing Impaired Provide discussion questions to hearing-impaired students before discussion. Assign another student to record the answers to the questions when they are discussed. Remind hearing students to face hearing-impaired students during the discussion if possible. [L2]
IS **Auditory-Musical**

Curriculum Connection

History Have students research alchemy. During the Middle Ages, alchemists searched for a way to turn common metals into gold. Though unsuccessful, they were precursors to modern chemists. Much of alchemy was based on Aristotle's idea that matter tries to reach perfection. Alchemists concluded that there must be a way to turn other metals into gold, since it was the "perfect" metal.
[L3] **IS** **Linguistic**

Ionic Compounds Ions of opposite charges attract one another to form electrically neutral compounds called ionic compounds. Table salt is made of sodium (Na) and chlorine (Cl) ions, as shown in **Figure 3B.** When they combine, a chlorine atom gains an electron from a sodium atom. The chlorine atom becomes a negatively charged ion, and the sodium atom becomes a positively charged ion. These oppositely charged ions then are attracted to each other and form the ionic compound sodium chloride, NaCl.

Ions are important in many life processes that take place in your body and in other organisms. For example, messages are sent along your nerves as potassium and sodium ions move in and out of nerve cells. Calcium ions are important in causing your muscles to contract. Ions also are involved in the transport of oxygen by your blood. The movement of some substances into and out of a cell would not be possible without ions.

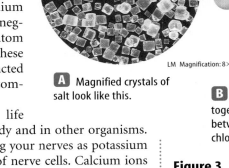

LM Magnification: 8×

A Magnified crystals of salt look like this.

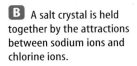

B A salt crystal is held together by the attractions between sodium ions and chlorine ions.

Figure 3 Table salt crystals are held together by ionic bonds.

Mixtures

Some substances, such as a combination of sugar and salt, can't change each other or combine chemically. A **mixture** is a combination of substances in which individual substances retain their own properties. Mixtures can be solids, liquids, gases, or any combination of them.

> ✓ **Reading Check** *Why is a combination of sugar and salt said to be a mixture?*

Most chemical reactions in living organisms take place in mixtures called solutions. You've probably noticed the taste of salt when you perspire. Sweat is a solution of salt and water. In a solution, two or more substances are mixed evenly. A cell's cytoplasm is a solution of dissolved molecules and ions.

Living things also contain mixtures called suspensions. A suspension is formed when a liquid or a gas has another substance evenly spread throughout it. Unlike solutions, the substances in a suspension eventually sink to the bottom. If blood, shown in **Figure 4,** is left undisturbed, the red blood cells and white blood cells will sink gradually to the bottom. However, the pumping action of your heart constantly moves your blood and the blood cells remain suspended.

Figure 4 When a test tube of whole blood is left standing, the blood cells sink in the watery plasma.

SECTION 1 Chemistry of Life **69**

Activity

Organic Compounds Display a Food Guide Pyramid and discuss the types of organic compounds represented by foods in each group. Ask students to use this information to create a bulletin board display of foods rich in carbohydrates, lipids, and proteins. Have students illustrate the display with pictures of the foods. [L2]

Fun Fact

A paste made of meat tenderizer and water is often used to treat bee and jellyfish stings. An enzyme in the meat tenderizer helps to break down the proteins in the venom, making the area less painful.

Reading Check

Answer fats, oils, and phospholipids

Table 2 Organic Compounds Found in Living Things

	Carbohydrates	Lipids	Proteins	Nucleic Acids
Elements	carbon, hydrogen, and oxygen	carbon, oxygen, hydrogen, and phosphorus	carbon, oxygen, hydrogen, nitrogen, and sulfur	carbon, oxygen, hydrogen, nitrogen, and phosphorus
Examples	sugars, starch, and cellulose	fats, oils, waxes, phospholipids, and cholesterol	enzymes, skin, and hair	DNA and RNA
Function	supply energy for cell processes; form plant structures; short-term energy storage	store large amounts of energy long term; form boundaries around cells	regulate cell processes and build cell structures	carry hereditary information; used to make proteins

Topic: Air Quality
Visit life.msscience.com for Web links to information about air quality.

Activity Organic compounds such as soot, smoke, and ash can affect air quality. Look up the air quality forecast for today. List three locations where the air quality forecast is good, and three locations where it is unhealthy.

Organic Compounds

You and all living things are made up of compounds that are classified as organic or inorganic. Rocks and other nonliving things contain inorganic compounds, but most do not contain large amounts of organic compounds. **Organic compounds** always contain carbon and hydrogen and usually are associated with living things. One exception would be nonliving things that are products of living things. For example, coal contains organic compounds because it was formed from dead and decaying plants. Organic molecules can contain hundreds or even thousands of atoms that can be arranged in many ways. **Table 2** compares the four groups of organic compounds that make up all living things—carbohydrates, lipids, proteins, and nucleic acids.

Carbohydrates Carbohydrates are organic molecules that supply energy for cell processes. Sugars and starches are carbohydrates that cells use for energy. Some carbohydrates also are important parts of cell structures. For example, a carbohydrate called cellulose is an important part of plant cells.

Lipids Another type of organic compound found in living things is a lipid. Lipids do not mix with water. Lipids such as fats and oils store and release even larger amounts of energy than carbohydrates do. One type of lipid, the phospholipid, is a major part of cell membranes.

Reading Check   *What are three types of lipids?*

Science Journal

CFCs Have students research and summarize in their Science Journals the organic compounds known as chlorofluorocarbons (CFCs). Summaries should include a description of the composition of these compounds, their use as refrigerants, and a description of how the use of these substances has impacted the environment. [L3] [P]

Proteins Organic compounds called proteins have many important functions in living organisms. They are made up of smaller molecules called amino acids. Proteins are the building blocks of many structures in organisms. Your muscles contain large amounts of protein. Proteins are scattered throughout cell membranes. Certain proteins called **enzymes** regulate nearly all chemical reactions in cells.

Nucleic Acids Large organic molecules that store important coded information in cells are called nucleic acids. One nucleic acid, deoxyribonucleic acid, or DNA—genetic material—is found in all cells at some point in their lives. It carries information that directs each cell's activities. Another nucleic acid, ribonucleic acid, or RNA, is needed to make enzymes and other proteins.

Inorganic Compounds

Most **inorganic compounds** are made from elements other than carbon. Generally, inorganic molecules contain fewer atoms than organic molecules. Inorganic compounds are the source for many elements needed by living things. For example, plants take up inorganic compounds from the soil. These inorganic compounds can contain the elements nitrogen, phosphorus, and sulfur. Many foods that you eat contain inorganic compounds. **Table 3** shows some of the inorganic compounds that are important to you. One of the most important inorganic compounds for living things is water.

Table 3 Some Inorganic Compounds Important in Humans	
Compound	**Use in Body**
Water	makes up most of the blood; most chemical reactions occur in water
Calcium phosphate	gives strength to bones
Hydrochloric acid	breaks down foods in the stomach
Sodium bicarbonate	helps the digestion of food to occur
Salts containing sodium, chlorine, and potassium	important in sending messages along nerves

Mini LAB

Observing How Enzymes Work

Procedure
1. Get two small cups of **prepared gelatin** from your teacher. Do not eat or drink anything in lab.
2. On the gelatin in one of the cups, place a piece of **fresh pineapple.**
3. Let both cups stand undisturbed overnight.
4. Observe what happens to the gelatin.

Analysis
1. What effect did the piece of fresh pineapple have on the gelatin?
2. What does fresh pineapple contain that caused it to have the effect on the gelatin you observed?
3. Why do the preparation directions on a box of gelatin dessert tell you not to mix it with fresh pineapple?

Mini LAB

Purpose to observe the effects of enzymes on gelatin L1 LS
Visual-Spatial

Materials two small cups of prepared gelatin, one slice of fresh pineapple

Teaching Strategies
• To prepare gelatin, add only half the amount of water indicated on the gelatin package.
• After students add pineapple to one cup, allow both cups of gelatin to sit overnight.

Analysis
1. The gelatin under the fresh pineapple turned to a liquid.
2. an enzyme
3. The gelatin would not solidify if in contact with fresh pineapple.

Assessment

Performance Have students design an experiment to show conclusively that fresh pineapple contains enzymes that keep gelatin from becoming solid. They can repeat the experiment using canned pineapple. Use **Performance Assessment in the Science Classroom**, p. 95.

Teacher FYI

Water Life on Earth could not have evolved without water. Wherever life is found, water is found. Life is found in water at all temperatures. Bacteria can live under snow and in the near-boiling water of hot springs.

Curriculum Connection

Health Provide students with copies of the periodic table. Ask them to research which elements are important for good health. They can find this information on food labels, in reference books, and on the Internet. Ask students to shade each element they discover on the table and to share their results with the class. L2 LS **Interpersonal**

Make a Model

Water Molecule Have students make a model of a water molecule. They may use foam balls or colored marshmallows to represent the atoms, and toothpicks to hold them together. L2 **LS** **Kinesthetic**

Applying Math

National Math Standards
Correlation to Mathematics Objectives
1, 9

Answers to Practice Problems

1. Calculate the infant's water weight and the adult's water weight, then subtract to find the difference.
   Infant: $78/100 = x \div 3.2$ kg
   $x = (78 \times 3.2) \div 100$
   $x = 2.496$ kg of water;
   Adult: $60 \div 100 = x \div 95$ kg
   $x = (60 \times 95) \div 100$
   $x = 57$ kg of water;
   Difference: 57 kg $- 2.496$ kg
   $= 54.504$ kg

2. Calculate the adult woman's water weight and the adult man's water weight, then subtract to find the difference, as in problem 1. The man has 19.5 kg more water than the woman.

Importance of Water Some scientists hypothesize that life began in the water of Earth's ancient oceans. Chemical reactions might have occurred that produced organic molecules. Similar chemical reactions can take place in cells in your body.

Living things are composed of more than 50 percent water and depend on water to survive. You can live for weeks without food but only for a few days without water. **Figure 5** shows where water is found in your body. Although seeds and spores of plants, fungi, and bacteria can exist without water, they must have water if they are to grow and reproduce. All the chemical reactions in living things take place in water solutions, and most organisms use water to transport materials through their bodies. For example, many animals have blood that is mostly water and moves materials. Plants use water to move minerals and sugars between the roots and leaves.

Applying Math   Solve an Equation

CALCULATE THE IMPORTANCE OF WATER All life on Earth depends on water for survival. Water is the most vital part of humans and other animals. It is required for all of the chemical processes that keep us alive. At least 60 percent of an adult human body consists of water. If an adult man weighs 90 kg, how many kilograms of water does his body contain?

Solution

1 *This is what you know:*
- adult human body = 60% water
- man = 90 kg

2 *This is what you need to find:*
How many kilograms of water does the adult man have?

3 *This is the procedure you need to use:*
- Set up the ratio: $60/100 = x/90$.
- Solve the equation for x: $(60 \times 90)/100$.
- The adult man has 54 kg of water.

4 *Check your answer:*
Divide your answer by 90, then multiply by 100. You should get 60%.

Practice Problems

1. A human body at birth consists of 78 percent water. This gradually decreases to 60 percent in an adult. Assume a baby weighed 3.2 kg at birth and grew into an adult weighing 95 kg. Calculate the approximate number of kilograms of water the human gained.

2. Assume an adult woman weighs 65 kg and an adult man weighs 90 kg. Calculate how much more water, in kilograms, the man has compared to the woman.

 Science Online
For more practice, visit
life.msscience.com/
math_practice

Curriculum Connection

Art Have students cut out pictures from magazines that illustrate water use by organisms, in industry, and in the environment. Then, have each student make a water collage using the pictures they chose. Display collages in the classroom. L1 **LS** **Visual-Spatial**

Characteristics of Water The atoms of a water molecule are arranged in such a way that the molecule has areas with different charges. Water molecules are like magnets. The negative part of a water molecule is attracted to the positive part of another water molecule just like the north pole of a magnet is attracted to the south pole of another magnet. This attraction, or force, between water molecules is why a film forms on the surface of water. The film is strong enough to support small insects because the forces between water molecules are stronger than the force of gravity on the insect.

When heat is added to any substance, its molecules begin to move faster. Because water molecules are so strongly attracted to each other, the temperature of water changes slowly. The large percentage of water in living things acts like an insulator. The water in a cell helps keep its temperature constant, which allows life-sustaining chemical reactions to take place.

You've seen ice floating on water. When water freezes, ice crystals form. In the crystals, each water molecule is spaced at a certain distance from all the others. Because this distance is greater in frozen water than in liquid water, ice floats on water. Bodies of water freeze from the top down. The floating ice provides insulation from extremely cold temperatures and allows living things to survive in the cold water under the ice.

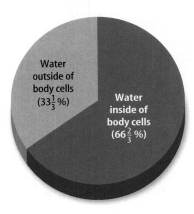

Figure 5 About two-thirds of your body's water is located within your body's cells. Water helps maintain the cells' shapes and sizes. One-third of your body's water is outside of your body's cells.

---

section 1 review

Summary

The Nature of Matter
- Atoms are made up of protons, neutrons, and electrons.
- Elements are made up of only one kind of atom.
- Compounds are made up of two or more elements.

Mixtures
- Solutions are made of two or more substances and are mixed evenly, whereas substances in suspension eventually will sink to the bottom.

Organic Compounds
- All living things contain organic compounds.

Inorganic Compounds
- Water is one of the most important inorganic compounds for living things.

Self Check

1. **Compare and contrast** atoms and molecules.
2. **Describe** the differences between an organic and an inorganic compound. Given an example of each type of compound.
3. **List** the four types of organic compounds found in all living things.
4. **Infer** why life as we know it depends on water.
5. **Think Critically** If you mix salt, sand, and sugar with water in a small jar, will the resulting mixture be a suspension, a solution, or both?

Applying Skills

6. **Interpret** Carefully observe **Figure 1** and determine how many protons, neutrons, and electrons an atom of oxygen has.

 life.msscience.com/self_check_quiz

SECTION 1 Chemistry of Life **73**

SECTION 1 Chemistry of Life **73**

1 Motivate

Bellringer

Section Focus Transparencies also are available on the Interactive Chalkboard CD-ROM.

L2 **ELL**

Tie to Prior Knowledge

Cell Parts Use an overhead transparency to review the parts of a cell. Point out that the cell membrane helps a cell maintain a balance between the cell and materials, such as water, salt, and sugars, in its environment.

Virtual Labs

Water Loss or Gain *Under what conditions do cells gain or lose water?*

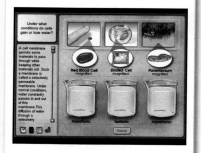

Moving Cellular Materials

as you read

What You'll Learn

- **Describe** the function of a selectively permeable membrane.
- **Explain** how the processes of diffusion and osmosis move molecules in living cells.
- **Explain** how passive transport and active transport differ.

Why It's Important

Cell membranes control the substances that enter and leave the cells in your body.

Review Vocabulary
cytoplasm: constantly moving gel-like mixture inside the cell membrane that contains hereditary material and is the location of most of a cell's life process

New Vocabulary
- passive transport
- diffusion
- equilibrium
- osmosis
- active transport
- endocytosis
- exocytosis

Figure 6 A cell membrane, like a screen, will let some things through more easily than others. Air gets through a screen, but insects are kept out.

Passive Transport

"Close that window. Do you want to let in all the bugs and leaves?" How do you prevent unwanted things from coming through the window? As seen in **Figure 6,** a window screen provides the protection needed to keep unwanted things outside. It also allows some things to pass into or out of the room like air, unpleasant odors, or smoke.

Cells take in food, oxygen, and other substances from their environments. They also release waste materials into their environments. A cell has a membrane around it that works for a cell like a window screen does for a room. A cell's membrane is selectively permeable (PUR mee uh bul). It allows some things to enter or leave the cell while keeping other things outside or inside the cell. The window screen also is selectively permeable based on the size of its openings.

Things can move through a cell membrane in several ways. Which way things move depends on the size of the molecules or particles, the path taken through the membrane, and whether or not energy is used. The movement of substances through the cell membrane without the input of energy is called **passive transport.** Three types of passive transport can occur. The type depends on what is moving through the cell membrane.

Section 2 Resource Manager

Chapter *FAST FILE* Resources
Transparency Activity, p. 43
Directed Reading for Content Mastery, p. 18
MiniLAB, p. 4
Enrichment, p. 29

Reinforcement, p. 26
Lab Activity, pp. 9–10
Lab Worksheet, pp. 5–6
Life Science Critical Thinking/Problem Solving, p. 15

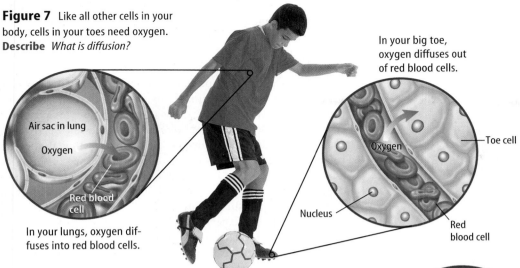

Figure 7 Like all other cells in your body, cells in your toes need oxygen. **Describe** *What is diffusion?*

In your big toe, oxygen diffuses out of red blood cells.

Air sac in lung

Oxygen

Red blood cell

In your lungs, oxygen diffuses into red blood cells.

Oxygen

Toe cell

Nucleus

Red blood cell

Diffusion

Diffusion Molecules in solids, liquids, and gases move constantly and randomly. You might smell perfume when you sit near or as you walk past someone who is wearing it. This is because perfume molecules randomly move throughout the air. This random movement of molecules from an area where there is relatively more of them into an area where there is relatively fewer of them is called **diffusion.** Diffusion is one type of cellular passive transport. Molecules of a substance will continue to move from one area into another until the relative number of these molecules is equal in the two areas. When this occurs, **equilibrium** is reached and diffusion stops. After equilibrium occurs, it is maintained because molecules continue to move.

Reading Check *What is equilibrium?*

Every cell in your body uses oxygen. When you breathe, how does oxygen get from your lungs to cells in your big toe? Oxygen is carried throughout your body in your blood by the red blood cells. When your blood is pumped from your heart to your lungs, your red blood cells do not contain much oxygen. However, your lungs have more oxygen molecules than your red blood cells do, so the oxygen molecules diffuse into your red blood cells from your lungs, as shown in **Figure 7.** When the blood reaches your big toe, there are more oxygen molecules in your red blood cells than in your big toe cells. The oxygen diffuses from your red blood cells and into your big toe cells, as shown also in **Figure 7.**

Mini LAB

Observing Diffusion

Procedure

1. Use two clean glasses of equal size. Label one *Hot,* then fill it until half full with **very warm water.** Label the other *Cold,* then fill it until half full with **cold water. WARNING:** *Do not use boiling hot water.*
2. Add one drop of **food coloring** to each glass. Carefully release the drop just at the water's surface to avoid splashing the water.
3. Observe the water in the glasses. Record your observations immediately and again after 15 min.

Analysis

1. Describe what happens when food coloring is added to each glass.
2. How does temperature affect the rate of diffusion?

Try at Home

Figure 7 the random movement of molecules from where there is more of them to where there is fewer of them

Mini LAB

Purpose to investigate the effect of temperature on diffusion rate
L1 ELL COOP LEARN LS **Logical-Mathematical**

Materials two clean glasses, very warm water, cold water, food coloring, dropper, marker or wax pencil, clock, labels

Teaching Strategies
• Have students record how long it takes the food coloring to diffuse evenly throughout each beaker.
• Caution students not to move the water-filled beakers.

Analysis
1. The food coloring spreads throughout the water; it spreads faster in the hot water.
2. Heat increases the rate of diffusion.

Assessment

Performance To further assess understanding of the effect of temperature on diffusion, have students repeat the activity using ice water instead of hot water. Use **Performance Assessment in the Science Classroom,** p. 105. L1

Try at Home

Reading Check

Answer when the relative number of molecules of a substance is equal in the two areas

Teacher FYI

Membranes A permeable membrane allows all molecules to pass through. An impermeable membrane doesn't allow any to pass. Only some molecules can pass through a semi-permeable membrane—usually only small molecules that can pass through quickly.

Selectively Permeable Membrane

Materials sand, salt, marbles, water, kitchen strainer

Estimated Time five minutes

Procedure Pour different substances through the kitchen strainer. Select some substances that will pass through the strainer and some that will not.

Inquiry Lab

Observing the Effect of Salt on Plants

Purpose to design an experiment to grow plants treated with salt

Possible Materials container, soil, fast-growing plants or seeds such as grass or radishes, table salt or road salt

Estimated Time one month

Teaching Strategies

• Students can vary the amount of salt, and whether it is added to the soil or to leaves.

• Students can predict what the effect of the salt will be by testing rate of growth, plant height, plant color, and leaf number. L2

For additional inquiry activities, see *Science Inquiry Labs.*

Caption Answer

Figure 8 diffusion of water through a cell membrane

Reading Check

Answer Because there are fewer water molecules around the carrot cells than inside the carrot cells, water leaves the carrot and moves into the salt solution.

Osmosis—The Diffusion of Water Remember that water makes up a large part of living matter. Cells contain water and are surrounded by water. Water molecules move by diffusion into and out of cells. The diffusion of water through a cell membrane is called **osmosis.**

If cells weren't surrounded by water that contains few dissolved substances, water inside of cells would diffuse out of them. This is why water left the carrot cells in this chapter's Launch Lab. Because there were relatively fewer water molecules in the salt solution around the carrot cells than in the carrot cells, water moved out of the cells and into the salt solution.

Losing water from a plant cell causes its cell membrane to come away from its cell wall, as shown on the left in **Figure 8.** This reduces pressure against its cell wall, and a plant cell becomes limp. If the carrot sticks were taken out of salt water and put in pure water, the water around the cells would move into them and they would fill with water. Their cell membranes would press against their cell walls, as shown on the right in **Figure 8,** pressure would increase, and the cells would become firm. That is why the carrot sticks would be crisp again.

Reading Check *Why do carrots in salt water become limp?*

Osmosis also takes place in animal cells. If animal cells were placed in pure water, they too would swell up. However, animal cells are different from plant cells. Just like an overfilled water balloon, animal cells will burst if too much water enters the cell.

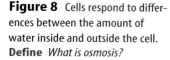

Figure 8 Cells respond to differences between the amount of water inside and outside the cell. **Define** *What is osmosis?*

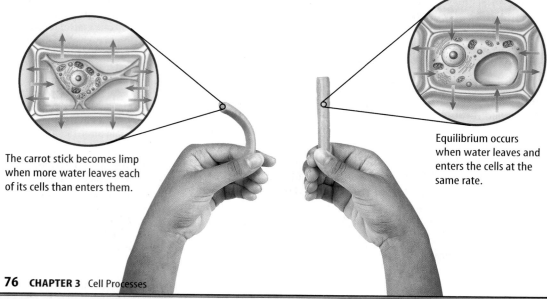

The carrot stick becomes limp when more water leaves each of its cells than enters them.

Equilibrium occurs when water leaves and enters the cells at the same rate.

LAB DEMONSTRATION

Purpose to observe diffusion

Materials self-sealing plastic sandwich bag, cooked rice, tincture of iodine, 8-oz clear plastic cups, tablespoon

Preparation Half-fill the plastic cups with water and add 6 drops of tincture of iodine. Cook rice before class.

Procedure Seal a sandwich bag containing 2 tbsp of rice, and place it into the water that contains iodine. Observe after 10 min.

Expected Outcome Iodine molecules will move through the plastic bag, turning the rice blue-black. Iodine turns blue-black in the presence of starch.

Assessment

What did you observe? The rice inside the plastic bag turned blue-black. Explain what occurred. Iodine molecules diffused from an area where there was a large number of iodine molecules (outside the bag) to an area where there were few iodine molecules (inside the bag).

Facilitated Diffusion Cells take in many substances. Some substances pass easily through the cell membrane by diffusion. Other substances, such as glucose molecules, are so large that they can enter the cell only with the help of molecules in the cell membrane called transport proteins. This process, a type of passive transport, is known as facilitated diffusion. Have you ever used the drive through at a fast-food restaurant to get your meal? The transport proteins in the cell membrane are like the drive-through window at the restaurant. The window lets you get food out of the restaurant and put money into the restaurant. Similarly, transport proteins are used to move substances into and out of the cell.

Active Transport

Imagine that a football game is over and you leave the stadium. As soon as you get outside of the stadium, you remember that you left your jacket on your seat. Now you have to move against the crowd coming out of the stadium to get back in to get your jacket. Which required more energy—leaving the stadium with the crowd or going back to get your jacket? Something similar to this happens in cells.

Sometimes, a substance is needed inside a cell even though the amount of that substance inside the cell is already greater than the amount outside the cell. For example, root cells require minerals from the soil. The roots of the plant in **Figure 9** already might contain more of those mineral molecules than the surrounding soil does. The tendency is for mineral molecules to move out of the root by diffusion or facilitated diffusion. But they need to move back across the cell membrane and into the cell just like you had to move back into the stadium. When an input of energy is required to move materials through a cell membrane, **active transport** takes place.

Active transport involves transport proteins, just as facilitated diffusion does. In active transport, a transport protein binds with the needed particle and cellular energy is used to move it through the cell membrane. When the particle is released, the transport protein can move another needed particle through the membrane.

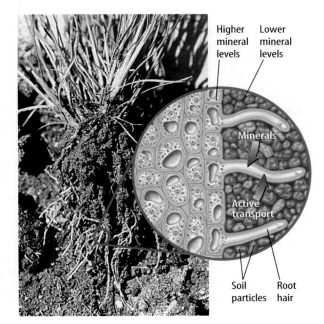

Figure 9 Some root cells have extensions called root hairs that may be 5 mm to 8 mm long. Minerals are taken in by active transport through the cell membranes of root hairs.

Transport Proteins Your health depends on transport proteins. Sometimes transport proteins are missing or do not function correctly. What would happen if proteins that transport cholesterol across membranes were missing? Cholesterol is an important lipid used by your cells. Write your ideas in your Science Journal.

Discussion

Salt and Thirst Why do salty foods make you thirsty? The salt present in the food causes water to leave your cells; the lost water needs to be replaced by the body.

Caption Answer

Figure 8 The diffusion of water through a cell membrane.

Use an Analogy

Active and Passive Transport Have students compare active and passive transport with the energy they must exert to get a bicycle to the top of a hill and then ride it back down. Students must exert energy to get the bicycle up the hill. In the same way, the cell uses energy to move substances from areas of low concentration to areas of high concentration. Students do not need to exert energy to ride the bicycle down the hill. In passive transport, cells do not have to use energy to move substances from areas of high concentration to areas of low concentration. L2 IS **Logical-Mathematical**

Text Question Answer

going back for the jacket

Transport Proteins Cholesterol would not be transported to different areas of the body. Without cholesterol, the body could not synthesize bile acids, steroid hormones, or Vitamin D.

Research Have students research the "good" types and "bad" types of cholesterol. Why does the body need cholesterol? They should include why the body needs "good" cholesterol and why certain types of cholesterol are bad for people's health. Students can design a health pamphlet on the ways to lower health risks associated with high cholesterol. L2

Cultural Diversity

Preserving Foods A practical use of osmosis is the drying and salting of food. Have students report on the processes and uses of dried and salted foods in Native American and other cultures. For example, the French developed a vegetable dehydrator in 1795. Both processes remove water from cells in order to preserve the food. In drying, water evaporates. In salting, a salt solution is used to remove water from cells. L2

Teacher FYI

Membranes Cell membranes contain spaces through which some substances (water molecules, mineral ions, sugar molecules) can pass easily. The spaces are too small for large molecules to pass through. Some ions cannot pass through membranes due to their charge. These move into a cell via channels or active transport.

Word Meaning Have students use a dictionary to find the meanings of the prefixes *endo-* and *exo-* ("taking in" and "turning out"). Ask them to find examples of other words that make use of these prefixes, and to explain how the meaning of the prefix relates to the meaning of the word. *Possible answers: endoskeleton, a skeleton that is inside the body; exoskeleton, a skeleton that is outside the body* L2

3 Assess

DAILY INTERVENTION

Checking for Understanding

Visual-Spatial Have students make a poster that diagrams the processes of endocytosis and exocytosis. Ask them to draw the processes in a step-wise manner with labels. Discuss how the processes are similar and how they differ. L2

Reteach

Diffusion Place two or three drops of vanilla extract inside a balloon. Blow up the balloon and tie it. Have students observe the balloon until they can smell the vanilla. Then have them explain why they smell the vanilla outside the balloon. *Diffusion has taken place across the membrane.* L2

✓ Assessment

Oral Would a cell placed in syrup lose or gain water? Explain. *It would lose water; water molecules move by diffusion from areas of high concentration to areas of low concentration.*

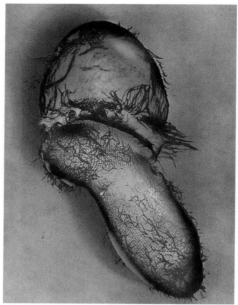

Color-enhanced TEM Magnification: 1,400×

Figure 10 One-celled organisms like this egg-shaped one can take in other one-celled organisms using endocytosis.

Endocytosis and Exocytosis

Some molecules and particles are too large to move by diffusion or to use the cell membrane's transport proteins. Large protein molecules and bacteria, for example, can enter a cell when they are surrounded by the cell membrane. The cell membrane folds in on itself, enclosing the item in a sphere called a vesicle. Vesicles are transport and storage structures in a cell's cytoplasm. The sphere pinches off, and the resulting vesicle enters the cytoplasm. A similar thing happens when you poke your finger into a partially inflated balloon. Your finger is surrounded by the balloon in much the same way that the protein molecule is surrounded by the cell membrane. This process of taking substances into a cell by surrounding it with the cell membrane is called **endocytosis** (en duh si TOH sus). Some one-celled organisms, as shown in **Figure 10,** take in food this way.

The contents of a vesicle can be released by a cell using the process called **exocytosis** (ek soh si TOH sus). Exocytosis occurs in the opposite way that endocytosis does. A vesicle's membrane fuses with a cell's membrane, and the vesicle's contents are released. Cells in your stomach use this process to release chemicals that help digest food. The ways that materials can enter or leave a cell are summarized in **Figure 11.**

section 2 review

Summary

Passive Transport
- Cells take in substances and release waste through their cell membranes.
- Facilitated diffusion and osmosis are types of passive transport.

Active Transport
- Transport proteins are involved in active transport.
- Transport proteins can be reused many times.

Endocytosis and Exocytosis
- Vesicles are formed when a cell takes in a substance by endocytosis.
- Contents of a vesicle are released to the outside of a cell by exocytosis.

Self Check

1. **Describe** how cell membranes are selectively permeable.
2. **Compare and contrast** the processes of osmosis and diffusion.
3. **Infer** why endocytosis and exocytosis are important processes to cells.
4. **Think Critically** Why are fresh fruits and vegetables sprinkled with water at produce markets?

Applying Skills

5. **Communicate** Seawater is saltier than tap water. Explain why drinking large amounts of seawater would be dangerous for humans.

 life.msscience.com/self_check_quiz

section 2 review

1. They allow some molecules to pass through, but not others.
2. In both, molecules move from areas with many molecules to areas with few molecules. Osmosis is the diffusion of water across a cell membrane; diffusion can apply to any form of matter.
3. Molecules and particles that are too large to move by diffusion or by the cell's transport proteins can move into and out of cells using endocytosis and exocytosis.
4. Water will diffuse into the fruits and vegetables and keep them crisp.
5. The high levels of salt in seawater would cause water to move out of the cells, resulting in dehydration.

Figure 11

A flexible yet strong layer, the cell membrane is built of two layers of lipids (gold) pierced by protein "passageways" (purple). Molecules can enter or exit the cell by slipping between the lipids or through the protein passageways. Substances that cannot enter or exit the cell in these ways may be surrounded by the membrane and drawn into or expelled from the cell.

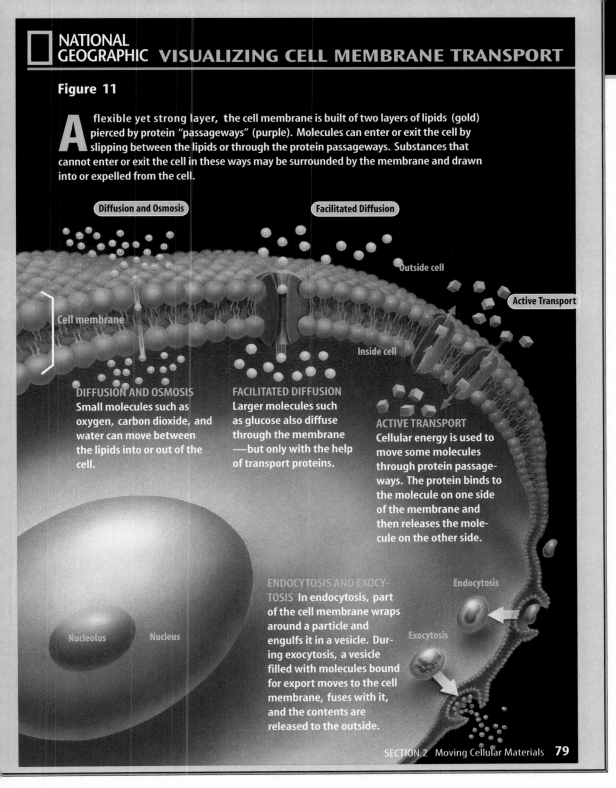

Diffusion and Osmosis

Facilitated Diffusion

Outside cell

Active Transport

Cell membrane

Inside cell

DIFFUSION AND OSMOSIS Small molecules such as oxygen, carbon dioxide, and water can move between the lipids into or out of the cell.

FACILITATED DIFFUSION Larger molecules such as glucose also diffuse through the membrane —but only with the help of transport proteins.

ACTIVE TRANSPORT Cellular energy is used to move some molecules through protein passageways. The protein binds to the molecule on one side of the membrane and then releases the molecule on the other side.

ENDOCYTOSIS AND EXOCYTOSIS In endocytosis, part of the cell membrane wraps around a particle and engulfs it in a vesicle. During exocytosis, a vesicle filled with molecules bound for export moves to the cell membrane, fuses with it, and the contents are released to the outside.

Endocytosis

Exocytosis

Nucleolus   Nucleus

SECTION 2 Moving Cellular Materials **79**

Visualizing Cell Membrane Transport

Have students examine the pictures and read the captions. Then ask students the following questions.

Why do some substances move through the cell membrane through exocytosis and endocytosis instead of one of the other transport methods? These substances, which include proteins and nucleic acids, are too large to use the other methods. For example, cholesterol enters by endocytosis; neurotransmitters exit by exocytosis.

Which transport method(s) is like floating downstream? Which is like paddling upstream? Why? In diffusion (osmosis and facilitated diffusion), a substance moves from an area of higher concentration to an area of lower concentration. This does not require energy because it goes with the flow, like floating downstream. In active transport, the substance must go against the concentration gradient which, like paddling upstream, requires energy.

Activity

Cell Membrane Transport Have students make a model of a cell that illustrates one type of cell membrane transport. L2
IS **Kinesthetic**

Visual Learning

Figure 11 Transport of a molecule across a cell membrane can occur in several ways, such as diffusion and osmosis, facilitated diffusion, active transport, and endocytosis and exocytosis. Have students make an outline of the transport of a molecule across a membrane by using this figure. L2 P

Differentiated Instruction

English-Language Learners Pair students and on flashcards have them write key terms and definitions that deal with the movement of cellular materials. Students should include diffusion, osmosis, facilitated diffusion, active transport, exocytosis and endocytosis on their cards. L2

Challenge Have students investigate transport proteins and the substances each transports. Students can make a card game to teach other students what they learned. L3

Real-World Question

Purpose to observe and measure the amount of water diffusing through an egg membrane

L2 IS **Logical-Mathematical**

Process Skills observe and infer, measure, communicate, recognize cause and effect, form operational definitions

Time Required 50 minutes to set up, 5 minutes each day to observe, 15 minutes to summarize

Procedure

Alternate Materials Food containers with lids may be used to hold the unshelled egg.

Teaching Strategy Cover raw eggs with vinegar. Leave undisturbed for two or three days until the shells dissolve.

Troubleshooting

- Remind students to handle unshelled eggs carefully.
- Thick syrup works better than thin syrup.
- Make sure students replace lids on containers.

Conclude and Apply

1. water— increased in size; corn syrup—decreased in size
2. about 30 mL of water entered; about 40 mL of water left
3. The eggshell is not permeable to water and syrup.
4. cell membrane

Observing Osmosis

It is difficult to observe osmosis in cells because most cells are so small. However, a few cells can be seen without the aid of a microscope. Try this lab to observe osmosis.

Real-World Question

How does osmosis occur in an egg cell?

Materials

unshelled egg*	distilled water (250 mL)
balance	light corn syrup (250 mL)
spoon	500-mL container

*an egg whose shell has been dissolved by vinegar

Goals

- **Observe** osmosis in an egg cell.
- **Determine** what affects osmosis.

Safety Precautions

WARNING: *Eggs may contain bacteria. Avoid touching your face.*

Procedure

1. Copy the table below into your Science Journal and use it to record your data.

Egg Mass Data

	Beginning Egg Mass	Egg Mass After Two Days
Distilled water		
Corn syrup		

2. Obtain an unshelled egg from your teacher. Handle the egg gently. Use a balance to find the egg's mass and record it in the table.

3. Place the egg in the container and add enough distilled water to cover it.

4. **Observe** the egg after 30 min, one day, and two days. After each observation, record the egg's appearance in your Science Journal.

5. After day two, remove the egg with a spoon and allow it to drain. Find the egg's mass and record it in the table.

6. Empty the container, then put the egg back in. Now add enough corn syrup to cover it. Repeat steps 4 and 5.

Conclude and Apply

1. **Explain** the difference between what happened to the egg in water and in corn syrup.
2. **Calculate** the mass of water that moved into and out of the egg.
3. **Hypothesize** why you used an unshelled egg for this investigation.
4. **Infer** what part of the egg controlled water's movement into and out of the egg.

Communicating Your Data

Compare your conclusions with those of other students in your class. **For more help, refer to the** Science Skill Handbook.

✔ Assessment

Performance Have students place ten dried beans in water overnight. Direct them to explain their observations. Use **Performance Assessment in the Science Classroom,** p. 97 L2

Communicating Your Data

Students should discuss why their conclusions did or did not agree with those of other students.

Energy for Life

Trapping and Using Energy

Think of all the energy that players use in a basketball game. Where does the energy come from? The simplest answer is "from the food they eat." The chemical energy stored in food molecules is changed inside of cells into forms needed to perform all the activities necessary for life. In every cell, these changes involve chemical reactions. All of the activities of an organism involve chemical reactions in some way. The total of all chemical reactions in an organism is called **metabolism.**

The chemical reactions of metabolism need enzymes. What do enzymes do? Suppose you are hungry and decide to open a can of spaghetti. You use a can opener to open the can. Without a can opener, the spaghetti is unusable. The can of spaghetti changes because of the can opener, but the can opener does not change. The can opener can be used again later to open more cans of spaghetti. Enzymes in cells work something like can openers. The enzyme, like the can opener, causes a change, but the enzyme is not changed and can be used again, as shown in **Figure 12.** Unlike the can opener, which can only cause things to come apart, enzymes also can cause molecules to join. Without the right enzyme, a chemical reaction in a cell cannot take place. Each chemical reaction in a cell requires a specific enzyme.

as you read

What You'll Learn
- **List** the differences between producers and consumers.
- **Explain** how the processes of photosynthesis and respiration store and release energy.
- **Describe** how cells get energy from glucose through fermentation.

Why It's Important
Because of photosynthesis and respiration, you use the Sun's energy.

🔎 **Review Vocabulary**
mitochondrion: cell organelle that breaks down lipids and carbohydrates and releases energy

New Vocabulary
- metabolism
- photosynthesis
- respiration
- fermentation

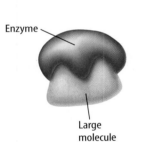
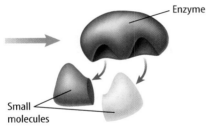

Enzyme

Enzyme

Large molecule

Small molecules

The enzyme attaches to the large molecule it will help change.

The enzyme causes the larger molecule to break down into two smaller molecules. The enzyme is not changed and can be used again.

Figure 12 Enzymes are needed for most chemical reactions that take place in cells.
Determine *What is the sum of all chemical reactions in an organism called?*

SECTION 3 Energy for Life **81**

Bellringer

Section Focus Transparencies also are available on the Interactive Chalkboard CD-ROM.
L2 ELL

Tie to Prior Knowledge

Energy Sources Display pictures of people using energy—playing sports, gardening, working, and so on. Ask students to identify the source of this energy. chemical bonds in food Then ask where the energy in the food came from. It was derived from plants that captured the Sun's energy. L2

Caption Answer
Figure 12 metabolism

Section 3 Resource Manager

Chapter *FAST FILE* Resources
Transparency Activity, p. 44
Directed Reading for Content Mastery, pp. 19, 20
Lab Activity, pp. 11–14
Enrichment, p. 30

Reinforcement, p. 27
Lab Worksheet, pp. 7–8
Life Science Critical Thinking/Problem Solving, p. 15
Lab Management and Safety, p. 63

Activity

Bubbles Pick a leaf from a plant that has been exposed to sunlight for a few hours. Submerge it in water. Observe the surface of the leaf. What forms on the leaf? Why? Bubbles; the leaf is giving off oxygen. L2

Use an Analogy

Construction and Photosynthesis Compare the construction of a house to photosynthesis. Building a house is a physical process that requires the putting together of raw materials. Photosynthesis is a chemical process of putting raw materials together. They both require raw materials and result in a usable product. [IS] **Logical-Mathematical**

Caption Answer

Figure 13 carbon dioxide, water, light energy, and chlorophyll

IDENTIFYING Misconceptions

Plant Food Some students may think that plants obtain food from the soil. Plants take in a variety of minerals and other substances from the soil, but these are not used as food. They are dissolved in water and absorbed through the plant's roots. Once absorbed, they are transported to structures in the plant where they are needed. The food of plants—glucose—is produced by plants in the chloroplasts of their cells from carbon dioxide and water and using light energy.

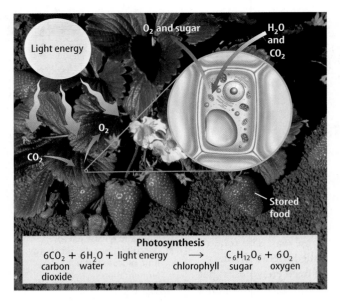

Figure 13 Plants use photosynthesis to make food.
Determine *According to the chemical equation, what raw materials would the plant in the photo need for photosynthesis?*

Photosynthesis

$$6CO_2 + 6H_2O + \text{light energy} \longrightarrow C_6H_{12}O_6 + 6O_2$$

carbon dioxide, water, light energy, chlorophyll, sugar, oxygen

Photosynthesis Living things are divided into two groups—producers and consumers—based on how they obtain their food. Organisms that make their own food, such as plants, are called producers. Organisms that cannot make their own food are called consumers.

If you have ever walked barefoot across a sidewalk on a sunny summer day, you probably moved quickly because the sidewalk was hot. Sunlight energy was converted into thermal energy and heated the sidewalk. Plants and many other producers can convert light energy into another kind of energy—chemical energy. The process they use is called photosynthesis. During **photosynthesis,** producers use light energy to make sugars, which can be used as food.

Producing Carbohydrates Producers that use photosynthesis are usually green because they contain a green pigment called chlorophyll (KLOR uh fihl). Chlorophyll and other pigments are used in photosynthesis to capture light energy. In plant cells, these pigments are found in chloroplasts.

The captured light energy powers chemical reactions that produce sugar and oxygen from the raw materials, carbon dioxide and water. For plants, the raw materials come from air and soil. Some of the captured light energy is stored in the chemical bonds that hold the sugar molecules together. **Figure 13** shows what happens during photosynthesis in a plant. Enzymes also are needed before these reactions can occur.

Storing Carbohydrates Plants make more sugar during photosynthesis than they need for survival. Excess sugar is changed and stored as starches or used to make other carbohydrates. Plants use these carbohydrates as food for growth, maintenance, and reproduction.

Why is photosynthesis important to consumers? Do you eat apples? Apple trees use photosynthesis to produce apples. Do you like cheese? Some cheese comes from milk, which is produced by cows that eat plants. Consumers take in food by eating producers or other consumers. No matter what you eat, photosynthesis was involved directly or indirectly in its production.

Differentiated Instruction

Challenge There are certain plants, such as the Indian pipe (*Monotropa uniflora*) and dodder (*Cuscuta*), that lack chlorophyll. Have students research these plants and write a report about how they obtain food to present to the class. L2

Science Journal

Energy and Photosynthesis In their Science Journals, have students list all the foods they eat in one day. Have them to divide the list into two groups: (1) foods formed directly by photosynthesis, (2) foods not formed directly by photosynthesis. Use the lists to help students see that all food energy comes from photosynthesis, whether directly or indirectly. L2

Respiration Imagine that you get up late for school. You dress quickly, then run three blocks to school. When you get to school, you feel hot and are breathing fast. Why? Your muscle cells use a lot of energy when you run. To get this energy, muscle cells break down food. Some of the energy from the food is used when you move and some of it becomes thermal energy, which is why you feel warm or hot. Most cells also need oxygen to break down food. You were breathing fast because your body was working to get oxygen to your muscles. Your muscle cells were using the oxygen for the process of respiration. During **respiration,** chemical reactions occur that break down food molecules into simpler substances and release their stored energy. Just as in photosynthesis, enzymes are needed for the chemical reactions of respiration.

✔ Reading Check *What must happen to food molecules for respiration to take place?*

Breaking Down Carbohydrates The food molecules most easily broken down by cells are carbohydrates. Respiration of carbohydrates begins in the cytoplasm of the cell. The carbohydrates are broken down into glucose molecules. Each glucose molecule is broken down further into two simpler molecules. As the glucose molecules are broken down, energy is released.

The two simpler molecules are broken down again. This breakdown occurs in the mitochondria of the cells of plants, animals, fungi, and many other organisms. This process uses oxygen, releases much more energy, and produces carbon dioxide and water as wastes. When you exhale, you breathe out carbon dioxide and some of the water.

Respiration occurs in the cells of all living things. **Figure 14** shows how respiration occurs in one consumer. As you are reading this section of the chapter, millions of cells in your body are breaking down glucose, releasing energy, and producing carbon dioxide and water.

Microbiologist Dr. Harold Amos is a microbiologist who has studied cell processes in bacteria and mammals. He has a medical degree and a doctorate in bacteriology and immunology. He has also received many awards for his scientific work and his contributions to the careers of other scientists. Research microbiology careers, and write what you find in your Science Journal.

Figure 14 Producers and consumers carry on respiration that releases energy from foods.

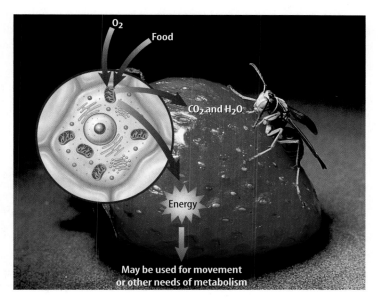

O₂
Food
CO_2 and H_2O
Energy
May be used for movement or other needs of metabolism

Microbiologist Scientists in the field of microbiology study organisms of microscopic or submicroscopic size. A bachelor's degree is required to work in this field. Students interested in a career in microbiology should study sciences, math, and Latin.

Use Science Words

Word Origin Have students study the parts of the word *photosynthesis.* It comes from the Greek *photo, syn-,* and *thesis.* Have them find the meaning of these words and word parts and describe how the word is defined. photo: "light;" syn-: "together;" thesis: "to place;" Photosynthesis uses light to place compounds together. ⟨L2⟩

✔ Reading Check

Answer They must be broken down into simpler substances and their stored energy released.

⬙ IDENTIFYING Misconceptions

Plant Gases Students often think that plants do not use oxygen, only that they produce oxygen and use carbon dioxide during photosynthesis. See page F at the beginning of this chapter for teaching strategies that address this misconception.

✔ Active Reading

Buddy Interviews This strategy helps students understand and clarify the reading. Have students interview one another to find out what helps them to understand what they are reading, how they find answers, and how they assimilate new vocabulary terms. Have students use Buddy Interviews to help them master photosynthesis and respiration. ⟨L2⟩

Teacher FYI

Athletes' Oxygen The body of an average person running a 100-yard dash in 12 seconds would require 6 L (1.6 gal.) of air. The person's lungs could supply only about 1.2 L of air. As a result, oxygen debt would occur, and the muscles would produce lactic acid. Most athletes take in at least 10 percent more oxygen than the average person; trained marathon runners take in up to 45 percent more oxygen. They have more efficient respiratory and circulatory systems and can exert greater effort without incurring oxygen debt.

Discussion

Yeast Why do bakers use yeast for breadmaking? Yeast carry out processes that release energy in the absence of oxygen and produce carbon dioxide, which causes bread to rise.

Quick Demo

Fermentation

Materials sugar, water, jar, yeast

Estimated Time five minutes to prepare, several hours before class; 10 minutes to observe

Procedure Prepare a sugar solution by mixing 1 tablespoon of sugar with 1 cup of warm water. Add some yeast to the solution a few hours before class and cover it. Have students note the odor of alcohol and the bubbles of carbon dioxide. Point out that these products result from alcoholic fermentation.

Topic: Beneficial Microorganisms
Visit life.msscience.com for Web links to information about how microorganisms are used to produce many useful products.

Activity Find three other ways that microorganisms are beneficial.

Figure 15 Organisms that use fermentation produce several different wastes.

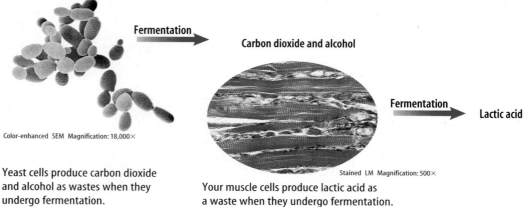

Color-enhanced SEM Magnification: 18,000×

Yeast cells produce carbon dioxide and alcohol as wastes when they undergo fermentation.

Stained LM Magnification: 500×

Your muscle cells produce lactic acid as a waste when they undergo fermentation.

84 CHAPTER 3 Cell Processes

Fermentation Remember imagining you were late and had to run to school? During your run, your muscle cells might not have received enough oxygen, even though you were breathing rapidly. When cells do not have enough oxygen for respiration, they use a process called **fermentation** to release some of the energy stored in glucose molecules.

Like respiration, fermentation begins in the cytoplasm. Again, as the glucose molecules are broken down, energy is released. But the simple molecules from the breakdown of glucose do not move into the mitochondria. Instead, more chemical reactions occur in the cytoplasm. These reactions release some energy and produce wastes. Depending on the type of cell, the wastes may be lactic acid or alcohol and carbon dioxide, as shown in **Figure 15.** Your muscle cells can use fermentation to change the simple molecules into lactic acid while releasing energy. The presence of lactic acid is why your muscle cells might feel stiff and sore after you run to school.

 Reading Check *Where in a cell does fermentation take place?*

Some microscopic organisms, such as bacteria, carry out fermentation and make lactic acid. Some of these organisms are used to produce yogurt and some cheeses. These organisms break down a sugar in milk and release energy. The lactic acid produced causes the milk to become more solid and gives these foods some of their flavor.

Have you ever used yeast to make bread? Yeasts are one-celled living organisms. Yeast cells use fermentation and break down sugar in bread dough. They produce alcohol and carbon dioxide as wastes. The carbon dioxide waste is a gas that makes bread dough rise before it is baked. The alcohol is lost as the bread bakes.

Cultural Diversity

Fermenting Food Lactic acid fermentation by bacteria is responsible for a number of foods from different cultures. Have students research these foods and report their findings to the class in oral reports. Possible topics: Hawaiian *poi*, Japanese soy sauce, Korean *kimchi*, German sauerkraut, yogurt. L3

CO_2, H_2O

Photosynthesis
(producers)

Respiration
(all living things)

Sugars, O_2

Figure 16 The chemical reactions of photosynthesis and respiration could not take place without each other.

Related Processes How are photosynthesis, respiration, and fermentation related? Some producers use photosynthesis to make food. All living things use respiration or fermentation to release energy stored in food. If you think carefully about what happens during photosynthesis and respiration, you will see that what is produced in one is used in the other, as shown in **Figure 16.** These two processes are almost the opposite of each other. Photosynthesis produces sugars and oxygen, and respiration uses these products. The carbon dioxide and water produced during respiration are used during photosynthesis. Most life would not be possible without these important chemical reactions.

section 3 review

Summary

Trapping and Using Energy

- Metabolism is the total of all chemical reactions in an organism.
- During photosynthesis, light energy is used to make sugars.
- Chlorophyll and other pigments capture light energy.
- Consumers take in energy by eating producers and other consumers.
- Living cells break down glucose and release energy. This is called respiration.
- Fermentation changes simple molecules and releases energy.
- Without photosynthesis and respiration, most life would not be possible.

Self Check

1. **Explain** the difference between producers and consumers and give three examples of each.
2. **Infer** how the energy used by many living things on Earth can be traced back to sunlight.
3. **Compare and contrast** respiration and fermentation.
4. **Think Critically** How can some indoor plants help to improve the quality of air in a room?

Applying Math

5. **Solve** Refer to the chemical equation for photosynthesis. Calculate then compare the number of carbon, hydrogen, and oxygen atoms before and after photosynthesis.

 Science Online life.msscience.com/self_check_quiz

section 3 review

1. Producers make food. Consumers get energy by eating producers, food made by producers, or other consumers. Examples will vary.
2. Energy used by living things is released from food molecules during cellular respiration. Photosynthetic producers convert light energy—usually from the Sun—into the chemical energy in the sugar molecules that they produce. Consumers get this energy by eating producers or other consumers that eat producers.
3. The amount of energy released by fermentation is less than that released by respiration.
4. Plants remove carbon dioxide from the air, use it in photosynthesis, and produce oxygen.
5. The number of atoms is the same before and after photosynthesis; $C = 6$, $H = 12$, $O = 18$.

Visual Learning

Figure 16 The arrows in the figure illustrate the interdependence of photosynthesis and respiration. Producers take in carbon dioxide and water, undergo photosynthesis, and produce oxygen and sugars. Other living organisms take in oxygen and sugars, undergo respiration, and give off carbon dioxide and water. Have students create an events chain concept map to illustrate what is occurring in the pictures in this figure. L2 P

3 Assess

DAILY INTERVENTION

Checking for Understanding

Logical-Mathematical Using a three-column chart, have students brainstorm with the class about different organisms and whether they use photosynthesis, respiration, or fermentation. Discuss how these processes are related and under what circumstances an organism would use them. L2

Reteach

Using Energy Have students identify organisms that photosynthesize and those that respire. Only organisms with chlorophyll photosynthesize; all organisms respire. L1

☑ Assessment

Content Have students make a table to compare and contrast photosynthesis and respiration. Use **Performance Assessment in the Science Classroom,** p. 109. L2

BENCH TESTED

▶ Real-World Question

Purpose Students observe photosynthesis and respiration in plants and infer whether the processes occur in light or darkness. L2 **ELL** COOP LEARN **IS** Visual-Spatial

Process Skills measure, observe, infer, communicate, compare and contrast, recognize cause and effect, separate and control variables, interpret data

Time Required 50 minutes (leave overnight if using artificial light)

Safety Precautions Students should use care when working with chemicals.

▶ Procedure

Tie to Prior Knowledge Most students are aware that plants use light energy to make food and that photosynthesis will occur in the tube placed near the light.

Troubleshooting *Elodea* should be kept in the dark for two days before the activity. Use sharp scissors to make a clean diagonal cut at the bottom of each stem.

Goals
- **Observe** green water plants in the light and dark.
- **Determine** whether plants carry on photosynthesis and respiration.

Materials
16-mm test tubes (3)
150-mm test tubes with stoppers (4)
*small, clear-glass baby food jars with lids (4)
test-tube rack
stirring rod
scissors
carbonated water (5 mL)
bromthymol blue solution in dropper bottle
aged tap water (20 mL)
*distilled water (20 mL)
sprigs of *Elodea* (2)
*other water plants
*Alternate materials

Safety Precautions
🌊 ♨ 📛 🧤 🔥 ☹ 🥽 ✋

WARNING: *Wear splash-proof safety goggles to protect eyes from hazardous chemicals.*

Photosynthesis and Respiration

LM Magnification: 225×

▶ Real-World Question

Every living cell carries on many chemical processes. Two important chemical processes are respiration and photosynthesis. All cells, including the ones in your body, carry on respiration. However, some plant cells can carry on both processes. In this experiment you will investigate when these processes occur in plant cells. How could you find out when plants were using these processes? Are the products of photosynthesis and respiration the same? When do plants carry on photosynthesis and respiration?

▶ Procedure

1. In your Science Journal, copy and complete the test-tube data table as you perform this lab.

Test-Tube Data		
Test Tube	Color at Start	Color After 30 Minutes
1	yellow	blue
2	yellow	yellow
3	blue	yellow
4	blue	blue

Alternative Inquiry Lab

Photosynthesis and Respiration To make this Lab an Inquiry Lab, have students relate the problem to nature. What happens to plants during periods without light? Have students brainstorm additional questions that interest them and design experiments to explore them. Students can observe photosynthesis and respiration in plants. They can use *Elodea* or other water plants and the materials described above to set up the experiment. Unsafe or impractical questions should be eliminated.

---

2. Label each test tube using the numbers *1, 2, 3,* and *4.* Pour 5 mL of aged tap water into each test tube.

3. Add 10 drops of carbonated water to test tubes *1* and *2.*

4. Add 10 drops of bromthymol blue to all of the test tubes. Bromthymol blue turns green to yellow in the presence of an acid.

5. Cut two 10-cm sprigs of *Elodea.* Place one sprig in test tube *1* and one sprig in test tube *3.* Stopper all test tubes.

6. Place test tubes *1* and *2* in bright light. Place tubes *3* and *4* in the dark. Observe the test tubes for 45 min or until the color changes. Record the color of each of the four test tubes.

● *Analyze Your Data*

1. **Identify** what is indicated by the color of the water in all four test tubes at the start of the activity.

2. **Infer** what process occurred in the test tube or tubes that changed color after 30 min.

● *Conclude and Apply*

1. **Describe** the purpose of test tubes *2* and *4* in this experiment.

2. **Explain** whether or not the results of this experiment show that photosynthesis and respiration occur in plants.

Communicating Your Data

Choose one of the following activities to **communicate** your data. Prepare an oral presentation that explains how the experiment showed the differences between products of photosynthesis and respiration. Draw a cartoon strip to **explain** what you did in this experiment. Use each panel to show a different step. **For more help, refer to the** Science Skill Handbook.

● *Analyze Your Data*

Expected Outcome Most results will reflect that plants used carbon dioxide in the light and gave off carbon dioxide in the dark.

Answers to Questions

1. Test tubes 1 and 2 contain carbon dioxide. Tubes 3 and 4 do not.
2. They underwent photosynthesis or respiration.

Error Analysis Have students compare their results and explain why any differences occurred. L2

● *Conclude and Apply*

1. Tubes 2 and 4 were controls.
2. Yes, the experimental results showed that both processes happen in plant cells. In test tube 1, the green plant used carbon dioxide for photosynthesis. In test tube 3, the green plant gave off carbon dioxide as a result of respiration.

☑ Assessment

Oral How are fermentation and respiration similar? Both processes release energy through the breakdown of other substances. Use **Performance Assessment in the Science Classroom,** p. 99. L2

Differentiated Instruction

Visually Impaired Pair students who are visually impaired with those who can describe to them the colors in the test tubes and other observations, both before and after the experiment. L2

Communicating Your Data

Students should use data from the experiment for the presentation or cartoon.

Understanding Literature

Personification When she states that the tulip inspires love.

Respond to the Reading

1. Possible answers: The tulip bulb is buried deep in the ground; the tulip is a hardy plant.
2. the yellow color at the base of each petal
3. **Linking Science and Writing** As they observe the plant, students should record the change in the plant's growth.

 **Plant Dormancy**

Plant stems play a part in the transport of materials from roots to leaves. Stems vary greatly in size and shape from one plant species to another. Some grow entirely underground and other stems can store water and nutrients. Plants often store food in their stems during their growth period. When a plant's growth stops, this stored food enables them to survive dormancy. Dormancy occurs during a cold winter or a long dry period. The dormant plant uses the stored food to begin growing when conditions again become favorable.

from "Tulip"
by Penny Harter

I watched its first green push
through bare dirt, where the builders
had dropped boards, shingles,
plaster—
killing everything.
    I could not recall what grew there,
what returned each spring,
but the leaves looked tulip,
and one morning it arrived,
a scarlet slash against the aluminum siding.
    Mornings, on the way to my car,
I bow to the still bell
of its closed petals; evenings,
it greets me, light ringing
at the end of my driveway.
    Sometimes I kneel
to stare into the yellow throat . . . .
It opens and closes my days.
It has made me weak with love . . . .

Understanding Literature

Personification Using human traits or emotions to describe an idea, animal, or inanimate object is called personification. When the poet writes that the tulip has a "yellow throat," she uses personification. Where else does the poet use personification?

Respond to the Reading

1. Why do you suppose the tulip survived the builders' abuse?
2. What is the yellow throat that the narrator is staring into?
3. **Linking Science and Writing** Keep a gardener's journal of a plant for a month, describing weekly the plant's condition, size, health, color, and other physical qualities.

 Because most chemical reactions in plants take place in water, plants must have water in order to grow. The water carries nutrients and minerals from the soil into the plant. The process of active transport allows needed nutrients to enter the roots. The cell membranes of root cells contain proteins that bind with the needed nutrients. Cellular energy is used to move these nutrients through the cell membrane.

Resources for Teachers and Students

Tulipa: A Photographer's Botanical, by Christopher Baker (Photographer), Willem Lemmers, Emma Sweeny, and Michael Pollan, Artisan, 1999

Photosynthesis, by Krishna Rao and David O. Hall, Cambridge University Press, 1999

Plant Identification Terminology: An Illustrated Glossary, by James G. Harris and Melinda Woolf Harris, Spring Lake Publishers, 2001

American Society for Microbiology, Office of Education, 1325 Massachusetts Avenue, NW, Washington, DC 20005–4171

Reviewing Main Ideas

Section 1 — Chemistry of Life

1. Matter is anything that has mass and takes up space.

2. Energy in matter is in the chemical bonds that hold matter together.

3. All organic compounds contain the elements hydrogen and carbon. The organic compounds in living things are carbohydrates, lipids, proteins, and nucleic acids.

4. Organic and inorganic compounds are important to living things.

Section 2 — Moving Cellular Materials

1. The selectively permeable cell membrane controls which molecules can pass into and out of the cell.

2. In diffusion, molecules move from areas where there are relatively more of them to areas where there are relatively fewer of them.

3. Osmosis is the diffusion of water through a cell membrane.

4. Cells use energy to move molecules by active transport but do not use energy for passive transport.

5. Cells move large particles through cell membranes by endocytosis and exocytosis.

Section 3 — Energy for Life

1. Photosynthesis is the process by which some producers change light energy into chemical energy.

2. Respiration that uses oxygen releases the energy in food molecules and produces waste carbon dioxide and water.

3. Some one-celled organisms and cells that lack oxygen use fermentation to release small amounts of energy from glucose. Wastes such as alcohol, carbon dioxide, and lactic acid are produced.

Visualizing Main Ideas

Copy and complete the following table on energy processes.

Energy Processes

	Photosynthesis	Respiration	Fermentation
Energy source	light	food (glucose)	food (glucose)
In plant and animal cells, occurs in	chloroplast	mitochondria	cytoplasm
Reactants are	water, carbon dioxide	glucose, oxygen	glucose, oxygen
Products are	glucose, oxygen	water, carbon dioxide	lactic acid, alcohol, carbon dioxide

 life.msscience.com/interactive_tutor

CHAPTER STUDY GUIDE 89

Reviewing Main Ideas

Summary statements can be used by students to review the major concepts of the chapter.

Visualizing Main Ideas

See student page.

Visit life.msscience.com
/self_check_quiz
/interactive_tutor
/vocabulary_puzzlemaker
/chapter_review
/standardized_test

Assessment Transparency

For additional assessment questions, use the *Assessment Transparency* located in the transparency book.

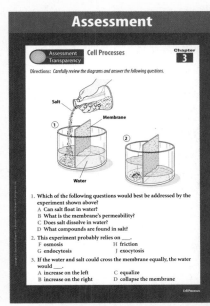

◇ Identifying Misconceptions

Assess

Discussion Do animals ever give off oxygen as a product of their metabolic activities? No Explain Oxygen is given off as a product of photosynthesis, thus only organisms that can carry out photosynthesis produce this gas. Animals are not photosynthetic organisms. What products do plants release during their metabolic processes? both oxygen and carbon dioxide

Specifically reinforce the idea that plants carry out both photosynthesis and respiration.

Expected Outcome At this point students should understand and be able to explain the complementary processes of photosynthesis and respiration in plants and animals.

Using Vocabulary

1. osmosis
2. enzymes
3. by endocytosis
4. inorganic compound
5. photosynthesis
6. organic compounds
7. respiration
8. metabolism

Checking Concepts

9. C	13. D
10. B	14. C
11. A	15. A
12. B	16. C

Using Vocabulary

active transport p. 77	metabolism p. 81
diffusion p. 75	mixture p. 69
endocytosis p. 78	organic compound p. 70
enzyme p. 71	osmosis p. 76
equilibrium p. 75	passive transport p. 74
exocytosis p. 78	photosynthesis p. 82
fermentation p. 84	respiration p. 83
inorganic compound p. 71	

Use what you know about the vocabulary words to answer the following questions.

1. What is the diffusion of water called?

2. What type of protein regulates nearly all chemical reactions in cells?

3. How do large food particles enter an amoeba?

4. What type of compound is water?

5. What process is used by some producers to convert light energy into chemical energy?

6. What type of compounds always contain carbon and hydrogen?

7. What process uses oxygen to break down glucose?

8. What is the total of all chemical reactions in an organism called?

Checking Concepts

Choose the word or phrase that best answers the question.

9. What is it called when cells use energy to move molecules?
   A) diffusion
   B) osmosis
   C) active transport
   D) passive transport

Use the photo below to answer question 10.

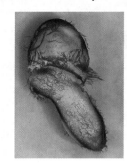

10. What cell process is occurring in the photo?
    A) osmosis
    B) endocytosis
    C) exocytosis
    D) diffusion

11. What occurs when the number of molecules of a substance is equal in two areas?
    A) equilibrium
    B) metabolism
    C) fermentation
    D) cellular respiration

12. Which of the following substances is an example of a carbohydrate?
    A) enzymes
    B) sugars
    C) waxes
    D) proteins

13. What is RNA an example of?
    A) carbon dioxide
    B) water
    C) lipid
    D) nucleic acid

14. What organic molecule stores the greatest amount of energy?
    A) carbohydrate
    B) water
    C) lipid
    D) nucleic acid

15. Which of these formulas is an example of an organic compound?
    A) $C_6H_{12}O_6$
    B) NO_2
    C) H_2O
    D) O_2

16. What are organisms that cannot make their own food called?
    A) biodegradables
    B) producers
    C) consumers
    D) enzymes

Science online life.msscience.com/vocabulary_puzzlemaker

Use the Exam*View*® Pro Testmaker CD-ROM to:
- create multiple versions of tests
- create modified tests with one mouse click for inclusion students
- edit existing questions and add your own questions
- build tests aligned with state standards using built-in State Curriculum Tags
- change English tests to Spanish with one mouse click and vice versa

Thinking Critically

17. Concept Map Copy and complete the events-chain concept map to sequence the following parts of matter from smallest to largest: *atom*, *electron*, and *compound*.

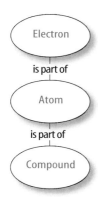

Electron

is part of

Atom

is part of

Compound

Use the table below to answer question 18.

Photosynthesis in Water Plants

Beaker Number	Distance from Light (cm)	Bubbles per Minute
1	10	45
2	30	30
3	50	19
4	70	6
5	100	1

18. Interpret Data Water plants were placed at different distances from a light source. Bubbles coming from the plants were counted to measure the rate of photosynthesis. What can you say about how the distance from the light affected the rate?

19. Infer why, in snowy places, salt is used to melt ice on the roads. Explain what could happen to many roadside plants as a result.

 Science**Online** life.msscience.com/chapter_review

20. Draw a conclusion about why sugar dissolves faster in hot tea than in iced tea.

21. Predict what would happen to the consumers in a lake if all the producers died.

22. Explain how meat tenderizers affect meat.

23. Form a hypothesis about what will happen to wilted celery when placed in a glass of plain water.

Performance Activities

24. Puzzle Make a crossword puzzle with words describing ways substances are transported across cell membranes. Use the following words in your puzzle: *diffusion, osmosis, facilitated diffusion, active transport, endocytosis,* and *exocytosis.* Make sure your clues give good descriptions of each transport method.

Applying Math

25. Light and Photosynthesis Using the data from question 18, make a line graph that shows the relationship between the rate of photosynthesis and the distance from light.

26. Importance of Water Assume the brain is 70% water. If the average adult human brain weighs 1.4 kg, how many kilograms of water does it contain?

Use the equation below to answer question 27.

Photosynthesis
$$6CO_2 + 6H_2O + \text{light energy} \longrightarrow C_6H_{12}O_6 + 6O_2$$
carbon dioxide   water   chlorophyll   sugar   oxygen

27. Photosynthesis Refer to the chemical equation above. If 18 CO_2 molecules and 18 H_2O molecules are used with light energy to make sugar, how many sugar molecules will be produced? How many oxygen molecules will be produced?

Thinking Critically

17. See student page.

18. The closer a plant is to light, the faster its rate of photosynthesis.

19. Plants die as water molecules move out of the cells into the salty soil.

20. The molecules in hot water move faster than those in cold. These faster-moving molecules bump into the sugar molecules more often and more vigorously, dissolving the sugar faster.

21. Consumers would also die; they depend on producers for food.

22. The enzymes increase the rate at which protein bonds are broken; this makes the meat more tender.

23. Wilted celery will become crisp as water molecules move by osmosis into its cells to reach equilibrium.

Performance Activities

24. Definitions in the chapter for these terms can be used. Use **PASC,** p. 91.

Applying Math

National Math Standards

1, 2, 5, 6, 9

25.

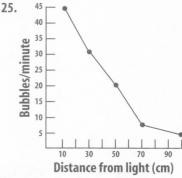

26. 0.98 kg

27. 3 sugar molecules and 18 oxygen molecules will be produced.

✔ Assessment   Resources

Reproducible Masters

Chapter *Fast File* Resources
  Chapter Review, pp. 35–36
  Chapter Tests, pp. 37–40
  Assessment Transparency Activity, p. 47

Glencoe Science Web site
  Chapter Review Test
  Standardized Test Practice

Glencoe Technology

- Assessment Transparency
- Exam*View*® Pro Testmaker
- MindJogger Videoquiz
- Interactive Chalkboard
- Virtual Labs CD-ROM

FAST FILE

Answer Sheet A practice answer sheet can be found at life.msscience.com/answer_sheet.

Name   **Date**   **Class**

Assessment   **Student Recording Sheet**   *Use with pages 788–789 of the Student Edition*

Standardized Test Practice

Part 1   **Multiple Choice**
Select the best answer from the choices given and fill in the corresponding oval.

1. Ⓐ Ⓑ Ⓒ Ⓓ   8. Ⓐ Ⓑ Ⓒ Ⓓ
2. Ⓐ Ⓑ Ⓒ Ⓓ   9. Ⓐ Ⓑ Ⓒ Ⓓ
3. Ⓐ Ⓑ Ⓒ Ⓓ   10. Ⓐ Ⓑ Ⓒ Ⓓ
4. Ⓐ Ⓑ Ⓒ Ⓓ   11. Ⓐ Ⓑ Ⓒ Ⓓ
5. Ⓐ Ⓑ Ⓒ Ⓓ   12. Ⓐ Ⓑ Ⓒ Ⓓ
6. Ⓐ Ⓑ Ⓒ Ⓓ   13. Ⓐ Ⓑ Ⓒ Ⓓ
7. Ⓐ Ⓑ Ⓒ Ⓓ   14. Ⓐ Ⓑ Ⓒ Ⓓ

Part 2   **Constructed Response/Grid In**
Record and bubble in your answers on the grids below.

15.   16.   17.

Record your answers for Questions 18–21 on a separate sheet of paper.

S A M P L E

Part 1 **Multiple Choice**

1. C
2. B
3. D
4. A
5. B
6. B
7. A
8. D
9. C
10. C

Part 2 **Short Response**

11. An atom has a nucleus that contains the protons and neutrons. Protons are positively charged particles and neutrons have no charge. Electrons are negatively charged particles that are found outside the nucleus and participate in chemical reactions.

12. It helps to break down the food for digestion so that the body is better able to release the chemical energy stored in the food.

Part 1 Multiple Choice

Record your answers on the answer sheet provided by your teacher or on a sheet of paper.

1. An element cannot be broken down by chemical reactions and is made up of only one kind of
   A. electron.
   C. atom.
   B. carbohydrate.
   D. molecule.

Use the illustration below to answer questions 2 and 3.

2. What kind of chemical compound do salt and water form?
   A. covalent
   B. ionic
   C. solution
   D. lipid

3. Salt is very important in the human body. What kind of compound is salt?
   A. organic
   B. carbohydrate
   C. protein
   D. inorganic

4. A cell that contains 40% water is placed in a solution that is 20% water. The cell and the solution will reach equilibrium when they both contain how much water?
   A. 30%
   C. 60%
   B. 40%
   D. 20%

5. All chemical reactions in living things take place in what kind of a solution?
   A. protein
   C. gas
   B. water
   D. solid

6. The sum of all the chemical reactions in an organism is
   A. respiration.
   C. fermentation.
   B. metabolism.
   D. endocytosis.

7. What is needed for all chemical reactions in cells?
   A. enzymes
   C. DNA
   B. lipids
   D. cell membrane

8. The carbon dioxide that you exhale is a product of
   A. osmosis.
   B. DNA synthesis.
   C. photosynthesis.
   D. respiration.

9. Matter cannot be held together or broken apart without
   A. gas.
   B. liquid.
   C. energy.
   D. temperature.

Use the table below to answer question 10.

Cell Substances		
Organic Compound	**Flexibility**	**Found in**
Keratin	Not very flexible	Hair and skin of mammals
Collagen	Not very flexible	Skin, bones, and tendons of mammals
Chitin	Very rigid	Tough outer shell of insects and crabs
Cellulose	Very flexible	Plant cell walls

10. According to this information, which organic compound is the least flexible?
    A. keratin
    B. collagen
    C. chitin
    D. cellulose

---

13. Ice floats because the space between water molecules is greater in ice than in liquid. Fish are able to live in the water under the ice.

14. Photosynthesis produces more sugar than the plant needs for survival. This extra sugar is stored in the potato as starch.

15. Respiration releases more energy for an athlete's muscles.

Fermentation; a product of fermentation is lactic acid and the buildup of lactic acid will make muscles sore.

16. salt—inorganic; fat—organic, lipid; skin—organic, protein; DNA—organic, nucleic acid; sugar—organic, carbohydrate; water—inorganic; potassium salt—inorganic

17. Selectively permeable means that only certain molecules are allowed to pass across the membrane. For proper cell function, what enters and leaves a cell needs to be controlled.

18. Source—the Sun; they take place in the chloroplast of a plant cell.

Part 2 | Short Response/Grid In

Record your answers on the answer sheet provided by your teacher or on a sheet of paper.

11. Explain the structure of an atom.

12. How does chewing food affect your body's ability to release the chemical energy of the food?

13. Ice fishing is a popular sport in the winter. What properties of water is this sport based on?

14. Explain where the starch in a potato comes from.

15. Does fermentation or respiration release more energy for an athlete's muscles? Which process would be responsible for making muscles sore?

Use the table below to answer question 16.

Classification of Compounds			
Compound	Organic	Inorganic	Type of organic compound
Salt			
Fat			
Skin			
DNA			
Sugar			
Water			
Potassium			

16. Copy and complete the table above. Identify each item as inorganic or organic. If the item is an organic compound further classify it as a protein, carbohydrate, lipid or nucleic acid.

17. Define selectively permeable and discuss why it is important for the cell membrane.

18. What is the source of energy for the photosynthesis reactions and where do they take place in a cell?

Part 3 | Open Ended

Record your answers on a sheet of paper.

19. Give examples of each of the four types of organic molecules and why they are needed in a plant cell.

20. Trace the path of how oxygen molecules are produced in a plant cell to how they are used in human cells.

21. Describe four ways a large or small molecule can cross the cell membrane.

22. Discuss how water is bonded together and the unique properties that result from the bonds.

Use the illustration below to answer question 23.

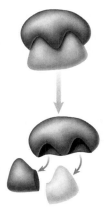

23. Describe in detail what process is taking place in this diagram and its significance for a cell.

24. How do plants use carbon dioxide? Why would plants need oxygen?

Test-Taking Tip

Diagrams Study a diagram carefully, being sure to read all labels and captions.

larger molecules cross the cell membrane. Water moves across the cell membrane by osmosis. Osmosis is the movement of water from areas of high concentration to areas of low concentration. Active transport of molecules across the cell membrane requires cellular energy. The cell membrane engulfs a particle for endocytosis and a vesicle fuses with the cell membrane to release particles from the cell in exocytosis.

22. A water molecule has an area of negative charge and an area of positive charge. The opposite charges attract water molecules to one another. This makes water a good insulator. In ice, the molecules are spaced further apart. This allows ice to float on water providing a layer of insulation for organisms living below the ice.

23. In this diagram an enzyme is being used for a chemical reaction. The enzyme causes the larger molecule to breakdown into smaller molecules. The enzyme is needed for this reaction and is reusable. This reaction is significant for a cell because enzymes are needed for most of the chemical reactions that take place in a cell.

24. Carbon dioxide is used in the process of photosynthesis. Carbon dioxide and water are converted to sugar molecules in the chloroplast. Energy from the Sun is used to drive this reaction. Oxygen is a product of this reaction and is used in plant cells for respiration.

Rubrics

For more help evaluating openended assessment questions, see the rubric on p. 10T.

Part 3 | Open Ended

19. Carbohydrates found in a plant cell are sugars, starch and cellulose. These molecules can be used for energy and cell structure. Lipids are fats, oils waxes, phospholipids and cholesterol. These molecules are sources of long term energy storage and are a component of cell boundaries. Enzymes are proteins and they regulate all chemical reactions in a cell. Nucleic acids carry the hereditary information and carry the code to make proteins.

20. Plants make sugar from carbon dioxide and water. The product of this process is oxygen. This oxygen is released into the air and inhaled by humans. The oxygen diffuses into the bloodstream in the lungs. It is then carried to the cells where it diffuses into the cells and is used in the mitochondria for respiration.

21. Molecules can move from areas of high concentration to areas of low concentration by diffusing across the cell membrane. Facilitated diffusion use transport proteins to help

chapter 4 Organizer

Section/Objectives	Standards		Labs/Features
	National	**State/Local**	
Chapter Opener	See pp. 16T–17T for a Key to Standards.		**Launch Lab:** Infer About Seed Growth, p. 95 **Foldables,** p. 95 A data-collection lab using Probeware technology can be found in **Probeware Labs,** pp. 1–4
Section 1 Cell Division and Mitosis ⏲ 2 sessions 📦 1 block 1. **Explain** why mitosis is important. 2. **Examine** the steps of mitosis. 3. **Compare** mitosis in plant and animal cells. 4. **List** two examples of asexual reproduction.	National Content Standards: UCP.1, UCP.2, UCP.3, A.1, A.2, C.1, C.2, C.3		**Integrate Career,** p. 97 **MiniLAB:** Modeling Mitosis, p. 101 **Lab:** Mitosis in Plant Cells, p. 103
Section 2 Sexual Reproduction and Meiosis ⏲ 2 sessions 📦 1 block 5. **Describe** the stages of meiosis and how sex cells are produced. 6. **Explain** why meiosis is needed for sexual reproduction. 7. **Name** the cells that are involved in fertilization. 8. **Explain** how fertilization occurs in sexual reproduction.	National Content Standards: UCP.1, UCP.2, A.1, C.1, C.2, C.3, C.5		**Integrate Chemistry,** p. 105 **Applying Science:** How can chromosome numbers be predicted? p. 107 **Visualizing Polyploidy in Plants,** p. 108
Section 3 DNA ⏲ 3 sessions 📦 1.5 blocks 9. **Identify** the parts of a DNA molecule and its structure. 10. **Explain** how DNA copies itself. 11. **Describe** the structure and function of each kind of RNA.	National Content Standards: UCP.1–UCP.5, A.1, A.2, C.1, C.2, C.3		**MiniLAB:** Modeling DNA Replication, p. 111 **Science Online,** p. 113 **Science Online,** p. 115 **Lab:** Mutations, p. 116 **Oops! Accidents in Science:** A Tangled Tale, p. 118

94A CHAPTER 4 Cell Reproduction

Lab Materials	Reproducible Resources	Section Assessment	Technology
Launch Lab: soaked bean seeds, water, paper towels, self-sealing plastic bags, magnifying lens	**Chapter *FAST FILE* Resources** Foldables Worksheet, p. 15 Directed Reading Overview, p. 17 Note-taking Worksheets, pp. 31–33	GLENCOE'S ASSESSMENT ADVANTAGE	**TeacherWorks** includes: • Interactive Teacher Edition • Lesson Planner with calendar • Access to all program blacklines • Correlations to standards • Web links 📼 Video Lab
MiniLAB: colored paper, poster board, markers, toothpicks, yarn, thread, glue, scissors **Lab:** prepared slide of onion root tip, microscope	**Chapter *FAST FILE* Resources** Transparency Activity, p. 42 MiniLAB, p. 3 Enrichment, p. 28 Reinforcement, p. 25 Transparency Activity, pp. 45–46 Lab Worksheet, pp. 5–6 Directed Reading, p. 18 Lab Activity, pp. 9–10	**Portfolio** Visual Learning, p. 97 **Performance** MiniLAB, p. 101 Applying Math, p. 102 **Content** Challenge, p. 99 Section Review, p. 102	🔦 Section Focus Transparency 🔦 Teaching Transparency 💿 Virtual Labs CD-ROM 🎧 Guided Reading Audio Program 💿 Interactive Chalkboard CD-ROM
Need materials? Contact Science Kit at 1-800-828-7777 or www.sciencekit.com on the Internet.	**Chapter *FAST FILE* Resources** Transparency Activity, p. 43 Enrichment, p. 29 Reinforcement, p. 26 Directed Reading, p. 18 **Life Science Critical Thinking/ Problem Solving,** p. 19 **Mathematics Skill Activities,** p. 3 **Performance Assessment in the Science Classroom,** p. 57	**Portfolio** Make a Model, p. 107 **Performance** Applying Science, p. 107 Applying Skills, p. 109 **Content** Challenge, p. 106 Section Review, p. 109	🔦 Section Focus Transparency 💿 Virtual Labs CD-ROM 🎧 Guided Reading Audio Program 💿 Interactive Chalkboard CD-ROM
MiniLAB: pencil, paper **Lab:** Web sites and other resources on mutations	**Chapter *FAST FILE* Resources** Transparency Activity, p. 44 MiniLAB, p. 4 Enrichment, p. 30 Reinforcement, p. 27 Directed Reading, pp. 19, 20 Lab Worksheet, pp. 7–8 Lab Activity, pp. 11–13 **Home and Community Involvement,** p. 36	**Portfolio** Curriculum Connection, p. 113 **Performance** MiniLAB, p. 111 Applying Skills, p. 115 **Content** Challenge, p. 114 Section Review, p. 115	🔦 Section Focus Transparency 💿 Virtual Labs CD-ROM 🎧 Guided Reading Audio Program 💿 Interactive Chalkboard CD-ROM 📼 Probeware Lab

End of Chapter Assessment

GLENCOE'S ASSESSMENT ADVANTAGE

Blackline Masters	Technology	Professional Series
Chapter *FAST FILE* Resources Chapter Review, pp. 35–36 Chapter Tests, pp. 37–40 **Standardized Test Practice,** pp. 19–22	📼 MindJogger Videoquiz 💿 Virtual Labs CD-ROM 💿 Exam*View*® Pro Testmaker 💿 TeacherWorks CD-ROM 💿 Interactive Chalkboard CD-ROM	**Performance Assessment in the Science Classroom (PASC)**

chapter 4 Cell Reproduction

Transparencies

Section Focus

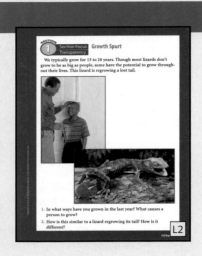

Section Focus Transparency 1 — Growth Spurt

We typically grow for 15 to 20 years. Though most lizards don't grow to be as big as people, some have the potential to grow throughout their lives. This lizard is regrowing a lost tail.

1. In what ways have you grown in the last year? What causes a person to grow?
2. How is this similar to a lizard regrowing its tail? How is it different?

L2

Section Focus Transparency 2 — I Think He Has Your Eyes

The Santa Gertrudis bull flourishes in the arid plains of Texas. The King Ranch developed the Santa Gertrudis by cross-breeding Brahman cattle with Shorthorns. As you can see, the Santa Gertrudis inherited characteristics from both of its parents.

1. Why might ranchers have wanted to cross-breed Brahmans and Shorthorns?
2. Which of the Santa Gertrudis' traits can you identify in the Brahman and the Shorthorn?

L2

Section Focus Transparency 3 — Curly Cat

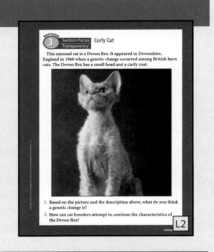

This unusual cat is a Devon Rex. It appeared in Devonshire, England in 1960 when a genetic change occurred among British barn cats. The Devon Rex has a small head and a curly coat.

1. Based on the picture and the description above, what do you think a genetic change is?
2. How can cat breeders attempt to continue the characteristics of the Devon Rex?

L2

This is a representation of key blackline masters available in the Teacher Classroom Resources. See Resource Manager boxes within the chapter for additional information.

Key to Teaching Strategies

The following designations will help you decide which activities are appropriate for your students.

L1 Level 1 activities should be appropriate for students with learning difficulties.

L2 Level 2 activities should be within the ability range of all students.

L3 Level 3 activities are designed for above-average students.

ELL ELL activities should be within the ability range of English-Language Learners.

COOP LEARN Cooperative Learning activities are designed for small group work.

LS Multiple Learning Styles logos, as described on page 12T, are used throughout to indicate strategies that address different learning styles.

P These strategies represent student products that can be placed into a best-work portfolio.

PBL Problem-Based Learning activities apply real-world situations to learning.

Assessment

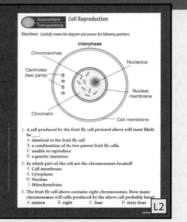

Assessment Transparency — Cell Reproduction

Directions: Carefully review the diagram and answer the following questions.

Interphase

1. A cell produced by the fruit fly cell pictured above will most likely be ___.
   A identical to the fruit fly cell
   B a combination of its two parent fruit fly cells
   C unable to reproduce
   D a genetic mutation
2. In which part of the cell are the chromosomes located?
   F Cell membrane
   G Cytoplasm
   H Nucleus
   J Mitochondrion
3. The fruit fly cell above contains eight chromosomes. How many chromosomes will cells produced by the above cell probably have?
   A sixteen   B eight   C four   D sixty-four

L2

Teaching

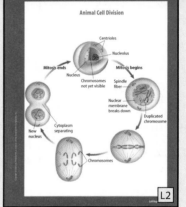

Teaching Transparency — Animal Cell Division

L2

Hands-on Activities

Student Text Lab Worksheet

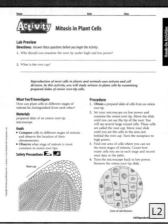

Activity — Mitosis in Plant Cells

Lab Preview
Directions: Answer these questions before you begin the Activity.
1. Why should you examine the root tip under high and low power?
2. What is the root cap?

L2

Laboratory Activities

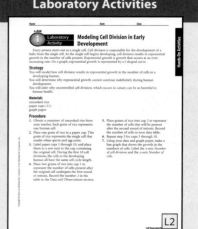

Laboratory Activity 1 — Modeling Cell Division in Early Development

L2

Meeting Different Ability Levels

Content Outline

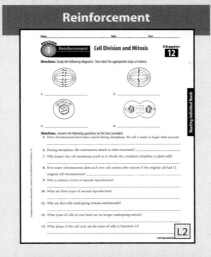

L2

Reinforcement

L2

Enrichment

L3

Directed Reading (English/Spanish)

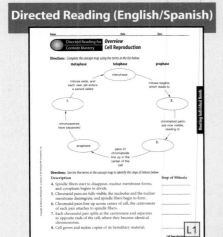

L1

Study Guide

Study Guide

Features
- Contains a study guide page for each section of the chapter
- Reviews key concepts
- Includes answer pages

L2

Reading Essentials

Reading Essentials for Glencoe Science
An Interactive Student Workbook

Features
- Condensed core content
- Actively involves students in reading
- Reinforces key vocabulary

L1

Assessment

Test Practice Workbook

L2

Glencoe Life Science

Chapter Review

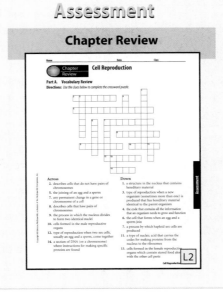

L2

Chapter Tests

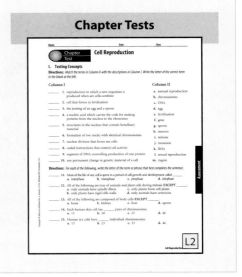

L2

Science Content Background

section 1 Cell Division and Mitosis

Results of Mitosis

Every species has a characteristic number of chromosomes in each cell. A cat has 38 chromosomes, whereas a potato and a chimpanzee each have 48 chromosomes. In all sexually reproducing organisms, chromosomes occur in homologous pairs. Except for some sex chromosomes, homologous chromosomes are of equal length and have the same genes at the same relative locations. The alleles may or may not be identical. For example, the gene for hair color would be at the same location on homologous chromosomes but may code for brunette on one chromosome and blonde on the other.

Teacher to Teacher

Patricia M. Horton, Mentor Teacher
Summit Intermediate School
Etiwanda, California

"To demonstrate osmosis, I put liquid starch in a plastic sandwich bag and close it with a twist tie. I then place the plastic bag into a beaker filled with a mixture of water and iodine. As the iodine moves through the plastic bag membrane, the starch begins to turn purple."

Patricia M. Horton

Reuters New Media Inc./Corbis

Animals and some plants have one pair of sex chromosomes. In most animals, including humans, the sex chromosomes of the female are truly homologous, whereas the male sex chromosomes are of unequal lengths and have many different genes. This is reversed in birds and butterflies, with males having the truly homologous sex chromosomes.

Asexual Reproduction

Eukaryotes, which include many protists, some fungi, and plants, reproduce asexually by mitosis. Prokaryotes, like bacteria, reproduce by fission. Depending on the organism, one or several new organisms can be created that are genetically identical to, or clones of, the original organism. Most animals do not use asexual reproduction. Recently scientists have been able to stimulate cells from adult animals to divide by mitosis and reproduce new animals that are clones of the organism from which the cells were taken.

section 2 Sexual Reproduction and Meiosis

Sexual Reproduction

Sex cells, or gametes, are the result of meiosis. Because of a process that happens at metaphase I called independent assortment, the possible combination of chromosomes for each sex cell varies every time sex cells form. When duplicated homologous chromosomes line up at a cell's center during metaphase I, there are no rules about how a particular pair is aligned relative to any other pair. The only requirement is that the alignment results in one half of each duplicated chromosome moving in one direction and the other half moving in the opposite direction during anaphase I. The offspring formed by fertilization has its own unique combination of genetic material. This produces variation between parents and offspring and may give offspring a better chance of surviving in a changing environment.

Meiosis and Sex Cells

This process is often called reduction division since the number of chromosomes in the cells produced is half that of the original cell. Meiosis provides for great diversity within a species because of the many ways the chromosomes can align during metaphase I. There are more than 8 million possible gametes that can be produced from the 23 pairs of human chromosomes.

In animals, meiosis results in haploid egg and sperm cells. In plants, meiosis results in haploid spores that later produce egg and sperm cells.

section 3 DNA

What is DNA?

The information in DNA that determines what an organism will be is contained in a code dictated by the order of subunits called nucleotides. A nucleotide consists of the sugar deoxyribose, a phosphate molecule, and one of the four possible nitrogen

bases. A DNA molecule is two chains of nucleotides. These two chains are antiparallel and run in opposite directions. One chain ends with a phosphate, and the other chain ends with deoxyribose. Just as the order of letters on this page determines what words you are reading, the order of nucleotides determines the message on the DNA. Because DNA is copied from one generation to the next, any change, or mutation, in a gene is also preserved. If the change occurs in cells that become gametes, it is passed on to future generations in a process called heredity.

A DNA Model

The process of DNA replication is directed by the enzyme called DNA polymerase. It moves along the separated DNA molecule and inserts the correct, complementary nucleotides onto the exposed nitrogen bases. This happens at many locations along the length of the DNA molecule simultaneously. Otherwise the time it would take to match up the millions of nitrogen bases would be astronomical.

Mutations

A change in a cell's genetic message is called a mutation. Some mutations affect the message itself, altering the sequence of DNA nucleotides. Other classes of mutations involve sequences of DNA that can move from place to place and are often called jumping genes. When a particular gene is mutated, its function is often destroyed.

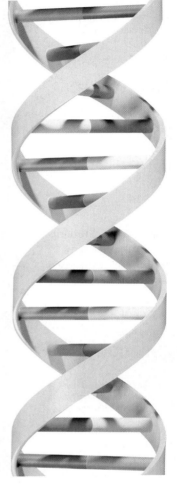

Michael Simpson/FPG International

---

chapter content resources

Internet Resources

For additional content background, visit **life.msscience.com** to:

- access your book online
- find references to related articles in popular science magazines
- access Web links with related content background
- access current events with science journal topics

Print Resources

James Watson & Francis Crick: Discovery of the Double Helix and Beyond (Makers of Modern Science), by David E. Newton and David B. Newton, Facts on File, Inc., 1992

DNA (Science Concepts), by Alvin Silverstein, Virginia B. Silverstein, Laura Silverstein Nunn, Twenty-First Century Books (E), 2002

My Name Is Gene, Second Edition, N.L. Eskeland, N.C. Bailey, Science2Discover, 2002

Chapter Vocabulary

mitosis, p. 98
chromosome, p. 98
asexual reproduction, p. 101
sexual reproduction, p. 104
sperm, p. 104
egg, p. 104
fertilization, p. 104
zygote, p. 104
diploid, p. 104
haploid, p. 105
meiosis, p. 105
DNA, p. 110
gene, p. 112
RNA, p. 112
mutation, p. 114

Science Journal Student responses will vary, but may include that cells split into two and that they reproduce so that an organism can grow.

with Image Bank

PowerPoint® Presentations

This CD-ROM is an editable Microsoft® PowerPoint® presentation that includes:
- a pre-made presentation for every chapter
- interactive graphics
- animations
- audio clips
- image bank
- all new section and chapter questions
- Standardized Test Practice
- transparencies
- pre-lab questions for all labs
- Foldables directions
- links to life.msscience.com

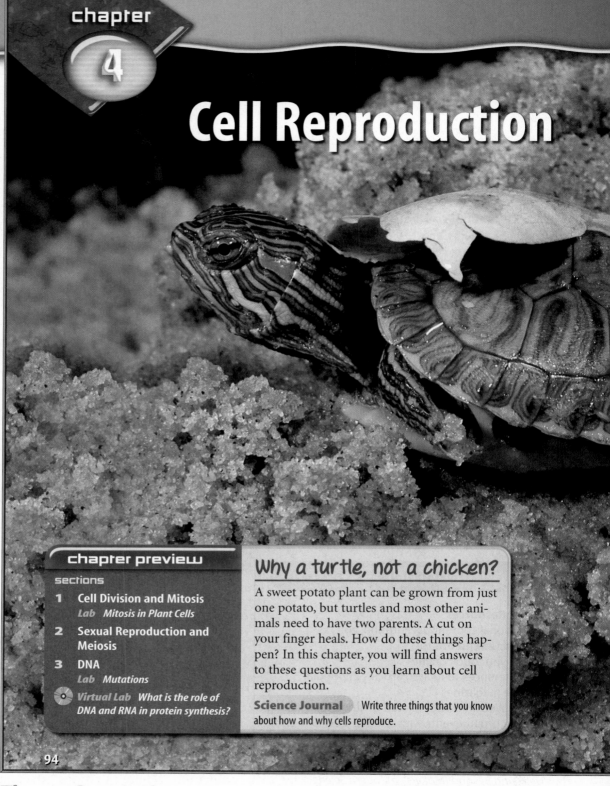

Cell Reproduction

chapter preview

sections

1 Cell Division and Mitosis
  Lab   Mitosis in Plant Cells

2 Sexual Reproduction and Meiosis

3 DNA
  Lab   Mutations

Virtual Lab   What is the role of DNA and RNA in protein synthesis?

Why a turtle, not a chicken?

A sweet potato plant can be grown from just one potato, but turtles and most other animals need to have two parents. A cut on your finger heals. How do these things happen? In this chapter, you will find answers to these questions as you learn about cell reproduction.

Science Journal Write three things that you know about how and why cells reproduce.

Theme Connection

Stability and Change DNA controls all cell activities by directing the production of proteins in living organisms. Changes in DNA can result in evolutionary changes that are inherited.

About the Photo

Hatchlings Turtles reproduce on land. Female turtles lay eggs, usually at night, and then bury them to protect them from predators, to keep the eggs moist, and to help maintain the proper temperature for development. Eggs usually hatch in 60–140 days. Hatchling turtles use an "egg tooth" to break their way out of the egg. Hatchlings usually emerge in early evening.

Start-Up Activities

Infer About Seed Growth

Most flower and vegetable seeds sprout and grow into entire plants in just a few weeks. Although all of the cells in a seed have information and instructions to produce a new plant, only some of the cells in the seed use the information. Where are these cells in seeds? Do the following lab to find out.

1. Carefully split open two bean seeds that have soaked in water overnight.

2. Observe both halves and record your observations.

3. Wrap all four halves in a moist paper towel. Then put them into a self-sealing, plastic bag and seal the bag.

4. Make observations every day for a few days.

5. **Think Critically** Write a paragraph that describes what you observe. Hypothesize which cells in seeds use information about how plants grow.

Science Online Preview this chapter's content and activities at life.msscience.com

FOLDABLES Study Organizer

How and Why Cells Divide
Make the following Foldable to help you organize information from the chapter about cell reproduction.

STEP 1 Draw a mark at the midpoint of a vertical sheet of paper along the side edge.

STEP 2 Turn the paper horizontally and fold the outside edges in to touch at the midpoint mark.

STEP 3 Use a pencil to draw a cell on the front of your Foldable as shown.

Analyze As you read the chapter, write under the flaps how cells divide. In the middle section, list why cells divide.

Launch LAB

Purpose Use the Launch Lab to introduce students to growth; as they read the chapter, they will understand that growth is the result of mitosis. L2 LS
Kinesthetic

Preparation Soak pinto beans or other large seeds for 24 hours.

Materials 2 soaked seeds, paper towels, self-sealing plastic bag, magnifying lens, water

Teaching Strategy After soaking, the seeds should split easily. If students have difficulty, forceps can be used to separate the seeds.

Think Critically

Students should observe and record the growth of a new plant from one-half of each seed. They should predict that the cells of the seed embryo are able to use the information needed to grow into a plant.

Assessment

Performance Have students repeat the experiment using corn seeds and observe the new plant that grows from each seed. Use **Performance Assessment in the Science Classroom**, p. 89. L2

FOLDABLES Study Organizer **Dinah Zike Study Fold**

Student preparation materials for this Foldable are available in the **Chapter FAST FILE Resources.**

Probeware Labs

This chapter's data-collection lab using Probeware technology is included on the *Video Labs CD-ROM.* See the *Probeware Lab Manual* pages 1–4 for student worksheets.

CHAPTER 4 Cell Reproduction **95**

section 1
Cell Division and Mitosis

1 Motivate

Bellringer

Section Focus Transparencies also are available on the Interactive Chalkboard CD-ROM.

 L2 ELL

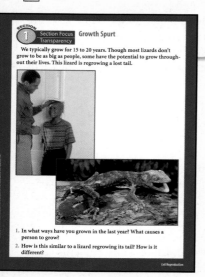

Tie to Prior Knowledge

Cell Functions Use a diagram or transparency to review the parts of a cell and their functions. Explain that mitosis involves only the nucleus.

as you read

What You'll Learn
- **Explain** why mitosis is important.
- **Examine** the steps of mitosis.
- **Compare** mitosis in plant and animal cells.
- **List** two examples of asexual reproduction.

Why It's Important
Your growth, like that of many organisms, depends on cell division.

Review Vocabulary
nucleus: organelle that controls all the activities of a cell and contains hereditary material made of proteins and DNA

New Vocabulary
- mitosis
- chromosome
- asexual reproduction

Why is cell division important?

What do you, an octopus, and an oak tree have in common? You share many characteristics, but an important one is that you are all made of cells—trillions of cells. Where did all of those cells come from? As amazing as it might seem, many organisms start as just one cell. That cell divides and becomes two, two become four, four become eight, and so on. Many-celled organisms, including you, grow because cell division increases the total number of cells in an organism. Even after growth stops, cell division is still important. Every day, billions of red blood cells in your body wear out and are replaced. During the few seconds it takes you to read this sentence, your bone marrow produced about six million red blood cells. Cell division is important to one-celled organisms, too—it's how they reproduce themselves, as shown in **Figure 1.** Cell division isn't as simple as just cutting the cell in half, so how do cells divide?

The Cell Cycle

A living organism has a life cycle. A life cycle begins with the organism's formation, is followed by growth and development, and finally ends in death. Right now, you are in a stage of your life cycle called adolescence, which is a period of active growth and development. Individual cells also have life cycles.

Figure 1 All organisms use cell division. Many-celled organisms, such as this octopus, grow by increasing the numbers of their cells.

Like this dividing amoeba, a one-celled organism reaches a certain size and then reproduces.

96 CHAPTER 4 Cell Reproduction

Section 1 Resource Manager

Chapter *FAST FILE* Resources
Transparency Activity, pp. 42, 45–46
Directed Reading for Content Mastery, pp. 17, 18
Note-taking Worksheets, pp. 31–33
Enrichment, p. 28
MiniLAB, p. 3

Lab Activity, pp. 9–10
Reinforcement, p. 25
Lab Worksheet, pp. 5–6

Figure 2 Interphase is the longest part of the cell cycle. **Identify** *When do chromosomes duplicate?*

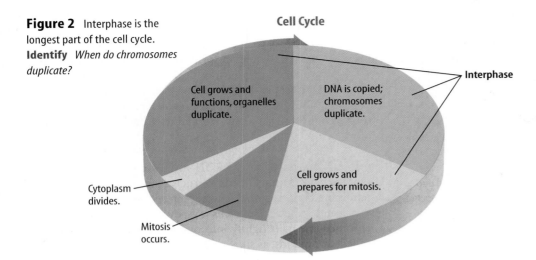

Cell Cycle

Cell grows and functions, organelles duplicate.

DNA is copied; chromosomes duplicate.

Interphase

Cell grows and prepares for mitosis.

Cytoplasm divides.

Mitosis occurs.

Length of Cycle The cell cycle, as shown in **Figure 2,** is a series of events that takes place from one cell division to the next. The time it takes to complete a cell cycle is not the same in all cells. For example, the cycle for cells in some bean plants takes about 19 h to complete. Cells in animal embryos divide rapidly and can complete their cycles in less than 20 min. In some human cells, the cell cycle takes about 16 h. Cells in humans that are needed for repair, growth, or replacement, like skin and bone cells, constantly repeat the cycle.

Interphase Most of the life of any eukaryotic cell—a cell with a nucleus—is spent in a period of growth and development called interphase. Cells in your body that no longer divide, such as nerve and muscle cells, are always in interphase. An actively dividing cell, such as a skin cell, copies its hereditary material and prepares for cell division during interphase.

Why is it important for a cell to copy its hereditary information before dividing? Imagine that you have a part in a play and the director has one complete copy of the script. If the director gave only one page to each person in the play, no one would have the entire script. Instead the director makes a complete, separate copy of the script for each member of the cast so that each one can learn his or her part. Before a cell divides, a copy of the hereditary material must be made so that each of the two new cells will get a complete copy. Just as the actors in the play need the entire script, each cell needs a complete set of hereditary material to carry out life functions.

After interphase, cell division begins. The nucleus divides, and then the cytoplasm separates to form two new cells.

INTEGRATE Career

Oncologist In most cells, the cell cycle is well controlled. Cancer cells, however, have uncontrolled cell division. Doctors who diagnose, study, and treat cancer are called oncologists. Someone wanting to become an oncologist must first complete medical school before training in oncology. Research the subspecialties of oncology. List and describe them in your Science Journal.

2 Teach

Caption Answer
Figure 2 during interphase

Visual Learning

Figure 2 Have students make an events chain concept map that outlines the steps of the cell cycle as illustrated in **Figure 2.** L2 LS **Visual-Spatial** P

INTEGRATE Career

Oncologist There are many oncology specialties, including medical oncology, pediatric oncology, radiation oncology, and surgical oncology. After completion of medical school and training in a specialty, physicians must pass a certifying exam.

Research Have students research ways that help prevent cancerous cells from forming. Some preventive measures include using sunscreen, not smoking, and eating certain foods. Can cancer be prevented completely? Are there vaccinations against cancer? Students can write a health pamphlet that encourages a healthy lifestyle to minimize cancer risks. L2

Science Journal

Life of a Cell Have students write creative stories about the life cycle of a cell from its beginning to its end. Have them use section vocabulary words as they describe what happens in the cell. L2 LS
Linguistic

SECTION 1 Cell Division and Mitosis **97**

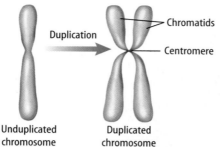

Figure 3 DNA is copied during interphase. An unduplicated chromosome has one strand of DNA. A duplicated chromosome has two identical DNA strands, called chromatids, that are held together at a region called the centromere.

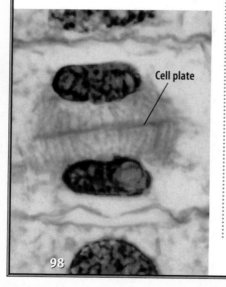

Figure 4 The cell plate shown in this plant cell appears when the cytoplasm is being divided. **Identify** *what phase of mitosis will be next.*

Mitosis

Mitosis (mi TOH sus) is the process in which the nucleus divides to form two identical nuclei. Each new nucleus also is identical to the original nucleus. Mitosis is described as a series of phases, or steps. The steps of mitosis in order are named prophase, metaphase, anaphase, and telophase.

Steps of Mitosis When any nucleus divides, the chromosomes (KROH muh sohmz) play the important part. A **chromosome** is a structure in the nucleus that contains hereditary material. During interphase, each chromosome duplicates. When the nucleus is ready to divide, each duplicated chromosome coils tightly into two thickened, identical strands called chromatids, as shown in **Figure 3.**

✔ Reading Check *How are chromosomes and chromatids related?*

During prophase, the pairs of chromatids are fully visible when viewed under a microscope. The nucleolus and the nuclear membrane disintegrate. Two small structures called centrioles (SEN tree olz) move to opposite ends of the cell. Between the centrioles, threadlike spindle fibers begin to stretch across the cell. Plant cells also form spindle fibers during mitosis but do not have centrioles.

In metaphase, the pairs of chromatids line up across the center of the cell. The centromere of each pair usually becomes attached to two spindle fibers—one from each side of the cell.

In anaphase, each centromere divides and the spindle fibers shorten. Each pair of chromatids separates, and chromatids begin to move to opposite ends of the cell. The separated chromatids are now called chromosomes. In the final step, telophase, spindle fibers start to disappear, the chromosomes start to uncoil, and a new nucleus forms.

Division of the Cytoplasm For most cells, after the nucleus has divided, the cytoplasm separates and two new cells are formed. In animal cells, the cell membrane pinches in the middle, like a balloon with a string tightened around it, and the cytoplasm divides. In plant cells, the appearance of a cell plate, as shown in **Figure 4,** tells you that the cytoplasm is being divided. New cell walls form along the cell plate, and new cell membranes develop inside the cell walls. Following division of the cytoplasm, most new cells begin the period of growth, or interphase, again. Review cell division for an animal cell using the illustrations in **Figure 5.**

Figure 5 Cell division for an animal cell is shown here. Each micrograph shown in this figure is magnified 600 times.

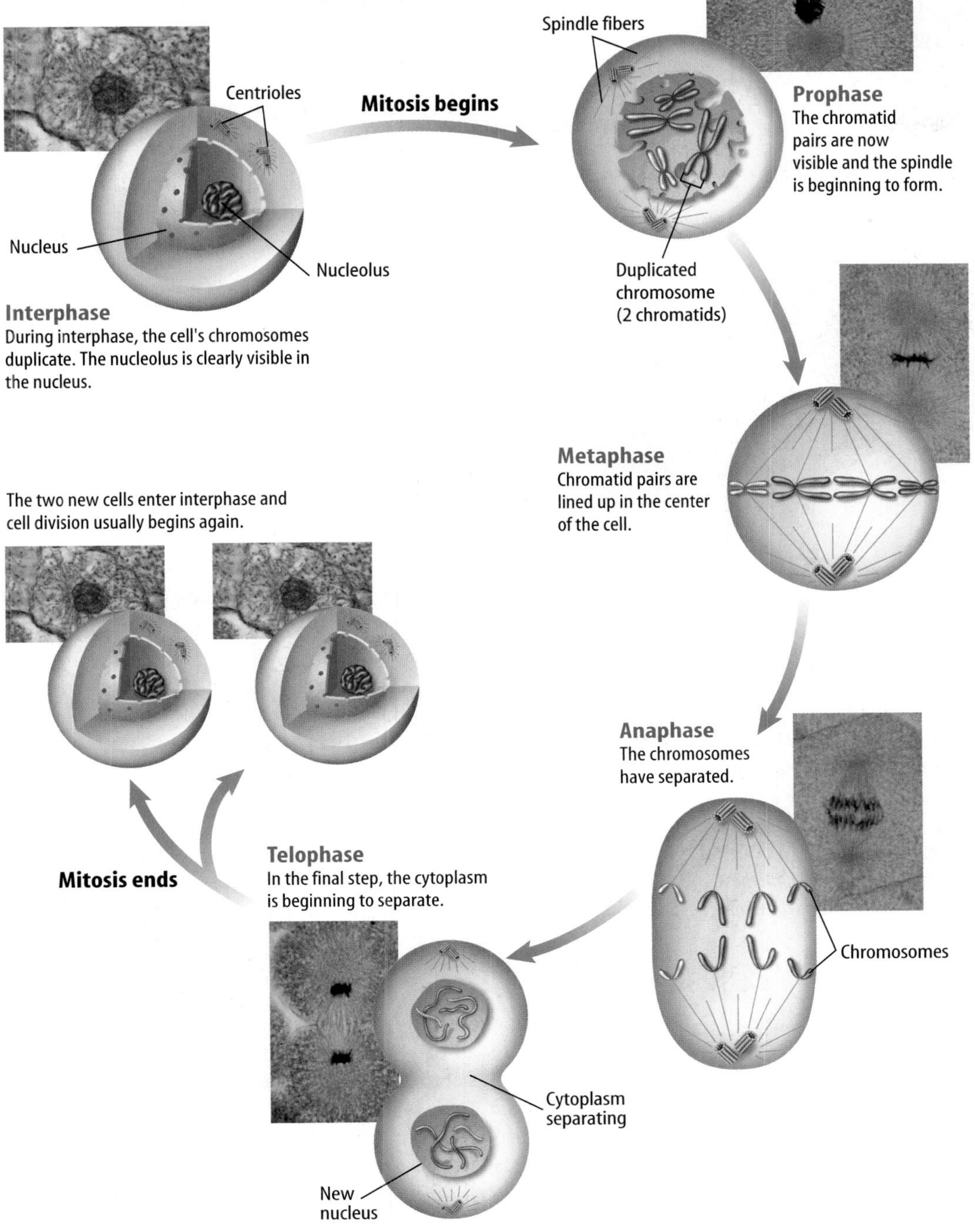
Centrioles
Mitosis begins
Nucleus
Nucleolus
Interphase
During interphase, the cell's chromosomes duplicate. The nucleolus is clearly visible in the nucleus.
Spindle fibers
Prophase
The chromatid pairs are now visible and the spindle is beginning to form.
Duplicated chromosome (2 chromatids)
Metaphase
Chromatid pairs are lined up in the center of the cell.
The two new cells enter interphase and cell division usually begins again.
Anaphase
The chromosomes have separated.
Chromosomes
Mitosis ends
Telophase
In the final step, the cytoplasm is beginning to separate.
Cytoplasm separating
New nucleus

Quick Demo

Mitosis

Materials microprojector, fertilized frog eggs

Estimated Time 10 minutes

Procedure Demonstrate mitotic cell divisions in the growth of fertilized frog eggs. The increasing numbers of cells can be seen readily during the early stages of tadpole development.

Teacher FYI

Interphase Duplication The fact that chromosomes are duplicated in the nucleus during interphase has been hypothesized for more than a hundred years, but evidence for the hypothesis did not appear until 1981.

Use Science Words

Word Meaning Explain that the word *mitosis* derives from the Greek word for "thread." Have students explain the derivation. During mitosis, the replicated chromosomes—threadlike structures—separate. Then point out that *phase* is another word for "stage." Have students use a dictionary to find the meanings of the prefixes *inter-* (between), *pro-* (before), *meta-* (after), *ana-* (up), and *telo-* (end). L2

Differentiated Instruction

Challenge Have students make a paper-and-string model of mitosis. The stages of mitosis can be connected using string, and colored string can be used to represent duplicated chromosomes. Students should include labels and descriptions of what occurs at each stage. The models can then be displayed in the classroom. L3

Curriculum Connection

Math It takes 15 minutes for certain embryo cells to divide. Have students calculate how many cells would be produced from one embryo cell after four hours. 240 minutes divided by 15 minutes = 16 cell divisions; $2^{16} = 65,536$ cells L2 LS **Logical-Mathematical**

SECTION 1 Cell Division and Mitosis 99

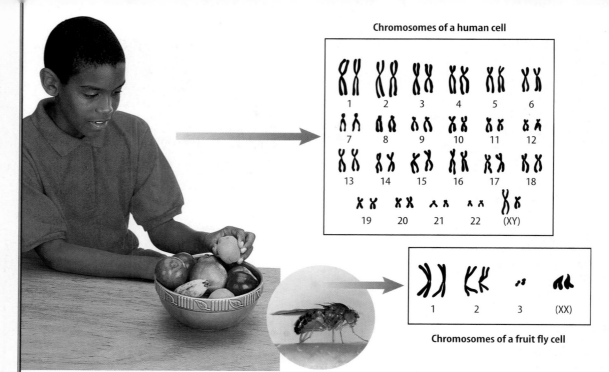

Chromosomes of a fruit fly cell

Discussion

Spinal Cord Damage Have students use their knowledge of the cell cycle to infer why even slight injuries to the brain and spinal cord can be serious and permanent. Because nerve cells do not undergo mitosis, damaged cells are not replaced, although some repair does occur. L2

Discussion

Nonliving Growth Many nonliving things such as icicles, stalagmites, crystals, and sand dunes appear to grow. Ask students to give examples of other nonliving things that appear to grow. Possible answers: highway systems, buildings, developments, shopping malls Have students distinguish between the processes involved in the growth of living things and the growth of nonliving things. In nonliving things, growth is caused by the surrounding environment. In living things, growth is caused by processes within the organism. L1

Caption Answer

Figure 6 the sex of the organism

Activity

Cancer Have students research and report on cancer. The report should include how cancer relates to mitosis and some of the technology used to diagnose and treat cancer. Display written reports.

Figure 6 Pairs of chromosomes are found in the nucleus of most cells. All chromosomes shown here are in their duplicated form. Most human cells have 23 pairs of chromosomes including one pair of chromosomes that help determine sex such as the XY pair above. Most fruit fly cells have four pairs of chromosomes.
Infer *What do you think the XX pair in fruit flies helps determine?*

Results of Mitosis You should remember two important things about mitosis. First, it is the division of a nucleus. Second, it produces two new nuclei that are identical to each other and the original nucleus. Each new nucleus has the same number and type of chromosomes. Every cell in your body, except sex cells, has a nucleus with 46 chromosomes—23 pairs. This is because you began as one cell with 46 chromosomes in its nucleus. Skin cells, produced to replace or repair your skin, have the same 46 chromosomes as the original single cell you developed from. Each cell in a fruit fly has eight chromosomes, so each new cell produced by mitosis has a copy of those eight chromosomes. **Figure 6** shows the chromosomes found in most human cells and those found in most fruit fly cells.

Each of the trillions of cells in your body, except sex cells, has a copy of the same hereditary material. Even though all actors in a play have copies of the same script, they do not learn the same lines. Likewise, all of your cells use different parts of the same hereditary material to become different types of cells.

Cell division allows growth and replaces worn out or damaged cells. You are much larger and have more cells than a baby mainly because of cell division. If you cut yourself, the wound heals because cell division replaces damaged cells. Another way some organisms use cell division is to produce new organisms.

100   CHAPTER 4 Cell Reproduction

 LAB DEMONSTRATION

Purpose to observe asexual reproduction in a sweet potato

Materials sweet potato with leaf buds, water, widemouthed glass jar, 4 toothpicks

Preparation Obtain a sweet potato that has purple leaf buds growing at its scarred end.

Procedure Fill a jar almost full of water, and place sweet potato with buds or scarred end up so at least half of the potato is in water. Toothpicks can hold the potato in place. Keep the water level constant and observe for three weeks.

Expected Outcome Students should observe the formation of roots and leaf growth.

Assessment

Ask students what part of the sweet potato produced leaves and roots. Leaves developed from the buds; roots grew from the bottom half of the sweet potato. Is this an example of sexual or asexual reproduction? Explain. Asexual; a new organism is produced from one parent. L2

Asexual Reproduction

Reproduction is the process by which an organism produces others of its same kind. Among living organisms, there are two types of reproduction—sexual and asexual. Sexual reproduction usually requires two organisms. In **asexual reproduction,** a new organism (sometimes more than one) is produced from one organism. The new organism will have hereditary material identical to the hereditary material of the parent organism.

Reading Check *How many organisms are needed for asexual reproduction?*

Cellular Asexual Reproduction Organisms with eukaryotic cells asexually reproduce by cell division. A sweet potato growing in a jar of water is an example of asexual reproduction. All the stems, leaves, and roots that grow from the sweet potato have been produced by cell division and have the same hereditary material. New strawberry plants can be reproduced asexually from horizontal stems called runners. **Figure 7** shows asexual reproduction in a potato and a strawberry plant.

Recall that mitosis is the division of a nucleus. However, bacteria do not have a nucleus so they can't use mitosis. Instead, bacteria reproduce asexually by fission. During fission, an organism whose cells do not contain a nucleus copies its genetic material and then divides into two identical organisms.

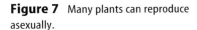

Figure 7 Many plants can reproduce asexually.

A new potato plant can grow from each sprout on this potato.

Infer *how the genetic material in the small strawberry plant above compares to the genetic material in the large strawberry plant.*

Mini LAB

Modeling Mitosis

Procedure
1. Make models of cell division using **materials supplied by your teacher.**
2. Use four chromosomes in your model.
3. When finished, arrange the models in the order in which mitosis occurs.

Analysis
1. In which steps is the nucleus visible?
2. How many cells does a dividing cell form?

Reading Check

Answer one

Mini LAB

Purpose Students will construct a model of mitosis. L2 ELL LS
Kinesthetic and Visual-Spatial

Materials colored paper, poster board, markers, toothpicks, yarn, thread, glue, scissors

Teaching Strategy Student models should resemble mitosis as shown in **Figure 5.**

Analysis
1. prophase and telophase
2. two new cells

Assessment

Performance Assess students' understanding of mitosis by making flash cards of the stages and having students arrange them in the proper order. Use **Performance Assessment in the Science Classroom,** p. 163.

Caption Answer
Figure 7 They are identical.

Visual Learning

Figure 6 Have students name the stage of mitosis that the human cell was in when the chromosomes were extracted from it. The cell was in either prophase or metaphase. Chromosomes are not visible during interphase even though they are duplicated. They are visible when they become coiled tightly at the beginning of prophase and throughout metaphase. Pairs separate during anaphase and telophase. L2

Science Journal

Cloning Have students use science reference books, newspapers, and the Internet to research cloning, a process that artificially reproduces an exact duplicate of a single parent. Have students write reports in their Science Journals on the medical uses as well as the negative ethical implications of cloning technology. L2 LS **Linguistic**

Observing Budding

Purpose to design an experiment to demonstrate yeast budding [L2]

Possible Materials package of yeast, sugar, warm water, microscope, microscope slides

Estimated Time one day

Teaching Strategies

• Mix a package of yeast, 1 tsp of sugar, and 0.5 L warm water. After a few hours in a warm place, budding yeast can be seen under a microscope.

• Students can infer why the water and sugar are necessary for yeast to undergo budding.

For additional inquiry activities, see *Science Inquiry Labs.*

Text Question Answer
Sea star numbers would increase.

3 Assess

DAILY INTERVENTION

Check for Understanding
Kinesthetic, Logical-Mathematical
Using marbles as cells, have students demonstrate five cell divisions, beginning with one cell, two cells, and three cells. Record results in a table. [L2]

Reteach

Cell Cycle Have students draw the nucleus or chromosomes on cell cycle outlines and describe what is occurring at each stage. [L1]
ELL **IS** **Visual-Spatial**

Figure 8 Some organisms use cell division for budding and regeneration.

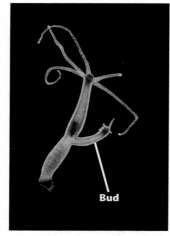

A Hydra, a freshwater animal, can reproduce asexually by budding. The bud is a small exact copy of the adult.

B This sea star is regenerating four new arms.

Budding and Regeneration Look at **Figure 8A.** A new organism is growing from the body of the parent organism. This organism, called a hydra, is reproducing by budding. Budding is a type of asexual reproduction made possible because of cell division. When the bud on the adult becomes large enough, it breaks away to live on its own.

Could you grow a new finger? Some organisms can regrow damaged or lost body parts, as shown in **Figure 8B.** Regeneration is the process that uses cell division to regrow body parts. Sponges, planaria, sea stars, and some other organisms can use regeneration for asexual reproduction. If these organisms break into pieces, a whole new organism will grow from each piece. Because sea stars eat oysters, oyster farmers dislike them. What would happen if an oyster farmer collected sea stars, cut them into pieces, and threw them back into the ocean?

section 1 review

Summary

The Cell Cycle

• The cell cycle is a series of events from one cell division to the next.

• Most of a eukaryotic cell's life is interphase.

Mitosis

• Mitosis is a series of four phases or steps.

• Each new nucleus formed by mitosis has the same number and type of chromosomes.

Asexual Reproduction

• In asexual reproduction, a new organism is produced from one organism.

• Cellular, budding, and regeneration are forms of asexual reproduction.

Self Check

1. **Define** mitosis. How does it differ in plants and animals?

2. **Identify** two examples of asexual reproduction in many-celled organisms.

3. **Describe** what happens to chromosomes before mitosis.

4. **Compare and contrast** the two new cells formed after mitosis and cell division.

5. **Think Critically** Why is it important for the nuclear membrane to disintegrate during mitosis?

Applying Math

6. **Solve One-Step Equations** If a cell undergoes cell division every 5 min, how many cells will there be after 1 h?

Science Online life.msscience.com/self_check_quiz

Assessment

Oral How is mitosis different from cell division? Mitosis is the division of the nucleus. Cell division includes mitosis and the division of the cytoplasm and its contents. Use **PASC,** p. 89. [L2]

section 1 review

1. a process in which a cell nucleus divides into two nuclei, each of which has the same genetic information; in animal cells, the cytoplasm divides as the cell membrane pinches in the middle of the cell; in plant cells, the appearance of the cell plate indicates that the cytoplasm is being divided.

2. Possible answers: budding and regeneration

3. The chromosomes duplicate.

4. They both have the same genetic information.

5. Otherwise, the chromosomes would not be able to move to opposite ends of the cell.

6. 60 minutes divided by 5 minutes = 12 cell divisions; 2^{12} = 4,096 cells

Mit💮sis in Plant Cells

Reproduction of most cells in plants and animals uses mitosis and cell division. In this lab, you will study mitosis in plant cells by examining prepared slides of onion root-tip cells.

● Real-World Question

How can plant cells in different stages of mitosis be distinguished from each other?

Goals

- **Compare** cells in different stages of mitosis and observe the location of their chromosomes.
- **Observe** what stage of mitosis is most common in onion root tips.

Materials

prepared slide of an onion root tip
microscope

Safety Precautions

● Procedure

1. Copy the data table in your Science Journal.

Number of Root-Tip Cells Observed

Stage of Mitosis	Number of Cells Observed	Percent of Cells Observed
Prophase	78	65
Metaphase	23	19
Anaphase	12	10
Telophase	7	6
Total	120	100

2. **Obtain** a prepared slide of cells from an onion root tip.

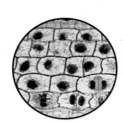

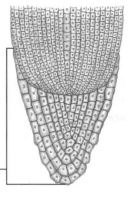

Zone of cell division   Root cap

3. Set your microscope on low power and examine the slide. The large, round cells at the root tip are called the root cap. Move the slide until you see the cells just behind the root cap. Turn to the high-power objective.

4. Find an area where you can see the most stages of mitosis. Count and record how many cells you see in each stage.

5. Return the nosepiece to low power. Remove the onion root-tip slide.

● Conclude and Apply

1. **Compare** the cells in the region behind the root cap to those in the root cap.

2. **Calculate** the percent of cells found in each stage of mitosis. Infer which stage of mitosis takes the longest period of time.

𝒞ommunicating
Your Data

Write and illustrate a story as if you were a cell undergoing mitosis. Share your story with your class. **For more help, refer to the** Science Skill Handbook.

𝒞ommunicating
Your Data

The story and drawings should include the stages in mitosis.

● Real-World Question

Purpose Students observe the stages of mitosis. L2 ELL LS **Visual-Spatial**

Process Skills observe, infer, compare and contrast

Time Required 40 minutes

● Procedure

Teaching Strategy Review the stages of mitosis before beginning the activity.

Troubleshooting Students may have difficulty locating all the phases. You may want to place an onion root tip slide on the microprojector and point out the phases.

● Conclude and Apply

1. The cells behind the root cap are smaller than those in the root cap. Mitosis occurs at a faster rate in cells behind the root cap.
2. See student page; prophase takes the longest.

☑ Assessment

Performance To further assess students' understanding of mitosis, give each one a sheet of paper listing a stage and have them describe what comes before and after that stage. Use **Performance Assessment in the Science Classroom,** p. 163. L2

Sexual Reproduction and Meiosis

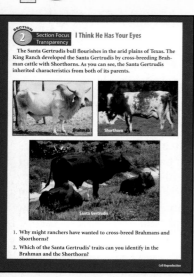
as you read

What You'll Learn

- **Describe** the stages of meiosis and how sex cells are produced.
- **Explain** why meiosis is needed for sexual reproduction.
- **Name** the cells that are involved in fertilization.
- **Explain** how fertilization occurs in sexual reproduction.

Why It's Important

Meiosis and sexual reproduction are the reasons why no one else is exactly like you.

⊙ Review Vocabulary

organism: any living thing; uses energy, is made of cells, reproduces, responds, grows, and develops

New Vocabulary

- sexual reproduction
- sperm
- egg
- fertilization
- zygote
- diploid
- haploid
- meiosis

Sexual Reproduction

Sexual reproduction is another way that a new organism can be produced. During **sexual reproduction,** two sex cells, sometimes called an egg and a sperm, come together. Sex cells, like those in **Figure 9,** are formed from cells in reproductive organs. **Sperm** are formed in the male reproductive organs. **Eggs** are formed in the female reproductive organs. The joining of an egg and a sperm is called **fertilization,** and the cell that forms is called a **zygote** (ZI goht). Generally, the egg and the sperm come from two different organisms of the same species. Following fertilization, cell division begins. A new organism with a unique identity develops.

Diploid Cells Your body forms two types of cells—body cells and sex cells. Body cells far outnumber sex cells. Your brain, skin, bones, and other tissues and organs are formed from body cells. A typical human body cell has 46 chromosomes. Each chromosome has a mate that is similar to it in size and shape and has similar DNA. Human body cells have 23 pairs of chromosomes. When cells have pairs of similar chromosomes, they are said to be **diploid** (DIH ployd).

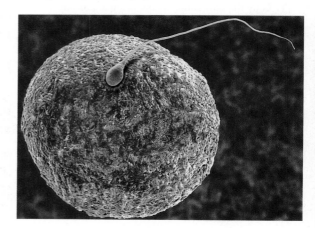

Figure 9 A human egg and a human sperm at fertilization.

Section 2 Resource Manager

Chapter *FAST FILE* Resources

Transparency Activity, p. 43

Directed Reading for Content Mastery, p. 18

Enrichment, p. 29

Reinforcement, p. 26

Life Science Critical Thinking/Problem Solving, p. 19

Mathematics Skill Activities, p. 3

Performance Assessment in the Science Classroom, p. 57

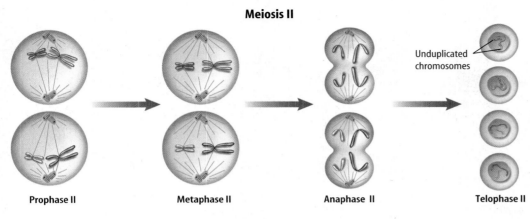

Meiosis II

Prophase II   Metaphase II   Anaphase II   Telophase II

Unduplicated chromosomes

Summary of Meiosis Two cells form during meiosis I. In meiosis II, both of these cells form two cells. The two divisions of the nucleus result in four sex cells. Each has one-half the number of chromosomes in its nucleus that was in the original nucleus. From a human cell with 46 paired chromosomes, meiosis produces four sex cells each with 23 unpaired chromosomes.

Applying Science

How can chromosome numbers be predicted?

Offspring get half of their chromosomes from one parent and half from the other. What happens if each parent has a different diploid number of chromosomes?

Identifying the Problem

A zebra and a donkey can mate to produce a zonkey. Zebras have a diploid number of 46. Donkeys have a diploid number of 62.

Solving the Problem

1. How many chromosomes would the zonkey receive from each parent?
2. What is the chromosome number of the zonkey?
3. What would happen when meiosis occurs in the zonkey's reproductive organs?
4. Predict why zonkeys are usually sterile.

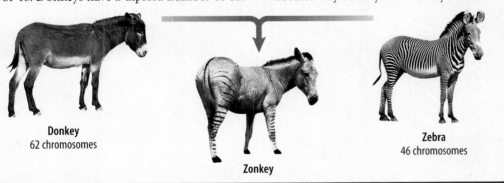

Donkey
62 chromosomes

Zonkey

Zebra
46 chromosomes

SECTION 2 Sexual Reproduction and Meiosis **107**

Make a Model

Stages of Meiosis Have students make a model of the stages of meiosis in an organism with three pairs of chromosomes. Have them use shapes to distinguish the chromosomes. L2 LS **Kinesthetic** P

Activity

Meiosis Lyrics Using one of their favorite songs, have students write substitute lyrics about what happens in meiosis. L2 LS **Auditory-Musical**

Applying Science

Answers

1. 23 from the zebra and 31 from the donkey
2. 54
3. Normal sex cells would not form because there are 8 unpaired chromosomes from the donkey.
4. Each sex cell could not have one-half the chromosomes of the original cell.

Quick Demo

Meiosis

Materials projecting microscope, prepared slides of lily anthers undergoing meiosis

Estimated Time 10 minutes

Procedure Demonstrate meiotic cell division in the lily anthers. Display the various stages of meiosis and have students draw what they see.

Active Reading

Flow Chart A flow chart helps students logically sequence events. Students will write major stages of the sequence in large ovals and write substages in smaller ovals under the larger ovals. Have students design a flow chart for a concept in this section. Sample flow chart: L2

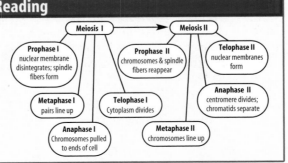

Visualizing Polyploidy in Plants

Have students examine the pictures and read the captions. Then ask the following questions.

What kinds of mistakes in meiosis or mitosis could result in a polyploid plant? A mistake that caused chromosome sets not to separate, allowing more than one full set to be present in a cell after division to form sex cells.

What is the main advantage of bananas being triploid? Triploid plants have very small seeds, so people can eat bananas without removing seeds.

Why wouldn't you find triploid peanuts in the grocery store? The part of a peanut plant you eat is a seed, but triploid plants have little or no seeds.

Activity

Plant Chromosomes Have students use pipe cleaners to model the chromosomes of one of the plants featured here. For example, a banana with 3 sets of 11 chromosomes, a strawberry with 8 sets of 7 chromosomes, or a peanut with 4 sets of 10 chromosomes. L2

NATIONAL GEOGRAPHIC VISUALIZING POLYPLOIDY IN PLANTS

Figure 12

You received a haploid (n) set of chromosomes from each of your parents, making you a diploid (2n) organism. In nature, however, many plants are polyploid—they have three (3n), four (4n), or more sets of chromosomes. We depend on some of these plants for food.

▲ **TRIPLOID** Bright yellow bananas typically come from triploid (3n) banana plants. Plants with an odd number of chromosome sets usually cannot reproduce sexually and have very small seeds or none at all.

▲ **TETRAPLOID** Polyploidy occurs naturally in many plants—including peanuts and daylilies—due to mistakes in mitosis or meiosis.

▼ **HEXAPLOID** Modern cultivated strains of oats have six sets of chromosomes, making them hexaploid (6n) plants.

▲ **OCTAPLOID** Polyploid plants often are bigger than nonpolyploid plants and may have especially large leaves, flowers, or fruits. Strawberries are an example of octaploid (8n) plants.

108

Visual Learning

Figure 13 Have students follow the unseparated chromosome pair through each stage of meiosis. How did this error affect the sex cells? Some had too many chromosomes; others not enough. L2

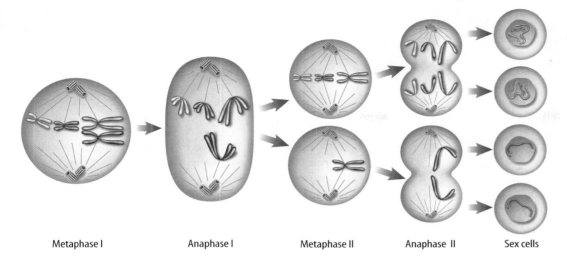

Metaphase I   Anaphase I   Metaphase II   Anaphase II   Sex cells

Mistakes in Meiosis Meiosis occurs many times in reproductive organs. Although mistakes in plants, as shown in **Figure 12,** are common, mistakes are less common in animals. These mistakes can produce sex cells with too many or too few chromosomes, as shown in **Figure 13.** Sometimes, zygotes produced from these sex cells die. If the zygote lives, every cell in the organism that grows from that zygote usually will have the wrong number of chromosomes. Organisms with the wrong number of chromosomes may not grow normally.

Figure 13 This diploid cell has four chromosomes. During anaphase I, one pair of duplicated chromosomes did not separate. **Infer** *how many chromosomes each sex cell usually has.*

section 2 review

Summary

Sexual Reproduction
- During sexual reproduction, two sex cells come together.
- Cell division begins after fertilization.
- A typical human body cell has 46 chromosomes, and a human sex cell has 23 chromosomes.

Meiosis and Sex Cells
- Each chromosome is duplicated before meiosis, then two divisions of the nucleus occur.
- During meiosis I, duplicated chromosomes are separated into new cells.
- Chromatids separate during meiosis II.
- Meiosis I and meiosis II result in four sex cells.

Self Check

1. **Describe** a zygote and how it is formed.
2. **Explain** where sex cells form.
3. **Compare** what happens to chromosomes during anaphase I and anaphase II.
4. **Think Critically** Plants grown from runners and leaf cuttings have the same traits as the parent plant. Plants grown from seeds can vary from the parent plants in many ways. Why can this happen?

Applying Skills

5. **Make and use a table** to compare mitosis and meiosis in humans. Vertical headings should include: *What Type of Cell (Body or Sex), Beginning Cell (Haploid or Diploid), Number of Cells Produced, End-Product Cell (Haploid or Diploid),* and *Number of Chromosomes in New Cells.*

Feature	Mitosis	Meiosis
Type of cell	Body cell	Sex cell
Beginning cell	Diploid	Diploid
Number of cells produced	Two	Four
End product	Diploid	Haploid
Number of chromosomes	Same as original cell	Half the original cell

section 2 review

1. A zygote is the cell that forms when a sperm fertilizes an egg.
2. Sperm cells form in male reproductive organs; egg cells form in female reproductive organs.
3. Anaphase I—duplicated chromosome pairs separate and move to opposite ends of the cell; anaphase II—chromatids separate and move to opposite ends of the cell.
4. Plants produced by asexual reproduction are the result of mitosis. Plants grown from seeds vary from their parents, because seeds are produced by sexual reproduction.
5. See table.

SECTION 3 | Section Focus Transparency | **Curly Cat**

This unusual cat is a Devon Rex. It appeared in Devonshire, England in 1960 when a genetic change occurred among British barn cats. The Devon Rex has a small head and a curly coat.

1. Based on the picture and the description above, what do you think a genetic change is?
2. How can cat breeders attempt to continue the characteristics of the Devon Rex?

Cell Reproduction

Tie to Prior Knowledge

Template Games Students should be familiar with template systems, such as keys and locks and peg-and-hole games. Ask for other examples. Use this knowledge to explain that DNA in the nucleus serves as a template for RNA.

Virtual Labs

Protein Synthesis *What is the role of DNA and RNA in protein synthesis?*

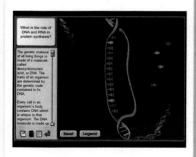

---

as you read

What **You'll Learn**

- **Identify** the parts of a DNA molecule and its structure.
- **Explain** how DNA copies itself.
- **Describe** the structure and function of each kind of RNA.

Why **It's Important**

DNA helps determine nearly everything your body is and does.

Review Vocabulary
heredity: the passing of traits from parents to offspring

New Vocabulary
- DNA
- gene
- RNA
- mutation

Figure 14 DNA is part of the chromosomes found in a cell's nucleus.

What is DNA?

Why was the alphabet one of the first things you learned when you started school? Letters are a code that you need to know before you learn to read. A cell also uses a code that is stored in its hereditary material. The code is a chemical called deoxyribonucleic (dee AHK sih ri boh noo klay ihk) acid, or **DNA.** It contains information for an organism's growth and function. **Figure 14** shows how DNA is stored in cells that have a nucleus. When a cell divides, the DNA code is copied and passed to the new cells. In this way, new cells receive the same coded information that was in the original cell. Every cell that has ever been formed in your body or in any other organism contains DNA.

INTEGRATE Chemistry

Discovering DNA Since the mid-1800s, scientists have known that the nuclei of cells contain large molecules called nucleic acids. By 1950, chemists had learned what the nucleic acid DNA was made of, but they didn't understand how the parts of DNA were arranged.

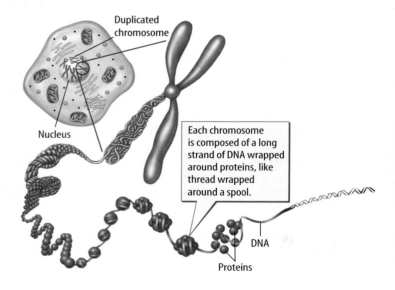

Duplicated chromosome

Nucleus

Each chromosome is composed of a long strand of DNA wrapped around proteins, like thread wrapped around a spool.

DNA

Proteins

110   CHAPTER 4 Cell Reproduction

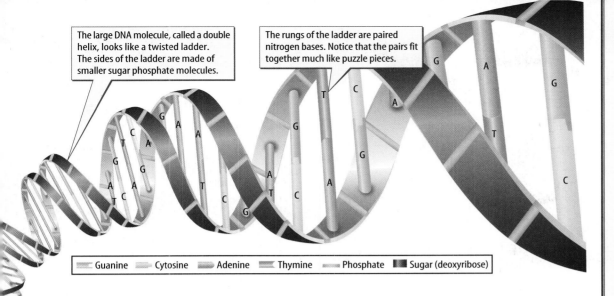

The large DNA molecule, called a double helix, looks like a twisted ladder. The sides of the ladder are made of smaller sugar phosphate molecules.

The rungs of the ladder are paired nitrogen bases. Notice that the pairs fit together much like puzzle pieces.

| Guanine | Cytosine | Adenine | Thymine | Phosphate | Sugar (deoxyribose) |

DNA's Structure In 1952, scientist Rosalind Franklin discovered that DNA is two chains of molecules in a spiral form. By using an X-ray technique, Dr. Franklin showed that the large spiral was probably made up of two spirals. As it turned out, the structure of DNA is similar to a twisted ladder. In 1953, using the work of Franklin and others, scientists James Watson and Francis Crick made a model of a DNA molecule.

A DNA Model What does DNA look like? According to the Watson and Crick DNA model, each side of the ladder is made up of sugar-phosphate molecules. Each molecule consists of the sugar called deoxyribose (dee AHK sih ri bohs) and a phosphate group. The rungs of the ladder are made up of other molecules called nitrogen bases. Four kinds of nitrogen bases are found in DNA—adenine (A duh neen), guanine (GWAH neen), cytosine (SI tuh seen), and thymine (THI meen). The bases are represented by the letters A, G, C, and T. The amount of cytosine in cells always equals the amount of guanine, and the amount of adenine always equals the amount of thymine. This led to the hypothesis that these bases occur as pairs in DNA. **Figure 14** shows that adenine always pairs with thymine, and guanine always pairs with cytosine. Like interlocking pieces of a puzzle, each base bonds only with its correct partner.

✔ **Reading Check** *What are the nitrogen base pairs in a DNA molecule?*

Mini LAB

Modeling DNA Replication

Procedure
1. Suppose you have a segment of DNA that is six nitrogen base pairs in length. On **paper,** using the letters A, T, C, and G, write a combination of six pairs, remembering that A and T are always a pair and C and G are always a pair.
2. Duplicate your segment of DNA. On paper, diagram how this happens and show the new DNA segments.

Analysis
Compare the order of bases of the original DNA to the new DNA molecules.

Try at Home

Mini LAB

Purpose Students will model DNA replication. L2 IS **Visual-Spatial**

Materials pencil and paper

Teaching Strategy Make sure students understand that they are to make up a sample strand of DNA, then make the complementary strand, then split the two strands and make those complementary strands, so they can see that the new strands are identical to the original.

Analysis
Answers will vary with the bases chosen, but bases should be in the same order as the original DNA.

Assessment

Performance Draw and label one strand of DNA. Have students draw the complementary strand. Use **Performance Assessment in the Science Classroom,** p. 127. L2

Try at Home

✔ **Reading Check**

Answer Adenine pairs with thymine, and guanine with cytosine.

Differentiated Instruction

English-Language Learners Use unifix cubes to demonstrate the various bases. Have students make their own models of base pairs, using a different color for each base. L2 ELL IS **Kinesthetic**

Use an Analogy

Morse Code Students are probably familiar with Morse code. Morse code uses only two symbols—the dot and the dash—in combinations to represent numbers and letters of the alphabet. DNA has four symbols. The order of nitrogen bases, rather than the sequence of dots and dashes, expresses the information needed for life processes.

Discussion

DNA Sequence How can you predict the base sequence of a second strand of DNA? by knowing the base-pairing rules and the sequence of the original DNA strand

Fun Fact

When students hear about the "code of life," they are hearing about the order of nitrogen bases in DNA.

Teacher **FYI**

Human Genome An individual's complete set of genetic material is its genome. In early 2001, it was announced that a working draft of the human genome had been mapped. The knowledge gained from the project will be a basis for studying human diseases and accelerating biomedical research.

Text Question Answer

It could cause serious health problems.

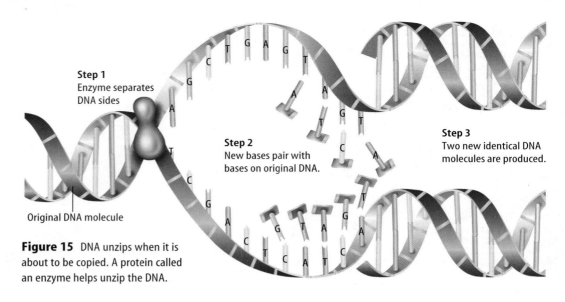

Step 1
Enzyme separates DNA sides

Step 2
New bases pair with bases on original DNA.

Step 3
Two new identical DNA molecules are produced.

Original DNA molecule

Figure 15 DNA unzips when it is about to be copied. A protein called an enzyme helps unzip the DNA.

Figure 16 This diagram shows just a few of the genes that have been identified on human chromosome 7. The bold print is the name that has been given to each gene.

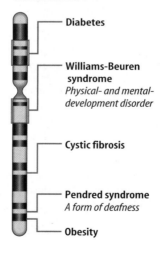

Chromosome 7

- Diabetes
- **Williams-Beuren syndrome**
  Physical- and mental-development disorder
- Cystic fibrosis
- **Pendred syndrome**
  A form of deafness
- Obesity

Copying DNA When chromosomes are duplicated before mitosis or meiosis, the amount of DNA in the nucleus is doubled. The Watson and Crick model shows how this takes place. The two sides of DNA unwind and separate. Each side then becomes a pattern on which a new side forms, as shown in **Figure 15.** The new DNA has bases that are identical to those of the original DNA and are in the same order.

Genes

Most of your characteristics, such as the color of your hair, your height, and even how things taste to you, depend on the kinds of proteins your cells make. DNA in your cells stores the instructions for making these proteins.

Proteins build cells and tissues or work as enzymes. The instructions for making a specific protein are found in a **gene** which is a section of DNA on a chromosome. As shown in **Figure 16,** each chromosome contains hundreds of genes. Proteins are made of chains of hundreds or thousands of amino acids. The gene determines the order of amino acids in a protein. Changing the order of the amino acids makes a different protein. What might occur if an important protein couldn't be made or if the wrong protein was made in your cells?

Making Proteins Genes are found in the nucleus, but proteins are made on ribosomes in cytoplasm. The codes for making proteins are carried from the nucleus to the ribosomes by another type of nucleic acid called ribonucleic acid, or **RNA.**

112 CHAPTER 4 Cell Reproduction

Science Journal

DNA as Evidence Have students research the use of DNA technology in law enforcement and write a report in their Science Journals. Have them use the Internet, news magazines, reference books, and interview forensic scientists. L2 **LS** **Linguistic**

Curriculum Connection

Math The DNA code is written in four "letters" and the cell "reads" the code in groups of three. Have students determine how many different ways the four "letters" (A, T, G, and C) can be arranged in groups of three. There are 64 possible combinations. L2 **LS** **Logical-Mathematical**

Ribonucleic Acid RNA is made in the nucleus on a DNA pattern. However, RNA is different from DNA. If DNA is like a ladder, RNA is like a ladder that has all its rungs sawed in half. Compare the DNA molecule in **Figure 14** to the RNA molecule in **Figure 17**. RNA has the bases A, G, and C like DNA but has the base uracil (U) instead of thymine (T). The sugar-phosphate molecules in RNA contain the sugar ribose, not deoxyribose.

The three main kinds of RNA made from DNA in a cell's nucleus are messenger RNA (mRNA), ribosomal RNA (rRNA), and transfer RNA (tRNA). Protein production begins when mRNA moves into the cytoplasm. There, ribosomes attach to it. Ribosomes are made of rRNA. Transfer RNA molecules in the cytoplasm bring amino acids to these ribosomes. Inside the ribosomes, three nitrogen bases on the mRNA temporarily match with three nitrogen bases on the tRNA. The same thing happens for the mRNA and another tRNA molecule, as shown in **Figure 17.** The amino acids that are attached to the two tRNA molecules bond. This is the beginning of a protein.

The code carried on the mRNA directs the order in which the amino acids bond. After a tRNA molecule has lost its amino acid, it can move about the cytoplasm and pick up another amino acid just like the first one. The ribosome moves along the mRNA. New tRNA molecules with amino acids match up and add amino acids to the protein molecule.

Science Online

Topic: The Human Genome Project
Visit life.msscience.com for Web links to information about the Human Genome Project.

Activity Find out when chromosomes 5, 16, 29, 21, and 22 were completely sequenced. Write about what scientists learned about each of these chromosomes.

Figure 17 Cells need DNA, RNA, and amino acids to make proteins.

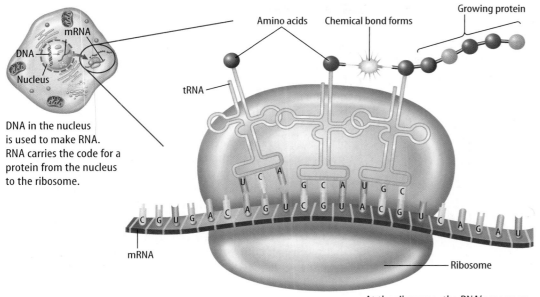

DNA in the nucleus is used to make RNA. RNA carries the code for a protein from the nucleus to the ribosome.

At the ribosome, the RNA's message is translated into a specific protein.

SECTION 3 DNA **113**

Make a Model

Protein Synthesis Have students draw a cell on a poster board and make a model demonstrating protein synthesis using materials such as craft sticks, beads, yarn, and so on. L2 LS **Visual-Spatial**

Activity

Corresponding Sequence On the board or an overhead transparency, write the sequence for one strand of DNA. Have students copy the sequence and write the corresponding sequence for mRNA and tRNA. L2 LS **Visual-Spatial**

Quick Demo

DNA Replication

Materials pipe cleaners in multiple colors

Estimated Time 5 minutes

Procedure Demonstrate the replication of DNA. Begin with two pipe cleaners of different colors, wrapped around one another as in a double helix. Unwind the strands and separate them. Wrap a new pipe cleaner around each strand, using the opposite color to demonstrate the complimentary strands.

Visual Learning

Figure 17 Have students make an events-chain concept map to outline the stages of protein synthesis. L2 LS **Visual-Spatial**

Curriculum Connection

History Have students study the history of DNA research. Then using poster board, students should draw and label a timeline showing the events of DNA research since DNA was first removed from a cell nucleus in 1869. L3 LS **Visual-Spatial and Kinesthetic** P

Cells in the iris of the eye produce proteins needed for eye color.

Muscle cells produce proteins that help make muscles move.

Cells in the stomach produce proteins necessary to digest food.

Figure 18 Each cell in the body produces only the proteins that are necessary to do its job.

Controlling Genes You might think that because most cells in an organism have exactly the same chromosomes and the same genes, they would make the same proteins, but they don't. In many-celled organisms like you, each cell uses only some of the thousands of genes that it has to make proteins. Just as each actor uses only the lines from the script for his or her role, each cell uses only the genes that direct the making of proteins that it needs. For example, muscle proteins are made in muscle cells, as represented in **Figure 18,** but not in nerve cells.

Cells must be able to control genes by turning some genes off and turning other genes on. They do this in many different ways. Sometimes the DNA is twisted so tightly that no RNA can be made. Other times, chemicals bind to the DNA so that it cannot be used. If the incorrect proteins are produced, the organism cannot function properly.

Mutations

Sometimes mistakes happen when DNA is being copied. Imagine that the copy of the script the director gave you was missing three pages. You use your copy to learn your lines. When you begin rehearsing for the play, everyone is ready for one of the scenes except for you. What happened? You check your copy of the script against the original and find that three of the pages are missing. Because your script is different from the others, you cannot perform your part correctly.

If DNA is not copied exactly, the proteins made from the instructions might not be made correctly. These mistakes, called **mutations,** are any permanent change in the DNA sequence of a gene or chromosome of a cell. Some mutations include cells that receive an entire extra chromosome or are missing a chromosome. Outside factors such as X rays, sunlight, and some chemicals have been known to cause mutations.

Reading Check *When are mutations likely to occur?*

Figure 19 Because of a defect on chromosome 2, the mutant fruit fly has short wings and cannot fly.
Predict *Could this defect be transferred to the mutant's offspring? Explain.*

Caption Answer
Figure 19 yes, if the defect is in its reproductive cells

Results of a Mutation Genes control the traits you inherit. Without correctly coded proteins, an organism can't grow, repair, or maintain itself. A change in a gene or chromosome can change the traits of an organism, as illustrated in **Figure 19.**

If the mutation occurs in a body cell, it might or might not be life threatening to the organism. However, if a mutation occurs in a sex cell, then all the cells that are formed from that sex cell will have that mutation. Mutations add variety to a species when the organism reproduces. Many mutations are harmful to organisms, often causing their death. Some mutations do not appear to have any effect on the organism, and some can even be beneficial. For example, a mutation to a plant might cause it to produce a chemical that certain insects avoid. If these insects normally eat the plant, the mutation will help the plant survive.

Topic: Fruit Fly Genes
Visit life.msscience.com for Web links to information about what genes are present on the chromosomes of a fruit fly.

Activity Draw a picture of one of the chromosomes of a fruit fly and label some of its genes.

section 3 review

Summary

What is DNA?

● Each side of the DNA ladder is made up of sugar-phosphate molecules, and the rungs of the ladder are made up of nitrogenous bases.

● When DNA is copied, the new DNA has bases that are identical to those of the original DNA.

Genes

● The instructions for making a specific protein are found in genes in the cell nucleus. Proteins are made on ribosomes in the cytoplasm.

● There are three main kinds of RNA—mRNA, rRNA, and tRNA.

Mutations

● If DNA is not copied exactly, the resulting mutations may cause proteins to be made incorrectly.

Self Check

1. **Describe** how DNA makes a copy of itself.

2. **Explain** how the codes for proteins are carried from the nucleus to the ribosomes.

3. **Apply** A strand of DNA has the bases AGTAAC. Using letters, show a matching DNA strand.

4. **Determine** how tRNA is used when cells build proteins.

5. **Think Critically** You begin as one cell. Compare the DNA in your brain cells to the DNA in your heart cells.

Applying Skills

6. **Concept Map** Using a Venn diagram, compare and contrast DNA and RNA.

7. **Use a word processor** to make an outline of the events that led up to the discovery of DNA. Use library resources to find this information.

DAILY INTERVENTION

Check for Understanding
Visual-Spatial Have students make puzzle pieces that represent the key elements in protein synthesis—three types of RNA, ribosome, amino acids, chemical bond, and protein. Working in pairs, the students can put the puzzle together to demonstrate the process of protein synthesis and students can test each other's ability to identify what each puzzle piece represents. L2

Reteach
DNA and Protein Have students make a drawing of DNA replication and protein synthesis. L2 [IS] **Visual-Spatial**

3 Assess

Assessment

Oral What are the three kinds of RNA and their functions? Messenger RNA, transfer RNA, and ribosomal RNA; mRNA is copied from DNA and moves from the nucleus to a ribosome; tRNA carries amino acids to ribosomes; rRNA makes up ribosomes. Use **Performance Assessment in the Science Classroom,** p. 89. L2

section 3 review

1. The two sides unwind and separate; a complementary strand is formed for each, and the resulting double-stranded DNA has one original strand and one new strand.

2. The codes are carried by mRNA from the nucleus to the ribosome.

3. TCATTG

4. The tRNA in the cytoplasm brings amino acids to the ribosomes. There, three nitrogen bases on the mRNA template match with three bases on the tRNA. The amino acids bond, and protein synthesis begins.

5. The DNA is identical.

6. Answers should be similar to the table for question 23 in the Chapter Review.

7. Students should be sure to include the contributions of Miescher, Griffith, Avery, Hershey, Chase, Chargraff, Wilkins, Franklin, Crick, and Watson.

Real-World Question

Purpose

Internet Students use Internet sites that can be accessed through life.msscience.com/internet_lab.

They will observe genetic traits and mutations in animals. [L2]

Process Skills collect data, observe, research, communicate, make and use tables, form a hypothesis, compare, describe, record

Time Required about three days

Make a Plan

Preparation

Internet To run through the steps that the students will follow, visit life.msscience.com/internet_lab.

Non-Internet Have students use books to select an animal and one of its traits to investigate.

LAB
Use the Internet

Mutations

Fantail pigeon

Goals
- **Observe** traits of various animals.
- **Research** how mutations become traits.
- **Gather** data about mutations.
- **Make** a frequency table of your findings and communicate them to other students.

Data Source

Science Online

Visit life.msscience.com/internet_lab for more information on common genetic traits in different animals, recessive and dominant genes, and data from other students.

Real-World Question

Mutations can result in dominant or recessive genes. A recessive characteristic can appear only if an organism has two recessive genes for that characteristic. However, a dominant characteristic can appear if an organism has one or two dominant genes for that characteristic. Why do some mutations result in more common traits while others do not? Form a hypothesis about how a mutation can become a common trait.

Make a Plan

1. **Observe** common traits in various animals, such as household pets or animals you might see in a zoo.
2. **Learn** what genes carry these traits in each animal.
3. **Research** the traits to discover which ones are results of mutations. Are all mutations dominant? Are any of these mutations beneficial?

White tiger

Alternative Inquiry Lab

Real-World Connection To broaden their knowledge of genetic traits and mutations in animals, have students meet with officials of an area zoo to find out how they maintain variety in the animals kept there. Also have them explore the Web sites of zoos on the Internet. To track what they learn, students can make a table of the different species that are found at the zoos they investigate. For species that are found at many zoos, what unique traits do species have at the different zoos? How do these zoos keep variety in the species of animals? Are their methods different for endangered or threatened species? Have students then make a chart showing some ways of maintaining variety in the species that are different from those at the area zoo. Have them present their findings to the area zoo officials.

▶ Follow Your Plan

1. Make sure your teacher approves your plan before you start.
2. Visit the link shown below to access different Web sites for information about mutations and genetics.
3. **Decide** if a mutation is beneficial, harmful, or neither. Record your data in your Science Journal.

▶ Analyze Your Data

1. **Record** in your Science Journal a list of traits that are results of mutations.
2. **Describe** an animal, such as a pet or an animal you've seen in the zoo. Point out which traits are known to be the result of a mutation.
3. **Make** a chart that compares recessive mutations to dominant mutations. Which are more common?
4. **Share** your data with other students by posting it at the link shown below.

Siberian Husky's eyes

▶ Conclude and Apply

1. **Compare** your findings to those of your classmates and other data at the link shown below. What were some of the traits your classmates found that you did not? Which were the most common?
2. Look at your chart of mutations. Are all mutations beneficial? When might a mutation be harmful to an organism?
3. **Predict** how your data would be affected if you had performed this lab when one of these common mutations first appeared. Do you think you would see more or less animals with this trait?
4. Mutations occur every day but we only see a few of them. Infer how many mutations over millions of years can lead to a new species.

Communicating Your Data

Find this lab using the link below. **Post** your data in the table provided. Combine your data with that of other students and make a chart that shows all of the data.

Science Online

life.msscience.com/internet_lab

Communicating Your Data

Have students use the Internet resources to collect pictures of the animal they are investigating. Have them find pictures that show the mutation.

✓ Assessment

Oral Students describe mutations they researched and discuss how helpful they are to animals. Show pictures of animals with the mutation. Use **Performance Assessment in the Science Classroom**, p. 143. [L2]

▶ Follow Your Plan

Teaching Strategy Have students use animal population data to see how often that mutation is found. [L2]

▶ Analyze Your Data

1. Answers will vary. Color can result from a mutation.
2. Answers will depend upon animals chosen.
3. Answers will vary, but dominant genes are not necessarily more common.
4. Students may need help posting data.

▶ Conclude and Apply

1. Answers will vary. Remind students that the most common traits may be the result of mutations.
2. Answers will vary. Have students think about the mutation they are investigating and how helpful or harmful it is to the animal.
3. If you had investigated the mutation when it first appeared, you may have seen fewer animals with the trait. With the passage of time, you can determine if the mutation is beneficial.
4. Organisms with mutations may be better suited to a particular environment. These traits would be passed on to their offspring. Many mutations may lead to a new species.

Content Background

Cytogenetics is the branch of science that studies heredity both through genetics and studies of the cell. In 1956, modern human cytogenetics began, thanks to the discovery of the number of human chromosomes present in each cell of the body. As early as 1905, scientists had determined that chromosomes are found in pairs, and in 1915 Thomas Hunt Morgan discovered that genes were found on chromosomes. It was not until 1952 that Dr. Hsu's work occurred, and 1953 when Watson and Crick used Rosalind Franklin's work to determine the structure of DNA. Studies of human chromosomes and genes have progressed at an astounding rate since that time. Scientists have determined the particular chromosome that carries the gene for many human diseases and other traits.

Discussion

Explain What type of mistake could the lab technician in Dr. Hsu's lab have made while mixing the solution to cause mysterious behavior of the chromosomes? Possible answer: The technician either added too little of the solute to a set amount of water, or too much water to a set amount of solute, causing the solution to have a higher water content than the cells.

Activity

Genetics Have students work in teams to research the major discoveries in the field of genetics. Have each team display their results on a time line made on a long piece of paper. Students should be encouraged to include discoveries from early research until present times and to include the names of the scientists who made the discoveries. L2

A Tangled Tale
How did a scientist get chromosomes to separate?

Thanks to chromosomes, each of us is unique!

Viewed under the microscope, chromosomes in cells sometimes look a lot like spaghetti. That's why scientists had such a hard time figuring out how many chromosomes are in each human cell. Imagine, then, how Dr. Tao-Chiuh Hsu (dow shew•SEW) must have felt when he looked into a microscope and saw "beautifully scattered chromosomes." The problem was, Hsu didn't know what he had done to separate the chromosomes into countable strands.

"I tried to study those slides and set up some more cultures to repeat the miracle," Hsu explained. "But nothing happened."

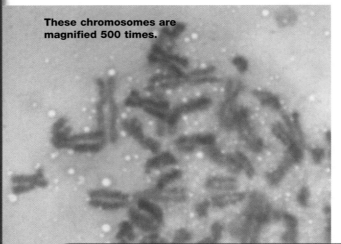
These chromosomes are magnified 500 times.

For three months Hsu tried changing every variable he could think of to make the chromosomes separate again. In April 1952, his efforts were finally rewarded. Hsu quickly realized that the chromosomes separated because of osmosis.

Osmosis is the movement of water molecules through cell membranes. This movement occurs in predictable ways. The water molecules move from areas with higher concentrations of water to areas with lower concentrations of water. In Hsu's case, the solution he used to prepare the cells had a higher concentration of water then the cell did. So water moved from the solution into the cell and the cell swelled until it finally exploded. The chromosomes suddenly were visible as separate strands.

What made the cells swell the first time? Apparently a technician had mixed the solution incorrectly. "Since nearly four months had elapsed, there was no way to trace who actually had prepared that particular [solution]," Hsu noted. "Therefore, this heroine must remain anonymous."

Research What developments led scientists to conclude that the human cell has 46 chromosomes? Visit the link shown to the right to get started.

Science Online
For more information, visit life.msscience.com/oops

Research As students research the history of research on human chromosomes, have them consider the rate at which discoveries occurred then and now. Point out that the Human Genome Project has increased the knowledge of genetics at an amazing rate. L2

Resources for Teachers and Students

DNA and Genetic Engineering (Cells & Life), by Robert Snedden, Heinemann Library, 2003

The Big Idea, by Paul Strathern. New York: Doubleday, 1999

Reviewing Main Ideas

Section 1   Cell Division and Mitosis

1. The life cycle of a cell has two parts—growth and development, and cell division.

2. In mitosis, the nucleus divides to form two identical nuclei. Mitosis occurs in four continuous steps, or phases—prophase, metaphase, anaphase, and telophase.

3. Cell division in animal cells and plant cells is similar, but plant cells do not have centrioles and animal cells do not form cell walls.

4. Organisms use cell division to grow, to replace cells, and for asexual reproduction. Asexual reproduction produces organisms with DNA identical to the parent's DNA. Fission, budding, and regeneration can be used for asexual reproduction.

Section 2   Sexual Reproduction and Meiosis

1. Sexual reproduction results when an egg and sperm join. This event is called fertilization, and the cell that forms is called the zygote.

2. Meiosis occurs in the reproductive organs, producing four haploid sex cells.

3. During meiosis, two divisions of the nucleus occur.

4. Meiosis ensures that offspring produced by fertilization have the same number of chromosomes as their parents.

Section 3   DNA

1. DNA is a large molecule made up of two twisted strands of sugar-phosphate molecules and nitrogen bases.

2. All cells contain DNA. The section of DNA on a chromosome that directs the making of a specific protein is a gene.

3. DNA can copy itself and is the pattern from which RNA is made. Messenger RNA, ribosomal RNA, and transfer RNA are used to make proteins.

4. Permanent changes in DNA are called mutations.

Visualizing Main Ideas

Think of four ways that organisms can use mitosis. Copy and complete the spider diagram below.

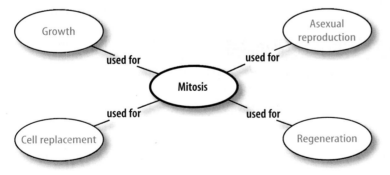

 life.msscience.com/interactive_tutor

CHAPTER STUDY GUIDE   **119**

Reviewing Main Ideas

Summary statements can be used by students to review the major concepts of the chapter.

Visualizing Main Ideas

See student page.

Visit life.msscience.com
/self_check_quiz
/interactive_tutor
/vocabulary_puzzlemaker
/chapter_review
/standardized_test

Assessment Transparency

For additional assessment questions, use the *Assessment Transparency* located in the transparency book.

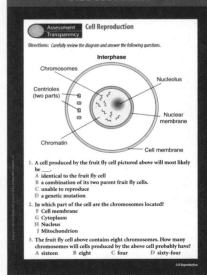

Using Vocabulary

1. Egg, sperm
2. Mitosis
3. DNA or RNA
4. gene
5. haploid
6. asexual reproduction
7. chromosome
8. Meiosis
9. Fertilization, meiosis, or sexual reproduction
10. mutation

Checking Concepts

11. D
12. D
13. B
14. C
15. A
16. A
17. D
18. C
19. B

Using Vocabulary

asexual reproduction p.101
chromosome p.98
diploid p.104
DNA p.110
egg p.104
fertilization p.104
gene p.112
haploid p.105
meiosis p.105
mitosis p.98
mutation p.114
RNA p.112
sexual reproduction p.104
sperm p.104
zygote p.104

Fill in the blanks with the correct vocabulary word or words.

1. _____ and _____ cells are sex cells.
2. _____ produces two identical cells.
3. An example of a nucleic acid is _____.
4. A(n) _____ is the code for a protein.
5. A(n) _____ sperm is formed during meiosis.
6. Budding is a type of _____.
7. A(n) _____ is a structure in the nucleus that contains hereditary material.
8. _____ produces four sex cells.
9. As a result of _____, a new organism develops that has its own unique identity.
10. An error made during the copying of DNA is called a(n) _____.

Checking Concepts

Choose the word or phrase that best answers the question.

11. Which of the following is a double spiral molecule with pairs of nitrogen bases?
    A) RNA
    B) amino acid
    C) protein
    D) DNA

12. What is in RNA but not in DNA?
    A) thymine
    B) thyroid
    C) adenine
    D) uracil

13. If a diploid tomato cell has 24 chromosomes, how many chromosomes will the tomato's sex cells have?
    A) 6
    B) 12
    C) 24
    D) 48

14. During a cell's life cycle, when do chromosomes duplicate?
    A) anaphase
    B) metaphase
    C) interphase
    D) telophase

15. When do chromatids separate during mitosis?
    A) anaphase
    B) prophase
    C) metaphase
    D) telophase

16. How is the hydra shown in the picture reproducing?
    A) asexually, by budding
    B) sexually, by budding
    C) asexually, by fission
    D) sexually, by fission

17. What is any permanent change in a gene or a chromosome called?
    A) fission
    B) reproduction
    C) replication
    D) mutation

18. What does meiosis produce?
    A) cells with the diploid chromosome number
    B) cells with identical chromosomes
    C) sex cells
    D) a zygote

19. What type of nucleic acid carries the codes for making proteins from the nucleus to the ribosome?
    A) DNA
    B) RNA
    C) protein
    D) genes

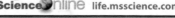 **Science** Online life.msscience.com/vocabulary_puzzlemaker

Use the Exam*View*® Pro Testmaker CD-ROM to:
- create multiple versions of tests
- create modified tests with one mouse click for inclusion students
- edit existing questions and add your own questions
- build tests aligned with state standards using built-in State Curriculum Tags
- change English tests to Spanish with one mouse click and vice versa

Thinking Critically

20. List the base sequence of a strand of RNA made using the DNA pattern ATCCGTC. Look at **Figure 14** for a hint.

21. **Predict** whether a mutation in a human skin cell can be passed on to the person's offspring. Explain.

22. **Explain** how a zygote could end up with an extra chromosome.

23. **Classify** Copy and complete this table about DNA and RNA.

DNA and RNA

	DNA	RNA
Number of strands	2	1
Type of sugar	deoxyribose	ribose
Letter names of bases	G, A, C, T	G, A, C, U
Where found	nucleus	nucleus & cytoplasm

24. **Concept Map** Make an events-chain concept map of what occurs from interphase in the parent cell to the formation of the zygote. Tell whether the chromosome's number at each stage is haploid or diploid.

25. **Concept Map** Copy and complete the events-chain concept map of DNA synthesis.

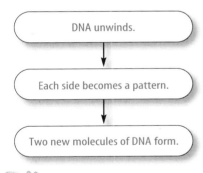

DNA unwinds.

↓

Each side becomes a pattern.

↓

Two new molecules of DNA form.

26. **Compare and Contrast** Meiosis is two divisions of a reproductive cell's nucleus. It occurs in a continuous series of steps. Compare and contrast the steps of meiosis I to the steps of meiosis II.

27. **Describe** what occurs in mitosis that gives the new cells identical DNA.

28. **Form a hypothesis** about the effect of an incorrect mitotic division on the new cells produced.

29. **Determine** how many chromosomes are in the original cell compared to those in the new cells formed by cell division. Explain.

Performance Activities

30. **Flash Cards** Make a set of 11 flash cards with drawings of a cell that show the different stages of meiosis. Shuffle your cards and then put them in the correct order. Give them to another student in the class to try.

Applying Math

31. **Cell Cycle** Assume an average human cell has a cell cycle of 20 hours. Calculate how many cells there would be after 80 hours.

Use the diagram below to answer question 32.

C G U G A C A G U C G U A C G U C A G A U

32. **Amino Acids** Sets of three nitrogen bases code for an amino acid. How many amino acids will make up the protein molecule that is coded for by the mRNA molecule above?

Thinking Critically

20. UAGGCAG

21. No; in order for a mutation to be passed to offspring, the mutation must take place in a sex cell.

22. This could happen if nondisjunction (failure of like chromosomes or chromatids to separate) occurs during anaphase I or II.

23. See student page.

24. The order of events given for meiosis should reflect **Figure 11** and formation of the zygote, **Figure 10**. The cell at the beginning of meiosis is diploid. The four cells at the end of meiosis are all haploid.

25. See student page.

26. Student answers should reflect the information in Section 2 and **Figure 11**.

27. the copying of chromosomes in interphase; the separation of the copies at anaphase; the separation of two new cells at telophase

28. Incorrect division can result in an incorrect number of chromosomes, often leading to abnormal offspring.

29. The number of chromosomes in the new cell are the same as in the original cell; DNA is copied before mitosis so new cells retained the correct number of chromosomes.

Performance Activities

30. Cards should be sequenced as shown in **Figure 11**. If interphase is included, it should come before prophase I. **Use Performance Assessment in the Science Classroom**, p. 163.

Applying Math

National Math Standards

1, 6, 9

31. 80 hours divided by 20 hours = 4 cycles; 2^4 = 16 cells

32. 7

☑ Assessment Resources

📁 Reproducible Masters

Chapter *Fast File* Resources
Chapter Review, pp. 35–36
Chapter Tests, pp. 37–40
Assessment Transparency Activity, p. 47

Glencoe Science Web site
Chapter Review Test
Standardized Test Practice

Glencoe Technology

🔹 Assessment Transparency
🔹 Exam*View*® Pro Testmaker
🔹 MindJogger Videoquiz
🔹 Interactive Chalkboard

FAST FILE

Answer Sheet A practice answer sheet can be found at life.msscience.com/answer_sheet.

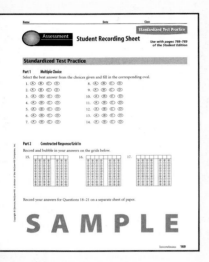

S A M P L E

Part 1 | Multiple Choice

Record your answers on the answer sheet provided by your teacher or on a sheet of paper.

1. What stage of the cell cycle involves growth and function?
   - A. prophase
   - B. interphase
   - C. mitosis
   - D. cytoplasmic division

2. During interphase, which structure of a cell is duplicated?
   - A. cell plate
   - B. mitochondrion
   - C. chromosome
   - D. chloroplast

Use the figure below to answer questions 3 and 4.

3. What form of asexual reproduction is shown here?
   - A. regeneration
   - B. cell division
   - C. sprouting
   - D. meiosis

4. How does the genetic material of the new organism above compare to that of the parent organism?
   - A. It is exactly the same.
   - B. It is a little different.
   - C. It is completely different.
   - D. It is haploid.

5. Organisms with three or more sets of chromosomes are called
   - A. monoploid.
   - B. diploid.
   - C. haploid.
   - D. polyploid.

6. If a sex cell has eight chromosomes, how many chromosomes will there be after fertilization?
   - A. 8
   - B. 16
   - C. 32
   - D. 64

Use the diagram below to answer questions 7 and 8.

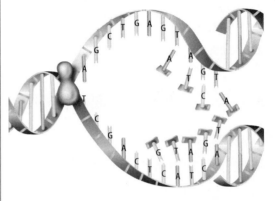

7. What does this diagram illustrate?
   - A. DNA duplication
   - B. RNA
   - C. cell reproduction
   - D. RNA synthesis

8. When does the process shown occur in the cell cycle?
   - A. prophase
   - B. metaphase
   - C. interphase
   - D. anaphase

9. Proteins are made of
   - A. genes
   - B. bases
   - C. amino acids
   - D. chromosomes

Part 2 | Short Response/Grid In

Record your answers on the answer sheet provided by your teacher or on a sheet of paper.

10. In the human body, which cells are constantly dividing? Why is this important? How can this be potentially harmful?

11. Arrange the following terms in the correct order: *fertilization, sex cells, meiosis, zygote, mitosis.*

12. What are the three types of RNA used during protein synthesis? What is the function of each type of RNA?

13. Describe the relationship between gene, protein, DNA and chromosome.

Use the table below to answer question 14.

Phase of Cell Cycle	Action within the Cell
Interphase	Chromosomes duplicate
Prophase	Chromosomes visible
Metaphase	Chromosomes line up in center of cell
Anaphase	Chromosomes have separated
Telophase	Cytoplasm separates

14. Fill in the blanks in the table with the appropriate term or definition.

15. What types of cells would constantly be in interphase?

16. Why is regeneration important for some organisms? In what way could regeneration of nerve cells be beneficial for humans?

17. What types of organisms are polyploidy? Why are they important?

18. What happens to chromosomes in meiosis I and meiosis II?

19. Describe several different ways that organisms can reproduce.

Part 3 | Open Ended

Record your answers on a sheet of paper.

Use the photo below to answer question 20.

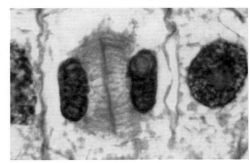

20. Is this a plant or an animal cell? Compare and contrast animal and plant cell division.

21. Describe in detail the structure of DNA.

Use the diagram below to answer question 22.

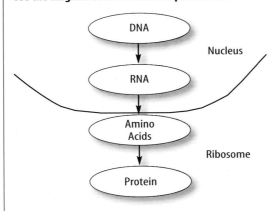

22. Discuss in detail what is taking place at each step of protein synthesis diagrammed above.

23. If a skin cell and a stomach cell have the same DNA then why are they so different?

24. What is mutation? Give examples where mutations could be harmful, beneficial or neutral.

ribosome, the message is translated to assemble amino acids into proteins.

23. A skin cell and stomach cell are so different because cells can turn genes on and off. Different genes in the skin cell are turned on so that it can carry out different functions than the stomach cell.

24. A mutation is a change in the sequence of DNA that codes for a gene or a change in the number chromosomes. There are many examples of harmful mutations; some could just cause the organism to not thrive in the environment and some may cause death. Beneficial mutations are those which benefit the organism's chance of survival. Neutral mutations do not benefit or harm the organism.

Rubrics

For more help evaluating open-ended assessment questions, see the rubric on p. 10T.

Part 3 | Open Ended

20. A plant cell appears in the picture. Cell division in a plant and animal cell are very similar. They both have interphase, mitosis and cytoplasmic division. The phases of mitosis are prophase, metaphase, anaphase and telophase. In prophase animal cells have centrioles and plant cells do not. In telophase, plant cells form a cell plate and animal cells do not.

21. DNA has a structure similar to a twisted ladder. The sides of the ladder are sugar-phosphate molecules and the rungs of the ladder are nitrogenous bases. RNA has only one side of the ladder with rungs of the nitrogenous bases. DNA and RNA both have the nitrogenous bases adenine, cytosine and guanine. RNA has uracil and DNA has thymine which pair with adenine.

22. In this diagram, DNA in the nucleus is used to make RNA. RNA carries the code for a protein from the nucleus to a ribosome. At the

Section/Objectives	Standards		Labs/Features
Chapter Opener	**National**	**State/Local**	**Launch Lab:** Who around you has dimples?, p. 125 **Foldables,** p. 125
	See pp. 16T–17T for a Key to Standards.		
Section 1 Genetics 🕐 2 sessions 📦 1 block 1. **Explain** how traits are inherited. 2. **Identify** Mendel's role in the history of genetics. 3. **Use** a Punnett square to predict the results of crosses. 4. **Compare and contrast** the difference between an individual's genotype and phenotype.	National Content Standards: UCP.1–UCP.3, UCP.5, A.1, A.2, C.1, C.2, G.2, G.3		**Science Online,** p. 127 **MiniLAB:** Comparing Common Traits, p. 128 **Visualizing Mendel's Experiments,** p. 129 **Applying Math:** Punnett Square, p. 131 **Lab:** Predicting Results, p. 133
Section 2 Genetics Since Mendel 🕐 2 sessions 📦 1 block 5. **Explain** how traits are inherited by incomplete dominance. 6. **Compare** multiple alleles and polygenic inheritance, and give examples of each. 7. **Describe** two human genetic disorders and how they are inherited. 8. **Explain** how sex-linked traits are passed to offspring.	National Content Standards: UCP.1–UCP.5, A.1, A.2, C.1, C.2, F.1, G.1		**Science Online,** p. 135 **MiniLAB:** Interpreting Polygenic Inheritance, p. 136 **Integrate Career,** p. 137
Section 3 Advances in Genetics 🕐 3 sessions 📦 1.5 blocks 9. **Evaluate** the importance of advances in genetics. 10. **Sequence** the steps in making genetically engineered organisms.	National Content Standards: UCP.1–UCP.5, A.1, A.2, C.1, C.2, F.3, F.5		**Integrate Environment,** p. 142 **Lab:** Tests for Color Blindness, p. 144 **Science Stats:** The Human Genome, p. 146

Glencoe Exclusive!
Teacher Works™
All-In-One Planner and Resource Center

Lab Materials	Reproducible Resources	Section Assessment	Technology
Launch Lab: Science Journal	**Chapter** *FAST FILE* **Resources** Foldables Worksheets, p. 13 Directed Reading Overview, p. 15 Note-taking Worksheets, pp. 29–31	GLENCOE'S **ASSESSMENT** ADVANTAGE	Teacher**Works** includes: • Interactive Teacher Edition • Lesson Planner with calendar • Access to all program blacklines • Correlations to standards • Web links
MiniLAB: pencil, paper **Lab:** paper bags (2), red beans (100), white beans (100)	**Chapter** *FAST FILE* **Resources** Transparency Activity, p. 40 MiniLAB, p. 3 Directed Reading, p. 16 Enrichment, p. 26 Reinforcement, p. 23 Lab Worksheet, pp. 5–6 Lab Activity, pp. 9–10, 11–12 **Mathematics Skill Activities,** p. 23	Portfolio Differentiated Instruction, p. 130 Performance MiniLAB, p. 128 Applying Math, p. 131 Applying Math, p. 132 Content Section Review, p. 132	Section Focus Transparency Virtual Labs CD-ROM Guided Reading Audio Program Interactive Chalkboard CD-ROM Video Lab
MiniLAB: paper, pencil, ruler *Need materials?* Contact Science Kit at 1-800-828-7777 or www.sciencekit.com on the Internet.	**Chapter** *FAST FILE* **Resources** Transparency Activity, p. 41 MiniLAB, p. 4 Enrichment, p. 27 Reinforcement, p. 24 Directed Reading, p. 16 Transparency Activity, pp. 43–44 **Life Science Critical Thinking/ Problem Solving,** p. 19	Portfolio Science Journal, p. 135 Performance MiniLAB, p. 136 Applying Skills, p. 140 Content Section Review, p. 140	Section Focus Transparency Teaching Transparency Virtual Labs CD-ROM Guided Reading Audio Program Interactive Chalkboard CD-ROM
Lab: white paper or poster board, colored markers	**Chapter** *FAST FILE* **Resources** Transparency Activity, p. 42 Enrichment, p. 28 Reinforcement, p. 25 Directed Reading, pp. 17, 18 Lab Worksheet, pp. 7–8 **Lab Management and Safety,** p. 74	Portfolio Assessment, p. 143 Performance Applying Skills, p. 143 Content Section Review, p. 143	Section Focus Transparency Virtual Labs CD-ROM Guided Reading Audio Program Interactive Chalkboard CD-ROM

End of Chapter Assessment

GLENCOE'S
ASSESSMENT
ADVANTAGE

Blackline Masters	Technology	Professional Series
Chapter *FAST FILE* **Resources** Chapter Review, pp. 33–34 Chapter Tests, pp. 35–38 **Standardized Test Practice,** pp. 23–26	MindJogger Videoquiz Virtual Labs CD-ROM ExamView® Pro Testmaker TeacherWorks CD-ROM Interactive Chalkboard CD-ROM	**Performance Assessment in the Science Classroom (PASC)**

Transparencies

Section Focus

SECTION 1 Section Focus Transparency — Pass It On

You may have noticed that tall parents often have tall children and dark-haired parents often have dark-haired children. Even though offspring are similar to their parents, they do not look exactly alike.

1. Do children ever look exactly the same? When?
2. How are the members of this family different? How are they the same?
3. Why can looking at a set of parents help you predict what their children might look like?

L2

SECTION 2 Section Focus Transparency — Dog Days

Humans have kept dogs for 12,000 to 14,000 years. At first, all dogs had jobs, such as herding or guarding. Today, some dogs have jobs, but many others are kept as pets.

1. What determines how big a dog can get?
2. Can a gray puppy and a brown puppy be littermates? How?
3. What environmental conditions could make one dog look different than its identical twin?

L2

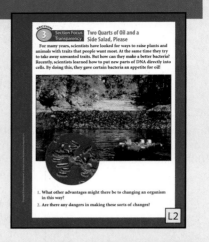

SECTION 3 Section Focus Transparency — Two Quarts of Oil and a Side Salad, Please

For many years, scientists have looked for ways to raise plants and animals with traits that people want most. At the same time they try to take away unwanted traits. But how can they make a better bacteria? Recently, scientists learned how to put new parts of DNA directly into cells. By doing this, they gave certain bacteria an appetite for oil!

1. What other advantages might there be to changing an organism in this way?
2. Are there any dangers in making these sorts of changes?

L2

This is a representation of key blackline masters available in the Teacher Classroom Resources. See Resource Manager boxes within the chapter for additional information.

Key to Teaching Strategies

The following designations will help you decide which activities are appropriate for your students.

L1 — Level 1 activities should be appropriate for students with learning difficulties.

L2 — Level 2 activities should be within the ability range of all students.

L3 — Level 3 activities are designed for above-average students.

ELL — ELL activities should be within the ability range of English-Language Learners.

COOP LEARN — Cooperative Learning activities are designed for small group work.

LS — Multiple Learning Styles logos, as described on page 12T, are used throughout to indicate strategies that address different learning styles.

P — These strategies represent student products that can be placed into a best-work portfolio.

PBL — Problem-Based Learning activities apply real-world situations to learning.

Assessment

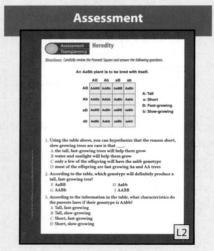

Assessment Transparency — Heredity

Directions: Carefully review the Punnett Square and answer the following questions.

An AaBb plant is to be bred with itself.

	AB	Ab	aB	ab
AB	AABB	AABb	AaBB	AaBb
Ab	AABb	AAbb	AaBb	Aabb
aB	AaBB	AaBb	aaBB	aaBb
ab	AaBb	Aabb	aaBb	aabb

A: Tall
a: Short
B: Fast-growing
b: Slow-growing

1. Using the table above, you can hypothesize that the reason short, slow growing trees are rare is that ___.
A the tall, fast-growing trees will help them grow
B water and sunlight will help them grow
C only a few of the offspring will have the aabb genotype
D most of the offspring are fast growing Aa and AA trees
2. According to the table, which genotype will definitely produce a tall, fast-growing tree?
F AaBB   H Aabb
G AABB   J AABB
3. According to the information in the table, what characteristics do the parents have if their genotype is AaBb?
A Tall, fast-growing
B Tall, slow-growing
C Short, fast-growing
D Short, slow-growing

L2

Teaching

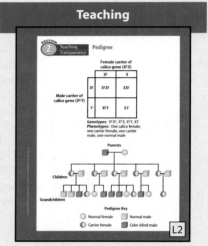

SECTION 2 Teaching Transparency — Pedigree

Female carrier of calico gene (X^C X)

	X^C	X
X^C	X^C X^C	X^C X
Y	X^C Y	X Y

Male carrier of calico gene (X^C Y)

Genotypes: X^C X^C, X^C X, X^C Y, X Y
Phenotypes: One calico female, one carrier female, one carrier male, one normal male

Parents

Children

Grandchildren

Pedigree Key
○ Normal female   □ Normal male
◑ Carrier female   ■ Color-blind male

L2

Hands-on Activities

Student Text Lab Worksheet

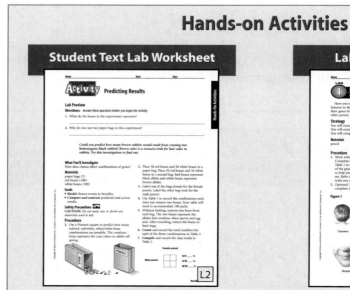

Activity — Predicting Results

Lab Preview
Directions: Answer these questions before you begin the Activity.
1. What do the beans in the experiment represent?

2. Why do you use two paper bags in this experiment?

Could you predict how many brown rabbits would result from crossing two heterozygous black rabbits? Brown color is a recessive trait for hair color in rabbits. Try this investigation to find out.

What You'll Investigate
How does chance affect combinations of genes?

Materials
paper bags (2)
red beans (100)
white beans (100)

Goals
• Model chance events in heredity.
• Compare and contrast predicted and actual results.

Safety Precautions
CAUTION: Do not taste, eat, or drink any materials used in lab.

Procedure
1. Use a Punnett square to predict how many red/red, red/white, white/white bean combinations are possible. These combinations represent the coat colors in rabbit offspring.

2. Place 50 red beans and 50 white beans in a paper bag. Place 50 red beans and 50 white beans in a second bag. Red beans represent black alleles and white beans represent brown alleles.
3. Label one of the bags female for the female parent. Label the other bag male for the male parent.
4. Use Table 1 to record the combination each time you remove two beans. Your table will need to accommodate 100 picks.
5. Without looking, remove one bean from each bag. The two beans represent the alleles that combine when sperm and egg join. After recording, return the beans to their bags.
6. Count and record the total numbers for each of the three combinations in Table 2.
7. Compile and record the class totals in Table 2.

L2

Laboratory Activities

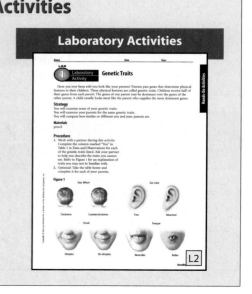

LAB 1 Laboratory Activity — Genetic Traits

Have you ever been told you look like your parents? Parents pass genes that determine physical features to their children. These physical features are called genetic traits. Children receive half of their genes from each parent. The genes of one parent may be dominant over the genes of the other parent. A child usually looks more like the parent who supplies the most dominant genes.

Strategy
You will examine some of your genetic traits.
You will examine your parents for the same genetic traits.
You will compare how similar or different you and your parents are.

Materials
pencil

Procedure
1. Work with a partner during this activity. Complete the column marked "You" in Table 1 in Data and Observations for each of the genetic traits listed. Ask your partner to help you describe the traits you cannot see. Refer to Figure 1 for an explanation of traits you may not be familiar with.
2. Optional: Take the table home and complete it for each of your parents.

Figure 1

L2

Resource Manager

Meeting Different Ability Levels

Content Outline
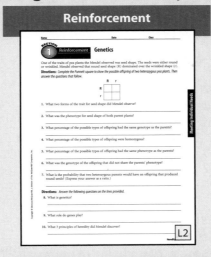

Reinforcement

Enrichment
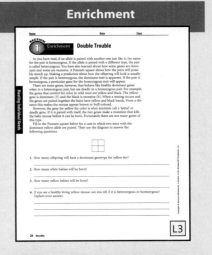

Directed Reading (English/Spanish)
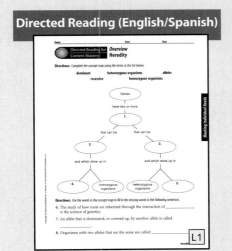

Study Guide

Reading Essentials

Assessment

Test Practice Workbook
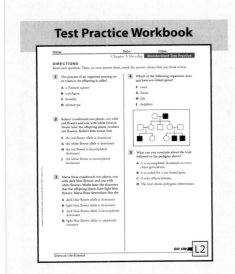

Chapter Review
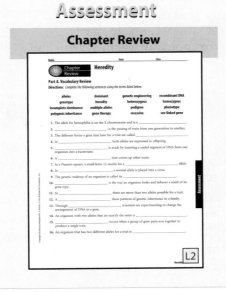

Chapter Tests
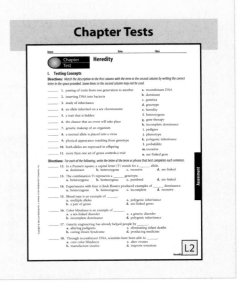

Science Content Background

section 1 Genetics

Mendelian Inheritance

Gregor Mendel, an Austrian monk, was the first scientist to bring an experimental and quantitative approach to genetics, the study of heredity. Mendelian inheritance reflects the mathematical rules of probability.

Dominant and Recessive Factors

In Mendel's experiments, the inheritance patterns of traits each possessed two alleles. The law of dominance explains that one trait, the dominant trait, is expressed in homozygous and heterozygous conditions. The recessive trait is expressed only in the homozygous condition.

Using a Punnett Square

Mendel developed the law of segregation, which shows that recessive alleles are not lost during meiosis. In Mendel's experiments with pea hybridization, the recessive trait reappeared in approximately one-fourth of the offspring produced by crossing two heterozygous pea plants.

section 2 Genetics Since Mendel

Other Modes of Inheritance

In incomplete dominance, the heterozygous condition results in an intermediate phenotype that appears to be a blend of the dominant and recessive traits. However, when heterozygous offspring are crossed, the next generation expresses the dominant, recessive, and intermediate phenotypes. In codominance, the heterozygous condition results in a phenotype that is a mixture of both dominant alleles. Sometimes there are multiple alleles for a trait, though each individual only carries two. Polygenic inheritance occurs when a trait is produced as a result of a group of genes. Mutations and chromosome disorders are caused by changes in genes.

Genetic Disorders

Many human disorders follow Mendelian inheritance patterns. Huntington's disease is carried on a dominant allele and causes lethal degeneration of the nervous system. Tay-Sachs is caused by a recessive allele and occurs most often in people of Jewish descent. Sickle-cell anemia is a recessive disorder that occurs most often in people of African descent. The red blood cells are malformed and cannot effectively transport oxygen.

section 3 Advances in Genetics

Benefits of Genetic Research

Advances made in the search for the molecular basis of inheritance are phenomenal. Technology is providing new tools to aid in research, genetic testing, and genetic counseling. Genetic engineering provides improved plants and efficient production of artificial chemicals such as insulin.

chapter content resources

Internet Resources

For additional content background, visit
life.msscience.com to:

- access your book online
- find references to related articles in popular science magazines
- access Web links with related content background
- access current events with science journal topics

Print Resources

Heredity Diseases, by Fern G. Brown, Franklin Watts, 1987

The Story of Science: The Treasure of Inheritance, by Roy A. Gallant, Benchmark Books, 2002

Genetics: The Study of Heredity (Investigating Science), by Ian Graham, Gareth Stevens, 2002

IDENTIFYING **Misconceptions**

Find Out What Students Think

Students may think that . . .

Dominant traits are the strongest, most superior, or most common traits in a population.
Genes coding for eye color in humans comes in two alleles. The dominant allele causes brown pigment to be produced in the iris, and the recessive allele does not produce a functional protein or pigment. Each person receives two alleles of each gene, one from each parent. If a person inherits at least one "brown" allele, the person's eyes will produce pigment. If a person has only recessive alleles, no pigment is made and the eyes appear blue. Human eye color is actually somewhat more complex than this, as it is controlled by several genes (not a single pair) as opposed to simple Mendelian inheritance. The greater the number of dominant alleles a person has, the darker the eyes appear.

Discussion
Ask the class, "If brown eyes are dominant over blue eyes, does this mean that someday all people will be brown-eyed?" Let students form small discussion groups. After a set time limit, let students present their answers and supporting evidence. Their answers will reveal their preconceived notions and their reasoning.

Promote Understanding

Activity
Group students in pairs, and give each pair an envelope containing five brown and five blue squares.

- Have each student draw one brown and one blue square. These squares represent the eye color alleles of an imaginary person. Ask what color of eyes the person has (brown).

- Tell students that their two imaginary people will have a child, so each must contribute one allele. Students should randomly draw a square from the envelope. Have students lay their contributed squares side by side and determine the eye color of the child.

- Count the number of blue-eyed and brown-eyed offspring produced in the class. Ask students why some of the brown-eyed parents had a child with blue eyes.

- Poll the class to see how many students have a widow's peak hairline (dominant) versus a straight hairline (recessive), and how many have a dimple in the chin (dominant) versus no dimple in the chin (recessive). These two traits have dominant forms that are usually infrequent in a population. L2

Assess
After completing the chapter, see *Identifying Misconceptions* in the Study Guide at the end of the chapter.

Heredity

Chapter Vocabulary

heredity, p. 126
alleles, p. 126
genetics, p. 126
hybrid, p. 128
dominant, p. 128
recessive, p. 128
Punnett square, p. 130
genotype, p. 130
phenotype, p. 130
homozygous, p. 130
heterozygous, p. 130
incomplete dominance, p. 134
polygenic inheritance, p. 136
sex-linked gene, p. 139
genetic engineering, p. 141

Science Journal Student responses will vary, but traits may include eye color, hair color, or shape of face. Students may respond that they can determine how traits were passed on to them by looking at their family history of those traits.

INTERACTIVE CHALKBOARD with Image Bank

PowerPoint® Presentations

This CD-ROM is an editable Microsoft® PowerPoint® presentation that includes:
- a pre-made presentation for every chapter
- interactive graphics
- animations
- audio clips
- image bank
- all new section and chapter questions
- Standardized Test Practice
- transparencies
- pre-lab questions for all labs
- Foldables directions
- links to life.msscience.com

chapter preview

sections

1 **Genetics**
   Lab Predicting Results

2 **Genetics Since Mendel**

3 **Advances in Genetics**
   Lab Tests for Color Blindness

   Virtual Lab How are traits passed from parents to offspring?

Why do people look different?

People have different skin colors, different kinds of hair, and different heights. Knowing how these differences are determined will help you predict when certain traits might appear. This will help you understand what causes hereditary disorders and how these are passed from generation to generation.

Science Journal Write three traits that you have and how you would determine how those traits were passed to you.

Theme Connection

Stability and Change Genes control stability through homeostasis at the organism level. Genetics provides background for understanding the changes involved in evolution.

About the Photo

Human Genome In 2001, the first draft of the human genome was published. The human genome contains approximately 30,000 genes. It is 25 times larger than any other genome sequenced so far. Despite the size of the human genome and the noticeable differences in human traits, any two humans differ in only about one or two nucleotide base pairs in every 1000 in their DNA sequence.

Start-Up Activities

Who around you has dimples?

You and your best friend enjoy the same sports, like the same food, and even have similar haircuts. But, there are noticeable differences between your appearances. Most of these differences are controlled by the genes you inherited from your parents. In the following lab, you will observe one of these differences.

1. Notice the two students in the photographs. One student has dimples when she smiles, and the other student doesn't have dimples.

2. Ask your classmates to smile naturally. In your Science Journal, record the name of each classmate and whether each one has dimples.

3. **Think Critically** In your Science Journal, calculate the percentage of students who have dimples. Are facial dimples a common feature among your classmates?

Classify Characteristics As you read this chapter about heredity, you can use the following Foldable to help you classify characteristics as inherited or not inherited.

STEP 1 Fold the top of a vertical piece of paper down and the bottom up to divide the paper into thirds.

STEP 2 Turn the paper horizontally; **unfold and label** the three columns as shown.

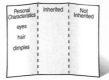

Read for Main Ideas Before you read the chapter, list personal characteristics and predict which are inherited or not inherited. As you read the chapter, check and change your list.

Preview this chapter's content and activities at life.msscience.com

---

Purpose Use the Launch Lab to introduce students to inheritance. Inform students that they will be learning about inheritance and genetics as they read the chapter. L2 ELL COOP LEARN LS **Logical-Mathematical**

Preparation Discuss the photograph as a class to ensure that students recognize what dimples are.

Teaching Strategy Record data for each class and have students compare their results with those of other classes.

Think Critically

Percentages will vary depending upon how many students in the class have and do not have dimples. Generally, the percentage of students having dimples falls between 10 and 40 percent.

Assessment

Oral Have students suggest other features that are inherited. Possible answers: hair color and texture, skin and eye color, height, shape of facial features. Use **Performance Assessment in the Science Classroom,** p. 89.

 Dinah Zike Study Fold

Student preparation materials for this Foldable are available in the **Chapter** *FAST FILE* **Resources.**

1 Motivate

Bellringer

Section Focus Transparencies also are available on the Interactive Chalkboard CD-ROM.

 L2 ELL

Tie to Prior Knowledge

Inherited Traits Show a picture of a mother dog and her puppies (or a cat and her kittens). Have students list characteristics of the offspring they think are inherited from the parents. Lead students to understand that all of the general physical traits, such as number of legs, length and shape of ears, eye color and shape, and so on, are inherited. L1

as you read

What You'll Learn

- **Explain** how traits are inherited.
- **Identify** Mendel's role in the history of genetics.
- **Use** a Punnett square to predict the results of crosses.
- **Compare and contrast** the difference between an individual's genotype and phenotype.

Why It's Important

Heredity and genetics help explain why people are different.

Review Vocabulary

meiosis: reproductive process that produces four haploid sex cells from one diploid cell

New Vocabulary

- heredity
- allele
- genetics
- hybrid
- dominant
- recessive
- Punnett square
- genotype
- phenotype
- homozygous
- heterozygous

Inheriting Traits

Do you look more like one parent or grandparent? Do you have your father's eyes? What about Aunt Isabella's cheekbones? Eye color, nose shape, and many other physical features are some of the traits that are inherited from parents, as **Figure 1** shows. An organism is a collection of traits, all inherited from its parents. **Heredity** (huh REH duh tee) is the passing of traits from parent to offspring. What controls these traits?

What is genetics? Generally, genes on chromosomes control an organism's form and function. The different forms of a trait that a gene may have are called **alleles** (uh LEELZ). When a pair of chromosomes separates during meiosis (mi OH sus), alleles for each trait also separate into different sex cells. As a result, every sex cell has one allele for each trait, as shown in **Figure 2.** The allele in one sex cell may control one form of the trait, such as having facial dimples. The allele in the other sex cell may control a different form of the trait—not having dimples. The study of how traits are inherited through the interactions of alleles is the science of **genetics** (juh NE tihks).

Figure 1 Note the strong family resemblance among these four generations.

Section 1 Resource Manager

Chapter FAST FILE Resources
- Transparency Activity, p. 40
- Directed Reading for Content Mastery, pp. 15, 16
- Note-taking Worksheets, pp. 29–31
- MiniLAB, p. 3
- Enrichment, p. 26

- Lab Activity, pp. 9–10, 11–12
- Lab Worksheet, pp. 5–6
- Reinforcement, p. 23

Home and Community Involvement, p. 36
Performance Assessment in the Science Classroom, p. 57
Mathematics Skill Activities, p. 23

Figure 2 An allele is one form of a gene. Alleles separate into separate sex cells during meiosis. In this example, the alleles that control the trait for dimples include *D,* the presence of dimples, and *d,* the absence of dimples.

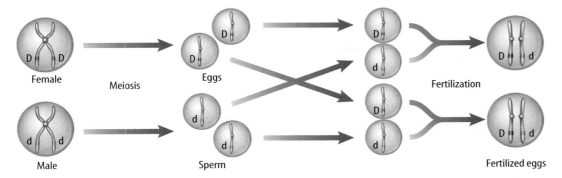

The alleles that control a trait are located on each duplicated chromosome.

During meiosis, duplicated chromosomes separate.

During fertilization, each parent donates one chromosome. This results in two alleles for the trait of dimples in the new individual formed.

Mendel—The Father of Genetics

Did you know that an experiment with pea plants helped scientists understand why your eyes are the color that they are? Gregor Mendel was an Austrian monk who studied mathematics and science but became a gardener in a monastery. His interest in plants began as a boy in his father's orchard where he could predict the possible types of flowers and fruits that would result from crossbreeding two plants. Curiosity about the connection between the color of a pea flower and the type of seed that same plant produced inspired him to begin experimenting with garden peas in 1856. Mendel made careful use of scientific methods, which resulted in the first recorded study of how traits pass from one generation to the next. After eight years, Mendel presented his results with pea plants to scientists.

Before Mendel, scientists mostly relied on observation and description, and often studied many traits at one time. Mendel was the first to trace one trait through several generations. He was also the first to use the mathematics of probability to explain heredity. The use of math in plant science was a new concept and not widely accepted then. Mendel's work was forgotten for a long time. In 1900, three plant scientists, working separately, reached the same conclusions as Mendel. Each plant scientist had discovered Mendel's writings while doing his own research. Since then, Mendel has been known as the father of genetics.

Science Online

Topic: Genetics
Visit life.msscience.com for Web links to information about early genetics experiments.

Activity List two other scientists who studied genetics, and what organism they used in their research.

Inquiry Lab

Observing Mendelian Genetics

Purpose to understand and observe the outcome of a cross between corn seedlings that are heterozygous for green pigment (*Cc*)

Possible Materials a flat of germinated albino corn

Estimated Time one class period

Teaching Strategies
• The dominant allele in corn is green pigment, so students can observe that most of the seedlings are green and they can predict why.
• Students can predict the genotypes of the green and albino seedlings.
• Students can count the number of green seedlings and the number of albino seedlings. They can predict what the ratio of green seedlings to albino seedlings should be and then calculate the actual ratio. Students can explain why the actual ratio may be different than the predicted ratio.
• Allow students to explore other questions that arise. L2

For additional inquiry activities, see *Science Inquiry Labs.*

Teacher FYI

Scientific Method Mendel's experiments illustrate the scientific method. Mendel worked with a single trait at a time, conducted carefully controlled experiments, collected and analyzed data, recorded his experiments so they could be repeated, worked with large samples, and shared results with his contemporaries.

Visual Learning

Figure 2 The arrows show how eggs and sperm, produced by meiosis, combine during fertilization. In this example, each parent was homozygous for a trait. What would the genotype of the fertilized eggs be if the female parent was heterozygous for the dimple trait (*Dd*)? One fertilized egg would be Dd and one would be dd.

Table 1 Traits Compared by Mendel

Traits	Shape of Seeds	Color of Seeds	Color of Pods	Shape of Pods	Plant Height	Position of Flowers	Flower Color
Dominant trait	Round	Yellow	Green	Full	Tall	At leaf junctions	Purple
Recessive trait	Wrinkled	Green	Yellow	Flat, constricted	short	At tips of branches	White

Genetics in a Garden

Each time Mendel studied a trait, he crossed two plants with different expressions of the trait and found that the new plants all looked like one of the two parents. He called these new plants **hybrids** (HI brudz) because they received different genetic information, or different alleles, for a trait from each parent. The results of these studies made Mendel even more curious about how traits are inherited.

Garden peas are easy to breed for pure traits. An organism that always produces the same traits generation after generation is called a purebred. For example, tall plants that always produce seeds that produce tall plants are purebred for the trait of tall height. **Table 1** shows other pea plant traits that Mendel studied.

Reading Check   *Why might farmers plant purebred crop seeds?*

Dominant and Recessive Factors In nature, insects randomly pollinate plants as they move from flower to flower. In his experiments, Mendel used pollen from the flowers of purebred tall plants to pollinate by hand the flowers of purebred short plants. This process is called cross-pollination. He found that tall plants crossed with short plants produced seeds that produced all tall plants. Whatever caused the plants to be short had disappeared. Mendel called the tall form the **dominant** (DAH muh nunt) factor because it dominated, or covered up, the short form. He called the form that seemed to disappear the **recessive** (rih SE sihv) factor. Today, these are called dominant alleles and recessive alleles. What happened to the recessive form? **Figure 3** answers this question.

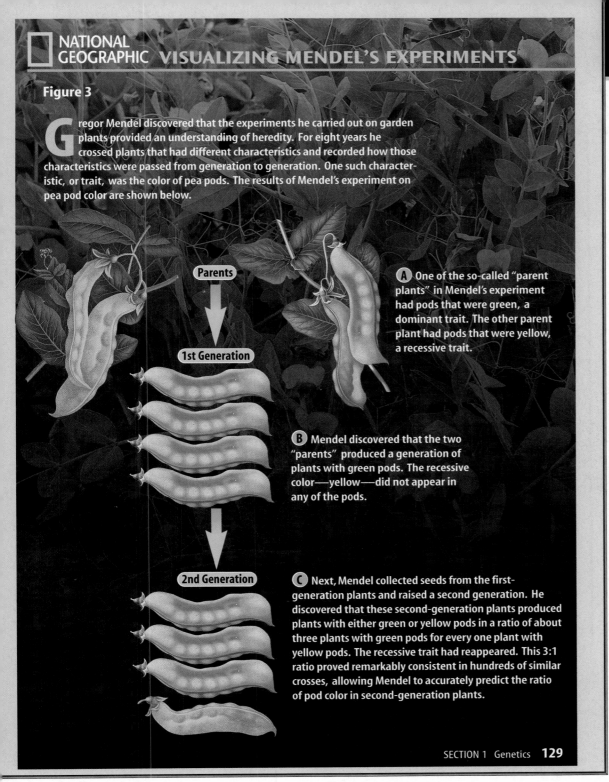

Figure 3

Gregor Mendel discovered that the experiments he carried out on garden plants provided an understanding of heredity. For eight years he crossed plants that had different characteristics and recorded how those characteristics were passed from generation to generation. One such characteristic, or trait, was the color of pea pods. The results of Mendel's experiment on pea pod color are shown below.

Parents

1st Generation

2nd Generation

A One of the so-called "parent plants" in Mendel's experiment had pods that were green, a dominant trait. The other parent plant had pods that were yellow, a recessive trait.

B Mendel discovered that the two "parents" produced a generation of plants with green pods. The recessive color—yellow—did not appear in any of the pods.

C Next, Mendel collected seeds from the first-generation plants and raised a second generation. He discovered that these second-generation plants produced plants with either green or yellow pods in a ratio of about three plants with green pods for every one plant with yellow pods. The recessive trait had reappeared. This 3:1 ratio proved remarkably consistent in hundreds of similar crosses, allowing Mendel to accurately predict the ratio of pod color in second-generation plants.

SECTION 1 Genetics **129**

NATIONAL GEOGRAPHIC

Visualizing Mendel's Experiments

Have students examine the pictures and read the captions. Then ask the following questions:

Why is it important that Mendel based his conclusions on the results of hundreds of pea plant crosses? It's important to have as much data as possible before drawing conclusions about any experiment, and in general, the larger the sample size, the more accurate the results will be.

Would the allele for the recessive trait of yellow pea pod color be present in the first generation of pea plants? Yes, the allele would be present, but it would not be expressed because none of the plants are homozygous recessive.

Activity

Mendel's Ratios Have students work in small groups. Using the example shown in the Visualizing, have the students use Mendel's ratios to determine the number of yellow pea plants in the second generation if the second generation of plants contained the following: 100 total plants (25), 300 total plants (75). L2

130 **CHAPTER 5** Heredity

Use an Analogy

Games of Chance The probability of genetic events is analogous to rolling a die and other games of chance.

Make a Model

Crossing Pea Plants Provide students with blocks of two different colors. Have them use the blocks to model the cross involving pea plant flowers described in the text. Help them use these tools to distinguish between genotype and phenotype, and homozygous and heterozygous. L2

Caption Answer

Figure 4 No; if red is recessive, then the genotype is homozygous recessive (rr), but if red is dominant, then the flower could be either homozygous (RR) or heterozygous (Rr).

Discussion

Allele Combinations Have students predict the possible allele combinations for a pea plant that is heterozygous for plant height, tall (Tt), and homozygous for seed shape, wrinkled (rr). The possible combinations are Tr and tr.

✓ Reading Check

Answer Homozygous organisms carry the same two alleles for a trait. Heterozygous organisms carry two different alleles for a trait.

Figure 4 This snapdragon's phenotype is red.
Determine *Can you tell what the flower's genotype for color is? Explain your answer.*

Using Probability to Make Predictions If you and your sister can't agree on what movie to see, you could solve the problem by tossing a coin. When you toss a coin, you're dealing with probabilities. Probability is a branch of mathematics that helps you predict the chance that something will happen. If your sister chooses tails while the coin is in the air, what is the probability that the coin will land tail-side up? Because a coin has two sides, there are two possible outcomes, heads or tails. One outcome is tails. Therefore, the probability of one side of a coin showing is one out of two, or 50 percent.

Mendel also dealt with probabilities. One of the things that made his predictions accurate was that he worked with large numbers of plants. He studied almost 30,000 pea plants over a period of eight years. By doing so, Mendel increased his chances of seeing a repeatable pattern. Valid scientific conclusions need to be based on results that can be duplicated.

Punnett Squares Suppose you wanted to know what colors of pea plant flowers you would get if you pollinated white flowers on one pea plant with pollen from purple flowers on a different plant. How could you predict what the offspring would look like without making the cross? A handy tool used to predict results in Mendelian genetics is the **Punnett** (PUH nut) **square.** In a Punnett square, letters represent dominant and recessive alleles. An uppercase letter stands for a dominant allele. A lowercase letter stands for a recessive allele. The letters are a form of code. They show the **genotype** (JEE nuh tipe), or genetic makeup, of an organism. Once you understand what the letters mean, you can tell a lot about the inheritance of a trait in an organism.

The way an organism looks and behaves as a result of its genotype is its **phenotype** (FEE nuh tipe), as shown in **Figure 4.** If you have brown hair, then the phenotype for your hair color is brown.

Alleles Determine Traits Most cells in your body have two alleles for every trait. These alleles are located on chromosomes within the nucleus of cells. An organism with two alleles that are the same is called **homozygous** (hoh muh ZI gus). For Mendel's peas, this would be written as *TT* (homozygous for the tall-dominant trait) or *tt* (homozygous for the short-recessive trait). An organism that has two different alleles for a trait is called **heterozygous** (he tuh roh ZI gus). The hybrid plants Mendel produced were all heterozygous for height, *Tt*.

✓ Reading Check
What is the difference between homozygous and heterozygous organisms?

Differentiated Instruction

Challenge Have students form Punnett squares that show the results of first- and second-generation crosses between organisms that are pure bred for two traits. What is the genotype of all of the first generation offspring? They are all heterozygous. Students should then cross the heterozygous offspring to determine the second-generation genotype. What is the ratio obtained in the second generation? 9:3:3:1 ratio L3 ELL COOP LEARN P

Making a Punnett Square In a Punnett square for predicting one trait, the letters representing the two alleles from one parent are written along the top of the grid, one letter per section. Those of the second parent are placed down the side of the grid, one letter per section. Each square of the grid is filled in with one allele donated by each parent. The letters that you use to fill in each of the squares represent the genotypes of possible offspring that the parents could produce.

Applying Math — Calculate Percentages

PUNNET SQUARE One dog carries heterozygous, black-fur traits (*Bb*), and its mate carries homogeneous, blond-fur traits (*bb*). Use a Punnett square to determine the probability of one of their puppies having black fur.

Solution

1 *This is what you know:*
- dominant allele is represented by *B*
- recessive allele is represented by *b*

2 *This is what you need to find out:*

What is the probability of a puppy's fur color being black?

3 *This is the procedure you need to use:*
- Complete the Punnett square.
- There are two *Bb* genotypes and four possible outcomes.
- %(black fur) =

$$\frac{\text{number of ways to get black fur}}{\text{number of possible outcomes}}$$

$$= \frac{2}{4} = \frac{1}{2} = 50\%$$

Black dog

	B	b
b	Bb	bb
b	Bb	bb

Blond dog

Genotypes of offspring:
2Bb, 2bb
Phenotypes of offspring:
2 black, 2 blond

4 *Check your answer:* $\frac{1}{2}$ of 4 is 2, which is the number of black dogs.

Practice Problems

1. In peas, the color yellow (*Y*) is dominant to the color green (*y*). According to the Punnett square, what is the probability of an offspring being yellow?

2. What is the probability of an offspring having the *yy* genotype?

Parent (Yy)

	Y	y
Y	YY	Yy
y	Yy	yy

Parent (Yy)

 For more practice, visit life.msscience.com/math_practice

Quick Demo

Beads as Traits

Materials string, colored beads

Estimated Time five minutes

Procedure Demonstrate alleles along a chromosome by stringing colored beads on a string. The colored beads represent genes for different traits along the chromosome. Create two strings of beads and bring the strands together to demonstrate the homozygous and heterozygous conditions.

Applying Math

National Math Standards
Correlation to Mathematics Objectives
1, 5, 9, 10

Answers to Practice Problems
1. 75% yellow
2. Genotype yy = 25%

Virtual Labs

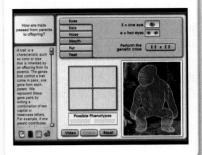

Inheriting Traits *How are traits passed from parents to offspring?*

Differentiated Instruction

Learning Disabled Have students choose one or two inherited traits (eye color, left- or right-handedness, and so on) and survey classmates to see how many of them display the characteristics. Results can be graphed. Other classrooms can be surveyed. Students can determine whether larger populations have the same ratio of the traits as subgroups. L1 COOP LEARN Interpersonal

Table 2 Have students relate the principles of heredity to genetic examples they have studied in this section.

3 Assess

DAILY INTERVENTION

Check for Understanding

Visual-Spatial Have students fill in a Punnett square on a large poster that shows the results of a trihybrid cross between individuals who are heterozygous for all three traits. L2

Reteach

Human Alleles Take the class to a paved portion of the school yard and have students role-play the alleles in a cross. Use masking tape to mark out a large Punnett square on the pavement. Assign students to be certain alleles and allow them to arrange themselves and announce the phenotypes and genotypes produced. L2 **ELL** **IS** Visual-Spatial

✔ Assessment

Performance Have students use a Punnett square to demonstrate their answer to Question 6. Use **Performance Assessment in the Science Classroom,** p. 97.

Principles of Heredity Even though Gregor Mendel didn't know anything about DNA, genes, or chromosomes, he succeeded in beginning to describe and mathematically represent how inherited traits are passed from parents to offspring. He realized that some factor in the pea plant produced certain traits. Mendel also concluded that these factors separated when the pea plant reproduced. Mendel arrived at his conclusions after years of detailed observation, careful analysis, and repeated experimentation. **Table 2** summarizes Mendel's principles of heredity.

Table 2 Principles of Heredity	
1	Traits are controlled by alleles on chromosomes.	
2	An allele's effect is dominant or recessive.	
3	When a pair of chromosomes separates during meiosis, the different alleles for a trait move into separate sex cells.	

section 1 review

Summary

Inheriting Traits
- Heredity is the passing of traits from parent to offspring.
- Genetics is the study of how traits are inherited through the interactions of alleles.

Mendel—The Father of Genetics
- In 1856, Mendel began experimenting with garden peas, using careful scientific methods.
- Mendel was the first to trace one trait through several generations.
- In 1900, three plant scientists separately reached the same conclusions as Mendel.

Genetics in a Garden
- Hybrids receive different genetic information for a trait from each parent.
- Genetics involves dominant and recessive factors.
- Punnett squares can be used to predict the results of a cross.
- Mendel's conclusions led to the principles of heredity.

Self Check

1. **Contrast** Alleles are described as being dominant or recessive. What is the difference between a dominant and a recessive allele?
2. **Describe** how dominant and recessive alleles are represented in a Punnett square.
3. **Explain** the difference between genotype and phenotype. Give examples.
4. **Infer** Gregor Mendel, an Austrian monk who lived in the 1800s, is known as the father of genetics. Explain why Mendel has been given this title.
5. **Think Critically** If an organism expresses a recessive phenotype, can you tell the genotype? Explain your answer by giving an example.

Applying Math

6. **Use Percentages** One fruit fly is heterozygous for long wings, and another fruit fly is homozygous for short wings. Long wings are dominant to short wings. Use a Punnett square to find the expected percent of offspring with short wings.

  life.msscience.com/self_check_quiz

---

section 1 review

1. A dominant allele is expressed if an allele pair is homozygous dominant or heterozygous. A recessive allele is expressed only when an allele pair is homozygous recessive.
2. Dominant alleles are represented with an uppercase letter, recessive alleles with a lowercase letter.
3. Genotype is the combination of alleles an organism contains; phenotype is the expression of the alleles in an organism. For example, a genotype might be Tt (heterozygous dominant), and the phenotype might be tall.
4. He was the first person to explain the mechanisms of heredity.
5. Yes, because two copies of the recessive allele must be present for the recessive phenotype to show up.
6. 50%

Predicting Results

Could you predict how many brown rabbits would result from crossing two heterozygous black rabbits? Try this investigation to find out. Brown color is a recessive trait for hair color in rabbits.

◉ Real-World Question

How does chance affect combinations of genes?

Goals
- **Model** chance events in heredity.
- **Compare and contrast** predicted and actual results.

Materials
paper bags (2)   white beans (100)
red beans (100)

Safety Precautions

WARNING: *Do not taste, eat, or drink any materials used in the lab.*

◉ Procedure

1. Use a Punnett square to predict how many red/red, red/white, and white/white bean combinations are possible. The combinations represent the coat colors in rabbit offspring.
2. Place 50 red beans and 50 white beans in a paper bag. Place 50 red beans and 50 white beans in a second bag. Red beans represent black alleles and white beans represent brown alleles.
3. Label one of the bags *Female* for the female parent. Label the other bag *Male* for the male parent.
4. Use a data table to record the combination each time you remove two beans. Your table will need to accommodate 100 picks.

5. Without looking, remove one bean from each bag. The two beans represent the alleles that combine when sperm and egg join. After recording, return the beans to their bags.
6. **Count** and record the total numbers for each of the three combinations in your data table.
7. **Compile and record** the class totals.

◉ Conclude and Apply

1. **Name** the combination that occurred most often.
2. **Calculate** the ratio of red/red to red/white to white/white. What hair color in rabbits do these combinations represent?
3. **Compare** your predicted (expected) results with your observed (actual) results.
4. **Hypothesize** how you could get predicted results to be closer to actual results.

Gene Combinations

Rabbits	Red/Red	Red/White	White/White
Your total			
Class total			

Communicating Your Data

Write a paragraph that clearly describes your results. Have another student read your paragraph. Ask if he or she could understand what happened. If not, rewrite your paragraph and have the other student read it again. **For more help, refer to the Science Skill Handbook.**

LAB **133**

✔ Assessment

Performance To further assess students' knowledge of probability, have them repeat the lab using three different kinds of beans. Use the **Performance Assessment in the Science Classroom,** p. 97. L2

Communicating Your Data

Students' paragraphs should indicate methods and results, as well as how the model relates to actual heredity principles.

◉ Real-World Question

Purpose Students use a model to investigate how the principles of heredity are related to chance. L2 ELL IN **Logical-Mathematical**

Process Skills predict, observe, record data, interpret data, use numbers, make and use tables

Time Required one class period

◉ Procedure

Safety Precautions Remind students not to eat or throw the beans.

Teaching Strategies
- All the beans should be approximately the same size.
- Emphasize the importance of completing all 100 trials.

Troubleshooting Explain to students that beans must be returned to the bag after each draw so that the probability of choosing the different color combinations remains the same throughout the lab.

◉ Conclude and Apply

1. red/white
2. Results should be close to 1:2:1; red/red represents a black rabbit, red/white represents a black rabbit, and white/white represents a brown rabbit.
3. Answers will vary, but should follow expected results closely.
4. A larger sample could be used or more trials done.

LAB 133

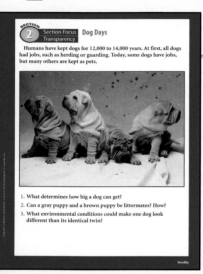

Tie to Prior Knowledge

Complex Inheritance Ask students if any of them have eye color different from either parent. Explain that some inherited traits involve more complex patterns of inheritance, and students will learn about them in this section.

Caption Answer

Figure 5 The palomino's coat color is intermediate between its parents' coat colors.

section 2

Genetics Since Mendel

as you read

What **You'll Learn**

- **Explain** how traits are inherited by incomplete dominance.
- **Compare** multiple alleles and polygenic inheritance, and give examples of each.
- **Describe** two human genetic disorders and how they are inherited.
- **Explain** how sex-linked traits are passed to offspring.

Why **It's Important**

Most of your inherited traits involve more complex patterns of inheritance than Mendel discovered.

🔍 **Review Vocabulary**

gene: section of DNA on a chromosome that contains instructions for making specific proteins

New Vocabulary

- incomplete dominance
- polygenic inheritance
- sex-linked gene

Figure 5 When a chestnut horse is bred with a cremello horse, all offspring will be palomino. The Punnett square shown on the opposite page can be used to predict this result. **Explain** *how the color of the palomino horse shows that the coat color of horses may be inherited by incomplete dominance.*

Incomplete Dominance

Not even in science do things remain the same. After Mendel's work was rediscovered in 1900, scientists repeated his experiments. For some plants, such as peas, Mendel's results proved true. However, when different plants were crossed, the results were sometimes different. One scientist crossed purebred red four-o'clock plants with purebred white four-o'clock plants. He expected to get all red flowers, but they were pink. Neither allele for flower color seemed dominant. Had the colors become blended like paint colors? He crossed the pink-flowered plants with each other, and red, pink, and white flowers were produced. The red and white alleles had not become blended. Instead, when the allele for white flowers and the allele for red flowers combined, the result was an intermediate phenotype—a pink flower.

When the offspring of two homozygous parents show an intermediate phenotype, this inheritance is called **incomplete dominance.** Other examples of incomplete dominance include the flower color of some plant breeds and the coat color of some horse breeds, as shown in **Figure 5.**

Chestnut horse

Cremello horse

Section 2 Resource Manager

Chapter *Fast File* Resources

Transparency Activity, pp. 41, 43–44
Directed Reading for Content Mastery, p. 16
MiniLAB, p. 4
Enrichment, p. 27
Reinforcement, p. 24

Life Science Critical Thinking/Problem Solving, p. 19

Multiple Alleles Mendel studied traits in peas that were controlled by just two alleles. However, many traits are controlled by more than two alleles. A trait that is controlled by more than two alleles is said to be controlled by multiple alleles. Traits controlled by multiple alleles produce more than three phenotypes of that trait.

Imagine that only three types of coins are made—nickels, dimes, and quarters. If every person can have only two coins, six different combinations are possible. In this problem, the coins represent alleles of a trait. The sum of each two-coin combination represents the phenotype. Can you name the six different phenotypes possible with two coins?

Blood type in humans is an example of multiple alleles that produce only four phenotypes. The alleles for blood types are called A, B, and O. The O allele is recessive to both the A and B alleles. When a person inherits one A allele and one B allele for blood type, both are expressed—phenotype AB. A person with phenotype A blood has the genetic makeup, or genotype—AA or AO. Someone with phenotype B blood has the genotype BB or BO. Finally, a person with phenotype O blood has the genotype OO.

Reading Check *What are the six different blood type genotypes?*

Palomino horse

Science Online

Topic: Blood Types
Visit life.msscience.com for Web links to information about the importance of blood types in blood transfusions.

Activity Make a chart showing which blood types can be used for transfusions into people with A, B, AB, or O blood phenotypes.

Punnett square

Chestnut horse (CC)

	C	C
C'	CC'	CC'
C'	CC'	CC'

Cremello horse (C'C')

Genotypes: All CC'
Phenotypes: All palomino horses

2 Teach

Discussion
Predicting Traits Discuss why traits governed by incomplete dominance or multiple alleles might be more difficult to study. Help students see that these patterns do not conform to Mendel's prediction of a simple 3:1 ratio.

Text Question Answer
Possible combinations: nickel, dime; nickel, quarter; dime, quarter; nickel, nickel; dime, dime; quarter, quarter

Fun Fact

Blood types are important to the health profession. Matching blood types—both AB, A, B, or O and Rh—is important in transfusions. The recessive blood type, O, occurs in more than 30 percent of Americans.

Reading Check

Answer AA, AO, AB, BB, BO, OO

Science Journal

Genetics of Flower Color Explain that in hibiscus flowers, red is dominant to white. Have students explain why they can tell the genotype of a red four-o'clock, but not of a red hibiscus. Four-o'clocks inherit color by incomplete dominance. A red four-o'clock must be homozygous. If it were heterozygous, it would be pink. A red hibiscus might be heterozygous or homozygous.

Word Origin Polygenic inheritance involves many genes. The prefix *poly-* means "many." Have students use a dictionary to find other words with this prefix and explain their meanings. Possible answers: polygon—many-sided figure; polychromatic—made of many colors

L2

Purpose to determine the inheritance pattern that controls hand span L2 ELL

LS Logical-Mathematical

Materials paper, pencil, ruler

Teaching Strategy It may be easier for students to have each subject place his or her hand on a piece of paper and mark the width of the hand span before measuring it.

Analysis

1. Answers will vary. Spans may range from 12.5 cm to 24 cm or more.
2. Hand spans are determined by polygenic inheritance, not by a simple Mendelian pattern.

Assessment

Oral Ask students to determine if identical twins have identical hand spans. The spans are usually very close, but not identical because of environmental factors that affect growth. Use **Performance Assessment in the Science Classroom,** p. 89.

✔ Reading Check

Answer amount of water or sunlight available, presence or absence of chemicals in soil

---

Interpreting Polygenic Inheritance

Procedure 🖐

1. Measure the hand spans of your classmates.
2. Using a **ruler,** measure from the tip of the thumb to the tip of the little finger when the hand is stretched out. Read the measurement to the nearest centimeter.
3. Record the name and hand-span measurement of each person in a data table.

Analysis

1. What range of hand spans did you find?
2. Are hand spans inherited as a simple Mendelian pattern or as a polygenic or incomplete dominance pattern? Explain.

Figure 6 Himalayan rabbits have alleles for dark-colored fur. However, this allele is able to express itself only at lower temperatures. Only the areas located farthest from the rabbit's main body heat (ears, nose, feet, tail) have dark-colored fur.

Polygenic Inheritance

Eye color is an example of a trait that is produced by a combination of many genes. **Polygenic** (pah lih JEH nihk) **inheritance** occurs when a group of gene pairs acts together to produce a trait. The effects of many alleles produces a wide variety of phenotypes. For this reason, it may be hard to classify all the different shades of eye color.

Your height and the color of your eyes and skin are just some of the many human traits controlled by polygenic inheritance. It is estimated that three to six gene pairs control your skin color. Even more gene pairs might control the color of your hair and eyes. The environment also plays an important role in the expression of traits controlled by polygenic inheritance. Polygenic inheritance is common and includes such traits as grain color in wheat and milk production in cows. Egg production in chickens is also a polygenic trait.

Impact of the Environment Your environment plays a role in how some of your genes are expressed or whether they are expressed at all, as shown in **Figure 6.** Environmental influences can be internal or external. For example, most male birds are more brightly colored than females. Chemicals in their bodies determine whether the gene for brightly colored feathers is expressed.

Although genes determine many of your traits, you might be able to influence their expression by the decisions you make. Some people have genes that make them at risk for developing certain cancers. Whether they get cancer might depend on external environmental factors. For instance, if some people at risk for skin cancer limit their exposure to the Sun and take care of their skin, they might never develop cancer.

✔ Reading Check

What environmental factors might affect the size of leaves on a tree?

✔ Active Reading

Reflective Journal In this strategy, students identify activities and what they learned and record responses to the activities. Have students divide pieces of paper into several columns. Have them record their thoughts under headings such as *What I did, What I learned, What questions do I have, What surprises did I experience,* and *Overall response.* Have students write a Reflective Journal entry for the MiniLAB. L2

Human Genes and Mutations

Sometimes a gene undergoes a change that results in a trait that is expressed differently. Occasionally errors occur in the DNA when it is copied inside of a cell. Such changes and errors are called mutations. Not all mutations are harmful. They might be helpful or have no effect on an organism.

Certain chemicals are known to produce mutations in plants or animals, including humans. X rays and radioactive substances are other causes of some mutations. Mutations are changes in genes.

Chromosome Disorders

In addition to individual mutations, problems can occur if the incorrect number of chromosomes is inherited. Every organism has a specific number of chromosomes. However, mistakes in the process of meiosis can result in a new organism with more or fewer chromosomes than normal. A change in the total number of human chromosomes is usually fatal to the unborn embryo or fetus, or the baby may die soon after birth.

Look at the human chromosomes in **Figure 7.** If three copies of chromosome 21 are produced in the fertilized human egg, Down's syndrome results. Individuals with Down's syndrome can be short, exhibit learning disabilities, and have heart problems. Such individuals can lead normal lives if they have no severe health complications.

INTEGRATE Career

Genetic Counselor Testing for genetic disorders may allow many affected individuals to seek treatment and cope with their diseases. Genetic counselors are trained to analyze a family's history to determine a person's health risk. Research what a genetic counselor does and how to become a genetic counselor. Record what you learn in your Science Journal.

INTEGRATE Career

Genetic Counselor The field of genetic counseling is the communication process that deals with the probability that a genetic disorder will occur within a family. Medical professionals specialized in medical genetics and counseling are called genetic counselors. They can help educate the public and help families find support and treatment for genetic disorders. To become a genetic counselor, you must earn a master's level degree and a certification test.

Figure 7 Humans usually have 23 pairs of chromosomes. Notice that three copies of chromosome 21 are present in this photo, rather than the usual two chromosomes. This change in chromosome number results in Down's syndrome. Chris Burke, a well-known actor, has this syndrome.

21

SECTION 2 Genetics Since Mendel **137**

LAB DEMONSTRATION

Purpose to show how mutations are passed to daughter cells

Materials blue and red overhead acetate, yarn, scissors, overhead projector

Preparation Cut out several 2-, 4-, and 6-cm long pairs of blue chromosomes. Cut one 4-cm long red chromosome.

Procedure Make a circle of yarn on the projector to represent a cell. Place the blue chromosome pairs in the cell. "Mutate" one chromosome from blue to red. Have the cell undergo mitosis.

Expected Outcome Daughter cells carry the mutation.

Assessment

What will happen when the cells carrying the mutation reproduce? The mutation will be reproduced. How might this explain a white stripe of hair on someone with black hair? The mutation is in the hair cells. It is passed along when the hair cells undergo mitosis.

Human Disorders Point out that about 600 simple recessive human disorders are presently known. Genetic disorders caused by dominant alleles are more common. An example is Huntington's disease, which usually does not express itself until the person is an adult. Why are fewer human genetic disorders recessive? Humans with recessive genetic disorders rarely live to a reproductive age.

✔ Reading Check

Answer Cystic fibrosis is a recessive disorder.

Caption Answer

Figure 8 The X chromosome is larger than the Y, and looks like an X. The Y chromosome looks like the V part of a Y.

Activity

Genetic Disorders Have students work in pairs to research genetic disorders. Student pairs can create a table that lists the disorder, its pattern of inheritance, and what characteristics someone with the disorder would have.

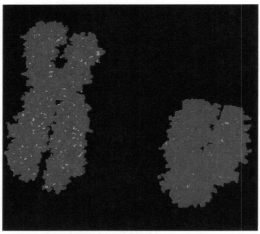

Color-enhanced SEM Magnification: 16000×

Figure 8 Sex in many organisms is determined by X and Y chromosomes.
Observe How do the X (left) and Y (right) chromosomes differ from one another in shape and size?

Recessive Genetic Disorders

Many human genetic disorders, such as cystic fibrosis, are caused by recessive genes. Some recessive genes are the result of a mutation within the gene. Many of these alleles are rare. Such genetic disorders occur when both parents have a recessive allele responsible for this disorder. Because the parents are heterozygous, they don't show any symptoms. However, if each parent passes the recessive allele to the child, the child inherits both recessive alleles and will have a recessive genetic disorder.

✔ Reading Check   *How is cystic fibrosis inherited?*

Cystic fibrosis is a homozygous recessive disorder. It is the most common genetic disorder that can lead to death among Caucasian Americans. In most people, a thin fluid is produced that lubricates the lungs and intestinal tract. People with cystic fibrosis produce thick mucus instead of this thin fluid. The thick mucus builds up in the lungs and makes it hard to breathe. This buildup often results in repeated bacterial respiratory infections. The thick mucus also reduces or prevents the flow of substances necessary for digesting food. Physical therapy, special diets, and new drug therapies have increased the life spans of patients with cystic fibrosis.

Sex Determination

What determines the sex of an individual? Much information on sex inheritance came from studies of fruit flies. Fruit flies have only four pairs of chromosomes. Because the chromosomes are large and few in number, they are easy to study. Scientists identified one pair that contains genes that determine the sex of the organism. They labeled the pair XX in females and XY in males. Geneticists use these labels when studying organisms, including humans. You can see human X and Y chromosomes in **Figure 8.**

Each egg produced by a female normally contains one X chromosome. Males produce sperm that normally have either an X or a Y chromosome. When a sperm with an X chromosome fertilizes an egg, the offspring is a female, XX. A male offspring, XY, is the result of a Y-containing sperm fertilizing an egg. What pair of sex chromosomes is in each of your cells? Sometimes chromosomes do not separate during meiosis. When this occurs, an individual can inherit an abnormal number of sex chromosomes.

Differentiated Instruction

English-Language Learners Have students work in pairs to create bookmarks using vocabulary and key terms from this section. Students can test each other's ability to pronounce and define each word. The bookmarks can be used to mark pages that contain words that students find difficult. L2

Teacher FYI

Genetic Disorders Most students will be aware of someone with a genetic disorder. Be sensitive to the possibility that students may have someone in their own family with a disorder.

Sex-Linked Disorders

Some inherited conditions are linked with the X and Y chromosomes. An allele inherited on a sex chromosome is called a **sex-linked gene.** Color blindness is a sex-linked disorder in which people cannot distinguish between certain colors, particularly red and green. This trait is a recessive allele on the X chromosome. Because males have only one X chromosome, a male with this allele on his X chromosome is color-blind. However, a color-blind female occurs only when both of her X chromosomes have the allele for this trait.

The allele for the distinct patches of three different colors found in calico cats is recessive and carried on the X chromosome. As shown in **Figure 9,** calico cats have inherited two X chromosomes with this recessive allele—one from both parents.

Pedigrees Trace Traits

How can you trace a trait through a family? A pedigree is a visual tool for following a trait through generations of a family. Males are represented by squares and females by circles. A completely filled circle or square shows that the trait is seen in that person. Half-colored circles or squares indicate carriers. A carrier is heterozygous for the trait, and it is not seen. People represented by empty circles or squares do not have the trait and are not carriers. The pedigree in **Figure 10** shows how the trait for color blindness is carried through a family.

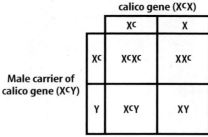

Female carrier of calico gene (X^CX)

	X^C	X
Male carrier of calico gene (X^CY) X^C	X^CX^C	XX^C
Y	X^CY	XY

Genotypes: X^CX^C, X^CX, X^CY, XY
Phenotypes: one calico female, one carrier female, one carrier male, one normal male

Figure 9 Calico cat fur is a homozygous recessive sex-linked trait. Female cats that are heterozygous are not calico but are only carriers. Two recessive alleles must be present for this allele to be expressed.
Determine *Why aren't all the females calico?*

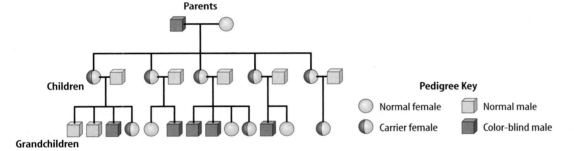

Parents

Children

Grandchildren

Pedigree Key

- ⬤ Normal female
- ◼ Normal male
- ◑ Carrier female
- ◼ Color-blind male

Figure 10 The symbols in this pedigree's key mean the same thing on all pedigree charts. The grandfather in this family was color-blind and married to a woman who was not a carrier of the color-blind allele.
Infer *why no women in this family are color-blind.*

Check for Understanding

Visual-Spatial Using colored pencils or markers and white paper, have students draw the outcome of crossing pea plants heterozygous for purple flowers. Extend this by having them show the outcome if pea plants' inheritance showed incomplete dominance and if inheritance was polygenic. The student's results can be displayed in the classroom. L2

Reteach

Inheritance Patterns Have students compare the three inheritance patterns in this section by making a chart. L1 IS **Visual-Spatial**

☑ Assessment

Process Have students prepare a table that lists types of inheritance, their descriptions, and examples of each. Use **Performance Assessment in the Science Classroom,** p. 109. L2

Shih Tzu

Black Labrador

Figure 11
A variety of traits are considered when breeding dogs.

Using Pedigrees A pedigree is a useful tool for a geneticist. Sometimes a geneticist needs to understand who has had a trait in a family over several generations to determine its pattern of inheritance. A geneticist determines if a trait is recessive, dominant, sex-linked, or has some other pattern of inheritance. When geneticists understand how a trait is inherited, they can predict the probability that a baby will be born with a specific trait.

Pedigrees also are important in breeding animals or plants. Because livestock and plant crops are used as sources of food, these organisms are bred to increase their yield and nutritional content. Breeders of pets and show animals, like the dogs pictured in **Figure 11,** also examine pedigrees carefully for possible desirable physical and ability traits. Issues concerning health also are considered when researching pedigrees.

section 2 review

Summary

Incomplete Dominance

- Incomplete dominance is when a dominant and recessive allele for a trait show an intermediate phenotype.
- Many traits are controlled by more than two alleles.
- A wide variety of phenotypes is produced by polygenic inheritance.

Human Genes and Mutations

- Errors can occur when DNA is copied.
- Mistakes in meiosis can result in an unequal number of chromosomes in sex cells.
- Recessive genes control many human genetic disorders.

Sex Determination

- An allele inherited on a sex chromosome is called a sex-linked gene.
- Pedigrees are visual tools to trace a trait through generations of a family.

Self Check

1. **Compare** how inheritance by multiple alleles and polygenic inheritance are similar.
2. **Explain** why a trait inherited by incomplete dominance is not a blend of two alleles.
3. **Discuss** Choose two genetic disorders and discuss how they are inherited.
4. **Apply** Using a Punnett square, explain why males are affected more often than females by sex-linked genetic disorders.
5. **Think Critically** Calico male cats are rare. Explain how such a cat can exist.

Applying Skills

6. **Predict** A man with blood type B marries a woman with blood type A. Their first child has blood type O. Use a Punnett square to predict what other blood types are possible for their offspring.
7. **Communicate** In your Science Journal, explain why offspring may or may not resemble either parent.

Science Online life.msscience.com/self_check_quiz

section 2 review

1. both result in many phenotypes
2. The two alleles are present in the offspring and can be passed on. Their DNA remains separate; it does not mix.
3. Answers will vary. Sample response: cystic fibrosis is inherited as a simple recessive trait.
4. Males only need to inherit one allele for the disorder to be affected. Females must inherit two alleles.
5. Possible answer: A male cat could inherit an extra X chromosome. Both X chromosomes may carry the recessive calico trait.
6. The Punnett square should show heterozygous parents with the alleles AO and BO.
7. There are many genes and combinations, so an individual may look very different from either parent.

section 3

Advances in Genetics

Why is genetics important?

If Mendel were to pick up a daily newspaper in any country today, he'd probably be surprised. News articles about developments in genetic research appear almost daily. The term *gene* has become a common word. The principles of heredity are being used to change the world.

Genetic Engineering

You may know that chromosomes are made of DNA and are in the nucleus of a cell. Sections of DNA in chromosomes that direct cell activities are called genes. Through **genetic engineering,** scientists are experimenting with biological and chemical methods to change the arrangement of DNA that makes up a gene. Genetic engineering already is used to help produce large volumes of medicine. Genes also can be inserted into cells to change how those cells perform their normal functions, as shown in **Figure 12.** Other research is being done to find new ways to improve crop production and quality, including the development of plants that are resistant to disease.

as you read

What You'll Learn

- **Evaluate** the importance of advances in genetics.
- **Sequence** the steps in making genetically engineered organisms.

Why It's Important

Advances in genetics can affect your health, the foods that you eat, and your environment.

Review Vocabulary

DNA: deoxyribonucleic acid; the genetic material of all organisms

New Vocabulary

- genetic engineering

Figure 12 DNA from one organism is placed into another species. This method is used to produce human insulin, human growth hormone, and other chemicals by bacteria.

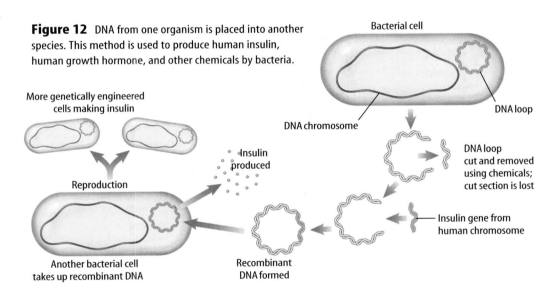

Bacterial cell
DNA chromosome
DNA loop
More genetically engineered cells making insulin
Reproduction
Insulin produced
DNA loop cut and removed using chemicals; cut section is lost
Another bacterial cell takes up recombinant DNA
Recombinant DNA formed
Insulin gene from human chromosome

SECTION 3   Advances in Genetics   **141**

1 Motivate

Bellringer

Section Focus Transparencies also are available on the Interactive Chalkboard CD-ROM.
L2 ELL

Tie to Prior Knowledge

Selective Breeding Explain that in selective breeding, specific crosses are made to accentuate a desired trait in offspring. Discuss with students how this might be advantageous to a plant breeder trying to produce a corn plant that has higher yields. Then explain that scientists are trying to find new ways to change traits without the time involved in selective breeding. They will learn about these techniques in this section.

Section 3 Resource Manager

Chapter FAST FILE Resources
Transparency Activity, p. 42
Directed Reading for Content Mastery, pp. 17, 18
Reinforcement, p. 25
Lab Worksheet, pp. 7–8
Enrichment, p. 28

Lab Management and Safety, p. 74

SECTION 3   Advances in Genetics   **141**

INTEGRATE
Environment

Genetically Engineered Crops Possible answer: The plants may pollinate other fields of the same crop unintentionally.

Career Have students research different careers in environmental science. They should discuss what type of study is required for the different careers and where an environmental scientist can find a job. Students should choose a specific environmental career and design a brochure that advertises how to become an environmental scientist. L2

Visual Learning

Figure 13 Explain that gene therapy is still in its infancy. As more is learned, the applications are likely to extend to many more genetic disorders. Remind students of the demonstration of a mutation in a cell being propagated by mitosis. How is gene therapy similar to the way a mutation is propagated through body cells? The mechanisms are similar, but in gene therapy, a mutation is corrected by the propagation, instead of spread.

Teacher FYI

Transferring a Gene Transgenesis is a genetic engineering process that involves transferring a gene from one organism into another. Using transgenesis, scientists have developed tomato plants that have increased resistance to disease and spoilage. Potato, cotton, and corn plants that have a natural resistance to insects, such as moth larvae and beetles, also have been developed.

INTEGRATE
Environment

Genetically Engineered Crops Crop plants are now being genetically engineered to produce chemicals that kill specific pests that feed on them. Some of the pollen from pesticide-resistant canola crops is capable of spreading up to 8 km from the plant, while corn and potato pollen can spread up to 1 km. What might be the effects of pollen landing on other plants?

Recombinant DNA Making recombinant DNA is one method of genetic engineering. Recombinant DNA is made by inserting a useful segment of DNA from one organism into a bacterium, as illustrated in **Figure 12.** Large quantities of human insulin are made by some genetically engineered organisms. People with Type 1 diabetes need this insulin because their pancreases produce too little or no insulin. Other uses include the production of growth hormone to treat dwarfism and chemicals to treat cancer.

Gene Therapy Gene therapy is a kind of genetic engineering. In gene therapy, a normal allele is placed in a virus, as shown in **Figure 13.** The virus then delivers the normal allele when it infects its target cell. The normal allele replaces the defective one. Scientists are conducting experiments that use this method to test ways of controlling cystic fibrosis and some kinds of cancer. More than 2,000 people already have taken part in gene therapy experiments. Gene therapy might be a method of curing several other genetic disorders in the future.

Figure 13 Gene therapy involves placing a normal allele into a cell that has a mutation. When the normal allele begins to function, a genetic disorder such as cystic fibrosis (CF) may be corrected.

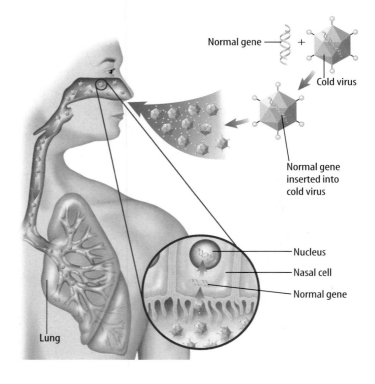

Normal gene + Cold virus

Normal gene inserted into cold virus

Nucleus

Nasal cell

Normal gene

Lung

Cultural Diversity

Genetic Engineering Research into genetic engineering, especially of crops, is taking place in many countries. Genetically engineered crops have already been planted in Europe, Canada, and the United States, though several countries in Europe have now banned the use of genetically engineered crops. Have students research to find out what countries could most benefit from agricultural advances involving genetic engineering. Have them research the staples of diets in those countries, and what, if any, research is being done on engineering those crops. Possible answer: Researchers at the International Rice Institute in the Philippines are working to produce new strains of rice. L2

Genetically Engineered Plants For thousands of years people have improved the plants they use for food and clothing even without the knowledge of genotypes. Until recently, these improvements were the results of selecting plants with the most desired traits to breed for the next generation. This process is called selective breeding. Recent advances in genetics have not replaced selective breeding. Although a plant can be bred for a particular phenotype, the genotype and pedigree of the plants also are considered.

Genetic engineering can produce improvements in crop plants, such as corn, wheat, and rice. One type of genetic engineering involves finding the genes that produce desired traits in one plant and then inserting those genes into a different plant. Scientists recently have made genetically engineered tomatoes with a gene that allows tomatoes to be picked green and transported great distances before they ripen completely. Ripe, firm tomatoes are then available in the local market. In the future, additional food crops may be genetically engineered so that they are not desirable food for insects.

**Reading Check** *What other types of traits would be considered desirable in plants?*

Because some people might prefer foods that are not changed genetically, some stores label such produce, as shown in **Figure 14.** The long-term effects of consuming genetically engineered plants are unknown.

Figure 14 Genetically engineered produce is sometimes labeled. This allows consumers to make informed choices about their foods.

✓ Reading Check

Answer Possible answers: increased growth rate, increased fruit size and production, reduced need for water, improved flavor, desirable flower color

3 Assess

DAILY INTERVENTION

Check for Understanding

Kinesthetic Have students make a time line for the future that shows their predictions about how advances in genetics might affect their life over the next ten years. They can include various gene therapies for genetic disorders and futuristic advancements in genetically engineered plants and crops. L2

Reteach

Flash Cards Have students make flash cards that illustrate steps in the process of genetic engineering. Have students practice identifying and ordering the steps using these cards. L2

✓ Assessment

Performance Have students make a model that demonstrates the process of genetic engineering. Use **Performance Assessment in the Science Classroom,** p. 123. L2 P

---

section 3 review

Summary

Why is genetics important?

- Developments in genetic research appear in newspapers almost daily.
- The world is being changed by the principles of heredity.

Genetic Engineering

- Scientists work with biological and chemical methods to change the arrangement of DNA that makes up a gene.
- One method of genetic engineering is making recombinant DNA.
- A normal allele is replaced in a virus and then delivers the normal allele when it infects its target cell.

Self Check

1. **Apply** Give examples of areas in which advances in genetics are important.
2. **Compare and contrast** the technologies of using recombinant DNA and gene therapy.
3. **Infer** What are some benefits of genetically engineered crops?
4. **Describe** how selective breeding differs from genetic engineering.
5. **Think Critically** Why might some people be opposed to genetically engineered plants?

Applying Skills

6. **Concept Map** Make an events-chain concept map of the steps used in making recombinant DNA.

Science Online life.msscience.com/self_check_quiz

SECTION 3 Advances in Genetics **143**

---

section 3 review

1. Answers may include agriculture, health, and medicine.
2. Recombinant DNA inserts a segment of DNA from an organism into a bacterium to produce needed substances. Gene therapy places a normal allele into a virus, which

delivers the allele to its target cell. There, it replaces the defective allele.
3. They may lead to increased crop production or be pest-resistant.
4. Selective breeding relies on natural, reproductive processes. Genetic engineering may take traits from

one organism and place them into another.
5. Some people are concerned about pesticide resistance in weeds or other unforeseen consequences.
6. Answers should reflect steps shown in **Figure 12.**

BENCH TESTED

▶ Real-World Question

Purpose Students will devise a method to test for color blindness, and administer the test to determine the percentage of affected individuals.

Process Skills interpret data, design an experiment, form a hypothesis, communicate, use numbers

Time Required one class period

Possible Materials colored markers, blank white paper

▶ Form a Hypothesis

Possible Hypothesis Students may hypothesize that color blindness will affect more males than females, because the allele for color blindness is carried on the X chromosome.

▶ Test Your Hypothesis

Possible Procedures Students may choose to create a picture or number out of green circles. They can then use circles of red, orange, or yellow to surround the picture or number. Using this test, students would determine whether individuals could see the "hidden" picture or number.

LAB — Design Your Own

Tests for Color Blindness

Goals
- **Design** an experiment that tests for a specific type of color blindness in males and females.
- **Calculate** the percentage of males and females with the disorder.

Possible Materials
white paper or poster board
colored markers: red, orange, yellow, bright green, dark green, blue
*computer and color printer
*Alternate materials

▶ Real-World Question

What do color-blind people see? People who have inherited color blindness can see most colors, but they have difficulty telling the difference between two specific colors. You have three genes that help you see color. One gene lets you see red, another blue, and the third gene allows you to see green. In the most common type of color blindness, red-green color blindness, the green gene does not work properly. What percentages of males and females in your school are color-blind?

▶ Form a Hypothesis

Based on your reading and your own experiences, form a hypothesis about how common color blindness is among males and females.

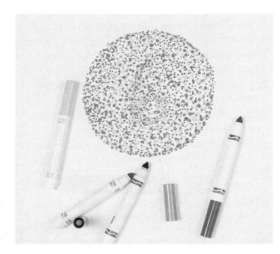

▶ Test Your Hypothesis

Make a Plan

1. Decide what type of color blindness you will test for—the common green-red color blindness or the more rare green-blue color blindness.

2. **List** the materials you will need and describe how you will create test pictures. Tests for color blindness use many circles of red, orange, and yellow as a background, with circles of dark and light green to make a picture or number. List the steps you will take to test your hypothesis.

3. Prepare a data table in your Science Journal to record your test results.

144   CHAPTER 5 Heredity

Alternative Inquiry Lab

Test for Color Blindness To make this Lab an Inquiry Lab, have students investigate color blindness in terms of traffic lights. Explain to students that the most common form of color blindness is red-green color blindness. Have students relate this to driving and stopping at traffic lights. What percentage of people in the school are color blind? What percentage of males and females are color blind? They can design test pictures and collect data from within the school. If a larger study is needed, students can test individuals outside of the school.

4. **Examine** your experiment to make sure all steps are in logical order.
5. **Identify** which pictures you will use as a control and which pictures you will use as variables.

Follow Your Plan

1. Make sure your teacher approves your plan before you start.
2. **Draw** the pictures that you will use to test for color blindness.
3. Carry out your experiment as planned and record your results in your data table.

Analyze Your Data

1. **Calculate** the percentage of males and females that tested positive for color blindness.
2. **Compare** the frequency of color blindness in males with the frequency of color blindness in females.

Conclude and Apply

1. **Explain** whether or not the results supported your hypothesis.
2. **Explain** why color blindness is called a sex-linked disorder.
3. **Infer** how common the color-blind disorder is in the general population.
4. **Predict** your results if you were to test a larger number of people.

Communicating Your Data

Using a word processor, write a short article for the advice column of a fashion magazine about how a color-blind person can avoid wearing outfits with clashing colors. **For more help, refer to the** Science Skill Handbook.

LAB **145**

Teaching Strategies
Allow students to test individuals outside of class. Encourage them to test family, friends, and other teachers. Have them turn in their results after one week.

Expected Outcome More males than females will test positive for color blindness.

Analyze Your Data

Answers to Questions

1. More males should test positive than females.
2. Males are much more likely to be color blind than females.

Error Analysis Have students compare results to identify errors in data collection. Some possible sources of error are colors on the test pictures not being right or students overhearing the results of others so as not to give a true result.

Conclude and Apply

1. Answers will vary.
2. The allele for this trait is only located on the X chromosome. Because males only have one X chromosome, males with this allele will be color blind. A female will be color blind only when both of her X chromosomes have the color blind allele.
3. Color blindness afflicts 8 percent of males and 0.04 percent of females.
4. A larger sample will give more accurate results.

Communicating Your Data

Students might suggest that matching colors be grouped in different areas of the closet, or that a tagging system be developed so that one group of matching clothing is labeled *A*, a second group is labeled *B*, and so on.

Assessment

Process Have students create a similar test for another type of color blindness. After getting results, have students make a bar graph showing the percentages of individuals affected with each type of color blindness. Use **Performance Assessment in the Science Classroom,** p. 105.

Content Background

The human genome project is making continual contributions to our knowledge of human genetics. Scientists involved in the project are quick to point out the many things they don't know, even though the genome is complete. Students may be curious to know whose genome is being sequenced. The government and private companies working on genomes are using several anonymous donors of various racial and ethnic backgrounds.

Discussion

Similar Genes Mice and humans have many similar genes. What is one characteristic or function shared by mice and humans that might be coded for by similar genes? Possible answer: Both mice and humans have digestive enzymes that could be coded for by similar genes.

Activity

Gene's Story Have students write a story from the point of view of a human gene. Students should include details such as which chromosome the gene is located on, the function of the gene, and whether the gene functions all the time or is switched on and off. Students can either use an imaginary gene, or an actual human gene. L2 IS **Linguistic**

Applying Math

Answer about 3 gigabytes (1 million base pairs = 1 megabyte; 3 billion base pairs = 3,000 megabytes)

SCIENCE Stats

The Human Genome

Did you know...

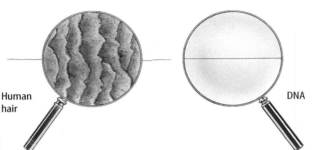

... The biggest advance in genetics in years took place in February 2001. Scientists successfully mapped the human genome. There are 30,000 to 40,000 genes in the human genome. Genes are in the nucleus of each of the several trillion cells in your body.

Centriole
Nucleus
Endoplasmic reticulum
Cytoplasm
Mitochondrion

Human hair

DNA

... The strands of DNA in the human genome, if unwound and connected end to end, would be more than 1.5 m long—but only about 130 trillionths of a centimeter wide. Even an average human hair is as much as 200,000 times wider than that.

... It would take about nine and one-half years to read aloud without stopping the 3 billion bits of instructions (called base pairs) in your genome.

Applying Math
If one million base pairs of DNA take up 1 megabyte of storage space on a computer, how many gigabytes (1,024 megabytes) would the whole genome fill?

Find Out About It
Human genome scientists hope to identify the location of disease-causing genes. Visit life.msscience.com/science_stats to research a genetic disease and share your results with your class.

Curriculum Connection

Art Have students use the Internet or print sources to find the names of artists who have created drawings and paintings that depict a molecule of DNA. Students then can either create a collage of copies of the drawings or paintings they find, or they can create their own drawing using colored pencils, markers, or crayons. Display the collages and artwork. L2

Write About It

Organize Information Have students make a chart with information they learn about genetic diseases. They can include columns to show whether the disease is dominant or recessive, sex-linked, and how genetic therapy may help treat the disease. L2

Reviewing Main Ideas

Section 1 Genetics

1. Genetics is the study of how traits are inherited. Gregor Mendel determined the basic laws of genetics.

2. Traits are controlled by alleles on chromosomes.

3. Some alleles can be dominant or recessive.

4. When a pair of chromosomes separates during meiosis, the different alleles move into separate sex cells. Mendel found that he could predict the outcome of genetic crosses.

Section 2 Genetics Since Mendel

1. Inheritance patterns studied since Mendel include incomplete dominance, multiple alleles, and polygenic inheritance.

2. These inheritance patterns allow a variety of phenotypes to be produced.

3. Some disorders are the results of inheritance and can be harmful and even deadly.

4. Pedigree charts help reveal patterns of the inheritance of a trait in a family. Pedigrees show that sex-linked traits are expressed more often in males than in females.

Section 3 Advances in Genetics

1. Genetic engineering uses biological and chemical methods to change genes.

2. Recombinant DNA is one method of genetic engineering to make useful chemicals, including hormones.

3. Gene therapy shows promise for correcting many human genetic disorders by inserting normal alleles into cells.

4. Breakthroughs in the field of genetic engineering are allowing scientists to do many things, such as producing plants that are resistant to disease.

Visualizing Main Ideas

Examine the following pedigree for diabetes and explain the inheritance pattern.

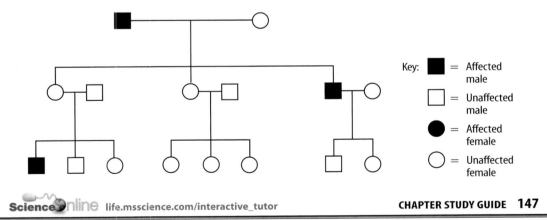

Key:
- ■ = Affected male
- □ = Unaffected male
- ● = Affected female
- ○ = Unaffected female

Science Online life.msscience.com/interactive_tutor

CHAPTER STUDY GUIDE 147

Identifying Misconceptions

Use this assessment as follow-up to page F at the beginning of this chapter.

Procedure Repeat the question: If brown eyes are dominant over blue eyes, does this mean that someday all people will be brown eyed? Have students write and diagram their answer.

Expected Outcome Students should show that brown-eyed parents can have blue-eyed children if both parents have one blue-eyed allele. It does not disappear in the parent, then reappear in the child. Students should show that they understand that a dominant allele is not stronger or more frequently expressed than a recessive allele. L2

chapter Study Guide **5**

Reviewing Main Ideas

Summary statements can be used by students to review the major concepts of the chapter.

Visualizing Main Ideas

See student page.

Visit life.msscience.com
- /self_check_quiz
- /interactive_tutor
- /vocabulary_puzzlemaker
- /chapter_review
- /standardized_test

Assessment Transparency

For additional assessment questions, use the *Assessment Transparency* located in the transparency book.

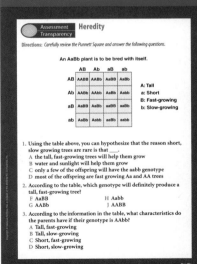

Assessment

Assessment Transparency **Heredity**

Directions: *Carefully review the Punnett Square and answer the following questions.*

An AaBb plant is to be bred with itself.

	AB	Ab	aB	ab
AB	AABB	AABb	AaBB	AaBb
Ab	AABb	AAbb	AaBb	Aabb
aB	AaBB	AaBb	aaBB	aaBb
ab	AaBb	Aabb	aaBb	aabb

A: Tall
a: Short
B: Fast-growing
b: Slow-growing

1. Using the table above, you can hypothesize that the reason short, slow growing trees are rare is that ___.
   A the tall, fast-growing trees will help them grow
   B water and sunlight will help them grow
   C only a few of the offspring will have the aabb genotype
   D most of the offspring are fast growing Aa and AA trees

2. According to the table, which genotype will definitely produce a tall, fast-growing tree?
   F AaBB   H Aabb
   G AABb   J AABB

3. According to the information in the table, what characteristics do the parents have if their genotype is AaBb?
   A Tall, fast-growing
   B Tall, slow-growing
   C Short, fast-growing
   D Short, slow-growing

Heredity

Using Vocabulary

1. alleles
2. phenotype
3. polygenic inheritance
4. dominant
5. Genetics
6. genotype
7. Genetic engineering
8. Punnett square
9. Heredity
10. sex-linked gene

Checking Concepts

11. C	14. C
12. A	15. D
13. C	16. B

Using Vocabulary

allele p. 126	hybrid p. 128
dominant p. 128	incomplete
genetic engineering p. 141	dominance p. 134
genetics p. 126	phenotype p. 130
genotype p. 130	polygenic inheritance p. 136
heredity p. 126	Punnett square p. 130
heterozygous p. 130	recessive p. 128
homozygous p. 130	sex-linked gene p. 139

Fill in the blanks with the correct word.

1. Alternate forms of a gene are called _____ .

2. The outward appearance of a trait is a(n) _____ .

3. Human height, eye color, and skin color are all traits controlled by _____ .

4. An allele that produces a trait in the heterozygous condition is _____ .

5. _____ is the branch of biology that deals with the study of heredity.

6. The actual combination of alleles of an organism is its _____ .

7. _____ is moving fragments of DNA from one organism and inserting them into another organism.

8. A(n) _____ is a helpful device for predicting the proportions of possible genotypes.

9. _____ is the passing of traits from parents to offspring.

10. Red-green color blindness and hemophilia are two human genetic disorders that are caused by a(n) _____ .

Checking Concepts

Choose the word or phrase that best answers the question.

11. Which of the following describes the allele that causes color blindness?
    A) dominant
    B) carried on the Y chromosome
    C) carried on the X chromosome
    D) present only in males

12. What is it called when the presence of two different alleles results in an intermediate phenotype?
    A) incomplete dominance
    B) polygenic inheritance
    C) multiple alleles
    D) sex-linked genes

13. What separates during meiosis?
    A) proteins   C) alleles
    B) phenotypes   D) pedigrees

14. What controls traits in organisms?
    A) cell membrane   C) genes
    B) cell wall   D) Punnett squares

15. What term describes the inheritance of cystic fibrosis?
    A) polygenic inheritance
    B) multiple alleles
    C) incomplete dominance
    D) recessive genes

16. What phenotype will the offspring represented in the Punnett square have?
    A) all recessive
    B) all dominant
    C) half recessive, half dominant
    D) Each will have a different phenotype.

	F	f
F	FF	Ff
F	FF	Ff

Science Online life.msscience.com/vocabulary_puzzlemaker

Use the ExamView® Pro Testmaker CD-ROM to:
- create multiple versions of tests
- create modified tests with one mouse click for inclusion students
- edit existing questions and add your own questions
- build tests aligned with state standards using built-in State Curriculum Tags
- change English tests to Spanish with one mouse click and vice versa

chapter Review 5

Thinking Critically

17. **Explain** the relationship between DNA, genes, alleles, and chromosomes.

18. **Classify** the inheritance pattern for each of the following:
    a. many different phenotypes produced by one pair of alleles
    b. many phenotypes produced by more than one pair of alleles; two phenotypes from two alleles; three phenotypes from two alleles.

Use the illustration below to answer question 19.

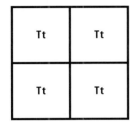

Tt	Tt
Tt	Tt

19. **Interpret Scientific Illustrations** What were the genotypes of the parents that produced the Punnett Square shown above?

20. **Explain** why two rabbits with the same genes might not be colored the same if one is raised in northern Maine and one is raised in southern Texas.

21. **Apply** Why would a person who receives genetic therapy for a disorder still be able to pass the disorder to his or her children?

22. **Predict** Two organisms were found to have different genotypes but the same phenotype. Predict what these phenotypes might be. Explain.

23. **Compare and contrast** Mendelian inheritance with incomplete dominance.

Performance Activities

24. **Newspaper Article** Write a newspaper article to announce a new, genetically engineered plant. Include the method of developing the plant, the characteristic changed, and the terms that you would expect to see. Read your article to the class.

25. **Predict** In humans, the widow's peak allele is dominant, and the straight hairline allele is recessive. Predict how both parents with widow's peaks could have a child without a widow's peak hairline.

26. **Use a word processor** or program to write predictions about how advances in genetics might affect your life in the next ten years.

Applying Math

27. **Human Genome** If you wrote the genetic information for each gene in the human genome on a separate sheet of 0.2-mm-thick paper and stacked the sheets, how tall would the stack be?

Use the table below to answer question 28.

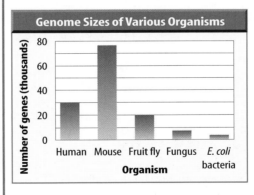

Genome Sizes of Various Organisms

28. **Genes** Consult the graph above. How many more genes are in the human genome than the genome of the fruit fly?

Thinking Critically

17. DNA is a chemical; a gene contains DNA; an allele is a form of a gene specific for a trait; genes are located on chromosomes.
18. (a) multiple allele inheritance (b) polygenic inheritance
19. TT and tt; both were purebred, one dominant, one recessive.
20. The coat colors of some rabbits are affected by temperature differences in the environment.
21. The normal allele is usually inserted only into the cells that cause the disorder. For this reason, the reproductive cells would not be changed by gene therapy.
22. The phenotypes would be the expression of a dominant trait.
23. Mendelian inheritance has two forms of an allele that produce only two phenotypes. Incomplete dominance also has two forms of an allele, but produces three phenotypes.

Performance Activities

24. Answers will vary, but should explain genetic engineering methods and how the methods can change the traits of organisms. Use **Performance Assessment in the Science Classroom,** p.141.
25. Both parents would have to be heterozygous to produce children without the widow's peak trait.
26. Answers may include increased food production, curing genetic disorders, or providing new medicines.

Applying Math

National Math Standards
1, 5, 9
27. 20 m
28. about 10,000 genes

☑ Assessment   Resources

📁 **Reproducible Masters**
Chapter *Fast File* Resources
  Chapter Review, pp. 33–34
  Chapter Tests, pp. 35–38
  Assessment Transparency Activity, p. 45
Glencoe Science Web site
  Chapter Review Test
  Standardized Test Practice

Glencoe Technology
  🖌 Assessment Transparency
  🌐 Exam*View*® Pro Testmaker
  💾 MindJogger Videoquiz
  🌐 Interactive Chalkboard

FAST FILE

Answer Sheet A practice answer sheet can be found at life.msscience.com/answer_sheet.

SAMPLE

Part 1 Multiple Choice

1. C	**6.** C
2. A	**7.** A
3. C	**8.** C
4. C	**9.** C
5. B	

Part 2 Short Response

10. 50%—heterozygous; 50%—homozygous; 75%—same phenotype as the parents

	F	f	
F	FF	Ff	FF – full
f	Ff	ff	ff – flat

Part 1 Multiple Choice

Record your answers on the answer sheet provided by your teacher or on a sheet of paper.

1. Heredity includes all of the following except
- **A.** traits.
- **B.** chromosomes.
- **C.** nutrients.
- **D.** phenotype.

2. What is a mutation?
- **A.** A change in a gene which is harmful, beneficial, or has no effect at all.
- **B.** A change in a gene which is only beneficial.
- **C.** A change in a gene which is only harmful.
- **D.** No change in a gene.

3. Sex of the offspring is determined by
- **A.** only the mother, because she has two X chromosomes.
- **B.** only the father, because he has one X and one Y chromosome.
- **C.** an X chromosome from the mother and either an X or Y chromosome from the father.
- **D.** mutations.

Use the pedigree below to answer questions 4–6.

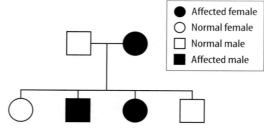

- ● Affected female
- ○ Normal female
- □ Normal male
- ■ Affected male

Huntington disease has a dominant (DD or Dd) inheritance pattern.

4. What is the genotype of the father?
- **A.** DD
- **B.** Dd
- **C.** dd
- **D.** D

5. What is the genotype of the mother?
- **A.** DD
- **B.** Dd
- **C.** dd
- **D.** D

6. The genotype of the unaffected children is
- **A.** DD.
- **B.** Dd.
- **C.** dd.
- **D.** D.

7. Manipulating the arrangement of DNA that makes up a gene is called
- **A.** genetic engineering.
- **B.** chromosomal migration.
- **C.** viral reproduction.
- **D.** cross breeding.

Use the Punnett square below to answer question 8.

		A	O
A		AA	AO
B		AB	BO

8. How many phenotypes would result from the following Punnett square?
- **A.** 1
- **B.** 2
- **C.** 3
- **D.** 4

9. Down's Syndrome is an example of
- **A.** incomplete dominance.
- **B.** genetic engineering.
- **C.** a chromosome disorder.
- **D.** a sex linked disorder.

Test-Taking Tip

Complete Charts Write directly on complex charts such as a Punnett square.

Question 10 Draw a Punnett square to answer all parts of the question.

150 STANDARDIZED TEST PRACTICE

---

11. If the flower color trait was an example of incomplete dominance, Mendel would have observed an intermediate phenotype when two purebred were crossed. Specifically, this phenotype would have been a light purple.

12. Heterozygous individuals are called carriers because they have or carry the recessive allele for a trait or disorder even though it is not present in their phenotype.

13. A body cell has a pair of alleles for each trait. Following meiosis, the sex cells only have one allele for each trait.

Part 2 | Short Response/Grid In

Record your answers on the answer sheet provided by your teacher or on a sheet of paper.

Use the table below to answer questions 10–11.

Some Traits Compared by Mendel			
Traits	**Shape of Seeds**	**Shape of Pods**	**Flower Color**
Dominant Trait	Round	Full	Purple
Recessive Trait	Wrinkled	Flat, constricted	White

10. Create a Punnett square using the *Shape of Pods* trait crossing heterozygous parents. What percentage of the offspring will be heterozygous? What percentage of the offspring will be homozygous? What percentage of the offspring will have the same phenotype as the parents?

11. Gregor Mendel studied traits in pea plants that were controlled by single genes. Explain what would have happened if the alleles for flower color were an example of incomplete dominance. What phenotypes would he have observed?

12. Why are heterozygous individuals called carriers for non-sex-linked and X-linked recessive patterns of inheritance?

13. How many alleles does a body cell have for each trait? What happens to the alleles during meiosis?

Part 3 | Open Ended

Record your answers on a sheet of paper.

14. Genetic counseling helps individuals determine the genetic risk or probability a disorder will be passed to offspring. Why would a pedigree be a very important tool for the counselors? Which patterns of inheritance (dominant, recessive, x-linked) would be the easiest to detect?

15. Explain the process of gene therapy. What types of disorders would this therapy be best suited? How has this therapy helped patients with cystic fibrosis?

Refer to the figure below to answer question 16.

16. What is the disorder associated with the karyotype shown above? How does this condition occur? What are the characteristics of someone with this disorder?

17. Explain why the parents of someone with cystic fibrosis do not show any symptoms. How are the alleles for cystic fibrosis passed from parents to offspring?

18. What is recombinant DNA and how is it used to help someone with Type I diabetes?

19. If each kernel on an ear of corn represents a separate genetic cross, would corn be a good plant to use to study genetics? Why or why not? What process could be used to control pollination?

---

16. Down's syndrome; chromosomal disorders can be a result of mistakes in the process of meiosis. Individuals with Down's syndrome can be short, exhibit learning disabilities, and have heart problems.

17. Cystic fibrosis is caused by recessive genes. Such genetic disorders occur when both parents have a recessive allele for the disorder. Because the parents are heterozygous, they don't show any symptoms. However, if each parent passes the recessive allele to the child, the child inherits both recessive alleles and will have a recessive genetic disorder.

18. Recombinant DNA is made by inserting a segment of DNA from one organism into a bacterium. Large quantities of human insulin are made by some genetically engineered organisms. People with Type I diabetes need this insulin because they produce too little or no insulin.

19. Corn would be a good plant to study genetics because you could see the offspring of many crosses on just one ear of corn and a corn stalk produces several ears of corn. This makes producing a large number of results easier. Valid scientific conclusions need to be based on results that can be duplicated. The corn plants would need to be pollinated by hand rather than letting insects randomly pollinate plants.

Rubrics

For more help evaluating open-ended assessment questions, see the rubric on p. 10T.

---

14. A pedigree is a very important tool for a genetic counselor because it is a visual means to trace a trait through a family. Any trait that has a dominant pattern of inheritance would be easy to detect because it would be present in every generation. Recessive disorders would be difficult to detect because the carriers would not display the phenotype. Environmental factors such as nutrition, lifestyle, habitat, and medical care would contribute to a person's phenotype.

15. Gene therapy is when a normal allele is placed in a virus and the virus delivers the normal allele when it infects its target cell. This type of therapy is best suited for single genes that are defective and would be very difficult to use with disorders that are polygenic. In cystic fibrosis patients, the normal allele is delivered into their lungs so it can begin to produce the normal thin fluid.

Section/Objectives	Standards		Labs/Features
	National	**State/Local**	
Chapter Opener	See pp. 16T–17T for a Key to Standards.		**Launch Lab:** Adaptation for a Hunter, p. 153 **Foldables,** p. 153
Section 1 Ideas About Evolution 🕐 2 sessions 📦 1 block 1. **Describe** Lamarck's hypothesis of acquired characteristics and Darwin's theory of natural selection. 2. **Identify** why variations in organisms are important. 3. **Compare and contrast** gradualism and punctuated equilibrium.	National Content Standards: UCP.1–UCP.5, A.1, A.2, C.1, C.4, C.5, G.1–G.3		**Science Online,** p. 156 **Applying Science:** Does natural selection take place in a fish tank?, p. 157 **Integrate Language Arts,** p. 158 **MiniLAB:** Relating Evolution to Species, p. 159 **Lab:** Hidden Frogs, p. 162
Section 2 Clues About Evolution 🕐 2 sessions 📦 1.5 blocks 4. **Identify** the importance of fossils as evidence of evolution. 5. **Explain** how relative and radiometric dating are used to estimate the age of fossils. 6. **List** examples of five types of evidence for evolution.	National Content Standards: UCP.1–UCP.5, A.1, A.2, F.1, G.2		**Science Online,** p. 165 **Visualizing the Geologic Time Scale,** p. 166 **Integrate Earth Science,** p. 167
Section 3 The Evolution of Primates 🕐 3 sessions 📦 2 blocks 7. **Describe** the differences among living primates. 8. **Identify** the adaptations of primates. 9. **Discuss** the evolutionary history of modern primates.	National Content Standards: UCP.1–UCP.5, A.1, A.2, C.1, C.5, G.1–G.3		**MiniLAB:** Living Without Thumbs, p. 171 **Lab:** Recognizing Variation in a Population, p. 174 **Science and History:** Fighting HIV, p. 176

Glencoe Exclusive!
Teacher Works™
All-In-One Planner and Resource Center

Lab Materials	Reproducible Resources	Section Assessment	Technology
Launch Lab: classified ads from the newspaper, white paper, black paper, hole punch, watch or clock with second hand	**Chapter FAST FILE Resources** Foldables Worksheet, p. 15 Directed Reading Overview, p. 17 Note-taking Worksheets, pp. 31–32	GLENCOE'S ASSESSMENT ADVANTAGE	TeacherWorks includes: • Interactive Teacher Edition • Lesson Planner with calendar • Access to all program blacklines • Correlations to standards • Web links
MiniLAB: lined paper **Lab:** cardboard form of a frog, colored markers, crayons, colored pencils, glue, beads, sequins, modeling clay	**Chapter FAST FILE Resources** Transparency Activity, p. 42 MiniLAB, p. 3 Enrichment, p. 28 Reinforcement, p. 25 Directed Reading, p. 18 Lab Activities, pp. 9–10, 11–14 Lab Worksheet, pp. 5–6 **Cultural Diversity,** p. 19 **Mathematics Skill Activities,** p. 1 **Science Inquiry Lab,** pp. 21–22	**Portfolio** Curriculum Connection, p. 159 **Performance** Applying Science, p. 157 MiniLAB, p. 159 Applying Math, p. 161 **Content** Section Review, p. 161	♦ Section Focus Transparency ◉ Virtual Labs CD-ROM ∩ Guided Reading Audio Program ◉ Interactive Chalkboard CD-ROM
Need materials? Contact Science Kit at 1-800-828-7777 or www.sciencekit.com on the Internet.	**Chapter FAST FILE Resources** Transparency Activity, p. 43 Enrichment, p. 29 Reinforcement, p. 26 Directed Reading, p. 19 Transparency Activity, pp. 45–46 **Life Science Critical Thinking/ Problem Solving,** p. 3	**Portfolio** Science Journal, p. 164 **Performance** Applying Math, p. 169 **Content** Section Review, p. 169	♦ Section Focus Transparency ♦ Teaching Transparency ◉ Virtual Labs CD-ROM ∩ Guided Reading Audio Program ◉ Interactive Chalkboard CD-ROM
MiniLAB: tape **Lab:** fruit and seeds from one plant species, metric ruler, magnifying lens, graph paper	**Chapter FAST FILE Resources** Transparency Activity, p. 44 MiniLAB, p. 4 Enrichment, p. 30 Reinforcement, p. 27 Directed Reading, pp. 19, 20 Lab Worksheet, pp. 7–8 **Lab Management and Safety,** p. 71	**Portfolio** MiniLAB Assessment, p. 171 **Performance** MiniLAB, p. 171 Applying Skills, p. 173 **Content** Section Review, p. 173	♦ Section Focus Transparency ◉ Virtual Labs CD-ROM ∩ Guided Reading Audio Program ◉ Interactive Chalkboard CD-ROM ▭ Video Lab

End of Chapter Assessment

GLENCOE'S ASSESSMENT ADVANTAGE

Blackline Masters	Technology	Professional Series
Chapter FAST FILE Resources Chapter Review, pp. 35–36 Chapter Tests, pp. 37–40 **Standardized Test Practice,** pp. 27–30	▭ MindJogger Videoquiz ◉ Virtual Labs CD-ROM ◉ ExamView® Pro Testmaker ◉ TeacherWorks CD-ROM ◉ Interactive Chalkboard CD-ROM	**Performance Assessment in the Science Classroom (PASC)**

Transparencies

Section Focus

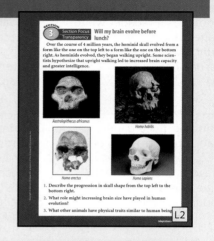

This is a representation of key blackline masters available in the Teacher Classroom Resources. See Resource Manager boxes within the chapter for additional information.

Key to Teaching Strategies

The following designations will help you decide which activities are appropriate for your students.

L1 Level 1 activities should be appropriate for students with learning difficulties.

L2 Level 2 activities should be within the ability range of all students.

L3 Level 3 activities are designed for above-average students.

ELL ELL activities should be within the ability range of English-Language Learners.

COOP LEARN Cooperative Learning activities are designed for small group work.

LS Multiple Learning Styles logos, as described on page 12T, are used throughout to indicate strategies that address different learning styles.

P These strategies represent student products that can be placed into a best-work portfolio.

PBL Problem-Based Learning activities apply real-world situations to learning.

Assessment

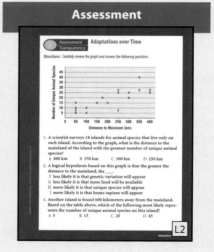

Teaching

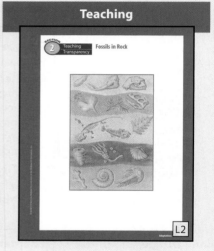

Hands-on Activities

Student Text Lab Worksheet

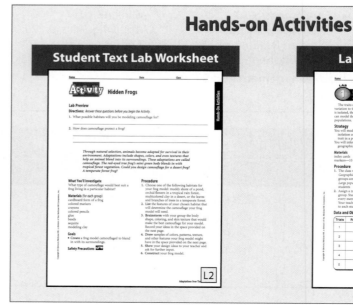

Laboratory Activities

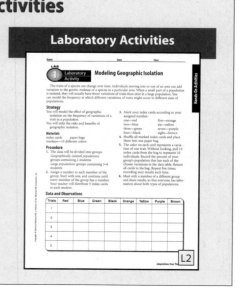

Meeting Different Ability Levels

Content Outline

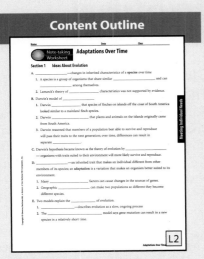

L2

Reinforcement

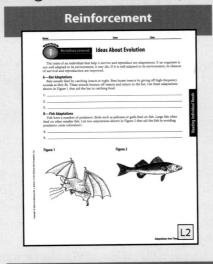

L2

Enrichment

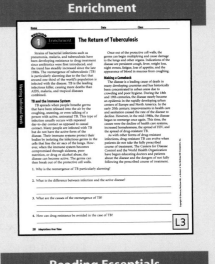

L3

Directed Reading (English/Spanish)

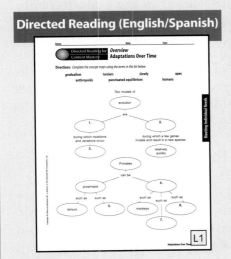

L1

Study Guide

Study Guide

Features
- Contains a study guide page for each section of the chapter
- Reviews key concepts
- Includes answer pages

L2

Reading Essentials

Reading Essentials for Glencoe Science
An Interactive Student Workbook

Features
- Condensed core content
- Actively involves students in reading
- Reinforces key vocabulary

L1

Assessment

Test Practice Workbook

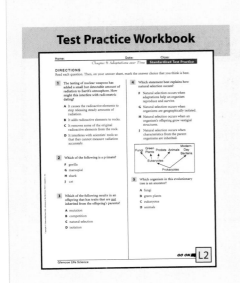

L2

Chapter Review

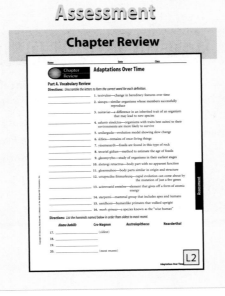

L2

Chapter Tests

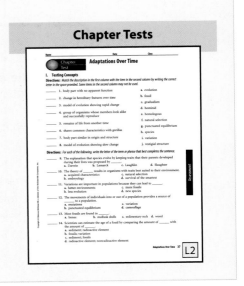

L2

Science Content Background

section 1 — Ideas About Evolution

Before Evolutionary Theories

Aristotle, a Greek philosopher, held a view that species were essentially perfect. Because species were considered to be well adapted, there was no discussion of evolution. Special Creation, with all species fixed, was the prevailing view. In addition, Carolus Linnaeus, father of taxonomy, organized the diversity of living things into a hierarchy of taxonomic categories that did not imply evolution.

Evolution by Natural Selection

In 1858, Charles Darwin and Alfred Wallace provided enough evidence to convince many scientists that evolution occurs. Their ideas differed from the prevailing views of their time in two important ways—species change, or evolve, and natural selection is the process by which this evolution occurs.

An important point about the discussions on natural selection and evolution is that Darwin's observations were not limited to those made during his trip on the HMS *Beagle*. Even as a young boy, Darwin was an avid collector of beetles and other information about natural history. Much of the evidence for his theory came from his own study of pigeons.

section 2 — Clues About Evolution

The Fossil Record

Some organisms which lived for only a short time in a certain environment formed fossils called index fossils. Index fossils are used by geologists to correlate rock strata across large areas.

Radioactive isotopes have half-lives that are not affected by environmental factors such as temperature or atmospheric pressure. Because the lengths of half-lives for radioactive isotopes of elements are known, an age estimate can be assigned to many rocks or fossils.

The evidence of evolution of species from the fossils record is compatible with other types of evidence for evolution. Transitional fossils have been located for some species, and species such as echinoderms have extensive fossil records that appear mostly complete.

section 3 — The Evolution of Primates

Ongoing Research

Discoveries regarding primate evolution occur regularly. DNA comparisons have been done in an attempt to establish a date for the evolution of modern humans. Results of these tests are currently being debated, repeated, and extended.

chapter content resources

Internet Resources

For additional content background, visit
life.msscience.com to:

- access your book online
- find references to related articles in popular science magazines
- access Web links with related content background
- access current events with science journal topics

Print Resources

Evolution: The Triumph of an Idea, by Carl Zimmer, Harper Collins Publishers, 2001

The Beak of the Finch, by Jonathan Weiner, Vintage Books, 1994

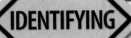

IDENTIFYING Misconceptions

Find Out What Students Think

Students may think that . . .

Environmental changes cause changes in traits that help organisms cope with the new environment.

Students often form a magical view of natural selection. They know that if pesticides are applied to a crop, some insects will survive and reproduce. However, rather than understanding that the insects that survived did so because of pre-exisiting traits, students often believe that the pesticide itself caused the insects to become resistant. In the same way they may believe that antibiotics cause bacteria to form antibiotic resistance, or that organisms develop new traits because they need them to survive in a new environment (e.g., giraffes having long necks).

Activity

Have students read the section in the text that describes how bacteria become resistant to penicillin. If possible, bring in an article from a popular science journal describing the problem of antibiotic resistance. Ask students to imagine a situation in which they were required to clean their desks and the counters of the room daily with antibiotic soap to kill *Salmonella* and *Staphylococcus* bacteria. Have students write a paragraph describing what would happen to the bacteria in the room. Students should understand that resistant strains of these bacteria could be selected for and become a problem in the room. Some students, however, may persist in believing that the resistant bacteria form because of the antibacterial soaps. L2

Promote Understanding

Activity

Divide the class into small groups, and give each group a bowl containing 10 beans of various, distinct colors (i.e., white, black, spotted, red). Only one bean should be red. Supply each group with bags of various colors of beans. Tell students that the beans represent a colony of bacteria, and the colors represent minor genetic variations in the same species. L2

- On your signal have each group "multiply" their beans. Since bacteria reproduce by cell division, have students simply add one new black bean for each black bean in the bowl, one red bean for every red bean in the bowl, and so on. Have students "multiply" their beans twice (for a total of 40 beans in the bowl).

- Next, tell students that an antibiotic has been spilled in the environment. The antibiotic works by destroying the bacterial cell wall. The genes that gave the red bacteria their color also gave them a cell wall that was particularly thick and resists the action of the antibiotic. All other bacteria were killed.

- Have students remove all beans from the bowl except the red beans. Now have them "multiply" the remaining (red) beans for two or three more generations. Point out that because the red "bacteria" already had a feature that allowed them to survive the antibiotic, only red "bacteria" remain.

Assess

After completing the chapter, see *Identifying Misconceptions* in the Study Guide at the end of the chapter.

Chapter Vocabulary

species, p. 154
evolution, p. 154
natural selection, p. 157
variation, p. 158
adaptation, p. 158
gradualism, p. 160
punctuated equilibrium, p. 160
sedimentary rock, p. 164
radioactive element, p. 165
embryology, p. 167
homologous, p. 168
vestigial structure, p. 168
primate, p. 170
hominid, p. 171
Homo sapiens, p. 172

Science Journal Answers will vary. Check that students understand that an adaptation is anything that helps an organism survive and reproduce in its environment. Also note that especially because of humans, many organisms are not well-adapted to their current habitats.

INTERACTIVE CHALKBOARD with Image Bank

PowerPoint® Presentations

This CD-ROM is an editable Microsoft® PowerPoint® presentation that includes:
- a pre-made presentation for every chapter
- interactive graphics
- animations
- audio clips
- image bank
- all new section and chapter questions
- Standardized Test Practice
- transparencies
- pre-lab questions for all labs
- Foldables directions
- links to life.msscience.com

Adaptations over Time

chapter preview

sections

1 Ideas About Evolution
Lab Hidden Frogs

2 Clues About Evolution

3 The Evolution of Primates
Lab Recognizing Variation in a Population

Virtual Lab How can natural selection be modeled?

Adaptation? No problem.

Cockroaches have existed for millions of years, yet they are still adapted to their environment. Since they first appeared, many species have disappeared, and other well-adapted species have evolved.

Science Journal Pick a favorite plant or animal and list in your Science Journal all the ways it is well-suited to its environment.

152

Theme Connection

Stability and Change Changes that occur during evolution can bring about stability by increasing variation within a population.

About the Photo

Successful Insects Cockroaches, and insects in general, are well-adapted to their environments. Separation of life stages reduces competition. Their body plan is particularly flexible for adaptation. By sheer numbers, insects are the most successful organisms on Earth.

Start-Up Activities

Adaptation for a Hunter

The cheetah is nature's fastest hunter, but it can run swiftly for only short distances. Its fur blends in with tall grass, making it almost invisible as it hides and waits for prey. Then the cheetah pounces, capturing the prey before it can run away.

1. Spread a sheet of newspaper classified ads on the floor.

2. Using a hole puncher, make 100 circles from each of the following types of paper: white paper, black paper, and classified ads.

3. Scatter all the circles on the newspaper on the floor. For 10 s, pick up as many circles as possible, one at a time. Have a partner time you.

4. Count the number of each kind of paper circle that you picked up. Record your results in your Science Journal.

5. **Think Critically** Which paper circles were most difficult to find? What can you infer about a cheetah's coloring from this activity? Enter your responses to these questions in your Science Journal.

Principles of Natural Selection Make the following Foldable to help you understand the process of natural selection.

STEP 1 Fold a sheet of paper in half lengthwise.

STEP 2 Fold paper down 2.5 cm from the top. (Hint: From the tip of your index finger to your middle knuckle is about 2.5 cm.)

STEP 3 Open and draw lines along the 2.5-cm fold and the center fold. **Label** as shown.

Summarize in a Table As you read, list the five principles of natural selection in the left-hand column. In the right-hand column, briefly write an example for each principle.

 Preview this chapter's content and activities at
life.msscience.com

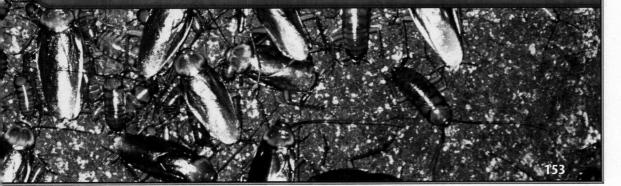

Bellringer

Section Focus Transparencies also are available on the Interactive Chalkboard CD-ROM.
L2 ELL

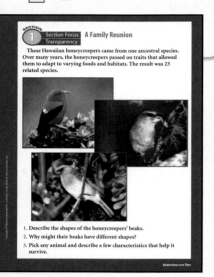

Tie to Prior Knowledge

Hypothesis v. Theory Reinforce the differences between the terms *hypothesis* and *theory*. A hypothesis is a testable prediction based on observations. Explain that a theory is not a guess, but rather an accepted explanation based on a large number of tests. Most scientists consider theories to be the best current explanation.

Caption Answer

Figure 1 Answers will vary.

What You'll Learn

- **Describe** Lamarck's hypothesis of acquired characteristics and Darwin's theory of natural selection.
- **Identify** why variations in organisms are important.
- **Compare and contrast** gradualism and punctuated equilibrium.

Why It's Important

The theory of evolution suggests why there are so many different living things.

Review Vocabulary
gene: a section of DNA that contains instructions for making specific proteins

New Vocabulary
- species
- evolution
- natural selection
- variation
- adaptation
- gradualism
- punctuated equilibrium

Figure 1 By studying fossils, scientists have traced the hypothesized evolution of the camel.
Discuss *the changes you observe in camels over time.*

Early Models of Evolution

Millions of species of plants, animals, and other organisms live on Earth today. Do you suppose they are exactly the same as they were when they first appeared—or have any of them changed? A **species** is a group of organisms that share similar characteristics and can reproduce among themselves to produce fertile offspring. Many characteristics of a species are inherited when they pass from parent to offspring. Change in these inherited characteristics over time is **evolution. Figure 1** shows how the characteristics of the camel have changed over time.

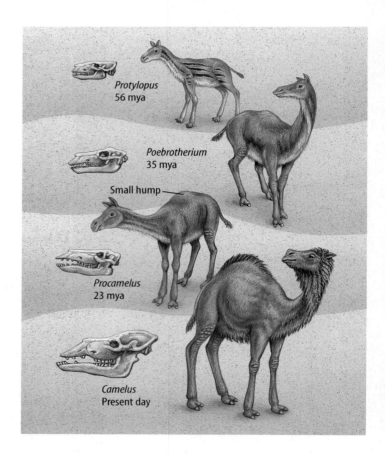

Protylopus
56 mya

Poebrotherium
35 mya

Small hump

Procamelus
23 mya

Camelus
Present day

---

154 CHAPTER 6 Adaptations over Time

Section 1 Resource Manager

Chapter *FAST FILE* Resources
Transparency Activity, p. 42
Directed Reading for Content Mastery, pp. 17, 18
Note-taking Worksheets, pp. 31–32
MiniLAB, p. 3
Enrichment, p. 28

Reinforcement, p. 26
Lab Worksheet, pp. 5–6
Lab Activities, pp. 9–10, 11–14
Mathematics Skill Activities, p. 1
Science Inquiry Labs, pp. 21–22

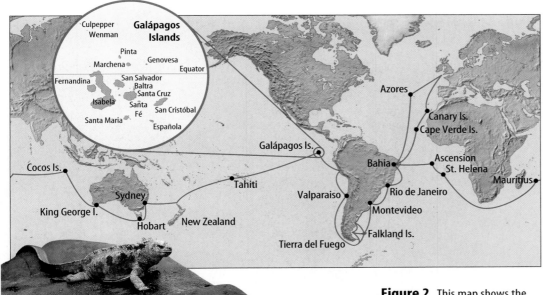

Figure 2 This map shows the route of Darwin's voyage on the HMS *Beagle*. Darwin noticed many species on the Galápagos Islands that he had not seen along the coast of South America, including the marine iguana. This species is the only lizard in the world known to enter the ocean and feed on seaweed.

Hypothesis of Acquired Characteristics In 1809, Jean Baptiste de Lamarck proposed a hypothesis to explain how species change over time. He suggested that characteristics, or traits, developed during a parent organism's lifetime are inherited by its offspring. His hypothesis is called the inheritance of acquired characteristics. Scientists collected data on traits that are passed from parents to offspring. The data showed that traits developed during a parent's lifetime, such as large muscles built by hard work or exercise, are not passed on to offspring. The evidence did not support Lamarck's hypothesis.

✔ **Reading Check** *What was Lamarck's explanation of evolution?*

Darwin's Model of Evolution

In December 1831, the HMS *Beagle* sailed from England on a journey to explore the South American coast. On board was a young naturalist named Charles Darwin. During the journey, Darwin recorded observations about the plants and animals he saw. He was amazed by the variety of life on the Galápagos Islands, which are about 1,000 km from the coast of Ecuador. Darwin hypothesized that the plants and animals on the Galápagos Islands originally must have come from Central and South America. But the islands were home to many species he had not seen in South America, including giant cactus trees, huge land tortoises, and the iguana shown in **Figure 2.**

✔ **Reading Check**

Answer Traits developed during a parent organism's lifetime are inherited by its offspring.

IDENTIFYING Misconceptions

Lamarck's Hypothesis Ask students to list the inadequacies of Lamarck's hypothesis. Students may agree with Lamarck until they critically examine the failures of this explanation. The primary failure of Lamarck's explanation is that acquired characteristics are not inherited. L3

Visual Learning

Figure 2 Ask students to explain why Darwin was able to use evidence from his voyage to develop his theory of evolution by natural selection. Many of the species in the Galápagos are unique to the islands but are similar to forms found on the mainland of South America.

Differentiated Instruction

Learning Disabled Allow students to use clay to make impressions of various items such as a comb, a key, etc. Plaster-of-paris can be poured into the impressions to form fossils. Place the plaster casts into a box. Allow students to try to identify the objects by reaching into the box without looking. You may use blindfolds if some students cannot resist the temptation to look. L1
⬛ Kinesthetic

Figure 3 Darwin observed that the beak shape of each species of Galápagos finch is related to its eating habits.

Finches that eat nuts and seeds have short, strong beaks for breaking hard shells.

Finches that feed on insects have long, slender beaks for probing beneath tree bark.

Finches with medium-sized beaks eat a variety of foods including seeds and insects.

Darwin's Observations Darwin observed 13 species of finches on the Galápagos Islands. He noticed that all 13 species were similar, except for differences in body size, beak shape, and eating habits, as shown in **Figure 3.** He also noticed that all the Galápagos finch species were similar to one finch species he had seen on the South American coast.

Darwin reasoned that the Galápagos finches must have had to compete for food. Finches with beak shapes that allowed them to eat available food survived longer and produced more offspring than finches without those beak shapes. After many generations, these groups of finches became separate species.

✔ Reading Check *How did Darwin explain the evolution of the different species of Galápagos finches?*

Natural Selection

After the voyage, Charles Darwin returned to England and continued to think about his observations. He collected more evidence on inherited traits by breeding racing pigeons. He also studied breeds of dogs and varieties of flowers. In the mid 1800s, Darwin developed a theory of evolution that is accepted by most scientists today. He described his ideas in a book called *On the Origin of Species,* which was published in 1859.

Darwin's Theory Darwin's observations led many other scientists to conduct experiments on inherited characteristics. After many years, Darwin's ideas became known as the theory of evolution by natural selection. **Natural selection** means that organisms with traits best suited to their environment are more likely to survive and reproduce. Their traits are passed to more offspring. All living organisms produce more offspring than survive. Galápagos finches lay several eggs every few months. Darwin realized that in just a few years, several pairs of finches could produce a large population. A population is all of the individuals of a species living in the same area. Members of a large population compete for living space, food, and other resources. Those that are best able to survive are more likely to reproduce and pass on their traits to the next generation.

The principles that describe how natural selection works are listed in **Table 1.** Over time, as new data was gathered and reported, changes were made to Darwin's original ideas about evolution by natural selection. His theory remains one of the most important ideas in the study of life science.

Table 1 The Principles of Natural Selection

1. Organisms produce more offspring than can survive.

2. Differences, or variations, occur among individuals of a species.

3. Some variations are passed to offspring.

4. Some variations are helpful. Individuals with helpful variations survive and reproduce better than those without these variations.

5. Over time, the offspring of individuals with helpful variations make up more of a population and eventually may become a separate species.

Applying Science

Teaching Strategy
Emphasize to students that there may be several correct answers for each journal entry.

Solving the Problem
June 6: none
July 22: 1 or none
July 24: 2, 3, or 4
July 28: 4 or 5
August 1: 1, 4, or none
August 12: 1 or none
August 15: 2, 3, or 5
August 18: 2, 3, or 4
August 20: 1 or none

Visual Learning

Table 1 Emphasize the importance of the principles of natural selection as mechanisms for evolution. Why is overproduction of offspring important? Overproduction results in a lack of resources, forcing animals to compete with one another. L2
[IS] **Logical-Mathematical**

Virtual Labs

Natural Selection *How can natural selection be modeled?*

Applying Science

Does natural selection take place in a fish tank?

Alejandro raises tropical fish as a hobby. Could the observations that he makes over several weeks illustrate the principles of natural selection?

Identifying the Problem
Alejandro keeps a detailed journal of his observations, some of which are given in the table to the right.

Solving the Problem
Refer to **Table 1** and match each of Alejandro's journal entries with the principle(s) it demonstrates. Here's a hint: *Some entries may not match any of the principles of natural selection. Some entries may match more than one principle.*

Fish Tank Observations

Date	Observation
June 6	6 fish are placed in aquarium tank.
July 22	16 new young appear.
July 24	3 young have short or missing tail fins. 13 young have normal tail fins.
July 28	Young with short or missing tail fins die.
August 1	2 normal fish die—from overcrowding?
August 12	30 new young appear.
August 15	5 young have short or missing tail fins. 25 young have normal tail fins.
August 18	Young with short or missing tail fins die.
August 20	Tank is overcrowded. Fish are divided equally into two tanks.

Differentiated Instruction

Learning Disabled Write the five principles of natural selection on a piece of colored paper. Cut the pieces apart to make a puzzle. Allow students to put the puzzle together to reinforce what they learn about natural selection. L1 [IS] **Visual-Spatial**

Caption Answers

Figure 4 Left Neither predators nor prey can detect the scorpion fish in its natural environment.

Figure 4 Right Predators might find it easily. Other lemurs might avoid it, preventing it from reproducing.

INTEGRATE
Language Arts

Evolution of English Etymology, the study of words, is in many ways a study of evolution. Discuss with students how their slang differs from yours and that of your parents.

Research Have students use the *Oxford English Dictionary* to investigate the history of words like house, man, nice, girl, brave, and hurry. They can then report to the class on the evolution of thse words.

INTEGRATE
Language Arts

Evolution of English
If someone from Shakespeare's time were to speak to you today, you probably would not understand her. Languages, like species, change over time. In your Science Journal, discuss some words or phrases that you use that your parents or teachers do not use correctly.

Figure 4 Variations that provide an advantage tend to increase in a population over time. Variations that result in a disadvantage tend to decrease in a population over time.

Variation and Adaptation

Darwin's theory of evolution by natural selection emphasizes the differences among individuals of a species. These differences are called variations. A **variation** is an inherited trait that makes an individual different from other members of its species. Variations result from permanent changes, or mutations, in an organism's genes. Some gene changes produce small variations, such as differences in the shape of human hairlines. Other gene changes produce large variations, such as an albino squirrel in a population of gray squirrels or fruit without seeds. Over time, more and more individuals of the species might inherit these variations. If individuals with these variations continue to survive and reproduce over many generations, a new species can evolve. It might take hundreds, thousands, or millions of generations for a new species to evolve.

Some variations are more helpful than others. An **adaptation** is any variation that makes an organism better suited to its environment. The variations that result in an adaptation can involve an organism's color, shape, behavior, or chemical makeup. Camouflage (KA muh flahj) is an adaptation. A camouflaged organism, like the one shown in **Figure 4,** blends into its environment and is more likely to survive and reproduce.

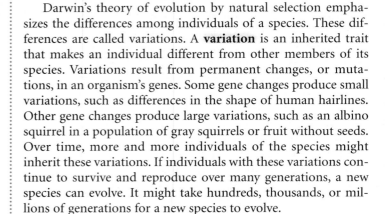
Albinism can prevent an organism from blending into its environment. **Infer** what might happen to an albino lemur in its natural environment.

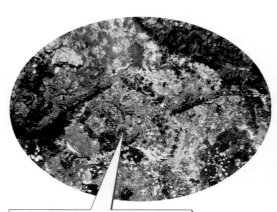
Camouflage allows organisms to blend into their environments. **Infer** how its coloration gives this scorpion fish a survival advantage.

⚗ LAB DEMONSTRATION

Purpose to observe variations

Materials pictures of various animal groups (i.e., cows, antelope, horses, wolves, rabbits), overhead projector

Preparation Make transparencies of pictures. Try to find pictures that show obvious differences (such as animals of different colors).

Procedure Have students observe each picture and list variations among the individuals in a group.

Expected Outcome Students will observe variations within a species.

Assessment

What causes differences between animals in the same species? genetic variations Do any of these variations aid in survival? If so, how? Answers will vary. Accept all reasonable answers.

European rabbits, like the one above, feed during the day and are fairly large.

Figure 5 About 600 years ago, European rabbits were introduced to the Canary Islands from a visiting Portuguese ship. The Canary Islands are in the Atlantic Ocean off the northwest coast of Africa. Over time, the Canary Island rabbits became a separate species.

Canary Island rabbits feed during the night. **Explain** *why large eyes might be considered a helpful adaptation in Canary Island rabbits.*

Caption Answer
Figure 5 Their large eyes help the rabbits see in the dark.

Changes in the Sources of Genes Over time, the genetic makeup of a species might change its appearance. For example, as the genetic makeup of a species of seed-eating Galápagos finch changed, so did the size and shape of its beak. Many kinds of environmental factors help bring about changes. When individuals of the same species move into or out of an area, they might bring in or remove genes and variations. Suppose a family from another country moves to your neighborhood. They might bring different foods, customs, and ways of speaking with them. In a similar way, when new individuals enter an existing population, they can bring in different genes and variations.

Geographic Isolation Sometimes mountains, lakes, or other geologic features isolate a small number of individuals from the rest of a population. Over several generations, variations that do not exist in the larger population might begin to be more common in the isolated population. Also, gene mutations can occur that add variations to populations. Over time, the two populations can become so different that they no longer can breed with each other. The two populations of rabbits shown in **Figure 5** have been geographically isolated from each other for thousands of generations.

Mini LAB

Relating Evolution to Species

Procedure
1. On a piece of **paper**, print the word *train*.
2. Add, subtract, or change one letter to make a new word.
3. Repeat step 2 with the new word.
4. Repeat steps 2 and 3 two more times.
5. Make a "family tree" that shows how your first word changed over time.

Analysis
1. Compare your tree to those of other people. Did you produce the same words?
2. How is this process similar to evolution by natural selection?

Mini LAB

Purpose Students practice classifying and sequencing. [L2]
[LS] **Visual-Spatial**

Teaching Strategy Have students think of each word as a species with the English language as the environment. Only useful changes that make other words will survive.

Analysis
1. Answers will vary. The same words will appear, but often in different places.
2. Answers will vary. Accept those that point out change over time, mutation, or adaptation.

Assessment

Performance To further assess students' understanding of evolution, have them make up and explain another hypothetical evolutionary schema using whatever shapes or materials they choose. Use **Performance Assessment in the Science Classroom,** p. 103.

SECTION 1 Ideas About Evolution **159**

Curriculum Connection

History Direct students to research the mid-nineteenth century to determine what daily life was like for Darwin and his peers. Students should make posters showing technologies used, dress of the period, and religious or political events. [L2] [LS] **Visual-Spatial** [P]

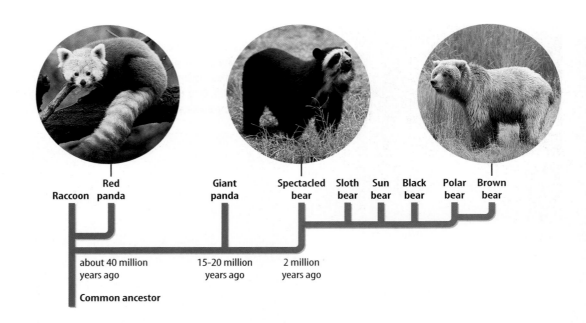

Raccoon | Red panda | Giant panda | Spectacled bear | Sloth bear | Sun bear | Black bear | Polar bear | Brown bear

about 40 million years ago

15-20 million years ago

2 million years ago

Common ancestor

Use Science Words

Word Origin Scientists once accepted that organisms evolve according to the gradualism model. *Gradus*, meaning a step, is the Latin word from which gradualism is derived. Ask students why this word is used. Gradualism seems to occur step by step.

L2 IS **Linguistic**

Caption Answer

Figure 6 Many changes occurred in a short time. Gradualism predicts slower changes.

Inquiry Lab

Investigating Selection

Purpose Help students see how natural selection works with pre-existing variation.

Possible Materials

• Iron nails, pennies, marbles, popcorn seeds, cereal
• Tweezers, fingers, magnets, spoons, clothespins

Estimated Time 25–30 minutes

Teaching Strategies

• Have students try to pick up as many nails as possible in 15s using the above materials.
• Then have them try to get popcorn with the same materials.
• How does this relate to natural selection?
• Allow students to think of other comparisons to natural selection. Discuss them as time allows. L2

For additional inquiry activities, see *Science Inquiry Labs.*

Figure 6 The hypothesized evolution of bears illustrates the punctuated equilibrium model of evolution.
Discuss *how the six species on the far right are explained better by punctuated equilibrium.*

The Speed of Evolution

Scientists do not agree on how quickly evolution occurs. Many scientists hypothesize that evolution occurs slowly, perhaps over tens or hundreds of millions of years. Other scientists hypothesize that evolution can occur quickly. Most scientists agree that evidence supports both of these models.

Gradualism Darwin hypothesized that evolution takes place slowly. The model that describes evolution as a slow, ongoing process by which one species changes to a new species is known as **gradualism.** According to the gradualism model, a continuing series of mutations and variations over time will result in a new species. Look back at **Figure 1,** which shows the evolution of the camel over tens of millions of years. Fossil evidence shows a series of intermediate forms that indicate a gradual change from the earliest camel species to today's species.

Punctuated Equilibrium Gradualism doesn't explain the evolution of all species. For some species, the fossil record shows few intermediate forms—one species suddenly changes to another. According to the **punctuated equilibrium** model, rapid evolution comes about when the mutation of a few genes results in the appearance of a new species over a relatively short period of time. The fossil record gives examples of this type of evolution, as you can see in **Figure 6.**

160 CHAPTER 6 Adaptations over Time

Curriculum Connection

Art Have students make a piece of art that shows their understanding of gradualism (i.e., a drawing that shows the slow evolution of one organism to another). In art, this process is called morphing.
L2 IS **Visual-Spatial**

Punctuated Equilibrium Today Evolution by the punctuated equilibrium model can occur over a few thousand or million years, and sometimes even faster. For example, many bacteria have changed in a few decades. The antibiotic penicillin originally came from the fungus shown in **Figure 7.** But many bacteria species that were once easily killed by penicillin no longer are harmed by it. These bacteria have developed resistance to the drug. Penicillin has been in use since 1943. Just four years later, in 1947, a species of bacteria that causes pneumonia and other infections already had developed resistance to the drug. By the 1990s, several disease-producing bacteria had become resistant to penicillin and many other antibiotics.

How did penicillin-resistant bacteria evolve so quickly? As in any population, some organisms have variations that allow them to survive unfavorable living conditions when other organisms cannot. When penicillin was used to kill bacteria, those with the penicillin-resistant variation survived, reproduced, and passed this trait to their offspring. Over a period of time, this bacteria population became penicillin-resistant.

Figure 7 The fungus growing in this petri dish is *Penicillium,* the original source of penicillin. It produces an antibiotic substance that prevents the growth of certain bacteria.

IDENTIFYING Misconceptions

Environmental Changes Many students think that environmental changes cause changes in traits that help organisms cope with the new environment. Refer to page F at the beginning of this chapter for teaching strategies that address this misconception.

3 Assess

DAILY INTERVENTION

Check for Understanding
Interpersonal Have students discuss why Darwin was impressed with the ability of humans to produce new breeds of plants and animals through artificial selection. He saw this as an analogy to the mechanism of evolution by natural selection. L2 COOP LEARN LS

Reteach
Types of Selection Have students list similarities between artificial selection, such as dog breeding, and natural selection. In both, specific traits are selected. L2

✓ Assessment

Performance To assess students' abilities to classify organisms by their variations, ask them to classify two species of birds that eat different types of foods. Use **Performance Assessment in the Science Classroom,** p. 121. L2

---

section 1 review

Summary

Early Models of Evolution
- Evolution is change in the characteristics of a species over time.
- Lamarck proposed the hypothesis of inherited acquired characteristics.

Natural Selection
- Darwin proposed evolution by natural selection, a process by which organisms best suited to their environments are most likely to survive and reproduce.
- Organisms have more offspring than can survive, individuals of a species vary, and many of these variations are passed to offspring.

Variation and Adaptation
- Adaptations are variations that help an organism survive or reproduce in its environment.
- Mutations are the source of new variations.

The Speed of Evolution
- Evolution may be a slow or fast process depending on the species under study.

Self Check

1. **Compare** Lamarck's and Darwin's ideas about how evolution takes place.
2. **Explain** why variations are important to understanding change in a population over time.
3. **Discuss** how the gradualism model of evolution differs from the punctuated equilibrium model of evolution.
4. **Describe** how geographic isolation contributes to evolution.
5. **Think Critically** What adaptations would be helpful for an animal species that was moved to the Arctic?
6. **Concept Map** Use information given in **Figure 6** to make a map that shows how raccoons, red pandas, giant pandas, polar bears, and black bears are related to a common ancestor.

Applying Math

7. **Use Percentages** The evolution of the camel can be traced back at least 56 million years. Use **Figure 1** to estimate the percent of this time that the modern camel has existed.

---

section 1 review

1. Lamarck thought acquired traits were passed to offspring; Darwin concluded that only inherited traits were passed to offspring.
2. If a population were genetically uniform, any harmful factor that affected one of them would affect all of them. Because of variation, some individuals in a population would not be affected by the adverse factor and would survive and reproduce.
3. Gradualism—species slowly evolve to become other species; punctuated equilibrium—species suddenly become other species in a relatively short amount of time.
4. Populations with different variations evolve independently, producing greater variation.
5. Possible answers: lighter coat color; traits for surviving extreme cold
6. The concept map should illustrate several species evolving from a common ancestor.
7. 2 million years/56 million years × 100% = approximately 4%

▶ Real-World Question

Purpose Students will explore how natural selection equips organisms for survival in their environment.

Process Skills observe, analyze, infer, formulate, model

Time Required 40 minutes

▶ Procedure

Teaching Strategies

- Obtain color photographs of frogs in natural settings to present examples of camouflage to students.

- Obtain color photographs of other camouflaged animals and ask students how natural selection has prepared them for survival in their environment.

Troubleshooting Provide students with pictures of different environments to serve as a reference.

▶ Conclude and Apply

1. Answer will vary, but students should consider the colors, patterns, and textures of the habitat.

2. Color patterns, textures, and body shapes that provide the best camouflage in an environment help those frogs avoid predators, and, through natural selection, these characteristics become dominant in a frog population.

3. The frog may not be properly camouflaged from predators in its new environment.

 Hidden Fr🐸gs

Through natural selection, animals become adapted for survival in their environment. Adaptations include shapes, colors, and even textures that help an animal blend into its surroundings. These adaptations are called camouflage. The red-eyed tree frog's mint green body blends in with tropical forest vegetation as shown in the photo on the right. Could you design camouflage for a desert frog? A temperate forest frog?

▶ Real-World Question

What type of camouflage would best suit a frog living in a particular habitat?

Goals

- **Create** a frog model camouflaged to blend in with its surroundings.

Materials (for each group)

cardboard form of a frog	glue
colored markers	beads
crayons	sequins
colored pencils	modeling clay

Safety Precautions

▶ Procedure

1. Choose one of the following habitats for your frog model: muddy shore of a pond, orchid flowers in a tropical rain forest, multicolored clay in a desert, or the leaves and branches of trees in a temperate forest.

2. **List** the features of your chosen habitat that will determine the camouflage your frog model will need.

3. **Brainstorm** with your group the body shape, coloring, and skin texture that would make the best camouflage for your model. Record your ideas in your Science Journal.

4. **Draw** in your Science Journal samples of colors, patterns, texture, and other features your frog model might have.

5. Show your design ideas to your teacher and ask for further input.

6. **Construct** your frog model.

▶ Conclude and Apply

1. **Explain** how the characteristics of the habitat helped you decide on the specific frog features you chose.

2. **Infer** how the color patterns and other physical features of real frogs develop in nature.

3. **Explain** why it might be harmful to release a frog into a habitat for which it is not adapted.

Communicating Your Data

Create a poster or other visual display that represents the habitat you chose for this activity. Use your display to show classmates how your design helps camouflage your frog model. **For more help, refer to the** Science Skill Handbook.

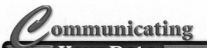 Assessment

Process Ask students to explain why the frog they have modeled would not be equipped to survive in a different environment. Use **Performance Assessment in the Science Classroom,** p. 89. L2

Communicating Your Data

Have students do library researches about their chosen habitats.

Clues About Evolution

Clues from Fossils

Imagine going on a fossil hunt in Wyoming. Your companions are paleontologists—scientists who study the past by collecting and examining fossils. As you climb a low hill, you notice a curved piece of stone jutting out of the sandy soil. One of the paleontologists carefully brushes the soil away and congratulates you on your find. You've discovered part of the fossilized shell of a turtle like the one shown in **Figure 8.**

The Green River Formation covers parts of Wyoming, Utah, and Colorado. On your fossil hunt, you learn that about 50 million years ago, during the Eocene Epoch, this region was covered by lakes. The water was home to fish, crocodiles, lizards, and turtles. Palms, fig trees, willows, and cattails grew on the lakeshores. Insects and birds flew through the air. How do scientists know all this? After many of the plants and animals of that time died, they were covered with silt and mud. Over millions of years, they became the fossils that have made the Green River Formation one of the richest fossil deposits in the world.

The turtle *Cistemum undatum* is from the same fossil formation.

The most abundant fossils are of a freshwater herring, *Knightia oecaena*, which is Wyoming's state fossil.

Figure 8 The desert of the Green River Formation is home to pronghorn antelope, elks, coyotes, and eagles. Fossil evidence shows that about 50 million years ago the environment was much warmer and wetter than it is today.

as you read

What You'll Learn

- **Identify** the importance of fossils as evidence of evolution.
- **Explain** how relative and radiometric dating are used to estimate the age of fossils.
- **List** examples of five types of evidence for evolution.

Why It's Important

The scientific evidence for evolution helps you understand why this theory is so important to the study of biology.

Review Vocabulary

epoch: next-smaller division of geological time after a period; is characterized by differences in life-forms that may vary regionally

New Vocabulary

- sedimentary rock
- radioactive element
- embryology
- homologous
- vestigial structure

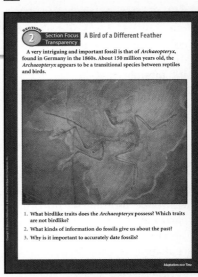

A Bird of a Different Feather

A very intriguing and important fossil is that of *Archaeopteryx*, found in Germany in the 1860s. About 150 million years old, the *Archaeopteryx* appears to be a transitional species between reptiles and birds.

1. What birdlike traits does the *Archaeopteryx* possess? Which traits are not birdlike?
2. What kinds of information do fossils give us about the past?
3. Why is it important to accurately date fossils?

Tie to Prior Knowledge

DNA Changes Review the structure and function of DNA with students while they study the evidence for evolution. Emphasize that changes in DNA provide the basis for evolution.

SECTION 2 Clues About Evolution **163**

Caption Answer

Figure 9 Imprint fossils, mineralized fossils, and cast fossils are the most common.

Activity

Collect Rocks Have groups of students collect rocks and fossils from your area. Allow them to research the types of rocks and fossils they find. If students will donate their finds to the school, you can quickly build a school collection of fossils and rocks to display. L2 ELL COOP LEARN IS **Interpersonal**

Activity

Rock Characteristics Bring in samples of igneous, metamorphic, and sedimentary rocks. Ask students to observe the differences. Explain that igneous rock was once molten, so no organism could have lived in it. Metamorphic rock has been reheated, so its structure has changed from the original. Any fossils contained in it are usually lost. Sedimentary rock has the best characteristics for the preservation of a fossil record. L2 ELL IS **Visual-Spatial**

Fun Fact

Scientists have successfully extracted DNA from frozen mammoths and used the information to evaluate the evolutionary relationships between living elephants and extinct species.

Figure 9 Examples of several different types of fossils are shown here.
Infer *which of these would most likely be found in a layer of sedimentary rock.*

Imprint fossils A leaf, feather, bones, or even the entire body of an organism can leave an imprint on sediment that later hardens to become rock.

Mineralized fossils Minerals can replace wood or bone to create a piece of petrified wood as shown to the left or a mineralized bone fossil.

Frozen fossils The remains of organisms like this mammoth can be trapped in ice that remains frozen for thousands of years.

Cast fossils Minerals can fill in the hollows of animal tracks, as shown to the right, a mollusk shell, or other parts of an organism to create a cast.

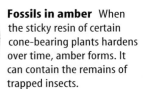

Fossils in amber When the sticky resin of certain cone-bearing plants hardens over time, amber forms. It can contain the remains of trapped insects.

Types of Fossils

INTEGRATE Earth Science

Most of the evidence for evolution comes from fossils. A fossil is the remains, an imprint, or a trace of a prehistoric organism. Several types of fossils are shown in **Figure 9.** Most fossils are found in sedimentary rock. **Sedimentary rock** is formed when layers of sand, silt, clay, or mud are compacted and cemented together, or when minerals are deposited from a solution. Limestone, sandstone, and shale are all examples of sedimentary rock. Fossils are found more often in limestone than in any other kind of sedimentary rock. The fossil record provides evidence that living things have evolved.

164 CHAPTER 6 Adaptations over Time

Teacher FYI

Incomplete Fossil Record The fossil record has always been incomplete because most organisms never become fossils. They are either decomposed or eaten before they have an opportunity to become fossilized.

Science Journal

The Grand Canyon Few places on Earth have as many layers of exposed sedimentary rock as the Grand Canyon. Have students visit the U.S. National Park Service at nps.gov/grca and research the Grand Canyon. Have them prepare an essay on what they would expect to see if they visited it. L2 IS **Linguistic** P

Determining a Fossil's Age

Paleontologists use detective skills to determine the age of dinosaur fossils or the remains of other ancient organisms. They can use clues provided by unique rock layers and the fossils they contain. The clues provide information about the geology, weather, and life-forms that must have been present during each geologic time period. Two basic methods—relative dating and radiometric dating—can be used, alone or together, to estimate the ages of rocks and fossils.

Relative Dating One way to find the approximate age of fossils found within a rock layer is relative dating. Relative dating is based on the idea that in undisturbed areas, younger rock layers are deposited on top of older rock layers, as shown in **Figure 10.** Relative dating provides only an estimate of a fossil's age. The estimate is made by comparing the ages of rock layers found above and below the fossil layer. For example, suppose a 50-million-year-old rock layer lies below a fossil, and a 35-million-year-old layer lies above it. According to relative dating, the fossil is between 35 million and 50 million years old.

> ✔ **Reading Check** *Why can relative dating be used only to estimate the age of a fossil?*

Radiometric Dating Scientists can obtain a more accurate estimate of the age of a rock layer by using radioactive elements. A **radioactive element** gives off a steady amount of radiation as it slowly changes to a nonradioactive element. Each radioactive element gives off radiation at a different rate. Scientists can estimate the age of the rock by comparing the amount of radioactive element with the amount of nonradioactive element in the rock. This method of dating does not always produce exact results, because the original amount of radioactive element in the rock can never be determined for certain.

Science Online

Topic: Fossil Finds
Visit life.msscience.com for Web links to information about recent fossil discoveries.

Activity Prepare a newspaper article describing how one of these discoveries was made, what it reveals about past life on Earth, and how it has impacted our understanding of what the past environments of Earth were like.

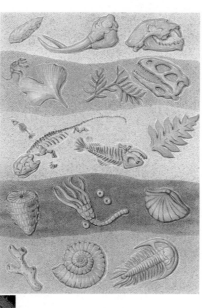

Figure 10 In Bryce Canyon, erosion by water and wind has cut through the sedimentary rock, exposing the layers.
Infer *the relative age of rocks in the lowest layers compared to the top layer.*

Quick Demo

Half-Lives

Materials two sets of jelly beans of different colors

Estimated Time five minutes

Procedure Take 40 beans of one color. Tell the class that they represent atoms of a radioactive isotope. After 30 seconds, replace 20 beans with beans of the other color. After another 30 seconds, replace half of the remaining beans of the first color. Repeat until all of the beans are of the new color. Ask students how many half-lives that took, and have them calculate how long decay would have taken with different half-lives. [L2]

> ✔ **Reading Check**

Answer Relative dating can only give a range, not an exact age.

Make a Model

Relative Dating Have students make a model showing how relative dating is used. Their model can show layers of sand, dirt, salt, cornmeal, or other materials in a plastic drink bottle or glass container. Several "fossils" should be placed in the model to explain their relative ages. Have each student present his or her model to the group. [L2] [IS] **Kinesthetic and Visual-Spatial**

Caption Answer

Figure 10 Assuming no disturbance, the bottom layers are older than the top layers.

Differentiated Instruction

Visually Impaired You can explain relative dating to visually impaired students by creating layers of different materials that the student can differentiate by touch. Use stiff cardboard or foam board and glue the materials in layers. Glue easily identifiable objects as analogies to fossils. [L1] **Kinesthetic and Visual-Spatial**

NATIONAL GEOGRAPHIC

Visualizing The Geologic Time Scale

Have students examine the pictures and read the captions. Then ask the following questions.

In the geologic time scale, which is longer—an era or a period? Students should note that an era is a longer time than a period.

The names of the geologic eras have Greek roots. *Ceno* means "recent" and *zoic* means "life." *Paleo* means "ancient." Infer the meaning of the Greek prefix *meso*. Meso means "middle," so mesozoic means "middle life."

Activity

Geologic Periods Have students work in teams to create a poster about one of the geologic periods shown in the feature. The poster should contain facts about the plants and animals that were alive during the period, as well as illustrations depicting the landforms and bodies of water that were present. The teams of students should present their findings to the class. L2

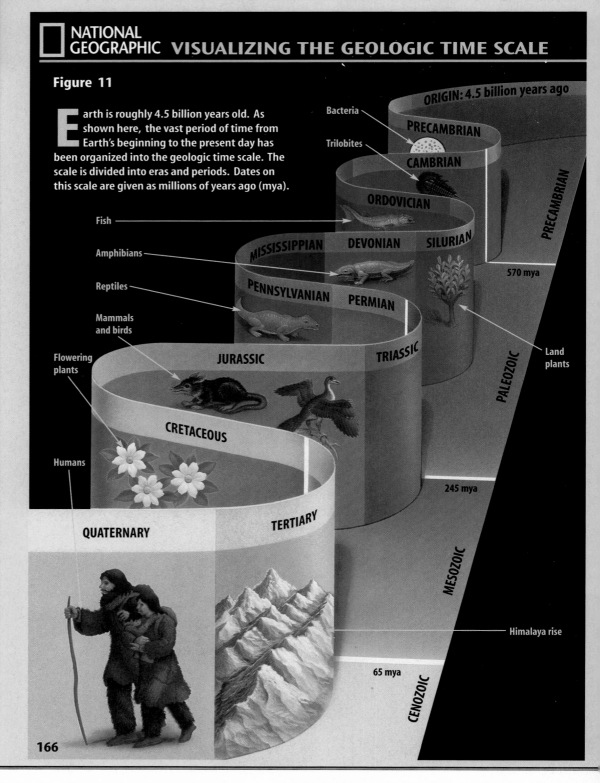

NATIONAL GEOGRAPHIC **VISUALIZING THE GEOLOGIC TIME SCALE**

Figure 11

Earth is roughly 4.5 billion years old. As shown here, the vast period of time from Earth's beginning to the present day has been organized into the geologic time scale. The scale is divided into eras and periods. Dates on this scale are given as millions of years ago (mya).

166

Curriculum Connection

Math Explain the vastness of geological, or "deep" time. A million years is only 0.02 percent of the total. Have students convert the eras and periods into percentages of the entire scale. L2
LS Logical-Mathematical

Differentiated Instruction

Challenge Have interested students research the Precambrian era, which accounts for about 90% of geologic time. Students should use a word processing program to prepare a short report of their findings. L3

Fossils and Evolution

Fossils provide a record of organisms that lived in the past. However, the fossil record is incomplete, or has gaps, much like a book with missing pages. The gaps exist because most organisms do not become fossils. By looking at fossils, scientists conclude that many simpler forms of life existed earlier in Earth's history, and more complex forms of life appeared later, as shown in **Figure 11.** Fossils provide indirect evidence that evolution has occurred on Earth.

Almost every week, fossil discoveries are made somewhere in the world. When fossils are found, they are used to help scientists understand the past. Scientists can use fossils to make models that show what the organisms might have looked like. From fossils, scientists can sometimes determine whether the organisms lived in family groups or alone, what types of food they ate, what kind of environment they lived in, and many other things about them. Most fossils represent extinct organisms. From a study of the fossil record, scientists have concluded that more than 99 percent of all organisms that have ever existed on Earth are now extinct.

More Clues About Evolution

Besides fossils, what other clues do humans have about evolution? Sometimes, evolution can be observed directly. Plant breeders observe evolution when they use cross-breeding to produce genetic changes in plants. The development of antibiotic resistance in bacteria is another direct observation of evolution. Entomologists have noted similar rapid evolution of pesticide-resistant insect species. These observations provide direct evidence that evolution occurs. Also, many examples of indirect evidence for evolution exist. They include similarities in embryo structures, the chemical makeup of organisms including DNA, and the way organisms develop into adults. Indirect evidence does not provide proof of evolution, but it does support the idea that evolution takes place over time.

Embryology The study of embryos and their development is called **embryology** (em bree AH luh jee). An embryo is the earliest growth stage of an organism. A tail and pharyngeal pouches are found at some point in the embryos of fish, reptiles, birds, and mammals, as **Figure 12** shows. Fish develop gills, but the other organisms develop other structures as their development continues. Fish, birds, and reptiles keep their tails, but many mammals lose theirs. These similarities suggest an evolutionary relationship among all vertebrate species.

Evolution in Fossils Many organisms have a history that has been preserved in sedimentary rock. Fossils show that the bones of animals such as horses and whales have become reduced in size or number over geologic time, as the species has evolved. In your Science Journal, explain what information can be gathered from changes in structures that occur over time.

Figure 12 Similarities in the embryos of fish, chickens, and rabbits show evidence of evolution. **Evaluate** *these embryos as evidence for evolution.*

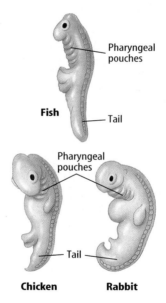

Fish — Pharyngeal pouches — Tail

Pharyngeal pouches — Tail

Chicken   Rabbit

SECTION 2 Clues About Evolution **167**

Use an Analogy

Geologic Time Use a length of rope or kite string as an analogy for the geologic time scale. Make knots to illustrate where the eras begin and end, and paint sections different colors to illustrate the periods. Another analogy for the geologic time scale is a clock. Use a wall clock and talk about the eras and periods as you advance the clock from 12:00. Make your conversion calculations before you begin.

Evolution in Fossils Changes in structures often mirror changes in the environment.

Teacher FYI

Family Trees Morphological and molecular studies indicate that marine mammals (e.g., whales, dolphins, porpoises) and some even-toed ungulates (e.g., hippos and cattle) share a common ancestor not shared by any other group. This implies that cattle and whales are more closely related than cattle and horses.

Caption Answer

Figure 12 Answers will vary. Accept answers that point out similarities.

Active Reading

Double Entry Journal In this strategy, the student takes notes and adds his or her own reflections while reading the text. Students are encouraged to explore ideas, make responses, and take risks in giving opinions about the reading. Have them divide a sheet of paper in half. On the left, have students identify a particular passage or quotation of significance in the reading. The reader records anything luminous, enigmatic, stimulating, or disturbing. On the right, the reader responds, questions, elaborates, makes personal connections, evaluates, reflects, analyzes, or interprets. Have students make a Double Entry Journal about evolution. L2

☑ Reading Check

Answer These structures often indicate that two or more species share common ancestors.

Teacher FYI

Evolution Evidence Pesticide resistance in insects, antibiotic resistance in bacteria, and observed differences in salamanders, frogs, and birds are all examples of direct evidence for evolution.

Discussion

Analogous Structures Structures that do not have a common origin but do appear similar are called analogous structures. What kinds of information would similar structures without a common origin provide? Such structures might indicate similar evolutionary solutions to similar environmental conditions.

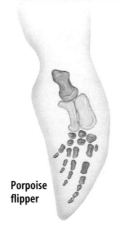
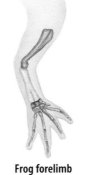
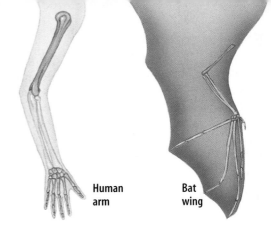

Porpoise flipper

Frog forelimb

Human arm

Bat wing

Figure 13 A porpoise flipper, frog forelimb, human arm, and bat wing are homologous. These structures show different arrangements and shapes of the bones of the forelimb. They have the same number of bones, muscles, and blood vessels, and they developed from similar tissues.

Homologous Structures What do the structures shown in **Figure 13** have in common? Although they have different functions, each of these structures is made up of the same kind of bones. Body parts that are similar in origin and structure are called **homologous** (hoh MAH luh gus). Homologous structures also can be similar in function. They often indicate that two or more species share common ancestors.

☑ Reading Check *What do homologous structures indicate?*

Vestigial Structures The bodies of some organisms include **vestigial** (veh STIH jee ul) **structures**—structures that don't seem to have a function. Vestigial structures also provide evidence for evolution. For example, manatees, snakes, and whales no longer have back legs, but, like all animals with legs, they still have pelvic bones. The human appendix is a vestigial structure. The appendix appears to be a small version of the cecum, which is an important part of the digestive tract of many mammals. Scientists hypothesize that vestigial structures, like those shown in **Figure 14,** are body parts that once functioned in an ancestor.

Figure 14 Humans have three small muscles around each ear that are vestigial. In some mammals, such as horses, these muscles are large. They allow a horse to turn its ears toward the source of a sound. Humans cannot rotate their ears, but some people can wiggle their ears.

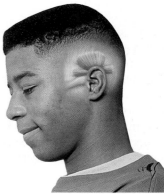

168 CHAPTER 6 Adaptations over Time

Cultural Diversity

Evolving Viruses The flu is an example of a sickness caused by a virus whose DNA evolves in order for it to survive. Every major flu epidemic has come from South China, where ducks, pigs, and humans are brought into daily contact. An avian flu transfers to pigs, as does a human flu variety. The viruses exchange pieces of genetic code to form a new flu strain. When the virus reinfects humans, it is different enough that antibodies made to fight the first form do not stop the new virus. That is why flu shots do not protect against all varieties.

DNA If you enjoy science fiction, you probably have read books or seen movies in which scientists re-create dinosaurs and other extinct organisms from DNA taken from fossils. DNA is the molecule that controls heredity and directs the development of every organism. In a cell with a nucleus, DNA is found in genes that make up the chromosomes. Scientists compare DNA from living organisms to identify similarities among species. Examinations of ancient DNA often provide additional evidence of how some species evolved from their extinct ancestors. By looking at DNA, scientists also can determine how closely related organisms are. For example, DNA studies indicate that dogs are the closest relatives of bears.

Similar DNA also can suggest common ancestry. Apes such as the gorillas shown in **Figure 15,** chimpanzees, and orangutans have 24 pairs of chromosomes. Humans have 23 pairs. When two of an ape's chromosomes are laid end to end, a match for human chromosome number 2 is formed. Also, similar proteins such as hemoglobin—the oxygen-carrying protein in red blood cells—are found in many primates. This can be further evidence that primates have a common ancestor.

Figure 15 Gorillas have DNA and proteins that are similar to humans and other primates.

3 Assess

DAILY INTERVENTION

Check for Understanding
Visual-Spatial Prepare a display of several lines of evidence that support evolution by natural selection.

Reteach
Fossils Show students examples of as many kinds of fossils as possible. Have students identify each type of fossil. L1
IS **Naturalist**

✓ Assessment

Performance Have students prepare a poster showing the time periods in which fish, amphibians, reptiles, birds, and mammals first appeared. Use **Performance Assessment in the Science Classroom,** p. 145. L2

section 2 review

Summary

Clues from Fossils
- Scientists learn about past life by studying fossils.

Determining a Fossil's Age
- The relative date of a fossil can be estimated from the ages of rocks in nearby layers.
- Radiometric dating using radioactive elements gives more accurate dates for fossils.

Fossils and Evolution
- The fossil record has gaps which may yet be filled with later discoveries.

More Clues About Evolution
- Homologous structures, similar embryos, or vestigial structures can show evolutionary relationships.
- Evolutionary relationships among organisms can be inferred from DNA comparisons.

Self Check

1. **Compare and contrast** relative dating and radiometric dating.
2. **Discuss** the importance of fossils as evidence of evolution and describe five different kinds of fossils.
3. **Explain** how DNA can provide some evidence of evolution.
4. **List** three examples of direct evidence for evolution.
5. **Interpret Scientific Illustrations** According to data in **Figure 11,** what was the longest geologic era? What was the shortest era? In what period did mammals appear?
6. **Think Critically** Compare and contrast the five types of evidence that support the theory of evolution.

Applying Math

7. **Use Percentages** The Cenozoic Era represents about 65 million years. Approximately what percent of Earth's 4.5-billion-year history does this era represent?

  life.msscience.com/self_check_quiz

section 2 review

1. Relative dating is used to find the approximate age of a rock layer by its position relative to other layers. Radiometric dating is used to date rocks by measuring relative amounts of radioactive and non-radioactive elements.
2. Fossils provide evidence of how species changed over time.

Organisms can be frozen in ice or trapped in amber. Minerals can replace wood or bone. There are also cast fossils and imprint fossils.
3. Organisms with similar DNA may have a common ancestor.
4. antibiotic resistance in bacteria, pesticide resistance in insects, and genetic changes in plants

5. Precambrian; Cenozoic; Jurassic
6. Students should compare and contrast vestigial structures, DNA, homologous structures, fossils, and embryology.
7. 65 million years/4,500 million years × 100 = 1.44%

The Evolution of Primates

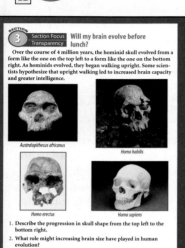
as you read

What You'll Learn
- **Describe** the differences among living primates.
- **Identify** the adaptations of primates.
- **Discuss** the evolutionary history of modern primates.

Why It's Important
Studying primate evolution will help you appreciate the differences among primates.

Review Vocabulary
opposable: can be placed against another digit of a hand or foot

New Vocabulary
- primate
- *Homo sapiens*
- hominid

Primates

Humans, monkeys, and apes belong to the group of mammals known as the **primates.** All primates have opposable thumbs, binocular vision, and flexible shoulders that allow the arms to rotate. These shared characteristics indicate that all primates may have evolved from a common ancestor.

Having an opposable thumb allows you to cross your thumb over your palm and touch your fingers. This means that you can grasp and hold things with your hands. An opposable thumb allows tree-dwelling primates to hold on to branches.

Binocular vision permits you to judge depth or distance with your eyes. In a similar way, it allows tree-dwelling primates to judge the distances as they move between branches. Flexible shoulders and rotating forelimbs also help tree-dwelling primates move from branch to branch. They also allow humans to do the backstroke, as shown in **Figure 16.**

Primates are divided into two major groups. The first group, the strepsirhines (STREP suh rines), includes lemurs and tarsiers like those shown in **Figure 17.** The second group, haplorhines (HAP luh rines), includes monkeys, apes, and humans.

Figure 16 The ability to rotate the shoulder in a complete circle allows humans to swim through water and tree-dwelling primates to travel through treetops.

Section 3 Resource Manager

Chapter *FAST FILE* Resources
Transparency Activity, p. 44
Directed Reading for Content Mastery, pp. 19, 20
MiniLAB, p. 4
Enrichment, p. 30

Reinforcement, p. 27
Lab Worksheet, pp. 7–8
Home and Community Involvement, p. 48
Lab Management and Safety, p. 71

Tarsier

Lemur

Figure 17 Tarsiers and lemurs are active at night. Tarsiers are commonly found in the rain forests of Southeast Asia. Lemurs live on Madagascar and other nearby islands.
List the traits that distinguish these animals as primates.

Hominids About 4 million to 6 million years ago, humanlike primates appeared that were different from the other primates. These ancestors, called **hominids,** ate both meat and plants and walked upright on two legs. Hominids shared some characteristics with gorillas, orangutans, and chimpanzees, but a larger brain separated them from the apes.

African Origins In the early 1920s, a fossil skull was discovered in a quarry in South Africa. The skull had a small space for the brain, but it had a humanlike jaw and teeth. The fossil, named *Australopithecus,* was one of the oldest hominids discovered. An almost-complete skeleton of *Australopithecus* was found in northern Africa in 1974. This hominid fossil, shown in **Figure 18,** was called Lucy and had a small brain but is thought to have walked upright. This fossil indicates that modern hominids might have evolved from similar ancestors.

Figure 18 The fossil remains of Lucy are estimated to be 2.9 million to 3.4 million years old.

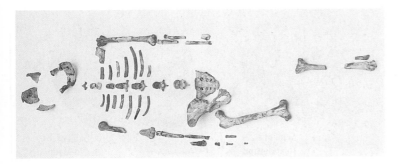

Mini LAB

Living Without Thumbs

Procedure
1. Using **tape,** fasten down each of your thumbs next to the palm of each hand.
2. Leave your thumbs taped down for at least 1 h. During this time, do the following activities: eat a meal, change clothes, and brush your teeth. Be careful not to try anything that could be dangerous.
3. Untape your thumbs, then write about your experiences in your **Science Journal.**

Analysis
1. Did not having use of your thumbs significantly affect the way you did anything? Explain.
2. Infer how having opposable thumbs could have influenced primate evolution.

Try at Home

Mini LAB

Purpose Students observe the function of opposable thumbs, and infer how they may have influenced primate evolution. L1 ELL IS Kinesthetic
Materials tape
Teaching Strategy Tell students it will be easier for them to tape both thumbs down if they use a roll of tape, rather than tape from a dispenser.
Safety Precautions Tell students not to try anything during this lab that could be dangerous without manual dexterity.
Analysis
1. Answers should indicate that students were negatively affected.
2. Possible answer: Opposable thumbs would allow for the use of tools, and tools are a foundation of modern civilization and technology.

Assessment
Performance Have students design a house with features that could be easily used by someone without thumbs. Use **Performance Assessment in the Science Classroom,** p. 123. P

Try at Home

Teacher FYI

Primate Existence Many types of primates existed in the Paleocene epoch. More modern forms are thought to have evolved during the Eocene epoch. There are presently about 200 species of primates, although there were more in the past.

Differentiated Instruction

English-Language Learners Have students look through old books and magazines for pictures or depictions of current primates and fossil hominids. Have them assemble these into a family tree that shows the relationships among these primates. L2 ELL Visual-Spatial

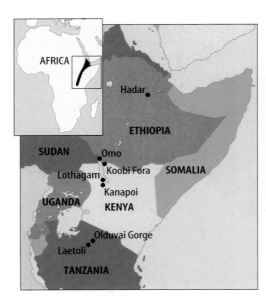

Figure 19 Many of the oldest humanlike skeletons have been found in this area of east Africa.

Early Humans In the 1960s in the region of Africa shown in **Figure 19,** a hominid fossil, which was more like present-day humans than *Australopithecus,* was discovered. The hominid was named *Homo habilis,* meaning "handy man," because simple stone tools were found near him. *Homo habilis* is estimated to be 1.5 million to 2 million years old. Based upon many fossil comparisons, scientists have suggested that *Homo habilis* gave rise to another species, *Homo erectus,* about 1.6 million years ago. This hominid had a larger brain than *Homo habilis. Homo erectus* traveled from Africa to Southeast Asia, China, and possibly Europe. *Homo habilis* and *Homo erectus* are thought to be ancestors of humans because they had larger brains and more humanlike features than *Australopithecus.*

✔ Reading Check *Why was* Homo habilis *given that name?*

Humans

The fossil record indicates that ***Homo sapiens*** evolved about 400,000 years ago. By about 125,000 years ago, two early human groups, Neanderthals (nee AN dur tawlz) and Cro-Magnon humans, as shown in **Figure 20,** probably lived at the same time in parts of Africa and Europe.

Neanderthals Short, heavy bodies with thick bones, small chins, and heavy browridges were physical characteristics of Neanderthals. Family groups lived in caves and used well-made stone tools to hunt large animals. Neanderthals disappeared from the fossil record about 30,000 years ago. They probably are not direct ancestors of modern humans, but represent a side branch of human evolution.

Figure 20 Compare the skull of a Neanderthal with the skull of a Cro-Magnon. **Describe** *what differences you can see between these two skulls.*

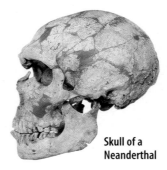

Skull of a
Neanderthal

Skull of a
Cro-Magnon

172 CHAPTER 6 Adaptations over Time

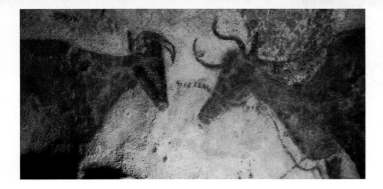

Figure 21 Paintings on cave walls have led scientists to hypothesize that Cro-Magnon humans had a well-developed culture.

Cro-Magnon Humans Cro-Magnon fossils have been found in Europe, Asia, and Australia and date from 10,000 to about 40,000 years in age. Standing about 1.6 m to 1.7 m tall, the physical appearance of Cro-Magnon people was almost the same as that of modern humans. They lived in caves, made stone carvings, and buried their dead. As shown in **Figure 21,** the oldest recorded art has been found on the walls of caves in France, where Cro-Magnon humans first painted bison, horses, and people carrying spears. Cro-Magnon humans are thought to be direct ancestors of early humans, *Homo sapiens,* which means "wise human." Evidence indicates that modern humans, *Homo sapiens sapiens,* evolved from *Homo sapiens.*

section 3 review

Summary

Primates
- Primates are an order of mammals characterized by opposable thumbs, binocular vision, and flexible shoulder joints.
- Primates are divided into strepsirrhines and haplorhines.
- Hominids are human ancestors that first appeared in Africa 4–6 million years ago.
- Hominids in the genus *Homo* first used tools and had larger brains than previous primates.

Humans
- *Homo sapiens* first appeared about 400,000 years ago.
- Cro-Magnon humans and Neanderthals coexisted in many places until Neanderthals disappeared about 30,000 years ago.
- *Homo sapiens* looked like modern humans and are believed to be our direct ancestors.

Self Check

1. **Describe** three kinds of evidence suggesting that all primates might have shared a common ancestor.
2. **Discuss** the importance of *Australopithecus*.
3. **Compare and contrast** Neanderthals, Cro-Magnon humans, and early humans.
4. **Identify** three groups most scientists consider to be direct ancestors of modern humans.
5. **Think Critically** Propose a hypothesis to explain why teeth are the most abundant fossil of hominids.

Applying Skills

6. **Concept Map** Make a concept map to show in what sequence hominids appeared. Use the following: *Homo sapiens sapiens,* Neanderthal, *Homo habilis, Australopithecus, Homo sapiens,* and Cro-Magnon human.
7. **Write** a story in your Science Journal about what life might have been like when both Neanderthals and Cro-Magnon humans were alive.

section 3 review

1. homologous structures; similar DNA; fossils
2. *Australopithecus,* an early hominid, had a small brain case but human-like jaws and teeth.
3. Neanderthals had short bodies with massive bones and heavy brow ridges. Cro-Magnon humans were taller, invented art, and made stone carvings. Cro-Magnon humans were very similar to early humans.
4. *Homo sapiens, Homo erectus,* and *Homo habilis*
5. Teeth are the hardest parts of an organism.
6. The concept map should be an events chain in the following order: *Australopithecus, Homo habilis,* Neanderthals, Cro-Magnon humans, *Homo sapiens,* and *Homo sapiens sapiens.*
7. Stories should indicate hardships that might result from being maladapted to their environment.

⊙ Real-World Question

Purpose Students design and carry out an experiment showing the variation in a population. L2
ELL COOP LEARN N **Logical-Mathematical**

Process Skills form a hypothesis, measure in SI, use numbers, interpret data, communicate, make and use tables, design an experiment

Time Required 45 minutes to plan the investigation, 45 minutes to complete the investigation

Safety Precautions Caution students not to put any materials into their mouths. Be sure students are not allergic to any plants used.

⊙ Form a Hypothesis

Possible Hypotheses Student hypotheses will vary. Possible hypotheses include: "A sample of peanuts will exhibit variations in numbers of seeds," or "A sample of peanuts will exhibit variations in length of seeds."

⊙ Test Your Hypothesis

Possible Procedures Procedures will vary. Most students will choose width or length to measure. Others may choose volume, number of seeds, or some other variable. Volume of fruit can be measured by water displacement. Students may want to design color charts to compare differences in fruit coloration.

LAB   Design Your Own

Goals
- **Design** an experiment that will allow you to collect data about variation in a population.
- **Observe, measure, and analyze** variations in a population.

Possible Materials
fruit and seeds from one plant species
metric ruler
magnifying lens
graph paper

Safety Precautions

🚫 🧤 👓 🧪

WARNING: *Do not put any fruit or seeds in your mouth.*

Recognizing Variation in a Population

⊙ Real-World Question

When you first observe a flock of pigeons, you might think all the birds look alike. However, if you look closer, you will notice minor differences, or variations, among the individuals. Different pigeons might have different color markings, or some might be smaller or larger than others. Individuals of the same species—whether they're birds, plants, or worms—might look alike at first, but some variations undoubtedly exist. According to the principles of natural selection, evolution could not occur without variations. What kinds of variations have you noticed among species of plants or animals? How can you measure variation in a plant or animal population?

⊙ Form a Hypothesis

Make a hypothesis about the amount of variation in the fruit and seeds of one species of plant.

174   CHAPTER 6 Adaptations over Time

Alternative Inquiry Lab

Plant Variation Allow students to choose a plant species to grow from seeds. When the plants flower, have them investigate variation in assorted plant traits. How do plants vary when flowering? Does that relate to variation in seeds? L3

Using Scientific Methods

⊙ Test Your Hypothesis

Make a Plan

1. As a group, agree upon and write out the prediction.
2. **List** the steps you need to take to test your prediction. Be specific. Describe exactly what you will do at each step. List your materials.
3. **Decide** what characteristic of fruit and seeds you will study. For example, you could measure the length of fruit and seeds or count the number of seeds per fruit.
4. **Design** a data table in your Science Journal to collect data about two variations. Use the table to record the data your group collects.
5. **Identify** any constants, variables, and controls of the experiment.
6. How many fruit and seeds will you examine? Will your data be more accurate if you examine larger numbers?
7. **Summarize** your data in a graph or chart.

Follow Your Plan

1. Make sure your teacher approves your plan before you start.
2. Carry out the experiment as planned.
3. While the experiment is going on, write down any observations you make and complete the data table in your Science Journal.

⊙ Analyze Your Data

1. **Calculate** the mean and range of variation in your experiment. The range is the difference between the largest and the smallest measurements. The mean is the sum of all the data divided by the sample size.
2. **Graph** your group's results by making a line graph for the variations you measured. Place the range of variation on the *x*-axis and the number of organisms that had that measurement on the *y*-axis.

⊙ Conclude and Apply

1. **Explain** your results in terms of natural selection.
2. **Discuss** the factors you used to determine the amount of variation present.
3. **Infer** why one or more of the variations you observed in this activity might be helpful to the survival of the individual.

Communicating Your Data

Create a poster or other exhibit that illustrates the variations you and your classmates observed.

LAB 175

Content Background

About the time of the 12th International Conference on AIDS in 1998, it had become clear that the powerful new drugs being used to attack HIV, called the protease inhibitors or the triple cocktail, would not bring the miracle that many had hoped they would. Between 10 and 50 percent of patients with AIDS who took protease inhibitors were later diagnosed with more virulent forms of HIV. As many as 4.5 percent of newly infected patients had drug-resistant strains of the virus.

If a person contracts HIV from another person with a resistant strain, it could be as if the person got infected in 1983 when there were no anti-retroviral drugs.

Discussion

New Approaches How would Wong-Stall's research avoid the pitfalls of the new drugs and vaccines to treat HIV and AIDS? Possible answer: Instead of depending on suppressing the virus with drugs, this new research would prevent the virus from multiplying by changing existing cell structure. This could eliminate the daily regimen of drugs.

Historical Significance

Have students research tuberculosis, or TB. Have students answer these questions:

• When and where was the first known outbreak of TB?

• At the height of the disease, how many people were infected with the disease?

• When was the TB vaccine introduced?

Explain that even though there is a TB vaccine, new drug-resistant strains of TB have recently been discovered. Because of these resistant strains, scientists are interested in the TB vaccine again.

Fighting HIV

The first cases of AIDS, or acquired immune deficiency syndrome, in humans were reported in the early 1980s. AIDS is caused by the human immunodeficiency virus, or HIV.

A major problem in AIDS research is the rapid evolution of HIV. When HIV multiplies inside a host cell, new versions of the virus are produced as well as identical copies of the virus that invaded the cell. New versions of the virus soon can outnumber the original version. A treatment that works against today's HIV might not work against tomorrow's version.

These rapid changes in HIV also mean that different strains of the virus exist in different places around the world. Treatments developed in the United States work only for people who contracted the virus in the United States. This leaves people in some parts of the world without effective treatments. So, researchers such as geneticist Flossie Wong-Staal at the University of California in San Diego, must look for new ways to fight the evolving virus.

Working Backwards

Flossie Wong-Staal is taking a new approach. First, her team identifies the parts of a human cell that HIV depends on and the parts of the human cell that HIV needs but the human cell doesn't need. Then the team looks for a way to remove—or inactivate—those unneeded parts. This technique limits the virus's ability to multiply.

Wong-Staal's research combines three important aspects of science—a deep understanding of how cells and genes operate, great skill in the techniques of genetics, and great ideas. Understanding, skill, and great ideas are the best weapons so far in the fight to conquer HIV.

Wong-Staal was on one of the two teams that first identified HIV as the virus that causes AIDS.

Research Use the link to the right and other sources to determine which nations have the highest rates of HIV infection. Which nation has the highest rate? Where does the U.S. rank? Next, find data from ten years ago. Have the rankings changed?

Science Online

For more information, visit life.msscience.com/time

Research What might account for the difference in numbers of people infected in different countries? Possible answers: The rates vary with the availability of medicine and access to health care and with education about how HIV is transmitted. Explain that the largest number of new infections of HIV in the U.S. are among young people. Have students discuss possible reasons for this.

Resources for Teachers and Students

AIDS and STDs: Global Perspectives, Rachel Donatelle, Pearson Custom Publishing, New York, 1999

Global Responses to AIDS, by Cristiana Bestos, Indiana University Press, Bloomington, Indiana, 1999

Reviewing Main Ideas

Section 1 Ideas About Evolution

1. Evolution is one of the central ideas of biology. It explains how living things have changed in the past and is a basis for predicting how they might change in the future.

2. Charles Darwin developed the theory of evolution by natural selection to explain how evolutionary changes account for the diversity of organisms on Earth.

3. Natural selection includes concepts of variation, overproduction, and competition.

4. According to natural selection, organisms with traits best suited to their environment are more likely to survive and reproduce.

Section 2 Clues About Evolution

1. Fossils provide evidence for evolution.

2. Relative dating and radiometric dating can be used to estimate the age of fossils.

3. The evolution of antibiotic-resistant bacteria, pesticide-resistant insects, and rapid genetic changes in plant species provides direct evidence that evolution occurs.

4. Homologous structures, vestigial structures, comparative embryology, and similarities in DNA provide indirect evidence of evolution.

Section 3 The Evolution of Primates

1. Primates include monkeys, apes, and humans. Hominids are humanlike primates.

2. The earliest known hominid fossil is *Australopithecus*.

3. *Homo sapiens* are thought to have evolved from Cro-Magnon humans about 400,000 years ago.

Visualizing Main Ideas

Copy and complete the following spider map on evolution.

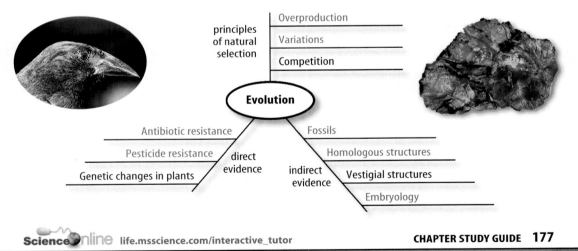

Reviewing Main Ideas

Summary statements can be used by students to review the major concepts of the chapter.

Visualizing Main Ideas

See student page.

Visit life.msscience.com
 /self_check_quiz
 /interactive_tutor
 /vocabulary_puzzlemaker
 /chapter_review
 /standardized_test

Assessment Transparency

For additional assessment questions, use the *Assessment Transparency* located in the transparency book.

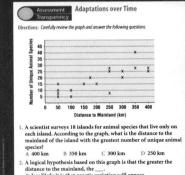

Identifying Misconceptions

Assess

Use this assessment as follow-up to page F at the beginning of this chapter.

Discussion After students complete the bean/bacteria activity, ask the following questions:

• Why did the red "bacteria" survive?

• Did the antibiotic cause the bacteria to have a thicker cell wall?

• When did the red bacteria's thick cell wall develop—before or after the antibiotic?

Expected Outcome Students should understand that the red bacteria's trait of a thicker cell wall existed before the antibiotic was introduced. The trait gave the bacterium an advantage that helped it survive. L2

Using Vocabulary

1. sedimentary rock
2. vestigial structures
3. homologous
4. primates
5. embryology, species, or variation
6. natural selection
7. *Homo sapiens*

Checking Concepts

8. C   12. A
9. B   13. C
10. D   14. D
11. D

Thinking Critically

15. The foot is from an aquatic bird with webbed feet for swimming.

16. Lamarck: Owls hunt at night and their eyes grow larger with use. The trait is passed on. Darwin: Larger owls' eyes were an advantage to survival. This inherited feature was passed on to offspring over many generations until owls became adapted for seeing prey at night with large eyes.

17. Answers will vary. Possible answer: Geographical isolation as a result of a volcanic eruption can divide a population. Two species may evolve.

18. Chameleons blend into their environment. This ability to change color helps protect them from predators.

19. Predators and competition for resources will eliminate many frogs. Only the most adapted will survive.

Using Vocabulary

adaptation p. 158
embryology p. 167
evolution p. 154
gradualism p. 160
hominid p. 171
Homo sapiens p. 172
homologous p. 168
natural selection p. 157

primate p. 170
punctuated equilibrium p. 160
radioactive element p. 165
sedimentary rock p. 164
species p. 154
variation p. 158
vestigial structure p. 168

Fill in the blanks with the correct vocabulary word or words.

1. _____ contains many different kinds of fossils.

2. The muscles that move the human ear appear to be _____.

3. Forelimbs of bats, humans, and seals are _____.

4. Opposable thumbs are a characteristic of _____.

5. The study of _____ can provide evidence of evolution.

6. The principles of _____ include variation and competition.

7. _____ likely evolved directly from Cro-Magnons.

Checking Concepts

Choose the word or phrase that best answers the question.

8. What is an example of adaptation?
   A) a fossil
   B) gradualism
   C) camouflage
   D) embryo

9. What method provides the most accurate estimate of a fossil's age?
   A) natural selection
   B) radiometric dating
   C) relative dating
   D) camouflage

10. What do homologous structures, vestigial structures, and fossils provide evidence of?
    A) gradualism   C) populations
    B) food choice   D) evolution

11. Which model of evolution shows change over a relatively short period of time?
    A) embryology
    B) adaptation
    C) gradualism
    D) punctuated equilibrium

12. What might a series of helpful variations in a species result in?
    A) adaptation   C) embryology
    B) fossils   D) climate change

Use the following chart to answer question 13.

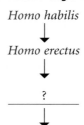

Homo habilis
↓
Homo erectus
↓
?
_____
↓
Homo sapiens

13. Which of the following correctly fills the gap in the line of descent from *Homo habilis*?
    A) Neanderthal
    B) *Australopithecus*
    C) Cro-Magnon human
    D) chimpanzee

14. What is the study of an organism's early development called?
    A) adaptation   C) natural selection
    B) relative dating D) embryology

 Science Online life.msscience.com/vocabulary_puzzlemaker

Use the Exam*View*® Pro Testmaker CD-ROM to:
- create multiple versions of tests
- create modified tests with one mouse click for inclusion students
- edit existing questions and add your own questions
- build tests aligned with state standards using built-in State Curriculum Tags
- change English tests to Spanish with one mouse click and vice versa

chapter Review **6**
6

Thinking Critically

15. **Predict** what type of bird the foot pictured at right would belong to. Explain your reasoning.

16. **Discuss** how Lamarck and Darwin would have explained the large eyes of an owl.

17. **Explain,** using an example, how a new species of organism could evolve.

18. **Identify** how the color-changing ability of chameleons is an adaptation.

19. **Form a hypothesis** as to why ponds are not overpopulated by frogs in summer. Use the concept of natural selection to help you.

20. **Sequence** Make an events-chain concept map of the events that led Charles Darwin to his theory of evolution by natural selection.

Use the table below to answer question 21.

Chemicals Present in Bacteria

Species 1	A, G, T, C, L, E, S, H
Species 2	A, G, T, C, L, D, H
Species 3	A, G, T, C, L, D, P, U, S, R, I, V
Species 4	A, G, T, C, L, D, H

21. **Interpret Data** Each letter above represents a chemical found in a species of bacteria. Which species are most closely related?

22. **Discuss** the evidence you would use to determine whether the evolution of a group were best explained by gradualism. How would this differ from a group that followed a punctuated equilibrium model?

23. **Describe** the processes a scientist would use to figure out the age of a fossil.

Science Online life.msscience.com/chapter_review

24. **Evaluate** the possibility for each of the five types of fossils in **Figure 9** to yield a DNA sample. Remember that only biological tissue will contain DNA.

Performance Activities

25. **Collection** With permission, collect fossils from your area and identify them. Show your collection to your class.

26. **Brochure** Assume that you are head of an advertising company. Develop a brochure to explain Darwin's theory of evolution by natural selection.

Applying Math

27. **Relative Age** The rate of radioactive decay is measured in half-lives—the amount of time it takes for one half of a radioactive element to decay. Determine the relative age of a fossil given the following information:
    - Rock layers are undisturbed.
    - The layer below the fossil has potassium-40 with a half-life of 1 million years and only one half of the original potassium is left.
    - The layer above the fossil has carbon-14 with a half-life of 5,730 years and one-sixteenth of the carbon isotope remains.

Use the graph below to answer question 28.

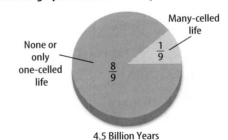

Many-celled life $\frac{1}{9}$

None or only one-celled life $\frac{8}{9}$

4.5 Billion Years

28. **First Appearances** If Earth is 4.5 billion years old, how long ago did the first many-celled life-forms appear?

Thinking Critically

20. Darwin did amateur studies in natural history as a boy. He became a naturalist aboard the *Beagle* and gathered information for five years. After returning to England, Darwin worked for the rest of his life to develop his theory.

21. Species 2 and 4 are the closest in relation; they have the same chemicals.

22. The best evidence will be from the fossil record. If species show slow changes over a long time, this would suggest gradualism. Punctuated equilibrium would be indicated if rapid change occurred in a short time followed by long periods with no change.

23. The layer of rock where it was formed would be noted. Radiometric dating would be done. Comparisons to other fossils would be made.

24. imprint fossils—the fossil is only an impression of an organism, no DNA will be present; mineralized fossils—minerals replace tissues, no DNA left to analyze; cast fossils—the DNA has been replaced; fossils in amber—if the DNA has not degraded, it might be available; frozen fossil—DNA has been extracted from frozen organisms (mammoths).

Performance Activities

25. Fossil collections will vary, depending on location. Students may get help from experts at a nearby university. Use **PASC,** p. 121.

26. The brochures should include the principles of natural selection, as found in **Table 1.** Use **PASC,** p. 129.

Applying Math

National Math Standards
1, 2, 5, 9

27. between 22,920 and 1 million years old

28. about 500 million years ago

☑ Assessment   Resources

📁 **Reproducible Masters**
Chapter *Fast File* Resources
   Chapter Review, pp. 35–36
   Chapter Tests, pp. 37–40
   Assessment Transparency Activity, p. 47
Glencoe Science Web site
   Chapter Review Test
   Standardized Test Practice

Glencoe Technology
   🖌 Assessment Transparency
   ◉ Exam*View*® Pro Testmaker
   📼 MindJogger Videoquiz
   ◉ Interactive Chalkboard

FAST FILE

Answer Sheet A practice answer sheet can be found at life.msscience.com/answer_sheet.

Part 1 | Multiple Choice

1. B
2. B
3. D
4. A
5. D
6. B

Part 1 | Multiple Choice

Record your answers on the answer sheet provided by your teacher or on a sheet of paper.

1. A species is a group of organisms
   A. that lives together with similar characteristics.
   B. that shares similar characteristics and can reproduce among themselves to produce fertile offspring.
   C. across a wide area that cannot reproduce.
   D. that chooses mates from among themselves.

2. Which of the following is considered an important factor in natural selection?
   A. limited reproduction
   B. competition for resources
   C. no variations within a population
   D. plentiful food and other resources

3. The marine iguana of the Galápagos Islands enters the ocean and feeds on seaweed. What is this an example of?
   A. adaptation
   B. gradualism
   C. survival of the fittest
   D. acquired characteristic

Use the illustration below to answer question 4.

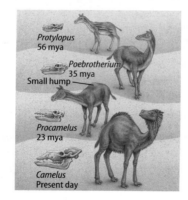

Protylopus 56 mya
Poebrotherium 35 mya
Small hump
Procamelus 23 mya
Camelus Present day

4. According to Lamarck's hypothesis of acquired characteristics, which statement best explains the changes in the camel over time?
   A. All characteristics developed during an individual's lifetime are passed on to offspring.
   B. Characteristics that do not help the animal survive are passed to offspring.
   C. Variation of the species leads to adaptation.
   D. Individuals moving from one area to another carry with them new characteristics.

Use the illustrations below to answer question 5.

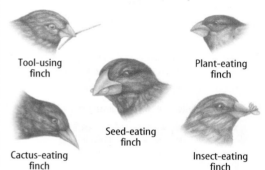

Tool-using finch
Plant-eating finch
Seed-eating finch
Cactus-eating finch
Insect-eating finch

5. What, besides competition for food, contributed to the evolution of the species of Darwin's finches?
   A. predation
   B. natural disaster
   C. DNA
   D. variation in beak shapes

6. Some harmless species imitate or mimic a poisonous species as a means for increased survival. What is this an example of?
   A. acquired characteristics
   B. adaptation
   C. variation
   D. geographic isolation

180 STANDARDIZED TEST PRACTICE

Part 2 | Short Response/Grid In

7. Camouflage is beneficial to a species because it helps the organism escape predation, which increases the chances of survival and reproduction.

8. The albino lemur would not be at a disadvantage in an environment with a lot of snow.

9. The level of variation is lower with an endangered species because the number of individuals is so low.

10. A variation that provides an advantage for an endangered species will increase the number of individuals and help the species to thrive again. A disadvantageous variation might cause the extinction of a species.

11. The Cro-Magnon humans had an adaptation that made them better suited for their environment thus allowing them to survive. The Neanderthals did not adapt to their environment over time and could not survive as a species.

Part 2 | Short Response/Grid In

Record your answers on the answer sheet provided by your teacher or on a sheet of paper.

7. How does camouflage benefit a species?

Use the photo below to answer question 8.

8. Describe an environment where the albino lemur would not be at a disadvantage.

9. Variation between members of a species plays an important role in Darwin's theory of evolution. What happens to variation in endangered species where the number of individuals is very low?

10. Describe what happens to an endangered species if a variation provides an advantage for the species. What would happen if the variation resulted in a disadvantage?

11. Using the theory of natural selection, hypothesize why the Cro-Magnon humans survived and the Neanderthals disappeared.

Test-Taking Tip

Never Leave Any Answer Blank Answer each question as best you can. You can receive partial credit for partially correct answers.

Question 16 If you cannot remember all primate characteristics, list as many as you can.

Part 3 | Open Ended

Record your answers on a sheet of paper.

12. What are the two groups of early humans that lived about 125,000 years ago in Africa and Europe? Describe their general appearance and characteristics. Compare these characteristics to modern humans.

13. Explain how bacterial resistance to antibiotics is an example of punctuated equilibrium.

14. Why are radioactive elements useful in dating fossils? Does this method improve accuracy over relative dating?

Use the illustrations below to answer question 15.

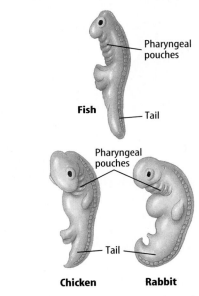

Pharyngeal pouches

Fish Tail

Pharyngeal pouches

Tail

Chicken **Rabbit**

15. Why would scientists study embryos? What features of these three embryos support evolution?

16. How does DNA evidence provide support that primates have a common ancestor?

which is based on the theory that older rock layers are underneath younger rock layers.

15. Scientists would study embryos because they are the earliest growth stage of an organism. The fish, chicken and rabbit embryos all have gill slits and tail at this stage. These similarities at this stage support an evolutionary relationship between all vertebrate species.

16. Scientists have compared the DNA of primates and it suggests common ancestry. Specifically the apes have 24 pairs of chromosomes and humans have 23 pairs of chromosomes. Two of the apes' chromosomes can be laid end to end and it will match with a human's number 2 chromosomes.

Rubrics

For more help evaluating open-ended assessment questions, see the rubric on p. 10T.

Part 3 | Open Ended

12. Neanderthals and Cro-Magnons. The Neanderthals had short, heavy bodies with thick bones, small chins and heavy brow ridges. They lived in family groups in caves and used well-made tools to hunt large animals. The Cro-Magnon people were similar to modern humans in appearance. They lived in caves, made stone carvings and buried their dead. Comparing the Neanderthals and Cro-Magnons to modern day humans could have a vast number of responses.

13. Punctuated equilibrium is when a species changes in a relatively short period of time. Bacteria became resistant to antibiotics over several decades.

14. Radioactive elements are useful in dating fossils because they decay at a constant rate. Each radioactive element gives off radiation at a different rate. Scientists can use the ratio of radioactive to nonradioactive elements in the rock to estimate the age. This method is much more accurate than relative dating

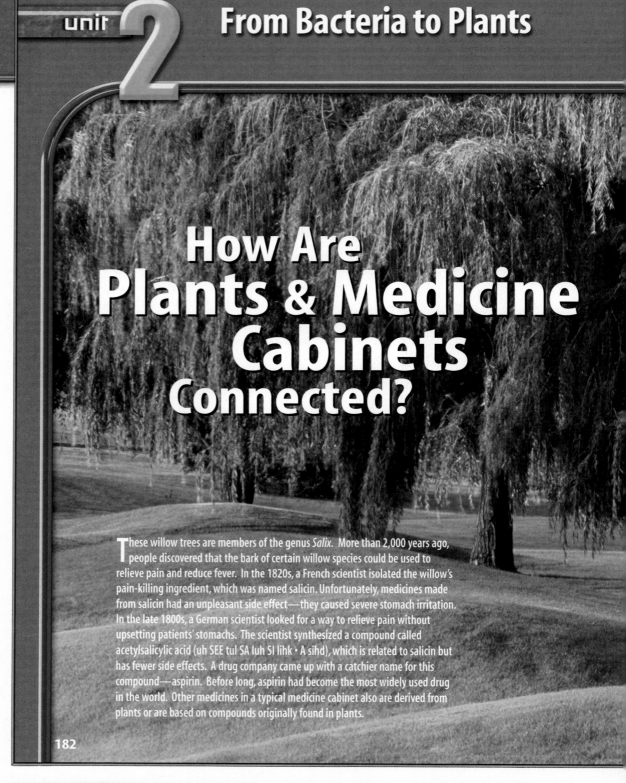

How Are Plants & Medicine Cabinets Connected?

These willow trees are members of the genus *Salix*. More than 2,000 years ago, people discovered that the bark of certain willow species could be used to relieve pain and reduce fever. In the 1820s, a French scientist isolated the willow's pain-killing ingredient, which was named salicin. Unfortunately, medicines made from salicin had an unpleasant side effect—they caused severe stomach irritation. In the late 1800s, a German scientist looked for a way to relieve pain without upsetting patients' stomachs. The scientist synthesized a compound called acetylsalicylic acid (uh SEE tul SA luh SI lihk • A sihd), which is related to salicin but has fewer side effects. A drug company came up with a catchier name for this compound—aspirin. Before long, aspirin had become the most widely used drug in the world. Other medicines in a typical medicine cabinet also are derived from plants or are based on compounds originally found in plants.

182

Unit Contents

Web Quest *Phytochemicals and a Healthy Diet* explores what phytochemicals are, in which foods they can be found, and their benefits in protecting humans from cancer and heart disease. Students will compare their personal diet with the optimum intake, and make informed decisions for their own recommended dietary plans. A list of questions will guide them as they investigate this important health topic.

PROJECT CRISS℠

Study Skills

Summarize Helping students to learn how to summarize is a method of increasing their comprehension and recall ability. On index cards, use the description frame, "A _____ is a kind of plant that…." The latter part of the sentence should include the plant's medicinal purpose or another use by humans. Students complete the sentence for each plant introduced in the unit.

NATIONAL GEOGRAPHIC

unit ⚡ projects

History Have students investigate drugs with plant origins to discover what plant it comes from, how it helps people, and how its medicinal properties first were used. Have students design a short slide presentation of their findings, and then add the location of the plant's origin to a class world-map display. If there are obvious concentrations of these plants, discuss what this might indicate.

Technology Have students design and construct a giant jigsaw puzzle illustrating the systems of a seed plant: seed, root, stem, leaf, and flower. Each informative-learning display should contain the labeled parts, a definition of the parts, and their functions.

Model Have pairs of students design a review game with cards or a game board that demonstrates the nitrogen and oxygen cycles, and how all life is interdependent. All game parts should be assembled in an environmentally friendly, student-made box with complete directions and user recommendations. Have students present their work, and then have students rotate through different stations as an end of unit review.

Additional Resources For more information, resources, and assessment rubrics, visit life.msscience.com/unit_project

unit ⚡ projects

Visit **life.msscience.com/unit_project** to find project ideas and resources. Projects include:
- **History** Design a slide show to present information on medicines derived from plants and where these plants grow.
- **Technology** Make your own giant jigsaw puzzle illustrating the five systems of a seed plant, including labels and functions of each plant part.
- **Model** Construct a review game demonstrating knowledge of nitrogen and oxygen cycles. The game and instructions should be assembled in an eco-friendly box.

WebQuest Discover *Phytochemicals and a Healthy Diet.* Compare your diet with the suggested diet that helps prevent cancer and heart disease.

NATIONAL GEOGRAPHIC   How Are Plants & Medicine Cabinets Connected?

Since prehistoric times, ancient cultures usually had individuals who understood the healing properties of plants.

The development of modern chemistry in the 1800s allowed the isolation of the active compounds in medicinal plant products. Many drugs, such as aspirin and quinine, that were originally plant derived are now only produced synthetically; the active ingredients being produced chemically.

Outside the industrialized world, the vast majority of people still are treated with medicines produced directly from plants. Many governments have recently allocated funds to assist in surveying and cataloging the uses of their countries' native plant species.

chapter 7 Organizer

Section/Objectives	Standards		Labs/Features
	National	State/Local	
Chapter Opener	See pp. 16T–17T for a Key to Standards.		**Launch Lab:** Why do bacteria form slime layers?, p. 185 **Foldables,** p. 185 A data-collection lab using Probeware technology can be found in **Probeware Labs,** pp. 9–11
Section 1 What are bacteria? 🕐 2 sessions 📦 1 block 1. **Identify** the characteristics of bacteria cells. 2. **Compare and contrast** aerobic and anaerobic organisms.	National Content Standards: UCP.1, UCP.2, UCP.5, A.1, A.2, C.1–C.5		**MiniLAB:** Modeling Bacteria Size, p. 187 **Science Online,** p. 189 **Integrate Earth Science,** p. 190 **Lab:** Observing Cyanobacteria, p. 192
Section 2 Bacteria in Your Life 🕐 3 sessions 📦 1.5 blocks 3. **Identify** some ways bacteria are helpful. 4. **Determine** the importance of nitrogen-fixing bacteria. 5. **Explain** how some bacteria can cause human disease.	National Content Standards: UCP.5, A.1, C.3–C.5, E.1, E.2, F.1, F.4, F.5		**MiniLAB:** Observing Bacterial Growth, p. 194 **Visualizing Nitrogen Fixing Bacteria,** p. 195 **Integrate Social Studies,** p. 196 **Science Online,** p. 197 **Applying Science:** Controlling Bacterial Growth, p. 198 **Lab:** Composting, p. 200 **Science Stats:** Unusual Bacteria, p. 202

Glencoe Exclusive!
TeacherWorks™
All-In-One Planner and Resource Center

Lab Materials	Reproducible Resources	Section Assessment	Technology
Launch Lab: synthetic kitchen sponge, water, hair-styling gel, plate, scissors	**Chapter *FAST FILE* Resources** Foldables Worksheet, p. 13 Directed Reading Overview, p. 15 Note-taking Worksheets, pp. 27–28	**GLENCOE'S ASSESSMENT ADVANTAGE**	**Teacher Works** includes: • Interactive Teacher Edition • Lesson Planner with calendar • Access to all program blacklines • Correlations to standards • Web links ▭ Video Lab
MiniLAB: meterstick, yarn or string **Lab:** prepared slides (or micrograph photos) of *Oscillatoria, Nostoc, Gloeocapsa,* and *Anabaena;* microscope	**Chapter *FAST FILE* Resources** Transparency Activity, p. 38 MiniLAB, p. 3 Enrichment, p. 25 Reinforcement, p. 23 Directed Reading, p. 16 Lab Worksheet, pp. 5–6 Lab Activity, pp. 9–10 Transparency Activity, pp. 41–43 **Home and Community Involvement,** p. 37 **Life Science Critical Thinking/ Problem Solving,** p. 1	**Portfolio** Science Journal, p. 189 **Performance** MiniLAB, p. 187 Applying Math, p. 191 **Content** Section Review, p. 191	⚲ Section Focus Transparency ⚲ Teaching Transparency ◉ Virtual Labs CD-ROM ∩ Guided Reading Audio Program ◉ Interactive Chalkboard CD-ROM
MiniLAB: 2–3 dried beans, distilled water, glass beaker **Lab:** 4 or more wide-mouth clear glass jars, soil, water, watering can, banana peel, apple core, scrap of newspaper, leaf, plastic candy wrapper, scrap of aluminum foil *Need materials?* Contact Science Kit at 1-800-828-7777 or www.sciencekit.com on the Internet.	**Chapter *FAST FILE* Resources** Transparency Activity, p. 39 MiniLAB, p. 4 Enrichment, p. 26 Reinforcement, p. 24 Directed Reading, pp. 17, 18 Lab Activity, pp. 11–12 Lab Worksheet, pp. 7–8 **Mathematics Skill Activities,** p. 19 **Reading and Writing Skill Activities,** p. 25 **Lab Management and Safety,** p. 58	**Portfolio** Cultural Diversity, p. 194 Science Journal, p. 198 **Performance** MiniLAB, p. 194 Applying Science, p. 198 Applying Skills, p. 199 **Content** Section Review, p. 199	⚲ Section Focus Transparency ◉ Virtual Labs CD-ROM ∩ Guided Reading Audio Program ◉ Interactive Chalkboard CD-ROM ▭ Probeware Lab

End of Chapter Assessment

GLENCOE'S ASSESSMENT ADVANTAGE

Blackline Masters	Technology	Professional Series
Chapter *FAST FILE* Resources Chapter Review, pp. 31–32 Chapter Tests, pp. 33–36 **Standardized Test Practice,** pp. 31–34	▭ MindJogger Videoquiz ◉ Virtual Labs CD-ROM ◉ Exam*View*® Pro Testmaker ◉ TeacherWorks CD-ROM ◉ Interactive Chalkboard CD-ROM	**Performance Assessment in the Science Classroom (PASC)**

Transparencies

Section Focus

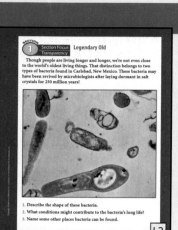

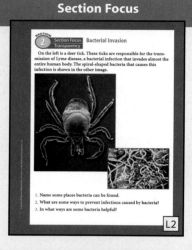

This is a representation of key blackline masters available in the Teacher Classroom Resources. See Resource Manager boxes within the chapter for additional information.

Key to Teaching Strategies

The following designations will help you decide which activities are appropriate for your students.

L1 Level 1 activities should be appropriate for students with learning difficulties.

L2 Level 2 activities should be within the ability range of all students.

L3 Level 3 activities are designed for above-average students.

ELL ELL activities should be within the ability range of English-Language Learners.

COOP LEARN Cooperative Learning activities are designed for small group work.

LS Multiple Learning Styles logos, as described on page 12T, are used throughout to indicate strategies that address different learning styles.

P These strategies represent student products that can be placed into a best-work portfolio.

PBL Problem-Based Learning activities apply real-world situations to learning.

Assessment

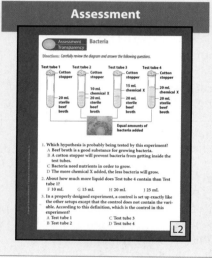

Teaching

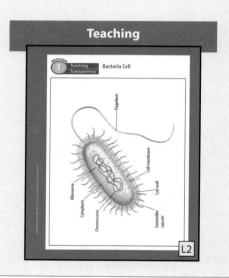

Hands-on Activities

Student Text Lab Worksheet

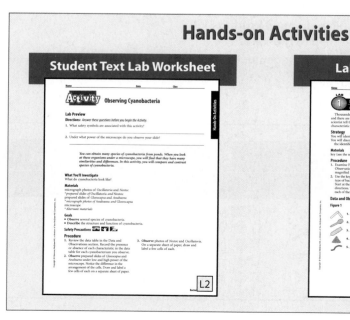

Laboratory Activities

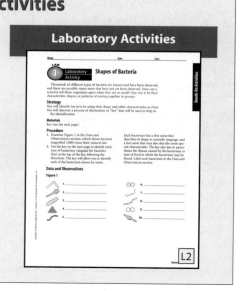

Resource Manager

Meeting Different Ability Levels

Content Outline
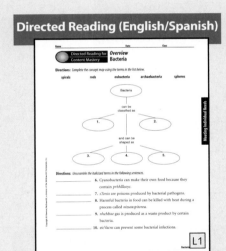

Reinforcement
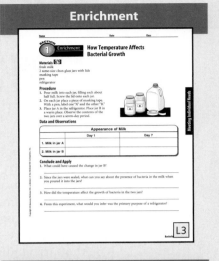

Enrichment

Directed Reading (English/Spanish)

Study Guide

Reading Essentials

Assessment

Test Practice Workbook
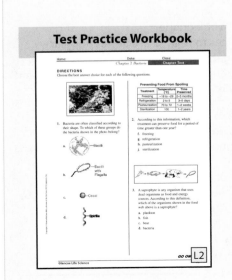

Chapter Review
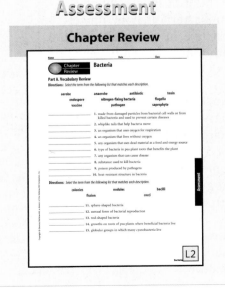

Chapter Tests
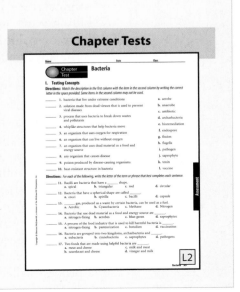

Science Content Background

section 1 What are bacteria?

Characteristics

The sizes of bacteria are genetically determined and are measured in microns—1 micron (mμ) = 0.001 mm. Most bacteria range from 0.2mμ to 2mμ in width and from 2mμ to 8mμ in length. Bacteria generally have a rigid cell wall that maintains the shape of the organism. Bacterial cell walls prevent cells from bursting in environments where the pressure in the cell is greater than the pressure in the surrounding medium or fluid. Bacterial cells usually die in environments where the external pressure is greater than the pressure in the cell. Bacteria have three basic shapes: rod-shaped bacilli (singular, *bacillus*), helical spirillia (singular, *spirillum*), and spherical cocci (singular, *coccus*). Some bacilli and spirillia possess flagella.

Eubacteria

Most named bacteria are members of Kingdom Eubacteria. The five major phylogenetic groups of eubacteria are based on comparisons of their ribosomal RNA.

Cyanobacteria, formerly called blue-green algae, are bacteria that contain chlorophyll, enabling them to make their own food. This process is similar to photosynthesis in plants. These organisms probably produced most of the original free oxygen in the atmosphere about 2.5 billion years ago. Cyanobacteria may be unicellular or colonial. Most live in freshwater, but some are symbiotic with fungi to form lichens.

Reproduction

Most bacteria reproduce by a process of cell division known as binary fission. In binary fission, the one or more circular or linear chromosomes of the bacterial cell are duplicated. The duplicated chromosomes attach to the cell membrane. Continued growth of the cell separates the chromosomes, and the cell membrane eventually pinches in two as a cell wall is deposited between the daughter cells. Some bacteria exchange genetic information through a process called conjugation.

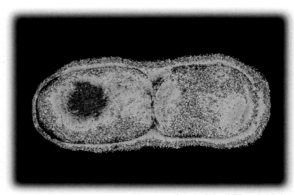

George Musil/Visuals Unlimited

section 2 Bacteria in Your Life

Beneficial Bacteria

Prokaryotes have a large impact on ecology. They and fungi are the organisms primarily responsible for the decay and recycling of materials. Of these materials, carbon and nitrogen are essential.

Nitrogen gas can be used as a source of nitrogen only by some eubacteria, including cyanobacteria. These organisms not only remove nitrogen from the air for their own use,

---

chapter content resources

Internet Resources

For additional content background, visit **life.msscience.com** to:

- access your book online
- find references to related articles in popular science magazines
- access Web links with related content background
- access current events with science journal topics

Print Resources

The Surprising Archaea: Discovering Another Domain of Life, by John L. Howland, Oxford University Press, 2000

The Secret Life of Germs: Observations and Lessons from a Microbe Hunter, by Philip M. Tierno Jr., PhD, Atria Books, 2001

Biodiversity of Microbial Life : Foundation of Earth's Biosphere, by James T. Staley and Anna-Louise Reysenbach, Wiley-Liss, 2001

but also change the nitrogen into compounds other organisms can use. This is important, because nitrogen is necessary in order for plants and animals to make amino acids and nucleic acids. Because the nitrogen content of the environment varies considerably in quantity and kinds of nitrogen-containing compounds, it is not surprising that organisms have evolved the ability to utilize more than one nitrogen source.

Antibiotics and Vaccines

An antibiotic is a chemical that is able to kill or inhibit the growth of bacteria. Thousands of antibiotics are known, but only a few have practical uses. Many types of microorganisms including bacteria, protists, and fungi, produce antibiotics.

The action of an antibiotic is dependent on its chemical structure. Certain antibiotics affect cell wall synthesis or destroy cell membrane permeability. Others act by inhibiting protein synthesis by causing the wrong amino acid to be inserted into the growing polypeptide chain of proteins in ribosomes. Broad spectrum antibiotics act on many different kinds of bacteria. Antibiotics, such as penicillin, act only on eubacteria. Other antimicrobials, such as cycloheximide, are active against eukaryotes but not prokaryotes.

Vaccines, on the other hand, are specific to certain bacteria or viruses. This is because a vaccine is made of damaged or killed bacterial cells or viruses. The white blood cells learn to recognize these pathogens and can respond quickly when they enter the body. It is important to note that antibiotics are taken after a bacterial pathogen enters the body, whereas a vaccine is a preventive measure.

Pasteurization

Pasteurization is achieved by passing milk continuously through a heat exchanger where its temperature quickly is raised to 71.6°C, held at that temperature for 15 s, and then quickly cooled. The process, named for Louis Pasteur,

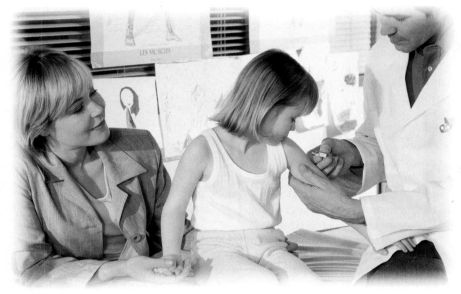

VCG/FPG International

was first used to control spoilage of wine and saved the wine industry in France. Pasteurization does not kill all the microbes present and should not be confused with sterilization, which uses high heat and pressure to kill all bacteria. Although pasteurization was originally used to kill organisms that cause tuberculosis, typhoid, and brucellosis, today it is used to increase the shelf life of milk.

Teacher to Teacher
Steve Federman, Teacher
Loveland Middle School
Loveland, Ohio

"To show students how using soap to wash your hands cleans away (but does not kill) germs, I sprinkle pepper (the 'germs') onto the surface of water placed in a low container or petri dish. I engage students in a conversation and have them predict what will happen when a drop of soap is placed along the inside edge of the container. I add a drop of soap and we watch what happens. The soap breaks the surface tension and quickly repels the pepper, similar to how soap repels germs off our hands."

Steve Federman

Chapter Vocabulary

flagella, p. 187
fission, p. 188
aerobe, p. 188
anaerobe, p. 188
antibiotic, p. 193
saprophyte, p. 194
nitrogen-fixing bacteria, p. 194
pathogen, p. 197
toxin, p. 197
endospore, p. 197
vaccine, p. 199

Science Journal   Student answers will vary. Beneficial bacteria include decomposer bacteria, such as those used in bioreactor landfills, and bacteria used to make yogurt, cheese, root beer, and other foods. Harmful bacteria include those that spoil food or cause disease. The beneficial list should be longer.

INTERACTIVE CHALKBOARD
with Image Bank

PowerPoint® Presentations

This CD-ROM is an editable Microsoft® PowerPoint® presentation that includes:

• a pre-made presentation for every chapter
• interactive graphics
• animations
• audio clips
• image bank
• all new section and chapter questions
• Standardized Test Practice
• transparencies
• pre-lab questions for all labs
• Foldables directions
• links to life.msscience.com

Bacteria

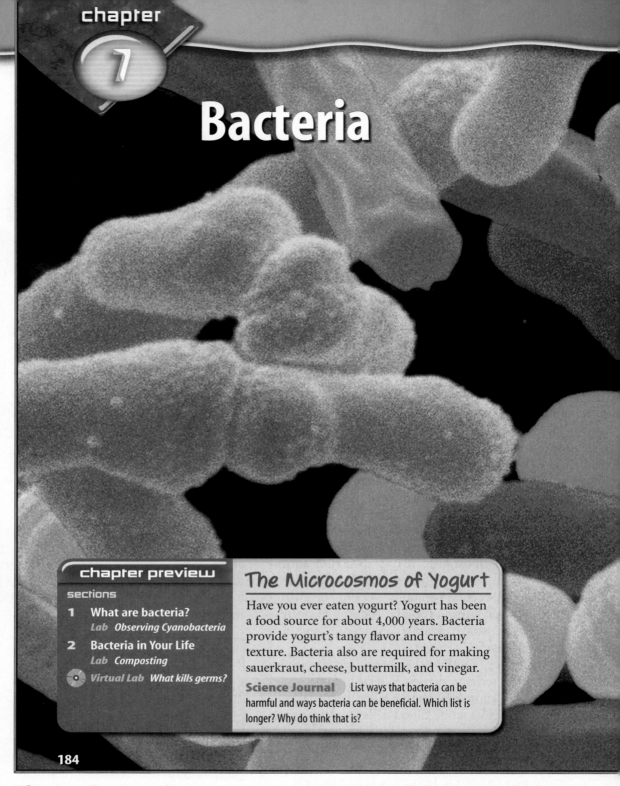

chapter preview

sections

1   **What are bacteria?**
    Lab Observing Cyanobacteria

2   **Bacteria in Your Life**
    Lab Composting

💿 *Virtual Lab What kills germs?*

The Microcosmos of Yogurt

Have you ever eaten yogurt? Yogurt has been a food source for about 4,000 years. Bacteria provide yogurt's tangy flavor and creamy texture. Bacteria also are required for making sauerkraut, cheese, buttermilk, and vinegar.

Science Journal   List ways that bacteria can be harmful and ways bacteria can be beneficial. Which list is longer? Why do think that is?

184

Theme Connection

Systems and Interactions The role of bacteria in maintaining a homeostatic balance is discussed. In addition to homeostasis, the ecological importance of bacteria is illustrated by using examples of niches filled by these organisms.

About the Photo

Yogurt Milk cultured by bacterial lactic acid fermentation is called yogurt. Cow's milk is used in the United States, but in other parts of the world, sheep's, goat's, or camel's milk may be used. *Lactobacillus GG* is one probiotic strain of bacteria found in yogurt. It can promote good health by protecting us against the excessive growth of potentially harmful bacteria in a human's intestines.

Start-Up Activities

Model a Bacterium's Slime Layer

Bacterial cells have a gelatinlike, protective coating on the outside of their cell walls. In some cases, the coating is thin and is referred to as a slime layer. A slime layer can help a bacterium attach to other surfaces. Dental plaque forms when bacteria with slime layers stick to teeth and multiply there. A slime layer also can reduce water loss from a bacterium. In this lab you will make a model of a bacterium's slime layer.

1. Cut two 2-cm-wide strips from the long side of a synthetic kitchen sponge.
2. Soak both strips in water. Remove them from the water and squeeze out the excess water. Both strips should be damp.
3. Completely coat one strip with hair-styling gel. Do not coat the other strip.
4. Place both strips on a plate (not paper) and leave them overnight.
5. **Think Critically** Record your observations of the two sponge strips in your Science Journal. Infer how a slime layer protects a bacterial cell from drying out. What environmental conditions are best for survival of bacteria?

Archaebacteria and Eubacteria Make the following Foldable to compare and contrast the characteristics of bacteria.

STEP 1 Fold one sheet of paper lengthwise.

STEP 2 Fold into thirds.

STEP 3 Unfold and draw overlapping ovals. Cut the top sheet along the folds.

STEP 4 Label the ovals as shown.

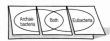

Archae-bacteria | Both | Eubacteria

Construct a Venn Diagram As you read the chapter, list the characteristics unique to archaebacteria under the left tab, those unique to eubacteria under the right tab, and those characteristics common to both under the middle tab.

Preview this chapter's content and activities at
life.msscience.com

185

Launch LAB

Purpose Use this Launch Lab to help students discover how the slime layer surrounding bacterial cells helps protect the cells from dehydration. ⌊L2⌋ ⌊IS⌋ **Kinesthetic**
Safety Precautions
Preparation Collect kitchen sponges, plates, and hair-styling gel. Locate areas where students can leave their sponges overnight.
Materials synthetic kitchen sponge; scissors; water; hair-styling gel; plate
Teaching Strategy Have students do this lab the day before you introduce the topic of bacteria slime layers. Use the activity to demonstrate the properties of a slime layer.

Think Critically

Students should find that the gel-treated sponge is still damp and adheres to the plate. The untreated sponge will have dried out. A slime layer seals moisture inside the bacteria cell. Bacteria cells thrive in moist, damp environmental conditions.

Assessment

Process Ask students to infer how Earth's nutrient cycles would be affected if bacteria cells did not have slime layers. Bacteria decompose dead and decaying materials into nutrients. Slime layers allow bacteria to lie dormant during drier conditions. Without slime layers, fewer bacteria would survive dry conditions, which would result in fewer nutrients being recycled. Use **Performance Assessment in the Science Classroom**, p. 89.

 Dinah Zike Study Fold

Student preparation materials for this Foldable are available in the **Chapter FAST FILE Resources.**

Probeware Labs

This chapter's data-collection lab using Probeware technology is included on the *Video Labs CD-ROM*. See the *Probeware Lab Manual* pages 9–11 for student worksheets.

What are bacteria?

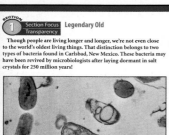
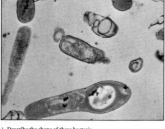

Caption Answer
Figure 1 sphere, rod, and spiral

Tie to Prior Knowledge
Living Things Review with students the characteristics of living things. Emphasize that bacterial cells have all of these characteristics, although they are smaller than the more familiar cells of plants and animals.

as you read

What You'll Learn
- Identify the characteristics of bacterial cells.
- Compare and contrast aerobic and anaerobic organisms.

Why It's Important
Bacteria are found almost everywhere and affect all living things.

Review Vocabulary
prokaryotic: cells without membrane-bound organelles

New Vocabulary
- flagella
- fission
- aerobe
- anaerobe

Figure 1 Bacteria can be found in almost any environment.
List *common terms that could be used to describe these cell shapes.*

Characteristics of Bacteria

For thousands of years people did not understand what caused disease. They did not understand the process of decomposition or what happened when food spoiled. It wasn't until the latter half of the seventeenth century that Antonie van Leeuwenhoek, a Dutch merchant, discovered the world of bacteria. Leeuwenhoek observed scrapings from his teeth using his simple microscope. Although he didn't know it at that time, some of the tiny swimming organisms he observed were bacteria. After Leeuwenhoek's discovery, it was another hundred years before bacteria were proven to be living cells that carry on all of the processes of life.

Where do bacteria live? Bacteria are almost everywhere— in the air, in foods that you eat and drink, and on the surfaces of things you touch. They are even found thousands of meters underground and at great ocean depths. A shovelful of soil contains billions of them. Your skin has about 100,000 bacteria per square centimeter, and millions of other bacteria live in your body. Some types of bacteria live in extreme environments where few other organisms can survive. Some heat-loving bacteria live in hot springs or hydrothermal vents—places where water temperature exceeds 100°C. Others can live in cold water or soil at 0°C. Some bacteria live in very salty water, like that of the Dead Sea. One type of bacteria lives in water that drains from coal mines, which is extremely acidic at a pH of 1.

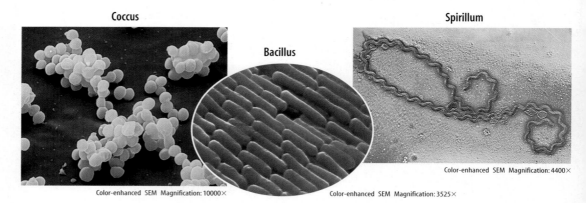

Coccus

Bacillus

Spirillum

Color-enhanced SEM Magnification: 10000×

Color-enhanced SEM Magnification: 3525×

Color-enhanced SEM Magnification: 4400×

Section 1 Resource Manager

Chapter *FAST FILE* Resources
Transparency Activity, pp. 38, 41–43
Directed Reading for Content Mastery, pp. 15, 16
MiniLAB, p. 3
Enrichment, p. 25

Note-taking Worksheets, pp. 27–28
Reinforcement, p. 23
Lab Activity, pp. 9–10
Lab Worksheet, pp. 5–6

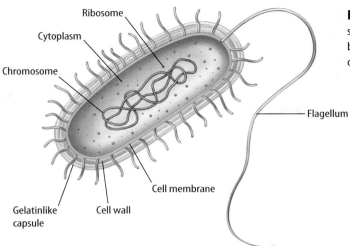

Figure 2 Bacterial cells are much smaller than eukaryotic cells. Most bacteria are about the size of some organelles found inside eukaryotic cells.

Ribosome
Cytoplasm
Chromosome
Flagellum
Cell membrane
Gelatinlike capsule
Cell wall

Structure of Bacterial Cells Bacteria normally have three basic shapes—spheres, rods, and spirals, as shown in **Figure 1.** Sphere-shaped bacteria are called cocci (KAHK si) (singular, *coccus*), rod-shaped bacteria are called bacilli (buh SIH li) (singular, *bacillus*), and spiral-shaped bacteria are called spirilla (spi RIH luh) (singular, *spirillum*). Bacteria are smaller than plant or animal cells. They are one-celled organisms that occur alone or in chains or groups.

A typical bacterial cell contains cytoplasm surrounded by a cell membrane and a cell wall, as shown in **Figure 2.** Bacterial cells are classified as prokaryotic because they do not contain a membrane-bound nucleus or other membrane-bound internal structures called organelles. Most of the genetic material of a bacterial cell is in its one circular chromosome found in the cytoplasm. Many bacteria also have a smaller circular piece of DNA called a plasmid. Ribosomes also are found in a bacterial cell's cytoplasm.

Special Features Some bacteria, like the type that causes pneumonia, have a thick, gelatinlike capsule around the cell wall. A capsule can help protect the bacterium from other cells that try to destroy it. The capsule, along with hairlike projections found on the surface of many bacteria, also can help them stick to surfaces. Some bacteria also have an outer coating called a slime layer. Like a capsule, a slime layer enables a bacterium to stick to surfaces and reduces water loss. Many bacteria that live in moist conditions also have whiplike tails called **flagella** to help them move.

✔ **Reading Check** *How do bacteria use flagella?*

Mini LAB

Modeling Bacteria Size

Procedure

1. One human hair is about 0.1 mm wide. Use a **meterstick** to measure a piece of **yarn or string** that is 10 m long. This yarn represents the width of your hair.
2. One type of bacteria is 2 micrometers long (1 micrometer = 0.000001 m). Measure another piece of yarn or string that is 20 cm long. This piece represents the length of the bacterium.
3. Find a large area where you can lay the two pieces of yarn or string next to each other and compare them.

Analysis

1. Calculate how much smaller the bacterium is than the width of your hair.
2. In your **Science Journal,** describe why a model is helpful to understand how small bacteria are.

Try at Home

SECTION 1 What are bacteria? **187**

---

2 Teach

Visual Learning

Figure 1 Emphasize that bacteria have three-dimensional shapes. Ask students to name common objects that are similar in shape to bacteria. *Balls are similar to cocci, lengths of thick wire are similar to bacilli, and wire spirals on notebooks are similar to spirilla.*

Figure 2 Emphasize that bacterial cells are small. Compare the size of a bacterium to another object you have studied. *Chloroplasts and mitochondria are about the same size as a bacterium.*

Mini LAB

Purpose to model the size of bacterial cells [L2]

IS Visual-Spatial

Materials 11 m of yarn or string; meterstick

Teaching Strategy Have students compare the sizes of bacteria and viruses. The diameter of the average virus is 100 nm, or 0.0000001 m, which is 10 times smaller than the average bacteria.

Analysis

1. 50 times smaller
2. Using models for size comparison allows one to understand the actual size of a bacterium.

Try at Home

✔ **Reading Check**

Answer to help them move

Curriculum Connection

Math Ask students whether they would rather have $10 every 20 minutes for 13 hours or start with one penny and have their money doubled every 20 minutes for 13 hours. *$400 by arithmetic growth or more than $5 trillion by exponential growth.* Point out that the growth rate of bacteria is like that of the penny. [L2] **IS** Logical-Mathematical

---

✔ Assessment

Oral Explain how the size of bacteria contributes to the spread of infection. *Their small size allows them to be transferred through the air when a person sneezes or coughs.* Use **Performance Assessment in the Science Classroom,** p. 87.

Fun Fact

Fission is also called binary fission. Binary fission is a quick and efficient means of producing many cells to utilize an energy resource.

Make a Model

Fission Have students use objects from home to make a model of bacteria undergoing fission. For instance, two golf balls could be used to model fission in cocci. L1 IS **Kinesthetic**

Discussion

Cocci Combinations Have groups of students discuss the possible combinations of cocci, such as pairs (diplococci), strands (streptococci), and clusters (staphylococci). Explain that different species of bacteria may assume all these shapes. L2 COOP LEARN IS **Interpersonal**

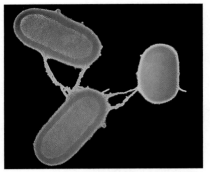

Color enhanced TEM Magnification: 5000×

Figure 3 Before dividing, these bacteria are exchanging DNA through the tubes that join them. This process is called conjugation.

Figure 4 Observing where bacteria can grow in tubes of a nutrient mixture shows you how oxygen affects different types of bacteria.

Reproduction Bacteria usually reproduce by fission. **Fission** is a process that produces two new cells with genetic material identical to each other and that of the original cell. It is the simplest form of asexual reproduction.

Some bacteria exchange genetic material through a process similar to sexual reproduction, as shown in **Figure 3.** Two bacteria line up beside each other and exchange DNA through a fine tube. This results in cells with different combinations of genetic material than they had before the exchange. As a result, the bacteria may acquire variations that give them an advantage for survival.

How Bacteria Obtain Food and Energy Bacteria obtain food in a variety of ways. Some make their food and others get it from the environment. Bacteria that contain chlorophyll or other pigments make their own food using energy from the Sun. Other bacteria use energy from chemical reactions to make food. Bacteria and other organisms that can make their own food are called producers.

Most bacteria are consumers. They do not make their own food. Some break down dead organisms to obtain energy. Others live as parasites of living organisms and absorb nutrients from their host.

Most organisms use oxygen when they break down food and obtain energy through a process called respiration. An organism that uses oxygen for respiration is called an **aerobe** (AY rohb). You are an aerobic organism and so are most bacteria. In contrast, an organism that is adapted to live without oxygen is called an **anaerobe** (AN uh rohb). Several kinds of anaerobic bacteria live in the intestinal tract of humans. Some bacteria cannot survive in areas with oxygen.

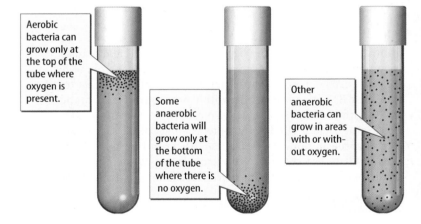

Aerobic bacteria can grow only at the top of the tube where oxygen is present.

Some anaerobic bacteria will grow only at the bottom of the tube where there is no oxygen.

Other anaerobic bacteria can grow in areas with or without oxygen.

188 CHAPTER 7 Bacteria

Differentiated Instruction

Learning Disabled Have pairs of students create flash cards that have the vocabulary for this chapter on one side and the definitions on the other. Allow students to practice using the vocabulary with their flash cards until they show proficiency with the terms. Students can also use flash cards to learn the names or structures of bacteria. L1 IS **Linguistic**

Teacher FYI

Scientific Drawings Leeuwenhoek was probably not the first person to observe bacteria, but he was the first to keep convincingly accurate records of his microscopic observations. He was also the first to illustrate fission in bacteria.

Figure 5 Many different bacteria can live in the intestines of humans and other animals. They often are identified based on the foods they use and the wastes they produce.

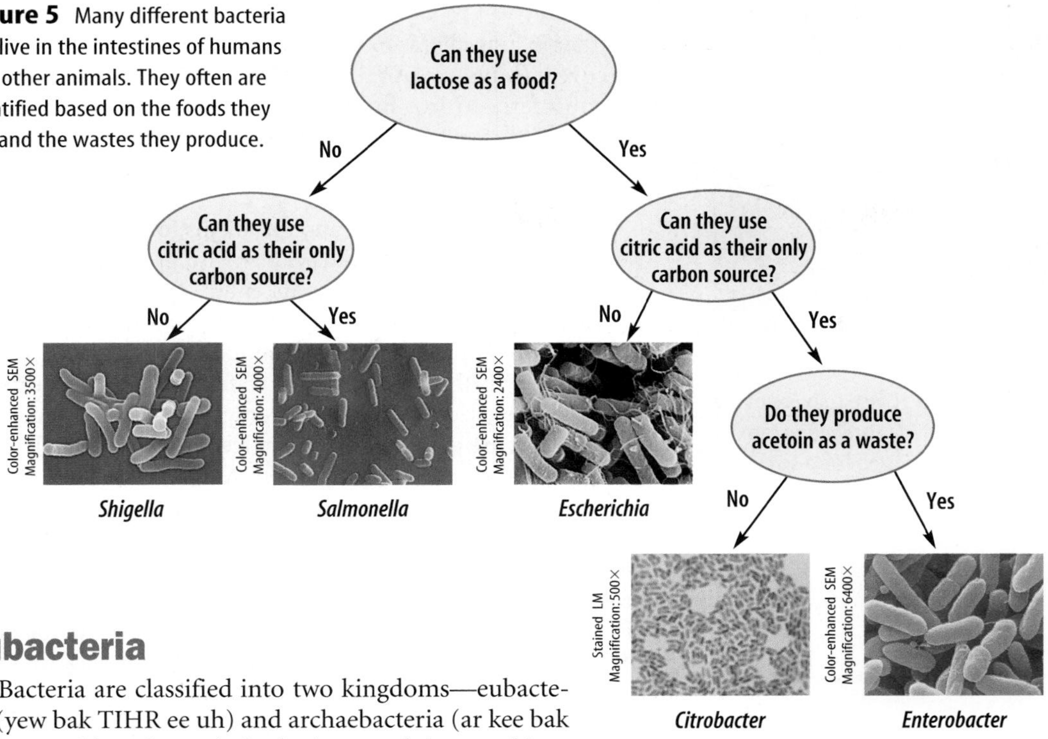

Can they use lactose as a food?
No
Yes
Can they use citric acid as their only carbon source?
No
Yes
Can they use citric acid as their only carbon source?
No
Yes
Do they produce acetoin as a waste?
No
Yes
Color-enhanced SEM Magnification: 3500×
Shigella
Color-enhanced SEM Magnification: 4000×
Salmonella
Color-enhanced SEM Magnification: 2400×
Escherichia
Stained LM Magnification: 500×
Citrobacter
Color-enhanced SEM Magnification: 6400×
Enterobacter

Eubacteria

Bacteria are classified into two kingdoms—eubacteria (yew bak TIHR ee uh) and archaebacteria (ar kee bak TIHR ee uh). Eubacteria is the larger of the two kingdoms. Scientists must study many characteristics in order to classify eubacteria into smaller groups. Most eubacteria are grouped according to their cell shape and structure, the way they obtain food, the type of food they consume, and the wastes they produce, as shown in **Figure 5.** Other characteristics used to group eubacteria include the method used for cell movement and whether the organism is an aerobe or anaerobe. New information about their genetic material is changing how scientists classify this kingdom.

Producer Eubacteria One important group of producer eubacteria is the cyanobacteria (si an oh bak TIHR ee uh). They make their own food using carbon dioxide, water, and energy from sunlight. They also produce oxygen as a waste. Cyanobacteria contain chlorophyll and another pigment that is blue. This pigment combination gives cyanobacteria their common name—blue-green bacteria. However, some cyanobacteria are yellow, black, or red. The Red Sea gets its name from red cyanobacteria.

Reading Check *Why are cyanobacteria classified as producers?*

Science Online

Topic: Producer Eubacteria
Visit life.msscience.com for Web links to information about the ways that producer bacteria make food.

Activity Construct a food web that illustrates a community that relies on producer bacteria as a source of energy.

Visual Learning

Figure 5 After discussing the phylogeny of bacteria, explain to students that phylogeny is based on the theory that organisms change over time and on their characteristics. Ask if these bacteria could ever be regrouped. Yes, organisms are often reclassified as new information is gained. With DNA technology, organisms are being reclassified often.

Use Science Words

Word Usage Have students use the words *aerobe* and *anaerobe* in sentences. An aerobe is a bacterium that requires oxygen. An anaerobe is a bacterium that lives without oxygen. L2 IS **Linguistic**

Reading Check

Answer They make their own food.

Science Journal

Bacteria in the News Ask students to find at least three recent newspaper or magazine articles that mention bacteria. Have them read the articles and prepare a written summary of what they learned and share with the class. L2 IS **Linguistic** P

Oscillatoria Have students make a wet mount to observe *Oscillatoria*. Point out that swaying movements are made as the bacteria secrete a slimy substance from their cells. L2 LS **Visual-Spatial**

INTEGRATE
Earth Science

Ocean Vents Where two of Earth's tectonic plates are splitting apart, ocean vents form. The conditions are hypothesized to be similar to those on early Earth. Some organisms that live near ocean vents include tube worms, clams, mussels, and bacteria.

Research Have students research a variety of organisms found at ocean vents and how they interact with each other. Students can construct an ocean vent food web and compare their food web to others in the class.

Quick Demo

Gram's Staining

Materials pictures of organisms that have been Gram-stained (include both gram-positive and gram-negative bacteria)

Estimated Time 15 minutes

Procedure Have students observe and compare the pictures of gram-positive and gram-negative organisms. Point out that the different colors are important in classification of bacteria. Have students look for a pattern between shape and the results of Gram's staining. L2 LS **Visual-Spatial**

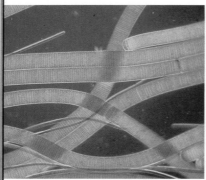
LM Magnification: 100×

Figure 6 These colonies of the cyanobacteria *Oscillatoria* can move by twisting like a screw.

INTEGRATE
Earth Science

Ocean Vents Geysers on the floor of the ocean are called ocean vents. Research to find out how ocean vents form and what conditions are like at an ocean vent. In your Science Journal, describe organisms that have been found living around ocean vents.

Figure 7 When stained with certain chemicals, bacteria with thin cell walls appear pink when viewed under a microscope. Those with thicker walls appear purple.

Importance of Cyanobacteria Some cyanobacteria live together in long chains or filaments, as shown in **Figure 6.** Many are covered with a gelatinlike substance. This adaptation enables cyanobacteria to live in groups called colonies. They are an important source of food for some organisms in lakes, ponds, and oceans. The oxygen produced by cyanobacteria is used by other aquatic organisms.

Cyanobacteria also can cause problems for aquatic life. Have you ever seen a pond covered with smelly, green, bubbly slime? When large amounts of nutrients enter a pond, cyanobacteria increase in number. Eventually the population grows so large that a bloom is produced. A bloom looks like a mat of bubbly green slime on the surface of the water. Available resources in the water are used up quickly and the cyanobacteria die. Other bacteria that are aerobic consumers feed on dead cyanobacteria and use up the oxygen in the water. As a result of the reduced oxygen in the water, fish and other organisms die.

Consumer Eubacteria Most consumer eubacteria are grouped into one of two categories based on the results of the Gram's stain. These results can be seen under a microscope after the bacteria are treated with certain chemicals that are called stains. As shown in **Figure 7,** gram-positive cells stain purple because they have thicker cell walls. Gram-negative cells stain pink because they have thinner cell walls.

The composition of the cell wall also can affect how a bacterium is affected by medicines given to treat an infection. Some antibiotics (an ti bi AH tihks) will be more effective against gram-negative bacteria than they will be against gram-positive bacteria.

One group of eubacteria is unique because they do not produce cell walls. This allows them to change their shape. They are not described as coccus, bacillus, or spirillum. One type of bacteria in this group, *Mycoplasma pneumoniae*, causes a type of pneumonia in humans.

Stained LM Magnification: 315×

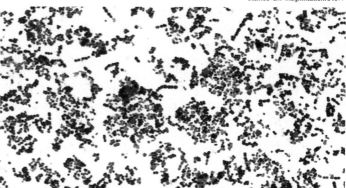

Differentiated Instruction

Learning Disabled If possible, bring in some pond water that has a mat of cyanobacteria on it. Place the mat in the light and ask what the bubbles are that appear in the mat. They are oxygen bubbles produced by photosynthesis. Then ask how large numbers of cyanobacteria can cause problems. When cyanobacteria die and decompose, oxygen levels drop. This can cause other organisms, such as fish, to die. L2 LS **Visual-Spatial**

Active Reading

Buddy Interviews This strategy helps students understand and clarify the reading. Have students interview one another to find out what helps them to understand what they are reading, how they find answers, and how they assimilate new vocabulary terms. Have students use Buddy Interviews to help them master concepts about bacteria.

Archaebacteria

Kingdom Archaebacteria contains certain kinds of bacteria that often are found in extreme conditions, such as hot springs. The conditions in which some archaebacteria live today are similar to conditions found on Earth during its early history. Archaebacteria are divided into groups based on where they live or how they get energy.

Salt-, Heat-, and Acid-Lovers One group of archaebacteria lives in salty environments such as the Great Salt Lake in Utah and the Dead Sea. Some of them require a habitat ten times saltier than seawater to grow.

Other groups of archaebacteria include those that live in acidic or hot environments. Some of these bacteria live near deep ocean vents or in hot springs where the temperature of the water is above 100°C.

Methane Producers Bacteria in this group of archaebacteria are anaerobic. They live in muddy swamps, the intestines of cattle, and even in you. Methane producers, as shown in **Figure 8,** use carbon dioxide for energy and release methane gas as a waste. Sometimes methane produced by these bacteria bubbles up out of swamps and marshes. These archaebacteria also are used in the process of sewage treatment. In an oxygen-free tank, the bacteria are used to break down the waste material that has been filtered from sewage water.

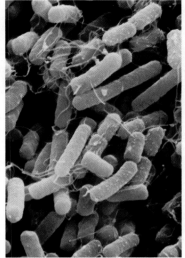

Color-enhanced SEM Magnification: 6000×

Figure 8 Some methane-producing bacteria live in the digestive tracts of cattle. They help digest the plants that cattle eat.

section 1 review

Summary

Characteristics of Bacteria

- Bacteria live almost everywhere and usually are one of three basic shapes.
- A bacterium lacks a nucleus, most bacteria reproduce asexually, and they can be aerobes or anaerobes.

Eubacteria

- Eubacteria are grouped by cell shape and structure, how they obtain food, and whether they are gram-positive or gram-negative.

Archaebacteria

- Archaebacteria can be found in extreme environments.
- Some break down sewage and produce methane.

Self Check

1. **List** three shapes of bacteria cells.
2. **Compare and contrast** aerobic organisms and anaerobic organisms.
3. **Explain** how most bacteria reproduce.
4. **Identify** who is given credit for first discovering bacteria.
5. **Think Critically** A pond is surrounded by recently fertilized farm fields. What effect would rainwater runoff from the fields have on the organisms in the pond?

Applying Math

6. **Solve One-Step Equations** Some bacteria reproduce every 20 min. Suppose that you have one bacterium. How long would it take for the number of bacteria to increase to more than 1 million?

DAILY INTERVENTION

Check for Understanding

Linguistic Have students research the cells of prokaryotes and eukaryotes to determine differences. Ask students how flagella of bacteria differ from flagella in other organisms, such as *Euglena*. Flagella of bacteria are simpler and are not surrounded by a membrane. L2

Reteach

Decomposers To demonstrate the role of bacteria as decomposers, bring a piece of decomposing fruit to class. Have students observe the process over a few days or a week. L2 IS **Visual-Spatial**

✔ Assessment

Performance To further assess students' abilities to observe cyanobacteria, set up a practical to have them identify organisms or answer questions about them. Use **Performance Assessment in the Science Classroom,** p. 89.

---

section 1 review

1. one-celled; cytoplasm surrounded by cell membrane and cell wall; circular or linear chromosome; ribosomes in cytoplasm; plasmid; no membrane-bound organelles
2. Aerobic: uses oxygen to live; anaerobic: can live without oxygen. Oxygen kills some anaerobes.
3. Fission; some bacteria also exchange genetic material in a process similar to sexual reproduction.
4. Antonie van Leeuwenhoek
5. It could potentially kill the pond organisms as cyanobacteria flourish, die, and decompose.
6. 6 hours and 40 minutes (1,048,576 bacteria)

▶ Real-World Question

Purpose Students will observe and record the characteristics of several cyanobacteria. L2 ELL
N Naturalist

Process Skills observe, classify, interpret data

Time Required 50 minutes

▶ Procedure

Alternate Materials In addition to the cyanobacteria listed, many others can be found in biological supply house catalogs.

Teaching Strategy Having prepared slides for use will be more interesting and visually stimulating for students than having them look at pictures.

Troubleshooting If students have trouble seeing the jellylike layer of the capsule, have them reduce the amount of light coming through the microscope's diaphragm.

▶ Conclude and Apply

1. You can infer that they are producers that carry on photosynthesis.
2. Cyanobacteria contain chlorophyll, which makes them photosynthetic eubacteria. They are green.

✔ Assessment

Performance Have students draw, label, and describe different cyanobacteria they observe. Use **Performance Assessment in the Science Classroom,** p. 127.

Observing Cyanobacteria

You can obtain many species of cyanobacteria from ponds. When you look at these organisms under a microscope, you will find that they have similarities and differences. In this lab, compare and contrast species of cyanobacteria.

▶ Real-World Question

What do cyanobacteria look like?

Goals
■ **Observe** several species of cyanobacteria.
■ **Describe** the structure and function of cyanobacteria.

Materials
micrograph photos of *Oscillatoria* and *Nostoc*
prepared slides of Oscillatoria *and* Nostoc
prepared slides of *Gloeocapsa* and *Anabaena*
micrograph photos of Anabaena *and* Gloeocapsa
microscope
Alternate materials

Safety Precautions
[safety symbols]

▶ Procedure

1. Copy the data table in your Science Journal. As you observe each cyanobacterium, record the presence or absence of each characteristic in the data table.
2. **Observe** prepared slides of *Gloeocapsa* and *Anabaena* under low and high power of the microscope. Notice the difference in the arrangement of the cells. In your Science Journal, draw and label a few cells of each.
3. **Observe** photos of *Nostoc* and *Oscillatoria*. In your Science Journal, draw and label a few cells of each.

▶ Conclude and Apply

1. **Infer** what the color of each cyanobacterium means.
2. **Explain** how you can tell by observing that a cyanobacterium is a eubacterium.

Communicating
Your Data

Compare your data table with those of other students in your class. **For more help, refer to the** Science Skill Handbook.

Cyanobacteria Observations				
Structure	***Anabaena***	***Gloeocapsa***	***Nostoc***	***Oscillatoria***
Filament or colony	filament	colony	filament	filament
Nucleus	no	no	no	no
Chlorophyll	yes	yes	yes	yes
Gel-like layer	yes	yes	yes	yes

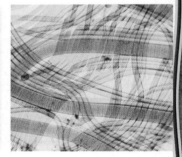

192 CHAPTER 7 Bacteria

Communicating
Your Data

Data tables should be the same for all students. Students who have differences should be prepared to explain them to others.

Bacteria in Your Life

Beneficial Bacteria

When you hear the word *bacteria,* you probably associate it with sore throats or other illnesses. However, few bacteria cause illness. Most are important for other reasons. The benefits of most bacteria far outweigh the harmful effects of a few.

Bacteria That Help You Without bacteria, you would not be healthy for long. Bacteria, like those in **Figure 9,** are found inside your digestive system. These bacteria are found in particularly high numbers in your large intestine. Most are harmless to you, and they help you stay healthy. For example, some bacteria in your intestines are responsible for producing vitamin K, which is necessary for normal blood clot formation.

Some bacteria produce chemicals called **antibiotics** that limit the growth of other bacteria. For example, one type of bacteria that is commonly found living in soil produces the antibiotic streptomycin. Another kind of bacteria, *Bacillus,* produces the antibiotic found in many nonprescription antiseptic ointments. Many bacterial diseases in humans and animals can be treated with antibiotics.

Lactobacillus LM Magnification: 250×

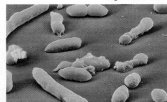

Klebsiella Color-enhanced TEM Magnification: 11000×

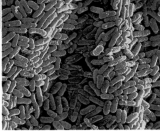

E. coli Color-enhanced SEM Magnification: 3200×

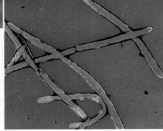

Fusobacterium Color-enhanced TEM Magnification: 3000×

Figure 9 Many types of bacteria live naturally in your large intestine. They help you digest food and produce essential vitamins.

---

as you read

What You'll Learn
- **Identify** some ways bacteria are helpful.
- **Determine** the importance of nitrogen-fixing bacteria.
- **Explain** how some bacteria can cause human disease.

Why It's Important
Discovering the ways bacteria affect your life can help you understand biological processes.

Review Vocabulary
disease: a condition with symptoms that interferes with normal body functions

New Vocabulary
- antibiotic
- saprophyte
- nitrogen-fixing bacteria
- pathogen
- toxin
- endospore
- vaccine

---

1 Motivate

INTERACTIVE CHALKBOARD
PowerPoint® Presentations

Bellringer

Section Focus Transparencies also are available on the Interactive Chalkboard CD-ROM.
L2 ELL

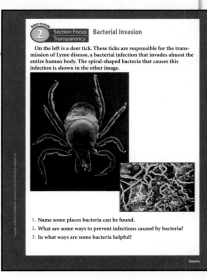

Tie to Prior Knowledge
Different Kinds of Bacteria Ask students if they have ever had a sore throat or eaten cheese. Explain that both of these experiences involve bacteria. In this section, they will learn about beneficial and harmful bacteria.

Virtual Labs

Germs *What kills germs?*

Section 2 Resource Manager

Chapter *FAST FILE* Resources

Transparency Activity, p. 39

Directed Reading for Content Mastery, pp. 17, 18

MiniLAB, p. 4

Enrichment, p. 26

Lab Activity, pp. 11–12

Reinforcement, p. 24

Lab Worksheet, pp. 11–12

Mathematics Skill Activities, p. 19

Lab Management and Safety, p. 58

Reading Check

Answer an organism that uses dead material as a food and energy source

Mini LAB

Purpose to observe and infer the growth rate of bacteria

L1 ELL COOP LEARN IS

Kinesthetic

Materials dried beans, distilled water, glass beaker

Teaching Strategies

• You may want to soak the beans for 24 hours prior to doing the lab, as this makes it easier for students to break them apart.

• Point out that the water's cloudiness indicates bacterial growth.

Safety Precautions Tell students to wash their hands after handling the materials and not to eat any of them.

Troubleshooting To avoid odors, caution students not to leave the beans and water in the classroom for more than five days.

Analysis

1. It usually takes 3–4 days.
2. the beans

Assessment

Process Have students hypothesize the doubling time of bacterial cells. Then have them design an experiment to test their hypothesis. Use **Performance Assessment in the Science Classroom,** p. 93.

Figure 10 Air is bubbled through the sewage in this aeration tank so that bacteria can break down much of the sewage wastes. **Determine** *whether the bacteria that live in this tank are aerobes or anaerobes.*

Mini LAB

Observing Bacterial Growth

Procedure

1. Obtain two or three **dried beans.**
2. Carefully break them into halves and place the halves into 10 mL of **distilled water** in a **glass beaker.**
3. Observe how many days it takes for the water to become cloudy and develop an unpleasant odor.

Analysis

1. How long did it take for the water to become cloudy?
2. What do you think the bacteria were using as a food source?

Bacteria and the Environment Without bacteria, there would be layers of dead material all over Earth deeper than you are tall. Consumer bacteria called saprophytes (SAP ruh fites) help maintain nature's balance. A **saprophyte** is any organism that uses dead organisms as food and energy sources. Saprophytic bacteria help recycle nutrients. These nutrients become available for use by other organisms. As shown in **Figure 10,** most sewage-treatment plants use saprophytic aerobic bacteria to break down wastes into carbon dioxide and water.

Reading Check *What is a saprophyte?*

Plants and animals must take in nitrogen to make needed proteins and nucleic acids. Animals can eat plants or other animals that contain nitrogen, but plants need to take nitrogen from the soil or air. Although air is about 78 percent nitrogen, neither animals nor plants can use it directly. **Nitrogen-fixing bacteria** change nitrogen from the air into forms that plants and animals can use. The roots of some plants such as peanuts and peas develop structures called nodules that contain nitrogen-fixing bacteria, as shown in **Figure 11.** It is estimated that nitrogen-fixing bacteria save U.S. farmers millions of dollars in fertilizer costs every year. Many of the cyanobacteria also can fix nitrogen and are important in providing nitrogen in usable forms to aquatic organisms.

Bioremediation Using organisms to help clean up or remove environmental pollutants is called bioremediation. One type of bioremediation uses bacteria to break down wastes and pollutants into simpler harmless compounds. Other bacteria use certain pollutants as a food source. Every year about five percent to ten percent of all wastes produced by industry, agriculture, and cities are treated by bioremediation. Sometimes bioremediation is used at the site where chemicals, such as oil, have been spilled. Research continues on ways to make bioremediation a faster process.

Teacher FYI

Bioremediation A wide variety of organic and toxic compounds have been broken down by bioremediation. Cleanup of oil spills by bioremediation is likely to increase in the future.

Cultural Diversity

In a Pickle Pickling is a process of food preservation that depends on the chemical process of fermentation and the inhibition of bacterial growth in a highly acidic solution. It is found in the cuisine of many cultures. Have students research different pickling processes and prepare lists of how and what products are pickled in different cultures. L2 P

VISUALIZING NITROGEN-FIXING BACTERIA

Figure 11

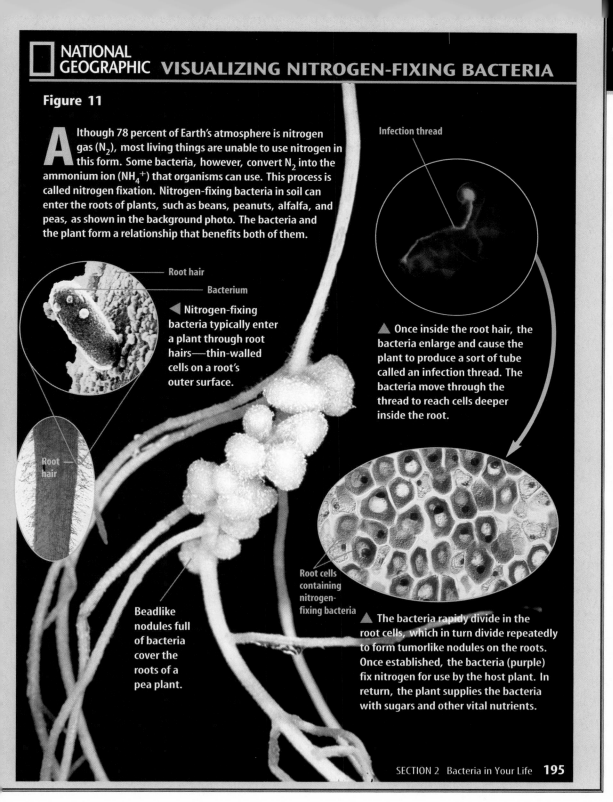

Although 78 percent of Earth's atmosphere is nitrogen gas (N_2), most living things are unable to use nitrogen in this form. Some bacteria, however, convert N_2 into the ammonium ion (NH_4^+) that organisms can use. This process is called nitrogen fixation. Nitrogen-fixing bacteria in soil can enter the roots of plants, such as beans, peanuts, alfalfa, and peas, as shown in the background photo. The bacteria and the plant form a relationship that benefits both of them.

Root hair

Bacterium

◀ Nitrogen-fixing bacteria typically enter a plant through root hairs—thin-walled cells on a root's outer surface.

Root hair

Beadlike nodules full of bacteria cover the roots of a pea plant.

Infection thread

▲ Once inside the root hair, the bacteria enlarge and cause the plant to produce a sort of tube called an infection thread. The bacteria move through the thread to reach cells deeper inside the root.

Root cells containing nitrogen-fixing bacteria

▲ The bacteria rapidly divide in the root cells, which in turn divide repeatedly to form tumorlike nodules on the roots. Once established, the bacteria (purple) fix nitrogen for use by the host plant. In return, the plant supplies the bacteria with sugars and other vital nutrients.

SECTION 2 Bacteria in Your Life **195**

Visualizing Nitrogen-Fixing Bacteria

Have students examine the pictures and read the captions. Then ask the following questions.

What is the "cost" to a plant for having nitrogen-fixing bacteria in its root cells? The "cost" to the plant is that the carbohydrates it makes are used by the bacteria.

When pea plants are producing peas, the nitrogen fixation of the associated bacteria dips to a low level. What would be a logical explanation for this? When producing peas, the plant has little extra sugar for the bacteria to use, so nitrogen fixation slows.

Make a Model

Nitrogen Fixation Have students model the relationship between plants and nitrogen fixation. Designate each student as either a plant or a nitrogen-fixing bacterium. Plants should carry two index cards, one labeled "sugars" and one labeled "nutrients." Bacteria should carry two index cards, each labeled "NH_4^+." Explain that each student must have one sugar and nutrient card and one NH_4^+ card to survive. Have the students exchange cards to meet their needs. [L1] [LS] **Interpersonal**

Activity

Fertilizer Direct interested students to examine the contents of different brands of garden and lawn fertilizer and infer why nitrogen is an ingredient in most of these products. Nitrogen is needed for plants to grow well. Nitrogen in the form provided by the fertilizers can be absorbed and used by plants.

Bioreactor Landfills More information about bioreactor landfills is available from the U.S. Environmental Protection Agency.

Science Journal

A Mutualist Relationship Have students explain in their Science Journals why "infection" of roots by nitrogen-fixing bacteria is beneficial for both plant and environment. Nitrogen gas in the atmosphere is unusable for most organisms. The bacteria fix nitrogen in a form that plants can use. After the plant dies, nitrogen is available for use by other organisms. L2 IS **Linguistic**

✔ **Reading Check**

Answer methane

Visual Learning

Figure 12 Enhance the impact of the photo by having students taste cheese curds. You may also have students bring various cheeses from home to taste. Point out that these foods were prepared by using beneficial bacteria. Caution students who may have food allergies to avoid tasting the cheeses. L1 ELL **Kinesthetic**

Bioreactor Landfills As Earth's population grows and produces more waste, traditional landfills, which take 30 to 100 years to decompose waste, no longer fulfill the need for solid-waste disposal. Bioreactor landfills, which take 5 to 10 years to decompose waste, are beginning to be used instead. Bioreactor landfills can use aerobic or anaerobic bacteria, or a combination of the two, for rapid degradation of wastes.

Figure 12 When bacteria such as *Streptococcus lactis* are added to milk, it causes the milk to separate into curds (solids) and whey (liquids). Other bacteria are added to the curds, which ripen into cheese. The type of cheese made depends on the bacterial species added to the curds.

Bacteria and Food Have you had any bacteria for lunch lately? Even before people understood that bacteria were involved, they were used in the production of foods. One of the first uses of bacteria was for making yogurt, a milk-based food that has been made in Europe and Asia for hundreds of years. Bacteria break down substances in milk to make many dairy products. Cheeses and buttermilk also can be produced with the aid of bacteria. Cheese making is shown in **Figure 12.**

Other foods you might have eaten also are made using bacteria. Sauerkraut, for example, is made with cabbage and a bacterial culture. Vinegar, pickles, olives, and soy sauce also are produced with the help of bacteria.

Bacteria in Industry Many industries rely on bacteria to make many products. Bacteria are grown in large containers called bioreactors. Conditions inside bioreactors are carefully controlled and monitored to allow for the growth of the bacteria. Medicines, enzymes, cleansers, and adhesives are some of the products that are made using bacteria.

Methane gas that is released as a waste by certain bacteria can be used as a fuel for heating, cooking, and industry. In landfills, methane-producing bacteria break down plant and animal material. The quantity of methane gas released by these bacteria is so large that some cities collect and burn it, as shown in **Figure 13.** Using bacteria to digest wastes and then produce methane gas could supply large amounts of fuel worldwide.

✔ **Reading Check** *What waste gas produced by some bacteria can be used as a fuel?*

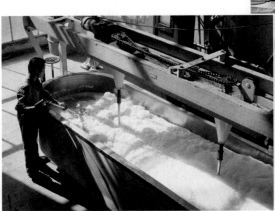

Curds and whey

Curds

LAB DEMONSTRATION

Purpose to observe the activity of bacteria
Materials plastic wastebasket, soil, paper, grass clippings, leaves, small sticks, dried food (avoid proteins and fats), bacteria culture, water, thermometer
Preparation Have students observe the materials and write down their predictions.

Procedure Mix materials, keeping the mixture as light as possible. Add small amounts of water. Take the mixture's temperature every two days and stir the compost pile. Add materials as needed.
Expected Outcome Students should observe the decay of organic materials.

Assessment

Why does the temperature rise above room temperature? As bacteria respire, they release heat. What happens to the paper and other organic material? It decays to form compost.

Figure 13 Methane gas produced by bacteria in this landfill is burning at the top of these collection tubes.

Science Online

Topic: Pathogens
Visit life.msscience.com for Web links to information about pathogenic bacteria and antibiotics.

Activity Compile a list of common antibiotics and the bacterial pathogens they are used to treat.

Harmful Bacteria

Not all bacteria are beneficial. Some bacteria are known as pathogens. A **pathogen** is any organism that causes disease. If you have ever had strep throat, you have had firsthand experience with a bacterial pathogen. Other pathogenic bacteria cause diphtheria, tetanus, and whooping cough in humans, as well as anthrax in humans and livestock.

How Pathogens Make You Sick Bacterial pathogens can cause illness and disease by several different methods. They can enter your body through a cut in the skin, you can inhale them, or they can enter in other ways. Once inside your body, they can multiply, damage normal cells, and cause illness and disease.

Some bacterial pathogens produce poisonous substances known as **toxins.** Botulism—a type of food poisoning that can result in paralysis and death—is caused by a toxin-producing bacterium. Botulism-causing bacteria are able to grow and produce toxins inside sealed cans of food. However, when growing conditions are unfavorable for their survival, some bacteria, like those that cause botulism, can produce thick-walled structures called **endospores.** Endospores, shown in **Figure 14,** can exist for hundreds of years before they resume growth. If the endospores of the botulism-causing bacteria are in canned food, they can grow and develop into regular bacterial cells and produce toxins again. Commercially canned foods undergo a process that uses steam under high pressure, which kills bacteria and most endospores.

Figure 14 Bacterial endospores can survive harsh winters, dry conditions, and heat.
Describe *possible ways endospores can be destroyed.*

LM Magnification: 600×

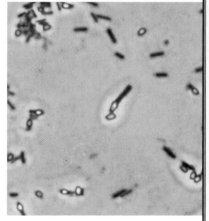

Figure 15 Pasteurization lowers the amount of bacteria in foods. Products, such as juice, ice cream, and yogurt, are pasteurized.

Pasteurization Unless it has been sterilized, all food contains bacteria. But heating food to sterilizing temperatures can change its taste. Pasteurization is a process of heating food to a temperature that kills most harmful bacteria but causes little change to the taste of the food. You are probably most familiar with pasteurized milk, but some fruit juices and other foods, as shown in **Figure 15,** also are pasteurized.

Applying Science

Controlling Bacterial Growth

Bacteria can be controlled by slowing or preventing their growth, or killing them. When trying to control bacteria that affect humans, it is often desirable just to slow their growth because substances that kill bacteria or prevent them from growing can harm humans. For example, bleach often is used to kill bacteria in bathrooms or on kitchen surfaces, but it is poisonous if swallowed. *Antiseptic* is the word used to describe substances that slow the growth of bacteria.

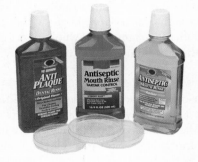

Identifying the Problem

Advertisers often claim that a substance kills bacteria, when in fact the substance only slows its growth. Many mouthwash advertisements make this claim. How could you test three mouthwashes to see which one is the best antiseptic?

Solving the Problem

1. Describe an experiment that you could do that would test which of three mouthwash products is the most effective antiseptic.

2. Identify the control in your experiment.

3. Read the ingredients labels on bottles of mouthwash. List the ingredients in the mouthwash. What ingredient do you think is the antiseptic? Explain.

Fun Fact

In the late 1970s and 1980s, Carl Woese studied bacteria classification by examining sequences of ribosomal RNA. He determined that archaebacteria are more closely related to animals, plants, and fungi than to other bacteria.

Figure 16 Each of these paper disks contains a different antibiotic. Clear areas where no bacteria are growing can be seen around four of the disks.

Infer *which one of these disks contains an antibiotic that is most effective against the bacteria growing on the plate.*

 INTEGRATE Health

Treating Bacterial Diseases Bacterial diseases in humans and animals usually are treated effectively with antibiotics. Penicillin, a well-known antibiotic, works by preventing bacteria from making cell walls. Without cell walls, certain bacteria cannot survive. **Figure 16** shows antibiotics at work.

Vaccines can prevent some bacterial diseases. A **vaccine** can be made from damaged particles taken from bacterial cell walls or from killed bacteria. Once the vaccine is injected, white blood cells in the blood recognize that type of bacteria. If the same type of bacteria enters the body at a later time, the white blood cells immediately attack them. Vaccines have been produced that are effective against many bacterial diseases.

section 2 review

Summary

Beneficial Bacteria
- Many types of bacteria help you stay healthy.
- Antibiotics are produced by some bacteria.
- Bacteria decompose dead material.
- Certain bacteria change nitrogen in the air to forms that other organisms can use.
- Some bacteria are used to remove pollutants.
- Bacteria help to produce some foods.

Harmful Bacteria
- Some bacteria cause disease.
- Some bacteria have endospores that enable them to adapt to harsh environments.

Self Check

1. **Explain** why saprophytic bacteria are helpful.
2. **Summarize** how nitrogen-fixing bacteria benefit plants and animals.
3. **List** three uses of bacteria in food production and other industry.
4. **Describe** how some bacteria cause disease.
5. **Think Critically** Why is botulism associated with canned foods and not fresh foods?

Applying Skills

6. **Measure in SI** Air can have more than 3,500 bacteria per cubic meter. How many bacteria might be in your classroom?

section 2 review

1. They recycle nutrients.
2. They change atmospheric nitrogen into a form that can be used by plants or animals.
3. Bacteria are used in making yogurt, sauerkraut, and other food products. Biotechnology industries use bacteria to produce medicines and other products. Methane gas can be produced in landfills.
4. Some bacteria produce toxins; others multiply in the body, damaging normal cells and causing illness and disease.
5. The bacteria that cause botulism are anaerobes, which grow in an oxygen-free environment, such as that in canned foods.
6. Measure the length, width, and height of the classroom in meters. Multiply these numbers to find the volume of air. Multiply the volume by 3,500 to obtain the number of bacteria per cubic meter.

Use an Analogy

Antibiotics Act Like Detergents Some antibiotics bind to fatlike molecules found in cell membranes. Just like detergents break up food and grease on dirty dishes, these antibiotics break up the fatlike molecules and destroy the cell membranes of harmful bacteria.

Caption Answer

Figure 16 The one that has the largest clear zone around it (at 10 o'clock) is most effective.

3 Assess

DAILY INTERVENTION

Check for Understanding

Visual-Spatial Students can demonstrate their understanding of the work of bacteria by bringing to class foods that are processed using bacteria or objects that show the effects of bacteria. L1

Reteach

Bacterial Processes Show students photographs of processes carried out by bacteria. Have students identify each process and its importance. L2 IS **Visual-Spatial**

✓ Assessment

Process Assess students' understanding of vaccines by having them make a concept map outlining what happens when someone receives a vaccination for a disease, and later is infected with that disease. The individual receives a vaccine, which enables their white blood cells to recognize and develop a defense against a particular disease-causing organism. When the organism later enters the individual's bloodstream, it is immediately recognized and killed by the white blood cells. Use **Performance Assessment in the Science Classroom,** p. 161.

⊙ Real-World Question

Purpose Students design an experiment to determine the types of materials that will decompose in a compost pile.
L2 IS **Visual-Spatial**

Process Skills compare, contrast, predict, describe, make a data table, interpret data

Time Required One 45-minute class period; three or four 20-minute observation periods over four weeks

Possible Materials wide mouth jars or flat baking pans, soil, food scraps (not fats or proteins), grass clippings, etc.

Safety Precautions 🥽 🧤 🔪 🧫

⊙ Form a Hypothesis

Possible Hypothesis Students should make a prediction about the materials they place in their jar. Students should explain why they made that prediction.

⊙ Test Your Hypothesis

Possible Procedure Bury food scraps, grass clippings, and leaf litter under 10 cm of soil in widemouthed jars or flat baking pans. Water, turn, and add layers of soil to the containers regularly. After the compost is established, place test items on the compost and bury them under 10 cm of soil. Examine the items once a week for signs of decomposition.

Teaching Strategy Encourage students to use common items such as pieces of polystyrene, notebook and glossy magazine paper, and biodegradable food items.

LAB Design Your Own

Composting

Goals
- **Predict** which of several items will decompose in a compost pile and which will not.
- **Demonstrate** the decomposition, or lack thereof, of several items.
- **Compare and contrast** the speed at which various items break down.

Possible Materials
widemouthed, clear-glass jars (at least 4)
soil
water
watering can
banana peel
apple core
scrap of newspaper
leaf
plastic candy wrapper
scrap of aluminum foil

Safety Precautions
🥽 🧤 🔪 🧫

⊙ Real-World Question

Over time, landfills fill up and new places to dump trash become more difficult to find. One way to reduce the amount of trash that must be dumped in a landfill is to recycle. Composting is a form of recycling that changes plant wastes into reusable, nutrient-rich compost. How do plant wastes become compost? What types of organisms can assist in the process? What types of items can be composted and what types cannot?

⊙ Form a Hypothesis

Based on readings or prior knowledge, form a hypothesis about what types of items will decompose in a compost pile and which will not.

Alternative Inquiry Lab

Perfect Compost Have students explore ideal conditions or materials for composting using food items, food packaging materials, potting soil, garden soil, sandy soil, clay soil, earthworms, isopods, shallow trays, and garden trowels. The initial set up should take one class session and then 10 min observation periods over several weeks. Students can test how well different types of soil degrade organic materials such as banana peels or apple cores, or how well the same type of soil affects the rate of decomposition of various food items and packaging materials. Students also can test whether or not earthworms, isopods, or other decomposing organisms will increase the rate of decomposition. Encourage students to create an outdoor compost pile to conduct their tests and use their test results to design an ideal compost pile for the school.

▶ Test Your Hypothesis

Make a Plan

1. **Decide** what items you are going to test. Choose some items that you think will decompose and some that you think will not.

2. **Predict** which of the items you chose will or will not decompose. Of the items that will, which do you think will decompose fastest? Slowest?

3. **Decide** how you will test whether or not the items decompose. How will you see the items? You may need to research composting in books, magazines, or on the Internet.

4. **Prepare** a data table in your Science Journal to record your observations.

5. **Identify** all constants, variables, and controls of the experiment.

Follow Your Plan

1. Make sure your teacher approves of your plan and your data table before you start.

2. **Observe** Set up your experiment and collect data as planned.

3. **Record Data** While doing the experiment, record your observations and complete your data tables in your Science Journal.

▶ Analyze Your Data

1. **Describe** your results. Did all of the items decompose? If not, which did and which did not?

2. Were your predictions correct? Explain.

3. **Compare** how fast each item decomposed. Which items decomposed fastest and which took longer?

▶ Conclude and Apply

1. What general statement(s) can you make about which items can be composted and which cannot? What about the speed of decomposition?

2. **Determine** whether your results support your hypothesis.

3. **Explain** what might happen to your compost pile if antibiotics were added to it.

4. **Describe** what you think happens in a landfill to items similar to those that you tested.

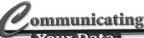

Point of View Write a letter to the editor of a local newspaper describing what you have learned about composting and encouraging more community composting.

▶ Analyze Your Data

Expected Outcome Student results should show various degrees of decay for the food items, natural-fiber clothing, and paper. Nonbiodegradable items will not show significant signs of decay.

Answers to Questions

1. Food items, paper, and clothing made of natural fibers will show various signs of decay, but non-degradable items, such as glass, plastic, or rocks, will not.
2. Answers will vary with results.
3. The food items will decay most rapidly, followed by clothing made of natural fibers. Moist items will decay more rapidly than drier items.

Error Analysis To avoid confusion when examining the composted items, students should use initially new items and make a record of the appearance of each item before it is composted.

▶ Conclude and Apply

1. Materials made of natural ingredients can be composted, but artificial items will not compost. Aerating the soil and keeping the compost moist increases decay.
2. Answers will vary.
3. Bacteria are the primary decomposing agents in compost piles. Killing bacteria would slow or stop the decay process.
4. Landfill items are frequently buried more deeply, are exposed to less moisture, and receive little or no aeration. Thus, items would decay more slowly in a landfill.

LAB 201

☑ Assessment

Performance With permission, have students plan and construct a school compost pile in a corner of the school property. Use **Performance Assessment in the Science Classroom,** p. 105.

Encourage students to access online resources to gather information on local landfills, compost sites, and recycling centers.

Content Background

There are many bacteria species that thrive in extreme environmental conditions. Thermophiles are bacteria that thrive at temperatures between 50°C and 60°C. Some even can live in hot springs and ocean hydrothermal vents, where temperatures can reach 110°C. Other bacteria, called psychrophiles, live at temperatures of 15°C to 20°C. Psychrophiles that live in the soil and water of arctic regions can survive temperatures as low as 0°C. Bacteria that live under extreme pressure are called barophiles. Those that live on the ocean floor at a depth of 7 km cannot survive at atmospheric pressure. Some species of bacteria, called acidophiles, can survive in a pH as low as 1 and are found in water that drains from coal mines, which contains high amounts of sulfuric acid and in hydrothermal vents.

Discussion

Unusual Bacteria What advantages do unusual bacteria have over other types of bacteria? Possible answer: These bacteria can survive in extreme environmental conditions.

Activity

Food Preservation Have students research different methods of food preservation, such as refrigeration, pasteurization, sterilization, pH alteration, radiation, and chemical preservatives, and discuss how the form of preservation relates to the basic survival or environmental requirements of many bacteria.

Applying Math

Answer 130 nanometers

SCIENCE Stats

Unusual Bacteria

Did you know...

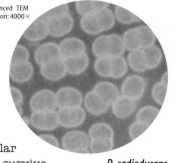
Color-enhanced TEM
Magnification: 4000×

D. radiodurans

...The hardiest bacteria, *Deinococcus radiodurans* (DE no KO kus·RA de oh DOOR anz), has a nasty odor, which has been described as similar to rotten cabbage. It might have an odor, but it can survive 3,000 times more radiation than humans because it quickly repairs damage to its DNA molecule. These bacteria were discovered in canned meat when they survived sterilization by radiation.

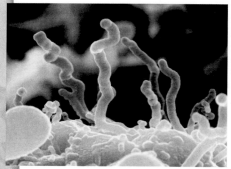
Nanobes

...The smallest bacteria, nanobes (NA nobes), are Earth's smallest living things. They have been found 5 km beneath the ocean floor near Australia. These tiny cells are 20 to 150 nanometers long. That means, depending on their size, it would take about 6,500,000 to 50,000,000 nanobes lined up to equal 1 m!

Applying Math What is the difference in size between the largest nanobe and the smallest nanobe?

...Earth's oldest living bacteria are thought to be 250 million years old. These ancient bacteria were revived from a crystal of rock salt buried 579 m below the desert floor in New Mexico.

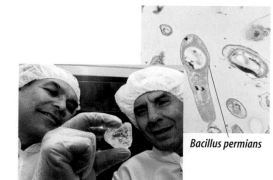
Bacillus permians

Find Out About It

Do research about halophiles, the bacteria that can live in highly salty environments. What is the maximum salt concentration in which extreme halophiles can survive? How does this compare to the maximum salt concentration at which nonhalophilic bacteria can survive? Visit life.msscience.com/science_stats to learn more.

Find Out About It

Have students list locations where halophiles can be found. ocean, Great Salt Lake, Dead Sea, salt licks, brine vats, salt flats Have students make a chart of the different types of halophiles, the salt concentration in which they can survive, and the number of times higher that is than the concentration in which nonhalophiles can survive. L3 **IS** **Logical-Mathematical**

Visual Learning

How hot can they get? How much higher temperatures can heat-resistant bacteria withstand than insects? about 60°C What is the minimum temperature needed to sterilize foods such as canned goods against heat-resistant bacteria? 120°C

Reviewing Main Ideas

Section 1 What are bacteria?

1. Bacteria can be found almost everywhere. They have one of three basic shapes—coccus, bacillus, or spirillum.

2. Bacteria are prokaryotic cells that usually reproduce by fission. All bacteria contain DNA, ribosomes, and cytoplasm but lack a membrane-bound nucleus.

3. Most bacteria are consumers, but some can make their own food. Anaeroic bacteria live without oxygen, but aerobic bacteria need oxygen to survive.

4. Cell shape and structure, how they get food, if they use oxygen, and their waste products can be used to classify eubacteria.

5. Cyanobacteria are producer eubacteria. They are an important source of food and oxygen for some aquatic organisms.

6. Archaebacteria are bacteria that often exist in extreme conditions, such as near ocean vents or in hot springs.

Section 2 Bacteria in Your Life

1. Most bacteria are helpful. They aid in recycling nutrients, fixing nitrogen, or helping in food production. They even can be used to break down pollutants.

2. Some bacteria that live in your body help you stay healthy and survive.

3. Other bacteria are harmful because they can cause disease in organisms.

4. Pasteurization can prevent the growth of harmful bacteria in food.

Visualizing Main Ideas

Copy and complete the following concept map on how bacteria affect the environment.

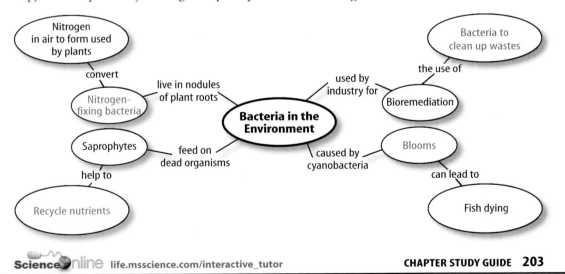

life.msscience.com/interactive_tutor

CHAPTER STUDY GUIDE **203**

---

chapter **7** **Study Guide**

Reviewing Main Ideas

Summary statements can be used by students to review the major concepts of the chapter.

Visualizing Main Ideas

See student page.

Science Online

Visit life.msscience.com
/self_check_quiz
/interactive_tutor
/vocabulary_puzzlemaker
/chapter_review
/standardized_test

Assessment Transparency

For additional assessment questions, use the *Assessment Transparency* located in the transparency book.

Assessment

Assessment Transparency **Bacteria**

Directions: *Carefully review the diagram and answer the following questions.*

Test tube 1	Test tube 2	Test tube 3	Test tube 4
Cotton stopper	Cotton stopper	Cotton stopper	Cotton stopper
	10 mL chemical X	15 mL chemical X	20 mL chemical X
20 mL sterile beef broth	20 mL sterile beef broth	20 mL sterile beef broth	20 mL sterile beef broth

Equal amounts of bacteria added

1. Which hypothesis is probably being tested by this experiment?
   A Beef broth is a good substance for growing bacteria.
   B A cotton stopper will prevent bacteria from getting inside the test tubes.
   C Bacteria need nutrients in order to grow.
   D The more chemical X added, the less bacteria will grow.

2. About how much more liquid does Test tube 4 contain than Test tube 1?
   F 10 mL   G 15 mL   H 20 mL   J 25 mL

3. In a properly designed experiment, a control is set up exactly like the other setups except that the control does not contain the variable. According to this definition, which is the control in this experiment?
   A Test tube 1   C Test tube 3
   B Test tube 2   D Test tube 4

Using Vocabulary

1. saprophyte
2. vaccine
3. pathogen
4. aerobe
5. fission
6. Nitrogen-fixing bacteria
7. anaerobe

Checking Concepts

8. D
9. A
10. D
11. A
12. A
13. B
14. C
15. D
16. B
17. C

Thinking Critically

18. Nitrogen would no longer be available in a form that plants could use; therefore, the plants would die unless fertilizer was added.

19. Bacteria can reproduce quickly, have means of moving, and can form endospores to survive extreme conditions. They can also exchange DNA, providing the population with variations that may be helpful.

Using Vocabulary

aerobe p. 188	nitrogen-fixing
anaerobe p. 188	bacteria p. 194
antibiotic p. 193	pathogen p. 197
endospore p. 197	saprophyte p. 194
fission p. 188	toxin p. 197
flagella p. 187	vaccine p. 199

Fill in the blanks with the correct word or words.

1. A(n) _____ uses dead organisms as a food source.
2. A(n) _____ can prevent some bacterial diseases.
3. A(n) _____ causes disease.
4. A bacterium that needs oxygen to carry out respiration is a(n) _____.
5. Bacteria reproduce using _____.
6. _____ are bacteria that convert nitrogen in the air to a form used by plants.
7. A(n) _____ can live without oxygen.

Checking Concepts

Choose the word or phrase that best answers the question.

8. What is a way of cleaning up an ecosystem using bacteria to break down harmful compounds?
 A) landfill **C)** toxic waste dumps
 B) waste storage **D)** bioremediation

9. What pigment do cyanobacteria need to make food?
 A) chlorophyll **C)** plasmids
 B) chromosomes **D)** ribosomes

10. Which of the following terms describes most bacteria?
 A) anaerobic **C)** many-celled
 B) pathogens **D)** beneficial

11. What is the name for rod-shaped bacteria?
 A) bacilli **C)** spirilla
 B) cocci **D)** colonies

12. What structure allows bacteria to stick to surfaces?
 A) capsule **C)** chromosome
 B) flagella **D)** cell wall

13. What organisms can grow as blooms in ponds?
 A) archaebacteria **C)** cocci
 B) cyanobacteria **D)** viruses

14. Which of these organisms are recyclers in the environment?
 A) producers **C)** saprophytes
 B) flagella **D)** pathogens

15. Which of the following is caused by a pathogenic bacterium?
 A) an antibiotic **C)** nitrogen fixation
 B) cheese **D)** strep throat

Use the photo below to answer questions 16 and 17.

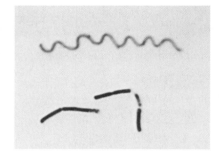

16. What shape are the gram-positive bacteria in the above photograph?
 A) coccus **C)** spirillum
 B) bacillus **D)** ovoid

17. What shape are the gram-negative bacteria in the above photograph?
 A) coccus **C)** spirillum
 B) bacillus **D)** ovoid

 life.msscience.com/vocabulary_puzzlemaker

Use the ExamView® Pro Testmaker CD-ROM to:
- create multiple versions of tests
- create modified tests with one mouse click for inclusion students
- edit existing questions and add your own questions
- build tests aligned with state standards using built-in State Curriculum Tags
- change English tests to Spanish with one mouse click and vice versa

Thinking Critically

18. Infer what would happen if nitrogen-fixing bacteria could no longer live on the roots of some plants.

19. Explain why bacteria are capable of surviving in almost all environments of the world.

20. Draw a conclusion as to why farmers often rotate crops such as beans, peas, and peanuts with other crops such as corn, wheat, and cotton.

21. Describe One organism that causes bacterial pneumonia is called pneumococcus. What is its shape?

22. List the precautions that can be taken to prevent food poisoning.

23. Concept Map Copy and complete the following events-chain concept map about the events surrounding a cyanobacteria bloom.

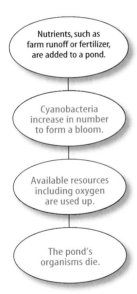

Nutrients, such as farm runoff or fertilizer, are added to a pond.

Cyanobacteria increase in number to form a bloom.

Available resources including oxygen are used up.

The pond's organisms die.

24. Design an experiment to decide if a kind of bacteria could grow anaerobically.

25. Describe the nitrogen-fixing process in your own words, using numbered steps. You will probably have more than four steps.

26. Infer the shape of pneumococcus bacteria.

Performance Activities

27. Poster Create a poster that illustrates the effects of bacteria. Use photos from magazines and your own drawings.

28. Poem Write a poem that demonstrates your knowledge of the importance of bacteria to human health.

Applying Math

Use the table below to answer questions 29 and 30.

Bacterial Reproduction Rates	
Temperature (°C)	Doubling Rate Per Hour
20.5	2.0
30.5	3.0
36.0	2.5
39.2	1.2

29. Doubling Rate Graph the data from the table above. Using the graph, determine where the doubling rate would be at 20°C. Where would the doubling rate be at 40°C?

30. Bacterial Reproduction Bacteria can reproduce rapidly. At 30.5°C, some species of bacteria can double their numbers in 3.0 hours. A biologist places a single bacterium on growth medium at 6:00 A.M. and incubates the bacteria until 4:00 P.M. the same afternoon. How many bacterium will there be?

Thinking Critically

20. Crops like beans, peas, and peanuts have nitrogen-fixing bacteria. These crops help to increase soil fertility.

21. spheres

22. using fresh foods, and cooking, serving, and storing them at safe temperatures, and washing hands, utensils and surfaces

23. See student page.

24. Place the organism in an environment without oxygen and measure its growth rate.

25. (1) Root hairs curl before infection by nitrogen-fixing bacteria. (2) Bacteria enter roots through an infection thread. (3) Pocketlike spaces within the root form and the cells begin to grow and divide. (4) Root nodules containing nitrogen-fixing bacteria form on the roots of legumes. (5) Atmospheric nitrogen is fixed and becomes available for other living things.

26. round because its name ends with "coccus"

Performance Activities

27. Posters should show beneficial and harmful effects of bacteria. Use **Performance Assessment in the Science Classroom,** p. 145.

28. Poems should demonstrate knowledge of the importance of bacteria to human health. Use **Performance Assessment in the Science Classroom,** p. 157.

Applying Math

National Math Standards
5, 6, 9

29. Graph should increase until a peak is reached, then decrease. Doubling rate will be almost 2.0 at 20°C.

30. eight bacteria

Assessment Resources

📁 **Reproducible Masters**
Chapter *Fast File* Resources
  Chapter Review, pp. 31–32
  Chapter Tests, pp. 33–36
  Assessment Transparency Activity, p. 43
Glencoe Science Web site
  Chapter Review Test
  Standardized Test Practice

Glencoe Technology
  Assessment Transparency
  ExamView® Pro Testmaker
  MindJogger Videoquiz
  Interactive Chalkboard

Answer Sheet A practice answer sheet can be found at life.msscience.com/answer_sheet.

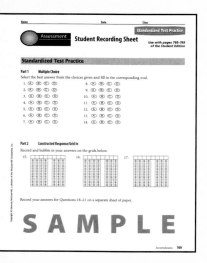

Part 1 Multiple Choice

1. C   6. D
2. B   7. B
3. A   8. A
4. C   9. C
5. A

Part 2 Short Response

10. Eubacteria are named according to cell shape and structure, how food is obtained, the wastes produced, the method of movement, and whether it's an aerobe or anaerobe.

11. An antiseptic is a substance that slows the growth of bacteria. Often a substance that is toxic to bacteria may also be toxic to human cells, so it could be dangerous to humans. Even if the substance isn't toxic to human cells, killing all bacteria could interfere with digestion.

Part 1 Multiple Choice

Record your answers on the answer sheet provided by your teacher or on a sheet of paper.

1. Most pathogenic bacteria are consumer eubacteria and are grouped according to what characteristic?
   - A. chlorophyll
   - B. ribosomes
   - C. cell wall
   - D. plasmids

2. Which of the following cannot be found in a bacterial cell?
   - A. ribosomes
   - B. nucleus
   - C. chromosome
   - D. cytoplasm

Use the photo below to answer questions 3 and 4.

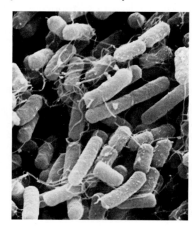

3. What shape are the bacterial cells shown above?
   - A. bacillus
   - B. coccus
   - C. spirillum
   - D. tubular

4. These bacteria are methane producers. Which of the following statements is true of these bacteria?
   - A. They are aerobic.
   - B. They are in Kingdom Eubacteria.
   - C. They are used in sewage treatment.
   - D. They live only near deep ocean vents.

5. Which of the following foods is not processed with the help of bacteria?
   - A. beef
   - B. cheese
   - C. yogurt
   - D. pickles

Use the photo below to answer questions 6 and 7.

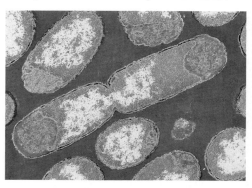

6. What process is occurring in the above photograph?
   - A. mitosis
   - B. fission
   - C. fusion
   - D. conjugation

7. The above is an example of what kind of reproduction?
   - A. sexual
   - B. asexual
   - C. meitotic
   - D. symbiotic

8. What characteristic probably was used in naming cyanobacteria?
   - A. pigments
   - B. slime layer
   - C. cell shape
   - D. cell wall

9. Each bacterium has
   - A. a nucleus.
   - B. mitochondria.
   - C. ribosomes.
   - D. a capsule.

Test-Taking Tip

Listen and Read Listen carefully to the instructions from the teacher and read the directions and each question carefully.

12. Nitrogen-fixing bacteria absorb nitrogen gas (N_2) from the air and convert the nitrogen to ammonium ion (NH_4^+), which plants can use.

13. The plant benefits by receiving nitrogen in a form it can utilize and the bacteria benefit by receiving food (sugars) and nutrients.

14. Bacteria and other decomposers break down dead plant material. This improves the quality of the soil because nutrients are released into the soil and are available for the next crop.

15. Bioremediation is the process of using living organisms to clean up environmental pollutants. Bacteria can be utilized for this process. Some types of bacteria can break down many organic chemicals, including petroleum products. The products of these processes either are harmless compounds or are easier to remove than the original pollutant.

16. Pasteurization is a process where food is heated to a temperature that kills most harmful bacteria but doesn't change the taste of the food. Sterilization heats food to higher temperatures to kill all bacteria present, but this often changes the taste of the food.

Part 2 | Short Response/Grid In

Record your answers on the answer sheet provided by your teacher or on a sheet of paper.

10. What characteristics can be used in naming eubacteria?

11. What does an antiseptic do? Why would an antiseptic be dangerous to humans if it killed all bacteria?

Use the photo below to answer questions 12 and 13.

12. The figure above shows plant roots that have nodules, which contain nitrogen-fixing bacteria. How does this benefit the plant?

13. This symbiotic relationship is mutualistic. Explain how bacteria benefit from this relationship.

14. What happens to dead plant material that is plowed into the soil following a crop harvest? Why is this plowing beneficial to the quality of the soil?

15. What is bioremediation? Give an example of how it is used.

16. Most of the dairy products that you buy are pasteurized. What is pasteurization? How is it different from sterilization?

Part 3 | Open Ended

Record your answers on a sheet of paper.

17. An antibiotic is prescribed to a patient to take for 10 days. After two days the patient feels better and stops taking the antibiotic. Several days later, the infection returns, but this time a greater amount of antibiotic was needed to cure the infection. Why? How could the patient have avoided the recurrence of the infection?

Use the photo below to answer questions 18 and 19.

18. Describe how aerobic bacteria in the wastewater treatment tank shown above clean the water. Where does the energy that was in the waste go?

19. Aerobic bacteria removed from the tanks, along with some solid waste, form sludge. After the sludge is dried, detoxified, and sterilized, it is either burned or applied to soil. What would be the benefit of applying it to soil? Why is it important to detoxify and sterilize the sludge first?

20. What causes a bloom of cyanobacteria? Explain how it can cause fish and other organisms in a pond to die.

that it contains organic molecules and nutrients that enrich the soil for growing plants. It is important to detoxify and sterilize the sludge before burning or applying it to soils, so that toxic substances are not released into the air, soil, or water, and infectious bacteria aren't released into the soil or water.

20. When a bloom of cyanobacteria develops in a pond, it quickly uses up available resources and the cyanobacteria die. The dead cyanobacteria no longer produce oxygen but are consumed by other aerobic bacteria that use up the available oxygen. The low oxygen level can kill fish and other organisms in the pond that depend on oxygen.

Rubrics

For more help evaluating openended assessment questions, see the rubric on p. 10T.

Part 3 | Open Ended

17. Even though the patient felt better, the bacterial infection wasn't completely gone. The bacteria that had some resistance to the antibiotic survived and multiplied. When the infection returned, many of the bacteria had greater resistance to the antibiotic, so it took a higher dose to kill the bacteria. The

patient could have avoided this problem by taking the antibiotic for the entire 10 days and stopping the initial infection completely.

18. The aerobic bacteria use oxygen to break down organic molecules (waste) in the water. The bacteria produce carbon dioxide and get energy from this process, so they

grow and divide. Some of the energy in the waste goes to the bacteria, some is in the carbon dioxide released and some is released as heat.

19. One benefit of burning the sludge is that it can be a source of energy for generating electricity. The benefit of applying sludge to soil is

Section/Objectives	Standards		Labs/Features
Chapter Opener	**National**	**State/Local**	**Launch Lab:** Dissect a Mushroom, p. 209
	See pp. 16T–17T for a Key to Standards.		**Foldables,** p. 209
Section 1 Protists ⏱ 3 sessions 📦 1.5 blocks 1. **Describe** the characteristics shared by all protist. 2. **Compare and contrast** the three groups of protists. 3. **List** examples of each of the three protist groups. 4. **Explain** why protists are so difficult to classify.	National Content Standards: UCP.1–UCP.5, A.1, A.2, C.1– C.5		**Science Online,** p. 214 **Integrate Health,** p. 217 **MiniLAB:** Observing Slime Molds, p. 218 **Applying Science:** Is it a fungus or a protist?, p. 219 **Lab:** Comparing Algae and Protozoans, p. 221
Section 2 Fungi ⏱ 4 sessions 📦 2 blocks 5. **Identify** the characteristics shared by all fungi. 6. **Classify** fungi into groups based on their methods of reproduction. 7. **Differentiate** between the imperfect fungi and all other fungi.	National Content Standards: UCP.1–UCP.3, UCP.5, A.1, A.2, F.1		**Science Online,** p. 223 **MiniLAB:** Interpreting Spore Prints, p. 225 **Visualizing Lichens as Air Quality Indicators,** p. 227 **Integrate Career,** p. 228 **Lab:** Creating a Fungus Field Guide, p. 230 **Science and Society:** Chocolate SOS, p. 232

Glencoe Exclusive!
Teacher Works™
All-In-One Planner and Resource Center

Lab Materials	Reproducible Resources	Section Assessment	Technology
Launch Lab: mushroom, hand lens	**Chapter FAST FILE Resources** Foldables Worksheet, p. 15 Directed Reading Overview, p. 17 Note-taking Worksheets, pp. 29–30	GLENCOE'S ASSESSMENT ADVANTAGE	TeacherWorks includes: • Interactive Teacher Edition • Lesson Planner with calendar • Access to all program blacklines • Correlations to standards • Web links
MiniLAB: live specimen of *Physarum polycephaalum,* hand lens **Lab:** cultures of *Paramecium, Amoeba, Euglena,* and *Spirogyra;* prepared slide of slime mold, microscope slides (4), coverslips (4), microscope, dropper	**Chapter FAST FILE Resources** Transparency Activity, p. 40 MiniLAB, p. 3 Enrichment, p. 27 Reinforcement, p. 25 Directed Reading, p. 18 Transparency Activity, pp. 43–44 Lab Worksheet, pp. 5–6 **Cultural Diversity,** p. 3 **Science Inquiry Labs,** pp. 11–12	Portfolio Science Journal, p. 212 Integrate Health, p. 217 Performance MiniLAB, p. 218 Applying Science, p. 219 Applying Skills, p. 220 Content Section Review, p. 220	Section Focus Transparency Teaching Transparency Guided Reading Audio Program Interactive Chalkboard CD-ROM
MiniLAB: several grocery-store mushrooms, unlined white paper **Lab:** Collection jars, hand lens, microscope, microscope slides and coverslips, field guide to fungi or club fungi, art supplies *Need materials?* Contact Science Kit at 1-800-828-7777 or www.sciencekit.com on the Internet.	**Chapter FAST FILE Resources** Transparency Activity, p. 41 MiniLAB, p. 4 Enrichment, p. 28 Reinforcement, p. 26 Directed Reading, pp. 19, 20 Lab Activities, pp. 9–10, 11–13 Lab Worksheet, pp. 7–8 **Mathematics Skill Activities,** p. 5 **Reading and Writing Skill Activities,** p. 37 **Lab Management and Safety,** p. 58	Portfolio Make a Model, p. 224 Performance MiniLAB, p. 225 Integrate Career, p. 228 Applying Math, p. 229 Content Section Review, p. 229	Section Focus Transparency Virtual Labs CD-ROM Guided Reading Audio Program Interactive Chalkboard CD-ROM

End of Chapter Assessment

GLENCOE'S ASSESSMENT ADVANTAGE

Blackline Masters	Technology	Professional Series
Chapter FAST FILE Resources Chapter Review, pp. 33–34 Chapter Tests, pp. 35–38 **Standardized Test Practice,** pp. 35–38	MindJogger Videoquiz Virtual Labs CD-ROM Exam*View*® Pro Testmaker TeacherWorks CD-ROM Interactive Chalkboard CD-ROM	**Performance Assessment in the Science Classroom (PASC)**

chapter 8 Protists and Fungi

Transparencies

Section Focus

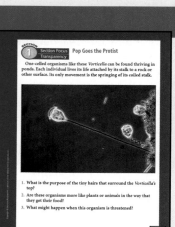

SECTION 1 Section Focus Transparency Pop Goes the Protist

One-celled organisms like these *Vorticella* can be found thriving in ponds. Each individual lives its life attached by its stalk to a rock or other surface. Its only movement is the springing of its coiled stalk.

1. What is the purpose of the tiny hairs that surround the *Vorticella's* top?
2. Are these organisms more like plants or animals in the way that they get their food?
3. What might happen when this organism is threatened?

L2

SECTION 2 Section Focus Transparency Dig It

Care for a truffle? Highly prized in Europe as a delicacy, truffles are a rare, fragrant, and flavorful variety of fungi. Because they can grow as much as 30 centimeters underground, people have trained pigs and dogs to hunt them by scent. The rarest truffles can be worth $3,000 per kilogram!

1. Do you think that truffles are classified as plants? Explain.
2. What other organisms resemble truffles?

L2

This is a representation of key blackline masters available in the Teacher Classroom Resources. See Resource Manager boxes within the chapter for additional information.

Key to Teaching Strategies

The following designations will help you decide which activities are appropriate for your students.

L1 Level 1 activities should be appropriate for students with learning difficulties.

L2 Level 2 activities should be within the ability range of all students.

L3 Level 3 activities are designed for above-average students.

ELL ELL activities should be within the ability range of English-Language Learners.

COOP LEARN Cooperative Learning activities are designed for small group work.

LS Multiple Learning Styles logos, as described on page 12T, are used throughout to indicate strategies that address different learning styles.

P These strategies represent student products that can be placed into a best-work portfolio.

PBL Problem-Based Learning activities apply real-world situations to learning.

Assessment

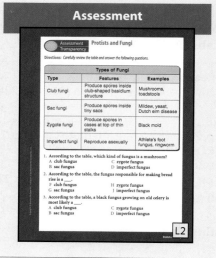

Assessment Transparency Protists and Fungi

Directions: *Carefully review the table and answer the following questions.*

Types of Fungi

Type	Features	Examples
Club fungi	Produce spores inside club-shaped basidium structure	Mushrooms, toadstools
Sac fungi	Produce spores inside tiny sacs	Mildew, yeast, Dutch elm disease
Zygote fungi	Produce spores in cases at top of thin stalks	Black mold
Imperfect fungi	Reproduce asexually	Athlete's foot fungus, ringworm

1. According to the table, which kind of fungus is a mushroom?
   A club fungus   C zygote fungus
   B sac fungus   D imperfect fungus
2. According to the table, the fungus responsible for making bread rise is a ___.
   F club fungus   H zygote fungus
   G sac fungus   J imperfect fungus
3. According to the table, a black fungus growing on old celery is most likely a ___.
   A club fungus   C zygote fungus
   B sac fungus   D imperfect fungus

L2

Teaching

SECTION 1 Teaching Transparency Protist Kingdom/Amoeba

Slime mold   Amoeba   Euglena   Dinoflagellate   Paramecium   Diatom   Macroalga

Food vacuole
Cytoplasm
Pseudopod
Nucleus
Cell membrane

L2

Hands-on Activities

Student Text Lab Worksheet

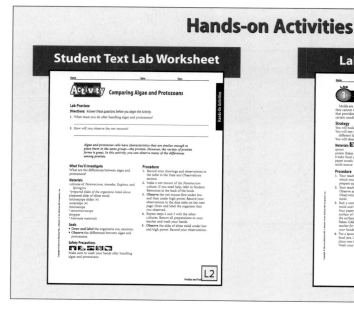

Activity Comparing Algae and Protozoans

L2

Laboratory Activities

LAB 1 Laboratory Activity Molds

L2

Meeting Different Ability Levels

Content Outline

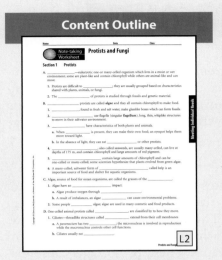

L2

Reinforcement

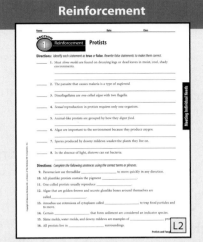

L2

Enrichment

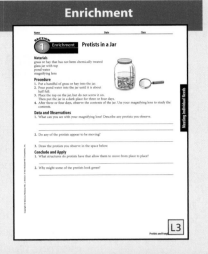

L3

Directed Reading (English/Spanish)

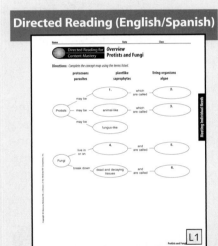

L1

Study Guide

Study Guide

Features
- Contains a study guide page for each section of the chapter
- Reviews key concepts
- Includes answer pages

L2

Reading Essentials

Reading Essentials for Glencoe Science
An Interactive Student Workbook

Features
- Condensed core content
- Actively involves students in reading
- Reinforces key vocabulary

L1

Assessment

Test Practice Workbook

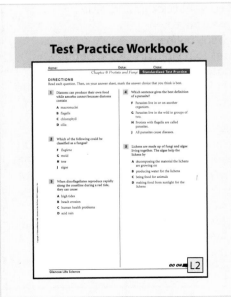

L2

Chapter Review

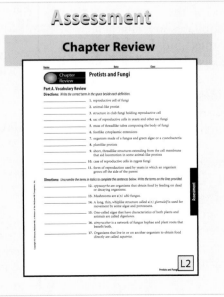

L2

Chapter Tests

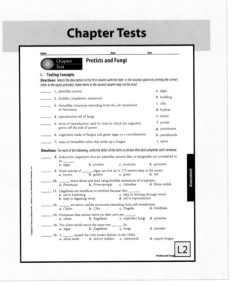

L2

Science Content Background

section 1

Protists

Evolution of Protists

Convenience is the primary reason for grouping all eukaryotes that are not animals, plants, or fungi into a single kingdom. Because the phyla of Kingdom Protista appear to have evolved independently from one another, protists pose several problems for taxonomists. One of the major theories of evolution explains how eukaryotic cells evolved. According to this theory, chloroplasts evolved from a cyanobacterium taken up by an ancestor. Mitochondria and other organelles are thought to have evolved from aerobic heterotrophic prokaryotes. In these cases, the prokaryotes evolved into the organelles through symbiotic relationships in which the smaller prokaryotes lived inside larger prokaryotes. These symbiotic relationships are somewhat similar to the symbiotic relationships that exist between humans and the anaerobic protists living in the human digestive tract.

Plantlike Protists

The chloroplasts of diatoms in the phylum Bacillariophyta most resemble those of the brown algae and dinoflagellates. Diatoms store their food reserves as a type of oil. This oil provides buoyancy to the diatoms, keeping them near the surface of the water, and thus near sunlight. Dinoflagellates are characterized by unique chromosomes and by an unusual form of mitosis that takes place within a nucleus whose nuclear membrane does not degenerate. Dinoflagellates are widespread as symbionts of corals. In this relationship, the dinoflagellates are responsible for much of the productivity of coral reefs.

The extreme diversity of the green algae in the phylum Chlorophyta is reflected by their abundance in marine, freshwater, and damp terrestrial environments, such as on tree trunks and in soil. Red algae lack centrioles and flagellated cells. For this reason, most taxonomists hypothesize that these organisms descended from the most ancient eukaryotes. Red algae have complex life cycles that involve alternation of generations. Brown algae also have alternating generations, with small gametophytes and large sporophytes.

Animal-like Protists

Most flagellates are nonparasitic. But some of the parasitic flagellates can be quite harmful to humans. These harmful parasites include *Trypanosoma*, which live in the bloodstreams of many vertebrates. These protozoans cause diseases such as sleeping sickness. They protect themselves from attack by the host's immune system by changing the molecular structure of their coats frequently.

Funguslike Protists

Phylum Myxomycota contains plasmodial slime molds. These slime molds form round spore-containing capsules under unfavorable environmental conditions such as starvation. These capsules then release spores that may undergo meiosis.

chapter content resources

Internet Resources

For additional content background, visit **life.msscience.com** to:

- access your book online
- find references to related articles in popular science magazines
- access Web links with related content background
- access current events with science journal topics

Print Resources

Free-Living Freshwater Protozoa: A Color Guide, by D.J. Patterson, ASM Press and Manson Publishing, 1996

Microbes: An Invisible Universe, by Howard Gest, ASM Press, 2003

Mr. Bloomfield's Orchard: The Mysterious World of Mushrooms, by Nicholas P. Money, Oxford University Press, 2002

Protists and Fungi, by Gareth Stevens Publishing, Gareth Stevens Publishing, 2003

Fungi

Club Fungi

Basidiomycota includes about 25,000 species of mushrooms, puffballs, shelf fungi, and rusts. Some species of this phylum form mycorrhizae. Others are plant parasites that cause considerable damage each year. Basidiomycotes are named for club-shaped structures that form the sexual spores.

Sac Fungi

Ascomycota is the largest group of fungi accounting for 75 percent of all described fungi. These fungi are named for the sac in which their sexual spores are produced. Yeast are sac fungi that are important in baking and brewing.

Zygote Fungi

Phylum Zygomycota is made up of about 600 species of fungi, including mycorrhizae, an important group that forms mutually beneficial relationships with the roots of most species of plants. Sexual reproduction in this group occurs when appropriate mating strains grow together and produce resistant spores called zoosporangia.

Imperfect Fungi

Fungal species with no known or observed method of sexual reproduction are classified in the phylum Deuteromycota. Some members of this phylum are responsible for producing the colors and flavors of several types of cheese.

Teacher to Teacher

Jeff Remington
Palmyra Middle School
Palmyra, Pennsylvania

"I call this activity *Microbes in Your World*. I have my students bring in any product that might be influenced by a microbe, or used to combat microbes. For example, antibacterial soap, antiseptic mouthwash, adhesive bandages, blue cheese, canned food items, yogurt, etc. As students share about the relationship of their product to microbes, an interesting class discussion opens up, including an awareness of the huge economic impact of microbes."

Jeff Remington

Antman/The Image Works

Chapter Vocabulary

protist, p. 210
algae, p. 211
flagellum, p. 212
protozoan, p. 215
cilia, p. 215
pseudopod, p. 216
hyphae, p. 222
saprophyte, p. 222
spore, p. 223
basidium, p. 224
ascus, p. 224
budding, p. 224
sporangium, p. 225
lichen, p. 226
mycorrhizae, p. 226

Science Journal Student responses will vary. They may include: edible mushrooms, cheese manufacturing (for example, bleu cheese), olive oil industry, and pesticides.

PowerPoint® Presentations

This CD-ROM is an editable Microsoft® PowerPoint® presentation that includes:
- a pre-made presentation for every chapter
- interactive graphics
- animations
- audio clips
- image bank
- all new section and chapter questions
- Standardized Test Practice
- transparencies
- pre-lab questions for all labs
- Foldables directions
- links to life.msscience.com

Protists and Fungi

chapter preview

sections

1 Protists
Lab Comparing Algae and Protozoans

2 Fungi
Lab Creating a Fungus Field Guide

Virtual Lab How can microscopic protists and fungi be characterized?

Fungi—Terrestrial Icebergs

A mushroom is like the tip of an iceberg; a small, visible portion of an extensive fungal network that grows under the soil. Many fungi and plant roots interact. These fungi help provide water and nutrients to these plants in exchange for carbohydrates that plants produce.

Science Journal What other ways might fungi benefit other organisms and the environment?

Theme Connection

Systems and Interactions Changes over time and ecological relationships of protists and fungi are discussed.

About the Photo

Fungi—Terrestrial Icebergs More than eight percent of terrestrial plant species' roots form associations with fungal hyphae in the soil called mycorrhizae. These symbiotic relationships enable the plants and the fungi to flourish. The network of hyphae in the soil collects water and nutrients and supply them to the plant roots with which they're associated. In return, the plants provide sugars for the fungi.

Start-Up Activities

Dissect a Mushroom

It is hard to tell by a mushroom's appearance whether it is safe to eat or is poisonous. Some edible mushrooms are so highly prized that people keep their location a secret for fear that others will find their treasure. Do the lab below to learn about the parts of mushrooms.

1. Obtain a mushroom from your teacher.
2. Using a magnifying lens, observe the underside of the mushroom cap. Then carefully pull off the cap and observe the gills, which are the thin, tissuelike structures. Hundreds of thousands of tiny reproductive structures called spores form on these gills.
3. Use your fingers or forceps to pull the stalk apart lengthwise. Continue this process until the pieces are as small as you can get them.
4. **Think Critically** In your Science Journal, write a description of the parts of the mushroom, and make a labeled drawing of the mushroom and its parts.

 Compare Protists and Fungi
Make the following Foldable to help you see how protists and fungi are similar and different.

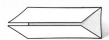 **Fold** the top of a vertical piece of paper down and the bottom up to divide the paper into thirds.

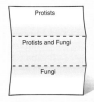 **Unfold and label** the three sections as shown.

Read for Main Ideas As you read the chapter, write information about each type of organism in the appropriate section, and information that they share in the middle section.

Preview this chapter's content and activities at life.mssience.com

---

1 Motivate

Bellringer

Section Focus Transparencies also are available on the Interactive Chalkboard CD-ROM.

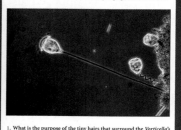

Pop Goes the Protist

One-celled organisms like these *Vorticella* can be found thriving in ponds. Each individual lives its life attached by its stalk to a rock or other surface. Its only movement is the springing of its coiled stalk.

1. What is the purpose of the tiny hairs that surround the *Vorticella's* top?
2. Are these organisms more like plants or animals in the way that they get their food?
3. What might happen when this organism is threatened?

Tie to Prior Knowledge

Classification Review classification with students. Explain that protists have some characteristics of animals, plants, and fungi.

Caption Answer

Figure 1 All are eukaryotic and appear to be able to move. They might live in a moist or wet environment.

---

section 1 Protists

as you read

What You'll Learn

- **Describe** the characteristics shared by all protists.
- **Compare and contrast** the three groups of protists.
- **List** examples of each of the three protist groups.
- **Explain** why protists are so difficult to classify.

Why It's Important

Many protists are important food sources for other organisms.

Review Vocabulary

asexual reproduction: requires only one parent to produce a new genetically identical individual

New Vocabulary

- protist
- algae
- flagellum
- protozoan
- cilia
- pseudopod

What is a protist?

Look at the organisms in **Figure 1.** As different as they appear, all of these organisms belong to one kingdom—the protist kingdom. A **protist** is a one- or many-celled organism that lives in moist or wet surroundings. All protists have eukaryotic cells—cells that have a nucleus and other internal, membrane-bound structures. Some protists are plantlike. They contain chlorophyll and make their own food. Other protists are animal-like. They do not have chlorophyll and can move. Some protists have a solid or a shell-like structure on the outside of their bodies.

Protist Reproduction Protists usually reproduce asexually by cell division. During cell division, the hereditary material in the nucleus is duplicated, the nucleus divides, and then the cytoplasm usually divides. The result is two new cells that are genetically identical. Asexual reproduction of many-celled protists occurs by regeneration. Parts of the organism can break off and grow into entirely new organisms that are genetically identical.

Most protists also can reproduce sexually. During sexual reproduction, the process of meiosis produces sex cells. Two sex cells join to form a new organism that is genetically different from the two organisms that were the sources of the sex cells. How and when sexual reproduction occurs depends on the specific type of protist.

Figure 1 The protist kingdom is made up of a variety of organisms. **Describe** *the characteristics that the organisms below have in common.*

| Slime mold | Amoeba | Euglena | Dinoflagellate | Paramecium | Diatom | Macroalga |

210 CHAPTER 8 Protists and Fungi

Section 1 Resource Manager

Chapter *Fast File* Resources

Transparency Activity, pp. 40, 43–44

Directed Reading for Content Mastery, pp. 17, 18

Note-taking Worksheets, pp. 29–30

Enrichment, p. 27

MiniLAB, p. 3

Lab Worksheet, pp. 5–6

Cultural Diversity, p. 3

Life Science Critical Thinking/Problem Solving, p. 1

Performance Assessment in the Science Classroom, p. 59

Classification of Protists

Not all scientists agree about how to classify the organisms in this group. Protists usually are divided into three groups—plantlike, animal-like, and funguslike—based on whether they share certain characteristics with plants, animals, or fungi. **Table 1** shows some of these characteristics. As you read this section, you will understand some of the problems of grouping protists in this way.

Evolution of Protists Although protists that produce a hard outer covering have left many fossils, other protists lack hard parts, so few fossils of these organisms have been found. But, by studying the genetic material and structure of modern protists, scientists are beginning to understand how they are related to each other and to other organisms. Scientists hypothesize that the common ancestor of most protists was a one-celled organism with a nucleus and other cellular structures. However, evidence suggests that protists with the ability to make their own food could have had a different ancestor than protists that cannot make their own food.

Plantlike Protists

Protists in this group are called plantlike because, like plants, they contain the pigment chlorophyll in chloroplasts and can make their own food. Many of them have cell walls like plants, and some have structures that hold them in place just as the roots of a plant do, but these protists do not have roots.

Plantlike protists are known as **algae** (AL jee) (singular, *alga*). As shown in **Figure 2,** some are one cell and others have many cells. Even though all algae have chlorophyll, not all of them look green. Many have other pigments that cover up their chlorophyll.

Table 1 Characteristics of Protist Groups

Plantlike	Animal-Like	Funguslike
Contain chlorophyll and make their own food using photosynthesis	Cannot make their own food; capture other organisms for food	Cannot make their own food; absorb food from their surroundings
Have cell walls	Do not have cell walls	Some organisms have cell walls; others do not
No specialized ways to move from place to place	Have specialized ways to move from place to place	Have specialized ways to move from place to place

Color-enhanced SEM
Magnification: 3100×

Figure 2 Algae exist in many shapes and sizes. Microscopic algae (left photo) are found in freshwater and salt water. You can see some types of green algae growing on rocks, washed up on the beach, or floating in the water.

2 Teach

Discussion

Characteristics Use information presented in **Table 1** to lead a discussion of the characteristics of the groups of protists. Allow students to compare and contrast the groups using these characteristics.

Activity

Pond Water Have students bring in pond water. Allow students to observe wet-mount slides of the water. They should observe a variety of algae. Use a dichotomous key to identify the algae. L2 ELL IS **Visual-Spatial**

Make a Model

Algae After students have looked at various algae under the microscope, have them make models to show what they look like. Materials for models might include clay, polystyrene, or plaster of paris. L2 ELL IS **Kinesthetic**

Figure 3 The cell walls of diatoms contain silica, the main element in glass. The body of a diatom is like a small box with a lid. The pattern of dots, pits, and lines on the cell wall's surface is different for each species of diatom.

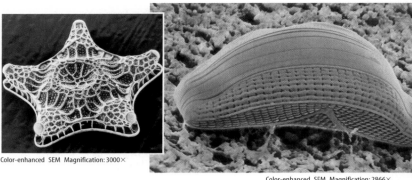

Color-enhanced SEM Magnification: 3000× — Color-enhanced SEM Magnification: 2866×

Diatoms Extremely large populations of diatoms exist. Diatoms, shown in **Figure 3,** are found in freshwater and salt water. They have a golden-brown pigment that covers up the green chlorophyll. Diatoms secrete glasslike boxes around themselves. When the organisms die, these boxes sink. Over thousands of years, they can collect and form deep layers.

Dinoflagellates Another group of algae is called the dinoflagellates, which means "spinning flagellates." Dinoflagellates, as shown in **Figure 4,** have two flagella. A **flagellum** (plural, *flagella*) is a long, thin, whiplike structure used for movement. One flagellum circles the cell like a belt, and another is attached to one end like a tail. As the two flagella move, they cause the cell to spin. Because many of the species in this group produce a chemical that causes them to glow at night, they are known as fire algae. Almost all dinoflagellates live in salt water. While most contain chlorophyll, some do not and must feed on other organisms.

Figure 4 Most dinoflagellates live in the sea. Some are free living and others are parasites. Still others, like the *Spiniferites* cyst (right photo), can produce toxins that make other organisms sick.
Determine *how euglenoids are similar to plants and animals.*

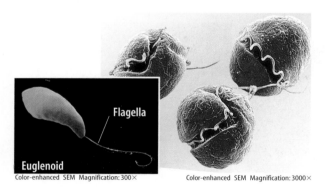

Flagella

Euglenoid
Color-enhanced SEM Magnification: 300× — Color-enhanced SEM Magnification: 3000×

Euglenoids Protists that have characteristics of both plants and animals are known as the euglenoids (yoo GLEE noydz). Many of these one-celled algae have chloroplasts, but some do not. Those with chloroplasts, like *Euglena* shown in **Figure 4,** can produce their own food. However, when light is not present, *Euglena* can feed on bacteria and other protists. Although *Euglena* has no cell wall, it does have a strong, flexible layer inside the cell membrane that helps it move and change shape. Many euglenoids move by whipping their flagella. An eyespot, an adaptation that is sensitive to light, helps photosynthetic euglenoids move toward light.

Red Algae Most red algae are many-celled and, along with the many-celled brown and green algae, sometimes are called seaweeds. Red algae contain chlorophyll, but they also produce large amounts of a red pigment. Some species of red algae can live up to 200 m deep in the ocean. They can absorb the limited amount of light at those depths to carry out the process of photosynthesis. **Figure 5** shows the depths at which different types of algae can live.

Green Algae There are more than 7,000 species of green algae in this diverse group of organisms. These algae, like the one shown in **Figure 6,** contain large amounts of chlorophyll. Green algae can be one-celled or many-celled. They are the most plant-like of all the algae. Because plants and green algae are similar in their structure, chlorophyll, and how they undergo photosynthesis, some scientists hypothesize that plants evolved from ancient, many-celled green algae. Although most green algae live in water, you can observe types that live in other moist environments, including on damp tree trunks and wet sidewalks.

Brown Algae As you might expect from their name, brown algae contain a brown pigment in addition to chlorophyll. They usually are found growing in cool, saltwater environments. Brown algae are many-celled and vary greatly in size. An important food source for many fish and invertebrates is a brown alga called kelp. Kelp, shown in **Figure 6,** forms a dense mat of stalks and leaflike blades where small fish and other animals live. Giant kelp is the largest organism in the protist kingdom and can grow to be 100 m in length.

> **Reading Check** What is kelp?

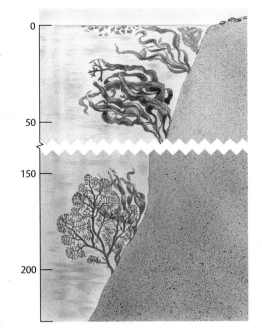

Figure 5 Green algae are found closer to the surface. Brown algae can grow from a depth of about 35 m. Red algae are found in the deepest water at 175 m to 200 m.

Figure 6 Green algae (left photo) often can be seen on the surface of ponds in the summer. Giant kelp, a brown alga, can form forests like this one located off the coast of California. Extracts from kelp add to the smoothness and spreadability of products such as cheese spreads and mayonnaise.

SECTION 1 Protists **213**

Science Online

Topic: Red Tides

Visit life.msscience.com for Web links to information about red tides and dinoflagellate blooms.

Activity Determine where red tides occur more frequently. Construct a map of the world and indicate where red tides have occurred in the last five years.

Figure 7 Carrageenan, a substance extracted from Irish moss, is used for thickening dairy products such as chocolate milk.

Importance of Algae

Have you thought about how important grasses are as a food source for animals that live on land? Cattle, deer, zebras, and many other animals depend on grasses as their main source of food. Algae sometimes are called the grasses of the oceans. Most animals that live in the oceans eat either algae for food or other animals that eat algae. You might think many-celled, large algae like kelp are the most important food source, but the one-celled diatoms and dinoflagellates are a more important food source for many organisms. Algae, such as *Euglena*, also are an important source of food for organisms that live in freshwater.

Algae and the Environment Algae are important in the environment because they produce oxygen as a result of photosynthesis. The oxygen produced by green algae is important for most organisms on Earth, including you.

Under certain conditions, algae can reproduce rapidly and develop into what is known as an algal bloom. Because of the large number of organisms in a bloom, the color of the water appears to change. Red tides that appear along the east and Gulf coasts of the United States are the result of dinoflagellate blooms. Toxins produced by the dinoflagellates can cause other organisms to die and can cause health problems in humans.

Algae and You People in many parts of the world eat some species of red and brown algae. You probably have eaten foods or used products made with algae. Carrageenan (kar uh JEE nuhn), a substance found in the cell walls of red algae, has gelatinlike properties that make it useful to the cosmetic and food industries. It is usually processed from the red alga Irish moss, shown in **Figure 7.** Carrageenan gives toothpastes, puddings, and salad dressings their smooth, creamy textures. Another substance, algin (AL juhn), found in the cell walls of brown algae, also has gelatinlike properties. It is used to thicken foods such as ice cream and marshmallows. Algin also is used in making rubber tires and hand lotion.

Ancient deposits of diatoms are mined and used in insulation, filters, and road paint. The cell walls of diatoms produce the sparkle that makes some road lines visible at night and the crunch you might feel in toothpaste.

✔ Reading Check What are some uses by humans of algae?

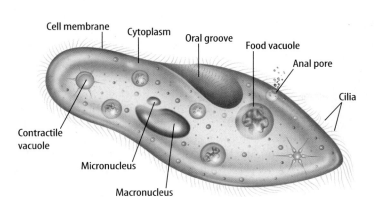

Cell membrane · Cytoplasm · Oral groove · Food vacuole · Anal pore · Cilia · Contractile vacuole · Micronucleus · Macronucleus

Figure 8 *Paramecium* is a typical ciliate found in many freshwater environments. These rapidly swimming protists consume bacteria.

Infer *Locate the vacuoles in the photo. What is their function?*

Animal-Like Protists

One-celled, animal-like protists are known as **protozoans.** Usually protozoans are classified by how they move. These complex organisms live in or on other living or dead organisms that are found in water or soil. Many protozoans have specialized vacuoles for digesting food and getting rid of excess water.

Ciliates As their name suggests, these protists have **cilia** (SIH lee uh)—short, threadlike structures that extend from the cell membrane. Ciliates can be covered with cilia or have cilia grouped in specific areas on the surface of the cell. The cilia beat in a coordinated way similar to rowboat oars. As a result, the organism moves swiftly in any direction. Organisms in this group include some of the most complex, one-celled protists and some of the largest, one-celled protists.

A typical ciliate is *Paramecium,* shown in **Figure 8.** *Paramecium* has two nuclei—a macronucleus and a micronucleus—another characteristic of the ciliates. The micronucleus is involved in reproduction. The macronucleus controls feeding, the exchange of oxygen and carbon dioxide, the amount of water and salts entering and leaving *Paramecium,* and other functions of *Paramecium.*

Ciliates usually feed on bacteria that are swept into the oral groove by the cilia. Once the food is inside the cell, a vacuole forms around it and the food is digested. Wastes are removed through the anal pore. Freshwater ciliates, like *Paramecium,* also have a structure called the contractile vacuole that helps get rid of excess water. When the contractile vacuole contracts, excess water is ejected from the cell.

SECTION 1 Protists **215**

Caption Answer
Figure 8 The contractile vacuoles are star-shaped. Their function is to eliminate excess water from the cell. Food vacuoles digest food.

Use Science Words
Word Meaning Have students determine the meanings of the prefix *pro-* and the suffix *-zoa* in the word *protozoan.* Ask them how these relate to the meaning of the word. *Pro-* comes from the Greek word, meaning "before," and *-zoa* comes from the Greek word for "animal." So, a protozoan is an organism that probably evolved before animals.

Use an Analogy
Cilia and Oars To help students visualize the beating of cilia, show them a photograph of a rowing crew. All members move together so that their oars are all in the same position at the same time. This propels the boat through the water as cilia propel a paramecium or other ciliate through its watery medium.

IDENTIFYING Misconceptions

Flagella and Cilia Function Point out that the use of the words *hairlike* and *threadlike* as they refer to flagella and cilia relate to how the organelles appear. They function more like oars or propellers.

Curriculum Connection

Math A paramecium may be about 0.1 cm long. Giant kelp may be 100 m long. How many times larger is giant kelp than a paramecium? 0.1 cm/paramecium × 1 m/100 cm × 1 giant kelp/100 m = 100,000 times larger L2 LS **Logical-Mathematical**

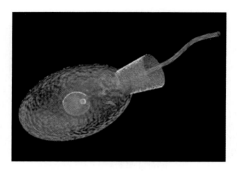

Figure 9 *Proterospongia* is a rare, freshwater protist. Some scientists hypothesize that this flagellate might share an ancestor with ancient animals.

Flagellates Protozoans called flagellates move through their watery environment by whipping their long flagella. Many species of flagellates live in freshwater, though some are parasites that harm their hosts.

Proterospongia, shown in **Figure 9,** is a member of one group of flagellates that might share an ancestor with ancient animals. These flagellates often grow in colonies of many cells that are similar in structure to cells found in animals called sponges. Like sponge cells, when *Proterospongia* cells are in colonies, they perform different functions. Moving the colony through the water or dividing, which increases the colony's size, are two examples of jobs that the cells of *Proterospongia* carry out.

Movement with Pseudopods Some protozoans move through their environments and feed using temporary extensions of their cytoplasm called **pseudopods** (SEW duh pahdz). The word *pseudopod* means "false foot." These organisms seem to flow along as they extend their pseudopods. They are found in freshwater and saltwater environments, and certain types are parasites in animals.

The amoeba shown in **Figure 10** is a typical member of this group. To obtain food, an amoeba extends the cytoplasm of a pseudopod on either side of a food particle such as a bacterium. Then the two parts of the pseudopod flow together and the particle is trapped. A vacuole forms around the trapped food. Digestion takes place inside the vacuole.

Although some protozoans of this group, like the amoeba, have no outer covering, others secrete hard shells around themselves. The white cliffs of Dover, England are composed mostly of the remains of some of these shelled protozoans. Some shelled protozoa have holes in their shells through which the pseudopods extend.

Figure 10 In many areas of the world, a disease-causing species of amoeba lives in the water. If it enters a human body, it can cause dysentery—a condition that can lead to a severe form of diarrhea.

Infer why an amoeba is classified as a protozoan.

LM Magnification: 85×

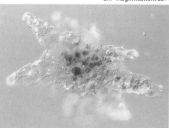

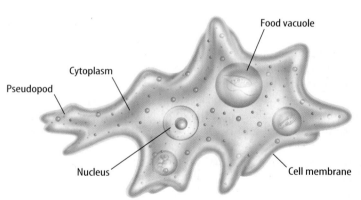

Food vacuole

Cytoplasm

Pseudopod

Nucleus

Cell membrane

LAB DEMONSTRATION

Purpose to observe how amoebas capture prey

Materials amoeba culture, small ciliates, projecting microscope, slide and coverslip, dropper

Preparation Have all necessary equipment set up before class starts. Pre-stained amoe-bas and ciliates may be helpful to obtain.

Procedure A drop of amoeba and a drop of prey per slide are sufficient. Observe under low power, then high power with the projecting microscope.

Expected Outcome Students should observe amoebas extending pseudopodia and cap-turing prey in food vacuoles.

Assessment

When is the organism captured? when the pseudopod completely envelopes it Is the prey still alive after capture? The prey lives for some time before digestive fluids kill it.

Name _____

Chapter 2 Section 1 Viruses

A. Virus–a nonliving strand of hereditary material surrounded by a
_____ coating

B. Virus multiplication–viruses can make copies of themselves only inside a living
_____ cell.

    1. _____ viruses–make the host cell produce new viruses,
which kills the host cell.

    2. _____ viruses–hide in the host cell without destroying it

        a. Virus hereditary material becomes part of the _____
cell's hereditary material.

        b. Latent viruses can become _____ and then destroy the
host cells.

C. Fighting viruses

    1.   Vaccines–damaged _____ which allow the host to
        fight some diseases

D. Research with viruses– One experimental method, called
_____, uses viruses to replace defective cell
hereditary material with normal cell hereditary material.

Figure 11 Asexual reproduction of the malaria parasite takes place inside a human host. Sexual reproduction takes place in the intestine of a mosquito.

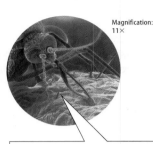

Magnification: 11×

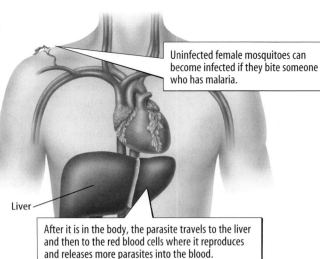

Uninfected female mosquitoes can become infected if they bite someone who has malaria.

Plasmodium lives in the salivary glands of certain female mosquitoes. The parasite can be transferred to a human's blood if an infected mosquito bites them.

Liver

After it is in the body, the parasite travels to the liver and then to the red blood cells where it reproduces and releases more parasites into the blood.

Other Protozoans One group of protozoans has no way of moving on their own. All of the organisms in this group are parasites of humans and other animals. These protozoans have complex life cycles that involve sexual and asexual reproduction. They often live part of their lives in one animal and part in another. The parasite that causes malaria is an example of a protozoan in this group. **Figure 11** shows the life cycle of the malaria parasite.

Importance of Protozoans

Like the algae, some protozoans are an important source of food for larger organisms. When some of the shelled protozoans die, they sink to the bottom of bodies of water and become part of the sediment. Sediment is a buildup of plant and animal remains and rock and mineral particles. The presence of these protists in sediments is used sometimes by field geologists as an indicator species. This tells them where petroleum reserves might be found beneath the surface of Earth.

Reading Check *Why are shelled protozoans important?*

One type of flagellated protozoan lives with bacteria in the digestive tract of termites. Termites feed mainly on wood. These protozoans and bacteria produce wood-digesting enzymes that help break down the wood. Without these organisms, the termites would be less able to use the chemical energy stored in wood.

INTEGRATE Health

African Sleeping Sickness The flagellate *Trypanosoma* is carried by the tsetse fly in Africa and causes African sleeping sickness in humans and other animals. It is transmitted to other organisms during bites from the fly. The disease affects the central nervous system. Research this disease and create a poster showing what you learn.

INTEGRATE Health

African Sleeping Sickness African sleeping sickness is prevalent in sub-Saharan Africa. Some regions are uninhabitable because of the risk of becoming infected. There are several varieties, caused by different species of protozoa, which differ slightly in their symptoms and severity. Early symptoms usually include fever and inflammation of the lymph nodes. More advanced symptoms may include a sensation of pain, severe headaches, mental dullness and apathy, tremors, paralysis, chorea, and profound sleepiness. These symptoms are often followed by coma and death, though in some cases the individual develops a tolerance and lives for many years as a carrier. Posters may relate the numbers of cases each year, the number of deaths, the vector, and locations of infestations. **P**

Research Some students may research possible cures.

Reading Check

Answer The presence of these organisms in sediment can indicate where petroleum may be found.

Curriculum Connection

Math Have students analyze the following story by making a graph. A person who contracted malaria had the following body temperatures (°C) at the given times. Day 1: 1:00 P.M., 39.4° (chills); 6:00 P.M., 38.3° (sweating); Day 2: 1:00 A.M., 36.1°; 6:00 A.M., 36.7°; 1:00 P.M., 36.1°; 6:00 P.M., 37.2°; Day 3: 1:00 A.M., 38.3° (chills); 6:00 A.M., 39.4°; 1:00 P.M., 39.4°; 6:00 P.M., 38.3° (sweating). When will the person have chills next? The person will have the chills next at 1:00 P.M. on Day 5. **L2 LS**

Logical-Mathematical

Purpose to observe the growth of slime molds and predict the best conditions for their growth

L2 | IS Visual-Spatial

Materials slime mold specimens, magnifying glass, pencil, paper

Teaching Strategy Obtain live specimens of slime mold from a biological supply company. *Physarum polycephalum* produces good results.

Safety Precaution Keep petri dishes closed.

Analysis

Lower temperatures and reduced humidity or the presence of food will result in the growth of the spore-producing form.

Assessment

Performance To assess students' understanding of slime molds, have them try to grow slime mold cultures on different surfaces with different nutrients. Use **Performance Assessment in the Science Classroom,** p. 97.

Caption Answer

Figure 12 Slime molds move and behave like animal-like protists during part of their life cycle, but, like fungi, they are decomposers that reproduce with spores.

Discussion

Fungi and Slime Molds Ask students to compare slime molds and fungi. Both are often found on decaying materials; both can reproduce by spore production.

Observing Slime Molds

Procedure

1. Obtain live specimens of the slime mold **Physarum polycephaalum** from your teacher.
2. Observe the mold once each day for four days.
3. Using a **magnifying lens,** make daily drawings and observations of the mold as it grows.

Analysis
Predict the growing conditions under which the slime mold will change from the amoeboid form to the spore-producing form.

Figure 12 Slime molds come in many different forms and colors ranging from brilliant yellow or orange to rich blue, violet, pink, and jet black.
Compare and contrast *how slime molds are similar to protists and fungi.*

Magnification: 3×

Magnification: 5.25×

218 CHAPTER 8 Protists and Fungi

Disease in Humans The protozoans that may be most important to you are the ones that cause diseases in humans. In tropical areas, flies or other biting insects transmit many of the parasitic flagellates to humans. A flagellated parasite called *Giardia* can be found in water that is contaminated with wastes from humans or wild or domesticated animals. If you drink water directly from a stream, you could get this diarrhea-causing parasite.

Some amoebas also are parasites that cause disease. One parasitic amoeba, found in ponds and streams, can lead to a brain infection and death.

Funguslike Protists

Funguslike protists include several small groups of organisms such as slime molds, water molds, and downy mildews. Although all funguslike protists produce spores like fungi, most of them can move from place to place using pseudopods like the amoeba. All of them must take in food from an outside source.

Slime Molds As shown in **Figure 12,** slime molds are more attractive than their name suggests. Slime molds form delicate, weblike structures on the surface of their food supply. Often these structures are brightly colored. Slime molds have some protozoan characteristics. During part of their life cycle, slime molds move by means of pseudopods and behave like amoebas.

Most slime molds are found on decaying logs or dead leaves in moist, cool, shady environments. One common slime mold sometimes creeps across lawns and mulch as it feeds on bacteria and decayed plants and animals. When conditions become less favorable for slime molds, reproductive structures form on stalks and spores are produced.

Differentiated Instruction

Learning Disabled After having students observe the movement of a slime mold under the microscope, have them perform these same movements as a group. The cytoplasm streams in one direction and then slows to a stop. Then the cytoplasm flows in the opposite direction, but not as far, before stopping. In this way, the slime mold creeps across a surface. L1 | IS Kinesthetic

Water Molds and Downy Mildews

Most members of this large, diverse group of funguslike protists live in water or moist places. Like fungi, they grow as a mass of threads over a plant or animal. Digestion takes place outside of these protists, then they absorb the organism's nutrients. Unlike fungi, the spores these protists produce have flagella. Their cell walls more closely resemble those of plants than those of fungi.

Some water molds are parasites of plants, and others feed on dead organisms. Most water molds appear as fuzzy, white growths on decaying matter, as shown in **Figure 13**. If you have an aquarium, you might see water molds attack a fish and cause its death. Another important type of protist is a group of plant parasites called downy mildew. Warm days and cool, moist nights are ideal growing conditions for them. They can live on aboveground parts of many plants. Downy mildews weaken plants and even can kill them.

Figure 13 Water mold, the threadlike material seen in the photo, grows on a dead salamander. In this case, the water mold is acting as a decomposer. This important process will return nutrients to the water.

 **Reading Check** *How do water molds affect organisms?*

Applying Science

Is it a fungus or a protist?

Slime molds, such as the pipe cleaner slime shown in the photograph to the right, can be found covering moist wood. They can be white or bright red, yellow, or purple. If you look at a piece of slime mold on a microscope slide, you will see that the cell nuclei move back and forth as the cytoplasm streams along. This streaming of the cytoplasm is how a slime mold creeps over the wood.

Identifying the Problem

Should slime molds be classified as protists or as fungi?

Solving the Problem

1. What characteristics do slime molds share with protists? How are slime molds similar to protozoans and algae?

2. What characteristics do slime molds share with fungi? What characteristics do slime molds have that are different from fungi?
3. What characteristics did you compare to decide what group slime molds should be classified in? What other characteristics could scientists examine to help classify slime molds?

Applying Science

Answers

1. eukaryotic organisms; usually live in moist or wet surroundings; creep across surfaces and engulf food in ways similar to amoebas.
2. grow on decaying matter and reproduce with spores; Unlike fungi, slime molds sometimes engulf food and move.
3. Answers will vary. Scientists could examine cell structure.

Inquiry Lab

Protist Zoo

Purpose to determine the best growing conditions for protists

Possible Materials water (tap, bottled, pond, stream), large jars, small aquariums, garden fertilizer, rocks, leaf litter (stream, forest), microscope, balance, microscope slides, eyedropper, pond life and protist guidebooks

Estimated Time two class sessions

Teaching Strategies

• Students can design an experiment to test various conditions protists need to grow. For example, jars can be filled with different types of water, a stream rock added to each jar, and the jars left in sunlight for a week.
• Students can use microscopes to search water samples and identify and record the diversity of protists in each test jar.
• A variety of environmental conditions can be tested, such as the amount of light or nutrients.

For additional inquiry activities, see *Science Inquiry Labs.*

Differentiated Instruction

Challenge Students can make a flipbook for one type of protist. On each page of the flipbook, they should show one stage of that protist's movement. When the pages are placed together and flipped through rapidly, the protist should appear to move. The book will be more interesting if it has more pages showing small sections of movement, and the organism consuming food. L3 **LS** **Visual-Spatial**

Figure 14 Downy mildews can have a great impact on agriculture and economies when they infect potatoes, sugar beets, grapes, and melons like those above.

Importance of the Funguslike Protists

Some of the organisms in this group are important because they help break down dead organisms. However, most funguslike protists are important because of the diseases they cause in plants and animals. One species of water mold that causes lesions in fish can be a problem when the number of this species in a given area is high. Fish farms and salmon spawning in streams can be greatly affected by a water mold spreading throughout the population. Water molds cause disease in other aquatic organisms including worms and even diatoms.

Economic Effects Downy mildews can have a huge effect on economies as well as social history. One of the most well-known members of this group caused the Irish potato famine during the 1840s. Potatoes were Ireland's main crop and the primary food source for its people. When the potato crop became infected with downy mildew, potatoes rotted in the fields, leaving many people with no food. A downy mildew infection of grapes in France during the 1870s nearly wiped out the entire French wine industry. Downy mildews, as shown in **Figure 14,** continue to infect crops such as lettuce, corn, and cabbage, as well as tropical avocados and pineapples.

section ① review

Summary

What is a protist?
- Protists can reproduce asexually or sexually.

Plantlike Protists
- Algae can make their own food.
- Euglenoids are both animal-like and plantlike.
- Seaweeds are many-celled algae.
- Green algae are an important source of oxygen and food for many organisms on Earth.
- Algae can be used to thicken food or cosmetics.

Animal-like Protists
- Protozoans are one-celled consumers. Some protozoans are parasites.
- Some protozoans form symbiotic relationships; other protozoans can cause disease.

Funguslike Protists
- Funguslike protists take in energy from other organisms.

Self Check

1. **Identify** the characteristics common to all protists.
2. **Compare and contrast** the characteristics of animal-like, plantlike, and funguslike protists.
3. **Explain** how plantlike protists are classified into different groups.
4. **Classify** What protozoan characteristics do scientists use to organize protozoans into groups?
5. **Think Critically** Why are there few fossils of certain groups of protists?

Applying Skills

6. **Make and Use a Table** Make a table of the positive and negative effects that protists might have on your life and health.
7. **Use a spreadsheet** to make a table that compares the characteristics of the three groups of protozoans. Include *example organisms, method of transportation,* and *other characteristics.*

section ① review

1. one-celled or many-celled organisms that live in moist or wet surroundings; possess membrane-bound nuclei; protists may be plantlike, animal-like, or funguslike
2. Algae are plantlike protists with chloroplasts and cell walls. Protozoans are one-celled animal-like protists that lack cell walls and cannot produce their own food. Funguslike protists are all consumers that produce spores.
3. by their structure and the pigments they contain
4. by their method of movement
5. Protists are small and do not have hard parts that are fossilized easily. The protists decay rapidly, leaving no trace of their existence.
6. Check student tables for accuracy.
7. Tables should accurately display information from this section.

Comparing Algae and Protozoans

Algae and protozoans have characteristics that are similar enough to place them in the same group—the protists. However, the variety of protist forms is great. In this lab, you can observe many of the differences among protists.

Real-World Question

What are the differences between algae and protozoans?

Goals
- **Draw and label** the organisms you examine.
- **Observe** the differences between algae and protozoans.

Materials
cultures of *Paramecium, Amoeba, Euglena,* and *Spirogyra*
*prepared slides of the organisms listed above
prepared slide of slime mold
microscope slides (4)
coverslips (4)
microscope
*stereomicroscope
dropper
*Alternate materials

Safefy Precautions

Procedure
1. Copy the data table in your Science Journal.
2. Make a wet mount of the *Paramecium* culture. If you need help, refer to Student Resources at the back of the book.

Magnification: 50×

Protist Observations		
Protist	**Drawing**	**Observations**
Paramecium		
Amoeba	Student drawings should resemble group features described in this section.	
Euglena		
Spirogyra		
Slime mold		

3. **Observe** the wet mount first under low and then under high power. Record your observations in the data table. Draw and label the organism that you observed.
4. Repeat steps 2 and 3 with the other cultures. Return all preparations to your teacher and wash your hands.
5. **Observe** the slide of slime mold under low and high power. Record your observations.

Conclude and Apply
1. **Describe** the structure used for movement by each organism that moves.
2. **List** the protists that make their own food and explain how you know that they can.
3. **Identify** the protists you observed with animal-like characteristics.

Communicating Your Data

Share the results of this lab with your classmates. **For more help, refer to the** Science Skill Handbook.

LAB 221

Communicating Your Data

Students should have similar results. They may communicate by using drawings or written descriptions of their observations.

✔ Assessment

Performance To further assess students' abilities to classify algae and protozoans, have them make and view wet mounts of scrapings from fish tanks. Use **Performance Assessment in the Science Classroom,** p. 121.

Real-World Question

Purpose Students will observe the differences between algae and protozoans. L2 IS **Visual-Spatial**

Process Skills observe and infer, classify, make and use tables, compare and contrast

Time Required 50 minutes

Procedure

Materials Prepared slides of protozoans and algae may be used. All live specimens should be obtained from a supply house. Do not use parasitic forms.

Safety Precautions Remind students to be careful when plugging and unplugging the microscope. Water should be kept away from the outlet.

Teaching Strategies
- Use a videotape of the organisms to prepare students for what they will see.
- Remind students that algae and protozoans are protists.

Troubleshooting Maintain separate cultures for each organism. Prevent students from using the same dropper for more than one culture.

Conclude and Apply

1. Paramecia use cilia; amoebas use pseudopods; euglenas use flagella.
2. *Spirogyra* and *Euglena* make their own food; they contain chloroplasts for photosynthesis.
3. *Paramecium, Euglena, Amoeba,* slime mold

Tie to Prior Knowledge

Fungi Have students relate examples of fungi they know about. Students will likely know about toadstools and fungi used in food. Explain that fungi are in their own kingdom.

as you read

What You'll Learn
- **Identify** the characteristics shared by all fungi.
- **Classify** fungi into groups based on their methods of reproduction.
- **Differentiate** between the imperfect fungi and all other fungi.

Why It's Important
Fungi are important sources of food and medicines, and they help recycle Earth's wastes.

Review Vocabulary
photosynthesis: a process in which chlorophyll containing organisms use energy from light and change carbon dioxide and water into simple sugars and oxygen gas

New Vocabulary
- hyphae
- saprophyte
- spore
- basidium
- ascus
- budding
- sporangium
- lichen
- mycorrhizae

Figure 15 The hyphae of fungi are involved in the digestion of food, as well as reproduction.

What are fungi?

Do you think you can find any fungi in your house or apartment? You have fungi in your home if you have mushroom soup or fresh mushrooms. What about that package of yeast in the cupboard? Yeasts are a type of fungus used to make some breads and cheeses. You also might find fungus growing on a loaf of bread or an orange, or mildew fungus growing on your shower curtain.

Origin of Fungi Although fossils of fungi exist, most are not useful in determining how fungi are related to other organisms. Some scientists hypothesize that fungi share an ancestor with ancient, flagellated protists and slime molds. Other scientists hypothesize that their ancestor was a green or red alga.

Structure of Fungi Most species of fungi are many-celled. The body of a fungus is usually a mass of many-celled, thread-like tubes called **hyphae** (HI fee), as shown in **Figure 15.** The hyphae produce enzymes that help break down food outside of the fungus. Then, the fungal cells absorb the digested food. Because of this, most fungi are known as saprophytes. **Saprophytes** are organisms that obtain food by absorbing dead or decaying tissues of other organisms. Other fungi are parasites. They obtain their food directly from living things.

Stained LM Magnification: 175×

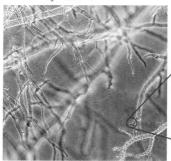

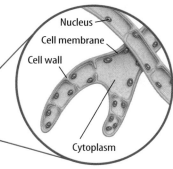

Nucleus
Cell membrane
Cell wall
Cytoplasm

Threadlike, microscopic hyphae make up the body of a fungus.

The internal structure of hyphae.

222 CHAPTER 8 Protists and Fungi

Other Characteristics of Fungi What other characteristics do all fungi share? Because some fungi grow anchored in soil and have a cell wall around each cell, fungi once were classified as plants. But fungi don't have the specialized tissues and organs of plants, such as leaves and roots. Unlike most plants, fungi do not contain chlorophyll and cannot undergo photosynthesis.

Fungi grow best in warm, humid areas, such as tropical forests or between toes. You need a microscope to see some fungi, but in Michigan one fungus was found growing underground over an area of about 15 hectares. In the state of Washington, another type of fungus found in 1992 was growing throughout nearly 600 hectares of soil.

Reproduction Asexual and sexual reproduction in fungi usually involves the production of spores. A **spore** is a waterproof reproductive cell that can grow into a new organism. In asexual reproduction, cell division produces spores. These spores will grow into new fungi that are genetically identical to the fungus from which the spores came.

Fungi are not identified as either male or female. Sexual reproduction can occur when the hyphae of two genetically different fungi of the same species grow close together. If the hyphae join, a reproductive structure will grow, as shown in **Figure 16.** Following meiosis in these structures, spores are produced that will grow into fungi. These fungi are genetically different from either of the two fungi whose hyphae joined during sexual reproduction. Fungi are classified into three main groups based on the type of structure formed by the joining of hyphae.

Reading Check *How are fungi classified?*

ScienceOnline

Topic: Unusual Fungi
Visit life.msscience.com for Web links to information about *Armillaria ostoyae* and other unusual fungi.

Activity Prepare an informational brochure about unusual fungi. Include illustrations and descriptions of at least three different kinds. Where do you find these fungi?

Color-enhanced LM Magnification: 30×

A Two hyphae fuse.

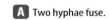

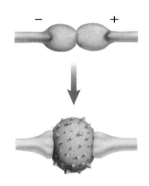

B Reproductive structure forms.

Figure 16 When two genetically different fungi of the same species meet, a reproductive structure, in this case a zygospore **B**, will be formed. The new fungi will be genetically different from either of the two original fungi.

SECTION 2 Fungi **223**

2 Teach

Activity

Rising Dough Mix some yeast suspension with flour and water and put it in a warm place. Ask students to predict what will happen over the course of the day. The dough will rise as the yeast's respiratory processes produce carbon dioxide. L2

Discussion

Classification of Fungi Have students discuss why fungi are no longer classified as plants. Unlike most plants, fungi contain no chloroplasts. There are a few species of plants that don't have chlorophyll. These plants are similar to fungi in that they must absorb their energy from other organisms. Examples include Indian pipe *(Monotropa uniflora)* and sugar stick *(Allotropa virgata).*

Quick Demo
Food Mold
Materials variety of foods with mold growing on them, and plastic containers, covers, or storage bags
Estimated Time ten minutes
Procedure Show students the foods with mold growing on them. Have students identify what characteristics the different molds have in common. Ask them what the foods might have in common.
WARNING: *Before beginning, ask if any students have known allergies to fungal spores. Contact the school nurse if a student shows signs of an allergic reaction to fungal spores in demonstrations during this section. It is rare, but some students may experience breathing difficulties in the presence of fungal spores.*

Reading Check

Answer by the type of structure formed by the joining of hyphae

Visual Learning

Figure 16 Zygospores are diploid structures that are able to withstand periods of unfavorable environmental conditions by going into dormancy. Ask students what structure will eventually develop from the zygospore, when conditions are right. Meiosis occurs after dormancy, and hyphae grow from the zygospore. Sporangia are produced by the hyphae.

Figure 17 Club fungi, like this mushroom, form a reproductive structure called a basidium. Each basidium produces four balloonlike structures called basidiospores. Spores will be released from these as the final step in sexual reproduction.

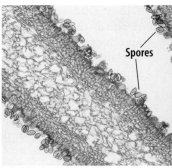

Spores

Stained LM Magnification: 18×

Club Fungi

The mushrooms shown in **Figure 17** are probably the type of fungus that you are most familiar with. The mushroom is only the reproductive structure of the fungus. Most of the fungus grows as hyphae in the soil or on the surface of its food source. These fungi commonly are known as club fungi. Their spores are produced in a club-shaped structure called a **basidium** (buh SIH dee uhm) (plural, *basidia*).

Sac Fungi

Yeasts, molds, morels, and truffles are all examples of sac fungi—a diverse group containing more than 30,000 different species. The spores of these fungi are produced in a little, saclike structure called an **ascus** (AS kus), as shown in **Figure 18.**

Although most fungi are many-celled, yeasts are one-celled organisms. Yeasts reproduce sexually by forming spores and reproduce asexually by budding, as illustrated in the right photo below. **Budding** is a form of asexual reproduction in which a new organism forms on the side of a parent organism. The two organisms are genetically identical.

Figure 18 The spores of a sac fungus are released when the tip of an ascus breaks open.

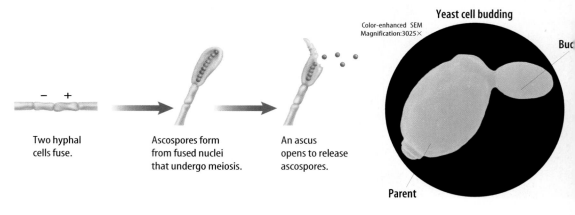

Two hyphal cells fuse.

Ascospores form from fused nuclei that undergo meiosis.

An ascus opens to release ascospores.

Color-enhanced SEM Magnification:3025×

Yeast cell budding

Bud

Parent

224 CHAPTER 8 Protists and Fungi

Figure 19 The black mold found growing on bread or fruit produces zygospores during sexual reproduction. Zygospores produce sporangia.

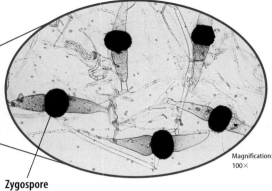

Magnification: 100×

Zygospore

Zygote Fungi and Other Fungi

The fuzzy black mold that you sometimes find growing on a piece of fruit or an old loaf of bread, as shown in **Figure 19,** is a type of zygospore fungus. Fungi that belong to this group produce spores in a round spore case called a **sporangium** (spuh RAN jee uhm) (plural, *sporangia*) on the tips of upright hyphae. When each sporangium splits open, hundreds of spores are released into the air. Each spore will grow and reproduce if it lands in a warm, moist area that has a food supply.

☑ Reading Check *What is a sporangium?*

Some fungi either never reproduce sexually or never have been observed reproducing sexually. Because of this, these fungi are difficult to classify. They usually are called imperfect fungi because there is no evidence that their life cycle has a sexual stage. Imperfect fungi reproduce asexually by producing spores. When the sexual stage of one of these fungi is observed, the species is classified immediately in one of the other three groups.

Penicillium is a fungus that is difficult to classify. Some scientists classify *Penicillium* as an imperfect fungi. Others think it should be classified as a sac fungus based on the type of spores it forms during asexual reproduction. Another fungus, which causes pneumonia, has been classified recently as an imperfect fungus. Like *Penicillium,* scientists do not agree about which group to place it in.

Mini LAB

Interpreting Spore Prints

Procedure

1. Obtain several **mushrooms from the grocery store** and let them age until the undersides look dark brown.
2. Remove the stems. Place the mushroom caps with the gills down on a piece of **unlined white paper.**
3. Let the mushroom caps sit undisturbed overnight and remove them from the paper the next day.

Analysis

1. **Draw** and label the results in your **Science Journal.** Describe the marks on the page and what might have made them.
2. **Estimate** the number of mushrooms that could be produced from a single mushroom cap.

Try at Home

Mini LAB

Purpose to observe spore prints
L1 ELL LS Visual-Spatial

Materials mushrooms, unlined white paper

Teaching Strategy Caution students not to disturb the mushrooms while spore prints are being made.

Safety Precautions Remind students not to eat anything used in the lab.

Troubleshooting Don't let mushrooms dry up and shrivel while waiting for them to age. Keep them moist.

Analysis

1. Sketches will vary. Brown lines will be parallel or concentric rings made by falling spores.
2. Count a few spores in one area and multiply by the total area of spore production.

Assessment

Performance To further assess understanding of mushrooms, have students carefully tease apart a bit of gill from under the cap and make a wet mount of an extremely small piece. Observe under a microscope. Students should draw and describe what they see in their Science Journals. Use **Performance Assessment in the Science Classroom,** p. 127.

Try at Home

SECTION 2 Fungi **225**

Differentiated Instruction

English-Language Learners Have students make flash cards with the name of a group of fungi and a picture on one side and the characteristics and an example on the other. Allow students to practice learning the fungi by using their flash cards.
L1 LS Linguistic

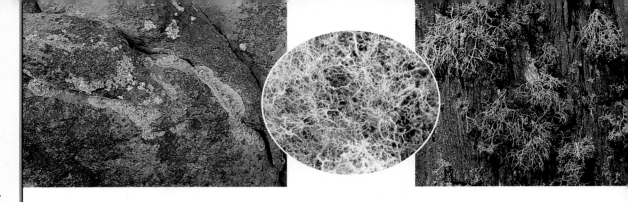

Figure 20 Lichens can look like a crust on bare rock, appear leafy, or grow upright. All three forms can grow near each other. **Determine** *one way lichens might be classified.*

Figure 22 Many plants, such as these orchids, could not survive without mycorrhizae to help absorb water and important minerals from soil.

Lichens

The colorful organisms in **Figure 20** are lichens. A **lichen** (LI kun) is an organism that is made of a fungus and either a green alga or a cyanobacterium. These two organisms have a relationship in which they both benefit. The alga or cyanobacterium lives among the threadlike strands of the fungus. The fungus gets food made by the green alga or cyanobacterium. The green alga or cyanobacterium gets a moist, protected place to live.

Importance of Lichens For many animals, including caribou and musk oxen, lichens are an important food source.

Lichens also are important in the weathering process of rocks. They grow on bare rock and release acids as part of their metabolism. The acids help break down the rock. As bits of rock accumulate and lichens die and decay, soil is formed. This soil supports the growth of other species.

Scientists also use lichens as indicator organisms to monitor pollution levels, as shown in **Figure 21.** Many species of lichens are sensitive to pollution. When these organisms show a decline in their health or die quickly, it alerts scientists to possible problems for larger organisms.

Fungi and Plants

Some fungi interact with plant roots. They form a network of hyphae and roots known as **mycorrhizae** (mi kuh RI zee). About 80 percent of plants develop mycorrhizae. The fungus helps the plant absorb more of certain nutrients from the soil better than the roots can on their own, while the plant supplies food and other nutrients to the fungi. Some plants, like the lady's slipper orchids shown in **Figure 22,** cannot grow without the development of mycorrhizae.

✔ Reading Check *Why are mycorrhizae so important to plants?*

226 CHAPTER 8 Protists and Fungi

Figure 21

Widespread, slow growing, and with long life spans, lichens come in many varieties. Lichens absorb water and nutrients mainly from the air rather than the soil. Because certain types are extremely sensitive to toxic environments, lichens make natural, inexpensive, air-pollution detectors.

Can you see a difference between these two red alder tree trunks? White lichens cover one trunk but not the other. Red alders are usually covered with lichens such as those seen in the photo on the left. Lichens could not survive on the tree on the right because of air pollution.

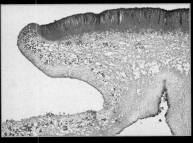

A lichen consists of a fungus and an alga or cyanobacterium living together in a partnership that benefits both organisms. In this cross section of a lichen (50x), reddish-stained bits of fungal tissue surround blue-stained algal cells.

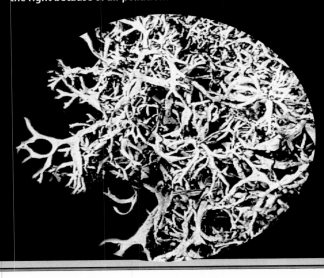

Evernia lichens, left, sicken and die when exposed to sulfur dioxide, a common pollutant emitted by coal-burning industrial plants such as the one above.

Visualizing Lichens as Air Quality Indicators

Have students examine the pictures and read the captions. Then ask the following questions.

If a tree has no lichens on its trunk, what does that indicate about the air quality in that area? Possible answer: The tree is in an area that has a source of air pollution.

Where do lichens get most of their nutrients? Lichens absorb water and nutrients from the air.

Activity

Lichen Map Have students make a map of the area surrounding the school. The area should encompass about 5 square km. Then have them indicate on the map which areas would most likely contain lichens. If there are no lichens in the area, have students discuss why that may be. [LS] **Naturalist**

Differentiated Instruction

Challenge Many current studies are trying to determine the effect that air pollution has on lichens. Have students research several different species of lichens and determine whether the lichens are sensitive to certain types of air pollution. Students can present their findings on a bulletin board. [L3]

Biotechnology Many pharmaceutical, diagnostic, agricultural, and environmental products that benefit society are the result of biotechnology. Some plants and animals have been genetically modified by biotechnology to improve them for human use. The United States is one of the world leaders in biotechnology research, development, and marketing.

Activity

Roles of Fungi Allow students to work in groups to develop and carry out interviews with local physicians concerning the role of fungi in the health field. Students will learn that fungi can cause infection in humans, but that some fungi are also used in the production of medicines. L2
COOP LEARN Interpersonal

Biotechnology Living cells and materials produced by cells are used in biotechnology to develop products that benefit society. Careers in biotechnology include laboratory research and development, quality control, biostatistician, and product development. Through biotechnology, some fungi have been developed that can be used as natural pesticides to control pests like termites, tent caterpillars, aphids, and citrus mites.

INTEGRATE Earth Science

Fossilized Fungus In 1999, scientists discovered a fossilized fungus in a 460 million-year-old rock. The fossil was a type of fungus that forms associations with plant roots. Scientists have known for many years that the first plants could not have survived moving from water to land alone. Early plants did not have specialized roots to absorb nutrients. Also, tubelike cells used for transporting water and nutrients to leaves were too simple.

Scientists have hypothesized that early fungi attached themselves to the roots of early plants, passing along nutrients taken from the soil. Scientists suggest that it was this relationship that allowed plants to move successfully from water onto land about 500 million years ago. Until the discovery of this fossil, no evidence had been found that this type of fungus existed at that time.

Importance of Fungi

As mentioned in the beginning of this chapter, some fungi are eaten for food. Cultivated mushrooms are an important food crop. However, wild mushrooms never should be eaten because many are poisonous. Some cheeses are produced using fungi. Yeasts are used in the baking industry. Yeasts use sugar for energy and produce alcohol and carbon dioxide as waste products. The carbon dioxide causes doughs to rise.

Agriculture Many fungi are important because they cause diseases in plants and animals. Many sac fungi are well-known by farmers because they damage or destroy plant crops. Diseases caused by sac fungi include Dutch elm disease, apple scab, and ergot disease of rye. Smuts and rust, shown in **Figure 23,** are club fungi. They cause billions of dollars worth of damage to food crops each year.

Figure 23 Rusts can infect the grains used to make many cereals including wheat (shown below), barley, rye, and oats. Not all fungi are bad for agriculture. Some are natural pesticides. This dead grasshopper (right) is infected with a fungal parasite.

Active Reading

Quickwrites This strategy, sometimes called freewrites, lets students use spontaneous writing to discover what they already know. Have students write a list of ideas about a topic, then share these ideas with the class. Next, have students write their ideas freely in a paragraph without worrying about punctuation, spelling, and grammar. Have students use a Quickwrite to discover what they know about the importance of fungi.

Health and Medicine Fungi can cause diseases in humans and animals. Ringworm and athlete's foot are skin infections caused by species of imperfect fungi. Other fungi can cause respiratory infections.

The effects of fungi on health and medicine are not all negative. Some species of fungi naturally produce antibiotics that keep bacteria from growing on or near them. The antibiotic penicillin is produced by the imperfect fungi *Penicillium*. This fungus is grown commercially, and the antibiotic is collected to use in fighting bacterial infections. Cyclosporine, an important drug used to help fight the body's rejection of transplanted organs, also is derived from a fungus. There are many more examples of breakthroughs in medicine as a result of studying and discovering new uses of fungi. In fact, there is a worldwide effort among scientists who study fungi to investigate soil samples to find more useful drugs.

Decomposers As important as fungi are in the production of different foods and medicines, they are most important as decomposers that break down organic materials. Food scraps, clothing, and dead plants and animals are made of organic material. Often found on rotting logs, as shown in **Figure 24,** fungi break down these materials. The chemicals in these materials are returned to the soil where plants can reuse them. Fungi, along with bacteria, are nature's recyclers. They keep Earth from becoming buried under mountains of organic waste materials.

Figure 24 Fungi have an important role as decomposers in nature.
Explain *why fungi are called nature's recyclers.*

Caption Answer
Figure 24 Fungi break down organic matter. The broken down materials that fungi do not use are left for other organisms to use.

3 Assess

DAILY INTERVENTION

Check for Understanding
Visual-Spatial Have students build a model of a lichen.

Reteach
Fungus Structure Show students various illustrations of fungi. Ask them to identify the parts of each fungus. L2 LS

✓ Assessment

Oral What has never been observed in any of the imperfect fungi? a sexual stage How do the imperfect fungi reproduce if they don't have a sexual stage? asexual spores

Virtual Labs

Traits *How can microscopic protists and fungi be characterized?*

---

section 2 review

Summary

What are fungi?
- Fungi are consumers and reproduce both sexually and asexually.
- There are three main classifications of fungi.

Lichens
- Lichens consist of a fungus and either a green alga or a cyanobacterium.
- They help break down rocks and form soil.

Fungi and Plants
- Mycorrhizae are a network of plant roots and fungi hyphae that interact to obtain nutrients.

Importance of Fungi
- Fungi are most important as decomposers.

Self Check

1. **List** characteristics common to all fungi.
2. **Explain** how fungi are classified into different groups.
3. **Compare and contrast** imperfect fungi and other groups of fungi.
4. **List** ways lichens are important.
5. **Think Critically** If an imperfect fungus was found to produce basidia under certain environmental conditions, how would the fungus be reclassified?

Applying Math

6. **Use Proportions** Of the 100,000 fungus species, approximately 30,000 are sac fungi. What percentage of fungus species are sac fungi?

---

section 2 review

1. Fungi cannot make their own food. Most fungi are many-celled saprophytes with a body made of hyphae. They grow anchored in soil and have cell walls.
2. by the structure formed by the joining of hyphae
3. Imperfect fungi have no known sexual stage in their life cycle; all other fungi do.
4. Lichens are an important food source for many animals, they help break down rocks into soil, and they are used to monitor pollution levels.
5. It would be reclassified as a club fungus belonging to division Basidiomycota.
6. $30{,}000/100{,}000 \times 100\% = 30\%$

BENCH TESTED

▶ *Real-World Question*

Purpose Students identify fungi and design a field guide for fungi in their area. **IS Kinesthetic and Visual-Spatial**

Process Skills identify, classify, analyze, and design

Time Required three class periods

Possible Materials Provide a wide selection of containers and other collection equipment. Provide students with detailed guidebooks to help them identify their discoveries. Encourage students to use a wide variety of art mediums including color pencils, markers, pastels, charcoal, paints, and photography.

Safety Precautions Caution students never to eat any fungi they collect and to thoroughly wash their hands after handling fungi.

▶ *Make a Model*

Possible Procedures

Discussion Tell students to think about methods for observing fungi. Have them consider features in their field guides that they would want to use to make identifying fungi easier. How will they group the organisms in the book? What type of diagrams or photographs will they include? How can they waterproof the pages of the field guide? What size should the field guide be?

Model and Invent

Creating a Fungus Field Guide

▶ *Real-World Question*

Whether they are hiking deep into a rain forest in search of rare tropical birds, diving to coral reefs to study marine worms, or peering into microscopes to identify strains of bacteria, scientists all over the world depend on reliable field guides. Field guides are books that identify and describe certain types of organisms or the organisms living in a specific environment. Scientists find field guides for a specific area especially helpful. How can you create a field guide for the club fungi living in your area? What information would you include in a field guide of club fungi?

▶ *Make A Model*

1. Decide on the locations where you will conduct your search.
2. Select the materials you will need to collect and survey club fungi.
3. Design a data table in your Science Journal to record the fungi you find.
4. Decide on the layout of your field guide. What information about the fungi you will include? What drawings you will use? How will you group the fungi?

Goals
- **Identify** the common club fungi found in the woods or grassy areas near your home or school.
- **Create** a field guide to help future science students identify these fungi.

Possible Materials
collection jars
magnifying lens
microscopes
microscope slides and coverslips
field guide to fungi or club fungi
art supplies

Safety Precautions

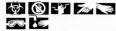

WARNING: *Do not eat any of the fungi you collect. Do not touch your face during the lab.*

5. **Describe** your plan to your teacher and ask your teacher how it could be improved.

6. **Present** your ideas for collecting and surveying fungi, and your layout ideas for your field guide to the class. Ask your classmates to suggest improvements in your plan.

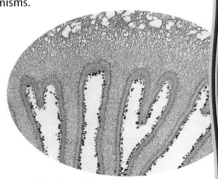

▶ Test Your Model

1. Search for samples of club fungi. **Record** the organisms you find in your data table. Use a fungus field guide to identify the fungi you discover. Do not pick or touch any fungi that you find unless you have permission.

2. Using your list of organisms, complete your field guide of club fungi as planned.

3. When finished, give your field guide to a classmate to identify a club fungus.

▶ Analyze Your Data

1. **Compare** the number of fungi you found to the total number of organisms listed in the field guide you used to identify the organisms.

2. **Analyze** the problems you may have had while collecting and identifying your fungi. Suggest steps you could take to improve your collection and identification methods.

3. **Analyze** the problems you had while creating your field guide. Suggest ways your field guide could be improved.

▶ Conclude and Apply

Infer why your field guide would be more helpful to future science students in your school than the fungus field guide you used to identify organisms.

*C*ommunicating
Your Data

Compare your field guide with those assembled by your classmates. Combine all the information on local club fungi compiled by your class to create a classroom field guide to club fungi.

Stained LM Magnification: 80×

LAB 231

Teaching Strategies

- Assign each student a "buddy." Students should be responsible for staying with their buddies at all times.
- Review any poisonous fungi found in your area. Emphasize that students should not touch these organisms.

▶ Test Your Model

Expected Outcome Students will design and create a field guide that illustrates and identifies the types of fungi found in local woods and grassy areas.

▶ Analyze Your Data

Student answers will vary depending upon individual research. Accept all reasonable answers.

▶ Conclude and Apply

Students should recognize that their field guides are specific to their area and are limited in scope. Larger field guides are more difficult to use.

✔ Assessment

Portfolio Ask students to draw a large colored picture of one of their fungi. Use **Performance Assessment in the Science Classroom,** p. 127.

*C*ommunicating
Your Data

Offer students who are interested the opportunity to purchase color photocopies of the classroom field guide.

Content Background

The cacao tree is a perennial that yields several harvests annually. On average, the cacao is 20 feet tall with 12-inch long shiny leaves. The cacao tree's pods contain beans with a high level of fat that are pulverized into a residue referred to as cocoa. Other uses for the cocoa bean include medication, cosmetics, and soap.

Witches' broom fungus is one of the most destructive. It infects the pods, making them unusable. Hard hit are the 5 to 6 million Brazilian small farmers who depend heavily on production of the cacao tree for their financial survival.

Discussion

Fighting Fungi with Fungi What are farmers currently doing to fight the fungal attacks on the cacaos? Possible answer: Using "good" fungi called *Trichoderma* to stop the spread of the "bad" fungi that is destroying the cacao trees.

Activity

Irish Potato Famine Use the Irish potato famine to illustrate how crop shortages can have devastating effects on a population. Use a team activity model. Have groups research the timetable for famine causes, and statistics. One group should be responsible for an illustration representing the time period. After each group has presented, lead a discussion on how the two crop shortages are similar and how they differ.

Investigate the Issue

Cacao Processing Lead a short discussion of each step that goes into cacao processing. Ask: Would chocolate bars still be easy to get if one group or part of the process was eliminated?

Chocolate SOS

Can a fungus protect cacao trees under attack?

Pods contain dozens of beans.

Losing Beans

Chocolate is made from seeds (cocoa beans) that grow in the pods on the tropical cacao tree. The monoculture (growing one type of crop) of modern fields has produced huge crops of cocoa beans, but also has enabled destructive fungi to sweep through cacao fields. A disease that attacks one plant of a species in a monoculture will rapidly spread to all plants in the monoculture. There are fewer healthy cacao trees today than there were several years ago. Since the blight began in the late 1980s, the world has lost three million tons of cocoa beans. Brazil, once the top producer and exporter of cocoa beans, harvested only 80,000 tons in 2000—the smallest harvest in 30 years.

A diseased pod from a cacao tree

Unless something stops the fungi that are destroying trees, there could be a lot less chocolate in the future. Your favorite chocolate bars could become more expensive and harder to find.

A Natural Cure

Farmers tried using traditional chemical sprays to fight the fungus, but they were ineffective because the tropical rains washed away the sprays. Now, agriculture scientists are working on a "natural solution" to the problem. They are using beneficial fungi (strains of *Trichoderma*) to fight the harmful fungi attacking the cocoa trees. When sprayed on trees, *Trichoderma* stops the spread of the harmful fungi. The test treatments in Brazil and Peru have reduced the destruction of the trees by between 30 and 50 percent.

Don't expect your favorite chocolate bars to disappear from stores anytime soon. Right now, world cocoa bean supplies still exceed demand. But if the spread of the epidemic can't be stopped, those chocolate bars could become slightly more expensive and a little harder to find.

Concept Map Use the library and other sources to learn the steps in making chocolate—from harvesting cacao beans to packing chocolate products for sale? Draw a concept map that shows the steps. Compare your concept map with those of your classmates.

Science Online

For more information, visit life.msscience.com/time

Concept Map Make sure student concept maps include the important role of farmers. Concept maps also should include shipping, sorting and cleaning, roasting, and winnowing the cocoa before being manufactured into chocolate. Discuss with students the necessity of each person and step in the process.

Resources for Teachers and Students

"Fighting a Fungal Siege on Cacao Farms." November 1999. *Agricultural Research*

"No Fun Fungi." May 26, 2000. *St. Louis Post-Dispatch*

Reviewing Main Ideas

Section 1 Protists

1. Protists are one-celled or many-celled eukaryotic organisms. They can reproduce asexually, resulting in two new cells that are genetically identical. Protists also can reproduce sexually and produce genetically different offspring.

2. The protist kingdom has members that are plantlike, animal-like, and funguslike.

3. Protists are thought to have evolved from a one-celled organism with a nucleus and other cellular structures.

4. Plantlike protists have cell walls and contain chlorophyll.

5. Animal-like protists can be separated into groups by how they move.

6. Funguslike protists have characteristics of protists and fungi.

Section 2 Fungi

1. Most species of fungi are many-celled. The body of a fungus consists of a mass of threadlike tubes.

2. Fungi are saprophytes or parasites—they feed off other things because they cannot make their own food.

3. Fungi reproduce using spores.

4. The three main groups of fungi are club fungi, sac fungi, and zygote fungi. Fungi that cannot be placed in a specific group are called imperfect fungi. Fungi are placed into one of these groups according to the structures in which they produce spores.

5. A lichen is an organism that consists of a fungus and a green alga or cyanobacterium.

Visualizing Main Ideas

Copy and complete the following concept map on a separate sheet of paper.

Importance of Fungi
- in — Food
  - examples — Mushrooms, Bread, Cheese
- in — Agriculture
  - examples — Plant disease, Natural pesticides
- in — Decomposers
  - example — Return nutrients to soil
- in — Health and medicine
  - examples — Skin infections, Respiratory infections, Penicillin

 life.msscience.com/interactive_tutor

CHAPTER STUDY GUIDE 233

Reviewing Main Ideas

Summary statements can be used by students to review the major concepts of the chapter.

Visualizing Main Ideas

See student page.

Science online

Visit life.msscience.com
/self_check_quiz
/interactive_tutor
/vocabulary_puzzlemaker
/chapter_review
/standardized_test

Assessment Transparency

For additional assessment questions, use the *Assessment Transparency* located in the transparency book.

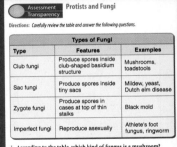

Assessment

Assessment Transparency — Protists and Fungi

Directions: Carefully review the table and answer the following questions.

Types of Fungi

Type	Features	Examples
Club fungi	Produce spores inside club-shaped basidium structure	Mushrooms, toadstools
Sac fungi	Produce spores inside tiny sacs	Mildew, yeast, Dutch elm disease
Zygote fungi	Produce spores in cases at top of thin stalks	Black mold
Imperfect fungi	Reproduce asexually	Athlete's foot fungus, ringworm

1. According to the table, which kind of fungus is a mushroom?
   A club fungus   C zygote fungus
   B sac fungus   D imperfect fungus

2. According to the table, the fungus responsible for making bread rise is a ___.
   F club fungus   H zygote fungus
   G sac fungus   J imperfect fungus

3. According to the table, a black fungus growing on old celery is most likely a ___.
   A club fungus   C zygote fungus
   B sac fungus   D imperfect fungus

Protists and Fungi

Using Vocabulary

1. spore
2. protist
3. cilia
4. algae
5. lichen
6. ascus
7. hyphae
8. pseudopod

Checking Concepts

9. B
10. D
11. D
12. A

13. B
14. B
15. B

Thinking Critically

16. no warmth, low humidity, low moisture
17. Accessory pigments help chlorophyll to be more efficient during photosynthesis.
18. Funguslike protists produce spores and take in food from an outside source like fungi. Unlike fungi, the funguslike protists usually move by using pseudopods.
19. When in association with certain mutualistic fungi, some plants are able to take in materials from their environment.
20. Fungi can digest food outside the organism. It secretes the enzymes, which help digest the fruit. Then the cells absorb the nutrients.

Using Vocabulary

algae p. 211	mycorrhizae p. 226
ascus p. 224	protist p. 210
basidium p. 224	protozoan p. 215
budding p. 224	pseudopod p. 216
cilia p. 215	saprophyte p. 222
flagellum p. 212	sporangium p. 225
hyphae p. 222	spore p. 223
lichen p. 226	

Write the vocabulary word that matches each of these descriptions.

1. reproductive cell of a fungus
2. organisms that are animal-like, plantlike, or funguslike
3. threadlike structures used for movement
4. plantlike protists
5. organism made up of a fungus and an alga or a cyanobacterium
6. reproductive structure made by sac fungi
7. threadlike tubes that make up the body of a fungus
8. structure used for movement formed by oozing cytoplasm

Checking Concepts

Choose the word or phrase that best answers the question.

9. Which type of protist captures food, does not have cell walls, and can move from place to place?
   - **A)** algae
   - **B)** protozoans
   - **C)** fungi
   - **D)** lichens

10. Which of the following organisms cause red tides when found in large numbers?
    - **A)** *Euglena*
    - **B)** diatoms
    - **C)** *Ulva*
    - **D)** dinoflagellates

11. Algae are important for which of the following reasons?
    - **A)** They are a food source for many aquatic organisms.
    - **B)** Parts of algae are used in foods that humans eat.
    - **C)** Algae produce oxygen as a result of the process of photosynthesis.
    - **D)** all of the above

12. Where would you most likely find fungus-like protists?
    - **A)** on decaying logs
    - **B)** in bright light
    - **C)** on dry surfaces
    - **D)** on metal surfaces

13. Where are spores produced in mushrooms?
    - **A)** sporangia
    - **B)** basidia
    - **C)** ascus
    - **D)** hyphae

14. Which of the following is used as an indicator organism?
    - **A)** club fungus
    - **B)** lichen
    - **C)** slime mold
    - **D)** imperfect fungus

Use the illustration below to answer question 15.

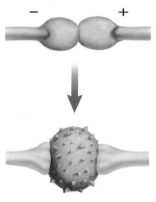

15. What is the reproductive structure, shown in the lower image above, called?
    - **A)** hypha
    - **B)** zygospore
    - **C)** basidium
    - **D)** ascus

 Science Online life.msscience.com/vocabulary_puzzlemaker

Use the Exam*View*® Pro Testmaker CD-ROM to:
- create multiple versions of tests
- create modified tests with one mouse click for inclusion students
- edit existing questions and add your own questions
- build tests aligned with state standards using built-in State Curriculum Tags
- change English tests to Spanish with one mouse click and vice versa

Thinking Critically

16. Identify what kind of environment is needed to prevent fungal growth.

17. Infer why algae contain pigments other than just chlorophyll.

18. Compare and contrast the features of fungi and funguslike protists.

19. List some advantages plants have when they form associations with fungi.

20. Explain the adaptations of fungi that enable them to get food.

21. Recognize Cause and Effect A leaf sitting on the floor of a rain forest will decompose in six weeks. A leaf on the floor of a temperate forest will take up to a year to decompose. Explain how this is possible.

22. Compare and Contrast Make a chart comparing and contrasting the different ways protists and fungi can obtain food.

23. Make and Use Tables Copy and complete the following table that compares the different groups of fungi.

Fungi Comparisons

Fungi Group	Structure Where Sexual Spores Are Produced	Examples
Club fungi	Basidium	Mushroom
Sac fungi	Ascus	Truffles
Zygospore fungi	Sporangium	Bread mold
Imperfect fungi	No sexual spores produced	*Penicillium*

24. Identify and Manipulate Variables and Controls You find a new and unusual fungus growing in your refrigerator. Design an experiment to determine to which fungus group it should be classified.

Performance Activities

25. Poster Research the different types of fungi found in the area where you live. Determine to which group each fungus belongs. Create a poster to display your results and share them with your class.

Applying Math

26. Lichen Growth Sometimes the diameter of a lichen colony is used to estimate the age of the rock it is growing on. In some climates, it may take 100 years for a lichen colony to increase its diameter by 50 mm. Estimate how old a rock tombstone is if the largest lichen colony growing on it has a diameter of 150 mm.

Use the graph below to answer question 27.

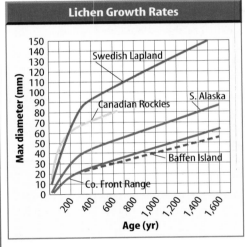

Lichen Growth Rates

27. Climate and Growth The graph above illustrates lichen growth rates in different climates. According to the graph, which climate is the most favorable for lichen growth? What is the difference between the diameter of a 200-year-old colony in the Swedish Lapland compared to a 200-year-old colony on Baffen Island?

Thinking Critically

21. Warm, moist environments such as those found in the rain forest are ideal for the growth of fungi. Therefore, fungi decompose dead organic materials more rapidly in rain forests than in cooler, drier temperate forests.

22. Charts will vary. Check charts for accuracy and completeness.

23. See student page.

24. Design will vary. Designs should include comparing the fungus with characteristics of different fungi and observing its sexual reproduction.

Performance Activities

25. Posters will vary. Most will have photos or drawings of various mushrooms or slime molds. Posters should contain information about the groups of fungi. Use **Performance Assessment in the Science Classroom,** p. 145.

Applying Math

National Math Standards
1, 2, 5, 9

26. 300 years old

27. Swedish Lapland; 50 mm

 Science Online life.msscience.com/chapter_review

☑ Assessment Resources

Reproducible Masters

Chapter *Fast File* Resources
Chapter Review, pp. 33–34
Chapter Tests, pp. 35–38
Assessment Transparency Activity, p. 45

Glencoe Science Web site
Chapter Review Test
Standardized Test Practice

Glencoe Technology

- Assessment Transparency
- Exam*View*® Pro Testmaker
- MindJogger Videoquiz
- Interactive Chalkboard

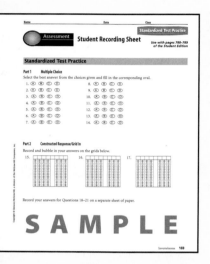

FAST FILE

Answer Sheet A practice answer sheet can be found at life.msscience.com/answer_sheet.

SAMPLE

Part 1 Multiple Choice

1. D	5. B
2. B	6. B
3. D	7. D
4. A	8. B

Part 2 Short Response

9. 200/35 = 5.7

10. Alga

11. Chlorophyll

12. During some part of their life cycle, slime molds move by means of pseudopods and behave like amoebas.

13. Saprophytes feed on dead or decaying tissues of other organisms. Parasites feed on living things.

14. Yeast is needed to make bread rise. Yeast is a one-celled fungus.

15. 15/600 = 40

Part 1 Multiple Choice

Record your answers on the answer sheet provided by your teacher or on a sheet of paper.

Use the illustration below to answer questions 1–3.

 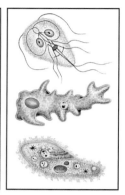

Group A   Group B

1. Which of the following organisms would belong in Group B?
   A) kelp   C) diatom
   B) grass   D) *Paramecium*

2. Which of the following is a characteristic of Group B?
   A) makes own food
   B) has specialized ways to move
   C) absorbs food from the surroundings
   D) has cell walls

3. Which of the following is NOT a method of moving used by the protists in Group B?
   A) pseudopod   C) flagella
   B) cilia   D) vacuole

Test-Taking Tip

Go at Your Own Pace Stay focused during the test and don't rush, even if you notice that other students are finishing the test early.

---

4. Which of the following is a protozoan?
   A) ciliate   C) kelp
   B) diatom   D) bacteria

Use the table below to answer questions 5–7.

Diseases Caused by Protozoans		
Disease	**Source**	**Protozoan**
Giardiasis	Contaminated water	*Giardia*
Malaria	Mosquito bite	*Plasmodium*
Dysentery	Contaminated water	*Entamoeba*
Sleeping sickness	Tsetse fly bite	*Trypanosoma*
Toxoplasmosis	Contaminated soil; eating undercooked meat that contains the organism	*Toxoplasma*

5. According to the chart, which of the following disease-carrying protozoan can be transmitted to humans by a bite from another animal?
   A) *Giardia*   C) *Entamoeba*
   B) *Plasmodium*   D) *Toxoplasma*

6. Based on the information in the chart, which disease can be prevented by purifying water used for drinking and cooking, and by washing fruits and vegetables?
   A) malaria   C) sleeping sickness
   B) dysentery   D) toxoplasmosis

7. According to the chart, which protozoan disease can be prevented by cooking meat thoroughly?
   A) malaria   C) sleeping sickness
   B) dysentery   D) toxoplasmosis

8. Where are the spores produced in the fuzzy black mold that grows on bread?
   A) basidia   C) ascus
   B) sporangia   D) hyphae

Part 3 Open Ended

16. Asexual reproduction requires only one parent organism and occurs by cell division. The new organism is genetically identical to the parent organism. Sexual reproduction requires two parent organisms. Two sex cells join to form a new organism that is genetically different from the two organisms that were the sources of the sex cells.

17. In many parts of the world, people eat red and brown algae. Carrageenan found in the cell walls of red algae is used in cosmetics, food, toothpastes, puddings, and salad dressings. Algin found in the cell walls of brown algae is used to thicken foods such as ice cream and marshmallows. Algin is also used in making tires and hand lotion. Diatoms are mined and used in insulation, filters, and road paint.

18. Downy mildews are funguslike protists. Like fungi, they grow as a mass of threads over a plant or animal. Digestion takes place outside of the downy mildew and they absorb the

Part 2 | Short Response/Grid In

Record your answers on the answer sheet provided by your teacher or on a sheet of paper.

9. Brown algae can grow at 35 m and red algae can grow at 200 m. Approximately how many times deeper than brown algae can red algae grow?

Use the illustration below to answer questions 10–11.

10. What type of protist is shown in the illustration above?

11. What pigment do all the organisms contain that absorbs light?

12. How are slime molds like protozoa?

13. How are saprophytes different from parasites?

14. Juan is making bread dough. "Don't forget to add fungus," Aunt Inez jokes. What did she mean?

15. One fungus found in Washington state was growing throughout 600 hectares of soil. Another fungus in Michigan was growing underground over an area of 15 hectares. How many times bigger was the fungus that was growing in Washington state?

Part 3 | Open Ended

Record your answers on a sheet of paper.

16. Compare and contrast asexual and sexual reproduction.

17. Discuss the ways that algae are useful for humans.

18. Compare and contrast fungi and downy mildews.

Use the table below to answer questions 19–21.

Newly Identified Organisms		
Characteristic	**Organism A**	**Organism B**
Movement	No	Yes
One-celled or many-celled	Many-celled	One-celled
Cell walls	Yes	No
Method of reproduction	Sexual	Sexual
Makes own food	Only some cells	No
Contains chlorophyll	Only found in some cells	No
Method of obtaining food	Made by some of the organism's cells; nutrients and water absorbed from surroundings	Sweeps food into oral groove
Where found	Bare rock	Freshwater

19. Dr. Seung discovered two new organisms. Their characteristics are listed in the table above. How would you classify organism B? How do you know?

20. What specialized way of moving would you expect to see if you examined organism B? Why?

21. How would you classify organism A? How do you know?

Rubrics

The following rubrics are sample scoring devices for short response and open-ended questions.

Short Response

Points	Description
2	The student demonstrates a thorough understanding of the science of the task. The response may contain minor flaws that do not detract from the demonstration of a thorough understanding.
1	The student has provided a response that is only partially correct.
0	The student has provided a completely incorrect solution or no response at all.

Open Ended

Points	Description
4	The student demonstrates a thorough understanding of the science of the task. The response may contain minor flaws that do not detract from the demonstration of a thorough understanding.
3	The student demonstrates an understanding of the science of the task. The response is essentially correct and demonstrates an essential but less than thorough understanding of the science.
2	The student demonstrates only a partial understanding of the science of the task. Although the student may have used the correct approach to a solution or may have provided a correct solution, the work lacks an essential understanding of the underlying science concepts.
1	The student demonstrates a very limited understanding of the science of the task. The response is incomplete and exhibits many flaws.
0	The student provides a completely incorrect solution or no response at all.

Section/Objectives	Standards		Labs/Features
Chapter Opener	**National**	**State/Local**	**Launch Lab:** How do you use plants?, p. 239 **Foldables,** p. 239
	See pp. 16T–17T for a Key to Standards.		
Section 1 An Overview of Plants ⏲ 2 sessions ▢ 1 block 1. **Identify** characteristics common to all plants. 2. **Explain** which plant adaptations make it possible for plants to survive on land. 3. **Compare and contrast** vascular and nonvascular plants.	National Content Standards: UCP.5, A.1, A.2, C.1–C.5		**Integrate History,** p. 242 **Visualizing Plant Classification,** p. 244
Section 2 Seedless Plants ⏲ 2 sessions ▢ 1 block 4. **Distinguish** between characteristics of seedless nonvascular plants and seedless vascular plants. 5. **Identify** the importance of some nonvascular and vascular plants.	National Content Standards: UCP.5, A.1, C.1–C.5, G.1–G.3		**MiniLAB:** Measuring Water Absorption by a Moss, p. 247 **Science Online,** p. 248 **Applying Science:** What is the value of rain forests?, p. 248
Section 3 Seed Plants ⏲ 3 sessions ▢ 1.5 blocks 6. **Identify** the characteristics of seed plants. 7. **Explain** the structures and functions of roots, stems, and leaves. 8. **Describe** the main characteristics and importance of gymnosperms and angiosperms. 9. **Compare** similarities and differences between monocots and dicots.	National Content Standards: UCP.2, UCP.5, A.1, C.1–C.5		**MiniLAB:** Observing Water Moving in a Plant, p. 253 **Integrate Health,** p. 255 **Science Online,** p. 259 **Lab:** Identifying Conifers, p. 261 **Lab:** Plants as Medicine, p. 262 **Oops! Accidents in Science:** A Loopy Idea Inspires a "Fastenating" Invention, p. 264

Lab Materials	Reproducible Resources	Section Assessment	Technology
Launch Lab: old magazines, scissors, paper and pencil	**Chapter FAST FILE Resources** Foldables Worksheet, p. 13 Directed Reading Overview, p. 15 Note-taking Worksheets, pp. 29–31	GLENCOE'S ASSESSMENT ADVANTAGE	Teacher**Works** includes: • Interactive Teacher Edition • Lesson Planner with calendar • Access to all program blacklines • Correlations to standards • Web links
Need materials? Contact Science Kit at 1-800-828-7777 or www.sciencekit.com on the Internet.	**Chapter FAST FILE Resources** Transparency Activity, p. 40 Enrichment, p. 26 Reinforcement, p. 23 Directed Reading, p. 16 **Cultural Diversity,** p. 19 **Life Science Critical Thinking/ Problem Solving,** p. 9	Portfolio Activity, p. 243 Performance Applying Skills, p. 245 Content Section Review, p. 245	Section Focus Transparency Virtual Labs CD-ROM Guided Reading Audio Program Interactive Chalkboard CD-ROM
MiniLAB: *sphagnum* moss, cheesecloth, spring scales, graduated cylinder, water, container for water	**Chapter FAST FILE Resources** Transparency Activity, pp. 41, 43–44 MiniLAB, p. 3 Enrichment, p. 27 Reinforcement, p. 24 Directed Reading, p. 17 **Home and Community Involvement,** p. 42 **Math Skill Activities,** p. 5	Portfolio Make a Model, p. 249 Performance MiniLab, p. 247 Applying Science, p. 248 Applying Math, p. 251 Content Section Review, p. 251	Section Focus Transparency Virtual Labs CD-ROM Guided Reading Audio Program Interactive Chalkboard CD-ROM Video Lab
MiniLAB: clear container, water, metric ruler, red food coloring, green onion, magnifying lens **Lab:** short branches of pine, cedar, spruce, Douglas fir, hemlock, fir, redwood, arborvitae, juniper **Lab:** no materials needed	**Chapter FAST FILE Resources** Transparency Activity, pp. 42, 43–44 MiniLAB, p. 4 Enrichment, p. 28 Reinforcement, p. 25 Directed Reading, pp. 17, 18 Lab Worksheets, pp. 5–6, 7–8 Transparency Activity, pp. 43–44 Lab Activities, pp. 9–10, 11–12 **Lab Management and Safety,** p. 61	Portfolio Curriculum Connection, p. 255 Performance MiniLab, p. 253 Applying Skills, p. 260 Content Section Review, p. 260	Section Focus Transparency Teaching Transparency Virtual Labs CD-ROM Guided Reading Audio Program Interactive Chalkboard CD-ROM

End of Chapter Assessment

GLENCOE'S ASSESSMENT ADVANTAGE

Blackline Masters	Technology	Professional Series
Chapter FAST FILE Resources Chapter Review, pp. 33–34 Chapter Tests, pp. 35–38 **Standardized Test Practice,** pp. 39–42	MindJogger Videoquiz Virtual Labs CD-ROM ExamView® Pro Testmaker TeacherWorks CD-ROM Interactive Chalkboard CD-ROM	**Performance Assessment in the Science Classroom (PASC)**

chapter **9** Plants

Transparencies

Section Focus

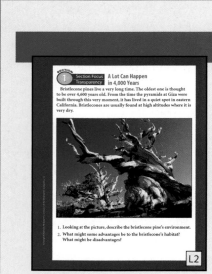

Section Focus Transparency 1 — A Lot Can Happen in 4,000 Years

Bristlecone pines live a very long time. The oldest one is thought to be over 4,600 years old. From the time the pyramids at Giza were built through this very moment, it has lived in a quiet spot in eastern California. Bristlecones are usually found at high altitudes where it is very dry.

1. Looking at the picture, describe the bristlecone pine's environment.
2. What might some advantages be to the bristlecone's habitat? What might be disadvantages?

L2

Section Focus Transparency 2 — A Fresh Start

After a forest fire has burned out, what happens to the barren acres of land? Will lush vegetation ever thrive in these areas again? Probably. In fact, it could even be better than before!

1. What life can you identify in the top picture?
2. What life can you identify in the bottom picture? What function might these first plants serve?

L2

Section Focus Transparency 3 — Rooted in Nature

Bonsai is an ancient method of growing trees or shrubs in small containers. The plants are kept small by pruning the branches and roots. Because some types of plants used for bonsai can live for more than 100 years, they are passed from generation to generation.

1. What are some advantages to having bonsai plants? What might some disadvantages be?
2. What qualities do you think would be important in practicing bonsai?

L2

This is a representation of key blackline masters available in the Teacher Classroom Resources. See Resource Manager boxes within the chapter for additional information.

Key to Teaching Strategies

The following designations will help you decide which activities are appropriate for your students.

L1 Level 1 activities should be appropriate for students with learning difficulties.

L2 Level 2 activities should be within the ability range of all students.

L3 Level 3 activities are designed for above-average students.

ELL ELL activities should be within the ability range of English-Language Learners.

COOP LEARN Cooperative Learning activities are designed for small group work.

LS Multiple Learning Styles logos, as described on page 12T, are used throughout to indicate strategies that address different learning styles.

P These strategies represent student products that can be placed into a best-work portfolio.

PBL Problem-Based Learning activities apply real-world situations to learning.

Assessment

Assessment Transparency — Plants

Directions: Carefully review the table and answer the following questions.

Watering and Plant Growth

Day	Plant A with no water	Plant B watered monthly	Plant C watered weekly	Plant D watered daily
1	10 cm	11 cm	12 cm	8 cm
5	10 cm	12 cm	13 cm	12 cm
10	10 cm	12 cm	15 cm	18 cm
15	10 cm	13 cm	17 cm	19 cm
20	10 cm	13 cm	20 cm	23 cm
25	10 cm	?	22 cm	27 cm

1. According to the table, which plant was the tallest on Day 5?
   A Plant A
   B Plant B
   C Plant C
   D Plant D
2. According to the table, which plant grew the most between Day 1 and Day 20?
   F Plant A   H Plant C
   G Plant B   J Plant D
3. If everything remains the same, what is a reasonable prediction for the height of Plant B on Day 25?
   A 10 cm   C 18 cm
   B 14 cm   D 24 cm

L2

Teaching

Teaching Transparency 3 — Monocots and Dicots

Monocot   Dicot

Vascular bundles   Vascular bundle

Cotyledon   Cotyledon

L2

Hands-on Activities

Student Text Lab Worksheet

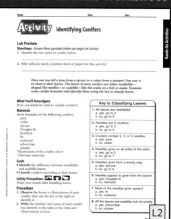

Activity — Identifying Conifers

Lab Preview
Directions: Answer these questions before you begin the Activity.
1. Identify the two types of conifer leaves.

2. Why will you need a separate sheet of paper for this activity?

How can you tell a pine from a spruce or a cedar from a juniper? One way is to observe their leaves. The leaves of most conifers are either needlelike—shaped like needles—or scalelike—like the scales on a fish or snake. Examine some conifer branches and identify them using the key to classify leaves.

What You'll Investigate
How can leaves be used to classify conifers?

Materials
short branches of the following conifers:
pine
cedar
spruce
Douglas fir
hemlock
fir
redwood
arborvitae
juniper
*illustrations of the conifers above
*Alternate materials

Goals
• Identify the difference between needlelike and scalelike leaves.
• Classify conifers according to their leaves.

Safety Precautions
Wash your hands after handling leaves.

Procedure
1. Observe the leaves or illustrations of each conifer, then use the key at the right to identify it.
2. Write the number and name of each conifer you identify in the table in the Data and Observations section.

Key to Classifying Leaves
1. All leaves are needlelike.
   a. yes, go to 2
   b. no, go to 8
2. Needles are in clusters.
   a. yes, go to 3
   b. no, go to 5
3. Clusters contain 2, 3, or 5 needles.
   a. yes, pine
   b. no, cedar
4. Needles grow on all sides of the stem.
   a. yes, go to 5
   b. no, go to 7
5. Needles grow from a woody peg.
   a. yes, spruce
   b. no, go to 6
6. Needles appear to grow from the branch.
   a. yes, Douglas fir
   b. no, hemlock
7. Most of the needles grow upward
   a. yes, fir
   b. no, redwood
8. All the leaves are scalelike but not prickly.
   a. yes, arborvitae
   b. no, juniper

L2

Laboratory Activities

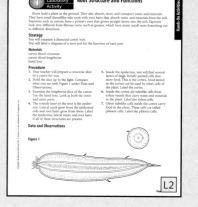

Laboratory Activity 1 — Root Structure and Functions

Roots hold a plant in the ground. They also absorb, store, and transport water and minerals. They have small threadlike side roots with root hairs that absorb water and minerals from the soil. Taproots, such as carrots, have a primary root that grows straight down into the soil. Taproots look very different from fibrous roots, such as grasses, which have many small roots branching out in different directions.

Strategy
You will examine a dissected carrot root.
You will label a diagram of a root and list the function of each part.

Materials
carrot sliced crosswise
carrot sliced lengthwise
hand lens

Procedure
1. Your teacher will prepare a crosswise slice of a carrot for you.
2. Hold the slice up to the light. Compare what you see with Figure 1 under Data and Observations.
3. Examine the lengthwise slice of the carrot. Use the hand lens. Look at both the inner and outer parts.
4. The outside layer of the root is the epidermis. Lateral roots grow from the epidermal cells and root hairs grow from them. Label the epidermis, lateral roots, and root hairs if all of these structures are present.
5. Inside the epidermis, you will find several layers of large, loosely packed cells that store food. This is the cortex. Food stored in the cortex can be used by other cells of the plant. Label the cortex.
6. Inside the cortex are tubelike cells from xylem vessels that carry water and minerals in the plant. Label the xylem cells.
7. Other tubelike cells inside the cortex carry food in the plant. These cells are called phloem cells. Label the phloem cells.

Data and Observations

Figure 1

L2

238C **CHAPTER 9** Plants

Meeting Different Ability Levels

Content Outline

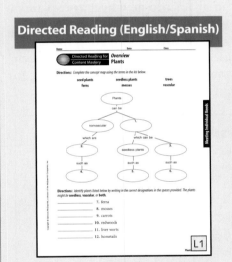

L2

Reinforcement

L2

Enrichment

L3

Directed Reading (English/Spanish)

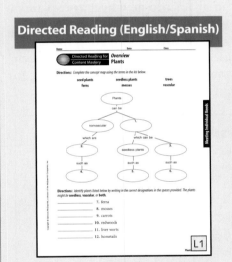

L1

Study Guide

Features
- Contains a study guide page for each section of the chapter
- Reviews key concepts
- Includes answer pages

L2

Reading Essentials

Reading Essentials for Glencoe Science
An Interactive Student Workbook

Features
- Condensed core content
- Actively involves students in reading
- Reinforces key vocabulary

L1

Assessment

Test Practice Workbook

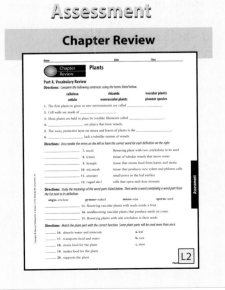

GO ON L2

Chapter Review

L2

Chapter Tests

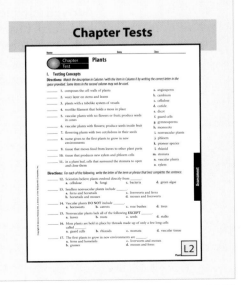

L2

Science Content Background

section 1 ## An Overview of Plants

Origin and Evolution of Plants

Plants probably share an ancestor with multicellular Chlorophyta, the green algae. Common characteristics of plants and green algae include pigments such as chlorophyll a and b and carotenoids, cell walls that consist primarily of cellulose, starch as the primary food-storage product, and similar cell division. Some plants, including mosses, liverworts, and ferns, have free-swimming sperm and require water for fertilization—another feature they have in common with green algae.

Adaptations to Land

Fibers are long, slender cells that are found in the vascular tissue of some plants. They usually contain an organic substance called lignin that makes the walls tough and hard. Fibers add extra support to many terrestrial plants. People weave the fibers of some plants to make products such as rope and cloth.

Classification of Plants

Classification of plants traditionally has been based on morphological characteristics such as the number and arrangement of leaves and the structure of flowers and fruit. Recently, genetic studies have been used to make minor changes in the classification of some plants. However, derived characteristics such as vascular tissue and seed formation and similar, easily observable characteristics are reliable features for classification.

For many years plants have been separated into divisions, but in 1993 the International Botanical Congress made the term *phylum* an acceptable alternative. You may wish to introduce the alternate term to your students.

section 2 ## Seedless Plants

Less Familiar Plants

Liverworts and hornworts are leafy with creeping gametophyte forms. Mosses have distinct leaflike and stemlike structures, but because they do not contain vascular tissue, they are not homologous to the leaves and stems of vascular plants. Some liverworts produce structures called gemma cups on their surfaces. Groups of cells in these structures are washed out of the cup when it rains. These cells can grow into new liverwort plants.

Seedless vascular plants include whisk ferns (Psilophyta), club mosses (Lycopoda), horsetails (Sphenophyta), and ferns (Pterophyta). In each of these divisions, motile sperm require water to swim to the egg.

Teacher to Teacher
Catherine C. Walker, Teacher
Martin Middle School
Raleigh, NC

"Writing vocabulary words on large index cards and posting them above the chalkboard helps my learning-disabled students. They can use these cards to spell the terms correctly on their tests and quizzes. It is like a word bank."

Catherine C. Walker

Pat Watson/The Image Works

headersegment**Helpingsegment

Helping You Prepare

section 3 Seed Plants

Origins

Seed plants appeared suddenly about 65 million years ago, at the beginning of the Cretaceous Period. These plants dominated the land. They developed sperm-containing pollen grains that could be transported from plant to plant without water. The development of an embryo inside a protective seed coat allowed seeds to survive harsh conditions for long periods. About 200,000 of the more than 260,000 species of plants in existence today are seed plants.

Vascular Tissue

The first vascular plants appeared no later than the early Silurian Period, some 430 million years ago. Early vascular plants had stems that formed as a result of primary growth—growth from plant tips. Stems had vascular cylinders with conducting functions, as they do in modern vascular plants. Secondary growth, found in conifers and some dicots, is an important early development. It arises by mitotic divisions of cambium tissues and increases the plant's girth.

Xylem tissue is made of tracheids and vessel elements that carry water and dissolved minerals. Tracheids are found in all plants with vascular tissue, but vessel elements are limited almost exclusively to angiosperms. Both are long, tube-like cells that have thick cell walls. Small openings called pits allow water to seep through the cell walls from tracheid to tracheid. Vessels lack transverse end walls and form continuous pipelines through which water can flow.

Unlike xylem tissue, phloem tissue is living. It is composed mostly of sieve-tube elements and companion cells. Sieve-tube elements are cells that carry the products of photosynthesis throughout the plant. Their cell walls are thinner than those of cells found in xylem. Cytoplasm

John Gerlach/Tom Stack & Associates

extends from one sieve-tube element to the next through structures called sieve plates. Since mature sieve-tube cells have no nuclei, companion cells help with their metabolism.

chapter content resources

Internet Resources

For additional content background, visit **life.msscience.com** to:

- access your book online
- find references to related articles in popular science magazines
- access Web links with related content background
- access current events with science journal topics

Print Resources

Biology of Plants, by Peter Raven, W.H. Freeman, 1999

The Botany Coloring Book, by Paul Young, Harper 1982

Botany for Gardeners, An Introduction and Guide, by Brian Capon, Timber Press, 1992

**CHAPTERsegment

CHAPTER 9 Helping You Prepare **238F**

Chapter Vocabulary

cuticle, p. 242
cellulose, p. 242
vascular plant, p. 245
nonvascular plant, p. 245
rhizoid, p. 246
pioneer species, p. 247
stomata, p. 253
guard cell, p. 253
xylem, p. 255
phloem, p. 255
cambium, p. 255
gymnosperm, p. 256
angiosperm, p. 257
monocot, p. 258
dicot, p. 258

Science Journal Student responses will vary. Most plants have stems, leaves or leaflike structures, roots or rootlike structures, and chlorophyll, and produce their own food through photosynthesis. All plants are multicellular. All plant cells are surrounded by a cell wall.

INTERACTIVE CHALKBOARD with Image Bank

PowerPoint® Presentations

This CD-ROM is an editable Microsoft® PowerPoint® presentation that includes:
- a pre-made presentation for every chapter
- interactive graphics
- animations
- audio clips
- image bank
- all new section and chapter questions
- Standardized Test Practice
- transparencies
- pre-lab questions for all labs
- Foldables directions
- links to life.msscience.com

chapter 9

Plants

chapter preview

sections

1 **An Overview of Plants**

2 **Seedless Plants**

3 **Seed Plants**
   Lab *Identifying Conifers*
   Lab *Plants as Medicine*

   Virtual Lab *What is the life cycle of a simple plant?*

How are all plants alike?

Plants are found nearly everywhere on Earth. A tropical rain forest like this one is crowded with lush, green plants. When you look at a plant, what do you expect to see? Do all plants have green leaves? Do all plants produce flowers and seeds?

Science Journal Write three characteristics that you think all plants have in common.

238

Theme Connection

Stability and Change This chapter emphasizes adaptations that allow plants to adapt, survive, and reproduce in various environments.

About the Photo

Forest Zones Tropical rain forests grow in equatorial regions with warm, wet weather. These forests can be divided into four zones. At the bottom is the shady forest floor. Next is the understory, a dark, cool region below the leaves of most rain forest trees. Next is the canopy, formed by the leafy treetops. Above that are the emergents—tall trees that rise above the canopy.

Start-Up Activities

How do you use plants?

Plants are just about everywhere—in parks and gardens, by streams, on rocks, in houses, and even on dinner plates. Do you use plants for things other than food?

1. Brainstorm with two other classmates and make a list of everything that you use in a day that comes from plants.
2. Compare your list with those of other groups in your class.
3. Search through old magazines for images of the items on your list.
4. As a class, build a bulletin board display of the magazine images.
5. **Think Critically** In your Science Journal, list things that were made from plants 100 years or more ago but today are made from plastics, steel, or some other material.

Preview this chapter's content and activities at
life.msscience.com

Plants Make the following Foldable to help identify what you already know, what you want to know, and what you learned about plants.

STEP 1 Fold a vertical sheet of paper from side to side. Make the front edge 1.25 cm shorter than the back edge.

STEP 2 Turn lengthwise and fold into thirds.

STEP 3 Unfold and cut only the top layer along both folds to make three tabs.

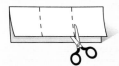

STEP 4 Label each tab as shown.

Identify Questions Before you read the chapter, write what you already know about plants under the left tab of your Foldable, and write questions about what you'd like to know under the center tab. After you read the chapter, list what you learned under the right tab.

An Overview of Plants

as you read

What You'll Learn

- **Identify** characteristics common to all plants.
- **Explain** which plant adaptations make it possible for plants to survive on land.
- **Compare and contrast** vascular and nonvascular plants.

Why It's Important

Plants produce food and oxygen, which are required for life by most organisms on Earth.

Review Vocabulary

species: closely related organisms that share similar characteristics and can reproduce among themselves

New Vocabulary

- cuticle
- cellulose
- vascular plant
- nonvascular plant

What is a plant?

What is the most common sight you see when you walk along nature trails in parks like the one shown in **Figure 1?** Maybe you've taken off your shoes and walked barefoot on soft, cool grass. Perhaps you've climbed a tree to see what things look like from high in its branches. In each instance, plants surrounded you.

If you named all the plants that you know, you probably would include trees, flowers, vegetables, fruits, and field crops like wheat, rice, or corn. Between 260,000 and 300,000 plant species have been discovered and identified. Scientists think many more species are still to be found, mainly in tropical rain forests. Plants are important food sources to humans and other consumers. Without plants, most life on Earth as we know it would not be possible.

Plant Characteristics Plants range in size from microscopic water ferns to giant sequoia trees that are sometimes more than 100 m in height. Most have roots or rootlike structures that hold them in the ground or onto some other object like a rock or another plant. Plants are adapted to nearly every environment on Earth. Some grow in frigid, ice-bound polar regions and others grow in hot, dry deserts. All plants need water, but some plants cannot live unless they are submerged in either freshwater or salt water.

Figure 1 All plants are many-celled and nearly all contain chlorophyll. Grasses, trees, shrubs, mosses, and ferns are all plants.

240 CHAPTER 9 Plants

Section 1 Resource Manager

Chapter *FAST FILE* Resources
Transparency Activity, p. 40
Directed Reading for Content Mastery, pp. 15, 16
Note-taking Worksheets, pp. 29–31
Enrichment, p. 26
Reinforcement, p. 23

Cultural Diversity, p. 19
Life Science Critical Thinking/Problem Solving, p. 9
Performance Assessment in the Science Classroom, p. 55

Plant Cells Like other living things, plants are made of cells. A plant cell has a cell membrane, a nucleus, and other cellular structures. In addition, plant cells have cell walls that provide structure and protection. Animal cells do not have cell walls.

Many plant cells contain the green pigment chlorophyll (KLOR uh fihl) so most plants are green. Plants need chlorophyll to make food using a process called photosynthesis. Chlorophyll is found in a cell structure called a chloroplast. Plant cells from green parts of the plant usually contain many chloroplasts.

Most plant cells have a large, membrane-bound structure called the central vacuole that takes up most of the space inside of the cell. This structure plays an important role in regulating the water content of the cell. Many substances are stored in the vacuole, including the pigments that make some flowers red, blue, or purple.

Origin and Evolution of Plants

Have plants always existed on land? The first plants that lived on land probably could survive only in damp areas. Their ancestors were probably ancient green algae that lived in the sea. Green algae are one-celled or many-celled organisms that use photosynthesis to make food. Today, plants and green algae have the same types of chlorophyll and carotenoids (kuh RAH tun oydz) in their cells. Carotenoids are red, yellow, or orange pigments that also are used for photosynthesis. These facts lead scientists to think that plants and green algae have a common ancestor.

Reading Check *How are plants and green algae alike?*

Fossil Record The fossil record for plants is not like that for animals. Most animals have bones or other hard parts that can fossilize. Plants usually decay before they become fossilized. The oldest fossil plants are about 420 million years old. **Figure 2** shows *Cooksonia,* a fossil of one of these plants. Other fossils of early plants are similar to the ancient green algae. Scientists hypothesize that some of these early plants evolved into the plants that exist today.

Cone-bearing plants, such as pines, probably evolved from a group of plants that grew about 350 million years ago. Fossils of these plants have been dated to about 300 million years ago. It is estimated that flowering plants did not exist until about 120 million years ago. However, the exact origin of flowering plants is not known.

Figure 2 This is a fossil of a plant named *Cooksonia.* These plants grew about 420 million years ago and were about 2.5 cm tall.

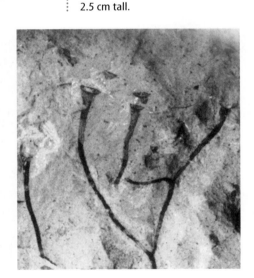

SECTION 1 An Overview of Plants **241**

Visual Learning

Figure 1 Which features of the organisms in the photo suggest they are plants? They are green, grow from soil, and have leaves and stems. L1

IDENTIFYING Misconceptions

Seeds Students may think that all plants produce seeds in flowers. Explain that some plants are seedless and do not make seeds, others produce seeds in cones.

Reading Check

Answer both have similar chlorophyll and carotenoids

Visual Learning

Figure 2 Point out to students the enlarged structures at the top of the *Cooksonia* stems. These are the plant's reproductive structures, where spores are produced. Explain to students that plants similar to this one grew in humid areas and were the main land plants on Earth for several million years.

Differentiated Instruction

Learning Disabled and Visually Impaired If possible, provide petrified wood or fossil casts of plants. Ask students what clues they have that these fossils were once living plants. The fossils may be shaped like plant stems or leaves. L1 IS **Kinesthetic**

Fun Fact

Luminous mosses glow with a greenish light. These mosses are found in caves and have cells shaped like tiny lenses that focus small amounts of light on the chloroplast.

Student results will vary. A source of information is USDA Forest Service.

✓ **Reading Check**

Answer to slow the loss of water

Quick Demo

Plant Cuticles

Materials water-filled spray mister, plant with waxy cuticle

Estimated Time 5 minutes

Procedure Mist water onto the leaves of an indoor plant that has a waxy cuticle. Allow students to observe how the water beads up and runs off the leaves. Ask students to explain how this demonstration shows that the cuticle slows the loss of water from the plant to the air. The cuticle works in both directions—it prevents water from entering or leaving the leaf. L2

Activity

Plant Anatomy Set up stations around the class that contain different plant parts. Have students write the name of each plant part and important information about each as they move from one station to another. L1 LS
Visual-Spatial

INTEGRATE History

Cellulose Plant cell walls are made mostly of cellulose. Anselme Payen, a French scientist, first isolated and identified the chemical composition of cellulose in 1838, while analyzing the chemical makeup of wood. Choose a type of wood and research to learn the uses of that wood. Make a classroom display of research results.

Figure 3 The alga *Spirogyra*, like all algae, must have water to survive. If the pool where it lives dries up, it will die.

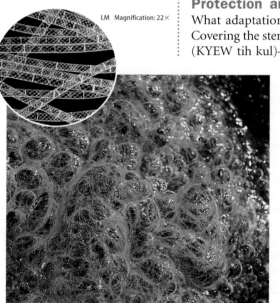
LM Magnification: 22×

Life on Land

Life on land has some advantages for plants. More sunlight and carbon dioxide—needed for photosynthesis—are available on land than in water. During photosynthesis, plants give off oxygen. Long ago, as more and more plants adapted to life on land, the amount of oxygen in Earth's atmosphere increased. This was the beginning for organisms that depend on oxygen.

Adaptations to Land

What is life like for green algae, shown in **Figure 3,** as they float in a shallow pool? The water in the pool surrounds and supports them as the algae make their own food through the process of photosynthesis. Because materials can enter and leave through their cell membranes and cell walls, the algae cells have everything they need to survive as long as they have water.

If the pool begins to dry up, the algae are on damp mud and are no longer supported by water. As the soil becomes drier and drier, the algae will lose water too because water moves through their cell membranes and cell walls from where there is more water to where there is less water. Without enough water in their environment, the algae will die. Plants that live on land have adaptations that allow them to conserve water, as well as other differences that make it possible for survival.

Protection and Support Water is important for plants. What adaptations would help a plant conserve water on land? Covering the stems, leaves, and flowers of many plants is a **cuticle** (KYEW tih kul)—a waxy, protective layer secreted by cells onto the surface of the plant. The cuticle slows the loss of water. The cuticle and other adaptations shown in **Figure 4** enable plants to survive on land.

✓ **Reading Check** *What is the function of a plant's cuticle?*

Supporting itself is another problem for a plant on land. Like all cells, plant cells have cell membranes, but they also have rigid cell walls outside the membrane. Cell walls contain **cellulose** (SEL yuh lohs), which is a chemical compound that plants can make out of sugar. Long chains of cellulose molecules form tangled fibers in plant cell walls. These fibers provide structure and support.

Teacher FYI

Gas Balance Almost all of the oxygen in Earth's atmosphere comes from the release of oxygen during photosynthesis. Plants also absorb carbon dioxide from the atmosphere during photosynthesis. The destruction of vast areas of tropical forest could affect the balance of these atmospheric gases.

Differentiated Instruction

Challenge How might animals have been affected if plants had not adapted to live on land? The evolution of land animals may not have been possible. Plants are the foundation of all land food chains and they produce much of the atmospheric oxygen that land animals need to live. L3

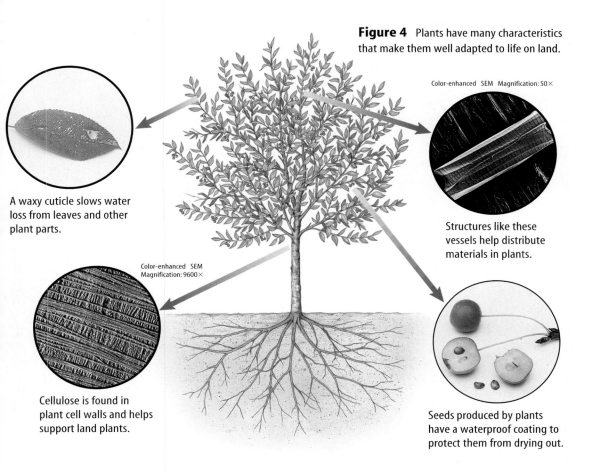

Figure 4 Plants have many characteristics that make them well adapted to life on land.

A waxy cuticle slows water loss from leaves and other plant parts.

Color-enhanced SEM Magnification: 50×

Structures like these vessels help distribute materials in plants.

Color-enhanced SEM Magnification: 9600×

Cellulose is found in plant cell walls and helps support land plants.

Seeds produced by plants have a waterproof coating to protect them from drying out.

Other Cell Wall Substances Cells of some plants secrete other substances into the cellulose that make the cell wall even stronger. Trees, such as oaks and pines, could not grow without these strong cell walls. Wood from trees can be used for construction mostly because of strong cell walls.

Life on land means that each plant cell is not surrounded by water and dissolved nutrients that can move into the cell. Through adaptations, structures developed in many plants that distribute water, nutrients, and food to all plant cells. These structures also help provide support for the plant.

Reproduction Changes in reproduction were necessary if plants were to survive on land. The presence of water-resistant spores helped some plants reproduce successfully. Other plants adapted by producing water-resistant seeds in cones or in flowers that developed into fruits.

Use Science Words

Word Meaning Have students compare the meaning of the word cuticle in relation to plants (protective layer on plant surface) and in relation to the human body (hardened skin at the base of nails). Both are derived from the Latin *cutis* meaning "skin." L2

LS Linguistic

Activity

Adaptation Posters Have students prepare posters that show examples of plant adaptations to life on land. L2 **LS** Visual-Spatial P

Use an Analogy

Plant Pipes Explain that vascular tissue in plants is somewhat like the plumbing in a building. Some pipes, analogous to xylem, bring water up into the building. Other pipes, analogous to phloem, transport materials away. Reinforce that phloem does NOT carry water—it carries dissolved sugars. L2

Discussion

Importance of Plants How have you used or depended upon plants today? oxygen, food, clothing, houses, furniture, books, paper, pencils, fuel L2

 LAB DEMONSTRATION

Purpose to model the function of plant cuticles
Materials water, paper towels, wax paper, paper clips, string
Preparation Tie the string so the towels can hang from it. Cut the towels and wax paper into 10-cm squares.

Procedure Wet three towel squares. Leave one uncovered. Cover one side of another with wax paper. Sandwich a third between two sheets of wax paper. Hang all three with clips. Have students observe how long it takes each towel to dry.
Expected Outcome Uncovered towels dry

more quickly than covered towels.

Assessment

How are towels covered with wax paper like plant leaves with cuticles? Wax paper prevents the towel from drying, as the cuticle prevents water loss from plants. L2

Visualizing Plant Classification

Have students examine the pictures and read the captions. Then ask the following question.

How might an injury to the stem of a vascular plant affect the rest of the plant? Possible answer: Since the stem transports water and nutrients absorbed by the roots to the rest of the plant, an injury could result in the plant becoming dry or some leaves dying from lack of nutrients.

Activity

Examining Seeds Provide students with magnifying lenses and the seeds of a variety of plants, such as sunflower, coconut, peanut, apple, orange, peach, and common garden plants. Have students examine the samples to identify similarities and differences. If fern spores are available, have students compare and contrast these structures with seeds. L2 LS **Visual-Spatial**

NATIONAL GEOGRAPHIC VISUALIZING PLANT CLASSIFICATION

Figure 5

Scientists group plants as either vascular—those with water- and food-conducting cells in their stems—or nonvascular. Vascular plants are further divided into those that produce spores and those that make seeds.

Sunflower

Joint fir

Cycad

Douglas fir

Ginkgo

Horsetail

Club moss

Fern

Moss

Liverwort

Hornwort

Vascular
Flowering
Seed vascular
Joint firs
Cycads
Conifers
Ginkgoes
Seedless vascular
Nonvascular
Mosses
Liverworts
Hornworts
Horsetails
Ferns
Club mosses

Differentiated Instruction

Challenge Have students investigate how nonvascular plants transport food and water to cells. Nonvascular plants have rhizoids, which are rootlike structures that collect water and nutrients from soil. The plant transports these materials throughout the rest of the body in one of two ways. Water and nutrients spread by diffusion or are carried by simple conducting tissues. Because both of these methods are very slow, plant size is limited. Usually nonvascular plants are no more than 2 cm in height. L3

Classification of Plants

The plant kingdom is classified into major groups called divisions. A division is the same as a phylum in other kingdoms. Another way to group plants is as vascular (VAS kyuh lur) or nonvascular plants, as illustrated in **Figure 5. Vascular plants** have tubelike structures that carry water, nutrients, and other substances throughout the plant. **Nonvascular plants** do not have these tubelike structures and use other ways to move water and substances.

Naming Plants Why do biologists call a pecan tree *Carya illinoiensis* and a white oak *Quercus alba*? They are using words that accurately name the plant. In the third century B.C., most plants were grouped as trees, shrubs, or herbs and placed into smaller groups by leaf characteristics. This simple system survived until late in the eighteenth century when a Swedish botanist, Carolus Linnaeus, developed a new system. His new system used many characteristics to classify a plant. He also developed a way to name plants called binomial nomenclature (bi NOH mee ul • NOH mun klay chur). Under this system, every plant species is given a unique two-word name like the names above for the pecan tree and white oak and for the two daisies in **Figure 6.**

Shasta daisy, *Chrysanthemum maximum*

African daisy, *Dimorphotheca aurantiaca*

Figure 6 Although these two plants are both called daisies, they are not the same species of plant. Using their binomial names helps eliminate the confusion that might come from using their common names.

section 1 review

Summary

What is a plant?
- All plant cells are surrounded by a cell wall.
- Many plant cells contain chlorophyll.

Origin and Evolution of Plants
- Ancestors of land plants were probably ancient green algae.

Adaptations to Land
- A waxy cuticle helps conserve water.
- Cellulose strengthens cell walls.

Classification of Plants
- The plant kingdom is divided into two groups—nonvascular plants and vascular plants.
- Vascular tissues transport nutrients.

Self Check

1. **List** the characteristics of plants.
2. **Compare and contrast** the characteristics of vascular and nonvascular plants.
3. **Identify** three adaptations that allow plants to survive on land.
4. **Explain** why binomial nomenclature is used to name plants.
5. **Thinking Critically** If you left a board lying on the grass for a few days, what would happen to the grass underneath the board? Why?

Applying Skills

6. **Form a hypothesis** about adaptations a land plant might undergo if it lived submerged in water.

3 Assess

DAILY INTERVENTION

Check for Understanding
Visual-Spatial Obtain a sunflower with stem and leaves, or a large color photograph of one. Direct students to pick out the characteristics that would help this plant survive on land. cuticle that protects leaves and stem from drying out, tall stem supported by cellulose, vascular structures to distribute materials throughout the plant, seeds protected by hard covering L2

Reteach

Algae Show students examples of a filamentous green alga and a green plant. Use live specimens or photographs. Compare the two by pointing out the structures present only on the green plant, and summarizing how each one contributes to the ability of plants to live on land. cuticle prevents water loss; roots or rootlike structures absorb water and nutrients from soil; stems or stemlike structures hold plant upright; photosynthesis takes place in leaves or leaflike structures; vascular tissues move water and food through plant L2

✓ Assessment

Oral Have students write additional questions not included in the Section Assessment and quiz each other. **Use Performance Assessment in the Science Classroom,** p. 91. L2

section 1 review

1. eukaryotic cells with cell walls; pigments for photosynthesis; most have roots, stems, and leaves
2. Both have eukaryotic cells with cell walls and carry out photosynthesis. Vascular plants have tubelike structures to carry materials; nonvascular plants do not.
3. Adaptations listed may include the cuticle, vascular tissue, and seeds.
4. It gives every species of plant a unique two-word name.
5. The grass might die. Light is needed for photosynthesis.
6. Possible answers: A thicker cuticle or a system for pumping water from cells could be needed; some might have a long stem to raise leaves above the water.

Seedless Plants

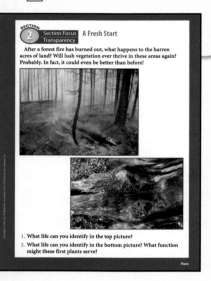
as you read

What You'll Learn
- **Distinguish** between characteristics of seedless nonvascular plants and seedless vascular plants.
- **Identify** the importance of some nonvascular and vascular plants.

Why It's Important
Seedless plants are among the first to grow in damaged or disturbed environments and help build soil for the growth of other plants.

Review Vocabulary
spore: waterproof reproductive cell

New Vocabulary
- rhizoid
- pioneer species

Figure 7 The seedless nonvascular plants include mosses, liverworts, and hornworts.

Seedless Nonvascular Plants

If you were asked to name the parts of a plant, you probably would list roots, stems, leaves, and flowers. You also might know that many plants grow from seeds. However, some plants, called nonvascular plants, don't grow from seeds and they do not have all of these parts. **Figure 7** shows some common types of nonvascular plants.

Nonvascular plants are usually just a few cells thick and only 2 cm to 5 cm in height. Most have stalks that look like stems and green, leaflike growths. Instead of roots, threadlike structures called **rhizoids** (RI zoydz) anchor them where they grow. Most nonvascular plants grow in places that are damp. Water is absorbed and distributed directly through their cell membranes and cell walls. Nonvascular plants also do not have flowers or cones that produce seeds. They reproduce by spores. Mosses, liverworts, and hornworts are examples of nonvascular plants.

Mosses Most nonvascular plants are classified as mosses, like the ones in **Figure 7.** They have green, leaflike growths arranged around a central stalk. Their rhizoids are made of many cells. Sometimes stalks with caps grow from moss plants. Reproductive cells called spores are produced in the caps of these stalks. Mosses often grow on tree trunks and rocks or the ground. Although they commonly are found in damp areas, some are adapted to living in deserts.

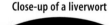
Close-up of moss plants

Close-up of a liverwort

Close-up of a hornwort

Section 2 Resource Manager

Figure 8 Mosses can grow in the thin layer of soil that covers these rocks.

Liverworts In the ninth century, liverworts were thought to be useful in treating diseases of the liver. The suffix *-wort* means "herb," so the word *liverwort* means "herb for the liver." Liverworts are rootless plants with flattened, leaflike bodies, as shown in **Figure 7.** They usually have one-celled rhizoids.

Hornworts Most hornworts are less than 2.5 cm in diameter and have a flattened body like liverworts, as shown in **Figure 7.** Unlike other nonvascular plants, almost all hornworts have only one chloroplast in each of their cells. Hornworts get their name from their spore-producing structures, which look like tiny horns of cattle.

 **Nonvascular Plants and the Environment** Mosses and liverworts are important in the ecology of many areas. Although they require moist conditions to grow and reproduce, many of them can withstand long, dry periods. They can grow in thin soil and in soils where other plants could not grow, as shown in **Figure 8.**

Spores of mosses and liverworts are carried by the wind. They will grow into plants if growing conditions are right. Mosses often are among the first plants to grow in new or disturbed environments, such as lava fields or after a forest fire. Organisms that are the first to grow in new or disturbed areas are called **pioneer species.** As pioneer plants grow and die, decaying material builds up. This, along with the slow breakdown of rocks, builds soil. When enough soil has formed, other organisms can move into the area.

 *Why are pioneer plant species important in disturbed environments?*

Mini LAB

Measuring Water Absorption by a Moss

Procedure
1. Place a few teaspoons of *Sphagnum* **moss** on a piece of **cheesecloth.** Gather the corners of the cloth and twist, then tie them securely to form a ball.
2. Weigh the ball.
3. Put 200 mL of **water** in a **container** and add the ball.
4. After 15 min, remove the ball and drain the excess water into the container.
5. Weigh the ball and measure the amount of water left in the container.
6. Wash your hands after handling the moss.

Analysis
In your **Science Journal,** calculate how much water was absorbed by the *Sphagnum* moss.

Curriculum Connection

Varieties of Ferns

Materials fronds from a variety of fern species, some with sori and with attached rhizomes, fern gametophytes (optional), magnifying lenses (optional)

Estimated Time 10–30 minutes

Procedure Have students note differences in shape, size, and color of fern fronds. Point out the location of sori on different species of ferns. Show students the rhizomes and, if possible, allow them to use magnifying lenses to observe a fern gametophyte.

Applying Science

Answers

1. Brazil
2. Answers should include some of the countries shaded on the map.
3. Some plants may become extinct before they can be studied.

Teacher FYI

Aspirin The active ingredient in aspirin is acetylsalicylic acid, which is also found in willow bark. This chemical interferes with the body's production of prostaglandins. These hormone-like substances aid transmission of pain signals to the brain and help raise body temperature to fight infection. That is why taking aspirin helps dull pain and fight fever.

Science Online

Topic: Medicinal Plants
Visit life.mssience.com for Web links to information about plants used as medicines.

Activity In your Science Journal, list four medicinal plants and their uses.

Seedless Vascular Plants

The fern in **Figure 9** is growing next to some moss plants. Ferns and mosses are alike in one way. Both reproduce by spores instead of seeds. However, ferns are different from mosses because they have vascular tissue. The vascular tissue in seedless vascular plants, like ferns, is made up of long, tubelike cells. These cells carry water, minerals, and food to cells throughout the plant. Why is vascular tissue an advantage to a plant? Nonvascular plants like the moss are usually only a few cells thick. Each cell absorbs water directly from its environment. As a result, these plants cannot grow large. Vascular plants, on the other hand, can grow bigger and thicker because the vascular tissue distributes water and nutrients to all plant cells.

Applying Science

What is the value of rain forests?

Throughout history, cultures have used plants for medicines. Some cultures used willow bark to cure headaches. Willow bark contains salicylates (suh LIH suh layts), the main ingredient in aspirin. Heart problems were treated with foxglove, which is the main source of digitalis (dih juh TAH lus), a drug prescribed for heart problems. Have all medicinal plants been identified?

Identifying the Problem

Tropical rain forests have the largest variety of organisms on Earth. Many plant species are still unknown. These forests are being destroyed rapidly. The map below shows the rate of destruction of the rain forests.

Some scientists estimate that most tropical rain forests will be destroyed in 30 years.

Solving the Problem

1. What country has the most rain forest destroyed each year?
2. Where can scientists go to study rain forest plants before the plants are destroyed?
3. Predict how the destruction of rain forests might affect research on new drugs from plants.

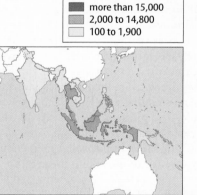

Deforested annually (km²)
- more than 15,000
- 2,000 to 14,800
- 100 to 1,900

Differentiated Instruction

Challenge Have motivated students read natural history books to find out why ferns have such common names as Boston fern, maidenhair fern, staghorn fern, cinnamon fern, hay-scented fern, and bracken fern. These names have to do with the shapes or scents of their leaves. L3

Visually Impaired Prepare samples of mosses, liverworts, and ferns for the class labeled with large print. Provide large magnifying glasses for closer observation of the plants. L2

Types of Seedless Vascular Plants

Besides ferns, seedless vascular plants include ground pines, spike mosses, and horsetails. About 1,000 species of ground pines, spike mosses, and horsetails are known to exist. Ferns are more abundant, with at least 12,000 known species. Many species of seedless vascular plants are known only from fossils. They flourished during the warm, moist period 360 million to 286 million years ago. Fossil records show that some horsetails grew 15 m tall, unlike modern species, which grow only 1 m to 2 m tall.

Ferns The largest group of seedless vascular plants is the ferns. They include many different forms, as shown in **Figure 10.** They have stems, leaves, and roots. Fern leaves are called fronds. Ferns produce spores in structures that usually are found on the underside of their fronds. Thousands of species of ferns now grow on Earth, but many more existed long ago. From clues left in rock layers, scientists infer that about 360 million years ago much of Earth was tropical. Steamy swamps covered large areas. The tallest plants were species of ferns. The ancient ferns grew as tall as 25 m—as tall as the tallest fern species alive today. Most modern tree ferns are about 3 m to 5 m in height and grow in tropical regions of the world.

Figure 9 The mosses and ferns pictured here are seedless plants. **Explain** *why the fern can grow taller than the moss.*

Figure 10 Ferns come in many different shapes and sizes.

The sword fern has a typical fern shape. Spores are produced in structures on the back of the frond.

This fern grows on other plants, not in the soil.
Infer *why it's called the staghorn fern.*

Tree ferns, like this one in Hawaii, grow in tropical areas.

Discussion

Mosses How can you tell the difference between true mosses and club mosses? True mosses produce spores in capsules on stalks. Club mosses produce spores at the end of stems in structures that look like tiny pine cones. [L2]

Reading Check

Answer at the ends of stems in structures that look like pine cones

---

Quick Demo

Horsetails

Materials horsetail plants (Latin name *Equisetum*)

Estimated Time 5 minutes

Procedure Demonstrate (and allow students to feel) how the grittiness of the plant's cell walls could be useful for scouring. [L2]
[IS] **Kinesthetic**

Caption Answer

Figure 12 in a conelike structure at the tips of some stems

Discussion

Tall Plants The presence of vascular tissue allows ferns to grow taller than other seedless, nonvascular plants. Why would this trait make them more successful than other seedless plants? The taller a plant can grow, the more likely it is that it will receive light and thus be able to photosynthesize.

Figure 11 Photographers once used the dry, flammable spores of club mosses as flash powder. It burned rapidly and produced the light that was needed to take photographs.

Figure 12 Most horsetails grow in damp areas and are less than 1 m tall.
Identify where spores would be produced on this plant.

Club Mosses Ground pines and spike mosses are groups of plants that often are called club mosses. They are related more closely to ferns than to mosses. These seedless vascular plants have needle-like leaves. Spores are produced at the end of the stems in structures that look like tiny pine cones. Ground pines, shown in **Figure 11,** are found from arctic regions to the tropics, but rarely in large numbers. In some areas, they are endangered because they have been over collected to make wreaths and other decorations.

Reading Check *Where are spores in club mosses produced?*

Spike mosses resemble ground pines. One species of spike moss, the resurrection plant, is adapted to desert conditions. When water is scarce, the plant curls up and seems dead. When water becomes available, the resurrection plant unfurls its green leaves and begins making food again. The plant can repeat this process whenever necessary.

Horsetails The stem structure of horsetails is unique among the vascular plants. The stem is jointed and has a hollow center surrounded by a ring of vascular tissue. At each joint, leaves grow out from around the stem. In **Figure 12,** you can see these joints. If you pull on a horsetail stem, it will pop apart in sections. Like the club mosses, spores from horsetails are produced in a conelike structure at the tips of some stems. The stems of the horsetails contain silica, a gritty substance found in sand. For centuries, horsetails have been used for polishing objects, sharpening tools, and scouring cooking utensils. Another common name for horsetails is scouring rush.

Importance of Seedless Plants

When many ancient seedless plants died, they became submerged in water and mud before they decomposed. As this plant material built up, it became compacted and compressed and eventually turned into coal—a process that took millions of years.

Today, a similar process is taking place in bogs, which are poorly drained areas of land that contain decaying plants. The plants in bogs are mostly seedless plants like mosses and ferns.

Differentiated Instruction

English-Language Learners Provide each student with a list of terms that can be used to describe nonvascular plants and seedless vascular plants. Have students write paragraphs that compare and contrast these plants using the terms given. Terms might include *nonvascular, mosses, rhizoids, moist, liverworts, ferns, leaves, roots,* and *horsetails.* [L2]

Visual Learning

Figure 13 If possible, have students examine samples of peat and coal. Remind them that peat is the first stage of coal formation. How does the appearance of peat differ from that of coal? Peat is lighter in color and isn't as rocklike as coal. [L2]

Peat When bog plants die, the waterlogged soil slows the decay process. Over time, these decaying plants are compressed into a substance called peat. Peat, which forms from the remains of sphagnum moss, is mined from bogs to use as a low-cost fuel in places such as Ireland and Russia, as shown in **Figure 13.** Peat supplies about one-third of Ireland's energy requirements. Scientists hypothesize that over time, if additional layers of soil bury, compact, and compress the peat, it will become coal.

Uses of Seedless Vascular Plants Many people keep ferns as houseplants. Ferns also are sold widely as landscape plants for shady areas. Peat and sphagnum mosses also are used for gardening. Peat is an excellent soil conditioner, and sphagnum moss often is used to line hanging baskets. Ferns also are used as weaving material for basketry.

Although most mosses are not used for food, parts of many other seedless vascular plants can be eaten. The rhizomes and young fronds of some ferns are edible. The dried stems of one type of horsetail can be ground into flour. Seedless plants have been used as folk medicines for hundreds of years. For example, ferns have been used to treat bee stings, burns, fevers, and even dandruff.

Figure 13 Peat is cut from bogs and used for a fuel in some parts of Europe.

---

section 2 review

Summary

Seedless Nonvascular Plants
- Seedless nonvascular plants include mosses, liverworts, and hornworts.
- They are usually only a few cells thick and no more than a few centimeters tall.
- They produce spores rather than seeds.

Seedless Vascular Plants
- Seedless vascular plants include ferns, club mosses, and horsetails.
- Vascular plants grow taller and can live farther from water than nonvascular plants.

Importance of Seedless Plants
- Nonvascular plants help build new soil.
- Coal deposits formed from ancient seedless plants that were buried in water and mud before they began to decay.

Self Check

1. **Compare and contrast** the characteristics of mosses and ferns.
2. **Explain** what fossil records tell about seedless plants that lived on Earth long ago.
3. **Identify** growing conditions in which you would expect to find pioneer plants such as mosses and liverworts.
4. **Summarize** the functions of vascular tissues.
5. **Think Critically** The electricity that you use every day might be produced by burning coal. What is the connection between electricity production and seedless vascular plants?

Applying Math

6. **Use Fractions** Approximately 8,000 species of liverworts and 9,000 species of mosses exist today. Estimate what fraction of these seedless nonvascular plants are mosses.

---

section 2 review

1. alike: reproduce by spores; different: unlike mosses, ferns have vascular tissue
2. Seedless plants dominated Earth long ago and grew much larger than they grow today.
3. in disturbed or new environments
4. The vascular system carries water, minerals, and food to plant cells. This allows the plant to grow bigger and thicker. The cells of vascular tissue also provide support.
5. Seedless plants (both vascular and nonvascular) formed ancient forests that decayed and became the coal we burn today as fuel.
6. 9/17

---

1 Motivate

Bellringer

Section Focus Transparencies also are available on the Interactive Chalkboard CD-ROM.

L2 ELL

1. What are some advantages to having bonsai plants? What might some disadvantages be?
2. What qualities do you think would be important in practicing bonsai?

Tie to Prior Knowledge

Edible Seeds Invite students to brainstorm a list of plant seeds that they eat or see regularly. Possible answers: any type of edible nut, sunflower seeds, sesame or poppy seeds, coconuts, seeds inside fruits L2

as you read

What You'll Learn

- **Identify** the characteristics of seed plants.
- **Explain** the structures and functions of roots, stems, and leaves.
- **Describe** the main characteristics and importance of gymnosperms and angiosperms.
- **Compare** similarities and differences between monocots and dicots.

Why It's Important

Humans depend on seed plants for food, clothing, and shelter.

Review Vocabulary
seed: plant embryo and food supply in a protective coating

New Vocabulary

- stomata
- guard cell
- xylem
- phloem
- cambium
- gymnosperm
- angiosperm
- monocot
- dicot

Characteristics of Seed Plants

What foods from plants have you eaten today? Apples? Potatoes? Carrots? Peanut butter and jelly sandwiches? All of these foods and more come from seed plants.

Most of the plants you are familiar with are seed plants. Most seed plants have leaves, stems, roots, and vascular tissue. They also produce seeds, which usually contain an embryo and stored food. The stored food is the source of energy for the embryo's early growth as it develops into a plant. Most of the plant species that have been identified in the world today are seed plants. The seed plants generally are classified into two major groups—gymnosperms (JIHM nuh spurmz) and angiosperms (AN jee uh spurmz).

Leaves Most seed plants have leaves. Leaves are the organs of the plant where the food-making process—photosynthesis—usually occurs. Leaves come in many shapes, sizes, and colors. Examine the structure of a typical leaf, shown in **Figure 14.**

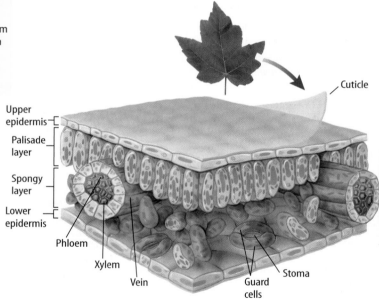

Cuticle

Upper epidermis

Palisade layer

Spongy layer

Lower epidermis

Phloem

Xylem

Vein

Guard cells

Stoma

Figure 14 The structure of a typical leaf is adapted for photosynthesis.
Explain why cells in the palisade layer have more chloroplasts than cells in the spongy layer.

252 CHAPTER 9 Plants

Section 3 Resource Manager

Chapter *FAST FILE* Resources
Transparency Activity, pp. 42, 43–44
Directed Reading for Content Mastery, pp. 17, 18
MiniLAB, p. 4
Enrichment, p. 28
Reinforcement, p. 25

Lab Activities, pp. 9–10, 11–12
Lab Worksheet, pp. 5–6, 7–8
Performance Assessment in the Science Classroom, p. 61
Lab Management and Safety, p. 61

Leaf Cell Layers A typical leaf is made of several different layers of cells. On the upper and lower surfaces of a leaf is a thin layer of cells called the epidermis, which covers and protects the leaf. A waxy cuticle coats the epidermis of some leaves. Most leaves have small openings in the epidermis called **stomata** (STOH muh tuh) (singular, *stoma*). Stomata allow carbon dioxide, water, and oxygen to enter into and exit from a leaf. Each stoma is surrounded by two **guard cells** that open and close it.

Just below the upper epidermis is the palisade layer. It consists of closely packed, long, narrow cells that usually contain many chloroplasts. Most of the food produced by plants is made in the palisade cells. Between the palisade layer and the lower epidermis is the spongy layer. It is a layer of loosely arranged cells separated by air spaces. In a leaf, veins containing vascular tissue are found in the spongy layer.

Stems The trunk of a tree is really the stem of the tree. Stems usually are located above ground and support the branches, leaves, and reproductive structures. Materials move between leaves and roots through the vascular tissue in the stem. Stems also can have other functions, as shown in **Figure 15.**

Plant stems are either herbaceous (hur BAY shus) or woody. Herbaceous stems usually are soft and green, like the stems of a tulip, while trees and shrubs have hard, rigid, woody stems. Lumber comes from woody stems.

Figure 15 Some plants have stems with special functions.

These potatoes are stems that grow underground and store food for the plant.

The stems of this cactus store water and can carry on photosynthesis.

Some stems of this grape plant help it climb on other plants.

Mini LAB

Observing Water Moving in a Plant

Procedure 🔧 📖 🚰 📋

1. Into a **clear container** pour **water** to a depth of 1.5 cm. Add 25 drops of **red food coloring** to the water.
2. Put the root end of a **green onion** into the container. Do not cut the onion in any way. Wash your hands.
3. The next day, examine the outside of the onion. Peel off the onion's layers and examine them. **WARNING:** *Do not eat the onion.*

Analysis
In your **Science Journal,** infer how the location of red color inside the onion might be related to vascular tissue.

Try at Home

---

2 Teach

Caption Answer

Figure 14 This layer is more likely to be exposed to the Sun.

Mini LAB

Purpose Students observe how water moves through vascular tissue. L2 IS **Visual-Spatial**

Materials water, clear container, red food coloring, green onion, magnifying lens, metric ruler

Teaching Strategy Have students predict what will happen to the green onion. Celery stems can be used in place of green onions.

Analysis
Food coloring and water moved into the onion's roots and up through its vascular tissue.

Assessment

Performance Have students identify vascular tissue in celery. Use **Performance Assessment in the Science Classroom,** p. 89.

Try at Home

Teacher FYI

Leaves Leaves come in a variety of sizes and shapes. Duckweed leaves are only millimeters across, while raffia palm leaves can be 20 m long and 2.4 m wide. Maples have broad, flat leaves; conifers have needlelike leaves. Cactus spines are modified leaves that reduce water loss and help protect the plant from hungry animals.

Figure 16 The root system of a tree can be as long as the tree can be tall.

Infer *why the root system of a tree would need to be so large.*

Roots Imagine a lone tree growing on top of a hill. What is the largest part of this plant? Maybe you guessed the trunk or the branches. Did you consider the roots, like those shown in **Figure 16?** The root systems of most plants are as large or larger than the aboveground stems and leaves.

Roots are important to plants. Water and other substances enter a plant through its roots. Roots have vascular tissue in which water and dissolved substances move from the soil through the stems to the leaves. Roots also act as anchors, preventing plants from being blown away by wind or washed away by moving water. Underground root systems support other plant parts that are aboveground—the stem, branches, and leaves of a tree. Sometimes, part of or all of the roots are aboveground, too.

Roots can store food. When you eat carrots or beets, you eat roots that contain stored food. Plants that continue growing from one year to the next use this stored food to begin new growth in the spring. Plants that grow in dry areas often have roots that store water.

Root tissues also can perform functions such as absorbing oxygen that is used in the process of respiration. Because water does not contain as much oxygen as air does, plants that grow with their roots in water might not be able to absorb enough oxygen. Some swamp plants have roots that grow partially out of the water and take in oxygen from the air. In order to perform all these functions, the root systems of plants must be large.

☑ Reading Check   *What are several functions of roots in plants?*

Visual Learning

Figure 16 How could planting a large tree such as this close to a building cause a problem? Students should infer that its extensive root system could interfere with the building's foundation or pipes leading into the building. L2

Vascular Tissue Three tissues usually make up the vascular system in a seed plant. **Xylem** (ZI lum) tissue is made up of hollow, tubular cells that are stacked one on top of the other to form a structure called a vessel. These vessels transport water and dissolved substances from the roots throughout the plant. The thick cell walls of xylem are also important because they help support the plant.

Phloem (FLOH em) is a plant tissue also made up of tubular cells that are stacked to form structures called tubes. Tubes are different from vessels. Phloem tubes move food from where it is made to other parts of the plant where it is used or stored.

In some plants, a cambium is between xylem and phloem. **Cambium** (KAM bee um) is a tissue that produces most of the new xylem and phloem cells. The growth of this new xylem and phloem increases the thickness of stems and roots. All three tissues are illustrated in **Figure 17.**

INTEGRATE Health

Vascular Systems Plants have vascular tissue, and you have a vascular system. Your vascular system transports oxygen, food, and wastes through blood vessels. Instead of xylem and phloem, your blood vessels include veins and arteries. In your Science Journal write a paragraph describing the difference between veins and arteries.

INTEGRATE Health

Vascular Systems Arteries carry blood away from the heart; veins carry blood toward the heart. Except for those vessels going to and from the lungs, arteries carry oxygen-rich blood, and veins carry oxygen-poor blood.

Career Medical scientists study human diseases and their cures. Similarly, plant pathologists study plant diseases and pests and develop methods for controlling these problems. Have students research other plant-related careers and share their findings with the class. Possible careers include horticulture, ecology, genetics, forestry, and food science. L2

Caption Answer
Figure 17 phloem

Figure 17 The vascular tissue of some seed plants includes xylem, phloem, and cambium. **Identify** *which of these tissues transports food throughout the plant.*

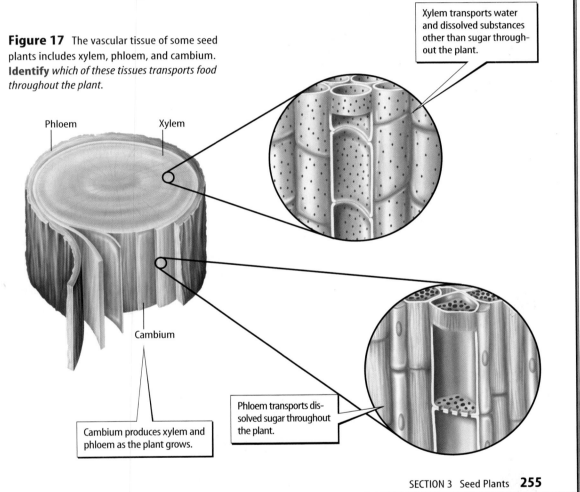

Phloem   Xylem

Xylem transports water and dissolved substances other than sugar throughout the plant.

Cambium

Cambium produces xylem and phloem as the plant grows.

Phloem transports dissolved sugar throughout the plant.

Fun Fact

An aphid drinks sap from plants by piercing the plant's phloem with its hollow mouthpart.

Curriculum Connection

History Theophrastus (ca. 372–ca. 287 B.C.) is known as the father of botany. His botanical works were so complete that nearly 1,800 years passed before any new discoveries were made. Have students research the name and contributions of other botanists and compile their findings into one time line. Bauhin, Linnaeus, Bailey, Gesner, Hales, Nageli, and Ray are botanists students may name. P
L3

Teacher FYI

Tree Rings The pattern of rings in tree trunks provides information about a tree's life. Good growth years produce wide rings. Slower growth, due to less favorable conditions, forms a narrower ring. If there is an extended dry period between two wet periods, two rings will be produced. Rings are wider on the sunny side of a tree.

256 CHAPTER 9 Plants

Discussion

Gymnosperms Is an apple tree a gymnosperm? Explain. No, it has seeds encased in fruits. Is a maple tree whose leaves turn golden and red in fall a gymnosperm? Explain. No, its seeds are enclosed in a dry, winged fruit.

Activity

Cones If possible, ask each student to find and bring to class a cone from a conifer in the area. Cones may be found in yards, in parks, and along routes to and from school. Have them compare and contrast the cones in class and make sketches and written descriptions of each type of cone. Discuss how the cones are alike and different. Although they have the same basic structure, they differ in size, color, and shape. L1 LS **Visual-Spatial**

Caption Answer

Figure 18 Most gymnosperms do not lose all of their leaves in the fall.

Reading Check

Answer Cones are the reproductive structures of the plants; seeds develop on female cones.

Figure 18 The gymnosperms include four divisions of plants.

Conifers are the largest, most diverse division. Most conifers are evergreen plants, such as this ponderosa pine (above).

About 100 species of cycads exist today. Only one genus is native to the United States.

More than half of the 70 species of gnetophytes, such as this joint fir, are in one genus.

The ginkgoes are represented by one living species. Ginkgoes lose their leaves in the fall.
Explain *how this is different from most gymnosperms.*

Gymnosperms

The oldest trees alive are gymnosperms. A bristlecone pine tree in the White Mountains of eastern California is estimated to be 4,900 years old. **Gymnosperms** are vascular plants that produce seeds that are not protected by fruit. The word *gymnosperm* comes from the Greek language and means "naked seed." Another characteristic of gymnosperms is that they do not have flowers. Leaves of most gymnosperms are needlelike or scalelike. Many gymnosperms are called evergreens because some green leaves always remain on their branches.

Four divisions of plants—conifers, cycads, ginkgoes, and gnetophytes (NE tuh fites)—are classified as gymnosperms. **Figure 18** shows examples of the four divisions. You are probably most familiar with the division Coniferophyta (kuh NIH fur uh fi tuh), the conifers. Pines, firs, spruces, redwoods, and junipers belong to this division. It contains the greatest number of gymnosperm species. All conifers produce two types of cones—male and female. Both types usually are found on the same plant. Cones are the reproductive structures of conifers. Seeds develop on the female cone but not on the male cone.

Reading Check
What is the importance of cones to gymnosperms?

Differentiated Instruction

English-Language Learners Bring branches from different conifers to class. Identify the tree species each branch is from and write the names on the board. Have students feel the differences in texture and shape of the leaves. Students should choose a branch, copy its name, and then write a description of it. L1 LS **Kinesthetic**

Active Reading

Think-Pair-Share This strategy encourages students to think first before discussing their ideas or thoughts about a topic. Ask students to respond to a question. After recording ideas, have partners share responses to the question. Finally, ask students to share responses with the class. Have students become involved in a Think-Pair-Share about seed plants. L2

Angiosperms

When people are asked to name a plant, most name an angiosperm. An **angiosperm** is a vascular plant that flowers and produces fruits with one or more seeds, such as the peaches shown in **Figure 19.** The fruit develops from a part or parts of one or more flowers. Angiosperms are familiar plants no matter where you live. They grow in parks, fields, forests, jungles, deserts, freshwater, salt water, and in the cracks of sidewalks. You might see them dangling from wires or other plants, and one species of orchid even grows underground. Angiosperms make up the plant division Anthophyta (AN thoh fi tuh). More than half of the known plant species belong to this division.

Flowers The flowers of angiosperms vary in size, shape, and color. Duckweed, an aquatic plant, has a flower that is only 0.1 mm long. A plant in Indonesia has a flower that is nearly 1 m in diameter and can weigh 9 kg. Nearly every color can be found in some flower, although some people would not include black. Multicolored flowers are common. Some plants have flowers that are not recognized easily as flowers, such as the flowers of ash trees, shown below.

Some flower parts develop into a fruit. Most fruits contain seeds, like an apple, or have seeds on their surface, like a strawberry. If you think all fruits are juicy and sweet, there are some that are not. The fruit of the vanilla orchid, as shown to the right, contains seeds and is dry.

Angiosperms are divided into two groups—the monocots and the dicots—shortened forms of the words *monocotyledon* (mah nuh kah tuh LEE dun) and *dicotyledon* (di kah tuh LEE dun).

Figure 19 Angiosperms have a wide variety of flowers and fruits.

The fruit of the vanilla orchid is the source of vanilla flavoring.

The flowers and fruit of a peach tree are typical of many angiosperms.

Ash flowers are not large and colorful. Their fruits are small and dry.

SECTION 3 Seed Plants **257**

Monocots and Dicots Prepare several lab stations to demonstrate different monocot or dicot characteristics. Have students rotate through the stations, making notes and sketches of each characteristic. When everyone has completed the activity, have students discuss how monocots and dicots are similar and different. L2 IS **Interpersonal**

Teacher FYI

Grasses Grasses make up the largest of all plant families. They are also the most widespread and can be found on almost every type of land surface and in every climate region on Earth. Sugarcane is a grass that grows in tropical areas to heights of 2 to 4.6 meters. This grass supplies more than half the world's sugar. Another grass is bamboo. Its strong, woody stems are used in some parts of the world as building materials and as water pipes. Bamboo is often used to make furniture.

Monocots and Dicots A cotyledon is part of a seed often used for food storage. The prefix *mono* means "one," and *di* means "two." Therefore, **monocots** have one cotyledon inside their seeds and **dicots** have two. The flowers, leaves, and stems of monocots and dicots are shown in **Figure 20.**

Many important foods come from monocots, including corn, rice, wheat, and barley. If you eat bananas, pineapple, or dates, you are eating fruit from monocots. Lilies and orchids also are monocots.

Dicots also produce familiar foods such as peanuts, green beans, peas, apples, and oranges. You might have rested in the shade of a dicot tree. Most shade trees, such as maple, oak, and elm, are dicots.

Figure 20 By observing a monocot and a dicot, you can determine their plant characteristics.

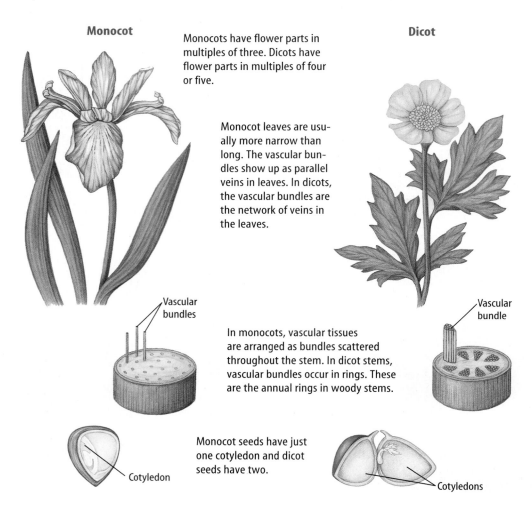

Monocot

Monocots have flower parts in multiples of three. Dicots have flower parts in multiples of four or five.

Monocot leaves are usually more narrow than long. The vascular bundles show up as parallel veins in leaves. In dicots, the vascular bundles are the network of veins in the leaves.

Dicot

Vascular bundles

In monocots, vascular tissues are arranged as bundles scattered throughout the stem. In dicot stems, vascular bundles occur in rings. These are the annual rings in woody stems.

Vascular bundle

Monocot seeds have just one cotyledon and dicot seeds have two.

Cotyledon

Cotyledons

258 CHAPTER 9 Plants

Differentiated Instruction

Challenge Have students survey the plants they find at a home and garden store, a grocery store, or a florist shop. Tell them to sketch the leaves and flowers of one monocot and one dicot and bring the sketches to class. Remind them to write down the names of the plants on the back of each sketch and whether the plant is a monocot or dicot. Have each student present his or her two sketches in class. Quiz class members on whether the plants are monocots or dicots, and have students give reasons for their choices. L3 IS **Visual-Spatial**

Petunias

Parsley

Pecan tree

Life Cycles of Angiosperms

Flowering plants vary greatly in appearance. Their life cycles are as varied as the kinds of plants, as shown in **Figure 21.** Some angiosperms grow from seeds to mature plants with their own seeds in less than a month. The life cycles of other plants can take as long as a century. If a plant's life cycle is completed within one year, it is called an annual. These plants must be grown from seeds each year.

Plants called biennials (bi EH nee ulz) complete their life cycles within two years. Biennials such as parsley store a large amount of food in an underground root or stem for growth in the second year. Biennials produce flowers and seeds only during the second year of growth. Angiosperms that take more than two years to grow to maturity are called perennials. Herbaceous perennials such as peonies appear to die each winter but grow and produce flowers each spring. Woody perennials such as fruit trees produce flowers and fruits on stems that survive for many years.

Importance of Seed Plants

What would a day at school be like without seed plants? One of the first things you'd notice is the lack of paper and books. Paper is made from wood pulp that comes from trees, which are seed plants. Are the desks and chairs at your school made of wood? They would need to be made of something else if no seed plants existed. Clothing that is made from cotton would not exist because cotton comes from seed plants. At lunchtime, you would have trouble finding something to eat. Bread, fruits, and potato chips all come from seed plants. Milk, hamburgers, and hot dogs all come from animals that eat seed plants. Unless you like to eat plants such as mosses and ferns, you'd go hungry. Without seed plants, your day at school would be different.

Figure 21 Life cycles of angiosperms include annuals, biennials, and perennials. Petunias, which are annuals, complete their life cycle in one year. Parsley plants, which are biennials, do not produce flowers and seeds the first year. Perennials, such as the pecan tree, flower and produce fruits year after year.

Topic: Renewable Resources
Visit life.msscience.com for Web links to information and recent news or magazine articles about the timber industry's efforts to replant trees.

Activity List in your Science Journal the species of trees that are planted and some of their uses.

Discussion
Planting Plan Why might it be a good idea to plant a flower garden with a mix of annuals and perennials? Students should infer that, aside from the desirability of variety in types of flowers, a garden of all annuals would be a lot of work because it would have to be replanted each year. A mix would include annuals that must be replanted and perennials that will bloom year after year.

Inquiry Lab

Observing Angiosperm Life Cycles
Purpose to explore flowering and seed production in an angiosperm
Estimated Time portions of several class sessions
Teaching Strategies
• Students can check with a local garden store to choose plants that flower relatively quickly and to find out about growth requirements.
• Students can start with seedlings in small pots and develop a plan for taking care of their plants as they grow.
• Allow students to explore questions that arise.
• Encourage students to regularly record observations about the changing characteristics of their growing plants. L2

For additional inquiry activities, see *Science Inquiry Labs.*

Teacher FYI
Asteraceae Dandelions, daisies, and sunflowers belong to the plant family called Asteraceae. What appears to be one flower is really a composite of many individual, small flowers called florets. In fact, the family name was once called Compositae.

Differentiated Instruction

Challenge If the only thing you know about a plant is that it contains 12 petals, why can't you say for sure whether it is a monocot or dicot? Monocots have petals in multiples of three; dicots have petals in multiples of four or five. Since 12 is divisible by three and four, this characteristic alone won't provide the answer. L3

DAILY INTERVENTION

Check for Understanding

Intrapersonal Have students write their own definitions of the following terms: *spore* reproductive structure in seedless plants; *vascular system* tissues that transport food and water throughout plant; *angiosperms* produce flowers and seeds enclosed in a fruit; *gymnosperms* produce seeds in cones L2

Reteach

Characteristics Emphasize the important characteristics that distinguish gymnosperms from angiosperms, or monocots from dicots. Prepare flash cards with a written or visual characteristic of one of the groups on each one. Quiz students by having them quickly respond as you hold up each card. L2

✔ Assessment

Performance Assess students' abilities to classify food plants by plant part. Give them several common fruits and vegetables and have students classify them as roots, stems, leaves, fruits, or flowers. roots: yams, beets, carrots; stems: asparagus, white potatoes, ginger; leaves: spinach, lettuce; fruits: tomatoes, cherries; flowers: broccoli, cauliflower Use **Performance Assessment in the Science Classroom,** p. 121. L2

Table 1 Some Products of Seed Plants		
From Gymnosperms		**From Angiosperms**
lumber, paper, soap, varnish, paints, waxes, perfumes, edible pine nuts, medicines		foods, sugar, chocolate, cotton cloth, linen, rubber, vegetable oils, perfumes, medicines, cinnamon, flavorings, dyes, lumber 

Products of Seed Plants Conifers are the most economically important gymnosperms. Most wood used for construction and for paper production comes from conifers. Resin, a waxy substance secreted by conifers, is used to make chemicals found in soap, paint, varnish, and some medicines.

The most economically important plants on Earth are the angiosperms. They form the basis of the diets of most animals. Angiosperms were the first plants that humans grew. They included grains, such as barley and wheat, and legumes, such as peas and lentils. Angiosperms are also the source of many of the fibers used in clothing. Besides cotton, linen fabrics come from plant fibers. **Table 1** shows just a few of the products of angiosperms and gymnosperms.

section 3 review

Summary

Characteristics of Seed Plants
- Leaves are organs in which photosynthesis takes place.
- Stems support leaves and branches and contain vascular tissues.
- Roots absorb water and nutrients from soil.

Gymnosperms
- Gymnosperms do not have flowers and produce seeds that are not protected by a fruit.

Angiosperms
- Angiosperms produce flowers that develop into a fruit with seeds.

Importance of Seed Plants
- The diets of most animals are based on angiosperms.

Self Check

1. **List** four characteristics common to all seed plants.
2. **Compare and contrast** the characteristics of gymnosperms and angiosperms.
3. **Classify** a flower with five petals as a monocot or a dicot.
4. **Explain** why the root system might be the largest part of a plant.
5. **Think Critically** The cuticle and epidermis of leaves are transparent. If they weren't, what might be the result?

Applying Skills

6. **Form a hypothesis** about what substance or substances are produced in palisade cells but not in xylem cells.

Science online life.msscience.com/self_check_quiz

section 3 review

1. Seed plants have roots, stems, leaves, vascular tissue, and produce seeds.
2. Gymnosperms produce seeds not protected by fruit; most have needlelike, evergreen leaves. Angiosperms produce flowers that become fruits that enclose seeds.
3. It is from a dicot.
4. Roots must absorb large amounts of water and nutrients and anchor plants.
5. Less light would reach the chloroplasts, which would reduce the rate of photosynthesis.
6. Students' hypotheses should include information that shows the connection between the presence of chloroplasts in cells and sugar production.

Identifying Conifers

How can you tell a pine from a spruce or a cedar from a juniper? One way is to observe their leaves. The leaves of most conifers are either needlelike—shaped like needles—or scale-like—shaped like the scales on a fish. Examine and identify some conifer branches using the key to the right.

◉ Real-World Question

How can leaves be used to classify conifers?

Goals

■ **Identify** the difference between needlelike and scalelike leaves.
■ **Classify** conifers according to their leaves.

Materials

short branches of the following conifers:

pine	Douglas fir	redwood
cedar	hemlock	arborvitae
spruce	fir	juniper

*illustrations of the conifers above
*Alternate materials

Safety Precautions 🌊 🧤 🧴
Wash your hands after handling leaves.

◉ Procedure

1. **Observe** the leaves or illustrations of each conifer, then use the key to identify it.
2. **Write** the number and name of each conifer you identify in your Science Journal.

◉ Conclude and Apply

1. **Name** two traits of hemlock leaves.
2. **Compare and contrast** pine and cedar leaves.

Key to Classifying Conifer Leaves

1. All leaves are needlelike.
   a. yes, go to 2
   b. no, go to 8

2. Needles are in clusters.
   a. yes, go to 3
   b. no, go to 4

3. Clusters contain two, three, or five needles.
   a. yes, pine
   b. no, cedar

4. Needles grow on all sides of the stem.
   a. yes, go to 5
   b. no, go to 7

5. Needles grow from a woody peg.
   a. yes, spruce
   b. no, go to 6

6. Needles appear to grow from the branch.
   a. yes, Douglas fir
   b. no, hemlock

7. Most of the needles grow upward.
   a. yes, fir
   b. no, redwood

8. All the leaves are scalelike but not prickly.
   a. yes, arborvitae
   b. no, juniper

𝒞ommunicating Your Data

Use the key above to identify conifers growing on your school grounds. Draw and label a map that locates these conifers. Post the map in your school. **For more help, refer to the** Science Skill Handbook.

LAB **261**

𝒞ommunicating Your Data

If possible, have students use a software program to draw their maps. Students can also use a word processing program to make a table that lists the types of conifers and their locations in and around the school grounds. L2

◉ Real-World Question

Purpose Students observe and classify conifer leaves. L2 ELL
IS **Logical-Mathematical**

Process Skills observe, classify, compare and contrast

Time Required 50 minutes

◉ Procedure

Safety Precautions Remind students not to eat any plant parts, and to wash their hands thoroughly after handling the leaves.

Teaching Strategy Provide magnifying lenses for students who want to have a closer look at the structures of the leaves.

◉ Conclude and Apply

1. Leaves are needlelike; needles grow on all sides of the stem.
2. Both have needlelike leaves with needles in clusters. Cedar leaves are usually flatter.

☑ Assessment

Process Direct students to come up with a classification chart similar to the one on this page to classify several broad leaves with very different characteristics. Have students test each other's classification systems. Use **Performance Assessment in the Science Classroom**, p. 121. L2

BENCH TESTED

◉ *Real-World Question*

Purpose

Internet Students use Internet sites that can be accessed through life.mssience.com/internet_lab.

They will investigate plants that are used as medicine. L2

Process Skills collect data, identify, research, review, compare and contrast, describe, record

Time Required three to six days

◉ *Make a Plan*

Preparation

Internet To run through the steps that the students will follow, visit life.mssience.com/internet_lab.

Non-Internet Sources Collect books and brochures about plants used as medicine.

LAB — Use the Internet

Plants as Medicine

Goals

- **Identify** two plants that can be used as a treatment for illness or as a supplement to support good health.
- **Research** the cultural and historical use of each of the two selected plants as medical treatments.
- **Review** multiple sources to understand the effectiveness of each of the two selected plants as a medical treatment.
- **Compare and contrast** the research and form a hypothesis about the medicinal effectiveness of each of the two plants.

Data Source

Science◉**nline**

Visit life.mssience.com/ internet_lab for more information about plants that can be used for maintaining good health and for data collected by other students.

◉ *Real-World Question*

You may have read about using peppermint to relieve an upset stomach, or taking *Echinacea* to boost your immune system and fight off illness. But did you know that pioneers brewed a cough medicine from lemon mint? In this lab, you will explore plants and their historical use in treating illness, and the benefits and risks associated with using plants as medicine. How are plants used in maintaining good health?

Echinacea

◉ *Make a Plan*

1. **Search** for information about plants that are used as medicine and identify two plants to investigate.
2. **Research** how these plants are currently recommended for use as medicine or to promote good health. Find out how each has been used historically.
3. **Explore** how other cultures used these plants as a medicine.

Mentha

Alternative Inquiry Lab

Real-World Connection Personally connect students to this lab by telling them that they are botanists exploring the Amazon rain forest. They discover plants not recorded in scientific literature. Native people use some of these plants to treat certain diseases. Have students design an experiment to test the properties of these plants. How would they determine if the plants contain substances that can cure or prevent cancer or other diseases? If time allows, provide students with plant materials and allow them to do similar experiments safely.

▶ Follow Your Plan

1. Make sure your teacher approves your plan before you start.
2. **Record** data you collect about each plant in your Science Journal.

▶ Analyze Your Data

1. **Write** a description of how different cultures have used each plant as medicine.
2. How have the plants you investigated been used as medicine historically?
3. **Record** all the uses suggested by different sources for each plant.
4. **Record** the side effects of using each plant as a treatment.

▶ Conclude and Apply

1. After conducting your research, what do you think are the benefits and drawbacks of using these plants as alternative medicines?
2. **Describe** any conflicting information about using each of these plants as medicine.
3. Based on your analysis, would you recommend the use of each of these two plants to treat illness or promote good health? Why or why not?
4. What would you say to someone who was thinking about using any plant-based, over-the-counter, herbal supplement?

𝒞ommunicating Your Data

Find this lab using the link below. Post your data for the two plants you investigated in the tables provided. **Compare** your data to those of other students. Review data that other students have entered about other plants that can be used as medicine.

Science Online

life.msscience.com/internet_lab

Monarda

▶ Follow Your Plan

Teaching Strategies Students should identify plants by common names and scientific names. L2

Troubleshooting Remind students that they may find conflicting information among their references.

▶ Analyze Your Data

Answers will be subjective and based on students' individual research.

▶ Conclude and Apply

Answers will be individualized and often based on students' opinions of their research. Look for depth and quality of research performed.

☑ Assessment

Portfolio Have students create a guide describing each of the plants they investigated. The guide should include a picture of the plant, how it promotes good health, and a summary of the plant's effectiveness. Use **Performance Assessment in the Science Classroom,** p. 129. L2

LAB 263

𝒞ommunicating Your Data

Suggest that students use a combination of their data and that obtained from others to draw their conclusions.

Oops! Accidents in SCIENCE

SOMETIMES GREAT DISCOVERIES HAPPEN BY ACCIDENT!

A LOOPY Idea Inspires a "Fastenating" Invention

A wild cocklebur plant inspired the hook-and-loop fastener.

Scientists often spend countless hours in the laboratory dreaming up useful inventions. Sometimes, however, the best ideas hit them in unexpected places at unexpected times. That's why scientists are constantly on the lookout for things that spark their curiosity.

One day in 1948, a Swiss inventor named George deMestral strolled through a field with his dog. When they returned home, deMestral discovered that the dog's fur was covered with cockleburs, parts of a prickly plant. These burs were also stuck to deMestral's jacket and pants. Curious about what made the burs so sticky, the inventor examined one under a microscope.

DeMestral noticed that the cocklebur was covered with lots of tiny hooks. By clinging to animal fur and fabric, this plant is carried to other places. While studying these burs, he got the idea to invent a new kind of fastener that could do the work of buttons, snaps, zippers, and laces—but better!

After years of experimentation, deMestral came up with a strong, durable hook-and-loop fastener made of two strips of nylon fabric. One strip has thousands of small, stiff hooks; the other strip is covered with soft, tiny loops. Today, this hook-and-loop fastening tape is used on shoes and sneakers, watchbands, hospital equipment, space suits, clothing, book bags, and more. You may have one of those hook-and-loop fasteners somewhere on you right now. They're the ones that go rrrrrrrip when you open them.

So, if you ever get a fresh idea that clings to your mind like a hook to a loop, stick with it and experiment! Who knows? It may lead to a fabulous invention that changes the world!

This photo provides a close-up view of a hook-and-loop fastener.

List Make a list of ten ways hook-and-loop tape is used today. Think of three new uses for it. Since you can buy strips of hook-and-loop fastening tape in most hardware and fabric stores, try out some of your favorite ideas.

Science online
For more information, visit life.msscience.com/oops

Reviewing Main Ideas

Section 1 — An Overview of Plants

1. Plants are made up of eukaryotic cells and vary greatly in size and shape.

2. Plants usually have some form of leaves, stems, and roots.

3. As plants evolved from aquatic to land environments, changes occurred in how they reproduced, supported themselves, and moved substances from one part of the plant to another.

4. The plant kingdom is classified into groups called divisions.

Section 2 — Seedless Plants

1. Seedless plants include nonvascular and vascular types.

2. Most seedless nonvascular plants have no true leaves, stems, or roots. Reproduction usually is by spores.

3. Seedless vascular plants have vascular tissues that move substances throughout the plant. These plants may reproduce by spores.

4. Many ancient forms of these plants underwent a process that resulted in the formation of coal.

Section 3 — Seed Plants

1. Seed plants are adapted to survive in nearly every environment on Earth.

2. Seed plants produce seeds and have vascular tissue, stems, roots, and leaves.

3. The two major groups of seed plants are gymnosperms and angiosperms. Gymnosperms generally have needlelike leaves and some type of cone. Angiosperms are plants that flower and are classified as monocots or dicots.

4. Seed plants are the most economically important plants on Earth.

Visualizing Main Ideas

Copy and complete the following concept map about the seed plants.

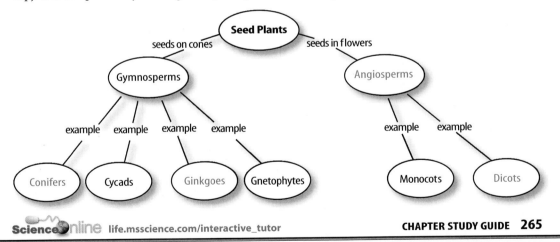

life.msscience.com/interactive_tutor

CHAPTER STUDY GUIDE 265

Reviewing Main Ideas

Summary statements can be used by students to review the major concepts of the chapter.

Visualizing Main Ideas

See student page.

Science Online

Visit life.msscience.com
/self_check_quiz
/interactive_tutor
/vocabulary_puzzlemaker
/chapter_review
/standardized_test

Assessment Transparency

For additional assessment questions, use the *Assessment Transparency* located in the transparency book.

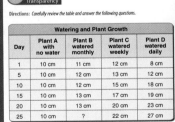

chapter 9 Review

Using Vocabulary

1. gymnosperm
2. monocot
3. rhizoid
4. xylem
5. nonvascular plant
6. cuticle
7. pioneer species
8. cellulose

Checking Concepts

9. C	14. C
10. A	15. A
11. C	16. D
12. B	17. C
13. D	18. A

Thinking Critically

19. The plant might lose so much water that it would wilt or die.
20. All flowering plants have vascular tissue.
21. Succulents grow naturally in dry environments.
22. They must grow in moist environments because they don't have vascular tissue for water or nutrient transport. All of their cells must absorb water from the environment.
23. Pioneer species help to break down rocks and make small pockets of soil needed by other, larger plants.

chapter 9 Review

Using Vocabulary

angiosperm p. 257	nonvascular plant p. 245
cambium p. 255	phloem p. 255
cellulose p. 242	pioneer species p. 247
cuticle p. 242	rhizoid p. 246
dicot p. 258	stomata p. 253
guard cell p. 253	vascular plant p. 245
gymnosperm p. 256	xylem p. 255
monocot p. 258	

Complete each analogy by providing the missing vocabulary word.

1. Angiosperm is to flower as _____ is to cone.

2. Dicot is to two seed leaves as _____ is to one seed leaf.

3. Root is to fern as _____ is to moss.

4. Phloem is to food transport as _____ is to water transport.

5. Vascular plant is to horsetail as _____ is to liverwort.

6. Cellulose is to support as _____ is to protect.

7. Fuel is to ferns as _____ is to bryophytes.

8. Cuticle is to wax as _____ is to fibers.

Checking Concepts

Choose the word or phrase that best answers the question.

9. Which of the following is a seedless vascular plant?
   A) moss   C) horsetail
   B) liverwort   D) pine

10. What are the small openings in the surface of a leaf surrounded by guard cells called?
    A) stomata   C) rhizoids
    B) cuticles   D) angiosperms

11. What are the plant structures that anchor the plant called?
    A) stems   C) roots
    B) leaves   D) guard cells

12. Where is most of a plant's new xylem and phloem produced?
    A) guard cell   C) stomata
    B) cambium   D) cuticle

13. What group has plants that are only a few cells thick?
    A) gymnosperms   C) ferns
    B) cycads   D) mosses

14. The oval plant parts shown to the right are found only in which plant group?
    A) nonvascular   C) gymnosperms
    B) seedless   D) angiosperms

15. What kinds of plants have structures that move water and other substances?
    A) vascular   C) nonvascular
    B) protist   D) bacterial

16. In what part of a leaf does most photosynthesis occur?
    A) epidermis   C) stomata
    B) cuticle   D) palisade layer

17. Which one of the following do ferns have?
    A) cones   C) spores
    B) rhizoids   D) seeds

18. Which of these is an advantage to life on land for plants?
    A) more direct sunlight
    B) less carbon dioxide
    C) greater space to grow
    D) less competition for food

266 CHAPTER REVIEW

 life.msscience.com/vocabulary_puzzlemaker

Use the Exam*View*® Pro Testmaker CD-ROM to:
- create multiple versions of tests
- create modified tests with one mouse click for inclusion students
- edit existing questions and add your own questions
- build tests aligned with state standards using built-in State Curriculum Tags
- change English tests to Spanish with one mouse click and vice versa

Thinking Critically

19. Predict what might happen if a land plant's waxy cuticle was destroyed.

20. Draw Conclusions On a walk through the woods with a friend, you find a plant neither of you has seen before. The plant has green leaves and yellow flowers. Your friend says it is a vascular plant. How does your friend know this?

21. Infer Plants called succulents store large amounts of water in their leaves, stems, and roots. In what environments would you expect to find succulents growing naturally?

22. Explain why mosses usually are found in moist areas.

23. Recognize Cause and Effect How do pioneer species change environments so that other plants can grow there?

24. Concept Map Copy and complete this map for the seedless plants of the plant kingdom.

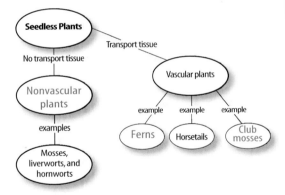

25. Interpret Scientific Illustrations Using **Figure 20** in this chapter, compare and contrast the number of cotyledons, bundle arrangement in the stem, veins in leaves, and number of flower parts for monocots and dicots.

 Science nline life.msscience.com/chapter_review

26. Sequence Put the following events in order to show how coal is formed from plants: *living seedless plants, coal is formed, dead seedless plants decay,* and *peat is formed.*

27. Predict what would happen if a ring of bark and camium layer were removed from around the trunk of a tree.

Performance Activities

28. Poem Choose a topic in this chapter that interests you. Look it up in a reference book, in an encyclopedia, or on a CD-ROM. Write a poem to share what you learn.

29. Display Use dried plant material, photos, drawings, or other materials to make a poster describing the form and function of roots, stems, and leaves.

Applying Math

Use the table below to answer questions 30–32.

Number of Stomata (per mm²)

Plant	Upper Surface	Lower Surface
Pine	50	71
Bean	40	281
Fir	0	228
Tomato	12	13

30. Gas Exchange What do the data in this table tell you about where gas exchange occurs in the leaf of each plant species?

31. Compare Leaf Surfaces Make two circle graphs—upper surface and lower surface—using the table above.

32. Guard Cells On average, how many guard cells are found on the lower surface of a bean leaf?

CHAPTER REVIEW 267

Thinking Critically

24. See student page.

25. Monocots have one seed leaf, scattered vascular bundles, parallel veins in leaves, and flower parts in multiples of three. Dicots have two seed leaves, vascular bundles in rings, a network of veins in leaves, and flower parts in multiples of four or five.

26. Living seedless plants, dead seedless plants decay, peat is formed, coal is formed.

27. The tree would probably die, because transport of water and food between roots and leaves would be interrupted.

Performance Activities

28. Have students share their poems with the class. Use **PASC,** p. 157.

29. Allow students to display their posters in the classroom or in other areas of the school.

Applying Math

National Math Standards
5, 6

30. Gas exchange for pine and tomato leaves is nearly the same on both the upper and lower surfaces because the number of stomata on each are about equal. Most of the gas exchange for bean leaves occurs on the lower surface. All gas exchange for fir needles happens on the lower surface.

31. The upper-surface graph should show 177° for pine, 141° for bean, and 42° for tomato. The lower-surface graph should show 43° for pine, 171° for bean, 138° for fir, and 8° for tomato.

32. 562 per mm²

☑ Assessment   Resources

Reproducible Masters
Chapter *Fast File* Resources
Chapter Review, pp. 33–34
Chapter Tests, pp. 35–38
Assessment Transparency Activity, p. 45
Glencoe Science Web site
Chapter Review Test
Standardized Test Practice

Glencoe Technology
- Assessment Transparency
- Exam*View*® Pro Testmaker
- MindJogger Videoquiz
- Interactive Chalkboard

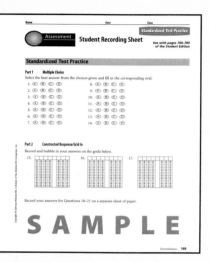

FAST FILE

Answer Sheet A practice answer sheet can be found at life.msscience.com/answer_sheet.

SAMPLE

Part 1 | Multiple Choice

1. C
2. B
3. B
4. D
5. D
6. D
7. B

Part 1 | Multiple Choice

Record your answers on the answer sheet provided by your teacher or on a sheet of paper.

1. Which of the following do plants use to photosynthesize?
  A. blood   **C.** chlorophyll
  B. iron   **D.** cellulose

2. Which of the following describes the function of the central vacuole in plant cells?
  A. It helps in reproduction.
  B. It helps regulate water content.
  C. It plays a key role in photosynthesis.
  D. It stores food.

Use the illustration below to answer questions 3 and 4.

Leaf Cross Section

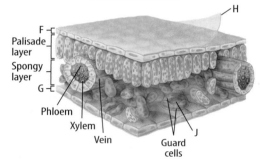

3. In the leaf cross section, what is indicated by H?
  A. upper epidermis
  B. cuticle
  C. stoma
  D. lower epidermis

4. What flows through the structure indicated by J?
  A. water only
  B. carbon dioxide and water only
  C. oxygen and carbon dioxide only
  D. water, carbon dioxide, and oxygen

5. In seed plants, vascular tissue refers to which of the following?
  A. xylem and phloem only
  B. xylem only
  C. phloem only
  D. xylem, phloem, and cambium

Use the illustration below to answer questions 6 and 7.

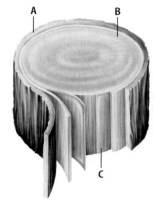

6. What is the function of the structure labeled C?
  A. It transports nutrients throughout the plant.
  B. It produces new xylem and phloem.
  C. It transports water from the roots to other parts of the plant.
  D. It absorbs water from outside the plant.

7. What type of vascular tissue is indicated by B?
  A. xylem   **C.** phloem
  B. cambium   **D.** cellulose

Test-Taking Tip

Eliminate Answer Choices If you don't know the answer to a multiple-choice question, eliminate as many incorrect choices as possible. Mark your best guess from the remaining answers before moving on to the next question.

268 STANDARDIZED TEST PRACTICE

Part 2 | Short Response/Grid In

8. Flower A—monocot; flower B—dicot. Monocot flower parts are multiples of three and leaves have parallel veins. Dicot flower parts are multiples of four or five and leaves have a network of veins.

9. sample answers: corn, rice, wheat, barley, banana trees, date palms

10. sample answers: apple tree, beans, orange tree, maple tree, oak tree

11. In general, the cuticle and the stomata help prevent water loss. Specific plants have other water-saving adaptations, such as the thick water-storage stems of cacti and succulents.

12. Pollen provides a way for sperm to travel to the egg without having to

swim through water. Tough seed coat protects plant embryo until enough water is present in the environment to permit growth.

13. nonvascular seedless plants: mosses, hornworts, or liverworts

14. conifer—gymnosperm; a vascular plant; reproductive structure is a cone; produces both male and female cones

Part 2 | Short Response/Grid In

Record your answers on the answer sheet provided by your teacher or on a sheet of paper.

Use the two illustrations below to answer questions 8–10.

A   B

8. Identify the flowers shown above as a monocot or a dicot. Explain the differences between the flowers of monocots and dicots.

9. Give three examples of plants represented by Plant A.

10. Give three examples of plants represented by Plant B.

11. How are plants that live on land able to conserve water?

12. Explain why reproductive adaptations were necessary in order for plants to survive on land.

13. You are hiking through a dense forest area and notice some unusual plants growing on the trunk of a tall tree. The plants are no taller than about 3 cm and have delicate stalks. They do not appear to have flowers. Based on this information, what type of plants would you say you found?

14. What is a conifer? To which major group of plants does it belong?

Part 3 | Open Ended

Record your answers on a sheet of paper.

Use the two diagrams below to answer questions 15–16.

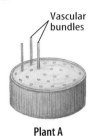 

Vascular bundles   Vascular bundles

Plant A   Plant B

15. Two plants, A and B, have stem cross sections as shown in the diagrams above. What does the different vascular bundle arrangement tell you about each plant?

16. Draw what the seed from each plant would look like.

17. Create a diagram that describes the life cycle of an annual angiosperm.

18. Discuss the importance of plants in your daily life. Give examples of plants or plant products that you use or consume regularly.

19. Compare and contrast vascular and non-vascular plants. Include examples of each type of plant.

20. Describe the group of plants known as the seedless vascular plants. How do these plants reproduce without seeds?

21. Explain what peat is and how it is formed. How is peat used today?

22. How would our knowledge of ancient plants be different if the fossil record for plants was as plentiful as it is for animals?

20. ferns, horsetails, spike mosses, ground pines, and club mosses; reproduce by spores instead of seeds

21. forms when bog plants die and are compressed in waterlogged soil; mined and used as low-cost fuel in some parts of the world

22. We would know about many other kinds of ancient plants, as well as how they reproduced, their environment, and what kinds of animals ate them.

Rubrics

For more help evaluating open-ended assessment questions, see the rubric on p. 10T.

Part 3 | Open Ended

15. The scattered arrangement in plant A indicates it is a monocot stem. The ringlike arrangement of the vascular bundles in plant B indicates it is a dicot.

16. monocot seed—one cotyledon; dicot seed—two cotyledons.

17. The diagram should include a seed, the seed growing into an immature plant, a mature plant with seed-producing flowers, and new seeds.

18. Responses will vary. Example items: clothing, food, rubber, paper, cotton, linen, medicines, wood and wood products.

19. Vascular plants have xylem and phloem tissues that distribute nutrients, food, and throughout the plant. Nonvascular plants do not. Both have leaves or leaflike structures for photosynthesis and a root or rootlike system for anchoring. Vascular—angiosperms, gymnosperms, and ferns. Nonvascular—mosses, liverworts, and hornworts.

Section/Objectives	Standards		Labs/Features
Chapter Opener	**National**	**State/Local**	**Launch Lab:** Do all fruits contain seeds?, p. 271 **Foldables,** p. 271
	See pp. 16T–17T for a Key to Standards.		A data-collection lab using Probeware technology can be found in the **Probeware Lab Manual,** pp. 17–20
Section 1 Introduction to Plant Reproduction ⏱ 2 sessions 📦 1 block 1. **Distinguish** between the two types of plant reproduction. 2. **Describe** the two stages in a plant's life cycle.	National Content Standards: UCP.1–UCP.3, UCP.5, A.1, A.2, C.1, C.2, C.5		**MiniLAB:** Observing Asexual Reproduction, p. 273 **Science Online,** p. 274
Section 2 Seedless Reproduction ⏱ 2 sessions 📦 1 block 3. **Examine** the life cycles of a moss and a fern. 4. **Explain** why spores are important to seedless plants. 5. **Identify** some special structures used by ferns for reproduction.	National Content Standards: UCP.1–UCP.3, UCP.5, A.1, A.2, C.1, C.2, C.5		**Integrate History,** p. 278 **Lab:** Comparing Seedless Plants, p. 280
Section 3 Seed Reproduction ⏱ 3 sessions 📦 1.5 blocks 6. **Examine** the life cycles of typical gymnosperms and angiosperms. 7. **Describe** the structure and function of the flower. 8. **Discuss** methods of seed dispersal in seed plants.	National Content Standards: UCP.1, UCP.2, UCP.5, A.1, A.2, C.1, C.2, C.4, C.5, F.2, G.2, G.3		**Science Online,** p. 282 **Integrate Environment,** p. 284 **MiniLAB:** Modeling Seed Dispersal, p. 288 **Visualizing Seed Dispersal,** p. 289 **Applying Math:** How many seeds will germinate?, p. 290 **Lab:** Germination Rate of Seeds, p. 292 **Science and Society:** Genetic Engineering, p. 294

Glencoe Exclusive!
TeacherWorks™
All-In-One Planner and Resource Center

Lab Materials	Reproducible Resources	Section Assessment	Technology
Launch Lab: 2 different types of grapes, plastic knife, paper towels	**Chapter FAST FILE Resources** Foldables Worksheet, p. 15 Directed Reading Overview, p. 17 Note-taking Worksheets, pp. 31–33	GLENCOE'S **ASSESSMENT** ADVANTAGE	**Teacher**Works includes: • Interactive Teacher Edition • Lesson Planner with calendar • Access to all program blacklines • Correlations to standards • Web links
MiniLAB: scissors, coleus or other houseplant, cup, water, small container of soil	**Chapter FAST FILE Resources** Transparency Activity, p. 42 MiniLAB, p. 3 Enrichment, p. 28 Reinforcement, p. 25 Directed Reading, p. 18 **Cultural Diversity,** p. 19	Portfolio Assessment, p. 275 Performance MiniLAB, p. 273 Applying Skills, p. 275 Content Section Review, p. 275	Section Focus Transparency Virtual Labs CD-ROM Guided Reading Audio Program Interactive Chalkboard CD-ROM
Lab: live mosses, liverworts, and ferns with gametophytes and sporophytes; magnifying lens; forceps; dropper; microscope slide and coverslip (2); microscope; dissecting needle; pencil with eraser	**Chapter FAST FILE Resources** Transparency Activity, p. 43 Enrichment, p. 29 Reinforcement, p. 26 Directed Reading, p. 18 Transparency Activity, pp. 45–46 Lab Worksheet, pp. 5–6	Portfolio Make a Model, p. 278 Performance Applying Math, p. 279 Content Section Review, p. 279	Section Focus Transparency Teaching Transparency Virtual Labs CD-ROM Guided Reading Audio Program Interactive Chalkboard CD-ROM Video Lab
MiniLAB: buttons, glue, paper, string, other common materials **Lab:** seeds, water, salt, potting soil, plant trays or plastic cups, thermometer, graduated cylinder, beakers *Need materials?* Contact Science Kit at 1-800-828-7777 or www.sciencekit.com on the Internet.	**Chapter FAST FILE Resources** Transparency Activity, p. 44 MiniLAB, p. 4 Enrichment, p. 30 Reinforcement, p. 27 Directed Reading, pp. 19, 20 Lab Activity, pp. 9–12, 13–14 Lab Worksheet, pp. 7–8 **Lab Management and Safety,** p. 38	Portfolio Activity, p. 283 Performance MiniLAB, p. 288 Applying Math, p. 290 Applying Skills, p. 291 Content Section Review, p. 291	Section Focus Transparency Virtual Labs CD-ROM Guided Reading Audio Program Interactive Chalkboard CD-ROM Probeware Lab

End of Chapter Assessment

GLENCOE'S **ASSESSMENT** ADVANTAGE

Blackline Masters	Technology	Professional Series
Chapter FAST FILE Resources Chapter Review, pp. 35–36 Chapter Tests, pp. 37–40 **Standardized Test Practice,** pp. 43–46	MindJogger Videoquiz Virtual Labs CD-ROM ExamView® Pro Testmaker TeacherWorks CD-ROM Interactive Chalkboard CD-ROM	**Performance Assessment in the Science Classroom (PASC)**

Transparencies

Section Focus

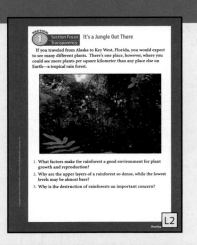

This is a representation of key blackline masters available in the Teacher Classroom Resources. See Resource Manager boxes within the chapter for additional information.

Key to Teaching Strategies

The following designations will help you decide which activities are appropriate for your students.

L1 Level 1 activities should be appropriate for students with learning difficulties.

L2 Level 2 activities should be within the ability range of all students.

L3 Level 3 activities are designed for above-average students.

ELL ELL activities should be within the ability range of English-Language Learners.

COOP LEARN Cooperative Learning activities are designed for small group work.

LS Multiple Learning Styles logos, as described on page 12T, are used throughout to indicate strategies that address different learning styles.

P These strategies represent student products that can be placed into a best-work portfolio.

PBL Problem-Based Learning activities apply real-world situations to learning.

Assessment

Teaching

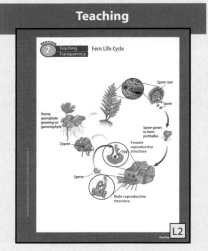

Hands-on Activities

Student Text Lab Worksheet

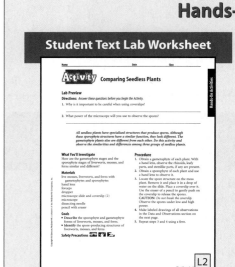

Laboratory Activities

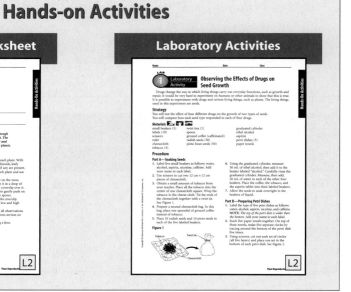

Meeting Different Ability Levels

Content Outline

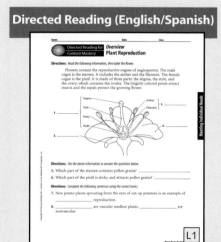

L2

Reinforcement

L2

Enrichment

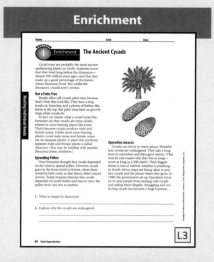

L3

Directed Reading (English/Spanish)

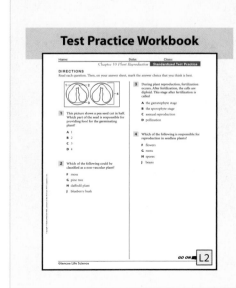

L1

Study Guide

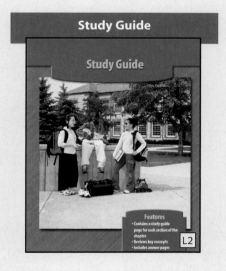

Study Guide

Features
- Contains a study guide page for each section of the chapter
- Reviews key concepts
- Includes answer pages

L2

Reading Essentials

Reading Essentials for Glencoe Science
An Interactive Student Workbook

Features
- Condensed core content
- Actively involves students in reading
- Reinforces key vocabulary

L1

Assessment

Test Practice Workbook

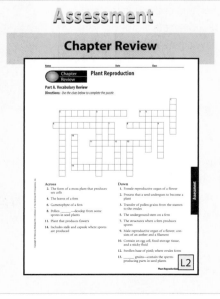

GO ON L2

Glencoe Life Science

Chapter Review

L2

Chapter Tests

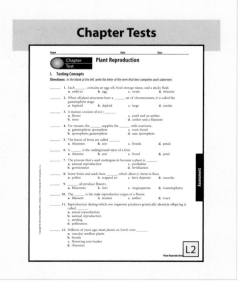

L2

Science Content Background

Introduction to Plant Reproduction
Types of Reproduction

Asexual reproduction is common in plants. It is most successful in appropriate environments that change little over long periods of time. The advantage of asexual reproduction is the ability to produce large numbers of offspring that have the same genetic makeup as the parent plant. As a result, asexual reproduction is equivalent to cloning. Many commercially grown plants, such as orchids and African violets, are routinely propagated asexually.

The genetic diversity of plants is increased through sexual reproduction. Sexual reproduction recombines genes, thus allowing plants to evolve and invade new habitats or adapt when the environment changes.

Teacher to Teacher
Steve Federman
Loveland Middle School
Loveland, Ohio

"Students in my class are thrilled to see the almost immediate germination of their seed necklaces, which have been placed under their clothing, next to the skin. Students place a moistened piece of cotton and a radish seed into a 2 $\times$ 2-inch resealable bag. With a hole punch, make a hole in the top corner of the bag and tie an 18-inch length of string or yarn through the hole. Wear it all day and see what sprouts!"

Steve Federman

Haploid and Diploid Stages

In all plant life cycles, there are haploid and diploid stages, referred to as an alternation of generations. Alternation of generations evolved with the ancestors of the plant kingdom, the ancient Chlorophyta, or green algae. A diploid sporophyte ($2n$) generation alternates with a haploid gametophyte generation (n). *Sporophyte* means "spore-producing" and *gametophyte* means "gamete-producing." These terms indicate the reproductive function of the plant. In some plants these are distinct organisms, but in others they are part of the larger organism.

Meiosis occurs in specialized cells of the sporophyte and results in the production of haploid (n) spores. Spores produce the gametophyte by mitosis. In time, gametophytes produce haploid gametes. A male and a female gamete unite to form a diploid zygote, the first cell in the multicellular sporophyte.

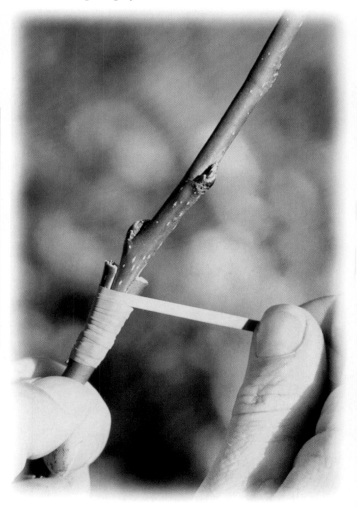

D. Cavagnaro/DRK Photo

section 2 Seedless Reproduction

Seedless Plants

In mosses, liverworts, and hornworts, the gametophyte is the familiar plant that makes its own food by photosynthesis. The sporophyte generation in mosses is found at the tip of the gametophyte and consists of a stalk with a capsule in which spores are produced by meiosis.

Fern spores germinate into a filamentous plant that eventually grows into an inconspicuous heart-shaped gametophyte called a prothallus. The gametophyte is independent and carries on photosynthesis. Fern sporophytes have leaves called fronds. Fronds produce spores in specialized packets called sori (singular, *sorus*) that are often misidentified as a plant disease.

section 3 Seed Reproduction

Gymnosperm Reproduction

Gymnosperms are unique among seed plants because the ovules of their seeds are not completely enclosed by tissue produced by the sporophyte.

The sporophytes, or 2*n* generations of gymnosperms, are familiar trees and shrubs like pines, junipers, and spruces. Ovulate (female) cones and pollen-bearing (male) cones are produced on separate stems. Female cones vary from the familiar woody cones to fleshy, berrylike cones. Berrylike cones are often colorful, such as the red ones on yews and the bluish ones on junipers. Many gymnosperm cones complete their life cycle in one year, but some take two or three years to mature.

All but about 35,000 of the 235,000 species of plants today are seed plants.

D. Cavagnaro/DRK Photo

Germination

Seeds are efficient units of dispersal for plants, and many have elaborate adaptations for moving away from the parent plant. Germination, the growth of a plant from a seed, is affected by many factors, such as temperature, light, moisture, and oxygen. Some seeds lay dormant, waiting for the appropriate set of conditions for germination.

---

chapter content resources

Internet Resources
For additional content background, visit **life.msscience.com** to:
- access your book online
- find references to related articles in popular science magazines
- access Web links with related content background
- access current events with science journal topics

Print Resources
Plant Biology, by Linda Graham, Prentice Hall, 2002
Plant Biology, Instant Notes Series, by A.J. Lack and D.E. Evans, Springer, 2001

---

chapter

10

Chapter Vocabulary

gametophyte stage, p. 275
spore, p. 275
sporophyte stage, p. 275
frond, p. 278
rhizome, p. 278
sori, p. 278
prothallus, p. 278
pollen grain, p. 281
pollination, p. 281
ovule, p. 283
stamen, p. 285
pistil, p. 285
ovary, p. 285
germination, p. 290

Science Journal Answers will vary. All gymnosperms and angiosperms reproduce by forming seeds, with the exception of a few varieties of angiosperms—such as seedless grapes and navel oranges—that have been developed through selective breeding and asexual reproduction to suppress seed production.

INTERACTIVE CHALKBOARD
with Image Bank

PowerPoint® Presentations

This CD-ROM is an editable Microsoft® PowerPoint® presentation that includes:

- a pre-made presentation for every chapter
- interactive graphics
- animations
- audio clips
- image bank
- all new section and chapter questions
- Standardized Test Practice
- transparencies
- pre-lab questions for all labs
- Foldables directions
- links to life.msscience.com

chapter
10

Plant Reproduction

chapter preview

sections

1 **Introduction to Plant Reproduction**

2 **Seedless Reproduction**
   Lab Comparing Seedless Plants

3 **Seed Reproduction**
   Lab Germination Rate of Seeds

   Virtual Lab What are the functions of the parts of a flower?

A Forest from Ashes

Saplings and other plants are growing among the remains of trees destroyed by fire. Where did these new plants come from? Some may have grown from seeds, and others may have grown from roots or stems that survived underground. These plants are the result of plant reproduction.

Science Journal List three plants that reproduce by forming seeds.

270

Theme Connection

Systems and Interactions This chapter emphasizes the mechanisms and systems of reproduction in plants.

About the Photo

Fire and Germination Fire is required for seed germination in some species, such as lodgepole pine and fireweed. Fire breaks down their tough seed coats, allowing water to enter and stimulate germination. Soil can be enriched by ashes and decaying plant material left behind by a fire, helping to support the growth of new plant cover.

Start-Up Activities

Do all fruits contain seeds?

You might know that most plants grow from seeds. Seeds are usually found in the fruits of plants. When you eat watermelon, it can contain many small seeds. Do some plants produce fruits without seeds? Do this lab to find out.

1. Obtain two grapes from your teacher. Each grape should be from a different plant.
2. Split each grape in half and examine the insides of each grape. **WARNING:** *Do not eat the grapes.*
3. **Think Critically** Were seeds found in both grapes? Hypothesize how new grape plants could be grown if no seeds are produced. In your Science Journal, list three other fruits you know of that do not contain seeds.

Preview this chapter's content and activities at life.msscience.com

---

Plant Reproduction Make the following Foldable to compare and contrast the sexual and asexual characteristics of a plant.

STEP 1 Fold one sheet of paper lengthwise.

STEP 2 Fold into thirds.

STEP 3 Unfold and draw overlapping ovals. Cut the top sheet along the folds.

STEP 4 Label the ovals as shown.

Construct a Venn Diagram As you read the chapter, list the characteristics unique to sexual reproduction under the left tab, those unique to asexual reproduction under the right tab, and those characteristics common to both under the middle tab.

Purpose Use the Launch Lab to introduce students to the ideas of sexual and asexual reproduction. Inform students that they will learn more about plant reproduction in this chapter. L1
ELL **LS** Visual-Spatial

Preparation Purchase both seedless and seeded grapes.
Materials grapes, plastic knife, paper towels

Teaching Strategies
• Be sure each student has both a seedless and a seeded grape.
• Have students cover their work surfaces with a paper towel.
• Be sure students wash their hands after handling the grapes.

Think Critically

Seeds were found in only one of the grapes. Hypotheses should indicate that some method other than seeds is responsible for producing seedless grape plants. Seedless fruits include bananas, some watermelons, and some oranges.

Assessment

Process Show students several fruits—some with seeds and some without. Have them classify the plants from which the fruits came as able to reproduce sexually or only asexually. Use **Performance Assessment in the Science Classroom,** p. 121. L2

Dinah Zike Study Fold

Student preparation materials for this Foldable are available in the **Chapter FAST FILE Resources.**

Probeware Labs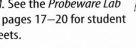

This chapter's data-collection lab using Probeware technology is included on the *Video Labs CD-ROM*. See the *Probeware Lab Manual* pages 17–20 for student worksheets.

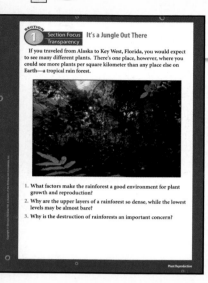
SECTION 1

Introduction to Plant Reproduction

as you read

What You'll Learn

- **Distinguish** between the two types of plant reproduction.
- **Describe** the two stages in a plant's life cycle.

Why It's Important

You can grow new plants without using seeds.

Review Vocabulary

fertilization: in sexual reproduction, the joining of a sperm and an egg

New Vocabulary

- spore
- gametophyte stage
- sporophyte stage

Types of Reproduction

Do people and plants have anything in common? You don't have leaves or roots, and a plant doesn't have a heart or a brain. Despite these differences, you are alike in many ways—you need water, oxygen, energy, and food to grow. Like humans, plants also can reproduce and make similar copies of themselves. Although humans have only one type of reproduction, most plants can reproduce in two different ways, as shown in **Figure 1.**

Sexual reproduction in plants and animals requires the production of sex cells—usually called sperm and eggs—in reproductive organs. The offspring produced by sexual reproduction are genetically different from either parent organism.

A second type of reproduction is called asexual reproduction. This type of reproduction does not require the production of sex cells. During asexual reproduction, one organism produces offspring that are genetically identical to it. Most plants have this type of reproduction, but humans and most other animals don't.

Figure 1 Many plants reproduce sexually with flowers that contain male and female parts. Other plants can reproduce asexually.

In crocus flowers, bees and other insects help get the sperm to the egg.

A cutting from this impatiens plant can be placed in water and will grow new roots. This new plant can then be planted in soil.

272 CHAPTER 10 Plant Reproduction

Figure 2 Asexual reproduction in plants takes many forms.

The eyes on these potatoes have begun to sprout. If a potato is cut into pieces, each piece that contains an eye can be planted and will grow into a new potato plant.

Grass plants spread by reproducing asexually.

Asexual Plant Reproduction Do you like to eat oranges and grapes that have seeds, or do you like seedless fruit? If these plants do not produce seeds, how do growers get new plants? Growers can produce new plants by asexual reproduction because many plant cells have the ability to grow into a variety of cell types. New plants can be grown from just a few cells in the laboratory. Under the right conditions, an entire plant can grow from one leaf or just a portion of the stem or root. When growers use these methods to start new plants, they must make sure that the leaf, stem, or root cuttings have plenty of water and anything else that they need to survive.

Asexual reproduction has been used to produce plants for centuries. The white potatoes shown in **Figure 2** were probably produced asexually. Many plants, such as lawn grasses also shown in **Figure 2,** can spread and cover wide areas because their stems grow underground and produce new grass plants asexually along the length of the stem.

Sexual Plant Reproduction Although plants and animals have sexual reproduction, there are differences in the way that it occurs. An important event in sexual reproduction is fertilization. Fertilization occurs when a sperm and egg combine to produce the first cell of the new organism, the zygote. How do the sperm and egg get together in plants? In some plants, water or wind help bring the sperm to the egg. For other plants, animals such as insects help bring the egg and sperm together.

✔ **Reading Check** *How does fertilization occur in plants?*

Observing Asexual Reproduction

Procedure 🌀 🈸 🗾
1. Using a pair of scissors, cut a stem with at least two pairs of leaves from a coleus or another houseplant.
2. Carefully remove the bottom pair of leaves.
3. Place the cut end of the stem into a cup that is half-filled with water for two weeks. Wash your hands.
4. Remove the new plant from the water and plant it in a small container of soil.

Analysis
1. Draw and label your results in your **Science Journal.**
2. Predict how the new plant and the plant from which it was taken are genetically related.

Purpose Students will observe the asexual reproduction of a houseplant. L2 ELL
IS **Kinesthetic**

Materials coleus plant, glass of water, scissors, container of soil

Teaching Strategy Tell students to choose a young stem rather than a tougher, older one.

Analysis
1. Drawings should show the growth of a new plant in the soil. Plants should have roots, stems, and leaves.
2. The plants are genetically identical.

Assessment

Performance Ask the students to repeat the lab with a different plant that can be propagated from a leaf or a root. Use **Performance Assessment in the Science Classroom,** p. 97.

Quick Demo

Observing Plant Runners

Materials any plant with runners, such as a strawberry plant or Bermuda grass

Estimated Time five minutes

Procedure Show students the plant's runners. Point out that runners are modified stems, and that new leaves and roots can grow from nodes along the runner.

✔ **Reading Check**

Answer Wind, water, or animals may carry the sperm to the egg in plants.

Differentiated Instruction

Challenge Encourage students to find out about asexual propagation techniques used by gardeners and farmers to produce identical plants. Examples include rooting, layering, or tissue culture. Ask each student to create a poster describing one of these techniques. L3

Teacher FYI

Plant Clones Tissue culture allows many plants to be grown quickly from one plant with a desirable trait. This method also produces disease-free plants. Plants routinely cloned using tissue culture include orchids, tobacco, chrysanthemums, potatoes, strawberries, asparagus, and gladioli.

Discussion

Cloning How does asexual reproduction in plants relate to cloning? A clone is an organism that is genetically identical to its parent. Any plant produced asexually is genetically identical to its parent plant, so it is also a clone of the parent.

Activity

Growing Potatoes Have students place a piece of potato with at least one eye in a clear plastic cup filled with moist soil. Students can observe the growth of roots and stems. Tell students that white potatoes sold in markets are grown this way. Ask students to explain what type of reproduction this activity represents.

Use Science Words

Word Meaning Have students research the meanings of the prefixes and suffixes that make up the words *sporophyte* and *gametophyte*. *Spor-* is derived from a Greek word meaning "seed;" *-phyte* from a Greek word meaning "plant;" *gamet-* from a Greek word meaning "to marry." Thus the gametophytes produce sex cells that will "marry" to form the sporophyte, or seed-producing stage in a plant's life cycle. L2 IS **Linguistic**

Figure 3 Some plants can fertilize themselves. Others require two different plants before fertilization can occur.

Flowers of pea plants contain male and female structures, and each flower can fertilize itself.

These holly flowers contain only male reproductive structures, so they can't fertilize themselves.

Compare the flowers of this female holly plant to those of the male plant.

Science Online

Topic: Male and Female Plants

Visit life.msscience.com for Web links to information about male and female plants.

Activity List four plants that have male and female reproductive structures on separate plants.

Reproductive Organs A plant's female reproductive organs produce eggs and male reproductive organs produce sperm. Depending on the species, these reproductive organs can be on the same plant or on separate plants, as shown in **Figure 3.** If a plant has both organs, it usually can reproduce by itself. However, some plants that have both sex organs still must exchange sex cells with other plants of the same type to reproduce.

In some plant species, the male and female reproductive organs are on separate plants. For example, holly plants are either female or male. For fertilization to occur, holly plants with flowers that have different sex organs must be near each other. In that case, after the eggs in female holly flowers are fertilized, berries can form.

Another difference between you and a plant is how and when plants produce sperm and eggs. You will begin to understand this difference as you examine the life cycle of a plant.

Plant Life Cycles

All organisms have life cycles. Your life cycle started when a sperm and an egg came together to produce the zygote that would grow and develop into the person you are today. A plant also has a life cycle. It can start when an egg and a sperm come together, eventually producing a mature plant.

Differentiated Instruction

Learning Disabled Have students draw a Venn diagram comparing the gametophyte and sporophyte generations, including the number of chromosomes in each and the process that begins each generation. *Meiosis, haploid, 1n, spores,* and *sex cells* apply to the gametophyte generation. *Fertilization, diploid,* and *2n* apply to the sporophyte generation. L3

Visual Learning

Figure 4 Plant life cycles can be very confusing. Help students break down the words *haploid* and *diploid* and relate them to the numbers of chromosomes contained in the cells of each plant stage. haploid—half the number of chromosomes; diploid—full number of chromosomes (or double the number of haploid chromosomes). L2

Two Stages During your life cycle, all structures in your body are formed by cell division and are made up of diploid cells—cells with a full set of chromosomes. However, sex cells form by meiosis and are haploid—they have half a set of chromosomes.

Plants have a two-stage life cycle, as shown in **Figure 4.** The two stages are the gametophyte (guh MEE tuh fite) stage and the sporophyte (SPOHR uh fite) stage.

Gametophyte Stage When reproductive cells undergo meiosis and produce haploid cells called **spores,** the **gametophyte stage** begins. Spores divide by cell division to form plant structures or an entire new plant. The cells in these structures or plants are haploid. Some of these cells undergo cell division and form sex cells.

Sporophyte Stage Fertilization—the joining of haploid sex cells—begins the **sporophyte stage.** Cells formed in this stage have the diploid number of chromosomes. Meiosis in some of these cells forms spores, and the cycle begins again.

✔ **Reading Check** *What process begins the sporophyte stage?*

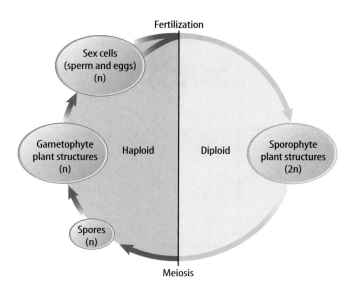

Figure 4 Plants produce diploid and haploid plant structures.
Identify *the process that begins the gametophyte stage.*

Asexual Reproduction What are the advantages and disadvantages of asexual reproduction? Advantages—usually faster than sexual reproduction; it takes only one plant, so there is no need to find a "mate"; and in a stable environment, lack of genetic variation may be advantageous. Disadvantages—does not provide genetic diversity because there is no genetic recombination.

Caption Answer
Figure 4 meiosis

Answer mitosis

3 Assess

DAILY INTERVENTION

Check for Understanding
Kinesthetic Have students write on separate index cards six terms associated with the alternation of generations: *fertilization, sporophyte plant, gametophyte plant, diploid, haploid,* and *meiosis.* Ask them to separate the cards into two sets, one for the gametophyte generation and one for the sporophyte generation. [L2]

Reteach
Plant Reproduction Have students work in small groups to prepare three multiple-choice questions about the general types of plant reproduction. Have groups take turns asking and answering each other's questions. [L2] COOP LEARN

---

section 1 review

Summary

Types of Reproduction
- Asexual reproduction results in offspring that are genetically identical to the parent plant.
- Sexual reproduction requires fertilization and results in offspring that are genetically different from either parent.
- Female reproductive organs produce eggs.
- Male reproductive organs produce sperm.

Plant Life Cycles
- The gametophyte stage of the plant life cycle begins with meiosis.
- The sporophyte stage begins with fertilization.

Self Check

1. **List** three differences between the gametophyte stage and the sporophyte stage of the plant life cycle.
2. **Describe** how plants reproduce asexually.
3. **Compare and contrast** sexual reproduction in plants and animals.
4. **Think Critically** You admire a friend's houseplant. What would you do to grow an identical plant?

Applying Skills

5. **Draw Conclusions** Using a microscope, you see that the nuclei of a plant's cells contain half the usual number of chromosomes. What is the life cycle stage of this plant?

---

section 1 review

1. gametophyte: haploid, produced by meiosis, produces sex cells; sporophyte: diploid, produced by mitosis, produces spores
2. Some plants grow asexually from leaves, stems, roots, runners, or other plant parts.
3. In animals, only sex cells are haploid. In plants, all the cells in the gametophyte stage of the life cycle are haploid.
4. A type of asexual reproduction (stem, leaf, or tip cutting); plants produced through these methods are identical to the parent plant.
5. Based on the haploid number of chromosomes, students should conclude that it is in the gametophyte stage.

✔ **Assessment**

Portfolio Have students write a poem that includes information about sexual and asexual reproduction. Use **Performance Assessment in the Science Classroom,** p. 151. [L2] [P]

Seedless Reproduction

as you read

What You'll Learn

■ **Examine** the life cycles of a moss and a fern.
■ **Explain** why spores are important to seedless plants.
■ **Identify** some special structures used by ferns for reproduction.

Why It's Important

Mosses help build new soil on bare rock or cooled lava, making it possible for other plants to take root.

◎ Review Vocabulary

photosynthesis: food-making process by which plants and many other producers use light energy to produce glucose and oxygen from carbon dioxide and water

New Vocabulary

● frond   ● sori
● rhizome   ● prothallus

The Importance of Spores

If you want to grow ferns and moss plants, you can't go to a garden store and buy a package of seeds—they don't produce seeds. You could, however, grow them from spores. The sporophyte stage of these plants produces haploid spores in structures called spore cases. When the spore case breaks open, the spores are released and spread by wind or water. The spores, shown in **Figure 5,** can grow into plants that will produce sex cells.

Seedless plants include all nonvascular plants and some vascular plants. Nonvascular plants do not have structures that transport water and substances throughout the plant. Instead, water and substances simply move from cell to cell. Vascular plants have tubelike cells that transport water and substances throughout the plant.

Nonvascular Seedless Plants

If you walked in a damp, shaded forest, you probably would see mosses covering the ground or growing on a log. Mosses, liverworts, and hornworts are all nonvascular plants.

The sporophyte stage of most nonvascular plants is so small that it can be easily overlooked. Moss plants have a life cycle typical of how sexual reproduction occurs in this plant group.

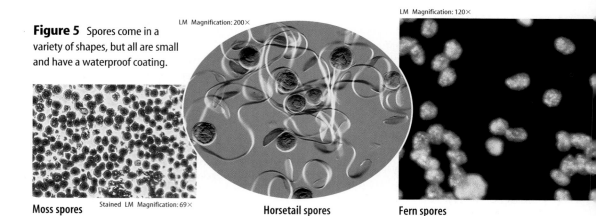

Figure 5 Spores come in a variety of shapes, but all are small and have a waterproof coating.

LM Magnification: 200×
LM Magnification: 120×
Stained LM Magnification: 69×

Moss spores   Horsetail spores   Fern spores

276 CHAPTER 10 Plant Reproduction

The Moss Life Cycle You recognize mosses as green, low-growing masses of plants. This is the gametophyte stage, which produces the sex cells. But the next time you see some moss growing, get down and look at it closely. If you see any brownish stalks growing up from the tip of the gametophyte plants, you are looking at the sporophyte stage. The sporophyte stage does not carry on photosynthesis. It depends on the gametophyte for nutrients and water. On the tip of the stalk is a tiny capsule. Inside the capsule millions of spores have been produced. When environmental conditions are just right, the capsule opens and the spores either fall to the ground or are blown away by the wind. New moss gametophytes can grow from each spore and the cycle begins again, as shown in **Figure 6.**

Figure 6 The life cycle of a moss alternates between gametophyte and sporophyte stages.
Identify *the structures that are produced by the gametophyte stage.*

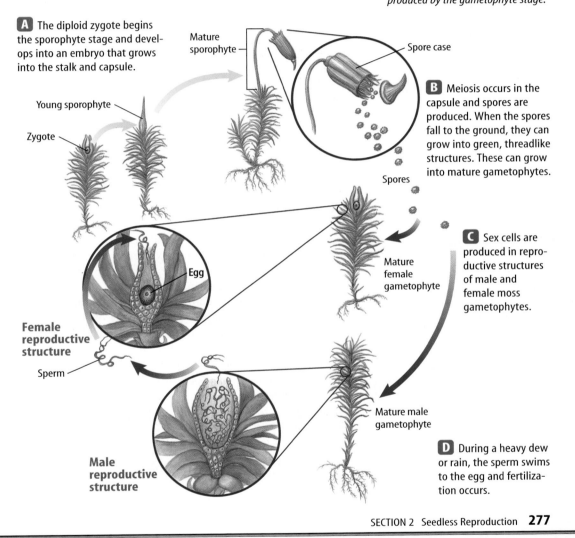

A The diploid zygote begins the sporophyte stage and develops into an embryo that grows into the stalk and capsule.

Mature sporophyte

Young sporophyte

Zygote

Spore case

B Meiosis occurs in the capsule and spores are produced. When the spores fall to the ground, they can grow into green, threadlike structures. These can grow into mature gametophytes.

Spores

Female reproductive structure

Egg

Mature female gametophyte

C Sex cells are produced in reproductive structures of male and female moss gametophytes.

Sperm

Male reproductive structure

Mature male gametophyte

D During a heavy dew or rain, the sperm swims to the egg and fertilization occurs.

SECTION 2 Seedless Reproduction **277**

Curriculum Connection

History Have students find out how humans have used moss gametophytes historically. Have students make posters to present their findings. Mosses were once used as bandages during wars because of their absorbency and antiseptic properties. L2 COOP LEARN

Differentiated Instruction

Visually Impaired Provide students with moss plants that include sporophytes, if possible, and a fern frond with well-developed sori. Allow students to use their sense of touch to explore the shape and texture of these plant structures. L2

2 Teach

Discussion

Moss Spores Explain that a single moss capsule may release 50 million spores. Ask students what advantages the production of so many spores provides to moss plants. It increases the likelihood that some spores will find a suitable environment and develop into new moss plants, thus aiding in the survival of the species.

Caption Answer
Figure 6 sex cells (eggs and sperm)

Activity

Terrariums Have the class make a terrarium that includes mosses. Have students observe these plants as they grow, mature, and produce spores from their capsules. L2

Visual Learning

Figure 6 Have students trace the different stages in the diagram, following the arrows. Again emphasize that the gametophyte produces sex cells (egg and sperm) that unite to form the sporophyte, which produces spores. Review with students the number of chromosomes contained by cells at each stage. Then give student pairs drawings of the stages of the moss life cycle on 3 × 5 cards. Have students sequence and label the drawings. L2

Teacher FYI

Vascular Tissue Some mosses possess strands of vascular tissue. This tissue is not arranged or differentiated to the extent found in true vascular plants.

Visual Learning

Figure 7 Ask students to explain why the balls of cells that grow in the cups shown in the picture are a form of asexual reproduction. These balls of cells do not need to be fertilized in order to grow into a new plant. Thus, they are a form of asexual reproduction.

Make a Model

Life Cycles Have students make drawings, flowcharts, or other models to show the stages of a moss's or fern's life cycle. Their models should include both gametophyte and sporophyte generations. L2 P

Discussion

Cycle Time Ask students to hypothesize how much time a plant spends in each phase of its life cycle. Allow them to explain their answers. Nonvascular plants spend most of their life cycle in the gametophyte phase. Most vascular plants spend most of their life cycle in the sporophyte stage. L2

Catapults Possible answers: machines that toss tennis balls; skeet throwers

Answer prothallus

Quick Demo

Seedless Plants

Materials photographs or transparencies of various fern and moss species

Estimated Time 15–20 minutes

Procedure Show students several species of seedless plants to demonstrate the variety of forms and the types of environments in which seedless plants live.

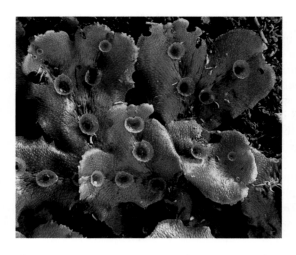

Figure 7 Small balls of cells grow in cuplike structures on the surface of the liverwort.

Catapults For thousands of years, humans have used catapults to launch objects. The spore cases of ferns act like tiny catapults as they eject their spores. In your Science Journal list tools, toys, and other objects that have used catapult technology throughout history.

Nonvascular Plants and Asexual Reproduction Nonvascular plants also can reproduce asexually. For example, if a piece of a moss gametophyte plant breaks off, it can grow into a new plant. Liverworts can form small balls of cells on the surface of the gametophyte plant, as shown in **Figure 7.** These are carried away by water and grow into new gametophyte plants if they settle in a damp environment.

Vascular Seedless Plants

Millions of years ago most plants on Earth were vascular seedless plants. Today they are not as widespread.

Most vascular seedless plants are ferns. Other plants in this group include horsetails and club mosses. All of these plants have vascular tissue to transport water from their roots to the rest of the plant. Unlike the nonvascular plants, the gametophyte of vascular seedless plants is the part that is small and often overlooked.

The Fern Life Cycle The fern plants that you see in nature or as houseplants are fern sporophyte plants. Fern leaves are called **fronds.** They grow from an underground stem called a **rhizome.** Roots that anchor the plant and absorb water and nutrients also grow from the rhizome. Fern sporophytes make their own food by photosynthesis. Fern spores are produced in structures called **sori** (singular, *sorus*), usually located on the underside of the fronds. Sori can look like crusty rust-, brown-, or dark-colored bumps. Sometimes they are mistaken for a disease or for something growing on the fronds.

If a fern spore lands on damp soil or rocks, it can grow into a small, green, heart-shaped gametophyte plant called a **prothallus** (proh THA lus). A prothallus is hard to see because most of them are only about 5 mm to 6 mm in diameter. The prothallus contains chlorophyll and can make its own food. It absorbs water and nutrients from the soil. The life cycle of a fern is shown in **Figure 8.**

Reading Check *What is the gametophyte plant of a fern called?*

Ferns may reproduce asexually, also. Fern rhizomes grow and form branches. New fronds and roots develop from each branch. The new rhizome branch can be separated from the main plant. It can grow on its own and form more fern plants.

278 CHAPTER 10 Plant Reproduction

Differentiated Instruction

Challenge Have students write essays that describe, compare, and contrast the life cycle of mosses and ferns. L3

Science Journal

Using Definitions *Frond* is the name given to leaves of ferns and palms. Have students look in a dictionary to find the derivation and meaning of the word *frond* and then write a paragraph in their journals to suggest why the word is used for these leaves. *Frond* comes from the Latin word for "leaf." L2

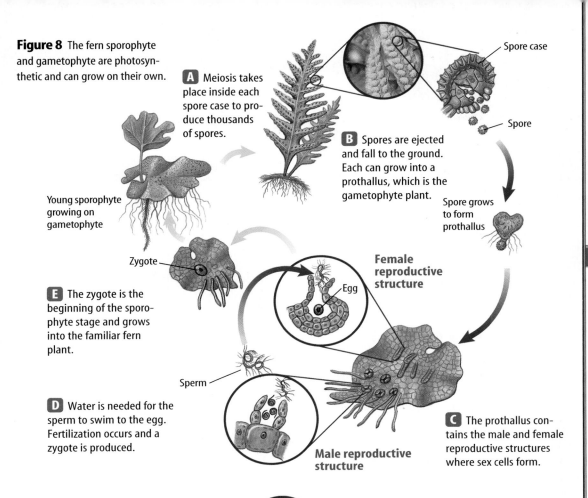

Figure 8 The fern sporophyte and gametophyte are photosynthetic and can grow on their own.

A Meiosis takes place inside each spore case to produce thousands of spores.

Spore case

Spore

B Spores are ejected and fall to the ground. Each can grow into a prothallus, which is the gametophyte plant.

Spore grows to form prothallus

Young sporophyte growing on gametophyte

Zygote

Female reproductive structure

Egg

E The zygote is the beginning of the sporophyte stage and grows into the familiar fern plant.

Sperm

D Water is needed for the sperm to swim to the egg. Fertilization occurs and a zygote is produced.

Male reproductive structure

C The prothallus contains the male and female reproductive structures where sex cells form.

---

section 2 review

Summary

The Importance of Spores
- Seedless plants reproduce by forming spores.
- Seedless plants include all nonvascular plants and some vascular plants.

Nonvascular Seedless Plants
- Spores are produced by the sporophyte stage and can grow into gametophyte plants.
- The sporophyte cannot photosynthesize.

Vascular Seedless Plants
- Fern sporophytes have green fronds that grow from an underground rhizome.

Self Check

1. **Describe** the life cycle of mosses.
2. **Explain** each stage in the life cycle of a fern.
3. **Compare and contrast** the gametophyte plant of a moss and the gametophyte plant of a fern.
4. **Describe** asexual reproduction in seedless plants.
5. **Think Critically** Why do some seedless plants reproduce only asexually during dry times of the year?

Applying Math

6. **Solve One-Step Equations** If moss spores are 0.1 mm in diameter, how many equal the diameter of a penny?

---

section 2 review

1. Spores land on the ground and grow into upright leafy gametophytes, which produce sex cells. Sperm swim in water to reach the egg, forming a zygote. The zygote grows and develops into a spore-producing sporophyte.

2. A spore grows into a heart-shaped gametophyte. The gametophyte produces sex cells that unite to form a zygote. The zygote grows into a spore-producing sporophyte.

3. A moss gametophyte is larger than the sporophyte and photosynthetic; ferns produce small, photosynthetic gametophytes.

4. Seedless plants reproduce asexually from plant parts, from small balls of cells that form on the gametophyte, or from rhizomes.

5. Sexual reproduction in these plants requires water.

6. The diameter of a penny is about 20 mm; about 200 spores needed.

Visual Learning

Figure 8 Again, have students trace with their fingers the sequence of events in a fern's life cycle. This time, have students explain the difference between the sporophyte and the gametophyte generations. L2

3 Assess

DAILY INTERVENTION

Check for Understanding

Interpersonal Have students work in pairs. One student in each pair describes the life cycle of a moss to their partner. The other student describes the life cycle of a fern. Have partners critique each other's descriptions, using the life cycle diagrams in this section as references. L2

Reteach

Life Cycle Terms Provide students with a list of the terms used in this section. Have students identify each term as being part of the moss life cycle, fern life cycle, or both. L2 **ELL** COOP LEARN **LS** Interpersonal

✓ Assessment

Performance Give each student a 3-in × 5-in card on which is written a description of a fern or moss structure. Have each student identify the structure. Assign students to two groups—one for students whose structure is part of the sporophyte stage, and one for students whose structure is part of the gametophyte stage of their plant's life cycle. Have students arrange themselves into a physical model of their plant's life cycle. Use **Performance Assessment in the Science Classroom,** p. 123. L2

Real-World Question

Purpose Students will observe the stages in the life cycles of liverworts, mosses, and ferns. L2
ELL COOP LEARN IN **Visual-Spatial**

Process Skills observe, classify, compare and contrast

Time Required 50 minutes

Safety Precautions Remind students not to eat any plant parts and to be careful when using microscopes.

Procedure

Teaching Strategy Make sure students have properly focused their microscopes.

Troubleshooting If moss spores are not released using water, add an equal amount of glycerin to the water.

Conclude and Apply

1. Moss gametophyte: green, low-growing structure with leaves in a whorl around a stalk; liverwort gametophyte: green, flat, leaflike form. Sporophytes of mosses are a nongreen stalk with a spore-containing capsule at the top. Liverwort sporophytes form on the gametophytes as green umbrella-like structures with spores in cases underneath. Fern gametophytes: green, heart-shaped structures; their sporophytes are familiar green plants.
2. gametophyte, sporophyte, rhizoids, spores, leaflike structures
3. Many spores do not land where conditions are right for growth. The greater the number of spores produced, the greater the chances that some will grow.

Comparing Seedless Plants

All seedless plants have specialized structures that produce spores. Although these sporophyte structures have a similar function, they look different. The gametophyte plants also are different from each other. Do this lab to observe the similarities and differences among three groups of seedless plants.

Real-World Question

How are the gametophyte stages and the sporophyte stages of liverworts, mosses, and ferns similar and different?

Goals
- **Describe** the sporophyte and gametophyte forms of liverworts, mosses, and ferns.
- **Identify** the spore-producing structures of liverworts, mosses, and ferns.

Materials
live mosses, liverworts, and ferns with gametophytes and sporophytes
microscope slides and coverslips (2)
magnifying lens   microscope
forceps   dissecting needle
dropper   pencil with eraser

Safety Precautions
⬚ ⬚ ⬚ ⬚

Procedure

1. Obtain a gametophyte of each plant. With a magnifying lens, observe the rhizoids, leafy parts, and stemlike parts, if any are present.
2. Obtain a sporophyte of each plant and use a magnifying lens to observe it.
3. Locate and remove a spore structure of a moss plant. Place it in a drop of water on a slide.

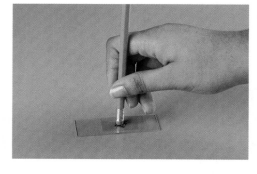

4. Place a coverslip over it. Use the eraser of a pencil to gently push on the coverslip to release the spores. **WARNING:** *Do not break the coverslip.* Observe the spores under low and high power.
5. Make labeled drawings of all observations in your Science Journal.
6. Repeat steps 3 and 4 using a fern.

Conclude and Apply

1. **Compare** the gametophyte's appearance to the sporophyte's appearance for each plant.
2. **List** structure(s) common to all three plants.
3. **Hypothesize** about why each plant produces a large number of spores.

Communicating Your Data

Prepare a bulletin board that shows differences between the sporophyte and gametophyte stages of liverworts, mosses, and ferns. **For more help, refer to the Science Skill Handbook.**

Communicating Your Data

The bulletin board should illustrate differences between the life cycle stages of the plants examined. Encourage students to use online resources to research photographs and information for the bulletin board.

☑ Assessment

Performance Assess students' understanding of the parts of mosses, liverworts, and ferns by having them identify parts of living specimens and by describing the functions of each. Use **Performance Assessment in the Science Classroom,** p. 89. L2

3 Seed Reproduction

The Importance of Pollen and Seeds

All the plants described so far have been seedless plants. However, the fruits and vegetables that you eat come from seed plants. Oak, maple, and other shade trees are also seed plants. All flowers are produced by seed plants. In fact, most of the plants on Earth are seed plants. How do you think they became such a successful group? Reproduction that involves pollen and seeds is part of the answer.

Pollen In seed plants, some spores develop into small structures called pollen grains. A **pollen grain,** as shown in **Figure 9,** has a water-resistant covering and contains gametophyte parts that can produce the sperm. The sperm of seed plants do not need to swim to the female part of the plant. Instead, they are carried as part of the pollen grain by gravity, wind, water currents, or animals. The transfer of pollen grains to the female part of the plant is called **pollination.**

After the pollen grain reaches the female part of a plant, sperm and a pollen tube are produced. The sperm moves through the pollen tube, then fertilization can occur.

Figure 9 The waterproof covering of a pollen grain is unique and can be used to identify the plant that it came from. This pollen from a ragweed plant is a common cause of hay fever.

as you read

What You'll Learn
- **Examine** the life cycles of typical gymnosperms and angiosperms.
- **Describe** the structure and function of the flower.
- **Discuss** methods of seed dispersal in seed plants.

Why It's Important
Seeds from cones and flowers produce most plants on Earth.

🔁 **Review Vocabulary**
gymnosperms: vascular plants that do not flower, generally have needlelike or scalelike leaves, and produce seeds that are not protected by fruit

New Vocabulary
- pollen grain
- pollination
- ovule
- stamen
- pistil
- ovary
- germination

INTERACTIVE CHALKBOARD
PowerPoint® Presentations

Bellringer

Section Focus Transparencies also are available on the Interactive Chalkboard CD-ROM.

L2 ELL

A Bee's-Eye View
A beautiful bright yellow flower you might notice in a field looks different to a bee. Bees can see ultraviolet light. To them the flower includes markings not visible to the human eye.

1. How do the ultraviolet markings help the bee?
2. How do the bee's actions benefit the flower?

Tie to Prior Knowledge

Seed Dispersal Ask students to recall a time when they dispersed seeds. One answer may be when they were eating fruit such as watermelon. Others may have actually planted seeds in a garden. Still others may have walked through a field and found seeds stuck to their clothing.

Color-enhanced SEM
Magnification: 3000×

SECTION 3 Seed Reproduction **281**

Section 3 Resource Manager

Chapter *FAST FILE* Resources
Transparency Activity, p. 44
Directed Reading for Content Mastery, pp. 19, 20
Enrichment, p. 30
MiniLAB, p. 4
Lab Activity, pp. 9–12, 13–14
Reinforcement, p. 27

Lab Worksheet, pp. 7–8
Reading and Writing Skill Activities, p. 1
Life Science Critical Thinking/Problem Solving, p. 8
Earth Science Critical Thinking/Problem Solving, p. 7
Home and Community Involvement, p. 41
Mathematics Skill Activities, p. 5
Lab Management and Safety, p. 38

Figure 10 Wings allow seeds to catch the wind and be dispersed farther from the parent plant.

✓ Reading Check

Answer seed coat, stored food, embryo

IDENTIFYING Misconceptions

Spores v. Pollen Students may hold the misconception that pollen grains are equivalent to spores, but there are some important differences. Spores of seedless plants are released into the environment and can grow into macroscopic gametophytes that may be male or female. Pollen grains contain so-called microspores that, when deposited onto female flowers, can grow into microscopic, male gametophytes of seed plants.

Figure 10 Seeds have three main parts—a seed coat, stored food, and an embryo. This pine seed also has a wing. **Infer** *the function of the wing.*

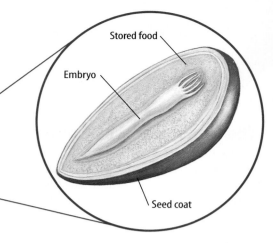

Stored food

Embryo

Seed coat

Science Online

Topic: Seed Banks

Visit life.msscience.com for Web links to information about conserving the seeds of many useful and endangered plants.

Activity List three organizations that manage seed banks, and give examples of the kinds of plants each organization works to conserve.

Seeds Following fertilization, the female part can develop into a seed. A seed consists of an embryo, stored food, and a protective seed coat, as shown in **Figure 10.** The embryo has structures that eventually will produce the plant's stem, leaves, and roots. In the seed, the embryo grows to a certain stage and then stops until the seed is planted. The stored food provides energy that is needed when the plant embryo begins to grow into a plant. Because the seed contains an embryo and stored food, a new plant can develop more rapidly from a seed than from a spore.

✓ Reading Check *What are the three parts of a seed?*

Gymnosperms (JIHM nuh spurmz) and angiosperms are seed plants. One difference between the two groups is the way seeds develop. In gymnosperms, seeds usually develop in cones—in angiosperms, seeds develop in flowers and fruit.

Gymnosperm Reproduction

If you have collected pine cones or used them in a craft project, you probably noticed that many shapes and sizes of cones exist. You probably also noticed that some cones contain seeds. Cones are the reproductive structures of gymnosperms. Each gymnosperm species has a different cone.

Gymnosperm plants include pines, firs, cedars, cycads, and ginkgoes. The pine is a familiar gymnosperm. Production of seeds in pines is typical of most gymnosperms.

Cones A pine tree is a sporophyte plant that produces male cones and female cones as shown in **Figure 11.** Male and female gametophyte structures are produced in the cones but you'd need a magnifying lens to see these structures clearly.

Curriculum Connection

Geography Gymnosperms are the dominant plant of the taiga biome. In North America, most of this area is located between 45° and 60° north latitude. Have students locate on a world map countries where taiga is the primary biome. Then have students list the climactic conditions of these areas. Canada, Norway, Sweden, and Russia are examples. These countries experience harsh winters and short summers. L2

A mature female cone consists of a spiral of woody scales on a short stem. At the base of each scale are two ovules. The egg is produced in the **ovule.** Pollen grains are produced in the smaller male cones. In the spring, clouds of pollen are released from the male cones. Anything near pine trees might be covered with the yellow, dustlike pollen.

Figure 11 Seed formation in pines, as in most gymnosperms, involves male and female cones.

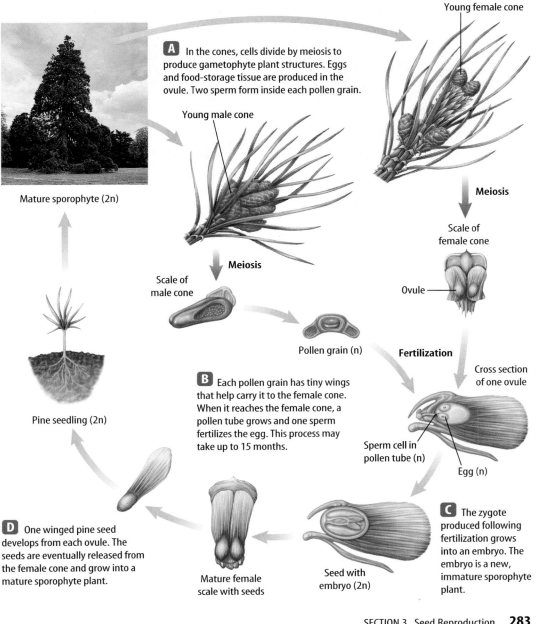

Mature sporophyte (2n)

A In the cones, cells divide by meiosis to produce gametophyte plant structures. Eggs and food-storage tissue are produced in the ovule. Two sperm form inside each pollen grain.

Young male cone

Young female cone

Meiosis

Scale of female cone

Ovule

Meiosis

Scale of male cone

Pollen grain (n)

Fertilization

Cross section of one ovule

Pine seedling (2n)

B Each pollen grain has tiny wings that help carry it to the female cone. When it reaches the female cone, a pollen tube grows and one sperm fertilizes the egg. This process may take up to 15 months.

Sperm cell in pollen tube (n)

Egg (n)

D One winged pine seed develops from each ovule. The seeds are eventually released from the female cone and grow into a mature sporophyte plant.

Mature female scale with seeds

Seed with embryo (2n)

C The zygote produced following fertilization grows into an embryo. The embryo is a new, immature sporophyte plant.

SECTION 3 Seed Reproduction **283**

Seed Germination Without forest fires, some types of cones would not open and new plants would not grow.

Teacher FYI

Self-pollination Self-pollinating plants usually produce flowers that are either not attractive to insects or have structures that hinder the movement of pollen from one plant to another. Genetic recombination in self-pollinating plants generally is not as extensive as in cross pollinating plants.

Quick Demo
Observing Pinecones

Materials two female pinecones, one green and one mature (if available, use a mature cone that has not yet released all of its seeds)

Estimated Time 5–10 minutes

Procedure Compare the tightly closed scales of the green cone with the looser, dryer scales of the mature cone. Loosen some of the scales on the mature cone and show students where the seeds are located. If a cone with seeds is unavailable, show students the two oval seed scars at the bottom of the scale and explain that this is where the seeds developed. When the seeds are mature, the cone opens and seeds are released. Pass both cones around the class for students to examine.

Seed Germination Some gymnosperm seeds will not germinate until the heat of a fire causes the cones to open and release the seeds. Without fires, these plants cannot reproduce. In your Science Journal, explain why some forest fires could be good for the environment.

Figure 12 Seed development can take more than one year in pines. The female cone looks different at various stages of the seed-production process.

Cone at pollination   Cone at the end of the first year   Mature, second-year cone

Gymnosperm Seeds Pollen is carried from male cones to female cones by the wind. However, most of the pollen falls on other plants, the ground, and bodies of water. To be useful, the pollen has to be blown between the scales of a female cone. There it can be trapped in the sticky fluid secreted by the ovule. If the pollen grain and the female cone are the same species, fertilization and the formation of a seed can take place.

If you are near a pine tree when the female cones release their seeds, you might hear a crackling noise as the cones' scales open. It can take a long time for seeds to be released from a female pine cone. From the moment a pollen grain falls on the female cone until the seeds are released, can take two or three years, as shown in **Figure 12.** In the right environment, each seed can grow into a new pine sporophyte.

Angiosperm Reproduction

You might not know it, but you are already familiar with angiosperms. If you had cereal for breakfast or bread in a sandwich for lunch, you ate parts of angiosperms. Flowers that you send or receive for special occasions are from angiosperms. Most of the seed plants on Earth today are angiosperms.

All angiosperms have flowers. The sporophyte plant produces the flowers. Flowers are important because they are reproductive organs. Flowers contain gametophyte structures that produce sperm or eggs for sexual reproduction.

284   CHAPTER 10   Plant Reproduction

 LAB DEMONSTRATION

Purpose to identify the parts of a flower

Materials a variety of monocot and dicot flowers, plastic knives, tape, paper

Preparation Collect or purchase enough flowers for one per student.

Safety Caution students to be careful with the knives.

Procedure Give each student a flower to dissect. As they work, have students tape each flower part in a line on the paper. Have students compare and contrast their dissections.

Expected Outcome Students should identify and compare flower parts and flowers.

Assessment

Have students describe any differences they have observed. The numbers of flower parts vary from plant to plant. Dicot flower parts occur in fours and fives; monocot flower parts occur in threes. L2

The Flower When you think of a flower, you probably imagine something with a pleasant aroma and colorful petals. Although many such flowers do exist, some flowers are drab and have no aroma, like the flowers of the maple tree shown in **Figure 13.** Why do you think such variety among flowers exists?

Most flowers have four main parts—petals, sepals, stamen, and pistil—as shown in **Figure 14.** Generally, the colorful parts of a flower are the petals. Outside the petals are usually leaflike parts called sepals. Sepals form the outside of the flower bud. Sometimes petals and sepals are the same color.

Inside the flower are the reproductive organs of the plant. The **stamen** is the male reproductive organ. Pollen is produced in the stamen. The **pistil** is the female reproductive organ. The **ovary** is the swollen base of the pistil where ovules are found. Not all flowers have every one of the four parts. Remember the holly plants you learned about at the beginning of the chapter? What flower part would be missing on a flower from a male holly plant?

✔ **Reading Check** *Where are ovules found in the flower?*

Figure 13 Maple trees produce clusters of flowers early in the spring.
Describe *how these flowers are different from those of the crocus shown in Figure 1.*

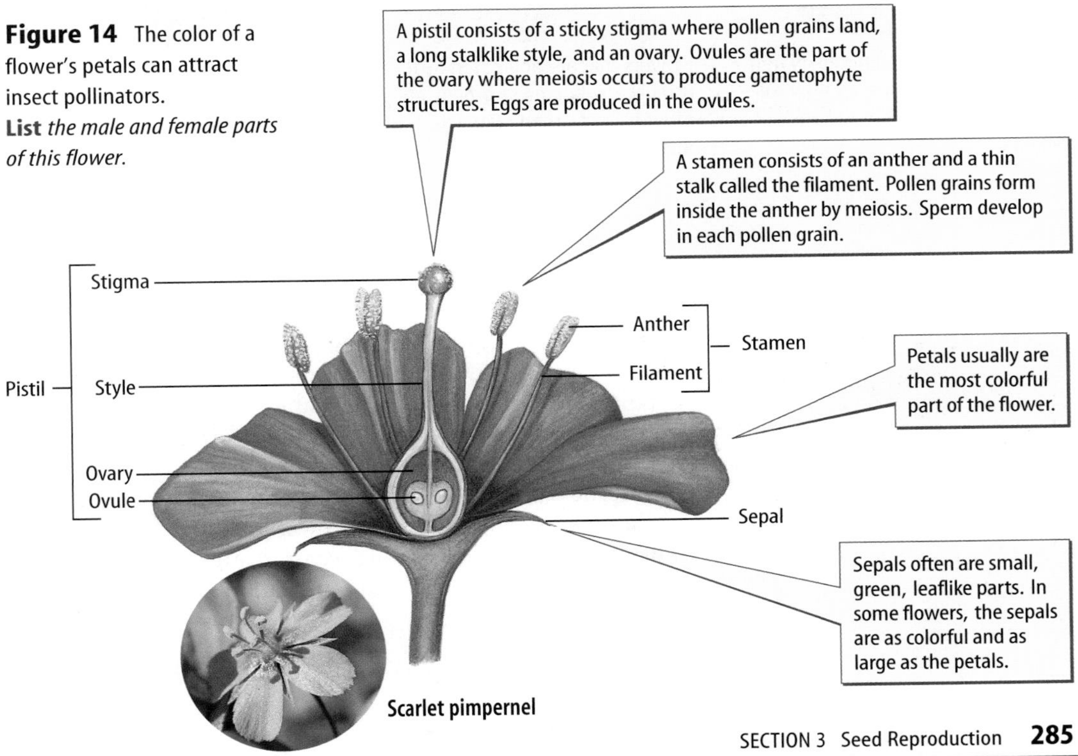

Figure 14 The color of a flower's petals can attract insect pollinators.
List *the male and female parts of this flower.*

A pistil consists of a sticky stigma where pollen grains land, a long stalklike style, and an ovary. Ovules are the part of the ovary where meiosis occurs to produce gametophyte structures. Eggs are produced in the ovules.

A stamen consists of an anther and a thin stalk called the filament. Pollen grains form inside the anther by meiosis. Sperm develop in each pollen grain.

Petals usually are the most colorful part of the flower.

Sepals often are small, green, leaflike parts. In some flowers, the sepals are as colorful and as large as the petals.

Stigma
Pistil
Style
Ovary
Ovule
Anther
Filament
Stamen
Sepal

Scarlet pimpernel

SECTION 3 Seed Reproduction **285**

Differentiated Instruction

Visually Impaired Provide visually impaired students with large plastic models of flowers so that they can tactilely identify the flower's structures. Allow these students to smell the scents of a variety of flowers to enrich their experience. L2
IS Kinesthetic

English-Language Learners Have students create a table that compares the life cycles of angiosperms and gymnosperms. Have them refer to the life cycle diagrams in this chapter. Their tables should have two columns with the labels: *Similarities* and *Differences.* L2

Inquiry Lab

Moss Life Cycle

Purpose Students design a moss habitat to observe the life cycle of a simple plant.

Possible Materials large jar, small aquarium, potting soil, plastic wrap, moss, thermometer, water, magnifying lens, masking tape

Estimated Time one class session; several observation periods over 2–3 weeks

Teaching Strategies

• With permission, students can collect moss from woodlands, moist walls, streamside rocks, or other moist, shady locations.

• Students can set up a terrarium in an aquarium by laying mats of moss over potting soil covered with plastic wrap that has holes punched in it.

• Students can use a magnifying lens to examine the moss as it develops through its life cycle.

• Encourage students to list observations and questions to explore through research and experiments.

For additional inquiry activities, see *Science Inquiry Labs.*

Figure 15 Looking at flowers will give you a clue about how each one is pollinated.

Honeybees are important pollinators. They are attracted to brightly colored flowers, especially blue and yellow flowers.

Flowers that are pollinated at night, like this cactus flower being pollinated by a bat, are usually white.

Flowers that are pollinated by hummingbirds usually are brightly colored, especially bright red and yellow.

Flowers that are pollinated by flies usually are dull red or brown. They often have a strong odor like rotten meat.

The flower of this wheat plant does not have a strong odor and is not brightly colored. Wind, not an animal, is the pollinator of wheat and most other grasses.

Importance of Flowers The appearance of a plant's flowers can tell you something about the life of the plant. Large flowers with brightly colored petals often attract insects and other animals, as shown in **Figure 15.** These animals might eat the flower, its nectar, or pollen. As they move about the flower, the animals get pollen on their wings, legs, or other body parts. Later, these animals spread the flower's pollen to other plants that they visit. Other flowers depend on wind, rain, or gravity to spread their pollen. Their petals can be small or absent. Flowers that open only at night, such as the cactus flower in **Figure 15,** usually are white or yellow and have strong scents to attract animal pollinators. Following pollination and fertilization, the ovules of flowers can develop into seeds.

✔ Reading Check *How do animals spread pollen?*

Differentiated Instruction

Learning Disabled Play "plant bingo." Have students make a game board by writing all the boldfaced terms from this section in squares on a sheet of paper. Then read a definition of a plant term. Students who can correctly identify the term can cover that term on their board. The first student to have all terms covered wins. L2

Visual Learning

Figure 15 After students have studied the pollination mechanisms shown, have them work in teams to write a short story about a particular kind of flower and its pollination mechanism. The story should include a day in the life of a flower. L2 COOP LEARN 🄸🄽 **Linguistic**

Angiosperm Seeds The development of angiosperm seeds is shown in **Figure 16.** Pollen grains reach the stigma in a variety of ways. Pollen is carried by wind, rain, or animals such as insects, birds, and mammals. A flower is pollinated when pollen grains land on the sticky stigma. A pollen tube grows from the pollen grain down through the style. The pollen tube enters the ovary and reaches an ovule. The sperm then travels down the pollen tube and fertilizes the egg in the ovule. A zygote forms and grows into the plant embryo.

Figure 16 In angiosperms, seed formation begins with the formation of sperm and eggs in the male and female flower parts.

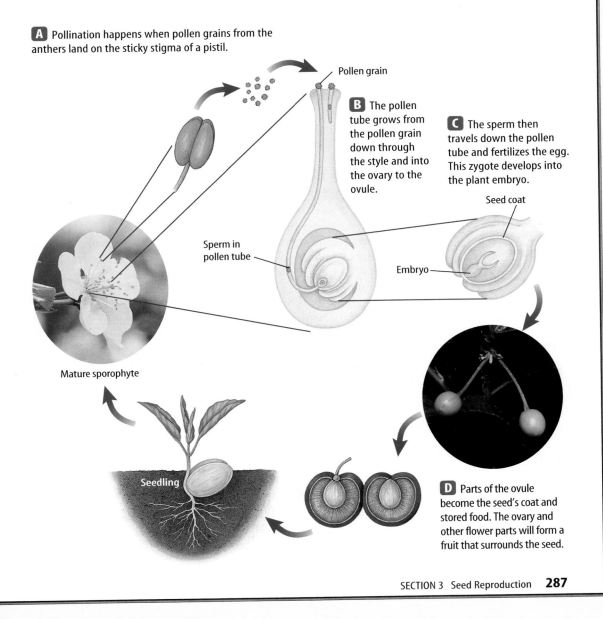

A Pollination happens when pollen grains from the anthers land on the sticky stigma of a pistil.

Pollen grain

B The pollen tube grows from the pollen grain down through the style and into the ovary to the ovule.

C The sperm then travels down the pollen tube and fertilizes the egg. This zygote develops into the plant embryo.

Seed coat

Sperm in pollen tube

Embryo

Mature sporophyte

Seedling

D Parts of the ovule become the seed's coat and stored food. The ovary and other flower parts will form a fruit that surrounds the seed.

SECTION 3 Seed Reproduction **287**

Visual Learning

Figure 16 After students have read and discussed the information, have them make an events chain concept map to summarize seed formation in angiosperms.
L2 IS **Visual-Spatial**

Teacher FYI

Bee Pollination Bees and flowers have a symbiotic, or mutually beneficial, relationship. More flowers are pollinated by bees than any other kind of insect. Many flowers also have a highly complicated structure that discourages self-pollination and encourages cross-pollination of plants with single flowers. This means that while a bee is getting nectar from the flower, it is able to touch the pistil, but not the stamen. As the bee is leaving, however, it is able to touch the stamen, but not the pistil. This way, the bee leaves pollen from another flower rather than the pollen from the flower from which the bee is taking nectar.

Virtual Labs

Flower Parts *What are the functions of the parts of a flower?*

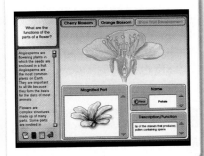

Cultural Diversity

Drip Irrigation Crop production on a Navajo reservation in Arizona was once limited because of the scarcity of water. In 1984, David Mazigh, manager of an experimental farm in Israel, was invited to visit the reservation. Mazigh shared his knowledge of drip irrigation with the Navajos. Some Israeli farmers use drip irrigation to get water to plants in their desert lands. Water is pumped from a well and mixed with fertilizer. The fertilizer solution travels in thick pipes to thin drip lines that lie beside rows of planted seeds in the fields. Small nozzles allow the solution to drip out, providing plants with a slow and constant supply of water and fertilizer. Encourage students to visit a garden store and examine the drip irrigation systems available for home use.

Use an Analogy

Clothing Fasteners The way many seeds attach themselves to passing animals is like the way that two pieces of hook and loop tape stick together. In fact, hook and loop tape was inspired by the mechanism cockleburs use to stick to fur and clothing.

Purpose Students infer possible methods of dispersal for a seed shaped like a button. L2 ELL
IS Logical-Mathematical

Materials button, **Figure 18**

Teaching Strategy Divide the class into groups. Ask each group to brainstorm possible dispersal methods for imaginary seeds shaped like other common items such as safety pins, cotton swab ends, and thumb tacks.

Analysis
1. Answer will vary depending on the button chosen and methods tried.
2. Answer will vary depending on the button chosen and methods tried.

Assessment

Process Ask students to infer how the weight and shape of a seed will determine whether the wind will disperse it. Seeds capable of wind dispersal must be lightweight. Their shapes must have maximum surface area exposure and have a shape that can trap air currents. Use **Performance Assessment in the Science Classroom,** p. 89.

✔ **Reading Check**

Answer Small seeds may become airborne when the plant releases them. Some seeds have winglike or feathery structures that allow them to move with air currents.

Figure 17 Seeds of land plants are capable of surviving unfavorable environmental conditions.
1. Immature plant
2. Cotyledon(s)
3. Seed coat
4. Endosperm

Mini LAB

Modeling Seed Dispersal

Procedure 👓
1. Find a **button** you can use to represent a seed.
2. Examine the seeds pictured in **Figure 18** and invent a way that your button seed could be dispersed by wind, water, on the fur of an animal, or by humans.
3. Bring your button seed to class and demonstrate how it could be dispersed.

Analysis
1. Explain how your button seed was dispersed.
2. In your **Science Journal,** write a paragraph describing your model. Also describe other ways you could model seed dispersal.

Try at Home

288 CHAPTER 10 Plant Reproduction

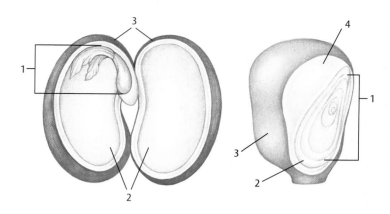

Seed Development Parts of the ovule develop into the stored food and the seed coat that surround the embryo, and a seed is formed, as shown in **Figure 17.** In the seeds of some plants, like beans and peanuts, the food is stored in structures called cotyledons. The seeds of other plants, like corn and wheat, have food stored in a tissue called endosperm.

Seed Dispersal

INTEGRATE Earth Science Sometimes, plants just seem to appear. They probably grew from a seed, but where did the seed come from? Plants have many ways of dispersing their seeds, as shown in **Figure 18.** Most seeds grow only when they are placed on or in soil. Do you know how seeds naturally get to the soil? For many seeds, gravity is the answer. They fall onto the soil from the parent plant on which they grew. However, in nature some seeds can be spread great distances from the parent plant.

Wind dispersal usually occurs because a seed has an attached structure that moves it with air currents. Some plants have very small seeds that become airborne when released by the plant.

✔ **Reading Check** *How can wind disperse seeds?*

Animals can disperse many seeds. Some seeds are eaten with fruits, pass through an animal's digestive system, and are dispersed as the animal moves from place to place. Seeds can be carried great distances and stored or buried by animals. Attaching to fur, feathers, and clothing is another way that seeds are dispersed by animals.

Water also disperses seeds. Raindrops can knock seeds out of a dry fruit. Some fruits and seeds float on flowing water or ocean currents. When you touch the seedpod of an impatiens flower, it explodes. The tiny seeds are ejected and spread some distance from the plant.

Teacher FYI

Wind Dispersal Seeds of maples, milkweed, elms, pines, cottonwoods, and other plants are dispersed by the wind.

288 CHAPTER 10 Plant Reproduction

Figure 18

Plants have many adaptations for dispersing seeds, often enlisting the aid of wind, water, or animals.

▲ Equipped with tiny hooks, burrs cling tightly to fur and feathers.

▼ Dandelion seeds are easily dislodged and sail away on a puff of wind.

▲ Pressure builds within the seedpods of this jewelweed plant until the pod bursts, flinging seeds far and wide.

▼ Some seeds buried by animals, such as this squirrel, go uneaten and sprout the next spring.

▲ Encased in a thick, buoyant husk, a coconut may be carried hundreds of kilometers by ocean currents.

▶ Blackberry seeds eaten by this white-footed mouse will pass through its digestive tract and be deposited in a new location.

Visualizing Seed Dispersal

Have students examine the pictures and read the captions. Then ask the following question.

What advantage does wide dispersal of seeds give a plant species? Possible answers: less competition for resources between parent plant and offspring, better chance of finding a suitable environment for growth

Activity

Chart Dispersal Have students complete a chart of the different methods of seed dispersal illustrated and give more examples for each method. L2

Sample chart:

Dispersal Method	Examples
In fur of animals	burdock, burr clover, foxtails, sticktights
Buried by animals	oak, pecan, pine
Excreted by animals	raspberries, strawberries, tomatoes
Floating	red mangroves, sedge
Shotgun dispersal	mistletoe, "touch-me-not" (impatiens), "squirting cucumbers" (ecballium), sandbox tree
Wind dispersal	maple, orchids, milkweed, tumbleweeds

Differentiated Instruction

Challenge Have students research the importance of bats and their role in pollination and seed dispersal in rain forests around the world. Have them make posters showing their results. Possible research findings: Bats are important in seed dispersal as they excrete seeds from the fruits they consume. Bats also are important in pollination of plants in tropical areas. Plants that rely on bats for pollination only bloom at night, when bats are active. L3

Teacher FYI

Seed Propulsion *Force* may be defined as a push or a pull. Some dry fruits open with such great force when ripe, that their seeds are dispersed some distance from the plants. Witch hazel seeds may be propelled more than 12 m by the force of its splitting ripe fruit.

Discussion

Germination Why might some gardeners soak their bean seeds before planting? Soaking softens the seed coat and speeds germination.

Activity

Collecting Seeds Have students collect as many different kinds of seeds as possible. Once collected, students can germinate the seeds and draw pictures of differences they note among the germinating seeds. They also can record and graph the various rates of germination. [L2] **ELL**
IS **Kinesthetic and Visual-Spatial**

Germination A series of events that results in the growth of a plant from a seed is called **germination.** When dispersed from the plant, some seeds germinate in just a few days and other seeds take weeks or months to grow. Some seeds can stay in a resting stage for hundreds of years. In 1982, seeds of the East Indian lotus sprouted after 466 years.

Seeds will not germinate until environmental conditions are right. Temperature, the presence or absence of light, availability of water, and amount of oxygen present can affect germination. Sometimes the seed must pass through an animal's digestive system before it will germinate. Germination begins when seed tissues absorb water. This causes the seed to swell and the seed coat to break open.

Applying Math   Calculate Using Percents

HOW MANY SEEDS WILL GERMINATE? The label on a packet of carrot seeds says that it contains about 200 seeds. It also claims that 95 percent of the seeds will germinate. How many seeds should germinate if the packet is correct?

Solution

1 *This is what you know:*
- quantity = 200
- percentage = 95

2 *This is what you need to find out:*

What is 95 percent of 200?

3 *This is the procedure you need to use:*
- Set up the equation for finding percentage:

$$\frac{95}{100} = \frac{x}{200}$$

- Solve the equation for x: $x = \dfrac{95 \times 200}{100}$

4 *Check your answer:*

Divide by 200 then multiply by 100. You should get the original percentage of 95.

Practice Problems

1. The label on a packet of 50 corn kernels claims that 98 percent will germinate. How many kernels will germinate if the packet is correct?

2. A seed catalog states that a packet contains 1,120 spinach seeds with a germination rate of 65 percent. How many spinach plants should the packet produce?

For more practice, visit life.msscience.com/math_practice

Differentiated Instruction

Learning Disabled To reinforce the conditions needed for germination, have students carry out this activity. Place a sponge in a shallow dish with enough water to soak the sponge. Be sure the sponge rises above the water level. Sprinkle a small amount of birdseed on the sponge. Pat the seeds into the sponge. Place the sponge in a bright but not sunny location. Add water to keep the sponge moist. Have students use magnifying lenses to examine the sponge each day. Have them record their observations as drawings with explanatory labels. Be sure they note when they see cracking in the seeds and the sprouting of the embryo. In five to seven days, the seedlings can be scraped off the sponge and into a container of potting soil. [L1]
ELL **IS** **Kinesthetic**

Figure 19 Seed germination results in a new plant.

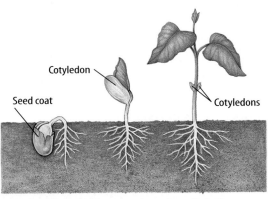

Seed coat

Cotyledon

Cotyledons

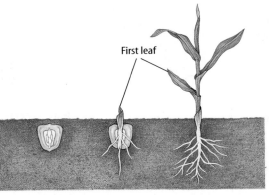

First leaf

In beans, the cotyledons rise above the soil. As the stored food is used, the cotyledons shrivel and fall off.

In corn, the stored food in the endosperm remains in the soil and is gradually used as the plant grows.

Next, a series of chemical reactions occurs that releases energy from the stored food in the cotyledons or endosperm for growth. Eventually, a root grows from the seed, followed by a stem and leaves as shown in **Figure 19.** After the plant emerges from the soil, photosynthesis can begin. Photosynthesis provides food as the plant continues to grow.

section 3 review

Summary

The Importance of Pollen and Seeds

- In seed plants, spores develop into pollen grains.
- Pollination is the transfer of pollen from a male plant part to a female plant part.

Gymnosperm Reproduction

- Cones are reproductive structures of gymnosperms.
- Seeds are produced in female cones.

Angiosperm Reproduction

- Flowers are reproductive structures of angiosperms.
- Female flower parts develop into seeds.

Seed Dispersal

- Seeds can be dispersed in several ways.
- Germination is the growth of a plant from a seed.

Self Check

1. **Compare and contrast** the life cycles of gymnosperms and angiosperms.
2. **Draw and label** a diagram showing all four parts of a flower.
3. **Describe** the three parts of a seed and their functions.
4. **Explain** the process of germination.
5. **Think Critically** Walnut trees produce edible seeds with a hard outer covering. Maple trees produce seeds with winglike edges. What type of seed dispersal applies to each type of tree?

Applying Skills

6. **Research information** to find out what conditions are needed for seed germination of three plants, such as corn, peas, and beans. How long does each type of seed take to germinate?

DAILY INTERVENTION

Check for Understanding

Linguistic Have students write a short paragraph describing how gymnosperm reproduction differs from reproduction in angiosperms. L2

Reteach

Flowers and Reproduction Bring in plants, flowers, and seeds to demonstrate the parts of a plant's life cycle. Have students sequence a plant's life cycle by using the plants and plant parts. Reproductive structures can be obtained by dissecting a flower. A magnifying lens may be needed to see the flower's reproductive parts. Have students write a paragraph that details the sequence of the plant's life cycle. L2 LS **Linguistic**

☑ Assessment

Process Assess students' abilities to observe and infer by giving students flowers and having them infer how each flower may be pollinated. Use **Performance Assessment in the Science Classroom,** p. 89. L2

section 3 review

1. The life cycles of angiosperms and gymnosperms are similar, except that angiosperms produce gametes in flowers and gymnosperms produce gametes in cones.
2. Students' diagrams should resemble **Figure 14.**
3. The seed coat protects the seed. The endosperm provides food for the growing embryo. The embryo contains immature leaves, stem, and root.
4. Seed absorbs water; energy is released from cotyledon or endosperm; embryo begins to grow; first root, then stem and leaves.
5. walnut: carried by animals or drops to the ground; maple: floats in the air or blown by wind
6. Answers will depend on seeds researched. Germination times can vary widely from species to species.

BENCH TESTED

Germination Rate of Seeds

▶ Real-World Question

Purpose Students design and carry out an experiment to explore how germination rate varies with an environmental factor.

L2 COOP LEARN

IS Logical-Mathematical

Process Skills design an experiment; collect, interpret, and analyze data; draw conclusions; communicate; make and use tables and graphs; compare and contrast; recognize cause and effect; form a hypothesis; manipulate and control variables; measure in SI

Time Required one class period, plus 10 min per day for two weeks

Alternate Materials Use any fast-germinating seeds. Epsom salts may be substituted for table salt. Seedling warming cables provide another variable to test.

Safety Precautions Have students review safety symbols and precautions on the student page.

▶ Form a Hypothesis

Possible Hypotheses Students may predict that seeds will germinate at a higher rate with water than with salt solutions. They may predict that warmer soil will increase the rate of germination. The presence and absence of light and planting depth are other variables that may be tested.

▶ Test Your Hypothesis

Possible Procedures Students will plant seeds in shallow trays or plastic cups. They may test one variable in their procedure.

Goals
- **Design** an experiment to test the effect of an environmental factor on seed germination rate.
- **Compare** germination rates under different conditions.

Possible Materials
seeds
water
salt
potting soil
plant trays or plastic cups
*seedling warming cables
thermometer
graduated cylinder
beakers
*Alternate materials

Safety Precautions

WARNING: *Some kinds of seeds are poisonous. Do not place any seeds in your mouth. Be careful when using any electrical equipment to avoid shock hazards.*

▶ Real-World Question

Many environmental factors affect the germination rate of seeds. Among these are soil temperature, air temperature, moisture content of soil, and salt content of soil. What happens to the germination rate when one of these variables is changed? How do environmental factors affect seed germination? Can you determine a way to predict the best conditions for seed germination?

▶ Form a Hypothesis

Based on your knowledge of seed germination, state a hypothesis to explain how environmental factors affect germination rates.

Alternative Inquiry Lab

Germination Rates To make this lab an inquiry lab, ask students how the germination rates for different types of seeds compare. The lab should take about one class session and several 5-minute observation periods over several weeks. Students can plant different types of seeds, such as bean seeds, mustard seeds, and alfalfa seeds, to compare their germination rates and establish exact environmental conditions as their controls. They can measure the amount of water, seed depth, mass of fertilizer, soil temperature, and air temperature. Encourage students to determine a method of measuring the amount of sunlight falling on each plant so that the amount of sunlight can be standardized. Students can construct data tables to record their data, and they can draw graphs to display their measurements.

⊙ Test Your Hypothesis

Make a Plan

1. As a group, agree upon and write your hypothesis and decide how you will test it. Identify which results will confirm the hypothesis.

2. **List** the steps you need to take to test your hypothesis. Be specific, and describe exactly what you will do at each step. List your materials.

3. **Prepare** a data table in your Science Journal to record your observations.

4. Reread your entire experiment to make sure that all of the steps are in a logical order.

5. **Identify** all constants, variables, and controls of the experiment.

Follow Your Plan

1. Make sure your teacher approves your plan and your data table before you proceed.

2. Use the same type and amount of soil in each tray.

3. While the experiment is going on, record your observations accurately and complete the data table in your Science Journal.

⊙ Analyze Your Data

1. **Compare** the germination rate in the two groups of seeds.

2. **Compare** your results with those of other groups.

3. Did changing the variable affect germination rates? Explain.

4. Make a bar graph of your experimental results.

⊙ Conclude and Apply

1. **Interpret** your graph to estimate the conditions that give the best germination rate.

2. **Describe** the conditions that affect germination rate.

Communicating
Your Data

Write a short article for a local newspaper telling about this experiment. Give some ideas about when and how to plant seeds in the garden and the conditions needed for germination.

LAB 293

Communicating
Your Data

Have students include graphs in their articles. [L2]

Students using salt solutions should be encouraged to use at least two solution strengths with distilled water as the control. If students use the warming cables as a variable, then seeds without added heat will be the control. If planting depth is the variable, the control is the recommended depth.

Teaching Strategy Have students examine seed packets to gain additional information about normal germination rates.

Troubleshooting Students may confuse rate of germination (how quickly seeds germinate) with germination rate (the percent of seeds that actually germinate).

Expected Outcome Some environmental conditions enhance seed germination; others do not.

⊙ Analyze Your Data

Answers to Questions

1. One group should have had a higher germination rate than the other.
2. Groups testing the same variable should have similar results.
3. Rates of germination and germination rates vary with environmental conditions for each variable, depending on species of plant tested.
4. Graphs should accurately reflect experimental data.

Error Analysis Have students try to explain differences in their results from others who tested the same variable.

⊙ Conclude and Apply

1. Graphs will vary, but each should indicate a range for best germination of the variable tested.
2. Answers may include water quality, amount of water, planting depth, and other similar variables.

TIME

SCIENCE AND Society

SCIENCE ISSUES THAT AFFECT YOU!

Content Background

Genetic engineering is possible because all living organisms, from viruses and single-celled bacteria to humans, use the same genetic code. This allows the possibility of combining DNA from various organisms. The resulting product is called *recombinant DNA*. Organisms that contain DNA from different species are called *transgenic*.

Discussion

Genetic Engineering What are some of the fears associated with the technology of genetic engineering? Possible answers: Bacteria and viruses that have been disabled may regain their ability to cause disease after they are injected; some viruses that are used cause very serious diseases prior to being disabled for such a use. L2

Investigate the Issue

Many of the fears regarding genetic engineering involve the use of this technology in altering many food items. Have students research and identify the foods that have already been subjected to this engineering. What are the goals of this work? Many possible answers: tomatoes with longer shelf life; corn and wheat with resistance to insects, etc. Some fears are that modified foods will produce new allergies, cause diseases, result in crop pests that are resistant to insecticides. L2

Genetic Engineering

Genetically modified "super" corn can resist heat, cold, drought, and insects.

What would happen if you crossed a cactus with a rose? Well, you'd either get an extra spiky flower, or a bush that didn't need to be watered very often. Until recently, this sort of mix was the stuff science fiction was made of. But now, with the help of genetic engineering, it may be possible.

Genetic engineering is a way of taking genes—sections of DNA that produce certain traits, like the color of a flower or the shape of a nose—from one species and giving them to another.

In 1983, the first plant was genetically modified, or changed. Since then, many crops in the U.S. have been modified in this way, including soybeans, potatoes, tomatoes, and corn.

One purpose of genetic engineering is to transfer an organism's traits. For example, scientists have changed lawn grass by adding to it the gene from another grass species. This gene makes lawn grass grow slowly, so it doesn't have to be mowed very often. Genetic engineering can also make plants that grow bigger and faster, repel insects, or resist herbicides. These changes could allow farmers to produce more crops with fewer chemicals. Scientists predict that genetic engineering soon will produce crops that are more nutritious and that can resist cold, heat, or even drought.

Genetic engineering is a relatively new process, and some people are worried about the long-term risks. One concern is that people might be allergic to modified foods and not realize it until it's too late. Other people say that genetic engineering is unnatural. Also, farmers must purchase the patented genetically modified seeds each growing season from the companies that make them, rather than saving and replanting the seeds from their current crops.

People in favor of genetic engineering reply that there are always risks with new technology, but proper precautions are being taken. Each new plant is tested and then approved by U.S. governmental agencies. And they say that most "natural" crops aren't really natural. They are really hybrid plants bred by agriculturists, and they couldn't survive on their own. As genetic engineering continues, so does the debate.

Debate Research the pros and cons of genetic engineering at the link shown to the right. Decide whether you are for or against genetic engineering. Debate your decision with a classmate.

Science Online

For more information, visit life.msscience.com/time

Debate Students can make displays illustrating the potential benefits and fears associated with genetic engineering technology. Help students use the results of their research to form arguments for their debate. You may wish to divide the class into two groups with opposing views. L2

Resources for Teachers and Students

"Are Bioengineered Foods Safe?," by Larry Thompson, January-February 2000, *FDA Consumer Magazine*

"Methods For Genetically Engineering a Plant," January-February 2000, *FDA Consumer Magazine*

Reviewing Main Ideas

Section 1   Introduction to Plant Reproduction

1. Plants reproduce sexually and asexually. Sexual reproduction involves the formation of sex cells and fertilization.

2. Asexual reproduction does not involve sex cells and produces plants genetically identical to the parent plant.

3. Plant life cycles include a gametophyte and a sporophyte stage. The gametophyte stage begins with meiosis. The sporophyte stage begins when the egg is fertilized by a sperm.

4. In some plant life cycles, the sporophyte and gametophyte stages are separate and not dependent on each other. In other plant life cycles, they are part of the same organism.

Section 2   Seedless Reproduction

1. For liverworts and mosses, the gametophyte stage is the familiar plant form. The sporophyte stage produces spores.

2. In ferns, the sporophyte stage is the familiar plant form.

3. Seedless plants, like mosses and ferns, use sexual reproduction to produce spores.

Section 3   Seed Reproduction

1. In seed plants the male reproductive organs produce pollen grains that eventually contain sperm. Eggs are produced in the ovules of the female reproductive organs.

2. The male and female reproductive organs of gymnosperms are called cones. Wind usually moves pollen from the male cone to the female cone for pollination.

3. The reproductive organs of angiosperms are in a flower. The male reproductive organ is the stamen, and the female reproductive organ is the pistil. Gravity, wind, rain, and animals can pollinate a flower.

4. Seeds of gymnosperms and angiosperms are dispersed in many ways. Wind, water, and animals spread seeds. Some plants can eject their seeds.

5. Germination is the growth of a plant from a seed.

Reviewing Main Ideas

Summary statements can be used by students to review the major concepts of the chapter.

Visualizing Main Ideas

See student page.

Science nline
Visit life.msscience.com
  /self_check_quiz
  /interactive_tutor
  /vocabulary_puzzlemaker
  /chapter_review
  /standardized_test

Assessment Transparency

For additional assessment questions, use the *Assessment Transparency* located in the transparency book.

Visualizing Main Ideas

Copy and complete the following table that compares reproduction in different plant groups.

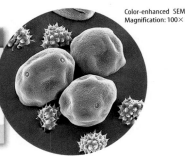

Color-enhanced SEM
Magnification: 100×

Plant Reproduction

Plant Group	Seeds?	Pollen?	Cones?	Flowers?
Mosses	No	No	No	No
Ferns	No	No	No	No
Gymnosperms	Yes	Yes	Yes	No
Angiosperms	Yes	Yes	No	Yes

 Science nline life.msscience.com/interactive_tutor

Assessment

1 Section Focus   **It's a Jungle Out There**
Transparency

If you traveled from Alaska to Key West, Florida, you would expect to see many different plants. There's one place, however, where you could see more plants per square kilometer than any place else on Earth—a tropical rain forest.

1. What factors make the rainforest a good environment for plant growth and reproduction?

2. Why are the upper layers of a rainforest so dense, while the lowest levels may be almost bare?

3. Why is the destruction of rainforests an important concern?

chapter 10 Review

Using Vocabulary

1. frond
2. ovule
3. gametophyte stage
4. gametophyte stage
5. rhizome; sori (either)
6. pistil
7. ovary

Checking Concepts

8. A	13. C
9. A	14. C
10. A	15. D
11. A	16. D
12. A	17. D

Thinking Critically

18. Large numbers of pollen grains increase the chances that any one pollen grain will be blown to a female cone and fertilize an ovule.

19. No; the embryo is the young plant; without it, no plant can grow.

20. Nonvascular plants and ferns require water to transport the sperm to egg cells.

21. The sporophyte is not photosynthetic, so it depends on the photosynthetic gametophyte for nutrition.

22. Brightly colored structures, scents, and flower form help to ensure pollination by specialized pollinators.

Using Vocabulary

frond p. 278	pollination p. 281
gametophyte stage p. 275	prothallus p. 278
germination p. 290	rhizome p. 278
ovary p. 285	sori p. 278
ovule p. 283	spore p. 275
pistil p. 285	sporophyte stage p. 275
pollen grain p. 281	stamen p. 285

Fill in the blank with the correct vocabulary word or words.

1. A(n) _____ is the leaf of a fern.

2. In seed plants, the _____ contains the egg.

3. The plant structures in the _____ are made up of haploid cells.

4. The green, leafy moss plant is part of the _____ in the moss life cycle.

5. Two parts of a sporophyte fern are a frond and _____.

6. The female reproductive organ of the flower is the _____.

7. The _____ is the swollen base of the pistil.

Checking Concepts

Choose the word or phrase that best answers the question.

8. How are colorful flowers usually pollinated?
   A) insects   C) clothing
   B) wind   D) gravity

9. What type of reproduction produces plants that are genetically identical?
   A) asexual   C) spore
   B) sexual   D) flower

10. Which of the following terms describes the cells in the gametophyte stage?
    A) haploid   C) diploid
    B) prokaryote   D) missing a nucleus

11. What structures do ferns form when they reproduce sexually?
    A) spores   C) seeds
    B) anthers   D) flowers

12. What contains food for the plant embryo?
    A) endosperm   C) stigma
    B) pollen grain   D) root

Use the photo below to answer question 13.

13. What disperses the seeds shown above?
    A) rain   C) wind
    B) animals   D) insects

14. What is the series of events that results in a plant growing from a seed?
    A) pollination   C) germination
    B) prothallus   D) fertilization

15. In seedless plants, meiosis produces what kind of plant structure?
    A) prothallus   C) flowers
    B) seeds   D) spores

16. Ovules and pollen grains take part in what process?
    A) germination
    B) asexual reproduction
    C) seed dispersal
    D) sexual reproduction

17. What part of the flower receives the pollen grain from the anther?
    A) sepal   C) stamen
    B) petal   D) stigma

296 CHAPTER REVIEW

Science Online life.msscience.com/vocabulary_puzzlemaker

Use the ExamView® Pro Testmaker CD-ROM to:
- create multiple versions of tests
- create modified tests with one mouse click for inclusion students
- edit existing questions and add your own questions
- build tests aligned with state standards using built-in State Curriculum Tags
- change English tests to Spanish with one mouse click and vice versa

Thinking Critically

18. **Explain** why male cones produce so many pollen grains.

19. **Predict** whether a seed without an embryo could germinate. Explain your answer.

20. **Discuss** the importance of water in the sexual reproduction of nonvascular plants and ferns.

21. **Infer** why the sporophyte stage in mosses is dependent on the gametophyte stage.

22. **List** the features of flowers that ensure pollination.

23. **Compare and contrast** the fern sporophyte and gametophyte stages.

24. **Interpret Scientific Illustrations** Using **Figure 16**, sequence these events.
    - pollen is trapped on the stigma
    - pollen tube reaches the ovule
    - fertilization
    - pollen released from the anther
    - pollen tube forms through the style
    - a seed forms

25. **Concept Map** Copy and complete this concept map of a typical plant life cycle.

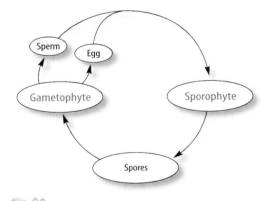

26. **Predict** Observe pictures of flowers or actual flowers and predict how they are pollinated. Explain your prediction.

Performance Activities

27. **Display** Collect several different types of seeds and use them to make a mosaic picture of a flower.

28. **Technical Writing** Write a newspaper story to tell people about the importance of gravity, water, wind, insects, and other animals in plant life cycles.

Applying Math

29. **Germination Rates** A seed producer tests a new batch of corn seeds before putting them on the market. The producer plants a sample of 150 seeds, and 110 of the seeds germinate. What is the germination rate for this batch of corn seeds?

30. **Seed Production** Each blossom on an apple tree, if fertilized, can become a fruit. Suppose an apple tree bears 1,200 blossoms in the spring. If 95 percent are pollinated, how many apples could the tree produce? If each apple contains five seeds, how many seeds would the tree produce?

Use the table below to answer question 31.

Onion Seed Data						
Temperature (°C)	10	15	20	25	30	35
Days to germinate	13	7	5	4	4	13

31. **Onion Seeds** Make a bar graph for the following data table about onion seeds. Put days on the horizontal axis and temperature on the vertical axis.

Thinking Critically

23. Haploid gametophyte stage—small and inconspicuous; diploid sporophyte stage—large and conspicuous; both stages are independent and photosynthetic.

24. 1—pollen is released from the anther; 2—pollen is trapped on the stigma; 3—pollen tube forms through style; 4—pollen tube reaches the ovule; 5—fertilization; 6—a seed forms

25. See student page.

26. Answers will vary depending on flowers observed.

Performance Activities

27. Seed mosaics will vary depending on seed selection and flower chosen. Look for all parts of a flower in the mosaics. Use **Performance Assessment in the Science Classroom,** p. 135.

28. Stories should include information about plant life cycles and the importance of mechanisms of pollination. Use **Performance Assessment in the Science Classroom,** p. 141.

Applying Math

National Math Standards
1, 2, 5, 9

29. $110 \div 150 = 0.73$, or 73%

30. $1,200 \times 0.95 = 1,140$; $1,140 \times 5 = 5,700$

31.

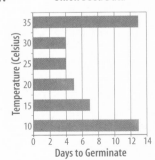

Onion Seed Data

Answer Sheet A practice answer sheet can be found at life.mssience.com/answer_sheet.

SAMPLE

Part 1 Multiple Choice

1. D
2. A
3. C
4. A
5. D
6. C
7. C
8. B

Part 1 Multiple Choice

Record your answers on the answer sheet provided by your teacher or on a sheet of paper.

1. Which statement applies to asexual reproduction?
   A. Sperm and egg are required.
   B. Offspring are genetically different from the parents.
   C. Most animals reproduce in this way.
   D. Offspring are genetically identical to the parent.

2. Which term describes the uniting of a sperm and egg to form a zygote?
   A. fertilization   C. pollination
   B. meiosis   D. germination

Use the picture below to answer questions 3 and 4.

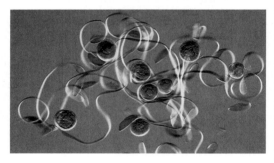

3. What is the primary method by which these horsetail spores are dispersed?
   A. water   C. wind
   B. insects D. grazing animals

Test-Taking Tip

Come Back To It Never skip a question. If you are unsure of an answer, mark your best guess on another sheet of paper and mark the question in your test booklet to remind you to come back to it at the end of the test.

298 STANDARDIZED TEST PRACTICE

4. The horsetail plant that produced these spores uses tubelike cells to transport water and other substances from one part of the plant to another. What type of plant is a horsetail?
   A. vascular   C. nonvascular
   B. seed   D. pollinated

5. Which of the following is a characteristic of angiosperms?
   A. production of cones
   B. seeds not protected by fruit
   C. growth from a rhizome
   D. production of flowers

Use the illustration below to answer questions 6 and 7.

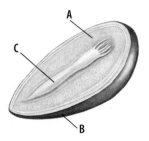

6. Structure B represents which part of this seed?
   A. stored food C. seed coat
   B. embryo   D. ovary

7. Which part(s) of this seed will grow into stems, roots, and leaves?
   A. A   C. C
   B. B   D. A and B

8. What causes seed germination to begin?
   A. warm temperature
   B. exposure to water
   C. at least 9 hours of daylight in a 24-hour period
   D. soil rich in organic material

Part 2 Short Response/Grid In

9. Uniting of sperm and egg is fertilization, required for sexual reproduction. Water, wind, gravity, and animals can help bring sperm and egg together.

10. Sketch should resemble the fern sporophyte in **Figure 8.**

11. Gymnosperm; male cones produce pollen grains; female cones pro-duce eggs that develop into seeds if fertilized by sperm from pollen grains.

12. to release the seeds

13. reproductive organs; size, color, smell, how pollinated, and whether they contain male structures, female structures, or both

14. carry seeds far from parent plant; digestive system can help break down seed coat, speeding germination

15. New plants can be produced asexu-ally along the stems, which grow and spread underground. In addition, grasses depend on wind for pollination.

Part 2 Short Response/Grid In

Record your answers on the answer sheet provided by your teacher or on a sheet of paper.

9. Sperm and eggs are found in different parts of plants. Explain why it is important for these cells to unite, and describe some factors in an environment that help unite them.

10. Make a sketch of a fern plant. Label the fronds, rhizome, roots, and sori.

Use the illustration below to answer questions 11 and 12.

11. What type of seed plant produces the structure shown here? Describe how it is involved in the reproduction of this plant.

12. Why are the scales open?

13. Describe the importance of flowers in angiosperms. What factors can differ from one flower to another?

14. Explain the role played by animals that eat fruits in the dispersal and germination of seeds.

15. Describe the characteristics of certain plants, such as grasses, that enable them to be distributed widely in an environment.

 life.msscience.com/standardized_test

Part 3 Open Ended

Record your answers on a sheet of paper.

16. You have a holly plant in your yard which, despite having ample water, sunlight, and fertilizer, has never produced berries. The flowers produced by this plant have only female structures. What could you do to help this plant produce berries?

17. Why is it important that spores produced during the gametophyte stage of a plant's life cycle be haploid cells?

18. Describe some of the factors that have contributed to the success of seed plants.

Use the illustration below to answer questions 19 and 20.

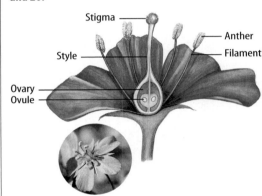

19. Describe the role of each structure labeled in this picture in the production of eggs or sperm.

20. Describe the process of pollination of this plant by insects.

21. Explain how a flower's appearance can indicate its method of pollination. Give three examples of flowers and the method of pollination for each.

21. A flower's characteristics, such as color, shape, and size of petals, can indicate method of pollination. White cactus flowers can be seen more easily at night by bats. Flowers with large petals provide landing places for insect pollinators. Hummingbirds with long beaks pollinate tubular-shaped flowers.

Rubrics

For more help evaluating open-ended assessment questions, see the rubric on p. 10T.

Part 3 Open Ended

16. A plant that produces male flowers could be planted near this female plant to increase the chances for pollination.

17. ensure the sporophyte plant will have the proper number of chromosomes

18. Sperm do not have to swim to egg. Stored food in seeds helps new plants develop rapidly. Seeds can be dispersed in a variety of ways: by wind, water, animals, or gravity.

19. Eggs produced in ovules contained in ovary; pollen grains form in anthers supported by filaments; sperm produced by pollen grains; stigma, supported by the style, is covered with a sticky substance that helps trap pollen grains that land on it; pollen grain germinates, growing a pollen tube through the style to the ovary.

20. Insects feed on nectar or pollen produced by the flower. As the insect feeds, pollen clings to its body. Some of that pollen rubs off onto the style when the insect visits another flower.

Section/Objectives	Standards		Labs/Features
Chapter Opener	**National**	**State/Local**	**Launch Lab:** Do plants lose water? p. 301 **Foldables**, p. 301
	See pp. 16T–17T for a Key to Standards.		
Section 1 Photosynthesis and Respiration 🕐 2 sessions 📦 1 block 1. **Explain** how plants take in and give off gases. 2. **Compare and contrast** photosynthesis and respiration. 3. **Discuss** why photosynthesis and respiration are important.	National Content Standards: UCP.1–UCP.3, UCP.5, A.1, A.2, C.1, C.3		**Integrate Career,** p. 303 **MiniLAB:** Inferring What Plants Need to Produce Chlorophyll, p. 305 **Science Online,** p. 306 **Lab:** Stomata in Leaves, p. 310
Section 2 Plant Responses 🕐 3 sessions 📦 1.5 blocks 4. **Identify** the relationship between a stimulus and a tropism in plants. 5. **Compare and contrast** long-day and short-day plants. 6. **Explain** how plant hormones and responses are related.	National Content Standards: UCP.1–UCP.3, UCP.5, A.1, A.2, C.1, C.3, C.5		**Integrate Physics,** p. 312 **Applying Math:** Growth Hormones, p. 313 **MiniLAB:** Observing Ripening, p. 314 **Visualizing Plant Hormones,** p. 315 **Science Online,** p. 316 **Lab:** Tropism in Plants, p. 318 **Science and Language Arts:** Sunkissed: An Indian Legend, p. 320

Glencoe Exclusive!
TeacherWorks™
All-In-One Planner and Resource Center

Lab Materials	Reproducible Resources	Section Assessment	Technology
Launch Lab: self-sealing plastic bag, aluminum foil, small potted plant	**Chapter *FAST FILE* Resources** Foldable Worksheet, p. 15 Directed Reading Overview, p. 17 Note-taking Worksheets, pp. 29–31	GLENCOE'S **ASSESSMENT** ADVANTAGE	TeacherWorks includes: • Interactive Teacher Edition • Lesson Planner with calendar • Access to all program blacklines • Correlations to standards • Web links
MiniLAB: black construction paper, plant with leaves, scissors, tape **Lab:** lettuce in dish of water, coverslip, microscope, microscope slide, salt solution, forceps *Need materials?* Contact Science Kit at 1-800-828-7777 or www.sciencekit.com on the Internet.	**Chapter *FAST FILE* Resources** Transparency Activity, p. 40 MiniLAB, p. 3 Enrichment, p. 27 Reinforcement, p. 25 Directed Reading, p. 18 Lab Worksheet, pp. 5–6 Transparency Activity, pp. 43–44 Lab Activity, pp. 9–10 **Life Science Critical Thinking/ Problem Solving,** p. 8	Portfolio Science Journal, p. 305 Performance MiniLAB, p. 305 Applying Math, p. 309 Content Section Review, p. 309	Section Focus Transparency Teaching Transparency Virtual Labs CD-ROM Guided Reading Audio Program Interactive Chalkboard CD-ROM
MiniLAB: 2 green bananas, paper bag **Lab:** paper towel, 30 × 30-cm sheet of aluminum foil, water, mustard seeds, marking pen, 1-L clear glass or plastic jar	**Chapter *FAST FILE* Resources** Transparency Activity, p. 41 MiniLAB, p. 4 Enrichment, p. 28 Reinforcement, p. 26 Directed Reading, pp. 19, 20 Lab Worksheet, pp. 7–8 Lab Activity, pp. 11–14 **Home and Community Involvement,** p. 45 **Lab Management and Safety,** p. 58	Portfolio Curriculum Connection, p. 316 Reteach, p. 317 Performance Applying Math, p. 313 MiniLAB, p. 314 Applying Skills, p. 317 Content Section Review, p. 317	Section Focus Transparency Virtual Labs CD-ROM Guided Reading Audio Program Interactive Chalkboard CD-ROM Video Lab

End of Chapter Assessment

GLENCOE'S **ASSESSMENT** ADVANTAGE

Blackline Masters	Technology	Professional Series
Chapter *FAST FILE* Resources Chapter Review, pp. 33–34 Chapter Tests, pp. 35–38 **Standardized Test Practice,** pp. 47–50	MindJogger Videoquiz Virtual Labs CD-ROM Exam*View*® Pro Testmaker TeacherWorks CD-ROM Interactive Chalkboard CD-ROM	**Performance Assessment in the Science Classroom (PASC)**

Transparencies

Section Focus

This is a representation of key blackline masters available in the Teacher Classroom Resources. See Resource Manager boxes within the chapter for additional information.

Key to Teaching Strategies

The following designations will help you decide which activities are appropriate for your students.

- L1   Level 1 activities should be appropriate for students with learning difficulties.

- L2   Level 2 activities should be within the ability range of all students.

- L3   Level 3 activities are designed for above-average students.

- ELL   ELL activities should be within the ability range of English-Language Learners.

- COOP LEARN   Cooperative Learning activities are designed for small group work.

- LS   Multiple Learning Styles logos, as described on page 12T, are used throughout to indicate strategies that address different learning styles.

- P   These strategies represent student products that can be placed into a best-work portfolio.

- PBL   Problem-Based Learning activities apply real-world situations to learning.

Assessment

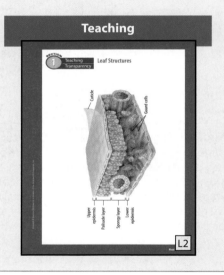

Teaching

Hands-on Activities

Student Text Lab Worksheet

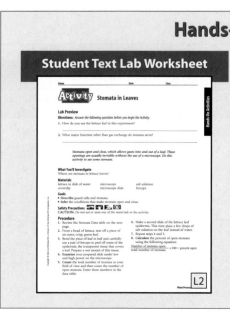

Laboratory Activities

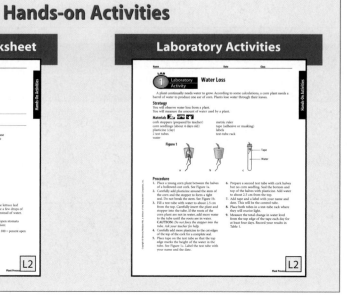

Meeting Different Ability Levels

Content Outline

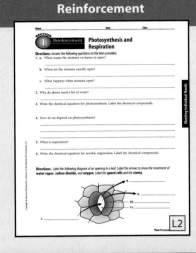

L2

Reinforcement

L2

Enrichment

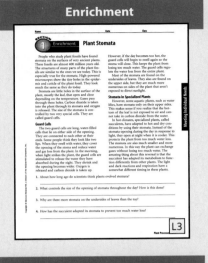

L3

Directed Reading (English/Spanish)

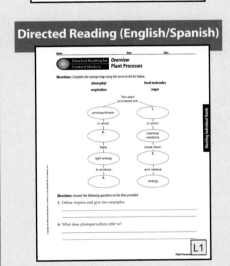

L1

Study Guide

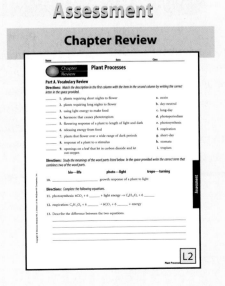

Study Guide

Features
- Contains a study guide page for each section of the chapter
- Reviews key concepts
- Includes answer pages

L2

Reading Essentials

Reading Essentials for Glencoe Science

An Interactive Student Workbook

Features
- Condensed core content
- Actively involves students in reading
- Reinforces key vocabulary

L1

Assessment

Test Practice Workbook

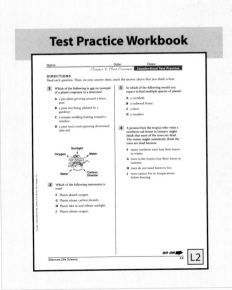

L2

Chapter Review

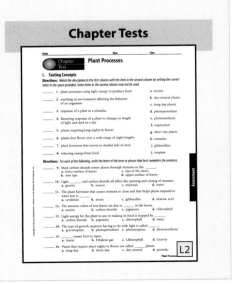

L2

Chapter Tests

L2

Science Content Background

section 1 — Photosynthesis and Respiration

The Food-Making Process

During the light-dependent portion of photosynthesis, a chemical reaction occurs between light and chlorophyll. Electrons from this reaction combine with hydrogen ions from water and store chemical energy called $NADPH + H^+$. The NADPH is the source of energy for the light-independent portion of photosynthesis, during which most plants utilize the NADPH energy to synthesize carbohydrates, including glucose, from carbon dioxide.

Respiration, the mechanism by which energy is released from stored fuel, is always preceded by glycolysis. Glycolysis, which occurs in cell cytoplasm, breaks down one glucose molecule into two molecules of pyruvic acid, producing a small amount of energy. If oxygen is not required or is unavailable during respiration, the process continues as anaerobic reactions, sometimes producing lactic acid. If alcohol is produced, the process is called fermentation. These two inefficient processes extract only a small amount of energy from the pyruvic acid. Aerobic respiration uses oxygen and releases all the energy in the chemical bonds of pyruvic acid. The end products of this process are carbon dioxide, water, and energy.

section 2 — Plant Responses

Types of Responses

Plant responses to external stimuli, called tropisms, are slow, permanent, directed growth movements. Plant responses to internal stimuli are faster and reversible.

Plant Hormones

Plant hormones, chemicals produced in specific plant cells, are transported to other sites in the plant, where they cause physiological changes. The hormone auxin causes cell walls to become more elastic and to stretch during active cell growth. It also suppresses lateral bud growth and prevents leaf abscission, or leaf drop. Ethylene regulates ripening of fruits. Abscisic acid, produced mainly in leaves and fruits, causes buds to become dormant. Gibberellins and cytokinins affect plant growth.

chapter content resources

Internet Resources

For additional content background, visit
life.msscience.com to:
- access your book online
- find references to related articles in popular science magazines
- access Web links with related content background
- access current events with science journal topics

Print Resources

Introductory Plant Biology, by Kingsley Stern, et.al., McGraw-Hill, 2002

Photo Atlas for Botany, by James Perry and David Morgan, Brooks Cole, 1998

The Botany of Desire, by Michael Pollan, Random House, 2001

IDENTIFYING Misconceptions

Find Out What Students Think

Students may think that . . .

Plants do not take in oxygen or give off carbon dioxide.

Photosynthesis is a plant's way of breathing.
Textbooks and science activity books frequently include diagrams showing a cycle in which plants produce oxygen and take in carbon dioxide and animals take in oxygen while giving off carbon dioxide. From diagrams like these, students draw the conclusion that plants exist to give off oxygen for the benefit of animals. They also equate photosynthesis with breathing because it involves taking in one gas and giving off another. Students who do know that plants can give off carbon dioxide often believe it only occurs in the dark, when the plant cannot get sunlight.

Activity
Write the words *oxygen, carbon dioxide, plant, animal, glucose, light,* and *water* on the board. Ask students to copy the words and then construct concept maps showing how all these terms interrelate. Students will most likely make diagrams showing oxygen moving from plant to animal and carbon dioxide moving from animal to plant. They may not know where to place glucose and water. [L2]

Promote Understanding

Demonstrations
After students have learned that glucose is a product of photosynthesis, ask them why they think plants make glucose. A possible answer may be "Plants make glucose for animals to eat." The following demonstrations will help students understand that plants make glucose for their own use. [L2]

- Show students a soaked bean seed. Open the seed and apply iodine as a test for starch. After several minutes the starchy endosperm of the seed should turn blue-black. Use a diagram or snap-lock beads to help explain that starch molecules are chains of glucose molecules. Explain that the bean plant stored starch in the bean seed. Ask students what advantage this might have for the plant. Some students may think that the starch is food for animals, while others may understand that it is food for the embryonic plant.

- Place viable bean seeds in a flask until it is one-third full. Add enough water to completely cover the seeds. Insert a stopper with a glass tube. Attach one end of a length of rubber tubing to the glass tube. Insert the other end into a small flask of limewater. Let the apparatus sit in a warm, well-lighted place. As the seeds absorb water and begin germination, they will metabolize the stored starch in their endosperm and will give off carbon dioxide. Carbon dioxide bubbling slowly through the limewater will cause the liquid to turn cloudy.

Assess
After completing the chapter, see *Identifying Misconceptions* in the Study Guide at the end of the chapter.

Chapter Vocabulary

Science Journal Answers will vary. If students understand that virtually all oxygen in Earth's atmosphere is produced by photosynthesis, they will answer that animal life would be impossible without green plants.

INTERACTIVE CHALKBOARD with Image Bank

PowerPoint® Presentations

This CD-ROM is an editable Microsoft® PowerPoint® presentation that includes:
- a pre-made presentation for every chapter
- interactive graphics
- animations
- audio clips
- image bank
- all new section and chapter questions
- Standardized Test Practice
- transparencies
- pre-lab questions for all labs
- Foldables directions
- links to life.msscience.com

Plant Processes

chapter preview

sections

1 Photosynthesis and Respiration
Lab Stomata in Leaves

2 Plant Responses
Lab Tropism in Plants

Virtual Lab Which colors of the light spectrum are most important for plant growth?

How did it get so big?

From crabgrass to giant sequoias, many plants start as small seeds. Some trees may grow to be more than 20 m tall. One tree can produce enough lumber to build a house. Where does all that wood come from? Did you know that plants are essential to the survival of all animals on Earth?

Science Journal Describe what would happen to life on Earth if all the green plants disappeared.

300

Theme Connection

Systems and Interactions The systems and structures involved in the processes of photosynthesis and respiration work together. Through interactions, these processes, along with the stimuli-response mechanisms discussed in the second part of the chapter, allow a plant to maintain homeostasis.

About the Photo

Earth's Oxygen Virtually all oxygen in Earth's atmosphere is produced during photosynthesis. The atmosphere contained little or no oxygen until biochemical reactions capable of capturing energy from light to support life first appeared billions of years ago. Plants also 'fix' carbon: they transform carbon dioxide gas into carbon-containing compounds that make up the bodies of living organisms, including the wood of trees.

Start-Up Activities

Do plants lose water?

Plants, like all other living organisms, are made of cells, reproduce, and need water to live. What would happen if you forgot to water a houseplant? From your own experiences, you probably know that the houseplant would wilt. Do the following lab to discover one way plants lose water.

1. Obtain a self-sealing plastic bag, some aluminum foil, and a small potted plant from your teacher.

2. Using the foil, carefully cover the soil around the plant in the pot. Place the potted plant in the plastic bag.

3. Seal the bag and place it in a sunny window. Wash your hands.

4. Observe the plant at the same time every day for a few days.

5. **Think Critically** Write a paragraph that describes what happened in the bag. If enough water is lost by a plant and not replaced, predict what will happen to the plant.

Photosynthesis and Respiration Make the following Foldable to help you distinguish between photosynthesis and respiration.

STEP 1 Fold a vertical sheet of paper in half from top to bottom.

STEP 2 Fold in half from side to side with the fold at the top.

STEP 3 Unfold the paper once. Cut only the fold of the top flap to make two tabs.

STEP 4 Turn the paper vertically and label the front tabs as shown.

Compare and Contrast As you read the chapter, write the characteristics of respiration and photosynthesis under the appropriate tab.

Preview this chapter's content and activities at
life.mssience.com

Purpose Use the Launch Lab to introduce students to plant processes. Inform students that they will be learning more about plant processes as they read the chapter. **ELL** **IS** **Kinesthetic** L2

Preparation The seedlings should be large enough to transpire an observable amount of water.

Materials large self-sealing plastic bags, seedling plants in pots, aluminum foil

Teaching Strategies

• Have students record their hypotheses about what will happen after the plants are sealed in the plastic bags.

• Discuss why the soil is covered with foil. to reduce evaporation from the soil

Think Critically

Students should explain that most of the water that gathers in the bag came from the plant. The plant will wilt or even die if it loses too much water. L2

Assessment

Process Have students diagram the pathway of water through a plant, drawing on prior knowledge to label their diagrams with terms such as *roots*, *stems*, *vascular tissue*, and *xylem*. Use **Performance Assessment in the Science Classroom**, p. 127. L2

 Dinah Zike Study Fold

Student preparation materials for this Foldable are available in the **Chapter *FAST FILE* Resources.**

section 1

Photosynthesis and Respiration

as you read

What You'll Learn

- **Explain** how plants take in and give off gases.
- **Compare and contrast** photosynthesis and respiration.
- **Discuss** why photosynthesis and respiration are important.

Why It's Important

Understanding photosynthesis and respiration in plants will help you understand how life exists on Earth.

Review Vocabulary

cellulose: chemical compound made of sugar; forms tangled fibers in plant cell walls and provides structure and support

New Vocabulary

- stomata
- photosynthesis
- chlorophyll
- respiration

Taking in Raw Materials

Sitting in the cool shade under a tree, you eat lunch. Food is one of the raw materials you need to grow. Oxygen is another. It enters your lungs and eventually reaches every cell in your body. Your cells use oxygen to help release energy from the food that you eat. The process that uses oxygen to release energy from food produces carbon dioxide and water as wastes. These wastes move in your blood to your lungs, where they are removed as gases when you exhale. You look up at the tree and wonder, "Does a tree need to eat? Does it use oxygen? How does it get rid of wastes?"

Movement of Materials in Plants Trees and other plants don't take in foods the way you do. Plants make their own foods using the raw materials water, carbon dioxide, and inorganic chemicals in the soil. Just like you, plants also produce waste products.

Most of the water used by plants is taken in through roots, as shown in **Figure 1.** Water moves into root cells and then up through the plant to where it is used. When you pull up a plant, its roots are damaged and some are lost. If you replant it, the plant will need extra water until new roots grow to replace those that were lost.

Leaves, instead of lungs, are where most gas exchange occurs in plants. Most of the water taken in through the roots exits through the leaves of a plant. Carbon dioxide, oxygen, and water vapor exit and enter the plant through openings in the leaf. The leaf's structure helps explain how it functions in gas exchange.

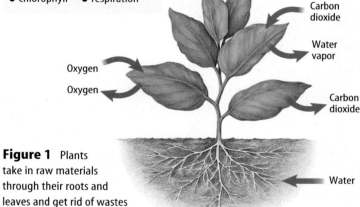

Carbon dioxide

Water vapor

Oxygen

Oxygen

Carbon dioxide

Water

Figure 1 Plants take in raw materials through their roots and leaves and get rid of wastes through their leaves.

302 CHAPTER 11 Plant Processes

Figure 2 A leaf's structure determines its function. Food is made in the inner layers. Most stomata are found on the lower epidermis.
Identify *the layer that contains most of the cells with chloroplasts.*

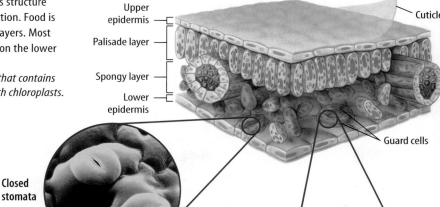

Upper epidermis
Palisade layer
Spongy layer
Lower epidermis
Cuticle
Guard cells

Closed stomata

Open stomata

Leaf Structure and Function A leaf is made up of many different layers, as shown in **Figure 2.** The outer cell layer of the leaf is the epidermis. A waxy cuticle that helps keep the leaf from drying out covers the epidermis. Because the epidermis is nearly transparent, sunlight—which is used to make food—reaches the cells inside the leaf. If you examine the epidermis under a microscope, you will see that it contains many small openings. These openings, called **stomata** (stoh MAH tuh) (singular, *stoma*), act as doorways for raw materials such as carbon dioxide, water vapor, and waste gases to enter and exit the leaf. Stomata also are found on the stems of many plants. More than 90 percent of the water plants take in through their roots is lost through the stomata. In one day, a growing tomato plant can lose up to 1 L of water.

Two cells called guard cells surround each stoma and control its size. As water moves into the guard cells, they swell and bend apart, opening a stoma. When guard cells lose water, they deflate and close the stoma. **Figure 2** shows closed and open stomata.

Stomata usually are open during the day, when most plants need to take in raw materials to make food. They usually are closed at night when food making slows down. Stomata also close when a plant is losing too much water. This adaptation conserves water, because less water vapor escapes from the leaf.

Inside the leaf are two layers of cells, the spongy layer and the palisade layer. Carbon dioxide and water vapor, which are needed in the food-making process, fill the spaces of the spongy layer. Most of the plant's food is made in the palisade layer.

INTEGRATE Career

Nutritionist Vitamins are substances needed for good health. Nutritionists promote healthy eating habits. Research to learn about other roles that nutritionists fulfill. Create a pamphlet to promote the career of nutritionist.

SECTION 1 Photosynthesis and Respiration **303**

Caption Answer
Figure 2 palisade layer

Visual Learning

Figure 2 Make sure students understand that the primary function of the stomata is to allow for the exchange of gases by the plant. L2

SECTION 1 Photosynthesis and Respiration **303**

Reading Check

Answer They contain a green pigment called chlorophyll that reflects green light.

Virtual Labs

Photosynthesis Which colors of the light spectrum are most important for plant growth?

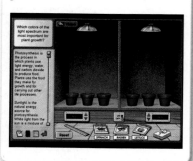

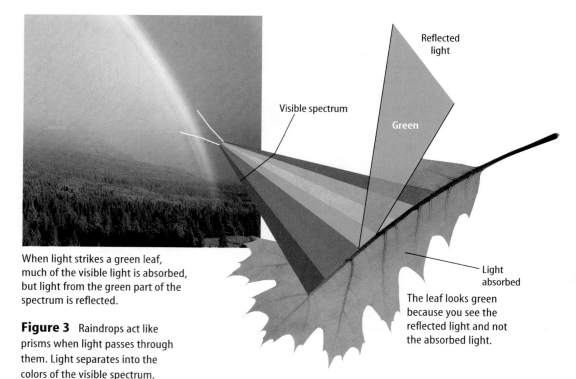

When light strikes a green leaf, much of the visible light is absorbed, but light from the green part of the spectrum is reflected.

Reflected light

Visible spectrum

Green

Light absorbed

The leaf looks green because you see the reflected light and not the absorbed light.

Figure 3 Raindrops act like prisms when light passes through them. Light separates into the colors of the visible spectrum. You see a rainbow when this happens.

Chloroplasts and Plant Pigments If you look closely at the leaf in **Figure 2,** you'll see that some of the cells contain small, green structures called chloroplasts. Most leaves look green because some of their cells contain so many chloroplasts. Chloroplasts are green because they contain a green pigment called **chlorophyll** (KLOR uh fihl).

Reading Check Why are chloroplasts green?

As shown in **Figure 3,** light from the Sun contains all colors of the visible spectrum. A pigment is a substance that reflects a particular part of the visible spectrum and absorbs the rest. When you see a green leaf, you are seeing green light energy reflected from chlorophyll. Most of the other colors of the spectrum, especially red and blue, are absorbed by chlorophyll. In the spring and summer, most leaves have so much chlorophyll that it hides all other pigments. In fall, the chlorophyll in some leaves breaks down and the leaves change color as other pigments become visible. Pigments, especially chlorophyll, are important to plants because the light energy that they absorb is used to make food. For plants, this food-making process—photosynthesis—happens in the chloroplasts.

LAB DEMONSTRATION

Purpose to show that the colors we see are the colors objects reflect

Materials prism, light source, objects of different colors

Preparation Collect materials and have them grouped together to save time.

Procedure Place a prism in a bright light source so that the colors of white light entering the prism separate. Place objects of different colors in the paths of the separated beams.

Expected Outcome Objects will absorb all colors except the color they reflect.

Assessment

What would happen if you placed a red rose with green leaves in a red beam of light in a darkened room? The rose would appear red and the leaves would appear black. L2

The Food-Making Process

Photosynthesis (foh toh SIHN thuh suhs) is the process during which a plant's chlorophyll traps light energy and sugars are produced. In plants, photosynthesis occurs only in cells with chloroplasts. For example, photosynthesis occurs only in a carrot plant's lacy green leaves, shown in **Figure 4.** Because a carrot's root cells lack chlorophyll and normally do not receive light, they can't perform photosynthesis. But excess sugar produced in the leaves is stored in the familiar orange root that you and many animals eat.

Besides light, plants also need the raw materials carbon dioxide and water for photosynthesis. The overall chemical equation for photosynthesis is shown below. What happens to each of the raw materials in the process?

$$6CO_2 + 6H_2O + \text{light energy} \xrightarrow{\text{chlorophyll}} C_6H_{12}O_6 + 6O_2$$

carbon dioxide   water   glucose   oxygen

Light-Dependent Reactions Some of the chemical reactions that take place during photosynthesis require light, but others do not. Those that need light can be called the light-dependent reactions of photosynthesis. During light-dependent reactions, chlorophyll and other pigments trap light energy that eventually will be stored in sugar molecules. Light energy causes water molecules, which were taken up by the roots, to split into oxygen and hydrogen. The oxygen leaves the plant through the stomata. This is the oxygen that you breathe. Hydrogen produced when water is split is used in photosynthesis reactions that occur when there is no light.

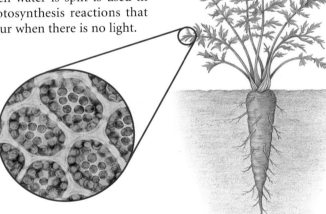

Figure 4 Because they contain chloroplasts, cells in the leaf of the carrot plant are the sites for photosynthesis.

Materials sprig of *Elodea*, test tube containing 5 mL of water and 1 mL of bromothymol blue

Estimated Time 10–20 minutes

Procedure Place the *Elodea* in the test tube. Have students note the yellow color. Place the tube in strong light. The solution should turn blue as *Elodea* takes up carbon dioxide in the presence of light.

Inquiry Lab

Comparing Leaf Surface Areas

Purpose measure differences in the leaf surface areas of different tree species

Possible Materials tree leaves, graph paper, metric ruler

Estimated Time 1 class session

Teaching Strategies

- Students can collect a variety of tree leaves of different sizes and determine how to calculate surface area.
- Students can trace leaf outlines on graph paper and count the squares of each leaf. Students will have to estimate fractions of squares in places where an entire square is not covered by the leaf outline.
- Students measure and calculate the area of each square, then calculate the area of each leaf by multiplying the area of one square times the number of squares the leaf outline occupies.
- Students can use math formulas for more rapid calculations. For example, they can trace squares or rectangles inside a leaf outline and calculate the area of these shapes using the formula $A = lw$ instead of counting those spaces.
- Students can research how the size of the leaves of different species affects the rate of tree growth and tree habitat. Allow students to explore other questions as they arise.

For additional inquiry activities, see *Science Inquiry Labs.*

Science Online

Topic: Plant Sugars

Visit life.msscience.com for Web links to information about sugars and related molecules produced by plants.

Activity List three sugar-containing molecules that plants produce.

Light-Independent Reactions Reactions that don't need light are called the light-independent reactions of photosynthesis. Carbon dioxide, the raw material from the air, is used in these reactions. The light energy trapped during the light-dependent reactions is used to combine carbon dioxide and hydrogen to make sugars. One important sugar that is made is glucose. The chemical bonds that hold glucose and other sugars together are stored energy. **Figure 5** compares what happens during each stage of photosynthesis.

What happens to the oxygen and glucose that were made during photosynthesis? Most of the oxygen from photosynthesis is a waste product and is released through stomata. Glucose is the main form of food for plant cells. A plant usually produces more glucose than it can use. Excess glucose is stored in plants as other sugars and starches. When you eat carrots, as well as beets, potatoes, or onions, you are eating the stored product of photosynthesis.

Glucose also is the basis of a plant's structure. You don't grow larger by breathing in and using carbon dioxide. However, that's exactly what plants do as they take in carbon dioxide gas and convert it into glucose. Cellulose, an important part of plant cell walls, is made from glucose. Leaves, stems, and roots are made of cellulose and other substances produced using glucose. The products of photosynthesis are used for plant growth.

Figure 5 Photosynthesis includes two sets of reactions, the light-dependent reactions and the light-independent reactions.
Describe *what happens to the glucose produced during photosynthesis.*

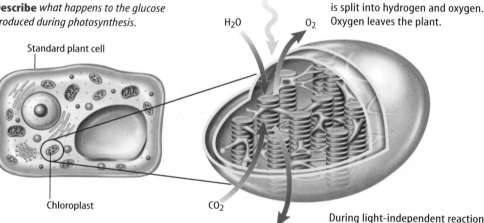

Standard plant cell

Chloroplast

Light

H_2O O_2

During light-dependent reactions, light energy is trapped and water is split into hydrogen and oxygen. Oxygen leaves the plant.

CO_2

$C_6H_{12}O_6$

During light-independent reactions, energy is used to combine carbon dioxide and hydrogen to make glucose and other sugars.

306 CHAPTER 11 Plant Processes

Differentiated Instruction

English-Language Learners Explain to students how a prefix can change the meaning of a word. Have them compare the terms *independent* and *dependent* and the terms *aerobic* and *anaerobic*. Explain that the prefixes *in-* and *a-* both mean 'not'. Since *aerobic* begins with an *a*, an *n* is added to it to make the word *anaerobic* easier to pronounce. [L2]
ELL Linguistic

Fun Fact

A place where food is stored or used in a plant is called a sink. Depending on the plant, roots, stems, and leaves can be sinks.

Figure 6 Tropical rain forests contain large numbers of photosynthetic plants.
Infer *why tropical forests are considered an important source of oxygen.*

Importance of Photosynthesis Why is photosynthesis important to living things? First, photosynthesis produces food. Organisms that carry on photosynthesis provide food directly or indirectly for nearly all the other organisms on Earth. Second, photosynthetic organisms, like the plants in **Figure 6,** use carbon dioxide and release oxygen. This removes carbon dioxide from the atmosphere and adds oxygen to it. Most organisms, including humans, need oxygen to stay alive. As much as 90 percent of the oxygen entering the atmosphere today is a result of photosynthesis.

The Breakdown of Food

Look at the photograph in **Figure 7.** Do the fox and the plants in the photograph have anything in common? They don't look alike, but the fox and the plants are made of cells that break down food and release energy in a process called respiration. How does this happen?

Respiration is a series of chemical reactions that breaks down food molecules and releases energy. Respiration occurs in cells of most organisms. The breakdown of food might or might not require oxygen. Respiration that uses oxygen to break down food chemically is called aerobic respiration. In plants and many organisms that have one or more cells, a nucleus, and other organelles, aerobic respiration occurs in the mitochondria (singular, *mitochondrion*). The overall chemical equation for aerobic respiration is shown below.

$$C_6H_{12}O_6 + 6O_2 \longrightarrow 6CO_2 + 6H_2O + \text{energy}$$

glucose   oxygen   carbon dioxide   water

Figure 7 You know that animals such as this red fox carry on respiration, but so do all the plants that surround the fox.

Figure 8 Aerobic respiration takes place in the mitochondria of plant cells. **Describe** *what happens to a molecule before it enters a mitochondrion.*

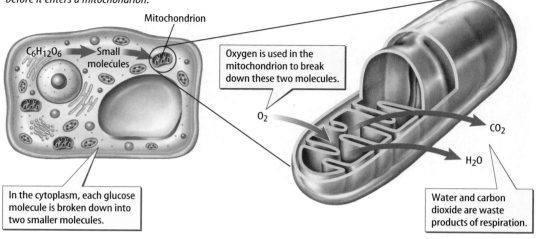

Mitochondrion

Oxygen is used in the mitochondrion to break down these two molecules.

$C_6H_{12}O_6$ → Small molecules

O_2

CO_2

H_2O

In the cytoplasm, each glucose molecule is broken down into two smaller molecules.

Water and carbon dioxide are waste products of respiration.

Figure 9 Plants use the energy released during respiration to carry out many functions.

Plant structure and function

Production of chlorophyll

Sprouting of seeds

Aerobic Respiration Before aerobic respiration begins, glucose molecules are broken down into two smaller molecules. This happens in the cytoplasm. The smaller molecules then enter a mitochondrion, where aerobic respiration takes place. Oxygen is used in the chemical reactions that break down the small molecules into water and carbon dioxide. The reactions also release energy. Every cell in the organism needs this energy. **Figure 8** shows aerobic respiration in a plant cell.

Importance of Respiration Although food contains energy, it is not in a form that can be used by cells. Respiration changes food energy into a form all cells can use. This energy drives the life processes of almost all organisms on Earth.

Reading Check *What organisms use respiration?*

Plants use energy produced by respiration to transport sugars and to open and close stomata. Some of the energy is used to produce substances needed for photosynthesis, such as chlorophyll. When seeds sprout, they use energy from the respiration of stored food in the seed. **Figure 9** shows some uses of energy in plants.

The waste product carbon dioxide is also important. Aerobic respiration returns carbon dioxide to the atmosphere, where it can be used again by plants and some other organisms for photosynthesis.

308 CHAPTER 11 Plant Processes

Visual Learning

Table 1 Comparing Photosynthesis and Aerobic Respiration

	Energy	Raw Materials	End Products	Where
Photosynthesis	stored	water and carbon dioxide	glucose and oxygen	cells with chlorophyll
Aerobic respiration	released	glucose and oxygen	water and carbon dioxide	cells with mitochondria

Comparison of Photosynthesis and Respiration

Look back in the section to find the equations for photosynthesis and aerobic respiration. You can see that aerobic respiration is almost the reverse of photosynthesis. Photosynthesis combines carbon dioxide and water by using light energy. The end products are glucose (food) and oxygen. During photosynthesis, energy is stored in food. Photosynthesis occurs only in cells that contain chlorophyll, such as those in the leaves of plants. Aerobic respiration combines oxygen and food to release the energy in the chemical bonds of the food. The end products of aerobic respiration are energy, carbon dioxide, and water. All plant cells contain mitochondria. Any cell with mitochondria can use the process of aerobic respiration. **Table 1** compares photosynthesis and aerobic respiration.

section 1 review

Summary

Taking in Raw Materials
- Leaves take in carbon dioxide that is used in photosynthesis.
- Oxygen and carbon dioxide are waste products of photosynthesis and respiration.

The Food-Making Process
- Photosynthesis takes place in chloroplasts.
- Photosynthesis is a series of chemical reactions that transforms energy from light into energy stored in the chemical bonds of sugar molecules.

The Breakdown of Food
- Aerobic respiration uses oxygen to release energy from food.
- Aerobic respiration takes place in mitochondria.

Self Check

1. **Describe** how gases enter and exit a leaf.
2. **Explain** why photosynthesis and respiration are important.
3. **Identify** what must happen to glucose molecules before respiration begins.
4. **Compare and contrast** the number of organisms that respire and the number that photosynthesize.
5. **Think Critically** Humidity is water vapor in the air. Infer how plants contribute to humidity.

Applying Math

6. **Solve One-Step Equations** How many CO_2 molecules result from the respiration of a glucose molecule ($C_6H_{12}O_6$)? Refer to the equation in this section.

 Science Online life.msscience.com/self_check_quiz

SECTION 1 Photosynthesis and Respiration **309**

section 1 review

1. Carbon dioxide and water vapor are exchanged by diffusion through the stomata on leaf surfaces.
2. Photosynthesis provides the basic food source used by most organisms on Earth, either directly or indirectly. Respiration releases the energy stored in the product of photosynthesis (glucose) for use in cells.
3. Glucose molecules must be broken down into simpler molecules in the cytoplasm before respiration can begin.
4. Only organisms that contain chlorophyll photosynthesize, but all organisms respire.
5. Plants transpire water from their leaves, contributing water vapor to the air and increasing humidity.
6. For every sugar molecule respired, six carbon dioxide molecules are produced.

Activity
Songs Have students make up songs that include the equations for photosynthesis and respiration. Then have them sing their songs to the class.

3 Assess

DAILY INTERVENTION

Check for Understanding
Logical-Mathematical Write the chemical equations for photosynthesis and respiration on the board. Have students identify which equation is for which process. Ask students to name each reactant and each product in the two equations. L2

Reteach
Light and Dark Have students place one plant in the light and another in a dark area while keeping all other variables constant. Have them observe the plants once each day for a week. Then have students explain any changes that occur. L2

✔ Assessment

Performance Using molecular model kits, have groups of students make the reactants of either photosynthesis or aerobic respiration. Exchange reactants between opposite groups and have them make the products of those reactants. Students should find that the reactants of one are the products of the other. Use **Performance Assessment in the Science Classroom**, p. 123. L3

Real-World Question

Purpose Students observe the activity of stomata in green plants. L2 **ELL** COOP LEARN
N **Visual-Spatial**

Process Skills observe and infer, recognize cause and effect

Time Required 45 minutes

Alternate Materials Romaine lettuce is recommended. Celery or onion epidermis may be substituted for lettuce.

Safety Precaution Emphasize that students should be careful when using microscopes.

Procedure

Teaching Strategy Remind students that osmosis is diffusion of water through a semipermeable membrane.

Troubleshooting If an alternative tissue is used, try the activity beforehand to make sure observations will be appropriate.

Conclude and Apply

1. the wet mount with plain water
2. Salt water causes water to leave the guard cells, causing them to become limp and close.
3. Stomata provide an entry and exit site in the leaf for gases such as carbon dioxide, oxygen, and water vapor.

Stomata in Leaves

Stomata open and close, which allows gases into and out of a leaf. These openings are usually invisible without the use of a microscope. Do this lab to see some stomata.

Real-World Question

Where are stomata in lettuce leaves?

Goals
- **Describe** guard cells and stomata.
- **Infer** the conditions that make stomata open and close.

Materials
lettuce in dish of water   microscope slide
coverslip   salt solution
microscope   forceps

Safety Precautions

WARNING: *Never eat or taste any materials used in the laboratory.*

Procedure

1. Copy the Stomata Data table into your Science Journal.
2. From a head of lettuce, tear off a piece of an outer, crisp, green leaf.
3. Bend the piece of leaf in half and carefully use a pair of forceps to peel off some of the epidermis, the transparent tissue that covers a leaf. Prepare a wet mount of this tissue.
4. Examine your prepared slide under low and high power on the microscope.
5. Count the total number of stomata in your field of view and then count the number of

Stomata Data (Sample data only)	Wet Mount	Salt-Solution Mount
Total Number of Stomata	50	60
Number of Open Stomata	40	5
Percent Open	80	8

open stomata. Enter these numbers in the data table.

6. Make a second slide of the lettuce leaf epidermis. This time place a few drops of salt solution on the leaf instead of water.
7. Wait a few minutes. Repeat steps 4 and 5.
8. **Calculate** the percent of open stomata using the following equation:

$$\frac{\text{number of open stomata}}{\text{total number of stomata}} \times 100 = \text{percent open}$$

Conclude and Apply

1. **Determine** which slide preparation had a greater percentage of open stomata.
2. **Infer** why fewer stomata were open in the salt-solution mount.
3. What can you infer about the function of stomata in a leaf?

Communicating Your Data

Collect data from your classmates and compare it to your data. Discuss any differences you find and why they occurred. **For more help, refer to the** Science Skill Handbook.

Assessment

Performance To further assess students' understanding of stomata, have them repeat the activity using one of the alternate materials and describe the outcome. Use **Performance Assessment in the Science Classroom,** p. 97. L2

Communicating Your Data

Data should be similar throughout the class. Differences might occur if students don't all use the same side of the leaf tissue. Upper and lower leaf surfaces often have different numbers of stomata.

section 2

Plant Responses

What are plant responses?

It's dark. You're alone in a room watching a horror film on television. Suddenly, the telephone near you rings. You jump, and your heart begins to beat faster. You've just responded to a stimulus. A stimulus is anything in the environment that causes a response in an organism. The response often involves movement either toward the stimulus or away from the stimulus. A stimulus may come from outside (external) or inside (internal) the organism. The ringing telephone is an example of an external stimulus. It caused you to jump, which is a response. Your beating heart is a response to an internal stimulus. Internal stimuli are usually chemicals produced by organisms. Many of these chemicals are hormones. Hormones are substances made in one part of an organism for use somewhere else in the organism.

All living organisms, including plants, respond to stimuli. Many different chemicals are known to act as hormones in plants. These internal stimuli have a variety of effects on plant growth and function. Plants respond to external stimuli such as touch, light, and gravity. Some responses, such as the response of the Venus's-flytrap plant in **Figure 10,** are rapid. Other plant responses are slower because they involve changes in growth.

as you read

***What* You'll Learn**

- **Identify** the relationship between a stimulus and a tropism in plants.
- **Compare and contrast** long-day and short-day plants.
- **Explain** how plant hormones and responses are related.

***Why* It's Important**

You will be able to grow healthier plants if you understand how they respond to certain stimuli.

🔍 **Review Vocabulary**
behavior: the way in which an organism interacts with other organisms and its environment

New Vocabulary
- tropism
- auxin
- photoperiodism
- long-day plant
- short-day plant
- day-neutral plant

Figure 10 A Venus's-flytrap has three small trigger hairs on the surface of its toothed leaves. When two hairs are touched at the same time, the plant responds by closing its trap in less than 1 second.

SECTION 2 Plant Responses **311**

1 Motivate

Bellringer

Section Focus Transparencies also are available on the Interactive Chalkboard CD-ROM.
L2 **ELL**

Tie to Prior Knowledge

Plant Parts Draw on the board a simple sketch of a flowering plant. Have students identify as many parts of the plant as they can and name the functions of those parts. L2

Fun Fact

The flowers of the Venus's flytrap plant form on a stalk that grows high above the leaves. This arrangement helps prevent pollinating insects from being trapped by the plant's toothed leaves.

Section 2 Resource Manager

Chapter *FAST FILE* Resources
Transparency Activity, p. 41
Directed Reading for Content Mastery, pp. 19, 20
MiniLAB, p. 4
Lab Activity, pp. 11–14
Reinforcement, p. 26

Enrichment, p. 28
Lab Worksheet, pp. 7–8
Mathematics Skill Activities, p. 25
Home and Community Involvement, p. 45
Performance Assessment in the Science Classroom, p. 61
Lab Management and Safety, p. 58

Caption Answer

Figure 11 stem

Discussion

Plant Responses Have students brainstorm a list of possible ways to determine the cause of various plant responses. Lead them to understand the difference between external and internal stimuli. External stimuli include touch, light, and gravity. Internal stimuli include hormones. L2

Activity

Pea Plant Small groups of students can grow a pea plant from seed. As the plant begins to grow, they place a stick in the pot. The stem and tendrils will respond by growing around the stick. Have students identify the type of response this illustrates. thigmatropism Challenge students to record and graph the growth of the pea plant. L3

Quick Demo

Carnivorous Plants

Materials Venus's flytrap plant, needle or sharp pencil

Estimated Time 10 minutes

Procedure Demonstrate the plant's response to touch. The trap of the Venus's flytrap is triggered when three or more of the sensitive hairs on the upper surfaces of the hinged leaves are touched. Use the tip of a needle or sharp pencil to stimulate the hairs. L3

Gravity Students may propose various experiments. Look for those that include a control and a method that would include a true test of the effects of gravity.

Figure 11 Tropisms are responses to external stimuli. **Identify** *the part of a plant that shows negative gravitropism.*

The pea plant's tendrils respond to touch by coiling around things.

This plant is growing toward the light, an example of positive phototropism.

This plant was turned on its side. With the roots visible, you can see that they are showing positive gravitropism.

INTEGRATE Physics

Gravity and Plants
Gravity is a stimulus that affects how plants grow. Can plants grow without gravity? In space the force of gravity is low. Write a paragraph in your Science Journal that describes your idea for an experiment aboard a space shuttle to test how low gravity affects plant growth.

Tropisms

Some responses of a plant to an external stimuli are called tropisms. A **tropism** (TROH pih zum) can be seen as movement caused by a change in growth and can be positive or negative. For example, plants might grow toward a stimulus—a positive tropism—or away from a stimulus—a negative tropism.

Touch One stimulus that can result in a change in a plant's growth is touch. When the pea plant, as shown in **Figure 11,** touches a solid object, it responds by growing faster on one side of its stem than on the other side. As a result the stem bends and twists around any object it touches.

Light Did you ever see a plant leaning toward a window? Light is an important stimulus to plants. When a plant responds to light, the cells on the side of the plant opposite the light get longer than the cells facing the light. Because of this uneven growth, the plant bends toward the light. This response causes the leaves to turn in such a way that they can absorb more light. When a plant grows toward light it is called a positive response to light, or positive phototropism, shown in **Figure 11.**

Gravity Plants respond to gravity. The downward growth of plant roots, as shown in **Figure 11,** is a positive response to gravity. A stem growing upward is a negative response to gravity. Plants also may respond to electricity, temperature, and darkness.

312 CHAPTER 11 Plant Processes

Visual Learning

Figure 11 Use these photographs to launch a discussion on plant responses caused by various external stimuli. Where have you seen responses such as these? How might they help a plant meet its needs? Answers will vary. Many of these responses help a plant grow toward the light, its source of energy. L2

Teacher FYI

Nastic Movements Unlike tropisms, nastic movements are independent of the direction of the stimulus. The most common are "sleep" or nyctinastic movements. These movements position leaves of some plants horizontally during the daylight and vertically at night. This response results from turgor pressure changes in cells.

Plant Hormones

Hormones control the changes in growth that result from tropisms and affect other plant growth. Plants often need only millionths of a gram of a hormone to stimulate a response.

Ethylene Many plants produce the hormone ethylene (EH thuh leen) gas and release it into the air around them. Ethylene is produced in cells of ripening fruit, which stimulates the ripening process. Commercially, fruits such as oranges and bananas are picked when they are unripe and the green fruits are exposed to ethylene during shipping so they will ripen. Another plant response to ethylene causes a layer of cells to form between a leaf and the stem. The cell layer causes the leaf to fall from the stem.

Applying Math — Calculate Averages

GROWTH HORMONES Gibberellins are plant hormones that increase growth rate. The graphs on the right show data from an experiment to determine how gibberellins affect the growth of bean seedlings. What is the average height of control bean seedlings after 14 days?

Solution

1 *This is what you know:*
- height of control seedlings after 14 days
- number of control seedlings

2 *This is what you need to find out:*
What is the average height of control seedlings after 14 days?

3 *This is the procedure you need to use:*
- Find the total of the seedling heights. $15 + 12 + 14 + 13 + 10 + 11 = 75$ cm
- Divide the height total by the number of control seedlings to find the average height. 75 cm/6 = 12.5 cm

4 *Check your answer:*
Multiply 12.5 cm by 6 and you should get 75 cm.

Control seedlings

Height (cm) after 14 days of growth

A B C D E F

Gibberellin-treated seedlings

Height (cm) after 14 days of growth

G H I J K L

Practice Problems

1. Calculate the average height of seedlings treated with gibberellin.

2. In an experiment, the heights of gibberellin-treated rose stems were 20, 26, 23, 24, 23, 25, and 26 cm. The average height of the controls was 23 cm. Did gibberellin have an effect?

For more practice, visit life.msscience.com/math_practice

Active Reading

Quickwrites This strategy, also called freewrites, lets students write spontaneously to discover what they already know. Students write a list of ideas about a topic, then share these ideas with the class. Next, students write their ideas freely in a paragraph without worrying about punctuation, spelling, and grammar. Have students do a Quickwrite to share ideas about plant responses. L2

Quick Demo

Rooting Hormone

Materials 2 coleus cuttings, rooting hormone, 2 soil-filled pots

Estimated Time 10 minutes setup; 10 minutes for observation and discussion

Procedure Apply rooting hormone to one cutting. Plant cuttings in separate pots. After several days, have students observe the roots of both stems and explain the results. *The cutting with the hormone should show greater root growth due to the presence of the chemical.* L2

Purpose to observe the effects of ethylene on ripening fruit L1 ELL IS Kinesthetic

Materials two green bananas, paper bag

Teaching Strategies
• Tell students to choose two green bananas that are at the same stage of ripeness.
• Students may eat the bananas after use.

Analysis
The green banana in the bag; the ethylene produced by the ripening banana was trapped in the bag, causing the fruit to ripen more quickly.

Assessment

Oral Have students explain their results to the class.

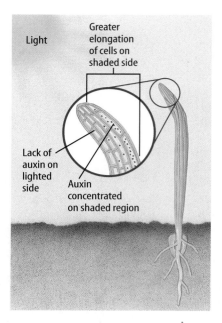

Figure 12 The concentration of auxin on the shaded side of a plant causes cells on that side to lengthen.

Mini LAB

Observing Ripening

Procedure
1. Place a **green banana** in a **paper bag.** Roll the top shut and place it on a table or counter.
2. Place another green banana near the paper bag.
3. After two days check the bananas to see how they have ripened. **WARNING:** *Do not eat the materials used in the lab.*

Analysis
Which banana ripened more quickly? Why?

Auxin Scientists identified the plant hormone, **auxin** (AWK sun) more than 100 years ago. Auxin is a type of plant hormone that causes plant stems and leaves to exhibit positive response to light. When light shines on a plant from one side, the auxin moves to the shaded side of the stem where it causes a change in growth, as shown in **Figure 12.** Auxins also control the production of other plant hormones, including ethylene.

✔ **Reading Check** *How are auxins and positive response to light related?*

Development of many parts of the plant, including flowers, roots, and fruit, is stimulated by auxins. Because auxins are so important in plant development, synthetic auxins have been developed for use in agriculture. Some of these synthetic auxins are used in orchards so that all plants produce flowers and fruit at the same time. Other synthetic auxins damage plants when they are applied in high doses and are used as weed killers.

Gibberellins and Cytokinins Two other groups of plant hormones that also cause changes in plant growth are gibberellins and cytokinins. Gibberellins (jih buh REH lunz) are chemical substances that were isolated first from a fungus. The fungus caused a disease in rice plants called "foolish seedling" disease. The fungus infects the stems of plants and causes them to grow too tall. Gibberellins can be mixed with water and sprayed on plants and seeds to stimulate plant stems to grow and seeds to germinate.

Like gibberellins, cytokinins (si tuh KI nunz) also cause rapid growth. Cytokinins promote growth by causing faster cell divisions. Like ethylene, the effect of cytokinins on the plant also is controlled by auxin. Interestingly, cytokinins can be sprayed on stored vegetables to keep them fresh longer.

Abscisic Acid Because hormones that cause growth in plants were known to exist, biologists suspected that substances that have the reverse effect also must exist. Abscisic (ab SIH zihk) acid is one such substance. Many plants grow in areas that have cold winters. Normally, if seeds germinate or buds develop on plants during the winter, they will die. Abscisic acid is the substance that keeps seeds from sprouting and buds from developing during the winter. This plant hormone also causes stomata to close and helps plants respond to water loss on hot summer days. **Figure 13** summarizes how plant hormones affect plants and how hormones are used.

Cultural Diversity

Ewiti Kurosawa Japanese scientist Ewiti Kurosawa discovered gibberellin while investigating the cause of "foolish seedling disease." He discovered that rice plants grew so tall that they fell over (thus, "foolish seedlings") after being infected with a fungus that secreted gibberellin. He named gibberellin after the genus of the fungus, *Gibberella fujikuroi.*

Differentiated Instruction

English-Language Learners Have students make flash cards by writing the name of a plant hormone on one side of an index card, and the effects of that hormone on the other side of the card. Let students work in pairs, using the flash cards to quiz each other about plant hormones. L1 ELL
COOP LEARN

Figure 13

Chemical compounds called plant hormones help determine how a plant grows. There are five main types of hormones. They coordinate a plant's growth and development, as well as its responses to environmental stimuli, such as light, gravity, and changing seasons. Most changes in plant growth are a result of plant hormones working together, but exactly how hormones cause these changes is not completely understood.

▲ ETHYLENE By controlling the exposure of these tomatoes to ethylene, a hormone that stimulates fruit ripening, farmers are able to harvest unripe fruit and make it ripen just before it arrives at the supermarket.

◄ GIBBERELLINS The larger mustard plant in the photo at left was sprayed with gibberellins, plant hormones that stimulate stem elongation and fruit development.

Lateral buds

Lateral branches

◄ CYTOKININS Lateral buds do not usually develop into branches. However, if a plant's main stem is cut, as in this bean plant, naturally occurring cytokinins will stimulate the growth of lateral branches, causing the plant to grow "bushy."

▼ AUXINS Powerful growth hormones called auxins regulate responses to light and gravity, stem elongation, and root growth. The root growth on the plant cuttings, center and right, is the result of auxin treatment.

▶ ABA (ABSCISIC ACID) In plants such as the American basswood, right, abscisic acid causes buds to remain dormant for the winter. When spring arrives, ABA stops working and the buds sprout.

SECTION 2 Plant Responses **315**

Visualizing Plant Hormones

Have students examine the pictures and read the captions. Then ask the following questions.

Which of the hormones here do not stimulate plant growth? What functions do these hormones serve? ABA causes dormancy instead of growth, and ethylene stimulates fruit ripening instead of growth. L2

How could farmers use plant hormones to enhance their profits? By controlling plant growth, budding, dormancy periods, and ripening of fruits, farmers can deliver more product to the market. L2

What plant hormone has most likely been studied by researchers working in space? Auxins, which control a plant's response to gravity, would be of great interest to those studying a plant's response to the reduced gravity in space. L2

Activity

Plant Hormones Have students work in teams to write a poem with five verses. Each verse should name a type of plant hormone, and tell the function of the hormone and the particular parts of the plant the hormone acts on. L2

Differentiated Instruction

Challenge Evidence exists that a plant hormone called florigen controls flowering in plants, but scientists haven't isolated it yet. Have students research some of the experiments scientists have done in their search for florigen. Students should report their findings to the class. L3

Visual Learning

Table 2 Ask students to identify the approximate time shown on the pie graphs for sunrise and sunset in early summer and early fall. summer: 5 A.M., 8 P.M.; fall: 6:30 A.M., 5:30 P.M. Ask students to calculate the number of hours of daylight and darkness shown in each pie graph. summer: daylight 15, darkness 9; fall: daylight 11, darkness 13

✔ Reading Check

Answer a specific amount of darkness, which varies depending on the species of plant

Activity

Florists Where do florists get the flowers they sell? Take the class on a field trip to a commercial greenhouse that supplies florist shops. Have students interview the staff to find out how they encourage plants to flower at times other than their normal flowering seasons. Growers often plan six to twelve months ahead to supply plants that are blooming out of season.

Discussion

Roses Some roses bloom more in the spring and fall than during the summer. What type of photoperiod is this? short-day

---

Science Online

Topic: Plant Pigments
Visit life.msscience.com for Web links to information about how plant pigments are involved in photoperiodism.

Activity Explain how day length affects a hormone that promotes flowering.

Figure 14 When short-day plants receive less darkness than required to produce flowers, they produce larger leaves instead.

Photoperiods

Sunflowers bloom in the summer, and cherry trees flower in the spring. Some plant species produce flowers at specific times during the year. A plant's response to the number of hours of daylight and darkness it receives daily is **photoperiodism** (foh toh PIHR ee uh dih zum).

Earth revolves around the Sun once each year. As Earth moves in its orbit, it also rotates. One rotation takes about 24 h. Because Earth is tilted about 23.5° from a line perpendicular to its orbit, the hours of daylight and darkness vary with the seasons. As you probably have noticed, the Sun sets later in summer than in winter. These changes in lengths of daylight and darkness affect plant growth.

Darkness and Flowers Many plants require a specific length of darkness to begin the flowering process. Generally, plants that require less than 10 h to 12 h of darkness to flower are called **long-day plants.** You may be familiar with some long-day plants such as spinach, lettuce, and beets. Plants that need 12 or more hours of darkness to flower are called **short-day plants.** Some short-day plants are poinsettias, strawberries, and ragweed. **Figure 14** shows what happens when a short-day plant receives less darkness than it needs to flower.

✔ Reading Check   *What is needed to begin the flowering process?*

Day-Neutral Plants Plants like dandelions and roses are **day-neutral plants.** They have no specific photoperiod, and the flowering process can begin within a range of hours of darkness.

In nature, photoperiodism affects where flowering plants can grow and produce flowers and fruit. Even if a particular environment has the proper temperature and other growing conditions for a plant, it will not flower and produce fruit without the correct photoperiod. **Table 2** shows how day length affects flowering in all three types of plants.

Sometimes the photoperiod of a plant has a narrow range. For example, some soybeans will flower with 9.5 h of darkness but will not flower with 10 h of darkness. Farmers must choose the variety of soybeans with a photoperiod that matches the hours of darkness in the section of the country where they plant their crop.

Curriculum Connection

Geography Have students research the place of origin for different plants and plot the locations on a world map. Challenge students to determine whether location of origin correlates with the length of darkness a plant needs to flower. L3 P

Table 2 Photoperiodism

	Long-Day Plants	Short-Day Plants	Day-Neutral Plants
Early Summer (clock: Noon, 6 AM, 6 PM, Midnight)			
Late Fall (clock: Noon, 6 AM, 6 PM, Midnight)			
	An iris is a long-day plant that is stimulated by short nights to flower in the early summer.	Goldenrod is a short-day plant that is stimulated by long nights to flower in the fall.	Roses are day-neutral plants and have no specific photoperiod.

Today, greenhouse growers are able to provide any length of artificial daylight or darkness. This means that you can buy short-day flowering plants during the summer and long-day flowering plants during the winter.

section 2 review

Summary

What are plant responses?
- Plants respond to both internal and external stimuli.

Tropisms
- Tropisms are plant responses to external stimuli, including touch, light, and gravity.

Plant Hormones
- Hormones control changes in plant growth, including changes that result from tropisms.

Photoperiods
- Long-day plants flower in late spring or summer.
- Short-day plants flower in late fall or winter.

Self Check

1. **List** one example of an internal stimulus and one example of an external stimulus in plants.
2. **Compare and contrast** photoperiodism and phototropism.
3. **Identify** the term that describes the photoperiod of red raspberries that produce fruit in late spring and in the fall.
4. **Distinguish** between abscisic acid and gibberellins.
5. **Think Critically** Describe the relationship between hormones and tropisms.

Applying Skills

6. **Compare and contrast** the responses of roots and stems to gravity.

 Science Online life.msscience.com/self_check_quiz

SECTION 2 Plant Responses **317**

section 2 review

1. Possible answers: Internal stimuli include hormones; external stimuli include environmental factors such as gravity and light.
2. Photoperiodism is a plant response to the length of the period of darkness; phototropism is any growth response to light.
3. short-day
4. Abscisic acid slows growth; gibberellins speed growth in plants.
5. Plant hormones are responsible for some tropisms.
6. Roots show positive gravitropism and grow downward. Stems show negative gravitropism and grow upward.

3 Assess

DAILY INTERVENTION

Check for Understanding

Auditory-Musical Ask student volunteers to describe plant responses that result from external stimuli. Have other students identify the stimulus causing that response. Also ask student volunteers to describe plant responses that result from internal stimuli, and have other students identify the hormone that causes the response. For example, the upward growth of stems is a response to the stimulus of light, which is external. The ripening of fruit is a response to the internal stimulus of the hormone ethylene. L2

Reteach

Tropism Chart Have students make a chart describing the various tropisms. For each tropism, they should include the stimulus, the response, and the effect on the plant. L2 P

☑ Assessment

Oral Ask students to compare and contrast the responses of roots, stems, and leaves to light. L2

Tropism in Plants

⊳ Real-World Question

Purpose Students experiment to observe plant responses to gravity. L2 ELL LS **Logical-Mathematical**

Process Skills observe and infer, communicate, make and use tables, compare and contrast, recognize cause and effect, manipulate and control variables, interpret data, use numbers

Time Required 1 class period to set up; 20 minutes one day each week for up to two weeks

Materials clear jar, marking pen, mustard seeds, aluminum foil, paper towel, water

Alternate Materials Bean seeds can be substituted for mustard seeds.

Safety Precautions Some kinds of seeds are poisonous. Do not allow students to put seeds in their mouths.

Goals
- **Describe** how roots and stems respond to gravity.
- **Observe** how changing the stimulus changes the growth of plants.

Materials
paper towel
30-cm × 30-cm sheet of aluminum foil
water
mustard seeds
marking pen
1-L clear-glass or plastic jar

Safety Precautions
⊠ 🔥 ☣ ⊘ ☤

WARNING: *Some kinds of seeds are poisonous. Do not put any seed in your mouth.*

⊳ Real-World Question

Grapevines can climb on trees, fences, or other nearby structures. This growth is a response to the stimulus of touch. Tropisms are specific plant responses to stimuli outside of the plant. One part of a plant can respond positively while another part of the same plant can respond negatively to the same stimulus. Gravitropism is a response to gravity. Why might it be important for some plant parts to have a positive response to gravity while other plant parts have a negative response? Do stems and roots respond to gravity in the same way? You can design an experiment to test how some plant parts respond to the stimulus of gravity.

Alternative Inquiry Lab

Testing for Gravitropism Encourage students to test and compare the effects of gravity on different types of houseplants or seeds. Students can put tape over the tops of pots that contains small houseplants such as ivy so that soil cannot spill. They also can plant mustard seeds or other seed varieties in small pots and tape over the tops of the pots. Students can hang their plants or planted seeds near a window. One pot can be hung right side up, another upside down, and others at various angles. Students can observe and measure the angle of the plant stems growing from each pot.

Procedure

1. Copy the data table on the right in your Science Journal.

2. Moisten the paper towel with water so that it's damp but not dripping. Fold it in half twice.

3. Place the folded paper towel in the center of the foil and sprinkle mustard seeds in a line across the center of the towel.

Response to Gravity		
Position of Arrow on Foil Package	Observations of Seedling Roots	Observations of Seedling Stems
Arrow up	Growing away from arrow	Growing toward arrow
Arrow down	Growing toward arrow	Growing away from arrow

4. Fold the foil around the towel and seal each end by folding the foil over. Make sure the paper towel is completely covered by the foil.

5. Use a marking pen to draw an arrow on the foil, and place the foil package in the jar with the arrow pointing upward.

6. After five days, carefully open the package and record your observations in the data table. (Note: *If no stems or roots are growing yet, reseal the package and place it back in the jar, making sure that the arrow points upward. Reopen the package in two days.*)

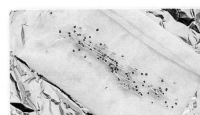

7. Reseal the foil package, being careful not to disturb the seedlings. Place it in the jar so that the arrow points downward instead of upward.

8. After five more days, reopen the package and observe any new growth of the seedlings' roots and stems. Record your observations in your data table.

Analyze Your Data

1. **Classify** the responses you observed as positive or negative tropisms.

2. **Explain** why the plants' growth changed when you placed them upside down.

Conclude and Apply

1. **Infer** why it was important that no light reach the seedlings during your experiment.

2. **Describe** some other ways you could have changed the position of the foil package to test the seedlings' response.

Communicating Your Data

Compare drawings you make of the growth of the seedlings before and after you turned the package. **Compare** your drawings with those of other students in your class. **For more help, refer to the Science Skill Handbook.**

Procedure

Teaching Strategy Explain that there might be more than one variable at work and that stems and roots might respond differently to these stimuli.

Troubleshooting Be sure that students always place the seeds back in the dish with the arrow pointing up.

Expected Outcome Roots will grow downward and shoots will grow upward.

Analyze Your Data

Answers to Questions

1. Stem growth upward is negative gravitropism; root growth downward is positive gravitropism.

2. The plants' growth continued to respond to the stimulus provided by gravity, even though the direction of this stimuli had changed.

Error Analysis Have students compare their data with that of others and explain any differences they encounter.

Conclude and Apply

1. If light reached the seedlings, they could have responded to it (phototropism), and results due to gravitropism would be uncertain.

2. Possible answers: The packages could have been laid flat or put on a spinning turntable.

Differentiated Instruction

Learning Disabled Provide clear directions both orally and in writing. Assign a buddy to each student to help him or her assemble the seed packets. L2

Communicating Your Data

Drawings will indicate that roots grow downward and shoots grow upward, notwithstanding the orientation of the seed.

✓ Assessment

Portfolio Have students make a labeled poster of their experimental results and share it with the class. Use **Performance Assessment in the Science Classroom,** p. 145. L2

Science and Language Arts

"Sunkissed: An Indian Legend"

as told by Alberto and Patricia De La Fuente

Understanding Literature

Legends and Oral Traditions Answers will vary but should include that a legend is usually a fictional story relaying information about a specific culture, in this case Mexican.

Respond to the Reading

1. The plants need the Sun to survive and grow.
2. The flowers need water to survive and grow.
3. **Linking Science and Writing** Remind students that good storytellers are enthusiastic and entertaining. An oral tradition is started because listeners want to pass the story along.

 Photosynthesis The study of photosynthesis began in 1771, with observations made by the English chemist Joseph Priestley. Priestley burned a candle in a closed container until the air in the container could no longer support combustion. He then placed a shoot of a plant in the container and discovered that after several days the plant had produced some substance (later recognized as oxygen) that enabled the confined air to again support combustion. In 1779 the Dutch physician Jan Ingenhousz showed that the plant must be exposed to light if oxygen is to be restored.

A long time ago, deep down in the very heart of the old Mexican forests, so far away from the sea that not even the largest birds ever had time to fly that far, there was a small, beautiful valley. A long chain of snow-covered mountains stood between the valley and the sea. . . . Each day the mountains were the first ones to tell everybody that Tonatiuh, the King of Light, was coming to the valley. . . .

"Good morning, Tonatiuh!" cried a little meadow. . . .

The wild flowers always started their fresh new day with a kiss of golden sunlight from Tonatiuh, but it was necessary to first wash their sleepy baby faces with the dew that Metztli, the Moon, sprinkled for them out of her bucket onto the nearby leaves during the night. . . .

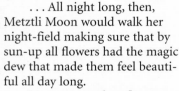

. . . All night long, then, Metztli Moon would walk her night-field making sure that by sun-up all flowers had the magic dew that made them feel beautiful all day long.

However, much as flowers love to be beautiful as long as possible, they want to be happy too. So every morning Tonatiuh himself would give each one a single golden kiss of such power that it was possible to be happy all day long after it. As you can see, then, a flower needs to feel beautiful in the first place, but if she does not feel beautiful, she will not be ready for her morning sun-kiss. If she cannot wash her little face with the magic dew, the whole day is lost.

Understanding Literature

Legends and Oral Traditions A legend is a traditional story often told orally and believed to be based on actual people and events. Legends are believed to be true even if they cannot be proved. "Sunkissed: An Indian Legend" is a legend about a little flower that is changed forever by the Sun. This legend also is an example of an oral tradition. Oral traditions are stories or skills that are handed down by word of mouth. What in this story indicates that it is a legend?

Respond to the Reading

1. What does this passage tell you about the relationship between the Sun and plants?
2. What does this passage tell you about the relationship between water and the growth of flowers?
3. **Linking Science and Writing** Create an idea for a fictional story that explains why the sky becomes so colorful during a sunset. Then retell your story to your classmates.

 The passage from "Sunkissed: An Indian Legend" does not teach us the details about photosynthesis or respiration. However, it does show how sunshine and water are important to plant life. The difference between the legend and the information contained in your textbook is this—photosynthesis and respiration can be proved scientifically, and the legend, although fun to read, cannot.

Resources for Teachers and Students

American Indian Myths and Legends by Richard Erdoes (Editor) and Alfonso Ortiz (Editor), Pantheon Books, 1985

Old Indian Legends by Zitkala-Sa, Sa Zitkala, and Angela Decora (Illustrator), University of Nebraska Press, 1985

Reviewing Main Ideas

Section 1 **Photosynthesis and Respiration**

1. Carbon dioxide and water vapor enter and leave a plant through openings in the epidermis called stomata. Guard cells cause a stoma to open and close.

2. Photosynthesis takes place in the chloroplasts of plant cells. Light energy is used to produce glucose and oxygen from carbon dioxide and water.

3. Photosynthesis provides the food for most organisms on Earth.

4. All organisms use respiration to release the energy stored in food molecules. Oxygen is used in the mitochondria to complete respiration in plant cells and many other types of cells. Energy is released and carbon dioxide and water are produced.

5. The energy released by respiration is used for the life processes of most living organisms, including plants.

6. Photosynthesis and respiration are almost the reverse of each other. The end products of photosynthesis are the raw materials needed for aerobic respiration. The end products of aerobic respiration are the raw materials needed for photosynthesis.

Section 2 **Plant Responses**

1. Plants respond positively and negatively to stimuli. The response may be a movement, a change in growth, or the beginning of some process such as flowering.

2. A stimulus from outside the plant is called a tropism. Outside stimuli include light, gravity, and touch.

3. The length of darkness each day can affect flowering times of plants.

4. Plant hormones cause responses in plants. Some hormones cause plants to exhibit tropisms. Other hormones cause changes in plant growth rates.

Visualizing Main Ideas

Copy and complete the following concept map on photosynthesis and respiration.

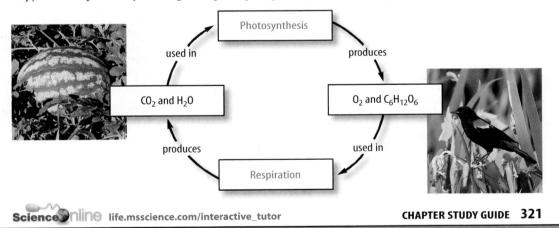

Photosynthesis

used in — produces

CO_2 and H_2O — O_2 and $C_6H_{12}O_6$

produces — used in

Respiration

Science Online life.msscience.com/interactive_tutor

CHAPTER STUDY GUIDE **321**

Reviewing Main Ideas

Summary statements can be used by students to review the major concepts of the chapter.

Visualizing Main Ideas

See student page.

Science Online

Visit life.msscience.com
  /self_check_quiz
  /interactive_tutor
  /vocabulary_puzzlemaker
  /chapter_review
  /standardized_test

Assessment Transparency

For additional assessment questions, use the *Assessment Transparency* located in the transparency book.

Assessment

Assessment Transparency **Plant Processes**

Directions: *Carefully review the diagram and answer the following questions.*

1. The plant in the diagram above, with light in position X, will most likely ___.
   A grow toward the light   C grow sideways
   B grow away from the light   D stop growing
2. According to this diagram, the light ___.
   F acts as an internal stimulus
   G burns the plant's sensitive stem
   H acts as an external stimulus
   J dries out the soil
3. If the plant moves, then it would most likely be reacting to the movement of the light, from position X to position Y, in order to ___.
   A shade it roots   C minimize respiration
   B absorb   D maximize phototropism

Plant Processes

◆Identifying Misconceptions

Assess

Use this assessment as follow-up to page F at the beginning of this chapter.
Procedure Give the following statements, and ask students to respond with "plants," "animals," or "both plants and animals": takes in oxygen; gives off carbon dioxide; takes in carbon dioxide; gives off oxygen; make glucose; uses glucose.

Expected Outcome Students should know that both plants and animals take in oxygen, give off carbon dioxide, and use glucose. Only plants give off oxygen, take in carbon dioxide, and make glucose.

Using Vocabulary

1. Auxin
2. Photosynthesis
3. Chlorophyll
4. short-day plant
5. respiration
6. long-day plant
7. tropism
8. stomata
9. Photoperiodism
10. day-neutral plants

Checking Concepts

11. C   15. D
12. D   16. C
13. D   17. A
14. A   18. B

Thinking Critically

19. Put them in a brown paper bag to retain ethylene.

20. a. positive response to light or negative response to gravity; b. positive response to gravity; c. positive response to light; d. positive response to touch

21. Oxygen is a by-product of photosynthesis. Until organisms that used carbon dioxide for photosynthesis evolved, little free oxygen was available.

22. Apple trees bloom in the spring when the days are short and nights are long. The number of dark hours in the summer is less than an apple tree's photoperiod.

23. Day-neutral plants will flower anywhere if they receive a minimum number of hours of darkness and if other environmental conditions are favorable. Long-day plants require the number of hours of darkness that occurs near the equator.

Using Vocabulary

auxin p. 314   photosynthesis p. 305
chlorophyll p. 304   respiration p. 307
day-neutral plant p. 316   short-day plant p. 316
long-day plant p. 316   stomata p. 303
photoperiodism p. 316   tropism p. 312

Fill in the blanks with the correct vocabulary word(s) from the list above.

1. _____ is a hormone that causes plant stems and leaves to exhibit positive phototropism.

2. _____ is a light-dependent process conducted by green plants but not by animals.

3. _____ is required for photosynthesis.

4. A poinsettia, often seen flowering during December holidays, is a(n) _____.

5. In most living things, energy is released from food by _____.

6. Spinach requires only ten hours of darkness to flower, which makes it a(n) _____.

7. A(n) _____ can cause a plant to bend toward light.

8. Plants usually take in carbon dioxide through _____.

9. _____ controls a plant's response to day length.

10. Plants that flower without regard to day length are _____.

Checking Concepts

Choose the word or phrase that best answers the question.

11. What raw material needed by plants enters through open stomata?
    A) sugar   C) carbon dioxide
    B) chlorophyll   D) cellulose

12. What is a function of stomata?
    A) photosynthesis
    B) to guard the interior cells
    C) to allow sugar to escape
    D) to permit the release of oxygen

13. What plant process produces water, carbon dioxide, and energy?
    A) cell division   C) growth
    B) photosynthesis D) respiration

14. What are the products of photosynthesis?
    A) glucose and oxygen
    B) carbon dioxide and water
    C) chlorophyll and glucose
    D) carbon dioxide and oxygen

15. What are plant substances that affect plant growth called?
    A) tropisms   C) germination
    B) glucose   D) hormones

16. Leaves change colors because what substance breaks down?
    A) hormone   C) chlorophyll
    B) carotenoid   D) cytoplasm

17. Which of these is a product of respiration?
    A) CO_2 C) C_2H_4
    B) O_2 D) H_2

Use the photo below to answer question 18.

18. What stimulus is this plant responding to?
    A) light   C) touch
    B) gravity   D) water

 Science Online life.msscience.com/vocabulary_puzzlemaker

Use the Exam*View*® Pro Testmaker CD-ROM to:
- create multiple versions of tests
- create modified tests with one mouse click for inclusion students
- edit existing questions and add your own questions
- build tests aligned with state standards using built-in State Curriculum Tags
- change English tests to Spanish with one mouse click and vice versa

Thinking Critically

19. Predict You buy pears at the store that are not completely ripe. What could you do to help them ripen more rapidly?

20. Name each tropism and state whether it is positive or negative.
  a. Stem grows up.
  b. Roots grow down.
  c. Plant grows toward light.
  d. A vine grows around a pole.

21. Infer Scientists who study sedimentary rocks and fossils suggest that oxygen was not in Earth's atmosphere until plantlike, one-celled organisms appeared. Why?

22. Explain why apple trees bloom in the spring but not in the summer.

23. Discuss why day-neutral and long-day plants grow best in countries near the equator.

24. Form a hypothesis about when guard cells open and close in desert plants.

25. Concept Map Copy and complete the following concept map about photoperiodism using the following information: flower year-round—*corn, dandelion, tomato*; flower in the spring, fall, or winter—*chrysanthemum, rice, poinsettia*; flower in summer—*spinach, lettuce, petunia*.

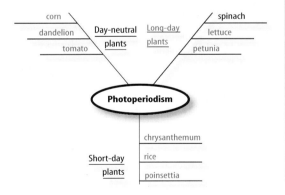

26. Compare and contrast the action of auxin and the action of ethylene on a plant.

Performance Activities

27. Coloring Book Create a coloring book of day-neutral plants, long-day plants, and short-day plants. Use pictures from magazines and seed catalogs to get your ideas. Label the drawings with the plant's name and how it responds to darkness. Let a younger student color the flowers in your book.

Applying Math

28. Stomata A houseplant leaf has 1,573 stomata. During daylight hours, when the plant is well watered, about 90 percent of the stomata were open. During daylight hours when the soil was dry, about 25 percent of the stomata remained open. How many stomata were open (a) when the soil was wet and (b) when it was dry?

Use the graph below to answer question 29.

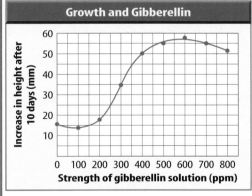

Growth and Gibberellin

29. Gibberellins The graph above shows the results of applying different amounts of gibberellin to the roots of bean plants. What effect did a 100-ppm solution of gibberellin have on bean plant growth? Which gibberellin solution resulted in the tallest plants?

Thinking Critically

24. Desert plants' stomata might open at night and close during the day in order to conserve moisture. This is opposite to most other plants.

25. See student page.

26. Both are hormones. Auxin makes stems grow toward light; ethylene makes fruit ripen.

Performance Activities

27. At a minimum each plant's drawing should include its name and photoperiod. Use **Performance Assessment in the Science Classroom,** p. 127.

Applying Math

National Math Standards
1, 5, 9

28. wet: 1,416; dry: 393

29. 100 ppm: no effect; 600 ppm

☑ Assessment Resources

📁 Reproducible Masters
Chapter *Fast File* Resources
  Chapter Review, pp. 33–34
  Chapter Tests, pp. 35–38
  Assessment Transparency Activity, p. 45
Glencoe Science Web site
  Chapter Review Test
  Standardized Test Practice

Glencoe Technology
  🔦 Assessment Transparency
  💿 Exam*View*® Pro Testmaker
  📺 MindJogger Videoquiz
  💿 Interactive Chalkboard

FAST FILE

Answer Sheet A practice answer sheet can be found at life.msscience.com/answer_sheet.

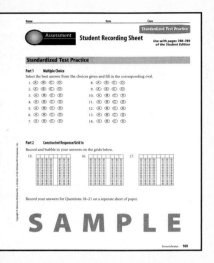

S A M P L E

Part 1 Multiple Choice

1. B   5. C   9. A
2. A   6. B   10. C
3. C   7. B
4. A   8. A

Part 2 Short Response

11. photosynthesis; amount of glucose and oxygen produced would also be limited

12. glucose. Extra glucose is stored in plants as sugars and starches, and is consumed by animals for food.

13. Respiration transforms energy stored in food into a form that can be used for transporting sugars, opening and closing stomata, producing chlorophyll, and other life processes.

Part 1 Multiple Choice

Record your answers on the answer sheet provided by your teacher or on a sheet of paper.

1. Which statement correctly describes the leaf epidermis?
   A. This is an inner cell layer of the leaf.
   B. This layer is nearly transparent.
   C. Food is made in this layer.
   D. Sunlight cannot penetrate this layer.

2. What happens when a plant is losing too much water?
   A. stomata close
   B. guard cells swell
   C. stomata open
   D. respiration increases

3. Which statement is TRUE?
   A. Changes in length of daylight and darkness have no effect on plant growth.
   B. Plants that need less than 10 to 12 hours of darkness to flower are called short-day plants.
   C. Plants that need 12 or more hours of darkness to flower are called short-day plants.
   D. Very few plants rely on a specific length of darkness to flower.

Use the illustration below to answer question 4.

Light

4. The plant above is showing a growth response that is controlled by
   A. auxin.   C. abscisic acid.
   B. gravity.   D. length of darkness.

Use the illustration below to answer questions 5 and 6.

5. What type of response is displayed by this plant?
   A. negative phototropism
   B. positive gravitropism
   C. positive phototropism
   D. negative gravitropism

6. What plant hormone is responsible for the response shown here?
   A. abscisic acid   C. a gibberellin
   B. auxin   D. a cytokinin

7. In which plant cell structure does respiration take place?
   A. nucleus   C. vacuole
   B. mitochondrion   D. cell wall

8. Which of these is NOT produced through aerobic respiration?
   A. glucose   C. water
   B. energy   D. carbon dioxide

9. Which plant hormone prevents the development of buds during the winter?
   A. abscisic acid   C. gibberellin
   B. auxin   D. cytokinin

10. What chemical absorbs light energy which plants use in photosynthesis?
    A. oxygen   C. chlorophyll
    B. hydrogen   D. glucose

324 STANDARDIZED TEST PRACTICE

---

14. Fruit picked and shipped when unripe can be moved longer distances for sale and has a longer shelf life before becoming overripe. Fruits are exposed to ethylene during shipping to promote ripening.

15. gravity, touch, light, electricity, temperature, darkness

16. They do not realize that short-day plants must be kept in darkness for at least 12 hours per day before they will flower.

17. Greenhouses can be set up to provide any needed length of artificial daylight or darkness, so both short-day and long-day plants can be forced to flower any time of the year.

18. leaves and stems; allow needed materials and wastes to enter and leave the plant

19. Chlorophyll reflects green light and absorbs most other colors and makes leaves appear green in spring and summer.

Part 2 | Short Response/Grid In

Record your answers on the answer sheet provided by your teacher or on a sheet of paper.

Use the illustration below to answer questions 11 and 12.

$$6CO_2 + 6H_2O + \text{light energy} \xrightarrow{\text{chlorophyll}} C_6H_{12}O_6 + 6O_2$$

11. Identify this process. How would this process change if the amount of available water was limited?

12. Based on this equation, what is the main food source for plant cells? How do animals use this food source?

13. Why is respiration necessary for plants? Describe some plant processes which require energy.

14. What advantage do growers gain by picking and shipping unripe fruit? What role does ethylene play in this commercial process?

15. Identify specific stimuli to which plants respond in the natural environment.

16. Many people who save poinsettia plants from Christmas cannot get them to flower the following Christmas. Why?

17. What effect have commercial greenhouses had on the availability of long-day and short-day plants year-round?

18. Where are stomata found on the leaf? What function do these structures perform?

19. Describe the relationship between chlorophyll and the color of leaves in spring and summer.

Part 3 | Open Ended

Record your answers on a sheet of paper.

20. Cellulose is an important component of plants. Describe its relationship to glucose. Identify cell and plant structures which contain significant amounts of cellulose.

21. Organisms which make their own food generate most of the oxygen in Earth's atmosphere. Trace the path of this element from a component of water in the soil to a gas in the air.

Use the illustration below to answer questions 22 and 23.

22. Explain how the tropism shown by this plant could help a gardener incorporate a larger number of plants into a small vegetable garden plot.

23. What advantages might thigmotropism, the response shown in this picture, provide for some plants?

24. The destruction of large areas of rain forest concerns scientists on many levels. Describe the relationship between environmental conditions for plant growth in rainforest regions, their relative rate of photosynthesis, and the amount of oxygen this process adds to the atmosphere.

Test-Taking Tip

Pace Yourself If you are taking a timed test, keep track of time during the test. If you find that you're spending too much time on a multiple-choice question, mark your best guess and move on.

Rubrics

The following rubrics are sample scoring devices for short response and open-ended questions.

Short Response

Points	Description
2	The student demonstrates a thorough understanding of the science of the task. The response may contain minor flaws that do not detract from the demonstration of a thorough understanding.
1	The student has provided a response that is only partially correct.
0	The student has provided a completely incorrect solution or no response at all.

Open Ended

Points	Description
4	The student demonstrates a thorough understanding of the science of the task. The response may contain minor flaws that do not detract from the demonstration of a thorough understanding.
3	The student demonstrates an understanding of the science of the task. The response is essentially correct and demonstrates an essential but less than thorough understanding of the science.
2	The student demonstrates only a partial understanding of the science of the task. Although the student may have used the correct approach to a solution or may have provided a correct solution, the work lacks an essential understanding of the underlying science concepts.
1	The student demonstrates a very limited understanding of the science of the task. The response is incomplete and exhibits many flaws.
0	The student provides a completely incorrect solution or no response at all.

Part 3 | Open Ended

20. made from glucose; major component of plant cell walls as well as leaves, stems, and roots

21. Water in soil is taken up by plant roots; light energy absorbed by leaves splits water molecules into oxygen and hydrogen atoms; oxygen exits through stomata into the atmosphere.

22. positive response to touch (thigmotropism); plants grow up on takes or trellises instead of sprawling on the ground

23. anchor the plant to a stable surface; raise the plant out of the shade and into a sunnier area

24. Materials necessary for photosynthesis are abundant in rain forest environments, making the rate of photosynthesis greater here than for plants in other areas of the world. Large-scale destruction of rain forest plants decreases the amount of oxygen produced through photosynthesis.

unit **3**   Animal Diversity

Unit Contents

WebQuest *Origins of Birds* will enable students to explore the evidence supporting the theory that birds descended from theropod dinosaurs. Students compare and contrast characteristics of birds and other groups of animals. Students will prepare a table of their new knowledge, and then use this information to answer the question: Are birds really dinosaurs?

How Are Animals & Airplanes Connected?

326

PROJECT
CRISS SM

Study Skills

Discussion Providing topics for discussion helps ensure that teams stay focused. At the end of the unit, group students for focused discussion in cooperative teams. Using a list of animals and their characteristics, students can determine the correct classification of each animal. Full-class discussion follows after the assignment.

NATIONAL GEOGRAPHIC

For thousands of years, people dreamed of flying like birds. Detailed sketches of flying machines were made about 500 years ago. Many of these machines featured mechanical wings that were intended to flap like the wings of a bird. But human muscles are not powerful enough to make such wings flap. Later, inventors studied birds such as eagles, which often glide through the air on outstretched wings. Successful gliders were built in the 1800s, but the gliders had no source of power to get them off the ground—and they were hard to control. Around 1900, two inventors studied bird flight more carefully and discovered that birds steer by changing the shape and position of their wings. The inventors built an engine-powered flying machine equipped with wires that could cause small changes in the shape and position of the wings. Though hardly as graceful as a soaring bird, the first powered, controlled flight took place in 1903, in the airplane seen here.

unit ⚡ projects

Visit **life.msscience.com/unit_project** to find project ideas and resources. Projects include:

- **History** Research Charles Darwin and his system for classifying animals. Write a time-travel interview to express your new knowledge.
- **Technology** Explore a biology-related career, and then write a want ad for a new job position.
- **Model** Study an animal, its characteristics, and habitat. Design a lunch bag with your new knowledge. A snack related to your animal may be placed inside to share with your classmates.

WebQuest Investigate *Origins of Birds* to learn about the theory that birds descended from theropod dinosaurs. Compare and contrast bird characteristics with other animals.

unit ⚡ projects

History Have students research the life of Charles Darwin and his involvement in animal species classification. Students will then write a time-travel interview with Darwin to demonstrate their new knowledge.

Career Have students choose a biology-related career to explore. Information should include courses required, advanced degrees, job location and availability, experience, and salary. Students will then write a want ad for their new job candidate.

Model Assign each student a different animal to research. Students should create an imaginative, yet informative, lunch bag to educate their classmates about their specific animal. On the bag should be the physical characteristics, prey-predator web, reproduction and life cycle, scientific name and classification, natural habitat and location, and a relevant, fun, learning activity. A snack related to the specific animal may be placed inside the bag to share with classmates.

Additional Resources For more information, resources, and assessment rubrics, visit life.msscience.com/unit_project

NATIONAL GEOGRAPHIC How Are Animals & Airplanes Connected?

Wings are complex, specialized adaptations. They enable birds to use a part of the environment not accessible to most other organisms. Their mastery of flight is reflected in the anatomical structures that allow them to modify the shape and angle of their wings. Their ability to steer and soar through the air provides them with a means of preying on other animals and of escaping predation themselves. It also allows them access to safe places for nesting. Other animals have developed wings that are different in structure, but these species achieve the same results as birds.

Section/Objectives	Standards		Labs/Features
	National	**State/Local**	
Chapter Opener	See pp. 16T–17T for a Key to Standards.		**Launch Lab:** Animal Symmetry, p. 329 **Foldables,** p. 329 A data-collection lab using Probeware technology can be found in **Probeware Labs,** pp. 17–20
Section 1 Is it an animal? ⏱ 2 sessions 📦 1 block 1. **Identify** the characteristics common to most animals. 2. **Determine** how animals meet their needs. 3. **Distinguish** between invertebrates and vertebrates.	National Content Standards: UCP.1–UCP.3, UCP.5, A.1, C.1, C.3, C.5, G.2		**Integrate Language Arts,** p. 331 **MiniLAB:** Modeling Animal Camouflage, p. 332 **Science Online,** p. 334
Section 2 Sponges and Cnidarians ⏱ 2 sessions 📦 1 block 4. **Describe** the characteristics of sponges and cnidarians. 5. **Explain** how sponges and cnidarians obtain food and oxygen. 6. **Determine** the importance of living coral reefs.	National Content Standards: UCP.2, UCP.5, A.1, A.2, C.1–C.5		**Integrate Chemistry,** p. 338 **Science Online,** p. 339 **Lab:** Observing a Cnidarian, p. 343
Section 3 Flatworms and Roundworms ⏱ 3 sessions 📦 1.5 blocks 7. **List** characteristics of flatworms and roundworms. 8. **Distinguish** between free-living and parasitic organisms. 9. **Identify** disease-causing flatworms and roundworms.	National Content Standards: UCP.2, UCP.5, A.1, A.2, C.1, C.3–C.5		**MiniLAB:** Observing Planarian Movement, p. 346 **Applying Math:** p. 347 **Visualizing Parasitic Worms,** p. 348 **Lab:** Comparing Free-Living and Parasitic Flatworms, pp. 350–351 **Science and History:** Sponges, p. 352

Lab Materials	Reproducible Resources	Section Assessment	Technology
Launch Lab: sheet of paper, scissors	**Chapter FAST FILE Resources** Foldables Worksheet, p. 15 Directed Reading Overview, p. 17 Note-taking Worksheets, pp. 31–33	GLENCOE'S **ASSESSMENT** ADVANTAGE	TeacherWorks includes: • Interactive Teacher Edition • Lesson Planner with calendar • Access to all program blacklines • Correlations to standards • Web links
MiniLAB: assorted materials such as paper, buttons, fabric scraps, and glitter; scissors; glue *Need materials?* Contact Science Kit at 1-800-828-7777 or www.sciencekit.com on the Internet.	**Chapter FAST FILE Resources** Transparency Activity, p. 42 MiniLAB, p. 3 Lab Activity, pp. 9–12 Enrichment, p. 28 Reinforcement, p. 25 Transparency Activity, pp. 45–46 Directed Reading, p. 18 **Cultural Diversity,** p. 21 **Science Inquiry Labs,** pp. XX	**Portfolio** Check for Understanding, p. 335 **Performance** MiniLab, p. 332 Applying Skills, p. 335 **Content** Section Review, p. 335	Section Focus Transparency Teaching Transparency Virtual Lab CD-ROM Guided Reading Audio Program Interactive Chalkboard CD-ROM
Lab: dropper, hydra culture, small dish, toothpick, *Daphnia* or brine shrimp, stereomicroscope	**Chapter FAST FILE Resources** Transparency Activity, p. 43 Enrichment, p. 29 Reinforcement, p. 26 Directed Reading, p. 19 Lab Worksheet, pp. 5–6 **Home and Community Involvement,** p. 38	**Portfolio** Curriculum Connection, p. 337 **Performance** Applying Math, p. 342 **Content** Section Review, p. 342	Section Focus Transparency Virtual Lab CD-ROM Guided Reading Audio Program Interactive Chalkboard CD-ROM Video Lab
MiniLAB: dropper, planarian culture, watch glass, water, stereomicroscope **Lab:** petri dish with planarian, compound microscope, prepared slide of a tapeworm, stereomicroscope, light source, small paintbrush, small piece of liver, dropper, water	**Chapter FAST FILE Resources** Transparency Activity, p. 44 MiniLAB, p. 4 Lab Activity, pp. 13–14 Enrichment, p. 30 Reinforcement, p. 27 Directed Reading, pp. 19, 20 Lab Worksheet, pp. 7–8 **Lab Management and Safety,** p. 43	**Portfolio** Science Journal, p. 346 **Performance** MiniLab, p. 346 Applying Math, p. 347 Applying Skills, p. 349 **Content** Section Review, p. 349	Section Focus Transparency Virtual Lab CD-ROM Guided Reading Audio Program Interactive Chalkboard CD-ROM Probeware Lab

End of Chapter Assessment

GLENCOE'S **ASSESSMENT** ADVANTAGE

Blackline Masters	Technology	Professional Series
Chapter FAST FILE Resources Chapter Review, pp. 35–36 Chapter Tests, pp. 37–40 **Standardized Test Practice,** pp. 51–54	MindJogger Videoquiz Virtual Labs CD-ROM ExamView® Pro Testmaker TeacherWorks CD-ROM Interactive Chalkboard CD-ROM	**Performance Assessment in the Science Classroom (PASC)**

Transparencies

Section Focus

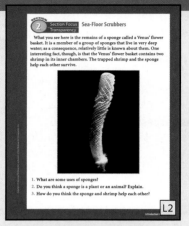

This is a representation of key blackline masters available in the Teacher Classroom Resources. See Resource Manager boxes within the chapter for additional information.

Key to Teaching Strategies

The following designations will help you decide which activities are appropriate for your students.

L1 Level 1 activities should be appropriate for students with learning difficulties.

L2 Level 2 activities should be within the ability range of all students.

L3 Level 3 activities are designed for above-average students.

ELL ELL activities should be within the ability range of English-Language Learners.

COOP LEARN Cooperative Learning activities are designed for small group work.

LS Multiple Learning Styles logos, as described on page 12T, are used throughout to indicate strategies that address different learning styles.

P These strategies represent student products that can be placed into a best-work portfolio.

PBL Problem-Based Learning activities apply real-world situations to learning.

Assessment

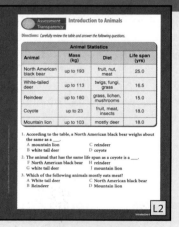

Teaching

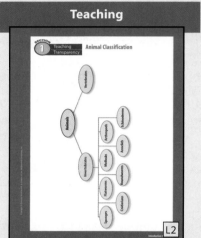

Hands-on Activities

Student Text Lab Worksheet

Lab Activities

Resource Manager

Meeting Different Ability Levels

Content Outline

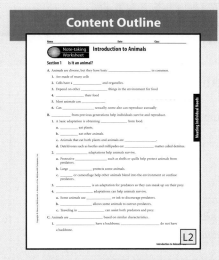

L2

Reinforcement

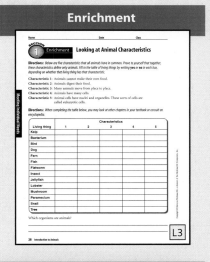

L2

Enrichment

L3

Directed Reading (English/Spanish)

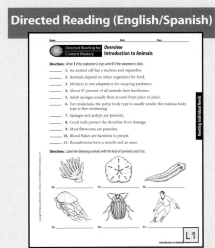

L1

Study Guide

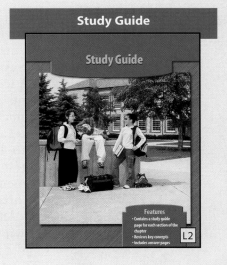

Study Guide

Features
- Contains a study guide page for each section of the chapter
- Reviews key concepts
- Includes answer pages

L2

Reading Essentials

Reading Essentials for Glencoe Science
An Interactive Student Workbook

Features
- Condensed core content
- Actively involves students in reading
- Reinforces key vocabulary

L1

Assessment

Test Practice Workbook

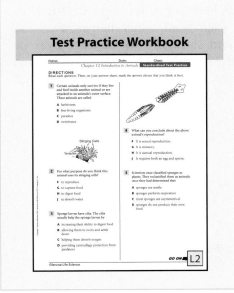

Glencoe Life Science

L2

Chapter Review

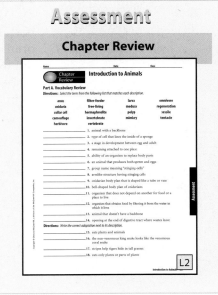

L2

Chapter Tests

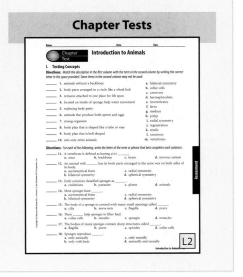

L2

Science Content Background

section 1 — Is it an animal?

Animal Characteristics

From sponges to monkeys there is considerable diversity in the animal kingdom. Yet there are characteristics that all animals share. Animals are heterotrophic—they consume parts of other organisms for their nutritional needs. Animals are composed of eukaryotic cells, which have nuclei and cell membranes.

Ken Lucas/Visuals Unlimited

How Animals Meet Their Needs

Animals have adaptions that make them either carnivores, herbivores, or omnivores. Consider the length of the alimentary canal. Many students are surprised to learn that herbivores have a much longer alimentary canal than do carnivores. The extra length is an adaption that helps with breaking down cellulose, the hard-to-digest plant material. The length of the human alimentary canal is between the lengths of herbivores and carnivores.

Another area where adaptations can be seen is with dentition. Herbivores have hard, flat molars that are used for grinding plant material. The sharp back teeth of a carnivore is for cutting and shredding meat.

Many land herbivores have eyes far apart on both sides of their head, which helps them spot predators. Land carnivores often have eyes in the front of their heads. This arrangement gives binocular vision, which better helps the predator estimate distance.

Sponges and Cnidarians
Sponges

Sponges belong to the phylum Porifera, which comes from the Latin words *porus*, which means "hole," and *ferre*, which means "to carry." They have this name because sponges carry materials in through their holes. The sponges your students typically encounter are artificial sponges. As a defense against bacteria, fungi, and predators, real sponges have chemical defenses. Scientists are studying these compounds to see if they can be used to combat human diseases.

Cnidarians

These animals belong to the aquatic invertebrate phylum called Cnidaria and are also called coelenterate animals. Sea anemones are carnivores, but they have symbiotic relationships with photosynthetic organisms that produce nutrients and oxygen for the anemone. For this reason, sea anemones will not survive for long in marine aquariums unless they contain proper lighting systems.

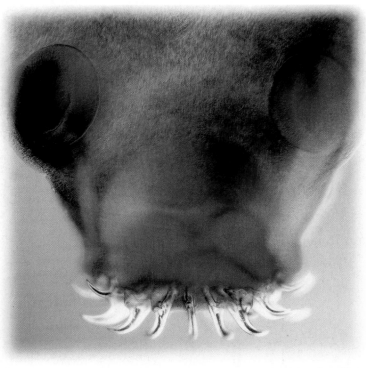

Alferd Pasieka/Science Library/Photo Researchers, Inc.

Flatworms and Roundworms
Flatworms

Flatworms belong to the phylum Platyhelminthes. The name comes from the Greek word *platys*, meaning "flat" and *helminthos*, meaning "worm." There are 3,500 species of tapeworms that live in different animals. The size of the worm usually varies with the organism in which it lives. For example, a tapeworm in a sperm whale may be 30 meters long.

Roundworms

Members of the phylum Nematoda are the simplest organisms that have tubelike digestive systems starting with a mouth and ending with an anus. These are abundant animals that live in large quantities in places as diverse as soils, plants, animals, freshwater, salt water, and even vinegar.

chapter content resources

Internet Resources

For additional content background, visit **life.msscience.com** to:

- access your book online
- find references to related articles in popular science magazines
- access Web links with related content background
- access current events with science journal topics

Print Resources

Coral Reefs: Ecology, Threats, and Conservation by Charles Sheppard, Voyageur Press, 2002

Parasitic Worms by Jim Flegg, Shire Publications, 1999

Invertebrate Zoology by Ellen Doris, Len Rubenstein, Thames & Hudson, 1993

Jellyfish to Insects: Projects With Biology (Hands on Science) by William Hemsley, Richard Hull, Gloucester Pr, 1991

Introduction to Animals

Chapter Vocabulary

Science Journal In this picture, students will find various corals, fishes, and sea aneome.

INTERACTIVE CHALKBOARD
with Image Bank

PowerPoint® Presentations

This CD-ROM is an editable Microsoft® PowerPoint® presentation that includes:

- a pre-made presentation for every chapter
- interactive graphics
- animations
- audio clips
- image bank
- all new section and chapter questions
- Standardized Test Practice
- transparencies
- pre-lab questions for all labs
- Foldables directions
- links to life.msscience.com

chapter preview

sections

1 Is it an animal?

2 Sponges and Cnidarians
Lab Observing a Cnidarian

3 Flatworms and Roundworms
Lab Comparing Free-living and Parasitic Flatworms

Virtual Lab How do sponges, cnidarians, flatworms, and roundworms obtain food?

Plant or Animal?

There are many animals on Earth, and not all look like a cat or a dog. A coral is an animal, and a coral reef is made of millions of these animals. By studying how animals are classified today, scientists can identify the relationships that exist among different animal groups.

Science Journal List all of the animals that you can identify in this picture.

328

Theme Connection

Stability and Change Changing environments lead to changes in the complexity of animals inhabiting these environments. The groups of animals from invertebrates to vertebrates show a trend toward increasing complexity.

About the Photo

Disappearing Reefs Coral reefs are often called the rain forests of the ocean because of the abundance of life there. Many animals in the ocean depend on the reef for food and protection, and coral polyps feed on plant and animal plankton. Unfortunately, coral reefs are disappearing at an alarming rate due to warmer waters and human activities.

Start-Up Activities

Animal Symmetry

The words *left* and *right* have meaning to you because your body has a left and a right side. But what is left or right to a jellyfish or sea star? How an animal's body parts are arranged is called symmetry. In the following lab, you will compare three types of symmetry found in animals.

1. On a piece of paper, draw three shapes—a circle, a triangle with two equal sides, and a free-form shape—then cut them out.

2. See how many different ways you can fold each shape through the center to make similar halves with each fold.

3. **Think Critically** Record which shapes can be folded into equal halves and which shapes cannot. Can any of the shapes be folded into equal halves more than one way? Which shape would be similar to a human? A sea star? A sponge?

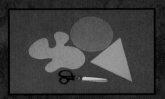

Animal Classification Make the following Foldable to help you classify the main characteristics of different animals.

STEP 1 **Fold** a piece of paper in half from top to bottom and then fold it in half again to divide it into fourths.

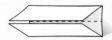

STEP 2 **Turn** the paper vertically, **unfold and label** the four columns as shown.

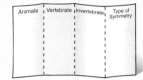

Read for Main Ideas As you read this chapter, list the characteristics of different animals in the appropriate column.

Preview this chapter's content and activities at life.msscience.com

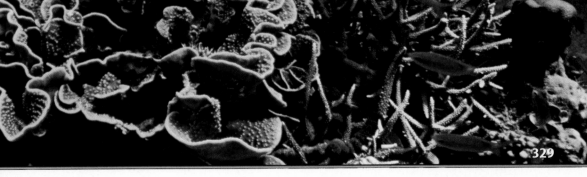

329

Launch LAB

Purpose Use this lab to introduce students to symmetry. Explain that in this chapter they will be learning about different types of symmetry and invertebrates [L2]

Preparation Cut out shapes that represent different animals with radial or bilateral symmetry. Show students the cutouts after they have finished the activity. Ask them to identify the type of symmetry of each.

Materials scissors, sheet of paper or colored construction paper

Teaching Strategy Have students compare the shapes they made with the shapes of animals from different phyla. Ask them to classify their "animals" into a phylum or to devise their own phyla for classifying organisms.

Safety Precaution Caution students to use scissors safely.

Think Critically

Answers will vary, but many of the shapes will have either radial or bilateral symmetry. triangle—human; circle—sea star; free-form shape—sponge.

Assessment

Performance Organize the class into groups and have each group make a poster display of their shapes. Similar shapes should be grouped together and classified. Use **Performance Assessment in the Science Classroom,** p. 145. [L2]

Probeware Labs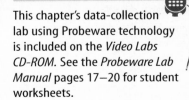

This chapter's data-collection lab using Probeware technology is included on the *Video Labs CD-ROM*. See the *Probeware Lab Manual* pages 17–20 for student worksheets.

FOLDABLES Study Organizer **Dinah Zike Study Fold**

Student preparation materials for this Foldable are available in the **Chapter FAST FILE Resources.**

Is it an animal?

1 Motivate

Bellringer

Section Focus Transparencies also are available on the Interactive Chalkboard CD-ROM.

Tie to Prior Knowledge

Animal Characteristics Ask what characteristics animals have that distinguish them from other living things. They cannot make their own food and most are capable of movement. Discuss the characteristics they have in common with all living things. They are made of cells, reproduce, grow, develop, respond, and have basic needs such as energy and water.

Caption Answer

Figure 1 These organisms are hydroids. They catch tiny plankton with their tentacles.

as you read

What You'll Learn

- **Identify** the characteristics common to most animals.
- **Determine** how animals meet their needs.
- **Distinguish** between invertebrates and vertebrates.

Why It's Important

Animals provide food, medicines, and companionship in your daily life.

Review Vocabulary

adapation: any variation that makes an organism better suited to its environment

New Vocabulary

- herbivore
- invertebrate
- carnivore
- radial symmetry
- omnivore
- bilateral
- vertebrate
  symmetry

Figure 1 These organisms look like plants, but they're one of the many plantlike animals that can be found growing on shipwrecks and other underwater surfaces.
Infer *how these animals obtain food.*

Animal Characteristics

From microscopic worms to giant whales, the animal kingdom includes an amazing variety of living things, but all of them have certain characteristics in common. What makes the animals in **Figure 1** different from plants? Is it because animals eat other living things? Is this enough information to identify them as animals? What characteristics do animals have?

1. Animals are made of many cells. Different kinds of cells carry out different functions such as sensing the environment, getting rid of wastes, and reproducing.

2. Animal cells have a nucleus and specialized structures inside the cells called organelles.

3. Animals depend on other living things in the environment for food. Some eat plants, some eat other animals, and some eat plants and animals.

4. Animals digest their food. The proteins, carbohydrates, and fats in foods are broken down into simpler molecules that can move into the animal's cells.

5. Many animals move from place to place. They can escape from their enemies and find food, mates, and places to live. Animals that move slowly or not at all have adaptations that make it possible for them to take care of these needs in other ways.

6. All animals are capable of reproducing sexually. Some animals also can reproduce asexually.

330 CHAPTER 12

Section 1 Resource Manager

Chapter *FAST FILE* Resources

Transparency Activity, pp. 42, 45–46

Directed Reading for Content Mastery, pp. 17, 18

Note-taking Worksheets, pp. 31–33

MiniLAB, p. 3

Lab Activity, pp. 9–12

Enrichment, p. 28

Reinforcement, p. 25

Figure 2 Animals eat a variety of foods.

Chitons eat algae from rocks.

A red-tailed hawk uses its sharp beak to tear the flesh.

Cardinal fish eat small invertebrates and some plant material.

How Animals Meet Their Needs

Any structure, process, or behavior that helps an organism survive in its environment is an adaptation. Adaptations are inherited from previous generations. In a changing environment, adaptations determine which individuals are more likely to survive and reproduce.

Adaptations for Obtaining Energy One of the most basic needs of animals is the need for food. All animals have adaptations that allow them to obtain, eat, and digest different foods. The chiton, shown in **Figure 2,** deer, some fish, and many insects are examples of herbivores. **Herbivores** eat only plants or parts of plants. In general, herbivores eat more often and in greater amounts than other animals because plants don't supply as much energy as other types of food.

 *Why are butterflies considered to be herbivores?*

Animals that eat only other animals, like the red-tailed hawk in **Figure 2,** are **carnivores.** Most carnivores capture and kill other animals for food. But some carnivores, called scavengers, eat only the remains of other animals. Animal flesh supplies more energy than plants do, so carnivores don't need to eat as much or as often as herbivores.

Animals that eat plants and animals or animal flesh are called **omnivores.** Bears, raccoons, robins, humans, and the cardinal fish in **Figure 2** are examples of omnivores.

Many beetles and other animals such as millipedes feed on tiny bits of decaying matter called detritus (dih TRI tus). They are called detritivores (dih TRI tih vorz).

INTEGRATE Language Arts

Carnivore Lore
Carnivores have always been written about as having great power and strength. Find a poem or short story about a carnivore and interpret what the author is trying to convey about the animal.

Quick Demo
Fish v. Plants
Materials classroom aquarium with both fish and live plants inside
Estimated Time 10 minutes
Procedure Have students observe the fish and plants in the classroom aquarium. Ask them to compare and contrast the two. Both are many-celled, reproduce sexually, and move. Green plants make their own food, but fish cannot. Animals can move from place to place. Plant movement is a result of growth and environmental stimulus. L1 **IS** **Visual-Spatial**

Activity

Energy Sources Display pictures of herbivores, carnivores, and omnivores on the bulletin board. Have students group them according to their source of obtaining energy. L1 COOP LEARN **IS** **Visual-Spatial**

Reading Check

Answer They feed on plant products.

Carnivore Lore Answers will vary depending on literary work chosen.

Differentiated Instruction

Challenge Have students research the characteristics of extinct animals, such as dinosaurs, and explain why they were classified as animals. L3

Teacher FYI

Animal Classification The branch of biology that deals with the study of animals is zoology. Early zoologists classified animals according to physical structure, where they lived, or economic use. Modern zoologists use cell structure and function, embryology, physiology, and genetics to classify animals.

Mini LAB

Purpose to model camouflage

L1 LS **Logical-Mathematical**

Materials assorted materials such as paper, buttons, and fabric scraps; scissors; glue

Safety Precautions

Teaching Strategy Encourage students to use the materials provided to make animals from various links in a food chain, and infer how camouflage assists both predator and prey in their survival.

Analysis

1. Generally, an animal will be well camouflaged in one environment and only partially camouflaged in other environments.
2. Answers will vary depending on students' designs.

Assessment

Process Have students place their animals in various locations in the room. How does changing an animal's environment affect it chances for survival? Most of the "animals" will no longer be camouflaged and have difficulty pursuing prey or fleeing from predators. Use **Performance Activities in the Science Classroom**, p. 89. L1

✔ Reading Check

Answer An animal can be mistaken for another type of animal. Sometimes this may save the animal's life, sometimes this may get the animal killed.

Caption Answer

Figure 4 The scarlet king snake's bands are nearly uniform in width and black alternates with red and yellow. The coral snake has wide and narrow bands and yellow alternates with red and black. The coral snake is venomous, while the king snake is not.

Figure 3 The pill bug's outer covering protects it and reduces moisture loss from its body.

Mini LAB

Modeling Animal Camouflage

Procedure

1. Pretend that a room in your home is the world of some fictitious animal. **From materials you can find around your home,** build a fictitious animal that would be camouflaged in this world.
2. Put your animal into its world and ask someone to find it.

Analysis

1. In how many places was your animal camouflaged?
2. What changes would increase its chances of surviving in its world?

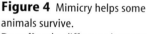

Figure 4 Mimicry helps some animals survive.
Describe the difference between the two snakes.

Physical Adaptations Some prey species have physical features that enable them to avoid predators. Outer coverings protect some animals. Pill bugs, as seen in **Figure 3,** have protective plates. Porcupines have sharp quills that prevent most predators from eating them. Turtles and many animals that live in water have hard shells that protect them from predators.

Size is also a type of defense. Large animals are usually safer than small animals. Few predators will attack animals such as moose or bison simply because they are so large.

Mimicry is an adaptation in which one animal closely resembles another animal in appearance or behavior. If predators cannot distinguish between the two, they usually will not eat either animal. The venomous coral snake and the nonvenomous scarlet king snake, shown in **Figure 4,** look alike. In some cases, this is a disadvantage for scarlet king snakes because people mistake them for coral snakes and kill them.

✔ Reading Check
How might mimicry be an advantage and a disadvantage for an animal?

Many animals, like the flounder in **Figure 5,** blend into their surrounding environment, enabling them to hide from their predators. English peppered moths are brown and speckled like the lichens (LI kunz) on trees, making it difficult for their predators to see them. Many freshwater fish, like the trout also in **Figure 5,** have light bellies and dark, speckled backs that blend in with the gravelly bottoms of their habitats when they are viewed from above. Any marking or coloring that helps an animal hide from other animals is called camouflage. Some animals, like the cuttlefish in **Figure 5,** have the ability to change their color depending on their surroundings.

Coral snake

Scarlet king snake

✔ Active Reading

Jigsaw In this collaborative learning technique, individuals become experts on a portion of a text and share their expertise with a small group, called their home group. Everyone shares responsibility for learning the assigned reading. Assign each person in each home group an expert number (1 through 5, for example). Have students gather into the expert groups that correspond to the number they were assigned. Have them read, discuss, and master chapter concepts and determine how best to teach them to their home groups. Have students return to their home groups and share the content they learned in their expert groups. Have students use the Jigsaw strategy as they study animal characteristics. L2

Bottom fish like this flounder, blend with the ocean floor.

A trout blends with the bottom of a stream.

Figure 5 Many types of animals blend with their surroundings.

Cuttlefish can be especially difficult to find because they can change color to blend with their surroundings.

Predator Adaptations

Camouflage is an adaptation for many predators so they can sneak up on their prey. Tigers have stripes that hide them in tall grasses. Killer whales are black on their upper surface and white underneath. When seen from above, the whale blends into the darkness of the deep ocean. The killer whale's white underside appears to be nearly the same color as the bright sky overhead when viewed from below. Adaptations such as these enable predators to hunt prey more successfully.

Behavioral Adaptations

In addition to physical adaptations, animals have behavioral adaptations that enable them to capture prey or to avoid predators. Chemicals are used by some animals to escape predators. Skunks spray attacking animals with a bad-smelling liquid. Some ants and beetles also use this method of defense. When squid and octopuses are threatened, they release a cloud of ink so they can escape, as shown in **Figure 6.**

Some animals are able to run faster than most of their predators. The Thomson's gazelle can run at speeds up to 80 km/h. A lion can run only about 36 km/h, so speed is a factor in the Thomson's gazelle's survival.

Traveling in groups is a behavior that is demonstrated by predators and prey. Herring swim in groups called schools that resemble an organism too large for a predator fish to attack. On the other hand, when wolves travel in packs, they can successfully hunt large prey that one predator alone could not capture.

Figure 6 An octopus's cloud of ink confuses a predator long enough for the octopus to escape.

333

Visual Learning

Figures 5 and 6 Have students look at the animals in these photos and list the adaptations they have for their particular environments, including those adaptations which allow them to escape predators.

IDENTIFYING Misconceptions

Color Change Students may think that chameleons change their color to match their background. However, this is not true. Each chameleon species has a particular range of color change it is capable of. Colors often include green, cream, yellow, and dark brown, often with spots of varying shades of the base color. The color change is brought about by environmental factors, such as light and temperature, as well as internal factors, such as sickness, pregnancy, and being threatened by a predator.

Fun Fact

Though insects make up the main portion of a chameleon's diet, large chameleons have been known to eat birds.

Differentiated Instruction

English-Language Learners Pair your ELL students with an English-speaking student. Have them make a poster of different adaptations of animals, including physical, predator, and behavioral adaptations. L2

Cultural Diversity

Animal Roles Discuss the ways in which animals are viewed in the United States—pets, food, recreation. Have students research the place of animals in other cultures. L3

Activity

Phylum Traits Organize the class into nine groups. Give each group an animal picture. Each animal should be from a different phylum (or major group). Have each group make a list of traits they can see and share their findings with the class. L1
COOP LEARN **IS** **Interpersonal**

IDENTIFYING Misconceptions

Invertebrate Traits Students may not think of invertebrates as animals. Elicit student help in writing on the chalkboard a list of familiar invertebrates and the characteristics they share with organisms more easily recognized as animals.

Quick Demo

Symmetry

Materials common objects around the classroom, Science Journals

Estimated Time 15 minutes

Procedure Compare symmetrical and asymmetrical objects. Use rocks, chalk, and other classroom objects. Have students list in their Science Journals as many asymmetrical items as they can find in the classroom. Repeat the activity with radially symmetrical and bilaterally symmetrical objects. L2 ELL **IS** **Visual-Spatial**

Figure 7 Animals can be classified into two large groups. These groups can be broken down further based on different animal characteristics.

Animals
Invertebrates — Vertebrates
Sponges · Flatworms · Mollusks · Arthropods
Cnidarians · Roundworms · Annelids · Echinoderms

Science Online

Topic: Animal Classification

Visit life.msscience.com for Web links to information about how the classification of an animal can change as new information is learned.

Activity Name a recent reclassification of an animal and one reason it was reclassified.

Animal Classification

Scientists have identified and named more than 1.8 million species of animals. It is estimated that there are another 3 million to 30 million more to identify and name. Animals can be classified into two major groups, as shown in **Figure 7.** All animals have common characteristics, but those in one group have more, similar characteristics because all the members of a group probably descended from a common ancestor. When a scientist finds a new animal, how does he or she begin to classify it?

Check for a Backbone To classify an animal, a scientist first looks to see whether or not the animal has a backbone. Animals with backbones are called **vertebrates.** Their backbones are made up of a stack of structures called vertebrae that support the animal. The backbone also protects and covers the spinal cord—a bundle of nerves that is connected to the brain. The spinal cord carries messages to all other parts of the body. It also carries messages from other parts of the body to the brain. Examples of vertebrates include fish, frogs, snakes, birds, and humans.

An animal without a backbone is classified as an **invertebrate.** About 97 percent of all animal species are invertebrates. Sponges, jellyfish, worms, insects, and clams are examples of invertebrates. Many invertebrates are well protected by their outer coverings. Some have shells, some have a skeleton on the outside of their body, and others have a spiny outer covering.

Symmetry After determining whether or not a backbone is present, a scientist might look at an animal's symmetry (SIH muh tree). Symmetry is how the body parts of an animal are arranged. Organisms that have no definite shape are called asymmetrical. Most sponges are asymmetrical animals.

Fun Fact

Animals with radial symmetry are common in the ocean, but all land animals have bilateral symmetry.

Figure 8 Symmetry is a characteristic of all animals. Sea urchins can sense things from all directions.

Most animals have bilateral symmetry like this crayfish. **Name** *the type of symmetry you have.*

Animals that have body parts arranged in a circle around a center point, the way spokes of a bicycle wheel are arranged, have **radial symmetry.** Hydras, jellyfish, sea urchins, like the one in **Figure 8,** and some sponges have radial symmetry.

Most animals have bilateral symmetry. In Latin, the word *bilateral* means "two sides." An animal with **bilateral symmetry,** like the crayfish shown in **Figure 8,** can be divided into right and left halves that are nearly mirror images of each other.

After an animal is classified as an invertebrate or a vertebrate and its symmetry is determined, other characteristics are identified that place it in one of the groups of animals with which it has the most characteristics in common. Sometimes a newly discovered animal is different from any existing group, and a new classification group is formed for that animal.

 Science nline life.msscience.com/self_check_quiz

Discussion

Sense Organs Where are the nerves and sense organs of animals with bilateral symmetry located? Why? In the front end; this arrangement allows animals to sense the environment as they move forward.

Caption Answer

Figure 8 bilateral

3 Assess

DAILY INTERVENTION

Check for Understanding

Visual-Spatial Have students make diagrams of a sea star, a butterfly, and a sponge, and label each diagram with the type of symmetry it represents. L1 LS P

Reteach

Animal Symmetry Have students look through magazines to find pictures of animals. Then have them work in groups to identify each animal's symmetry. L1
COOP LEARN LS **Visual-Spatial**

✓ Assessment

Content Place a number of pictures of animals on the bulletin board. Ask students to choose one and use the section on classification to explain how they would classify that organism. Use **Performance Assessment in the Science Classroom,** p. 121. L2

Tie to Prior Knowledge

Many-celled Organization Review how cells are organized into tissues, organs, systems, and organisms to help students understand the differences in the body structures of sponges and cnidarians.

as you read

What You'll Learn

- **Describe** the characteristics of sponges and cnidarians.
- **Explain** how sponges and cnidarians obtain food and oxygen.
- **Determine** the importance of living coral reefs.

Why It's Important

Sponges and cnidarians are important to medical research because they are sources of chemicals that fight disease.

⊙ Review Vocabulary
flagella: long, thin whiplike structures that grow from a cell

New Vocabulary
- sessile
- hermaphrodite
- polyp
- medusa
- tentacle
- stinging cell

Sponges

In their watery environments, sponges play many roles. They interact with many other animals such as worms, shrimp, snails, and sea stars. These animals live on, in, and under sponges. Sponges also are important as a food source for some snails, sea stars, and fish. Certain sponges contain photosynthetic bacteria and protists that provide oxygen and remove wastes for the sponge.

Only about 17 species of sponges are commercially important. Humans have long used the dried and cleaned bodies of some sponges for bathing and cleaning. Most sponges you see today are synthetic sponges or vegetable loofah sponges, but natural sea sponges like those in **Figure 9** still are available.

Today scientists are finding other uses for sponges. Chemicals made by sponges are being tested and used to make drugs that fight disease-causing bacteria, fungi, and viruses. These chemicals also might be used to treat certain forms of arthritis.

Origin of Sponges Fossil evidence shows that sponges appeared on Earth about 600 million years ago. Because sponges have little in common with other animals, many scientists have concluded that sponges probably evolved separately from all other animals. Sponges living today have many of the same characteristics as their fossilized ancestors.

Figure 9 Sponges can be found in a variety of habitats.

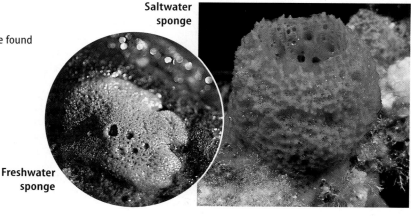

Saltwater sponge

Freshwater sponge

Section 2 Resource Manager

Chapter *FAST FILE* Resources
Transparency Activity, p. 43
Directed Reading for Content Mastery, p. 19
Enrichment, p. 29
Reinforcement, p. 26
Lab Worksheet, pp. 5–6

Life Science Critical Thinking/Problem Solving, p. 10
Earth Science Critical Thinking/Problem Solving, p. 1
Cultural Diversity, p. 7

Characteristics of Sponges

Most of the 5,000 species of sponges are found in warm, shallow salt water near coastlines, although some are found at ocean depths of 8,500 m or more. A few species, like the one in **Figure 9,** live in freshwater rivers, lakes, and streams. The colors, shapes, and sizes of sponges vary. Saltwater sponges are brilliant red, orange, yellow, or blue, while freshwater sponges are usually a dull brown or green. Some sponges have radial symmetry, but most are asymmetrical. Sponges can be smaller than a marble or larger than a compact car.

Adult sponges live attached to one place unless they are washed away by strong waves or currents. Organisms that remain attached to one place during their lifetimes are called **sessile** (SE sile). They often are found with other sponges in permanent groups called colonies. Early scientists classified sponges as plants because they didn't move. As microscopes were improved, scientists observed that sponges couldn't make their own food, so sponges were reclassified as animals.

Body Structure A sponge's body, like the one in **Figure 10,** is a hollow tube that is closed at the bottom and open at the top. The sponge has many small openings in its body. These openings are called pores.

Sponges have less complex body organization than other groups of animals. They have no tissues, organs, or organ systems. The body wall has two cell layers made up of several different types of cells. Those that line the inside of the sponge are called collar cells. The beating motion of the collar cells' flagella moves water through the sponge.

Many sponge bodies contain sharp, pointed structures called spicules (SPIH kyewlz). The soft-bodied, natural sponges that some people use for bathing or washing their cars have skeletons of a fibrous material called spongin. Other sponges contain spicules and spongin. Spicules and spongin provide support for a sponge and protection from predators.

Figure 10 Specialized cells, called collar cells, have flagella that move water through the pores in a sponge. Other cells filter microscopic food from the water as it passes through.

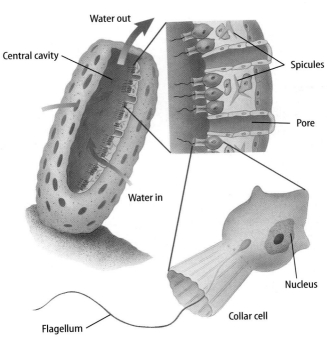

Water out

Central cavity

Spicules

Pore

Water in

Nucleus

Collar cell

Flagellum

SECTION 2 Sponges and Cnidarians **337**

---

2 Teach

Discussion

Sessile Animals Why are there no sessile animals on land? Sessile animals get their energy from food that passes by them. Food that swims or is suspended in water often cannot avoid sessile animals because of ocean currents.

Fun Fact

Of the thousands of sponge species, only about 100 species live in freshwater.

Inquiry Lab

Water-holding Capacity of Sponges

Purpose To explore and observe the ability of a sponge to hold water, have students design a method for testing which types of sponges hold more water.

Possible Materials water, various sponges, writing materials, a balance, a stopwatch or clock with a second hand

Estimated Time 1 class section

Teaching Strategies
- Students can compare the masses of wet and dry, and synthetic and natural sponges.
- Students can calculate the amount of water a sponge can hold.
- Students can also test absorption time to find what type of sponge absorbs more quickly.
- As part of the school's consumer awareness committe, students could test various consumer sponge products for their effectiveness and share their results with the school's custodian for purchase consideration.
- Allow students to explore questions as they arise. L2 PBL
LS **Logical-Mathematical**

For additional inquiry activities, see *Science Inquiry Labs.*

Differentiated Instruction

Visually Impaired Have students pass around different sponges, both natural and synthetic. Ask if they can feel any differences between the two types of sponges. L2

Curriculum Connection

Art Artists use sponges to create unique effects in their paintings. Painters use sponges for walls. Unlike brushes, which leave evidence of strokes, sponges provide a more natural texture. Have students use sponges to create a work of art for display in the classroom. L2 ELL LS **Kinesthetic and Visual-Spatial** P

Figure 11 Have students make an events chain concept map in which they sequence the events in sponge reproduction. L2 LS
Visual-Spatial

Quick Demo

Filtration

Materials soil, plant material, water, beaker, coffee filter, container

Estimated Time 15 minutes

Procedure Mix soil and plant material in a beaker of water. Pour the water mixture through a coffee filter into a container. Let students examine the filter contents and the container to see how sponge cells might filter food particles from water. L2
Visual-Spatial

Reading Check

Answer from water pulled in through their pores

INTEGRATE Chemistry

Spicule Composition The makeup of spicules reflects the composition of the water in which they live.

Research Look for possible uses for the substances that make up spicules.

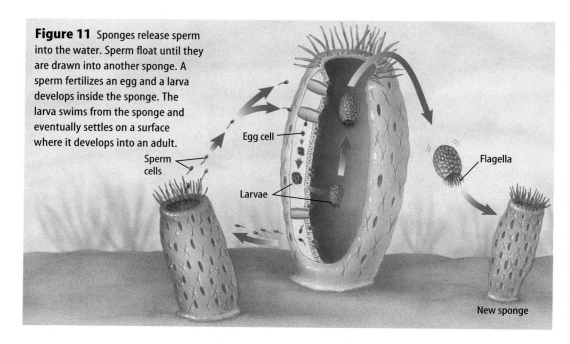
Figure 11 Sponges release sperm into the water. Sperm float until they are drawn into another sponge. A sperm fertilizes an egg and a larva develops inside the sponge. The larva swims from the sponge and eventually settles on a surface where it develops into an adult.

Egg cell

Sperm cells

Larvae

Flagella

New sponge

INTEGRATE Chemistry

Spicule Composition
Spicules of glass sponges are composed of silica. Other sponges have spicules of calcium carbonate. Relate the composition of spicules to the composition of the water in which the sponge lives. Write your answer in your Science Journal.

Obtaining Food and Oxygen Sponges filter microscopic food particles such as bacteria, algae, protists, and other materials from the water as it is pulled in through their pores. Oxygen also is removed from the water. The filtered water carries away wastes through an opening in the top of the sponge.

Reading Check *How do sponges get oxygen?*

Reproduction Sponges can reproduce sexually, as shown in **Figure 11.** Some species of sponges have separate sexes, but most sponge species are **hermaphrodites** (hur MA fruh dites)—animals that produce sperm and eggs in the same body. However, a sponge's sperm cannot fertilize its own eggs. After an egg is released, it might be fertilized and then develop into a larva (plural, *larvae*). The larva usually looks different from the adult form. Sponge larvae have cilia that allow them to swim. After a short time, the larvae settle down on objects where they will remain and grow into adult sponges.

Asexual reproduction occurs by budding or regeneration. A bud forms on a sponge, then drops from the parent sponge to grow on its own. New sponges also can grow by regeneration from small pieces of a sponge. Regeneration occurs when an organism grows new body parts to replace lost or damaged ones. Sponge growers cut sponges into pieces, attach weights to them, and put them back into the ocean to regenerate.

338 CHAPTER 12 Introduction to Animals

Curriculum Connection

Language Arts Have students research and report on *Xestospongi muta*, a barrel sponge that grows like a giant vase off the Cayman Islands. Sponges of this type are being tested for potential medicinal usage. L3

Cnidarians

Another group of invertebrates includes colorful corals, flowerlike sea anemones, tiny hydras, delicate jellyfish, and the iridescent Portuguese man-of-war, shown in **Figure 12.** These animals are classified as cnidarians (ni DAR ee uhnz).

Cnidarian Environments Most cnidarians live in salt water, although many types of hydras live in freshwater. Sea anemones and most jellyfish, also called jellies, live as individual organisms. Hydras and corals tend to form colonies.

Two Body Forms Cnidarians have two different body forms. The **polyp** (PAH lup) form, shown in **Figure 13** on the left, is shaped like a vase and usually is sessile. Sea anemones, corals, and hydras are cnidarians that live most of their lives as polyps. The **medusa** (mih DEW suh) form, shown in **Figure 13** on the right, is bell-shaped and free-swimming. A jelly spends most of its life as a medusa floating on ocean currents. Some species of jellies have tentacles that grow to 30 m and trail behind the animal.

> **Reading Check** *What are some possible benefits of having a medusa and a polyp form?*

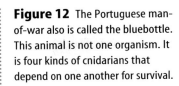

Figure 12 The Portuguese man-of-war also is called the bluebottle. This animal is not one organism. It is four kinds of cnidarians that depend on one another for survival.

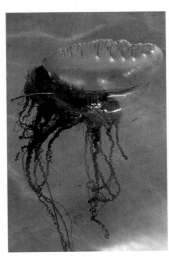

Figure 13 Cnidarians have medusa and polyp body forms.

Adult sea anemones are polyps that grow attached to the ocean bottom, a rock, coral, or any surface. They depend on the movement of water to bring them food.

Jellies can perform upward movements but must float to move downward.

Fun Fact

The lion's mane jelly (*Cyanea capillata*) is the largest true jelly. It can grow to 2.5m in diameter and have tentacles more than 30m long.

Cultural Diversity

Hydra The hydra was named for a mythical giant water monster with nine heads slain by Hercules, a Greek hero. Have students report on the Greek myth and explain how the real hydra is like the mythical one. The mythical hydra had nine heads. Each time Hercules cut off one head, it grew two back. A real hydra can be cut into pieces and each piece will generate a new hydra. [L3]

Figure 14 Tentacles surround the mouth of a sea anemone.

A Clown fish are protected from the sea anemone's sting by a special mucous covering. The anemone eats scraps that the fish drop, and the fish are protected from predators by the anemone's sting.

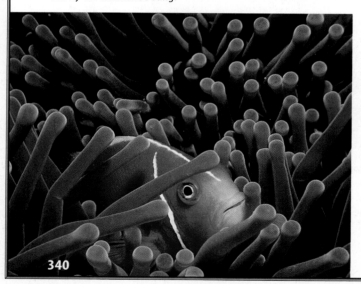

340

Body Structure All cnidarians have one body opening and radial symmetry. They have more complex bodies than sponges do. They have two cell layers that are arranged into tissues and a digestive cavity where food is broken down. In the two-cell-layer body plan of cnidarians, no cell is ever far from the water. In each cell, oxygen from the water is exchanged for carbon dioxide and other cell wastes.

Cnidarians have a system of nerve cells called a nerve net. The nerve net carries impulses and connects all parts of the organism. This makes cnidarians capable of some simple responses and movements. Hydras can somersault away from a threatening situation.

Armlike structures called **tentacles** (TEN tih kulz) surround the mouths of most cnidarians. Certain fish, shrimp, and other small animals live unharmed among the tentacles of large sea anemones, as shown in **Figure 14A.** The tentacles have stinging cells. A **stinging cell,** as shown in **Figure 14B,** has a capsule with a coiled, threadlike structure that helps the cnidarian capture food. Animals that live among an anemone's tentacles are not affected by the stinging cells. The animals are thought to help clean the sea anemone and protect it from certain predators.

Obtaining Food Cnidarians are predators. Some can stun their prey with nerve toxins produced by stinging cells. The threadlike structure in the stinging cell is sticky or barbed. When a cnidarian is touched or senses certain chemicals in its environment, the threadlike structures discharge and capture the prey. The tentacles bring the prey to the mouth, and the cnidarian ingests the food. Because cnidarians have only one body opening, undigested food goes back out through the mouth.

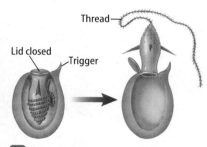

B A sea anemone's stinging cells have triggerlike structures. When prey brushes against the trigger, the thread is released into the prey. A toxin in the stinging cell stuns the prey.
Identify *the type of adaptation this is: physical, behavior, or predatory. Explain your answer.*

Fun Fact

A Portuguese man-of-war's float is filled with argon gas. No one knows why.

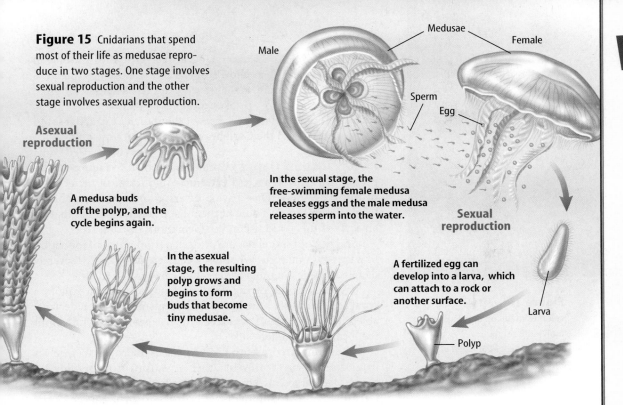

Figure 15 Cnidarians that spend most of their life as medusae reproduce in two stages. One stage involves sexual reproduction and the other stage involves asexual reproduction.

Asexual reproduction

A medusa buds off the polyp, and the cycle begins again.

In the asexual stage, the resulting polyp grows and begins to form buds that become tiny medusae.

Medusae

Male

Female

Sperm

Egg

In the sexual stage, the free-swimming female medusa releases eggs and the male medusa releases sperm into the water.

Sexual reproduction

A fertilized egg can develop into a larva, which can attach to a rock or another surface.

Larva

Polyp

Reproduction Cnidarians reproduce asexually and sexually, as shown in **Figure 15.** Polyp forms reproduce asexually by producing buds that eventually fall off the cnidarian and develop into new polyps. Polyps also reproduce sexually by producing eggs or sperm. Sperm are released into the water and fertilize the eggs, which also are released into the water.

Medusa (plural, *medusae*) forms of cnidarians have two stages of reproduction—a sexual stage and an asexual stage. Free-swimming medusae produce eggs or sperm and release them into the water. The eggs are fertilized by sperm from another medusa of the same species and develop into larvae. The larvae eventually settle down and grow into polyps. When young medusae bud off the polyp, the cycle begins again.

Origin of Cnidarians

The first cnidarians might have been on Earth more than 600 million years ago. Scientists hypothesize that the medusa body was the first form of cnidarian. Polyps could have formed from larvae of medusae that became permanently attached to a surface. Most of the cnidarian fossils are corals.

Differentiated Instruction

Challenge Have students investigate the relationship between some species of anemones and certain types of fish, such as the clownfish and the damselfish. Students should find that these animals have symbiotic relationships. L3

Teacher FYI

Coral Reef Types There are three types of coral reefs. Fringing reefs are submerged platforms of living coral that extend from the shore into the sea. Barrier reefs follow the shoreline but are separated from it by water. An atoll is a ring-shaped coral island in the open sea.

Figure 16 Coral reefs are colonies made up of many individual corals.
Infer the benefit of living in a colony for the corals.

Corals

INTEGRATE
Earth Science

The large coral reef formations found in shallow tropical seas are built as one generation of corals secretes their hard external skeletons on those of earlier generations. It takes millions of years for large reefs, such as those found in the waters of the Indian Ocean, the south Pacific Ocean, and the Caribbean Sea, to form.

Importance of Corals Coral reefs, shown in **Figure 16,** are productive ecosystems and extremely important in the ecology of tropical waters. They have a diversity of life comparable to tropical rain forests. Some of the most beautiful and fascinating animals of the world live in the formations of coral reefs.

Beaches and shorelines are protected from much of the action of waves by coral reefs. When coral reefs are destroyed or severely damaged, large amounts of shoreline can be washed away.

If you go scuba diving or snorkeling, you might explore a coral reef. Coral reefs are home for organisms that provide valuable shells and pearls. Fossil reefs can give geologists clues about the location of oil deposits.

Like sponges, corals produce chemicals to protect themselves from diseases or to prevent other organisms from settling on them. Medical researchers are learning that some of these chemicals might provide humans with drugs to fight cancer. Some coral is even used as a permanent replacement for missing sections of bone in humans.

section 2 review

Summary

Sponges
- Most sponges live in salt water, are sessile, and vary in size, color, and shape.
- A sponge has no tissues, organs, or organ systems.
- Sponges filter food from the water, and reproduce sexually and asexually.

Cnidarians
- Cnidarians live mostly in salt water and have two body forms: polyp and medusa.
- Cnidarians have nerve cells, tissues, and a digestive cavity.
- Corals are cnidarians that make up a diverse ecosystem called a coral reef.

Self Check

1. **Compare and contrast** how sponges and cnidarians get their food.
2. **Describe** the two body forms of cnidarians and tell how each reproduces.
3. **Infer** why most fossils of cnidarians are coral fossils. Would you expect to find a fossil sponge? Explain.
4. **Think Critically** What effect might the destruction of a large coral reef have on other ocean life?

Applying Math

5. **Solve One-Step Equations** A sponge 1 cm in diameter and 10 cm tall can move 22.5 L of water through its body each day. What volume of water will it pump through its body in 1 h? In 1 min?

Science Online life.msscience.com/self_check_quiz

section 2 review

1. Sponges: filter food out of the water; cnidarians: stinging cells on the tentacles paralyze an organism, tentacles pull the organism into the mouth.
2. polyps: vase-shaped, sessile, reproduce asexually by budding; medusae: bell-shaped, free-swimming, reproduce sexually by egg and sperm
3. Corals secrete a hard skeleton around themselves, which fossilizes easily. Fossil sponges would be rare, except for fossilized spicules.
4. There would be no homes for the animals that lived on the coral reef. Food supply would decrease.
5. The sponge will move about 0.94 L of water in one hour, and about 0.02 L of water per minute.

⊙bserving a Cnidarian

The hydra has a body cavity that is a simple, hollow sac. It is one of the few freshwater cnidarians.

⊙ Real-World Question

How does a hydra react to food and other stimuli?

Goals

- **Predict** how a hydra will respond to various stimuli.
- **Observe** how a hydra responds to stimuli.

Materials

dropper   toothpick
hydra culture   *Daphnia* or brine shrimp
small dish   stereomicroscope

Safety Precautions

⊙ Procedure

1. Copy the data table and use it to record your observations.

Hydra Observations

Features	Observations
Color	Answers will vary.
Number of tentacles	
Reaction to touch	
Reaction to food	

2. Use a dropper to place a hydra and some of the water in which it is living into a dish.
3. Place the dish on the stage of a stereomicroscope. Bring the hydra into focus. Record the hydra's color.
4. **Identify** and count the number of tentacles. Locate the mouth.

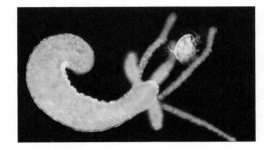

5. Study the basal disk by which the hydra attaches itself to a surface.
6. **Predict** what will happen if the hydra is touched with a toothpick. Carefully touch the tentacles with a toothpick. Describe the reaction in the data table.
7. Drop a *Daphnia* or a small amount of brine shrimp into the dish. Observe how the hydra takes in food. Record your observations.
8. Return the hydra to the culture.

⊙ Conclude and Apply

1. **Analyze** what happened when the hydra was touched. What happened to other areas of the animal?
2. **Describe** the advantages tentacles provide for hydra.

ℭommunicating Your Data

Compare your results with those of other students. Discuss whether all of the hydras studied had the same responses, and how the responses aid hydras in survival.

LAB   343

⊙ Real-World Question

Purpose to observe the structure and feeding method of a cnidarian
L1 ELL IS Interpersonal

Process Skills observe and infer, identify, predict, make and use tables

Time Required 40 minutes

Safety Precautions Caution students to use extreme care when working with live animals.

⊙ Procedure

Teaching Strategy Assign one person to place the hydra in the dish under the stereoscopic microscope and another to record the data.

Troubleshooting Place several coverslips into the jar the day before the hydra are needed. The hydra will probably cling to the coverslips. When you need hydra, remove the coverslips with forceps and place the coverslips directly into the dish that contains aquarium water.

⊙ Conclude and Apply

1. When certain parts were touched, other parts may have responded by stretching or contracting.
2. The tentacles wrap around food and bring it into the mouth. Stinging cells stun the prey.

ℭommunicating Your Data

Have students discuss their results in small groups. Then, copy the data table onto the board and fill it in as a class. L2

as you read

What You'll Learn
- **List** the characteristics of flatworms and roundworms.
- **Distinguish** between free-living and parasitic organisms.
- **Identify** disease-causing flatworms and roundworms.

Why It's Important
Many species of flatworms and roundworms cause disease in plants and animals.

Review Vocabulary
cilia: short, threadlike structures that aid in locomotion

New Vocabulary
- free-living organism
- anus

What is a worm?

Worms are invertebrates with soft bodies and bilateral symmetry. They have three tissue layers, as shown in **Figure 17,** which are organized into organs and organ systems.

Flatworms

As their name implies, flatworms have flattened bodies. Members of this group include planarians, flukes, and tapeworms. Some flatworms are free-living, but most are parasites, which means that they depend on another organism for food and a place to live. Unlike a parasite, a **free-living organism** doesn't depend on another organism for food or a place to live.

Planarians An example of a free-living flatworm is the planarian, as shown in **Figure 18.** It has a triangle-shaped head with two eyespots. Its one body opening—a mouth—is on the underside of the body. A muscular tube called the pharynx connects the mouth and the digestive tract. A planarian feeds on small organisms and dead bodies of larger organisms. Most planarians live under rocks, on plant material, or in freshwater. They vary in length from 3 mm to 30 cm. Their bodies are covered with fine, hairlike structures called cilia. As the cilia move, the worm is moved along in a slimy mucous track that is secreted from the underside of the planarian.

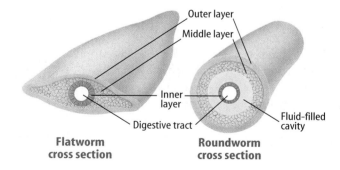

Figure 17 Worms have cells that are arranged into three specialized tissue layers and organs.

Outer layer
Middle layer
Inner layer
Digestive tract
Fluid-filled cavity

Flatworm cross section

Roundworm cross section

Section 3 Resource Manager

Chapter *FAST FILE* Resources
Transparency Activity, p. 44
Directed Reading for Content Mastery, pp. 19, 20
MiniLAB, p. 4
Enrichment, p. 30

Reinforcement, p. 27
Lab Worksheet, pp. 7–8
Lab Activity, pp. 13–14
Lab Management and Safety, p. 43

Figure 18 The planarian is a common freshwater flatworm.

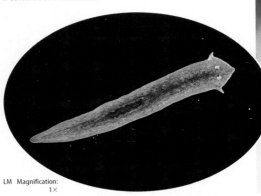

LM Magnification: 1×

The planarian's eyespots sense light.

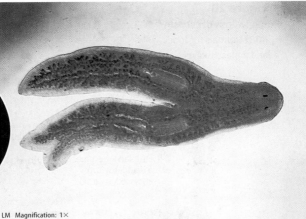

LM Magnification: 1×

Planarians can reproduce asexually by splitting, then regenerating the other half.

Planarians reproduce asexually by dividing in two, as shown in **Figure 18.** A planarian can be cut in two, and each piece will grow into a new worm. They also have the ability to regenerate. Planarians reproduce sexually by producing eggs and sperm. Most are hermaphrodites and exchange sperm with one another. They lay fertilized eggs that hatch in a few weeks.

Flukes All flukes are parasites with complex life cycles that require more than one host. Most flukes reproduce sexually. The male worm deposits sperm in the female worm. She lays the fertilized eggs inside the host. The eggs leave the host in its urine or feces. If the eggs end up in water, they usually infect snails. After they leave the snail, the young worms can burrow into the skin of a new host, such as a human, while he or she is standing or swimming in the water.

Of the many diseases caused by flukes, the most widespread one affecting humans is schistosomiasis (shis tuh soh MI uh sus). It is caused by blood flukes—flatworms that live in the blood, as shown in **Figure 19.** More than 200 million people, mostly in developing countries, are infected with blood flukes. It is estimated that 1 million people die each year because of them. Other types of flukes can infect the lungs, liver, eyes, and other organs of their host.

Reading Check *What is the most common disease that is caused by flukes?*

Figure 19 Female blood flukes deposit their eggs in the blood of their host. The eggs travel through the host and eventually end up in the host's digestive system.

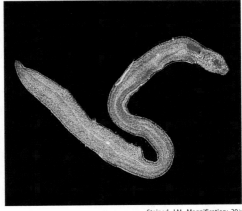

Stained LM Magnification: 20×

SECTION 3 Flatworms and Roundworms **345**

2 Teach

IDENTIFYING Misconceptions

Parasitic Purpose Students may think that because a parasite harms its host, it will always eventually kill the host. This may sometimes happen, but it is not in the parasite's best interest to kill its host. This would result in the parasite losing its food source.

Activity

Tapeworm Length Tapeworms as long as 9 m have been found in humans. Have students use a meterstick and measure 9 m to get an understanding of just how long tapeworms can be. L1 LS **Logical-Mathematical**

Reading Check

Answer schistosomiasis

Fun Fact

A cup of sand scooped from the bottom of the sea at wading depth contains about 50 to several hunderd marine animals, most commonly flatworms and roundworms.

Teacher FYI

Flatworm Respiration While flatworms do have well-developed organs, most do not have respiratory organs. Their flattened bodies enable all of their cells to exchange gases by diffusion.

Differentiated Instruction

Learning Disabled Have students select one type of worm described in this section. Have them design and construct a three-dimensional model of the worm and use the model to demonstrate its characteristics. L1 LS **Kinesthetic**

Mini LAB

Purpose to observe planarian movement L1 ELL LS **Kinesthetic and Visual-Spatial**

Materials planarian culture, dropper, watch glass, stereomicroscope, water

Teaching Strategy Planarians may be placed in water from the classroom aquarium.

Troubleshooting If planarians don't move, students may have to gently prod them with a small brush.

Analysis

1. Planarians ripple and flex their muscles in successive waves to propel themselves over surfaces.
2. Students may infer that movement is by means of muscular undulations on the underside of the planarian's body.
3. Planarians can move freely and are not confined within the body of another organism.

Assessment

Performance Have students feed the planarians pinhead-sized pieces of liver and describe their behavior. Use **Performance Activities in the Science Classroom,** p. 89. L1

Quick Demo

Tapeworm Characteristics

Materials preserved tapeworm specimens, stereomicroscope

Estimated Time 15 minutes

Procedure Obtain preserved tapeworm specimens from a local veterinarian or a biological supply company. Have students observe and list the characteristics of each. L2 LS **Visual-Spatial**

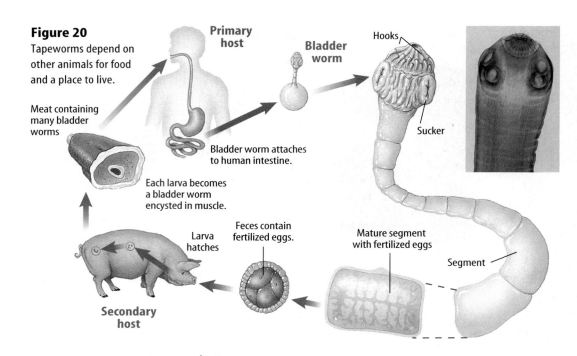

Figure 20
Tapeworms depend on other animals for food and a place to live.

Primary host

Bladder worm

Hooks

Sucker

Meat containing many bladder worms

Bladder worm attaches to human intestine.

Each larva becomes a bladder worm encysted in muscle.

Feces contain fertilized eggs.

Mature segment with fertilized eggs

Segment

Larva hatches

Secondary host

Mini LAB

Observing Planarian Movement

Procedure

1. Use a **dropper** to transfer a **planarian** to a **watch glass.**
2. Add enough **water** so the planarian can move freely.
3. Place the glass under a **stereomicroscope** and observe the planarian.

Analysis

1. Describe how a planarian moves in the water.
2. What body parts appear to be used in movement?
3. Explain why a planarian is a free-living flatworm.

Tapeworms Another type of flatworm is the tapeworm. These worms are parasites. The adult form uses hooks and suckers to attach itself to the intestine of a host organism, as illustrated in **Figure 20.** Dogs, cats, humans, and other animals are hosts for tapeworms. A tapeworm doesn't have a mouth or a digestive system. Instead, the tapeworm absorbs food that is digested by the host from its host's intestine.

A tapeworm grows by producing new body segments immediately behind its head. Its ribbonlike body can grow to be 12 m long. Each body segment has both male and female reproductive organs. The eggs are fertilized by sperm in the same segment. After a segment is filled with fertilized eggs, it breaks off and passes out of the host's body with the host's wastes. If another host eats a fertilized egg, the egg hatches and develops into an immature tapeworm called a bladder worm.

Origin of Flatworms

Because of the limited fossil evidence, the evolution of flatworms is uncertain. Evidence suggests that they were the first group of animals to evolve bilateral symmetry with senses and nerves in the head region. They also were probably the first group of animals to have a third tissue layer that develops into organs and systems. Some scientists hypothesize that flatworms and cnidarians might have had a common ancestor.

Science Journal

Controlling Flukes Have students research actions taken by the Department of Agriculture to control fluke infection in this country. Ask them to write the data as an article to be published in a consumer health magazine and include the article in their Science Journals. L2 LS **Linguistic** P

Differentiated Instruction

Challenge Health problems associated with infections by parasitic worms are often compounded by poverty, improper sanitation, and lack of governmental services to help infected people. Have students research some of the countries that are most affected by these parasites and report on what is being done to alleviate the health and social problems. L3

Roundworms

If you own a dog, you've probably had to get medicine from your veterinarian to protect it from heartworms—a type of roundworm. Roundworms also are called nematodes and more nematodes live on Earth than any other type of many-celled organism. It is estimated that more than a half million species of roundworms exist. They are found in soil, animals, plants, freshwater, and salt water. Some are parasitic, but most are free-living.

Roundworms are slender and tapered at both ends like the one in **Figure 21.** The body is a tube within a tube, with fluid in between. Most nematode species have male and female worms and reproduce sexually. Nematodes have two body openings, a mouth, and an anus. The **anus** is an opening at the end of the digestive tract through which wastes leave the body.

 **Reading Check** *What characteristics of roundworms might contribute to the success of the group?*

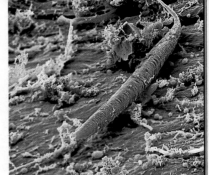
Color-enhanced SEM Magnification: 1000×

Figure 21 Some roundworms infect humans and other animals. Others infect plants, and some are free-living in the soil.

Discussion

Roundworm Adaptation How is the shape of a parasitic roundworm's body adapted to the worm's way of life? It is long and slender and has a pointed tip at either end. This shape enables it to move easily through the tissues of its host. L2

Reading Check

Answer Roundworms are probably so successful because they can live in a variety of environments. Accept all reasonable answers.

Applying Math

National Math Standards
Correlation to Mathematics Objectives
1, 2, 6, 9

Teaching Strategy
Follow the steps in the example problem, substituting the new values where necessary.

Answer to Practice Problems
1. 6 species of flatworms
2. 4%

Discussion

Parasitic Interactions Why is it an advantage to a parasite not to kill its host? A parasite depends on its host for nourishment and protection. If the parasite killed its host, the parasite would also likely die, as most adult parasites would not be able to find another host. L2

Applying Math — Use Percentages

SPECIES COUNTS In a forest ecosystem, about four percent of the 400 different animal species are roundworm species. How many roundworm species are in this ecosystem?

Solution

1 *This is what you know:*
- total animal species = 400
- roundworms species = 4% of total animal species

2 *This is what you must find out:*
How many roundworm species are in the ecosystem?

3 *This is the procedure you need to use:*
- Change 4% to a decimal. $\frac{4}{100} = 0.04$
- Use following equation:
  (roundworm-species percent as a decimal) × (total animal species) = number of roundworm species
- Substitute in known values:
  $0.04 \times 400 = 16$ roundworm species

4 *Check your answer:*
Divide 16 by 0.04 and you should get 400.

Practice Problems

1. Flatworms make up 1.5 percent of all animal species in the forest ecosystem. How many flatworms species probably are present?

2. If there are 16 bird species present, what percent of the animal species are the bird species?

 For more practice, visit life.msscience.com/math_practice

SECTION 3 Flatworms and Roundworms **347**

LAB DEMONSTRATION

Purpose to observe vinegar eels
Materials vinegar eel culture, dropper, projecting microscope, microscope slide, coverslip
Preparation Place a drop of the liquid containing vinegar eels onto a microscope slide. Gently add a coverslip.

Procedure Display vinegar eels under low power. Have students draw what they see and write a brief description.
Expected Outcome Students will observe small roundworms with jerky movements.

Assessment
What is the shape of the vinegar eels? round with pointed ends How do they move? with jerky movements Why are they called vinegar eels? They live in vinegar. L2

Visualizing Parasitic Worms

Have students examine the pictures and read the captions. Then ask the following questions.

Why do parasitic worms often cause weight loss in the host organism? Students should note that many of these types of worms infest the intestines, interfering with absorption of nutrients from food.

Identify one way you could reduce your chances of being infected with hookworms if you lived in a tropical climate. Hookworms usually enter through the skin of bare feet, so wearing shoes while outdoors is an effective way to reduce the risk of contracting hookworms.

Activity

Parasitic Worm Infestations Divide students into teams. Each team should research and compare the prevalence of human infestation with a specific species of parasitic worm in different parts of the world. Students should use a map when they present their findings to the class. Students should also identify any socioeconomic factors (i.e. limited access to health care) that cause certain areas to have a greater incidence of parasitic worm infestations. L2

NATIONAL GEOGRAPHIC VISUALIZING PARASITIC WORMS

Figure 22

Many diseases are caused by parasitic roundworms and flatworms that take up residence in the human body. Some of these diseases result in diarrhea, weight loss, and fatigue; others, if left untreated, can be fatal. Micrographs of several species of roundworms and flatworms and their magnifications are shown here.

▲ **6×** LIVER FLUKE Humans and other mammals ingest the larvae of these parasites by eating contaminated plant material. Immature flukes penetrate the intestinal wall and pass via the liver into the bile ducts. There they mature into adults that feed on blood and tissue.

▶ **78×** BLOOD FLUKE These parasites live as larvae in lakes and rivers and penetrate the skin of people wading in the water. After maturing in the liver, the flukes settle in veins in the intestine and bladder, causing schistosomiasis (shis tuh soh MI uh sus), which damages the liver and spleen.

▼ **125×** PINWORMS Typically inhabiting the large intestine, the female pinworm lays her eggs near the host's anus, causing discomfort. The micrograph below shows pinworm eggs on a piece of clear tape.

◀ **170×** ROUNDWORMS The roundworms that cause the disease trichinosis (trih kuh NOH sus) are eaten as larvae in undercooked infected meat. They mature in the intestine, then migrate to muscle tissue, where they form painful cysts.

▶ **200×** Trichina larvae in muscle tissue

Hookworm head
25×

▶ **4×** HOOKWORM These parasites enter their human hosts as larvae by penetrating the skin of bare feet. From there, they migrate to the lungs and eventually to the intestine, where they mature.

348 CHAPTER 12 Introduction to Animals

Differentiated Instruction

Challenge Have students research and diagram the complete life cycle of one of the parasitic worms shown in this feature. Students should present their diagrams to the class. L3 LS **Visual-Spatial**

Visual Learning

Figure 22 Have students create a table in which they list each of the diseases mentioned in this figure and what organism causes the disease. Students may do research to find methods of disease prevention for each listed disease. Any relevant information should be added to their table. L2 LS **Visual-Spatial**

Origin of Roundworms More than 550 million years ago, roundworms appeared early in animal evolution. They were the first group of animals to have a digestive system with a mouth and an anus. Scientists hypothesize that roundworms are more closely related to arthropods than to vertebrates. However, it is still unclear how roundworms fit into the evolution of animals.

Importance of Roundworms Some roundworms, shown in **Figure 22,** cause diseases in humans. Others are parasites of plants or of other animals, such as the fish shown in **Figure 23.** Some nematodes cause damage to fiber, agricultural products, and food. It is estimated that the worldwide annual amount of nematode damage is in the millions of dollars.

Not all roundworms are a problem for humans, however. In fact, many species are beneficial. Some species of roundworms feed on termites, fleas, ants, beetles, and many other types of insects that cause damage to crops and human property. Some species of beneficial nematodes kill other pests. Research is being done with nematodes that kill deer ticks that cause Lyme disease.

Roundworms also are important because they are essential to the health of soil. They provide nutrients to the soil as they break down organic material. They also help in cycling nutrients such as nitrogen.

Figure 23 This fish's fin is infected with parasitic roundworms. These roundworms damage the fin, which makes it difficult for the fish to swim and escape from predators.

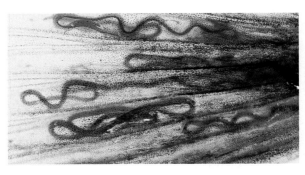

section 3 review

Summary

Common Characteristics
- Both flatworms and roundworms are invertebrates with soft bodies, bilateral symmetry, and three tissue layers that are organized into organs and organ systems.

Flatworms
- Flatworms have flattened bodies, and can be free-living or parasitic. They generally have one body opening.

Roundworms
- Also called nematodes, roundworms have a tube within a tube body plan. They have two openings: a mouth and an anus.

Self Check

1. **Compare and contrast** the body plan of a flatworm to the body plan of a roundworm.
2. **Distinguish** between a free-living flatworm and a parasitic flatworm.
3. **Explain** how tapeworms get energy.
4. **Identify** three roundworms that cause diseases in humans. How can humans prevent infection from each?
5. **Think Critically** Why is a flatworm considered to be more complex than a hydra?

Applying Skills

6. **Concept Map** Make an events-chain concept map for tapeworm reproduction.

 life.msscience.com/self_check_quiz

section 3 review

1. Flatworms have flattened bodies with one body opening, the mouth. Roundworms' bodies have a tube within a tube and fluid in between, and two body openings—a mouth and an anus.
2. Free-living flatworms find food in their environment; parasitic flatworms attach to a host and absorb food from the host.
3. They absorb food from the host's intestine.
4. Hookworm—wear shoes; *Trichinella*—cook meat thoroughly; Pinworm—wash hands
5. A hydra has two cell layers. A flatworm has three tissue layers, which are organized into organs and organ systems.
6. Student concept maps should be consistent with the information in this section.

BENCH TESTED

Real-World Question

Purpose Students compare and contrast free-living and parasitic worms. L2 COOP LEARN LS
Logical-Mathematical

Process Skills form a hypothesis, compare and contrast, observe and infer, communicate, classify, describe

Time Required 50 minutes

Materials

- Use prepared whole mount slides of tapeworms with heads and proglottids.
- Use a small brush to transfer planaria to culture dishes.
- Make sure the fed planaria are returned to a labeled dish so they will not be used again the same day.

Safety Precautions Caution students to use extreme care when working with live animals. Soft-bodied animals are easily injured.

Form a Hypothesis

Possible Hypothesis Most students will hypothesize that planarians have body parts for the environment in which they live and tapeworms have body parts for attaching to a host.

LAB

Comparing Free-Living and Parasitic Flatworms

Goals
- **Compare and contrast** the body parts and functions of free-living and parasitic flatworms.
- **Observe** how flatworms are adapted to their environments.

Possible Materials

petri dish with a planarian
compound microscope
prepared slide of a
    tapeworm
stereomicroscope
light source, such as a lamp
small paintbrush
small piece of liver
dropper
water

Safety Precautions

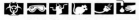

Real-World Question

How are the body parts of flatworms adapted to the environment in which they live? Are the adaptations of free-living flatworms and parasitic flatworms the same?

Form a Hypothesis

Form a hypothesis about what adaptations you think free-living and parasitic worms might have. What would be the benefits of these adaptations?

350

Alternative Inquiry Lab

Authentic Questions To make this Lab an Inquiry Lab, build on your students' experiences. Encourage them to use what they have learned to brainstorm questions about free-living and parasitic flatworms. Have each student choose one question to explore. Unsafe or impractical questions should be eliminated. Ask students to choose the materials they need to explore their questions. Students should have their plan approved before continuing. Conduct the experiments after all of the necessary materials have been gathered.

◉ Test Your Hypothesis

Make a Plan

1. As a group, make a list of possible ways you might design a procedure to compare and contrast types of flatworms. Your teacher will provide you with information on handling live flatworms.

2. Choose one of the methods you described in step 1. List the steps you will need to take to follow the procedure. Be sure to describe exactly what you will do at each step of the activity.

3. **List** the materials that you will need to complete your experiment.

4. If you need a data table, design one in your Science Journal so it is ready to use when your group begins to collect data.

Follow Your Plan

1. Make sure your teacher approves your plan before you start.

2. Carry out the experiment according to the approved plan.

3. While the experiment is going on, record any observations that you make and complete the data table in your Science Journal.

◉ Analyze Your Data

1. **Explain** how parasitic and free-living flatworms are similar.

2. **Describe** the differences between parasitic and free-living worms.

◉ Conclude and Apply

1. **Identify** which body systems are more developed in free-living flatworms.

2. **Identify** which body system is more complex in parasitic flatworms.

3. **Infer** which adaptations allow some flatworms to live as free-living organisms.

Communicating Your Data

Compare and discuss your experiment design and conclusions with other students. **For more help, refer to the** Science Skill Handbook.

LAB 351

✔ Assessment

Performance To further assess students' understanding of the differences between free-living and parasitic worms, assign them to different groups and have them use their drawings and observations to explain the differences. Assess explanations for accuracy. Use **Performance Assessment in the Science Classroom,** p. 99. L2

Communicating Your Data

Have students sketch the body designs of both types of worms, labeling the similarities and differences. L2

◉ Test Your Hypothesis

Possible Procedures One possible procedure is to observe the body structures of both free-living and parasitic worms using a hand lens or a stereomicroscope and prepared slides.

Expected Outcome

- Students' observations of planaria may include those already listed: planaria move with a gliding motion; the most sensitive body parts are those near the head; the tube-like structure (pharynx) pulls food into the body. Planarians have flat bodies. The mouth is on the bottom of the body. L2

- Students' observations of the tapeworm will include body parts adapted for attaching to a host and a well-developed reproductive system. L2

◉ Analyze Your Data

Answers to Questions

1. Both are invertebrates, have flattened bodies, and have three tissue layers organized into organs and organ systems.

2. Parasitic worms have body parts adapted for attaching to a host. Free-living flatworms have no such parts.

Error Analysis Have students compare their results and their hypotheses and explain why differences may have occurred. L2

◉ Conclude and Apply

1. The digestive and reproductive systems are better developed in free-living flatworms.

2. The reproductive system is more complex in parasitic worms.

3. cilia, feeding organs, light-sensitive behavior

TIME

Content Background

Members of the phylum Porifera are commonly called sponges. There are approximately 5,000 living sponge species. Sponges were long thought to be plants until scientists closely observed the way in which water was "ingested" by sponges. An enormous amount of water can pass through a sponge, sometimes 20,000 times its volume in a 24-hour period.

There are many different types of sponges. In the world's oceans, they can be quite colorful and beautiful. Sponges come in two basic types: encrusting and freestanding. Encrusting sponges typically cover hard surfaces in the same manner that mosses cover objects on land. Freestanding sponges sometimes grow into strange shapes, often reaching gigantic proportions.

Discussion

Sponge History Compare and contrast uses for sponges through history and their uses today. Possible answer: Sponges were used in more utilitarian ways, such as by the Greeks, who padded their helmets with them. They were also used to apply paint, to wipe surfaces, and to absorb liquids, just as they are today. L2

Historical Significance

Ask the students to compare natural to synthetic sponges. They can do this as a homework assignment or in class as a group activity. You might suggest that some students investigate the origin of the "loofah sponge," which is actually a member of the gourd family, Cucurbitaceae. Tell students to include a visual representation of sponges in their presentations. These can include photographs, drawings, models, or real-life sponges. L2

TIME SCIENCE AND HISTORY

A natural sponge

SPONGES

A common household item contains a lot of history

Sponges and baths. They go together like a hammer and nails. But sponges weren't always used just to scrub people and countertops. Some Greek artists dipped sponges into paint to dab on their artwork and crafts. Greek and Roman soldiers padded their helmets with soft sponges similar to modern padded bicycle helmets to soften enemies' blows. The Roman soldiers also used sponges like a canteen to soak up water from a nearby stream and squeeze it into their mouths. Sponges have appeared in artwork from prehistoric times and the Middle Ages, and are mentioned in Shakespeare's play Hamlet.

Natural sponges have been gathered over time from the Mediterranean, Caribbean Sea, and off the coast of Florida. Divers used to carry up the sponges from deep water, but today sponges are harvested in shallower water. Synthetic sponges, made of rubber or cellulose, are used more today than natural ones. Natural sponges absorb more water and last longer, but synthetic sponges are less expensive. Natural sponges may also cure diseases. Medical researchers hypothesize that an enzyme produced by sponges might help cure cancer. Who says natural sponges are washed up?

Brainstorm Work with your classmates to come up with as many sayings and phrases as you can using the word *sponge*. Use some of them in a story about sponges. Share your stories with the class.

Science Online
For more information, visit life.msscience.com/time

Brainstorm While brainstorming for the activity make use of the board to write down some of the students' suggestions. If possible use a theme related to the entire unit. Perhaps the setting of the story could be a coral reef, a salt-water aquarium, or a natural sponge retail store. Encourage students to use their imaginations for this exercise. L2

Resources for Teachers and Students

Sponges: Science Under the Sea, by Lynn M. Stone, The Rourke Book Company, 2002

Sponges: Filters of the Sea (Secrets Animal World), by Andreeu Llamas, Gabriel Casadevall and Ali Garousi (Ill.'s), Gareth Stevens, 1997

Reviewing Main Ideas

Section 1 — Is it an animal?

1. Animals are many-celled organisms that must find and digest their food.

2. Herbivores eat plants, carnivores eat animals or animal flesh, omnivores eat plants and animals, and detritivores feed on decaying plants and animals.

3. Animals have many ways to escape from predators such as speed, mimicry, protective outer coverings, and camouflage.

4. Invertebrates are animals without backbones. Animals that have backbones are called vertebrates.

5. When body parts are arranged the same way on both sides of the body, it is called bilateral symmetry. If body parts are arranged in a circle around a central point, it is known as radial symmetry. Animals without a specific central point are asymmetrical.

Section 2 — Sponges and Cnidarians

1. Adult sponges are sessile and obtain food by filtering water through their pores. Sponges can reproduce sexually and asexually.

2. Cnidarians are hollow-bodied animals with radial symmetry. Most have tentacles with stinging cells to obtain food.

3. Coral reefs have been deposited by reef-building corals over millions of years.

Section 3 — Flatworms and Roundworms

1. Flatworms have bilateral symmetry. Free-living and parasitic forms exist.

2. Roundworms have a tube-within-a-tube body plan and bilateral symmetry.

3. Flatworm and roundworm species can cause disease in humans.

Visualizing Main Ideas

Copy and complete the following concept map.

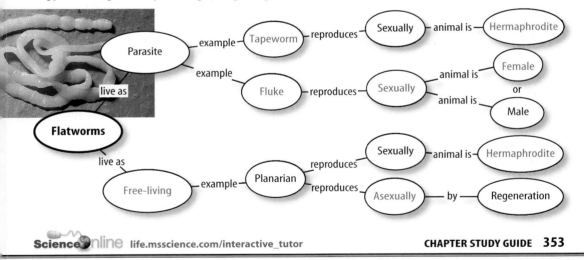

Science**Online** life.msscience.com/interactive_tutor

CHAPTER STUDY GUIDE 353

Reviewing Main Ideas

Summary statements can be used by students to review the major concepts of the chapter.

Visualizing Main Ideas

See student page.

Visit life.msscience.com
/self_check_quiz
/interactive_tutor
/vocabulary_puzzlemaker
/chapter_review
/standardized_test

Assessment Transparency

For additional assessment questions, use the *Assessment Transparency* located in the transparency book.

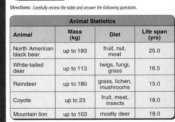

Assessment

Assessment Transparency — **Introduction to Animals**

Directions: Carefully review the table and answer the following questions.

Animal Statistics			
Animal	**Mass (kg)**	**Diet**	**Life span (yrs)**
North American black bear	up to 193	fruit, nut, meat	25.0
White-tailed deer	up to 113	twigs, fungi, grass	16.5
Reindeer	up to 180	grass, lichen, mushrooms	15.0
Coyote	up to 23	fruit, meat, insects	18.0
Mountain lion	up to 103	mostly deer	18.0

1. According to the table, a North American black bear weighs about the same as a ___.
   A mountain lion   C reindeer
   B white tail deer   D coyote

2. The animal that has the same life span as a coyote is a ___.
   F North American black bear   H reindeer
   G white tail deer   J mountain lion

3. Which of the following animals mostly eats meat?
   A White tail deer   C North American black bear
   B Reindeer   D Mountain lion

Introduction to Animals

chapter Review 12

chapter 12 Review

Using Vocabulary

1. invertebrate
2. radial symmetry
3. carnivore
4. herbivore
5. hermaphrodite
6. vertebrate
7. bilateral symmetry
8. polyp
9. sessile
10. medusa

Checking Concepts

11. D 16. C
12. A 17. C
13. A 18. A
14. A 19. B
15. A 20. B

Using Vocabulary

Find the correct vocabulary word(s).

1. animal without backbones
2. body parts arranged around a central point
3. animal that eat only other animals
4. animal that eat just plants
5. animal that produce sperm and eggs in one body
6. animal with backbones
7. body parts arranged similarly on both sides of the body
8. cnidarian body that is vase shaped
9. attached to one place
10. cnidarian body that is bell shaped

Checking Concepts

Choose the word or phrase that best answers the question.

11. Which of the following animals is sessile?
A) jellyfish C) planarian
B) roundworm D) sponge

12. What characteristic do all animals have?
A) digest their food
B) radial symmetry
C) free-living
D) polyp and medusa forms

13. Which term best describes a hydra?
A) carnivore C) herbivore
B) filter feeder D) parasite

14. Which animal has a mouth and an anus?
A) roundworm C) planarian
B) jellyfish D) tapeworm

15. What characteristic do scientists use to classify sponges?
A) material that makes up their skeletons
B) method of obtaining food
C) reproduction
D) symmetry

16. Which animal is a cnidarian?
A) fluke C) jellyfish
B) heartworm D) sponge

Use the photo below to answer question 17.

17. The photo above shows which hermaphroditic invertebrate organism?
A) fluke C) tapeworm
B) coral D) roundworm

18. How do sponges reproduce asexually?
A) budding C) medusae
B) polyps D) eggs and sperm

19. What is the young organism that the fertilized egg of a sponge develops into?
A) bud C) medusa
B) larva D) polyp

20. Which group do roundworms belong to?
A) cnidarians C) planarians
B) nematodes D) sponges

 Science online life.msscience.com/vocabulary_puzzlemaker

Use the ExamView® Pro Testmaker CD-ROM to:
- create multiple versions of tests
- create modified tests with one mouse click for inclusion students
- edit existing questions and add your own questions
- build tests aligned with state standards using built-in State Curriculum Tags
- change English tests to Spanish with one mouse click and vice versa

354 CHAPTER REVIEW

Thinking Critically

21. **Compare and contrast** the body organization of a sponge to that of a flatworm.

22. **Infer** the advantages of being able to reproduce sexually and asexually for animals like sponges, cnidarians, and flatworms.

23. **List** the types of food that sponges, hydras, and planarians eat. Explain why each organism eats a different size of particle.

24. **Compare and contrast** the medusa and polyp body forms of cnidarians.

25. **Infer** why scientists think the medusa stage was the first stage of the cnidarians.

26. **Form a hypothesis** about why cooking pork at high temperatures prevents harmful roundworms from developing, if they are present in the uncooked meat.

27. **Predict** what you can about the life of an organism that has no mouth or digestive system but has suckers and hooks on its head.

28. **Interpret Scientific Illustrations** Look at the photograph below. This animal escapes from predators by mimicry. Where in nature might you find the animal in this photo?

Performance Activities

29. **Report** Research tapeworms and other parasitic worms that live in humans. Find out how they are able to live in the intestines without being digested by the human host. Report your findings to the class.

 life.msscience.com/chapter_review

30. **Video Presentation** Create a video presentation using computer software or slides to illustrate the variety of sponges and cnidarians found on a coral reef.

Applying Math

31. **Reef Ecology** Coral reefs are considered the "rain forests of the ocean" due to the number of different species that depend on them. If scientists estimate that out of 4,000 species, 1,000 are from the coral reef ecosystem, what percentage of life is dependent on the reef?

Use the table below to answer questions 32 and 33.

Reef Area Data

Country/Geographical Location	Reef Area [km²]
Indonesia	51,000
Australia	49,000
Philippines	25,100
France	14,300
Papua, New Guinea	13,800
Fiji	10,000
Maledives	8,900
Saudi Arabia	6,700
Marshall Islands	6,100
India	5,800
United States	3,800
Other	89,800

32. **Reef Disappearance** Coral reefs are disappearing for many reasons, such as increased temperatures, physical damage, and pollution. In 2003, scientists predict that at the current rate of disappearance, in 2100 coral reefs will be gone. Use the table above to calculate the current rate of coral reef disappearance.

33. **Reef Locations** What percentage of coral reefs are off of the Australian coast?

✓ Assessment   Resources

📁 **Reproducible Masters**
Chapter *Fast File* Resources
  Chapter Review, pp. 35–36
  Chapter Tests, pp. 37–40
  Assessment Transparency Activity, p. 47
Glencoe Science Web site
  Chapter Review Test
  Standardized Test Practice

Glencoe Technology
  🖐 Assessment Transparency
  💿 Exam*View*® Pro Testmaker
  📼 MindJogger Videoquiz
  💿 Interactive Chalkboard

Thinking Critically

21. Sponges have two cell layers, little cell organization, and are asymmetrical; flatworms have three cell layers—organized into tissues, organs, and organ systems—and are bilaterally symmetrical.

22. Being able to reproduce sexually and asexually enables them to respond to changing conditions, survive poor conditions, and take advantage of favorable conditions.

23. Sponges eat bacteria, algae, and protozoans. Hydra eat small animals they capture with their tentacles. Planarians eat smaller animals or the remains of organisms. The size of a particle is determined by the size of the opening the organism has for ingesting food.

24. The medusa stage is bell-shaped and free-swimming. The polyp stage is vase-shaped and sessile.

25. The polyp stage develops from the medusa, a free-moving form. More polyp fossils exist, possibly indicating later existence on Earth.

26. Cysts are destroyed by heat; the worm has no protection and is killed.

27. It is a parasite.

28. on a plant

Performance Activities

29. Some parasites are protected by a thick mucus. The hosts may not have the enzymes to break down the mucus. Use **PASC,** p. 159.

30. Students should be able to identify each organism in their video presentation or slide show. Use **PASC,** p. 149.

Applying Math

National Math Standards
1, 6, 9
31. 25%
32. 2,931 km² per year.
33. 17%

Answer Sheet A practice answer sheet can be found at life.msscience.com/answer_sheet.

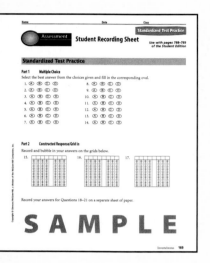

SAMPLE

Part 1 Multiple Choice

1. C   6. D
2. B   7. C
3. D   8. B
4. A   9. B
5. A   10. D

Part 2 Short Response

11. physical, like protective coverings, predator, such as camouflage, and behavioral, for example traveling in groups

12. invertebrate, because no backbone and radial symmetry; The parts are arranged around a central point.

13. Humans are vertebrates and have bilateral symmetry.

14. They filter food and oxygen from the water through pores.

Part 1 Multiple Choice

Record your answers on the answer sheet provided by your teacher or on a sheet of paper.

1. An animal that kills and then only eats other animals is an
   A) omnivore.   C) carnivore.
   B) herbivore.   D) scavenger.

2. An animal that does not have a backbone is called
   A) a vertebrate.   C) a hermaphrodite.
   B) an invertebrate.   D) a medusa.

Use the illustration below to answer questions 3 and 4.

3. This animal escapes from predators by using
   A) behavioral adaptation.
   B) predator adaptation.
   C) mimicry.
   D) physical adaptation.

4. Markings that help an animal hide from its predators are called
   A) camouflage.   C) behaviour.
   B) sessile.   D) mimicry.

5. Which of the following is not a cnidarian?
   A) coral   C) sea anemone
   B) hydra   D) sponge

Test-Taking Tip

Study Advice Do not "cram" the night before a test. It can hamper your memory and make you tired.

6. Animals that have body parts arranged around a center point
   A) exhibit radial symmetry.
   B) exhibit bilateral symmetry.
   C) exhibit asymmetry.
   D) exhibit no symmetry.

Use the photo below to answer questions 7 and 8.

7. This organism would typically be found in which environment?
   A) lake   C) ocean
   B) river   D) pond

8. It would likely spend most of its life
   A) floating on water currents.
   B) attached to rock or coral.
   C) grouped in a colony.
   D) dependent on three other cnidarians.

9. Worms have which type of symmetry?
   A) asymmetry
   B) bilateral symmetry
   C) radial symmetry
   D) no symmetry

10. Which animal's body has the least complex body organization?
    A) cnidarians   C) worms
    B) nematodes   D) sponges

15. asexually—budding or regeneration; sexually—some species are hermaphroditic, others have separate sexes

16. Cnidarians can be a sessile polyp or a free-swimming medusa.

17. It is a capsulelike cell with a trigger and lid and contains a toxin that stuns prey. When the trigger is touched by a prey, a coiled, thread-like structure is released and captures the prey.

18. Flatworms have flattened bodies, while roundworms have a tube-within-a-tube-body plan.

19. two digestive openings, a mouth, and an anus

Part 3 Open Ended

20. obtain and digest their food from living things, move, capable of reproducing sexually

21. herbivores, deer, eat plants; carnivores, lions, eat other animals; omnivores, humans, eat both plants and animals; detritivores, vultures, eat remains of organisms.

Part 2 | Short Response/Grid In

Record your answers on the answer sheet provided by your teacher or on a sheet of paper.

11. Name three adaptations, and give an example for each.

Use the photo below to answer questions 12 and 13.

12. What types of classification and symmetry does this animal have and why?

13. Compare and contrast this with the type of classification and symmetry you have as a human.

14. How do sponges get food and oxygen?

15. Explain how sponges reproduce. Do they have more than one method of reproduction?

16. Explain the two forms of cnidarians.

17. Describe structure of the stinging cells unique to cnidarians. What are the purposes of these cells?

18. Explain the primary difference between a roundworm and a flatworm.

19. Roundworms and flatworms are the simplest organism to have what feature?

Part 3 | Open Ended

Record your answers on a sheet of paper.

20. What are the characteristics that animals have in common and causes them to be included in their own kingdom?

21. Animals need energy. They get this from food. Explain the differences between herbivores, carnivores, omnivores and detritivores. Be sure to include examples of all categories.

22. Compare and contrast mimicry and camouflage. Give an example of both mimicry and camouflage.

Use the photo below to answer question 23.

23. How is this animal useful to humans?

24. Why is coral so important to us?

25. Explain how two types of animals may interact in a host and parasitic relationship. Include humans in this discussion.

26. Compare and contrast flatworms and roundworms. In your opinion, which are more developed? Defend your answer by providing examples.

Rubrics

The following rubrics are sample scoring devices for short response and open-ended questions.

Short Response

Points	Description
2	The student demonstrates a thorough understanding of the science of the task. The response may contain minor flaws that do not detract from the demonstration of a thorough understanding.
1	The student has provided a response that is only partially correct.
0	The student has provided a completely incorrect solution or no response at all.

Open Ended

Points	Description
4	The student demonstrates a thorough understanding of the science of the task. The response may contain minor flaws that do not detract from the demonstration of a thorough understanding.
3	The student demonstrates an understanding of the science of the task. The response is essentially correct and demonstrates an essential but less than thorough understanding of the science.
2	The student demonstrates only a partial understanding of the science of the task. Although the student may have used the correct approach to a solution or may have provided a correct solution, the work lacks an essential understanding of the underlying science concepts.
1	The student demonstrates a very limited understanding of the science of the task. The response is incomplete and exhibits many flaws.
0	The student provides a completely incorrect solution or no response at all.

22. Camouflage allows an animal to blend into the environment—flounder. Mimicry is when one organism looks or behaves like another—a viceroy butterfly looks like the poisonous monarch butterfly.

23. Sponges are a food source for other animals, have symbiotic relationships, used in bathing and cleaning, and are being studied for their medicinal value.

24. support a large diversity of life, break waves that would wash away large amounts of the coastlines, and chemicals secreted by coral polyps may be used medicinally

25. A blood fluke burrows into the skin of its host, a human.

26. Both—invertebrates, bilateral symmetry, soft bodies with three tissue layers; free living and parasitic forms, sexual reproduction; flatworms—flat bodies, one body opening, can regenerate; roundworms—cylindrical bodies with a fluid-filled cavity between its middle and inner layers, a mouth and an anus, cannot regenerate.

chapter (13) Organizer

Section/Objectives	Standards		Labs/Features
Chapter Opener	**National**	**State/Local**	**Launch Lab:** Mollusk Protection, p. 359 **Foldables,** p. 359
	See pp. 16T–17T for a Key to Standards.		
Section 1 Mollusks ⏱ 2 sessions 📦 1 block 1. **Identify** the characteristics of mollusks. 2. **Describe** gastropods, bivalves, and cephalopods. 3. **Explain** the environmental importance of mollusks.	National Content Standards: UCP.1–UCP.3, UCP.5, A.1, A.2, C.1–C.3		**Integrate Earth Science,** p. 363
Section 2 Segmented Worms ⏱ 2 sessions 📦 1 block 4. **Identify** the characteristics of segmented worms. 5. **Describe** the structures of an earthworm and how it takes in and digests food. 6. **Explain** the importance of segmented worms.	National Content Standards: UCP.1–UCP.3, UCP.5, A.1, A.2, C.1–C.3, C.5		**Science Online,** p. 368
Section 3 Arthropods ⏱ 2 sessions 📦 1 block 7. **Determine** the characteristics that are used to classify arthropods. 8. **Explain** how the structure of the exoskeleton relates to its function. 9. **Distinguish** between complete and incomplete metamorphosis.	National Content Standards: UCP.1, UCP.5, A.1, A.2, C.1–C.3, C.5, F.4		**MiniLAB:** Observing Metamorphosis, p. 372 **Integrate Social Studies,** p. 373 **Applying Math:** Silk Elasticity, p. 374 **Visualizing Arthropod Diversity,** p. 376 **Lab:** Observing a Crayfish, p. 379
Section 4 Echinoderms ⏱ 3 sessions 📦 1.5 blocks 10. **List** the characteristics of echinoderms. 11. **Explain** how sea stars obtain and digest food. 12. **Discuss** the importance of echinoderms.	National Content Standards: UCP.1–UCP.3, UCP.5, A.1, A.2, C.1–C.3, C.5		**MiniLAB:** Modeling the Strength of Tube Feet, p. 381 **Science Online,** p. 382 **Lab:** What do worms eat?, p. 384 **Science and Language Arts:** from "The Creatures on My Mind," p. 386

Glencoe Exclusive!
TeacherWorks™
All-In-One Planner and Resource Center

Lab Materials	Reproducible Resources	Section Assessment	Technology
Launch Lab: magnifying lens, clam shell	**Chapter** *FAST FILE* **Resources** Foldables Worksheet, p. 15 Directed Reading Overview, p. 17 Note-taking Worksheets, pp. 33–36	*GLENCOE'S* **ASSESSMENT** *ADVANTAGE*	**Teacher**Works includes: • Interactive Teacher Edition • Lesson Planner with calendar • Access to all program blacklines • Correlations to standards • Web links
	Chapter *FAST FILE* **Resources** Transparency Activity, p. 46 Enrichment, p. 29 Reinforcement, p. 25 Directed Reading, p. 18	Portfolio Visual Learning, p. 363 Performance Applying Skills, p. 364 Content Section Review, p. 364	Section Focus Transparency Virtual Labs CD-ROM Guided Reading Audio Program Interactive Chalkboard CD-ROM
Need materials? Contact Science Kit at 1-800-828-7777 or www.sciencekit.com on the Internet.	**Chapter** *FAST FILE* **Resources** Transparency Activity, p. 47 Lab Activity, pp. 9–12 Enrichment, p. 30 Reinforcement, p. 26 Transparency Activity, pp. 51–52 Directed Reading, p. 18	Portfolio Reteach, p. 369 Performance Applying Math, p. 369 Content Section Review, p. 369	Section Focus Transparency Teaching Transparency Virtual Labs CD-ROM Guided Reading Audio Program Interactive Chalkboard CD-ROM
MiniLAB: ripe banana, jar, cheesecloth, rubber band, magnifying lens **Lab:** crayfish in a small aquarium, uncooked ground beef, stirrer	**Chapter** *FAST FILE* **Resources** Transparency Activity, p. 48 MiniLAB, p. 3 Lab Activity, pp. 13–14 Enrichment, p. 31 Reinforcement, p. 27 Directed Reading, p. 19 Lab Worksheet, pp. 5–6	Portfolio Activity, p. 373 Performance MiniLAB, p. 372 Applying Math, p. 374 Applying Math, p. 378 Content Section Review, p. 378	Section Focus Transparency Virtual Labs CD-ROM Guided Reading Audio Program Interactive Chalkboard CD-ROM
MiniLAB: heavy book, clock or watch with second hand **Lab:** skins of 5 different fruits, wide-mouth jars, potting soil, humus, earthworms, black paper, masking tape, marker, rubber bands, peat moss, water	**Chapter** *FAST FILE* **Resources** Transparency Activity, p. 49 MiniLAB, p. 4 Enrichment, p. 32 Reinforcement, p. 28 Directed Reading, pp. 19, 20 Lab Worksheet, pp. 7–8	Portfolio Visual Learning, p. 381 Performance MiniLAB, p. 381 Applying Skills, p. 383 Content Section Review, p. 383	Section Focus Transparency Virtual Labs CD-ROM Guided Reading Audio Program Interactive Chalkboard CD-ROM Video Lab

End of Chapter Assessment

GLENCOE'S **ASSESSMENT** *ADVANTAGE*

Blackline Masters	Technology	Professional Series
Chapter *FAST FILE* **Resources** Chapter Review, pp. 39–40 Chapter Tests, pp. 41–44 **Standardized Test Practice, pp. 55–58**	MindJogger Videoquiz Virtual Labs CD-ROM Exam*View*® Pro Testmaker TeacherWorks CD-ROM Interactive Chalkboard CD-ROM	**Performance Assessment in the Science Classroom (PASC)**

Transparencies

Section Focus

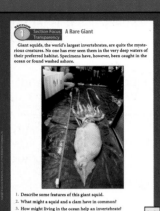

Section Focus Transparency 1 — A Rare Giant

Giant squids, the world's largest invertebrates, are quite the mysterious creatures. No one has ever seen them in the very deep waters of their preferred habitat. Specimens have, however, been caught in the ocean or found washed ashore.

1. Describe some features of this giant squid.
2. What might a squid and a clam have in common?
3. How might living in the ocean help an invertebrate?

Section Focus Transparency 2 — A Monster from the Deep?

Below is a close-up of an ice worm, a segmented worm that lives on underwater methane ice mounds, shown on the right. These worms are part of a recently discovered ecosystem 700 meters below the surface of the Gulf of Mexico.

1. How is this animal's body divided?
2. How is this animal similar to an earthworm?
3. What is unusual about worms living in mounds of ice 700 meters below the surface of the ocean?

Section Focus Transparency 3 — Natural Pest Control

The name ladybird beetle is commonly used for several different species of beetles. While a few ladybird beetles are harmful to crops, most of these beetles actually eat the pests that damage plants. This means they sometimes can be used instead of chemicals to protect crops.

1. What advantages do ladybird beetles have over chemicals for pest control?
2. Describe the appearance of this beetle. Does it look hard or soft on the outside?

This is a representation of key blackline masters available in the Teacher Classroom Resources. See Resource Manager boxes within the chapter for additional information.

Key to Teaching Strategies

The following designations will help you decide which activities are appropriate for your students.

L1 Level 1 activities should be appropriate for students with learning difficulties.

L2 Level 2 activities should be within the ability range of all students.

L3 Level 3 activities are designed for above-average students.

ELL ELL activities should be within the ability range of English-Language Learners.

COOP LEARN Cooperative Learning activities are designed for small group work.

LS Multiple Learning Styles logos, as described on page 12T, are used throughout to indicate strategies that address different learning styles.

P These strategies represent student products that can be placed into a best-work portfolio.

PBL Problem-Based Learning activities apply real-world situations to learning.

Assessment

Assessment Transparency — Mollusks, Worms, Arthropods, Echinoderms

Directions: Carefully review the graph and answer the following questions.

Southern Pine Beetle Infestations

1. According to the graph, which year had half the number of infestations that occurred in 1976?
A 1993   C 1984
B 1977   D 1991
2. According to the graph, the year that probably had the highest population of southern pine beetles was ___.
F 1992   H 1982
G 1976   I 1985
3. According to the graph, which year had twice as many infestations as 1977?
A 1986   C 1996
B 1991   D 1987

Teaching

Teaching Transparency 2 — Earthworm Anatomy

Hands-on Activities

Student Text Lab Worksheet

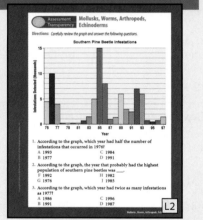

Activity — Observing a Crayfish

Lab Preview
Directions: Answer these questions before you begin the Activity.

1. What safety symbols are associated with this activity?

2. What type of outer covering do all arthropods have?

A crayfish has a segmented body and a fused head and thorax. It has a snout and eyes on movable eyestalks. Most crayfish have pincers. What are the pincers for?

What You'll Investigate
How does a crayfish use its appendages?

Materials
crayfish in a small aquarium
smocked ground beef
stirrer

Goals
• **Observe** a crayfish.
• **Determine** the function of pincers.

Safety Precautions
CAUTION: Use care when working with live animals.

Procedure
1. Use Table 1 to record all of your observations during this activity.
2. Your teacher will provide you with a crayfish in an aquarium. Leave the crayfish in the aquarium while you do the activity. Use the space in the Data and Observations section to draw your crayfish.
3. Gently touch the crayfish with the stirrer. How does the body feel?
4. Observe how the crayfish moves in the water.
5. Observe the compound eyes. On which body region are they located?
6. Drop a small piece of ground beef into the aquarium. Observe the crayfish's reaction. Wash your hands.
7. Return the aquarium to its proper place.

Laboratory Activities

Laboratory Activity 1 — Earthworm Anatomy

The earthworm is an invertebrate that has a segmented body and specialized body parts. Oxygen from the air moves into its body through its moist skin. Carbon dioxide moves out of its body through the skin. The earthworm has a series of enlarged tubes that act as hearts. The tubes pump blood through the blood vessels of an earthworm's body. The segmented body plan makes an earthworm's anatomy easy to study.

Strategy
You will observe the external parts of an earthworm.
You will dissect an earthworm.
You will identify the internal organs and organ systems of an earthworm.

Materials
earthworm (preserved)
paper towel
dissecting pan
hand lens
dissecting pins
dissecting scissors
dissecting needle

Visit the Glencoe Science Web site at science.glencoe.com for an alternate activity about earthworm anatomy.

Procedure
Part A—External Structure
1. Place a preserved earthworm lengthwise on a paper towel in the dissecting pan with the darker side up. This is the dorsal or top side.
2. Examine the external structure and identify the parts shown in Figure 1.
3. Run your fingers lightly along the top, bottom, and sides of the earthworm. The bristles that you feel are setae. Examine the setae with a hand lens. Estimate the number of setae on each segment.
4. Locate the mouth. The part that hangs over the mouth is called the prostomium.
5. Find the thickened band circling the body. This is the clitellum. It forms a cocoon for depositing the eggs during reproduction.
6. Locate the anus. See Figure 1.

Figure 1

Resource Manager

Meeting Different Ability Levels

Content Outline

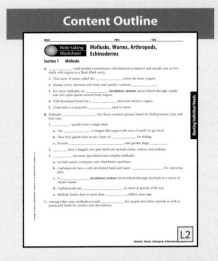

L2

Reinforcement

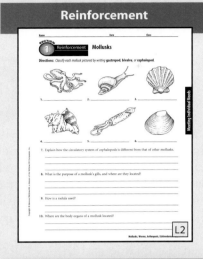

L2

Enrichment

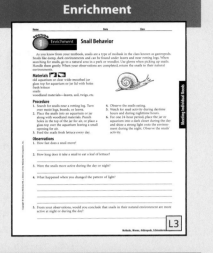

L3

Directed Reading (English/Spanish)

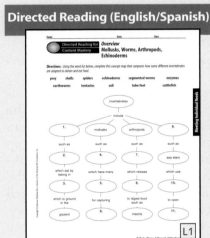

L1

Study Guide

L2

Reading Essentials

L1

Assessment

Test Practice Workbook

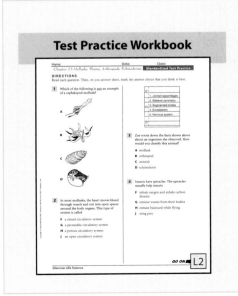

L2

Chapter Review

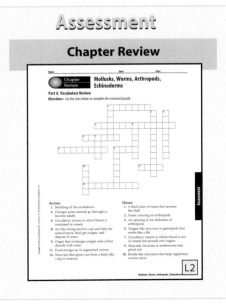

L2

Chapter Tests

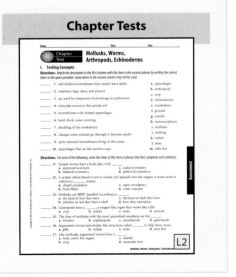

L2

Science Content Background

section 1
Mollusks
Characteristics of Mollusks

Mollusca is the second-largest phylum of animals. Mollusks can be found in freshwater and salt water and on land. A mollusk is an invertebrate that has a soft-body enclosed by a mantle and a muscular organ called the foot that is generally used for locomotion. In some mollusks, the mantle secretes a hard outer shell. As the animal grows, material is added to the shell that increases its size. In the cavity between the mantle and the body are the gills. A mollusk's gills are an adaptation that increases the surface area for the absorption of oxygen and the release of carbon dioxide. Mollusks that are filter feeders also use the gills to capture food.

Classification of Mollusks

Gastropoda, Bivalvia, and Cephalopoda are three familiar classes of mollusks. The class Gastropoda includes snails and slugs and is so named because the muscular foot is below the stomach. Gastropods have distinct heads and most have a shell. Bivalves do not have distinctive heads and have a two-part shell that is hinged together. They vary in size from tiny coquinas that are several millimeters long to giant clams that can be 1.5 m wide and weigh up to 270 kg. Bivalves and cephalopods have siphons through which water can be expelled forcefully. Cephalopods use this as a means of locomotion. The foot of a cephalopod is modified into several tentacles. Each tentacle has structures—usually suction cups—that can be used for capturing prey and locomotion.

section 2
Segmented Worms
Segmented Worm Characteristics

Segmented worms belong to the phylum Annelida. Although the most familiar annelid—the earthworm—is terrestrial, most annelids are marine animals. An annelid's body is made of segments that appear similar on the outside. Internally, each segment contains circulatory, excretory, and neural structures.

Earthworm Body Systems

Earthworms do not have eyes, but special sensors in their skin allow them to differentiate light and dark areas. They are negatively phototaxic, which means they move away from lighted areas.

The first segment of an earthworm contains the mouth and the last segment contains the anus. Soil enters the mouth and then a structure called the pharynx. The pharynx acts like a pump to push soil from the mouth through the esophagus into the crop. Annelids show variety in the forms of the pharynx, which often can be pushed out through their mouths. Some pharynxes contain sharp jaws for capturing prey or for eating plant materials.

> **Teacher to Teacher**
> Jeff Remington
> Palmyra Middle School
> Palmyra, Pennsylvania
>
> "I have my students 'pick-an-insect-parasite' and then research it. Students can share their findings with the class."
>
> *Jeff Remington*

Jeff Hunter/Image Bank

section 3

Arthropods
Characteristics of Arthropods

The first arthropods are thought to have existed in the oceans over 600 million years ago. They have evolved into countless forms and varieties—all based on the same general body plan. In addition to segmented bodies with exoskeletons and jointed appendages, arthropods have open circulatory systems, a brain, and a ventral nerve cord.

Insects

Class Insecta is the largest group of organisms on Earth and includes the only invertebrates capable of flight. Insects have evolved adaptations that allow them to live in nearly every environment.

The body of an insect is segmented. The head usually has compound eyes, antennae, and a mouth. Feeding adaptations include structures that allow insects to be carnivores, herbivores, omnivores, scavengers, or parasites. The thorax usually has legs and, if present, wings. The abdomen contains reproductive, digestive, excretory, and respiratory structures. Respiratory exchange in insects occurs in tubes called tracheae. These are connected to the outside by openings called spiracles.

While insects are commonly called bugs, entomologists, scientists who study insects, have a more restricted use of the term. The term bug is used to describe insects in the order Hemiptera. For entomologists, a cicada and a bed bug are bugs, but a fly and an ant are not.

Crustaceans

Most crustaceans are aquatic organisms. Unlike an insect, a crustacean has appendages on its abdomen as well as its thorax. Crustaceans are the only arthropods with two pair of antennae. They generally are classified into three groups. Decapods include lobsters, shrimp, crabs, and crawfish. The second group—the terrestrial and freshwater forms—includes sowbugs, sand fleas, and copepods. Barnacles make up the third group. They are free-swimming as larvae but sessile as adults.

section 4

Echinoderms
Echinoderm Characteristics

Sea stars, sea urchins, and sand dollars are examples of echinoderms. These invertebrates are not found on land or in freshwater, they are strictly saltwater organisms. Echinoderm larvae have bilateral symmetry but adult forms have radial symmetry. They have endoskeletons and a water vascular system that is not found in any other phyla.

---

chapter content resources

Internet Resources
For additional content background, visit
life.msscience.com to:
- access your book online
- find references to related articles in popular science magazines
- access Web links with related content background
- access current events with science journal topics

Print Resources
Earthworms, Leeches, and Sea Worms: Annelids by Beth Blexland, Chelsea House Publishing, 2002
Sorting Out Worms and Other Invertebrates: Everything You Want to Know About Insects, Corals, Mollusks, Sponges and More by Samuel G. Woods, Blackbirch Marketing, 1999
Butterflies, Bugs, and Worms (Young Discoverers: Biology Facts and Experiments Series) by Sally Morgan, Kingfisher Books, 1996

---

chapter 13

Chapter Vocabulary

mantle, p. 360
gill, p. 360
open circulatory system, p. 360
radula, p. 361
closed circulatory system, p. 362
setae, p. 365
crop, p. 366
gizzard, p. 366
appendage, p. 370
exoskeleton, p. 370
molting, p. 370
spiracle, p. 371
metamorphosis, p. 372
water-vascular system, p. 380
tube feet, p. 380

Science Journal Student answers will vary. Possible answers: mollusk—snail, slug, squid; worms—earthworm, leech, marine worm; arthropods—butterfly, bees, flies; echinoderms—sea star, sand dollar, sea cucumber

INTERACTIVE CHALKBOARD with Image Bank

PowerPoint® Presentations

This CD-ROM is an editable Microsoft® PowerPoint® presentation that includes:

- a pre-made presentation for every chapter
- interactive graphics
- animations
- audio clips
- image bank
- all new section and chapter questions
- Standardized Test Practice
- transparencies
- pre-lab questions for all labs
- Foldables directions
- links to life.mscience.com

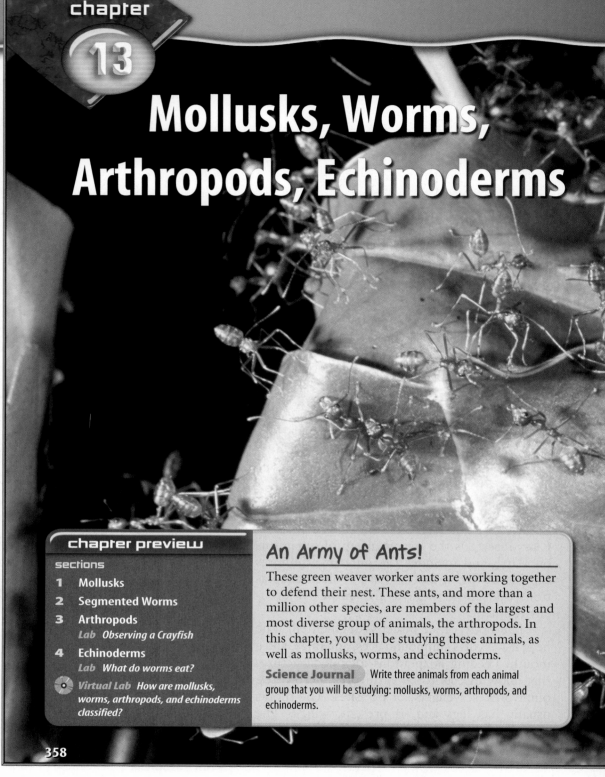

chapter 13

Mollusks, Worms, Arthropods, Echinoderms

chapter preview

sections

1 **Mollusks**

2 **Segmented Worms**

3 **Arthropods**
   Lab Observing a Crayfish

4 **Echinoderms**
   Lab What do worms eat?

⊙ *Virtual Lab How are mollusks, worms, arthropods, and echinoderms classified?*

An Army of Ants!

These green weaver worker ants are working together to defend their nest. These ants, and more than a million other species, are members of the largest and most diverse group of animals, the arthropods. In this chapter, you will be studying these animals, as well as mollusks, worms, and echinoderms.

Science Journal Write three animals from each animal group that you will be studying: mollusks, worms, arthropods, and echinoderms.

358

Theme Connection

Stability and Change and **Scale and Structure** Comparisons of the adaptations that have evolved in mollusks, segmented worms, arthropods, and echinoderms are explored.

About the Photo

Weaver Ants Green weaver ants build nests in trees or shrubs by binding leaves together with silk produced by their larvae. Individual colonies can be very large, with several nests spread over separate trees. They are aggressive and defend their nests, but their bites do not sting terribly. These ants sometimes are used in biological pest control because of their large population sizes and predatory habits.

Start-Up Activities

Mollusk Protection

If you've ever walked along a beach, especially after a storm, you've probably seen many seashells. They come in different colors, shapes, and sizes. If you look closely, you will see that some shells have many rings or bands. In the following lab, find out what the bands tell you about the shell and the organism that made it.

1. Use a magnifying lens to examine a clam's shell.

2. Count the number of rings or bands on the shell. Count as number one the large, top point called the crown.

3. Compare the distances between the bands of the shell.

4. **Think Critically** Do other students' shells have the same number of bands? Are all of the bands on your shell the same width? What do you think the bands represent, and why are some wider than others? Record your answers in your Science Journal.

Science Online Preview this chapter's content and activities at life.msscience.com

---

Study Organizer

Invertebrates Make the following Foldable to help you organize the main characteristics of the four groups of complex invertebrates.

STEP 1 Draw a mark at the midpoint of a sheet of paper along the side edge. Then **fold** the top and bottom edges in to touch the midpoint.

STEP 2 **Fold** in half from side to side.

STEP 3 **Turn** the paper vertically. **Open and cut** along the inside fold lines to form four tabs.

STEP 4 **Label** the tabs *Mollusks, Worms, Arthropods,* and *Echinoderms.*

Classify As you read the chapter, list the characteristics of the four groups of invertebrates under the appropriate tab.

Mollusks

Bellringer

Section Focus Transparencies also are available on the Interactive Chalkboard CD-ROM.

 L2 ELL

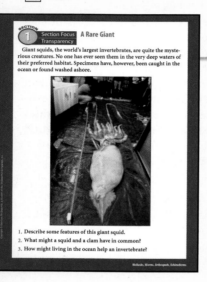

Section Focus Transparency   A Rare Giant

Giant squids, the world's largest invertebrates, are quite the mysterious creatures. No one has ever seen them in the very deep waters of their preferred habitat. Specimens have, however, been caught in the ocean or found washed ashore.

1. Describe some features of this giant squid.
2. What might a squid and a clam have in common?
3. How might living in the ocean help an invertebrate?

Mollusks, Worms, Arthropods, Echinoderms

Tie to Prior Knowledge

Mollusks Ask students to give examples of mollusks. Most will be familiar with mollusks such as oysters, clams, squid, garden snails, and octopuses. L2

as you read

What You'll Learn
- **Identify** the characteristics of mollusks.
- **Describe** gastropods, bivalves, and cephalopods.
- **Explain** the environmental importance of mollusks.

Why It's Important
Mollusks are a food source for many animals. They also filter impurities from the water.

Review Vocabulary
visceral mass: contains the stomach and other organs

New Vocabulary
- mantle
- gill
- open circulatory system
- radula
- closed circulatory system

Characteristics of Mollusks

Mollusks (MAH lusks) are soft-bodied invertebrates with bilateral symmetry and usually one or two shells. Their organs are in a fluid-filled cavity. The word *mollusk* comes from the Latin word meaning "soft." Most mollusks live in water, but some live on land. Snails, clams, and squid are examples of mollusks. More than 110,000 species of mollusks have been identified.

Body Plan All mollusks, like the one in **Figure 1,** have a thin layer of tissue called a mantle. The **mantle** covers the body organs, which are located in the visceral (VIH suh rul) mass. Between the soft body and the mantle is a space called the mantle cavity. It contains **gills**—the organs in which carbon dioxide from the mollusk is exchanged for oxygen in the water.

The mantle also secretes the shell or protects the body if the mollusk does not have a shell. The shell is made up of several layers. The inside layer is the smoothest. It is usually the thickest layer because it's added to throughout the life of the mollusk. The inside layer also protects the soft body.

The circulatory system of most mollusks is an open system. In an **open circulatory system,** the heart moves blood out into the open spaces around the body organs. The blood, which contains nutrients and oxygen, completely surrounds and nourishes the body organs.

Most mollusks have a well-developed head with a mouth and some sensory organs. Some mollusks, such as squid, have tentacles. On the underside of a mollusk is the muscular foot, which is used for movement.

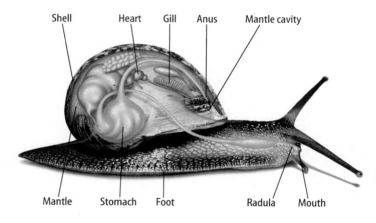

Shell   Heart   Gill   Anus   Mantle cavity

Mantle   Stomach   Foot   Radula   Mouth

Figure 1 The general mollusk body plan is shown by this snail. Most mollusks have a head, foot, and visceral mass.

360 CHAPTER 13 Mollusks, Worms, Arthropods, Echinoderms

Section 1 Resource Manager

Chapter *FAST FILE* Resources

Transparency Activity, p. 46

Directed Reading for Content Mastery, pp. 17, 18

Note-taking Worksheets, pp. 33–36

Enrichment, p. 29

Reinforcement, p. 25

Cultural Diversity, p. 3

Conch

Garden slugs

Figure 2 Conchs, sometimes called marine snails, have a single shell covering their internal organs. Garden slugs are mollusks without a shell.
Identify *the mollusk group that both conchs and garden slugs belong to.*

Classification of Mollusks

The first thing scientists look at when they classify mollusks is whether or not the animal has a shell. Mollusks that have shells are then classified by the kind of shell and kind of foot that they have. The three most common groups of mollusks are gastropods, bivalves, and cephalopods.

Gastropods The largest group of mollusks, the gastropods, includes snails, conchs like the one in **Figure 2,** abalones, whelks, sea slugs, and garden slugs, also shown in **Figure 2.** Conchs are sometimes called univalves. Except for slugs, which have no shell, gastropods have a single shell. Many have a pair of tentacles with eyes at the tips. Gastropods use a **radula** (RA juh luh)—a tonguelike organ with rows of teeth—to obtain food. The radula works like a file to scrape and tear food materials. That's why snails are helpful to have in an aquarium—they scrape the algae off the walls and keep the tank clean.

☑ Reading Check *How do gastropods get food?*

Slugs and many snails are adapted to life on land. They move by rhythmic contractions of the muscular foot. Glands in the foot secrete a layer of mucus on which they slide. Slugs and snails are most active at night or on cloudy days when they can avoid the hot Sun. Slugs do not have shells but are protected by a layer of mucus instead, so they must live in moist places. Slugs and land snails damage plants as they eat leaves and stems.

Use Science Words

Word Meaning Have students look up the words *mantle* and *radula* in a dictionary. Mantle comes from a Latin word meaning "cloak" and radula is Latin for "scraper." How is a mantle like a cloak? It covers and helps provide protection for the mollusk's body. How does having a scraper help a mollusk? It allows the mollusk to scrape food. L2 IS **Linguistic**

Caption Answer
Figure 2 gastropods

Use an Analogy

File Analogy Show students a steel file, and let them touch its surface. Use the file on a piece of scrap wood. Explain that a radula works in much the same way as the file as it scrapes algae from surfaces. L2

☑ Reading Check

Answer They use a tonguelike organ called a radula with rows of teeth for scraping and tearing algae from rocks.

Activity

Snail Observations Collect snails from a local pond or purchase them from a pet shop. Have students observe how the snails move. Have them examine the snails' eyes with a hand lens. Feed lettuce to the snails so students can observe their feeding method with a hand lens. L1 ELL IS **Visual-Spatial**

Differentiated Instruction

Challenge Why is an open circulatory system able to meet the needs of a gastropod? Gastropods move slowly and use energy at a low rate, so their needs for food and gas exchange are low. L3 IS **Logical-Mathematical**

English-Language Learners Make flashcards for this section, with English vocabulary words and definitions on one side, and the equivalent in the appropriate language of your student on the other side. You can pair your students up, or have your students work with the flashcards on their own. L2

Figure 3 Scallops force water between their valves to move away from sea stars and other predators. They can move up to 1 m with each muscular contraction.

Bivalves Mollusks that have a hinged, two-part shell joined by strong muscles are called bivalves. Clams, oysters, and scallops are bivalve mollusks and are a familiar source of seafood. These animals pull their shells closed by contracting powerful muscles near the hinge. To open their shells, they relax these muscles.

Bivalves are well adapted for living in water. For protection, clams burrow deep into the sand by contracting and relaxing their muscular foot. Mussels and oysters attach themselves with a strong thread or cement to a solid surface. This keeps waves and currents from washing them away. Scallops, shown in **Figure 3,** escape predators by rapidly opening and closing their shells. As water is forced out, the scallop moves rapidly in the opposite direction.

Cephalopods The most specialized and complex mollusks are the cephalopods (SE fuh luh pawdz). Squid, octopuses, cuttlefish, and chambered nautiluses belong to this group. The word *cephalopod* means "head-footed" and describes the body structure of these invertebrates. Cephalopods, like the cuttlefish in **Figure 4,** have a large, well-developed head. Their foot is divided into many tentacles with strong suction cups or hooks for capturing prey. All cephalopods are predators. They feed on fish, crustaceans, worms, and other mollusks.

Squid and octopuses have a well-developed nervous system and large eyes similar to human eyes. Unlike other mollusks, cephalopods have closed circulatory systems. In a **closed circulatory system,** blood containing food and oxygen moves through the body in a series of closed vessels, just as your blood moves through your blood vessels.

✔ Reading Check
What makes a cephalopod different from other mollusks?

Figure 4 Most cephalopods, like this cuttlefish, have an internal shell.
Infer *why an internal shell would be a helpful adaptation.*

LAB DEMONSTRATION

Purpose to observe mollusk traits

Materials squid, plastic tray, forceps, magnifying lens, goggles

Procedure As you demonstrate have students draw and label the body, head, eyes, tentacles, mouth, fins, beak, mantle and suction cups. Find the hard point at one end of the squid's fin (pen) and use forceps to pull it out.

Preparation Purchase squid from the supermarket. Wash the squid thoroughly before the demonstration.

Expected Outcome Students should observe mollusk traits in a squid.

Assessment

What are the suction cups used for? to capture and hold prey What mollusk traits were observed? soft body, head with eyes, foot divided into tentacles, internal shell (pen), beak used to tear food L2

Cephalopod Propulsion All cephalopods live in oceans and are adapted for swimming. Squid and other cephalopods have a water-filled cavity between an outer muscular covering and its internal organs. When the cephalopod tightens its muscular covering, water is forced out through an opening near the head, as shown in **Figure 5.** The jet of water propels the cephalopod backwards, and it moves away quickly. According to Newton's third law of motion, when one object exerts a force on a second object, the second object exerts a force on the first that is equal and opposite in direction. The movement of cephalopods is an example of this law. Muscles exert force on water under the mantle. Water being forced out exerts a force that results in movement backwards.

A squid can propel itself at speeds of more than 6 m/s using this jet propulsion and can briefly outdistance all but whales, dolphins, and the fastest fish. A squid even can jump out of the water and reach heights of almost 5 m above the ocean's surface. It then can travel through the air as far as 15 m. However, squid can maintain their top speed for just a few pulses. Octopuses also can swim by jet propulsion, but they usually use their tentacles to creep more slowly over the ocean floor.

Origin of Mollusks Some species of mollusks, such as the chambered nautilus, have changed little from their ancestors. Mollusk fossils date back more than 500 million years. Many species of mollusks became extinct about 65 million years ago. Today's mollusks are descendants of ancient mollusks.

Mollusk Extinction By about 65 million years ago, many mollusks had become extinct. What were the major physical events of the time that could have contributed to changing the environment? Write your answers in your Science Journal.

Visual Learning

Figure 5 Using this image and the text, have students write a paragraph describing how jet propulsion works, and how it can help a cephalopod escape from predators. L2 IS **Visual-Spatial and Linguistic** P

Discussion

Squid Adaptation How is a squid adapted for being a predator? It has tentacles with strong suckers for capturing prey, a well-developed nervous system, large eyes, and jet propulsion for rapid movement.

IDENTIFYING **Misconceptions**

Squid Size Students may have heard stories of giant squids battling with sperm whales, which may lead them to believe that all squids are giants. The squid most commonly sold in seafood markets, *Loligo*, is only about 30 cm (1 foot) long, and many other species are less than half that size.

Mollusk Extinction Sea levels were very low and the climate was dry.

Research What other animals were alive 245 million years ago? Research to find out the major characteristics of Earth at this time, and what animals are similar to the animals we have on Earth now.

Curriculum Connection

Literature Read Oliver Wendell Holmes' poem "The Chambered Nautilus," which was first published in 1858. The "ship of pearl" described in the poem is found in the Indian Ocean and the South Pacific Ocean. Have students draw the shell and write a report in their Science Journals about how the shell forms. L2 IS **Visual-Spatial and Linguistic**

Cultural Diversity

Contamination of Food Sources Mollusks are a food source the world over. Oysters, clams, squid, scallops, mussels, and octopuses are eaten by millions of people. In some ocean and bay fishing areas, pollution is causing problems for mollusks and the humans that eat them. Have students research the probable cultural and economic effects of pollution on mollusks and on the people who harvest them. L3

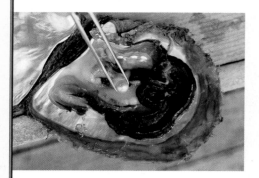

Figure 6 A pearl starts as an irritant—a grain of sand or a parasite—to an oyster. The oyster coats the irritant with a material that forms smooth, hard layers. It can take years for a pearl to form. Culturing pearls is a commercial industry in some countries.

Value of Mollusks

Mollusks have many uses. They are food for fish, sea stars, birds, and humans. Many people make their living raising or collecting mollusks to sell for food. Other invertebrates, such as hermit crabs, use empty mollusk shells as shelter. Many mollusk shells are used for jewelry and decoration. Pearls are produced by several species of mollusks, but most are made by mollusks called pearl oysters, shown in **Figure 6.** Mollusk shells also provide information about the conditions in an ecosystem, including the source and distribution of water pollutants. The internal shell of a cuttlefish is the cuttlebone, which is used in birdcages to provide birds with calcium. Squid and octopuses are able to learn tasks, so scientists are studying their nervous systems to understand how learning takes place and how memory works.

Even though mollusks are beneficial in many ways, they also can cause problems for humans. Land slugs and snails damage plants. Certain species of snails are hosts of parasites that infect humans. Shipworms, a type of bivalve, make holes in submerged wood of docks and boats, causing millions of dollars in damage each year. Because clams, oysters, and other mollusks are filter feeders, bacteria, viruses, and toxic protists from the water can become trapped in the animals. Eating these infected mollusks can result in sickness or even death.

 section 1 review

Summary

Mollusks
- The body plans of mollusks include a mantle, visceral mass, head, and foot.

Classification of Mollusks
- Gastropods typically have one shell, a foot, and eat using a radula.
- Bivalves have a hinged two-part shell, a muscular foot, and eat by filtering their food from the water.
- Cephalopods have a head, a foot which has been modified into tentacles, and a well-developed nervous system.

Value of Mollusks
- Mollusks are food for many animals, have commercial uses, and are used for research.

Self Check

1. **Explain** how a squid and other cephalopods can move so rapidly.
2. **Identify** some positive and negative ways that mollusks affect humans.
3. **Think Critically** Why is it unlikely that you would find garden slugs or land snails in a desert?

Applying Skills

4. **Interpret Scientific Illustrations** Observe the images of gastropods and bivalves in this section, and infer how bivalves are not adapted to life on land, but gastropods are.
5. **Use a Computer** Make a data table that compares and contrasts the following for gastropods, bivalves, and cephalopods: *methods for obtaining food, movement, circulation,* and *habitat.*

364 CHAPTER 13

 Science Online life.msscience.com/self_check_quiz

section 1 review

1. Jet propulsion; water is ejected through the funnel or siphon in one direction, moving the animal in the opposite direction.
2. Mollusks are used for food, jewelry, and research. They damage boats and docks. Eating those that contain disease-causing organisms can cause illness.
3. The desert is too dry. Slugs and snails require a moist environment.
4. Bivalves filter food from the water. They move slowly or remain attached to one place. Gastropods use their radula and teeth to eat plants and algae.
5. Check data tables for accuracy.

Segmented Worms

Segmented Worm Characteristics

The worms you see crawling across sidewalks after a rain and those used for fishing are called annelids (A nuh ludz). The word *annelid* means "little rings" and describes the bodies of these worms. They have tube-shaped bodies that are divided into many segments.

Have you ever watched a robin try to pull an earthworm out of the ground or tried it yourself? Why don't they slip out of the soil easily? On the outside of each body segment are bristlelike structures called **setae** (SEE tee). Segmented worms use their setae to hold on to the soil and to move. Segmented worms also have bilateral symmetry, a body cavity that holds the organs, and two body openings—a mouth and an anus. Annelids can be found in freshwater, salt water, and moist soil. Earthworms, like the one in **Figure 7,** marine worms, and leeches are examples of annelids.

Reading Check *What is the function of setae?*

Earthworm Body Systems

The most well-known annelids are earthworms. They have a definite anterior, or front end, and a posterior, or back end. Earthworms have more than 100 body segments. The segments can be seen on the outside and the inside of the body cavity. Each body segment, except for the first and last segments, has four pairs of setae. Earthworms move by using their setae and two sets of muscles in the body wall. One set of muscles runs the length of the body, and the other set circles the body. When an earthworm contracts its long muscles, it causes some of the segments to bunch up and the setae to stick out. This anchors the worm to the soil. When the circular muscles contract, the setae are pulled in and the worm can move forward.

Figure 7 One species of earthworm that lives in Australia can grow to be 3.3 m long.

as you read

What You'll Learn
- **Identify** the characteristics of segmented worms.
- **Describe** the structures of an earthworm and how it takes in and digests food.
- **Explain** the importance of segmented worms.

Why It's Important
Earthworms condition and aerate the soil, which helps increase crop yields.

⊙ Review Vocabulary
aerate: to supply with air

New Vocabulary
- setae
- crop
- gizzard

---

1 Motivate

INTERACTIVE CHALKBOARD
PowerPoint® Presentations

Bellringer

Section Focus Transparencies also are available on the Interactive Chalkboard CD-ROM.
L2 ELL

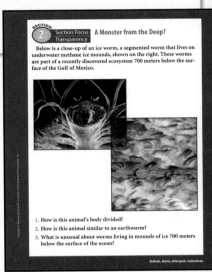

Tie to Prior Knowledge

Earthworm Observations Most students have seen earthworms. Discuss their observations about worms, where worms live, and what they eat. L2

Reading Check

Answer to hold onto soil and move

Section 2 Resource Manager

Chapter FAST FILE Resources
Transparency Activity, pp. 47, 51–52
Directed Reading for Content Mastery, p. 18
Lab Activity, pp. 9–12
Enrichment, p. 31
Reinforcement, p. 27

Performance Assessment in the Science Classroom, p. 55

Discussion

Annelids Display specimens (or pictures on a bulletin board) of annelids (clam worms, tube worms, fan worms, leeches, *Tubifex* worms, redworms and earthworms). Have students discuss how they are similar.

Activity

Sensory Maze Have several students set up a maze in the classroom, using desks and chairs. Blindfold volunteers who have not seen the maze, and ask them to find their way through it. Use this activity to help students understand that earthworms find food and escape predators without being able to see. L2 **Kinesthetic**

Quick Demo

Earthworm Anatomy

Materials preserved earthworm, dissecting tray, dissecting knife, dissecting probe, stereomicroscope (optional)

Estimated Time 20 minutes

Procedure Dissect a preserved earthworm, and have students examine its digestive, circulatory, excretory, reproductive, and nervous systems. L2 **Visual-Spatial**

Fun Fact

Even though earthworms do not have eyes, they have light receptors in the head that sense the presence of light.

Figure 8 Earthworm castings—also called vermicompost—are used as an organic fertilizer in gardens.
Infer *why earthworms are healthy to have in a garden or compost pile.*

Digestion and Excretion As an earthworm burrows through the soil, it takes soil into its mouth. Earthworms get energy from the bits of leaves and other organic matter found in the soil. The soil ingested by an earthworm moves to the **crop,** which is a sac used for storage. Behind the crop is a muscular structure called the **gizzard,** which grinds the soil and the bits of organic matter. This ground material passes to the intestine, where the organic matter is broken down and the nutrients are absorbed by the blood. Wastes leave the worm through the anus. When earthworms take in soil, they provide spaces for air and water to flow through it and mix the soil. Their wastes pile up at the openings to their burrows. These piles are called castings. Castings, like those in **Figure 8,** help fertilize the soil.

Circulation and Respiration Earthworms have a closed circulatory system, as shown in **Figure 9.** Two blood vessels along the top of the body and one along the bottom of the body meet in the front end of the earthworm. There, they connect to heartlike structures called aortic arches, which pump blood through the body. Smaller vessels go into each body segment.

Earthworms don't have gills or lungs. Oxygen and carbon dioxide are exchanged through their skin, which is covered with a thin film of watery mucus. It's important never to touch earthworms with dry hands or remove their thin mucous layer, because they could suffocate. But as you can tell after a rainstorm, earthworms don't survive in puddles of water either.

Figure 9 An earthworm's circulatory system includes five aortic arches that pump blood throughout its body.

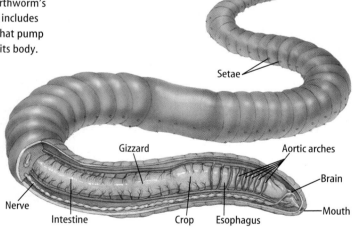

Setae

Gizzard

Aortic arches

Brain

Nerve

Intestine

Crop

Esophagus

Mouth

Differentiated Instruction

Challenge Have students research the major complex invertebrates in the chapter. Have them make identification cards of the ones in which they are most interested. On one side of the card, they can draw a picture of the invertebrate and on the other, give the name and major characteristics. A game can be played by keeping track of the number of organisms students can identify. L3

Teacher FYI

Soil Aeration Earthworm aeration of the soil is so beneficial that their presence in hundreds or thousands per hectare is a characteristic of a productive farm. *Lumbricus terrestris* ingests its own weight in soil and decaying matter every day. Earthworms survive in thin films of water in slightly moist soil, but if the soil becomes flooded, the worms can drown.

Nerve Response and Reproduction Earthworms have a small brain in their front segment. Nerves in each segment join to form a main nerve cord that connects to the brain. Earthworms respond to light, temperature, and moisture.

Earthworms are hermaphrodites (hur MA fruh dites)—meaning they produce sperm and eggs in the same body. Even though each worm has male and female reproductive structures, an individual worm can't fertilize its own eggs. Instead, it has to receive sperm from another earthworm in order to reproduce.

Marine Worms

More than 8,000 species of marine worms, or polychaetes, (PAH lee keets) exist, which is more than any other kind of annelid. Marine worms float, burrow, build structures, or walk along the ocean floor. Some polychaetes even produce their own light. Others, like the ice worms in **Figure 10,** are able to live 540 m deep. Polychaetes, like earthworms, have segments with setae. However, the setae occur in bundles on these worms. The word polychaete means "many bristles."

Sessile, bottom-dwelling polychaetes, such as the Christmas tree worms shown in **Figure 11,** have specialized tentacles that are used for exchanging oxygen and carbon dioxide and gathering food. Some marine worms build tubes around their bodies. When these worms are startled, they retreat into their tubes. Free-swimming polychaetes, such as the bristleworm shown in **Figure 11,** have a head with eyes; a tail; and parapodia (per uh POH dee uh). Parapodia are paired, fleshy outgrowths on each segment, which aid in feeding and locomotion.

Figure 10 Ice worms, a type of marine polychaete, were discovered first in 1997 living 540 m deep in the Gulf of Mexico.

Figure 11 These Christmas tree worms filter microorganisms from the water to eat. This bristleworm swims backwards and forwards, so it has eyes at both ends of its body.

Christmas tree worms

Bristleworm

SECTION 2 Segmented Worms **367**

Teacher FYI

Polychaetes Traits Polychaetes live in cracks and crevices in coral reefs, sand, mud, piles of rock, and in open water. Some build their own tube structures and burrows. Many are free-moving. Some polychaetes are brightly colored, iridescent, or even luminescent.

Visual Learning

Figure 11 Have students compare and contrast the marine worms found in this figure. L1
IS **Visual-Spatial**

Discussion

Wormy Words Have students discuss the meaning of "wormy" slang and colloquial expressions in the English language. Examples are: "the worm in the apple" (one bad thing in an otherwise good situation); "worm your way out of something" (get out of unpleasant situations using devious methods); describing a person as a "leech" (one who clings to another without contributing). L2

IDENTIFYING Misconceptions

Insects not Worms Make sure students understand that grubs and caterpillars are not annelids. They are insects in larval stages.

Differentiated Instruction

Challenge Have students research the economic importance of earthworms and how they are raised commercially. L3

Learning Disabled Have students make a picture dictionary illustrating the meaning of key words used in each section of this chapter. Have them begin by looking up the prefixes *exo-* and *endo-* in the dictionary. L2 IS **Visual-Spatial**

Science Online

Topic: Beneficial Leeches
Visit life.msscience.com for Web links to information about the uses of chemicals from leech saliva.

Activity Describe a possible use for leech saliva, and design a 30-second commercial on how you might sell it.

Figure 12 Medical leeches are used sometimes to prevent blood from clotting or accumulating in damaged skin.
Explain *how a leech can prevent blood clots.*

Leeches

A favorite topic for scary movies is leeches. If you've ever had to remove a leech from your body after swimming in a freshwater pond, lake, or river, you know it isn't fun. Leeches are segmented worms, but their bodies are not as round or as long as earthworms are, and they don't have setae. They feed on the blood of other animals. A sucker at each end of a leech's body is used to attach itself to an animal. If a leech attaches to you, you probably won't feel it. Leeches produce many chemicals, including an anesthetic (a nus THEH tihk) that numbs the wound so you don't feel its bite. After the leech has attached itself, it cuts into the animal and sucks out two to ten times its own weight in blood. Even though leeches prefer to eat blood, they can survive by eating aquatic insects and other organisms instead.

✔ **Reading Check** *Why is producing an anesthetic an advantage to a leech?*

Leeches and Medicine

Sometimes, leeches are used after surgery to keep blood flowing to the repaired area, as shown in **Figure 12.** For example, the tiny blood vessels in the ear quickly can become blocked with blood clots after surgery. To keep blood flowing in such places, physicians might attach leeches to the surgical site. As the leeches feed on the blood, chemicals in their saliva prevent the blood from coagulating. Besides the anti-clotting chemical, leech saliva also contains a chemical that dilates blood vessels, which improves the blood flow and allows the wound to heal more quickly. These chemicals are being studied to treat patients with heart or circulatory diseases, strokes, arthritis, or glaucoma.

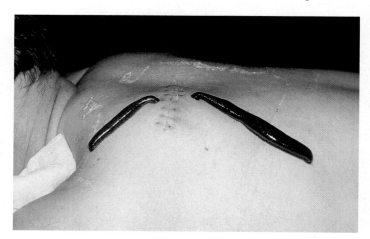

Science Journal

Annelids Have students research and report on annelids other than earthworms and leeches. Some examples are feather worms, fanworms, peacock worms, and giant tube worms that live in deep-sea vents. Have them include the structural differences among the worms in their reports. [L2]
LS Linguistic

Differentiated Instruction

Challenge Have students research and report on *Hirudo medicinalis.* This leech produces the anticoagulant hirudin. *Hirudo medicinalis,* the medicinal leech, feeds primarily on the blood of mammals, but it also sucks blood from amphibians, reptiles, and fish. It has three jaws with sharp teeth that make a Y-shaped incision in the skin of the host. After it feeds, the leech detaches from its host and may not feed again for as long as 18 months. [L3]

Value of Segmented Worms

Different kinds of segmented worms are helpful to other animals in a variety of ways. Earthworms help aerate the soil by constantly burrowing through it. By grinding and partially digesting the large amount of plant material in soil, earthworms speed up the return of nitrogen and other nutrients to the soil for use by plants.

Researchers are developing drugs based on the chemicals that come from leeches because leech saliva prevents blood clots. Marine worms and their larvae are food for many fish, invertebrates, and mammals.

Origin of Segmented Worms

Some scientists hypothesize that segmented worms evolved in the sea. The fossil record for segmented worms is limited because of their soft bodies. The tubes of marine worms are the most common fossils of the segmented worms. Some of these fossils date back about 620 million years.

Similarities between mollusks and segmented worms suggest that they could have a common ancestor. These groups were the first animals to have a body cavity with space for body organs to develop and function. Mollusks and segmented worms have a one-way digestive system with a separate mouth and anus. Their larvae, shown in **Figure 13,** are similar and are the best evidence that they have a common ancestor.

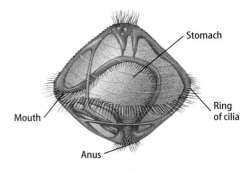

Mollusk larva

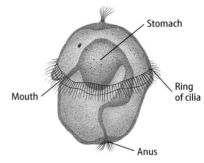

Annelid larva

Figure 13 Some mollusk larvae have many structures that are similar to those of some annelid larvae.

Visual Learning

Figure 13 Have students compare the structures of the larvae. L2

3 Assess

DAILY INTERVENTION

Check for Understanding
Kinesthetic Using modeling clay or dough, have students construct a new species of annelid. Their species must possess all of the characteristics of annelids including segments, bilateral symmetry, a body cavity that holds organs, and two digestive openings. Setae are optional. L2

Reteach
Mollusk and Segmented Worms Have students make a chart that compares the structures, environment, and ways of life (free-living or parasitic) of mollusks and segmented worms L2 P

✓ Assessment

Content Have students work in groups to list earthworm body systems, and external features. Use **Performance Assessment in the Science Classroom,** p. 169. L2

section 2 review

Summary

Segmented Worm Characteristics

- Segmented worms have tube-shaped bodies divided into many segments, bilateral symmetry, a body cavity with organs, and two body openings.
- Earthworms have a definite anterior and posterior end, a closed circulatory system, a small brain, and eat organic matter in the soil. Most segments have four pairs of setae.
- Polychaetes are marine worms with many setae occurring in bundles.
- Leeches are segmented worms that feed on the blood of other animals. They have no setae, but a sucker at each end of the body.

Self Check

1. **Define** setae and state their function.
2. **Describe** how an earthworm takes in and digests its food.
3. **Compare and contrast** how earthworms and marine worms exchange oxygen and carbon dioxide.
4. **Think Critically** What advantages do marine worms with tubes have over free-swimming polychaetes?

Applying Math

5. **Use Proportions** Suppose you find six earthworms in 10 cm^3 of soil. Based on this sample, calculate the number of earthworms you would find in 10 m^3 of soil.

 Scienceonline life.msscience.com/self_check_quiz

SECTION 2 Segmented Worms **369**

section 2 review

1. Setae are bristlelike structures on the outside of a segmented worm's body. They are used to hold on to the soil and to move.
2. It takes in soil, which moves through the digestive system. Food (plant and animal material in the soil) is removed from the soil and digested. Waste material leaves through the anus.
3. Earthworms obtain oxygen through their moist skin. Marine worms have specialized tentacles for obtaining oxygen.
4. Tube worms have a protective covering.
5. 6,000 earthworms

as you read

What You'll Learn
- **Determine** the characteristics that are used to classify arthropods.
- **Explain** how the structure of the exoskeleton relates to its function.
- **Distinguish** between complete and incomplete metamorphosis.

Why It's Important
Arthropods, such as those that carry diseases and eat crops, affect your life every day.

⊙ Review Vocabulary
venom: toxic fluid injected by an animal

New Vocabulary
- appendage
- exoskeleton
- molting
- spiracle
- metamorphosis

Characteristics of Arthropods

There are more than a million different species of arthropods, (AR thruh pahdz) making them the largest group of animals. The word *arthropoda* means "jointed foot." The jointed **appendages** of arthropods can include legs, antennae, claws, and pincers. Arthropod appendages are adapted for moving about, capturing prey, feeding, mating, and sensing their environment. Arthropods also have bilateral symmetry, segmented bodies, an exoskeleton, a body cavity, a digestive system with two openings, and a nervous system. Most arthropod species have separate sexes and reproduce sexually. Arthropods are adapted to living in almost every environment. They vary in size from microscopic dust mites to the large, Japanese spider crab, shown in **Figure 14.**

Segmented Bodies The bodies of arthropods are divided into segments similar to those of segmented worms. Some arthropods have many segments, but others have segments that are fused together to form body regions, such as those of insects, spiders, and crabs.

Exoskeletons All arthropods have a hard, outer covering called an **exoskeleton.** It covers, supports, and protects the internal body and provides places for muscles to attach. In many land-dwelling arthropods, such as insects, the exoskeleton has a waxy layer that reduces water loss from the animal.

An exoskeleton cannot grow as the animal grows. From time to time, the exoskeleton is shed and replaced by a new one in a process called **molting.** While the animals are molting, they are not well protected from predators because the new exoskeleton is soft. Before the new exoskeleton hardens, the animal swallows air or water to increase its exoskeleton's size. This way the new exoskeleton allows room for growth.

Figure 14 The Japanese spider crab has legs that can span more than 3 m.

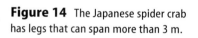

Insects

More species of insects exist than all other animal groups combined. More than 700,000 species of insects have been classified, and scientists identify more each year. Insects have three body regions—a head, a thorax, and an abdomen, as shown in **Figure 15.** However, it is almost impossible on some insects to see where one region stops and the next one begins.

Head An insect's head has a pair of antennae, eyes, and a mouth. The antennae are used for touch and smell. The eyes are simple or compound. Simple eyes detect light and darkness. Compound eyes, like those in **Figure 16,** contain many lenses and can detect colors and movement. The mouthparts of insects vary, depending on what the insect eats.

Thorax Three pairs of legs and one or two pairs of wings, if present, are attached to the thorax. Some insects, such as silverfish and fleas, don't have wings, and other insects have wings only for part of their lives. Insects are the only invertebrate animals that can fly. Flying allows insects to find places to live, food sources, and mates. Flight also helps them escape from their predators.

☑ Reading Check *How does flight benefit insects?*

Abdomen The abdomen has neither wings nor legs but it is where the reproductive structures are found. Females lay thousands of eggs, but only a fraction of the eggs develop into adults. Think about how overproduction of eggs might ensure that each insect species will continue.

Insects have an open circulatory system that carries digested food to cells and removes wastes. However, insect blood does not carry oxygen because it does not have hemoglobin. Instead, insects have openings called **spiracles** (SPIHR ih kulz) on the abdomen and thorax through which air enters and waste gases leave the insect's body.

Figure 15 One of the largest types of ants is the carpenter ant. Like all insects, it has a head, thorax, and abdomen.

Figure 16 Each compound eye is made up of small lenses that fit together. Each lens sees a part of the picture to make up the whole scene. Insects can't focus their eyes. Their eyes are always open and can detect movements.

Stained LM Magnification: 400×

SECTION 3 Arthropods **371**

Science Journal

Insect Societies Some insects, including ants, bees, termites, and wasps, live in highly organized societies. Each member has a specific job necessary for the survival of the colony. Have students choose a social insect and describe in their Science Journals the role of each member of the society. L2 **LS** **Linguistic**

Mini LAB

Observing Metamorphosis

Procedure 🔬 🧤

1. Place a 2-cm piece of ripe **banana** in a **jar** and leave it open.
2. Check the jar every day for two weeks. When you see fruit flies, cover the mouth of the jar with **cheesecloth.**
3. Identify, describe, and draw all the stages of metamorphosis that you observe.

Analysis

1. What type of metamorphosis do fruit flies undergo?
2. In which stages are the flies the most active?

From Egg to Adult Many insects go through changes in body form as they grow. This series of changes is called **metamorphosis** (me tuh MOR fuh sihs). Grasshoppers, silverfish, lice, and crickets undergo incomplete metamorphosis, shown in **Figure 17.** The stages of incomplete metamorphosis are egg, nymph, and adult. The nymph form molts several times before becoming an adult. Many insects—butterflies, beetles, ants, bees, moths, and flies—undergo complete metamorphosis, also shown in **Figure 17.** The stages of complete metamorphosis are egg, larva, pupa, and adult. Caterpillar is the common name for the larva of a moth or butterfly. Other insect larvae are called grubs, maggots, or mealworms. Only larval forms molt.

✔ **Reading Check** *When do grasshoppers molt?*

Figure 17 The two types of metamorphosis are shown here.

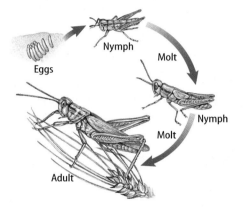

In incomplete metamorphosis, nymphs are smaller versions of their parents.

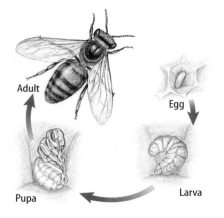

Many insects go through complete metamorphosis.

Visual Learning

Figure 17 Have students make a table in which they compare and contrast the two types of metamorphoses shown in this figure. L2 IS **Visual-Spatial**

Differentiated Instruction

Visually Impaired Purchase a variety of scientifically accurate, arthropod models. As a visually impaired student touches and describes each feature of a model, have a sighted student name the feature and record the description. Together, they should devise a classification system for the arthropod models. L2 COOP LEARN IS **Kinesthetic, Interpersonal**

Figure 18 Feeding adaptations of insects include different mouthparts.

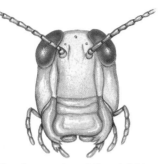

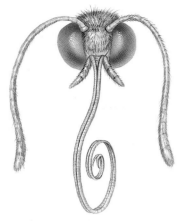

Grasshoppers have left and right mouthparts called mandibles that enable them to chew through tough plant tissues.

Butterflies and other nectar eaters have a long siphon that enables them to drink nectar from flowers.

Mosquitoes have mouths that are adapted for piercing skin and sucking blood.

Obtaining Food Insects feed on plants, the blood of animals, nectar, decaying materials, wood in houses, and clothes. Mouthparts of insects, such as those in **Figure 18,** are as diverse as the insects themselves. Grasshoppers and ants have large mandibles (MAN duh bulz) for chewing plant tissue. Butterflies and honeybees are equipped with siphons for lapping up nectar in flowers. Aphids and cicadas pierce plant tissues and suck out plant fluids. Praying mantises eat other animals. External parasites, such as mosquitoes, fleas, and lice, drink the blood and body fluids of other animals. Silverfish eat things that contain starch and some moth larvae eat wool clothing.

Insect Success Because of their tough, flexible, waterproof exoskeletons; their ability to fly; rapid reproductive cycles; and small sizes, insects are extremely successful. Most insects have short life spans, so genetic traits can change more quickly in insect populations than in organisms that take longer to reproduce. Because insects generally are small, they can live in a wide range of environments and avoid their enemies. Many species of insects can live in the same area and not compete with one another for food, because many are so specialized in what they eat.

Protective coloration, or camouflage, allows insects to blend in with their surroundings. Many moths resting on trees look like tree bark or bird droppings. Walking sticks and some caterpillars resemble twigs. When a leaf butterfly folds its wings it looks like a dead leaf.

Arachnids

Spiders, scorpions, mites, and ticks are examples of arachnids (uh RAK nudz). They have two body regions—a head-chest region called the cephalothorax (se fuh luh THOR aks) and an abdomen. Arachnids have four pairs of legs but no antennae. Many arachnids are adapted to kill prey with venom glands, stingers, or fangs. Others are parasites.

Scorpions Arachnids that have a sharp, venom-filled stinger at the end of their abdomen are called scorpions. The venom from the stinger paralyzes the prey. Unlike other arachnids, scorpions have a pair of well-developed appendages—pincers—with which they grab their prey. The sting of a scorpion is painful and can be fatal to humans.

Applying Math — Use Percentages

SILK ELASTICITY A strand of spider's silk can be stretched from 65 cm to 85 cm before it loses its elasticity—the ability to snap back to its original length. Calculate the percent of elasticity of spider's silk.

Solution

1. *This is what you know:*
   - original length of silk strand = 65 cm
   - stretched length of silk strand = 85 cm

2. *This is what you need to find out:*

   percent of elasticity

3. *This is the procedure you need to use:*
   - Find the difference between the stretched and original length. 85 cm − 65 cm = 20 cm
   - $\dfrac{\text{difference in length}}{\text{original length}} \times 100 = \%$ of elasticity
   - $\dfrac{20 \text{ cm}}{65 \text{ cm}} \times 100 = 30.7 \%$ of elasticity

4. *Check your answer:* Multiply 30.7% by 65 cm and you should get 20 cm.

Practice Problems

1. A 40-cm strand of nylon can be stretched to a length of 46.5 cm before losing its elasticity. Calculate the percent of elasticity for nylon and compare it to that of spider's silk.

2. Knowing the elasticity of spider's silk, what was the original length of a silk strand when the difference between the two strands is 44 cm?

For more practice, visit life.msscience.com/ math_practice

374 CHAPTER 13 Mollusks, Worms, Arthropods, Echinoderms

Science Journal

Careers Students may be interested in careers related to arthropods. Suggest that they research different types of careers in the field of entomology and record in their Science Journals what skills and education are needed and what the jobs entail. L2 IS **Linguistic**

Cultural Diversity

Origin of Silk Silk moth cocoons are one continuous strand of silk. According to Chinese legends, silk cloth originated around 3000 B.C. It is said that a cocoon fell into an empress' tea. The tea dissolved the substance that glued the cocoon together, revealing the long silk strand. Several strands were woven into a thread and, eventually, silk fabric was woven.

Spiders Because spiders can't chew their food, they release enzymes into their prey that help digest it. The spider then sucks the predigested liquid into its mouth.

Oxygen and carbon dioxide are exchanged in book lungs, illustrated in **Figure 19.** Openings on the abdomen allow these gases to move into and out of the book lungs.

Mites and Ticks Most mites are animal or plant parasites. However, some are not parasites, like the mites that live in the follicles of human eyelashes. Most mites are so small that they look like tiny specs to the unaided eye. All ticks are animal parasites. Ticks attach to their host's skin and remove blood from their hosts through specialized mouthparts. Ticks often carry bacteria and viruses that cause disease in humans and other animals. Diseases carried by ticks include Lyme disease and Rocky Mountain spotted fever.

Centipedes and Millipedes

Two groups of arthropods—centipedes and millipedes—have long bodies with many segments and many legs, antennae, and simple eyes. They can be found in damp environments, including in woodpiles, under vegetation, and in basements. Centipedes and millipedes reproduce sexually. They make nests for their eggs and stay with them until the eggs hatch.

Compare the centipede and millipede in **Figure 20.** How many pairs of legs does the centipede have per segment? How many pairs of legs does the millipede have per segment? Centipedes hunt for their prey, which includes snails, slugs, and worms. They have a pair of venomous claws that they use to inject venom into their prey. Their pinches are painful to humans but usually aren't fatal. Millipedes feed on plants and decaying material and often are found under the damp plant material.

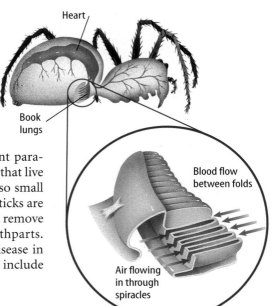

Heart

Book lungs

Blood flow between folds

Air flowing in through spiracles

Figure 19 Air circulates between the moist folds of the book lungs bringing oxygen to the blood.

Figure 20 Centipedes are predators—they capture and eat other animals. Millipedes eat plants or decaying plant material.

Centipede

Millipede

SECTION 3 Arthropods **375**

NATIONAL GEOGRAPHIC

Visualizing Arthropod Diversity

Have students examine the pictures and read the captions. Then ask the following questions.

What different types of locomotion are used by arthropods? Students should note that arthropods walk, fly and swim. Barnacles usually do not move from place to place under their own power.

What characteristic of a Monarch butterfly allows it to survive the changing weather in its environment? A monarch's wings allow it to migrate to a warmer climate when temperatures become too cold.

Activity

Model Arthropods Have students work in pairs to make a model of one of the arthropods pictured. Students should research the characteristics of the arthropod they have chosen to model, and incorporate their findings into their model. Have students present their models to the class. L2

Activity

Venn Diagram Have students make a Venn diagram that compares the characteristics of three of the pictured arthropods. Have students do further research to increase the number of characteristics included in their diagram. L2

NATIONAL GEOGRAPHIC VISUALIZING ARTHROPOD DIVERSITY

Figure 21

Some 600 million years ago, the first arthropods lived in Earth's ancient seas. Today, they inhabit nearly every environment on Earth. Arthropods are the most abundant and diverse group of animals on Earth. They range in size from nearly microscopic mites to spindly, giant Japanese spider crabs with legs spanning more than 3 m.

▲ **LOBSTER** Like crabs, lobsters are crustaceans that belong to the group called Decapoda, which means "ten legs." It's the lobster's tail, however, that interests most seafood lovers.

◄ **GRASS SPIDER** Grass spiders spin fine, nearly invisible webs just above the ground.

◄ **GOOSENECK BARNACLE** Gooseneck barnacles typically live attached to objects that float in the ocean. They use their long, feathery setae to strain tiny bits of food from the water.

▼ **MONARCH BUTTERFLY** Monarchs are a common sight in much of the United States during the summer. In fall, they migrate south to warmer climates.

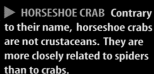

◄ **HISSING COCKROACH** Most cockroaches are considered to be pests by humans, but hissing cockroaches, such as this one, are sometimes kept as pets.

▶ **HORSESHOE CRAB** Contrary to their name, horseshoe crabs are not crustaceans. They are more closely related to spiders than to crabs.

▶ **CENTIPEDE** One pair of legs per segment distinguishes a centipede from a millipede, which has two pairs of legs per body segment.

376

Active Reading

Jigsaw Place students in five cooperative groups. Each group is to be responsible for studying and summarizing one of the five types of arthropods discussed in this section—insects, arachnids, centipedes, millipedes, and crustaceans. Once finished, each group is to direct the discussion on the type of arthropod it was responsible for learning about. Instruct groups to include drawings and several examples of their type of arthropod. L2 COOP LEARN **IS** Interpersonal

Crustaceans

Crabs, crayfish, shrimp, barnacles, pill bugs, and water fleas are crustaceans. Crustaceans and other arthropods are shown in **Figure 21.** Crustaceans have one or two pairs of antennae and mandibles, which are used for crushing food. Most crustaceans live in water, but some, like the pill bugs shown in **Figure 22,** live in moist environments on land. Pill bugs are common in gardens and around house foundations. They are harmless to humans.

Crustaceans, like the blue crab shown in **Figure 22,** have five pairs of legs. The first pair of legs are claws that catch and hold food. The other four pairs are walking legs. They also have five pairs of appendages on the abdomen called swimmerets. They help the crustacean move and are used in reproduction. In addition, the swimmerets force water over the feathery gills where the oxygen and carbon dioxide are exchanged. If a crustacean loses an appendage, it will grow back, or regenerate.

Value of Arthropods

Arthropods play several roles in the environment. They are a source of food for many animals, including humans. Some humans consider shrimp, crab, crayfish, and lobster as food delicacies. In Africa and Asia, many people eat insect larvae and insects such as grasshoppers, termites, and ants, which are excellent sources of protein.

Agriculture would be impossible without bees, butterflies, moths, and flies that pollinate crops. Bees manufacture honey, and silkworms produce silk. Many insects and spiders are predators of harmful animal species, such as stableflies. Useful chemicals are obtained from some arthropods. For example, bee venom is used to treat rheumatic arthritis.

Not all arthropods are useful to humans. Almost every cultivated crop has some insect pest that feeds on it. Many arthropods—mosquitoes, tsetse flies, fleas, and ticks—carry human and other animal diseases. In addition, weevils, cockroaches, carpenter ants, clothes moths, termites, and carpet beetles destroy food, clothing, and property.

Insects are an important part of the ecological communities in which humans live. Removing all of the insects would cause more harm than good.

Pill bugs

Crab

Figure 22 The segments in some crustaceans, such as this crab, aren't obvious because they are covered by a shieldlike structure. Pill bugs—also called roly polys—are crustaceans that live on land.
Compare and contrast *pill bugs to centipedes and millipedes.*

Discussion

Insect Survival How does meta-morphosis contribute to the success and survival of insect species? There is no competition between larvae and adults for food; insects can survive harsh and cold weather while protected as pupae. L2

3 Assess

DAILY INTERVENTION

Check for Understanding

Linguistic Have students explain why arthropods molt several times during their lives. L2 LS

Reteach

Arthropod Characteristics Give each group a dissecting tray containing a preserved millipede, centipede, crayfish, grasshopper, and spider. Have the students list the characteristics of the animals and determine how the five organisms are similar and how they are different. L1

COOP LEARN LS **Kinesthetic**

✓ Assessment

Content Ask students to write in their Science Journals how incomplete and complete meta-morphosis are similar and how they are different. Both are a series of changes. In complete metamorphoses, the young look very different from the adults. Use **Performance Assessment in the Science Classroom,** p. 175. L2

Figure 23 More than 15,000 species of trilobites have been classified. They are one of the most recognized types of fossils.

Controlling Insects One common way to control problem insects is by insecticides. However, many insecticides also kill helpful insects. Another problem is that many toxic substances that kill insects remain in the environment and accumulate in the bodies of animals that eat them. As other animals eat the contaminated animals, the insecticides can find their way into human food. Humans also are harmed by these toxins.

Different types of bacteria, fungi, and viruses are being used to control some insect pests. Natural predators and parasites of insect pests have been somewhat successful in controlling them. Other biological controls include using sterile males or naturally occurring chemicals that interfere with the reproduction or behavior of insect pests.

Origin of Arthropods Because of their hard body parts, arthropod fossils, like the one in **Figure 23,** are among the oldest and best-preserved fossils of many-celled animals. Some are more than 500 million years old. Because earthworms and leeches have individual body segments, scientists hypothesize that arthropods probably evolved from an ancestor of segmented worms. Over time, groups of body segments fused and became adapted for locomotion, feeding, and sensing the environment. The hard exoskeleton and walking legs allowed arthropods to be among the first successful land animals.

section 3 review

Summary

Characteristics of Arthropods

- All arthropods have jointed appendages, bilateral symmetry, a body cavity, a digestive system, a nervous system, segmented bodies, and an exoskeleton.

Arthropod Types

- Insects have three body segments—head, thorax, and abdomen—a pair of antennae, and three pairs of legs. They go through complete or incomplete metamorphosis.
- Arachnids have two body segments—a cephalothorax and an abdomen—four pairs of legs, and no antennae.
- Centipedes and millipedes have long bodies with many segments and legs.
- Crustaceans have five pairs of legs and five pairs of appendages called swimmerets.

Self Check

1. **Infer** the advantages and disadvantages of an exoskeleton.
2. **Compare and contrast** the stages of complete and incomplete metamorphosis.
3. **List** four ways arthropods obtain food.
4. **Evaluate** the impact of arthropods.
5. **Concept Map** Make an events-chain concept map of complete metamorphosis and one of incomplete metamorphosis.
6. **Think Critically** Choose an insect you are familiar with and explain how it is adapted to its environment.

Applying Math

7. **Make a Graph** Of the major arthropod groups, 88% are insects, 7% are arachnids, 3% are crustaceans, 1% are centipedes and millipedes, and all others make up 1%. Show this data in a circle graph.

Science online life.msscience.com/self_check_quiz

section 3 review

1. advantages: prevents dehydration, supports and protects body; disadvantages: body outgrows exoskeleton, animal vulnerable to predators while new exoskeleton hardens
2. Incomplete has a nymph stage between egg and adult; complete has a larva and pupa stage

between egg and adult.
3. Arthropods obtain food by chewing, piercing and sucking, lapping up nectar, and eating other animals.
4. Arthropods are a food source, they pollinate crops, prey on harmful organisms, and can be used medicinally. Arthropods destroy crops, carry

disease, and destroy property.
5. Make sure students include all stages in both concept maps.
6. Answers will vary. Look for understanding of insect adaptations.
7. Graph segments should be proportional and labeled.

Observing a Crayfish

BENCH TESTED

A crayfish has a segmented body and a fused head and thorax. It has a snout and eyes on movable eyestalks. Most crayfish have pincers.

⬤ Real-World Question

How does a crayfish use its appendages?

Goals
- **Observe** a crayfish.
- **Determine** the function of pincers.

Materials
crayfish in a small aquarium
uncooked ground beef
stirrer

Safety Precautions 🔲🔲🔲🔲🔲

⬤ Procedure

1. Copy the data table and use it to record all of your observations during this lab.

Crayfish Observations

Body Region	Number of Appendages	Function
Head	5 pairs	sense environment; hold and chew food
Thorax	5 pairs	capture food; defense; walking
Abdomen	5 pairs	create water currents to help crayfish move; reproduction

2. Your teacher will provide you with a crayfish in an aquarium. Leave the crayfish in the aquarium while you do the lab. Draw your crayfish.

3. Gently touch the crayfish with the stirrer. How does the body feel?

4. **Observe** how the crayfish moves in the water.

5. **Observe** the compound eyes. On which body region are they located?

6. Drop a small piece of ground beef into the aquarium. Observe the crayfish's reaction. Wash your hands.

7. Return the aquarium to its proper place.

⬤ Conclude and Apply

1. **Infer** how the location of the eyes is an advantage for the crayfish.

2. **Explain** how the structure of the pincers aids in getting food.

3. **Infer** how the exoskeleton provides protection.

Communicating Your Data

Compare your observations with those of other students in your class. **For more help, refer to the** Science Skill Handbook.

LAB 379

⬤ Real-World Question

Purpose Students observe crayfish structure and determine appendage use. L2
IS **Visual-Spatial**

Process Skills observe, interpret data, infer, compare and contrast

Time Required 35 minutes

⬤ Procedure

Alternate Materials Preserved crayfish may be used.

Teaching Strategy Crayfish may be obtained from a local stream or a biological supply company. If obtained locally, return them to the stream when the activity is completed.

Troubleshooting Students may not be able to count the appendages of the crayfish in the aquarium. Use a transparency of a crayfish on the overhead projector to help them.

⬤ Conclude and Apply

1. Crayfish conceal themselves under rocks and in mud. The eyes at the end of stalks allow the crayfish to see without revealing their bodies.
2. The two-piece structure works like a clamp to capture prey and the serrated edges help hold prey.
3. The hard exoskeleton protects it from predators and from falling debris.

✔ Assessment

Performance To expand students' understanding of crayfish, have them put a plastic bag containing ice cubes at one end of a long aquarium and a bag of warm water at the other end. Observe crayfish response. Have students infer how this response is reflected in nature. Remove bags when finished. Use **Performance Assessment in the Science Classroom,** p. 89.

Communicating Your Data

Have students put together a bulletin board on which crayfish drawings can be displayed. Copy the data table onto the board and fill it in as a class.

Echinoderms

as you read

What **You'll Learn**

- **List** the characteristics of echinoderms.
- **Explain** how sea stars obtain and digest food.
- **Discuss** the importance of echinoderms.

Why **It's Important**

Echinoderms are a group of animals that affect oceans and coastal areas.

Review Vocabulary
epidermis: outer, thinnest layer of skin

New Vocabulary
- water-vascular system
- tube feet

Echinoderm Characteristics

Echinoderms (ih KI nuh durm) are found in oceans all over the world. The term *echinoderm* is from the Greek words *echinos* meaning "spiny" and *derma* meaning "skin." Echinoderms have a hard endoskeleton covered by a thin, bumpy, or spiny epidermis. They are radially symmetrical, which allows them to sense food, predators, and other things in their environment from all directions.

All echinoderms have a mouth, stomach, and intestines. They feed on a variety of plants and animals. For example, sea stars feed on worms and mollusks, and sea urchins feed on algae. Others feed on dead and decaying matter called detritus (de TRI tus) found on the ocean floor.

Echinoderms have no head or brain, but they do have a nerve ring that surrounds the mouth. They also have cells that respond to light and touch.

Water-Vascular System A characteristic unique to echinoderms is their water-vascular system. It allows them to move, exchange carbon dioxide and oxygen, capture food, and release wastes. The **water-vascular system,** as shown in **Figure 24,** is a network of water-filled canals with thousands of tube feet connected to it. **Tube feet** are hollow, thin-walled tubes that each end in a suction cup. As the pressure in the tube feet changes, the animal is able to move along by pushing out and pulling in its tube feet.

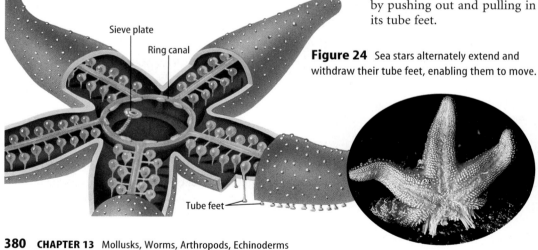

Sieve plate

Ring canal

Tube feet

Figure 24 Sea stars alternately extend and withdraw their tube feet, enabling them to move.

Section 4 Resource Manager

Chapter *FAST FILE* Resources
Transparency Activity, p. 49
Directed Reading for Content Mastery, pp. 19, 20
MiniLAB, p. 4
Enrichment, p. 32

Reinforcement, p. 28
Lab Worksheet, pp. 7–8
Lab Management and Safety, p. 73

Types of Echinoderms

Approximately 6,000 species of echinoderms are living today. Of those, more than one-third are sea stars. The other groups include brittle stars, sea urchins, sand dollars, and sea cucumbers.

Sea Stars Echinoderms with at least five arms arranged around a central point are called sea stars. The arms are lined with thousands of tube feet. Sea stars use their tube feet to open the shells of their prey. When the shell is open slightly, the sea star pushes its stomach through its mouth and into its prey. The sea star's stomach surrounds the soft body of its prey and secretes enzymes that help digest it. When the meal is over, the sea star pulls its stomach back into its own body.

☑ Reading Check *What is unusual about the way that sea stars eat their prey?*

Sea stars reproduce sexually when females release eggs and males release sperm into the water. Females can produce millions of eggs in one season.

Sea stars also can repair themselves by regeneration. If a sea star loses an arm, it can grow a new one. If enough of the center disk is left attached to a severed arm, a whole new sea star can grow from that arm.

Brittle Stars Like the one in **Figure 25,** brittle stars have fragile, slender, branched arms that break off easily. This adaptation helps a brittle star survive attacks by predators. While the predator is eating a broken arm, the brittle star escapes. Brittle stars quickly regenerate lost parts. They live hidden under rocks or in litter on the ocean floor. Brittle stars use their flexible arms for movement instead of their tube feet. Their tube feet are used to move particles of food into their mouth.

Figure 25 A brittle star's arms are so flexible that they wave back and forth in the ocean currents. They are called brittle stars because their arms break off easily if they are grabbed by a predator.

Mini LAB

Modeling the Strength of Tube Feet

Procedure
1. Hold your arm straight out, palm up.
2. Place a **heavy book** on your hand.
3. Have your partner time how long you can hold your arm up with the book on it.

Analysis
1. Describe how your arm feels after a few minutes.
2. If the book models the sea star and your arm models the clam, infer how a sea star successfully overcomes a clam to obtain food.

Try at Home

---

2 Teach

Mini LAB

Purpose to model how sea stars can open clam shells held closed by muscles L1 IS **Kinesthetic**

Materials heavy books, clock with a second hand

Teaching Strategies
• Make sure the books students use are heavy but not too heavy to lift.
• As students try this lab, suggest they imagine this is a life-or-death struggle as it is for the sea star and clam.

Analysis
1. arm muscles tire
2. Sea stars pull on a clam by using the suction power of their tube feet. Eventually, the muscles of the clam tire and the shell opens.

Assessment

Performance Have students wet suction cups and press them against a variety of surfaces. Ask students whether they can pick up an object with a suction cup and to compare this to tube feet. Yes; tube feet act like suction cups. Use **Performance Assessment in the Science Classroom,** p. 97.

Try at Home

☑ Reading Check

Answer They expel their stomach to eat.

Visual Learning

Figure 25 Have students study the brittle star in its natural environment. Then, have them make a list of its adaptations to this environment. L2 P

Differentiated Instruction

Learning Disabled Have learning disabled students make a picture dictionary illustrating the meaning of unfamiliar terms in this chapter. Have them write their words on cards and keep the cards in alphabetical order. L1 IS **Visual-Spatial**

Figure 26 Like all echinoderms, sand dollars and sea urchins are radially symmetrical.

Sand dollars live on ocean floors where they can burrow into the sand.

Sea urchins use tube feet and their spines to move around on the bottom of the ocean.

Science Online

Topic: Humans and Echinoderms

Visit life.msscience.com for Web links to information about how echinoderms are used by humans.

Activity Choose one or two uses and write an essay on why echinoderms are important to you.

Sea Urchins and Sand Dollars Another group of echinoderms includes sea urchins, sea biscuits, and sand dollars. They are disk- or globe-shaped animals covered with spines. They do not have arms, but sand dollars have a five-pointed pattern on their surface. **Figure 26** shows living sand dollars, covered with stiff, hairlike spines, and sea urchins with long, pointed spines that protect them from predators. Some sea urchins have sacs near the end of the spines that contain toxic fluid that is injected into predators. The spines also help in movement and burrowing. Sea urchins have five toothlike structures around their mouth.

Sea Cucumbers The animal shown in **Figure 27** is a sea cucumber. Sea cucumbers are soft-bodied echinoderms that have a leathery covering. They have tentacles around their mouth and rows of tube feet on their upper and lower surfaces. When threatened, sea cucumbers may expel their internal organs. These organs regenerate in a few weeks. Some sea cucumbers eat detritus, and others eat plankton.

✔ **Reading Check** *What makes sea cucumbers different from other echinoderms?*

Figure 27 Sea cucumbers have short tube feet, which they use to move around.
Describe *the characteristics of sea cucumbers.*

382 CHAPTER 13

Differentiated Instruction

Value of Echinoderms

Echinoderms are important to the marine environment because they feed on dead organisms and help recycle materials. Sea urchins control the growth of algae in coastal areas. Sea urchin eggs and sea cucumbers are used for food in some places. Many echinoderms are used in research and some might be possible sources of medicines. Sea stars are important predators that control populations of other animals. However, because sea stars feed on oysters and clams, they also destroy millions of dollars' worth of mollusks each year.

Origin of Echinoderms Like the example in **Figure 28,** a good fossil record exists for echinoderms. Echinoderms date back more than 400 million years. The earliest echinoderms might have had bilateral symmetry as adults and may have been attached to the ocean floor by stalks. Many larval forms of modern echinoderms are bilaterally symmetrical.

Scientists hypothesize that echinoderms more closely resemble animals with backbones than any other group of invertebrates. This is because echinoderms have complex body systems and an embryo that develops the same way that the embryos of animals with backbones develop.

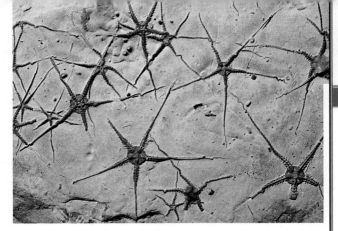

Figure 28 *Ophiopinna elegans* was a brittle star that lived about 165 million years ago.
Explain *the origins of echinoderms.*

section 4 review

Summary

Echinoderm Characteristics

- Echinoderms have a hard endoskeleton and are covered by thin, spiny skin.

- They are radially symmetrical. They have no brain or head, but have a nerve ring, and respond to light and touch.

- They have a specialized water-vascular system, which helps them move, exchange gases, capture food, and release wastes.

Types of Echinoderms

- The largest group of echinoderms is sea stars.

- Other groups include brittle stars, sea urchins and sand dollars, and sea cucumbers.

Self Check

1. **Explain** how echinoderms move and get their food.

2. **Infer** how sea urchins are beneficial.

3. **List** the methods of defense that echinoderms have to protect themselves from predators.

4. **Think Critically** Why would the ability to regenerate lost body parts be an important adaptation for sea stars, brittle stars, and other echinoderms?

Applying Skills

5. **Form a Hypothesis** Why do you think echinoderms live on the ocean floor?

6. **Communicate** Choose an echinoderm and write about it. Describe its appearance, how it gets food, where it lives, and other interesting facts.

 Scienceonline life.msscience.com/self_check_quiz

SECTION 4 Echinoderms **383**

DAILY INTERVENTION

Check for Understanding
Linguistic Have students explain why echinoderms have few predators. L2 IS

Reteach
Echinoderm Characteristics Have students look at either photographs or specimens of various echinoderms and list the major characteristics of each type. L2

✓ Assessment

Oral Infer why echinoderms are bottom dwellers. The tube feet are on the ventral side. Use **Performance Assessment in the Science Classroom,** p. 89. L2

Virtual Labs

 **Classify** *How are mollusks, worms, arthropods, and echinoderms classified?*

section 4 review

1. through the use of tube feet
2. They control the growth of algae. Their eggs are used as food by some people.
3. They have hard endoskeletons and spines, they regenerate rapidly, some have poison glands, and sea cucumbers can expel and regenerate their digestive systems.
4. Sea stars are dependent upon their arms (which contain tube feet) to move and obtain food. They could not survive without them.
5. With the exception of the brittle star, echinoderms have no means of movement except for their tube feet. Living on the ocean floor allows them to feed on other organisms and hide under debris.
6. Check students' work.

⊙ Real-World Question

Purpose Students experiment to determine the foods preferred by earthworms. L2 IS **Kinesthetic and Logical-Mathematical**

Process Skills identify and control variables, compare and contrast, observe and infer

Time Required one class period

⊙ Procedure

Materials Be certain students do not pack the materials into their jars tightly. Soil and humus should be sprinkled into the jar to allow sufficient air pockets to form.

Alternate Materials Decomposing leaf litter can replace humus, and melon or cantaloupe rinds can replace banana peels.

Safety Precautions Students should thoroughly wash their hands after handling lab materials. Caution students not to eat foods during science class. Caution students to moisten their hands before handling earthworms and to handle them gently.

Teaching Strategies

- Ask students to capture worms from their home gardens or yards to be used in the activity.
- Inspect each group's jar before they start the final stages of the experiment.

What do w⊙rms eat?

Goals
- ■ **Construct** five earthworm habitats.
- ■ **Test** different foods to determine which ones earthworms eat.

Materials
orange peels
apple peels
banana skin
kiwi fruit skin
watermelon rind
*skins of five
    different fruits
widemouthed jars (5)
potting soil
water
humus
*peat moss
earthworms
black construction paper
    (5 sheets)
masking tape
marker
rubber bands (5)
*Alternate materials

Safety Precautions

WARNING: *Do not handle earthworms with dry hands. Do not eat any materials used in the lab.*

⊙ Real-World Question

Earthworms are valuable because they improve the soil in which they live. There can be 50,000 earthworms living in one acre. Their tunnels increase air movement through the soil and improve water drainage. As they eat the decaying material in soil, their wastes can enrich the soil. Other than decaying material, what else do earthworms eat? Do they have favorite foods?

⊙ Procedure

1. Pour equal amounts of soil into each of the jars. Do not pack the soil. Leave several centimeters of space at the top of each jar.

2. Sprinkle equal amounts of water into each jar to moisten the soil. Avoid pouring too much water into the jars.

3. Pour humus into each of your jars to a depth of 2 cm. The humus should be loose.

4. Add watermelon rinds to the first jar, orange peels to the second, apple peels to the third, kiwi fruit skins to the fourth, and a banana peel to the fifth jar. Each jar should have 2 cm of fruit skins on top of the layer of humus.

384 CHAPTER 13

Alternative Inquiry Lab

Asking Questions To extend this lab, make it an inquiry lab. Build on student experiences by encouraging them to use what they have learned to brainstorm questions about the eating habits of worms. Have each student choose one question to explore. Unsafe or impractical questions should be eliminated. Ask them to choose the materials they need to explore their questions. Students should have their plan approved before continuing. Conduct the experiments after all of the necessary materials have been gathered.

5. Add five earthworms to each jar.

6. Wrap a sheet of black construction paper around each jar and secure it with a rubber band.

7. Using the masking tape and marker, label each jar with the type of fruit it contains.

8. Copy the data table below in your Science Journal.

9. Place all of your jars in the same cool, dark place. Observe your jars every other day for a week and record your observations in your data table.

Fruit Wastes

Date	Watermelon rind	Orange peels	Apple peels	Kiwi skins	Banana peels
		Answers will vary.			

▶ Analyze Your Data

1. **Record** the changes in your data table.

2. **Compare** the amount of skins left in each jar.

3. **Record** which fruit skin had the greatest change. The least?

▶ Conclude and Apply

1. **Infer** the type of food favored by earthworms.

2. **Infer** why some of the fruit skins were not eaten by the earthworms.

3. **Identify** a food source in each jar other than the fruit skins.

4. **Predict** what would happen in the jars over the next month if you continued the experiment.

Communicating Your Data

Use the results of your experiment and information from your reading to help you write a recipe for an appetizing dinner that worms would enjoy. Based on the results of your experiment, add other fruit skins or foods to your menu you think worms might like.

LAB 385

Tie to Prior Knowledge Most students know that worms create rich soil by decomposing organic matter.

▶ Analyze Your Data

Expected Outcome Softer fruit skins such as apples and pears will be consumed by the worms first, and thicker skins will be decomposed last or possibly not at all.

Answers to Questions

1. Check students' data tables.
2. The apple peel will disappear during the week. The other types of fruit skins may show varying degrees of decomposition.
3. Apple peels; answers on the least change will vary depending on thickness of peel, usually watermelon rind, but accept all reasonable answers.

Error Analysis Have each student group occasionally examine the jars of other groups to compare the decay process occurring in the jars. Ask groups to list plausible explanations to explain differences in decomposition rates.

▶ Conclude and Apply

1. apple peels
2. Watermelon rinds, orange peels, and banana skins are thicker and difficult for earthworms to digest.
3. soil and humus
4. The less digestible fruit skins would begin to decay, enabling the earthworms to consume them.

Communicating Your Data

Ask students to research vermicomposting, or composting using worms. They can find what foods should be avoided when composting, which types of worms are the best to use, and the best way to set up a vermicomposting bin. L2

from "The Creatures on My Mind"
by Ursula K. Le Guin

Understanding Literature

Personal Experience Narrative
Answers might include that insects lack the same sensory system as do humans; others may say that there is no way of knowing how insects feel.

Respond to the Reading

1. Possible answer: by flying into the light fixture
2. adult stage
3. **Linking Science and Writing** Have students consider the circumstances of the experience. Was a real or imagined danger involved?

Arthropods Although many people are horrified by arthropods, particularly insects, the majority of these animals are beneficial to Earth's ecosystems. Most of the world's flowering plants are pollinated by arthropods. Other arthropods, such as larger crustaceans like lobster and shrimp, are used for food. Smaller crustaceans are major components of ocean and wetland food chains.

However, some arthropods do pose threats to animals as well as to agriculture. For example, some insects can devastate crops, and others can carry diseases such as malaria, yellow fever (via mosquitoes) and typhus (via lice).

When I stayed for a week in New Orleans… I had an apartment with a balcony… But when I first stepped out on it, the first thing I saw was a huge beetle. It lay on its back directly under the light fixture. I thought it was dead, then saw its legs twitch and twitch again. Big insects horrify me. As a child I feared moths and spiders, but adolescence cured me, as if those fears evaporated in the stew of hormones. But I never got enough hormones to make me easy with the large, hard-shelled insects: wood roaches, June bugs, mantises, cicadas. This beetle was a couple of inches long; its abdomen was ribbed, its legs long and jointed; it was dull reddish brown; it was dying. I felt a little sick seeing it lie there twitching, enough to keep me from sitting out on the balcony that first day… And if I had any courage or common sense, I kept telling myself, I'd… put it out of its misery. We don't know what a beetle may or may not suffer…

Understanding Literature

Personal Experience Narrative In this passage, the author uses her personal experience to consider her connection to other living things. In this piece, the author recounts a minor event in her life when she happens upon a dying beetle. The experience allows the author to pose some important questions about another species and to think about how beetles might feel when they die. How do you think the beetle is feeling?

Respond to the Reading

1. How do you suppose the beetle injured itself?
2. From the author's description, in what stage of development is the beetle?
3. **Linking Science and Writing** Write about a personal experience that caused you to think about an important question or topic in your life.

The author names several arthropod species in the passage, including insects and an arachnid. Beetles, June bugs, mantises, cicadas, and moths are all insects. The spider is an arachnid. Of the arthropods the author names, can you tell which ones go through a complete metamorphosis?

Resources for Teachers and Students

Bugs: Insects, Spiders, Centipedes, Millipedes and Other Closely Related Arthropods, by Frank Lowenstein and Sheryl Lechner, Black Dog & Leventhal Publishing, December 1999

National Audubon Society Field Guide to North American Insects and Spiders, by Lorus J. Milne and Susan Rayfield (Illustrator), Knopf Publishing, November 1980

Reviewing Main Ideas

Section 1 Mollusks

1. Mollusks are soft-bodied invertebrates that usually are covered by a hard shell. They move using a muscular foot.

2. Mollusks with one shell are gastropods. Bivalves have two shells. Cephalopods have an internal shell and a foot that is divided into tentacles.

Section 2 Segmented Worms

1. Segmented worms have tube-shaped bodies divided into sections, a body cavity that holds the internal organs, and bristlelike structures called setae to help them move.

2. An earthworm's digestive system has a mouth, crop, gizzard, intestine, and anus. Polychaetes are marine worms. Leeches are parasites that attach to animals and feed on their blood.

Section 3 Arthropods

1. More than a million species of arthropods exist, which is more than any other group of animals. Most arthropods are insects.

2. Arthropods are grouped by number of body segments and appendages. Exoskeletons cover, protect, and support arthropod bodies.

3. Young arthropods develop either by complete metamorphosis or incomplete metamorphosis.

Section 4 Echinoderms

1. Echinoderms have a hard, spiny exoskeleton covered by a thin epidermis.

2. Most echinoderms have a water-vascular system that enables them to move, exchange carbon dioxide and oxygen, capture food, and give off wastes.

Visualizing Main Ideas

Copy and complete the following concept map about insects.

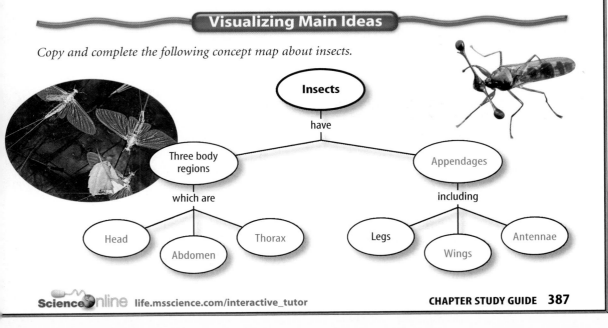

Science Online life.msscience.com/interactive_tutor

CHAPTER STUDY GUIDE **387**

Reviewing Main Ideas

Summary statements can be used by students to review the major concepts of the chapter.

Visualizing Main Ideas

See student page.

Science **Online**

Visit life.msscience.com
/self_check_quiz
/interactive_tutor
/vocabulary_puzzlemaker
/chapter_review
/standardized_test

Assessment Transparency

For additional assessment questions, use the *Assessment Transparency* located in the transparency book.

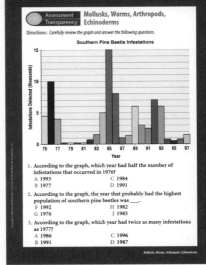

Using Vocabulary

1. mantle
2. setae, crop
3. exoskeleton
4. spiracles
5. Tube feet
6. radula
7. open circulatory system

Checking Concepts

8. C	12. D
9. D	13. A
10. A	14. A
11. C	15. B

Using Vocabulary

appendage p. 370	molting p. 370
closed circulatory system p. 362	open circulatory system p. 360
crop p. 366	radula p. 361
exoskeleton p. 370	setae p. 365
gill p. 360	spiracle p. 371
gizzard p. 366	tube feet p. 380
mantle p. 360	water-vascular system p. 380
metamorphosis p. 372	

Fill in the blanks with the correct vocabulary word or words.

1. Mollusk shells are secreted by the _____.

2. As earthworms move through soil using their _____, they take in soil, which is stored in the _____.

3. The _____ covers and protects arthropod bodies.

4. Insects exchange oxygen and carbon dioxide through _____.

5. _____ act like suction cups and help sea stars move and feed.

6. Snails use a(n) _____ to get food.

7. The blood of mollusks moves in a(n) _____.

Checking Concepts

Choose the word or phrase that best answers the question.

8. What structure covers organs of mollusks?
   A) gills   C) mantle
   B) food   D) visceral mass

9. What structures do echinoderms use to move and to open shells of mollusks?
   A) mantle   C) spines
   B) calcium plates   D) tube feet

10. Which organism has a closed circulatory system?
    A) earthworm   C) slug
    B) octopus   D) snail

11. What evidence suggests that arthropods might have evolved from annelids?
    A) Arthropods and annelids have gills.
    B) Both groups have species that live in salt water.
    C) Segmentation is present in both groups.
    D) All segmented worms have setae.

Use the photo below to answer questions 12 and 13.

12. Which of the following correctly describes the arthropod pictured above?
    A) three body regions, six legs
    B) two body regions, eight legs
    C) many body segments, ten legs
    D) many body segments, one pair of legs per segment

13. What type of arthropod is this animal?
    A) annelid   C) insect
    B) arachnid   D) mollusk

14. Which is an example of an annelid?
    A) earthworm   C) slug
    B) octopus   D) snail

15. Which sequence shows incomplete metamorphosis?
    A) egg—larvae—adult
    B) egg—nymph—adult
    C) larva—pupa—adult
    D) nymph—pupa—adult

 Science Online life.msscience.com/vocabulary_puzzlemaker

Use the ExamView® Pro Testmaker CD-ROM to:
- create multiple versions of tests
- create modified tests with one mouse click for inclusion students
- edit existing questions and add your own questions
- build tests aligned with state standards using built-in State Curriculum Tags
- change English tests to Spanish with one mouse click and vice versa

Thinking Critically

Use the photo below to answer question 16.

16. **Describe** how this animal obtains food.

17. **Compare** the ability of clams, oysters, scallops, and squid to protect themselves.

18. **Compare and contrast** an earthworm gizzard to teeth in other animals.

19. **Explain** the evidence that mollusks and annelids may share a common ancestor.

20. **Infer** how taking in extra water or air after molting, but before the new exoskeleton hardens, helps an arthropod.

21. **Classify** the following animals into arthropod groups: *spider, pill bug, crayfish, grasshopper, crab, silverfish, cricket, wasp, scorpion, shrimp, barnacle, tick,* and *butterfly.*

22. **Compare and Contrast** Copy and complete this Venn diagram to compare and contrast arthropods to annelids.

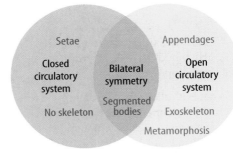

Annelids   **Arthropods**

Setae

Closed circulatory system

Bilateral symmetry

Segmented bodies

No skeleton

Appendages

Open circulatory system

Exoskeleton

Metamorphosis

 Science Online life.msscience.com/chapter_review

23. **Recognize Cause and Effect** If all the earthworms were removed from a hectare of soil, what would happen to the soil? Why?

24. **Research Information** The suffix *-ptera* means "wings." Research the meaning of the prefix listed below and give an example of a member of each insect group.

Diptera   Homoptera
Orthoptera   Hemiptera
Coleoptera

Performance Activities

25. **Construct** Choose an arthropod that develops through complete metamorphosis and construct a three-dimensional model for each of the four stages.

Applying Math

Use the table below to answer questions 26 and 27.

Described Species	
Type of Organism	Number of Described Species
Anthropods	1,065,000
Land plants	270,000
Fungi	72,000
Mollusks	70,000
Nematodes	25,000
Birds	10,000
Mammals	5,000
Bacteria	4,000
Other	145,000

26. **Arthropods** Using the table above, what percentage of organisms are arthropods? Mollusks?

27. **Species Distribution** Make a bar graph that shows the number of described species listed in the table above.

Thinking Critically

16. Gastropods use their radula to tear plant materials and scrape algae and plant material.

17. Clams burrow into the sand; oysters attach themselves by strong sticky threads to rocks; scallops eject water and move by rapidly opening and closing their shells; a squid ejects water and escapes by jet propulsion. Oysters, clams, and scallops also have hard shells.

18. Grit in the earthworm gizzard grinds soil in the same way that teeth break up and grind food in the mouth.

19. A space in the body to hold organs is present in both groups. The larvae of both groups are similar.

20. It provides room in which to grow before the next molt.

21. arachnids: spider, tick, scorpion; crustaceans: pill bug, crayfish, crab, shrimp, barnacle; insects: grasshopper, silverfish, cricket, wasp, butterfly

22. See student page.

23. The soil would become packed and hardened. It would be less fertile because of the lack of earthworm wastes.

24. Gastropods have only one shell.

25. Diptera: two wings, flies; Orthoptera: straight wings, grasshoppers; Coleoptera: shielded wings, beetles; Homoptera: whole wings, leaf hoppers; Hemiptera: half wings, water bugs

Performance Activities

26. Models will vary. Use **PASC**, p. 123.

Applying Math

National Math Standards

1, 5, 9

27. 64% arthropods, 4% mollusks (1,666,000 total species described)

28. Check students' graphs.

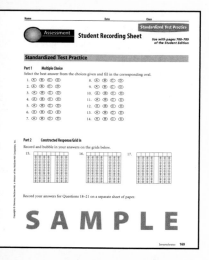

FAST FILE

Answer Sheet A practice answer sheet can be found at life.msscience.com/answer_sheet.

S A M P L E

Part 1 | Multiple Choice

1. C
2. B
3. C
4. D
5. A
6. C
7. D
8. C
9. D
10. A
11. B

Part 1 | Multiple Choice

Record your answers on the answer sheet provided by your teacher or on a sheet of paper.

1. Which of the following is not a mollusk?
   A. clam
   C. crab
   B. snail
   D. squid

Use the illustration below to answer questions 2 and 3.

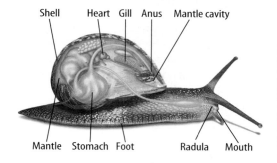

Shell Heart Gill Anus Mantle cavity

Mantle Stomach Foot Radula Mouth

2. This mollusk uses which of the following to exchange carbon dioxide with oxygen from the water?
   A. radula
   B. gill
   C. mantle
   D. shell

3. Which structure covers the body organs of this mollusk?
   A. radula
   B. gill
   C. mantle
   D. shell

4. Which is the largest group of mollusks?
   A. cephalopods
   C. monovalves
   B. bivalves
   D. gastropods

5. Which openings allow air to enter an insect's body?
   A. spiracles
   C. thorax
   B. gills
   D. setae

390 STANDARDIZED TEST PRACTICE

Use the photo below to answer questions 6 and 7.

6. This organism is an example of what type of mollusk?
   A. gastropod
   C. cephalopod
   B. bivalve
   D. monovalve

7. How do these animals move?
   A. a muscular foot
   B. tentacles
   C. contraction and relaxation
   D. jet propulsion

8. What does the word annelid mean?
   A. segmented
   C. little rings
   B. bristled
   D. worms

9. What are bristlelike structures on the outside of each body segment of annelids called?
   A. crops
   C. radula
   B. gizzards
   D. setae

10. What is the largest group of animals?
    A. arthropods
    C. gastropods
    B. cephalopods
    D. annelids

11. What is it called when an arthropod loses its exoskeleton and replaces it with a new one?
    A. shedding
    C. manging
    B. molting
    D. exfoliating

Part 2 | Short Response/Grid In

12. they use tube feet to pry open the shells of their prey, push their stomach outside of their body into the prey and digest its soft body

13. regeneration

14. they scrape and tear food using their radula

15. a closed circulatory system to carry food and oxygen

16. jet propulsion; they take in water and force it out through an opening near the head

17. Sexually; they are hermaphrodites, but cannot fertilize themselves.

18. Blood and oxygen are not contained in blood vessels, the blood completely surrounds the organs; insects, snails, leeches

19. An irritant in some mollusks is coated by a material that forms smooth, hard layers.

Part 2 | Short Response/Grid In

Record your answers on the answer sheet provided by your teacher or on a sheet of paper.

12. Describe how a sea star captures and consumes its prey.

13. Explain how sea stars repair or replace lost or damaged body parts.

14. Describe how gastropods, such as snails and garden slugs, eat.

Use the photo below to answer questions 15 and 16.

15. Describe this animal's vascular system. How is it used?

16. This animal has a unique method of movement. What is it and how does it work?

17. Describe the type of reproductive system found in earthworms.

18. What is an open circulatory system? Give three examples of animals that have an open circulatory system.

19. How are pearls formed in clams, oysters, and some other gastropods?

 life.msscience.com/standardized_test

Part 3 | Open Ended

Record your answers on a sheet of paper.

Use the photo below to answer questions 20 and 21.

20. Name and describe the phylum that this sea star belongs to.

21. This animal has a vascular system that is unique. Describe it.

22. What structures allow an earthworm to move? Describe its locomotion.

23. There are more species of insects than all other animal groups combined. In all environments, they have to compete with one another for survival. How do so many insects survive?

24. Insect bodies are divided into three segments. What are these three segments and what appendages and organs are in/on each part?

Test-Taking Tip

Show Your Work For constructed-response questions, show all of your work and any calculations on your answer sheet.

Question 22 Write out all of the adaptations that insects have for survival and determine which are the most beneficial to the success of the group.

Rubrics

The following rubrics are sample scoring devices for short response and open-ended questions.

Short Response

Points	Description
2	The student demonstrates a thorough understanding of the science of the task. The response may contain minor flaws that do not detract from the demonstration of a thorough understanding.
1	The student has provided a response that is only partially correct.
0	The student has provided a completely incorrect solution or no response at all.

Open Ended

Points	Description
4	The student demonstrates a thorough understanding of the science of the task. The response may contain minor flaws that do not detract from the demonstration of a thorough understanding.
3	The student demonstrates an understanding of the science of the task. The response is essentially correct and demonstrates an essential but less than thorough understanding of the science.
2	The student demonstrates only a partial understanding of the science of the task. Although the student may have used the correct approach to a solution or may have provided a correct solution, the work lacks an essential understanding of the underlying science concepts.
1	The student demonstrates a very limited understanding of the science of the task. The response is incomplete and exhibits many flaws.
0	The student provides a completely incorrect solution or no response at all.

Part 3 | Open Ended

20. echinoderm; bumpy skin, water-vascular system, radially symmetrical, mouth, stomach, and intestines, no brain

21. water-vascular system—a network of water-filled canals with thousands of tube feet

22. setae and two sets of muscles in the body; the long muscles contract and push the setae out anchoring the worm to the soil; the circular muscles contract and pull the setae in moving the worm forward

23. a short lifespan allows genetic traits to change quickly, specialized diet helps them avoid competition, flying, and other adaptations such as camouflage

24. a head with eyes, antennae, and mouthparts, thorax with one or two pair of wings, if present, and three pairs of legs, and abdomen with the digestive and reproductive organs

Section/Objectives	Standards		Labs/Features
Chapter Opener	**National**	**State/Local**	**Launch Lab:** Snake Hearing, p. 393 **Foldables,** p. 393
	See pp. 16T–17T for a Key to Standards.		
Section 1 Chordates and Vertebrates ⏱ 2 sessions 🧊 1 block 1. **List** the characteristics of all chordates. 2. **Identify** characteristics shared by vertebrates. 3. **Differentiate** between ectotherms and endotherms.	National Content Standards: UCP.1–UCP.4, A.1, A.2, C.1–C.3, C.5		**Lab:** Endotherms and Ectotherms, p. 398
Section 2 Fish ⏱ 2 sessions 🧊 1 block 4. **List** the characteristics of the three classes of fish. 5. **Explain** how fish obtain food and oxygen and reproduce. 6. **Describe** the importance and origin of fish.	National Content Standards: UCP.1–UCP.5, A.1, A.2, C.1–C.3, C.5, F.1		**Integrate Health,** p. 402 **MiniLAB:** Modeling How Fish Adjust to Different Depths, p. 403 **Applying Math:** Density of a Fish, p. 404
Section 3 Amphibians ⏱ 2 sessions 🧊 1 block 7. **Describe** the adaptations amphibians have for living in water and living on land. 8. **List** the kinds of amphibians and the characteristics of each. 9. **Explain** how amphibians reproduce and develop.	National Content Standards: UCP.1–UCP.5, A.1, A.2, C.1–C.3, C.5		**Science Online,** p. 409 **MiniLAB:** Describing Frog Adaptations, p. 410
Section 4 Reptiles ⏱ 3 sessions 🧊 1.5 blocks 10. **List** the characteristics of reptiles. 11. **Determine** how reptile adaptations enable them to live on land. 12. **Explain** the importance of the amniotic egg.	National Content Standards: UCP.1–UCP.5, A.1, A.2, C.1–C.3, C.5, F.4, F.5		**Science Online,** p. 413 **Visualizing Extinct Reptiles,** p. 416 **Integrate History,** p. 417 **Lab:** Water Temperature and the Respiration Rate of Fish, p. 418 **Science and Society:** Venom, p. 420

Lab Materials	Reproducible Resources	Section Assessment	Technology
Launch Lab: tuning fork	**Chapter *FAST FILE* Resources** Foldables Worksheet, p. 17 Directed Reading Overview, p. 19 Note-taking Worksheets, pp. 35–38	GLENCOE'S **ASSESSMENT** ADVANTAGE	TeacherWorks includes: • Interactive Teacher Edition • Lesson Planner with calendar • Access to all program blacklines • Correlations to standards • Web links
Lab: fiberfill, cloth, thermometer	**Chapter *FAST FILE* Resources** Transparency Activity, p. 48 Lab Activity, pp. 9–10 Enrichment, p. 31 Reinforcement, p. 27 Directed Reading, p. 20 Lab Worksheet, pp. 5–6	Portfolio Science Journal, p. 395 Performance Applying Skills, p. 397 Content Section Review, p. 397	🔦 Section Focus Transparency 💿 Virtual Labs CD-ROM 🎧 Guided Reading Audio Program 💿 Interactive Chalkboard CD-ROM
MiniLAB: 2 balloons, large bowl, water	**Chapter *FAST FILE* Resources** Transparency Activity, p. 49 MiniLAB, p. 3 Enrichment, p. 32 Reinforcement, p. 28 Directed Reading, p. 20 **Mathematics Skill Activities,** p. 49	Portfolio Differentiated Instruction, p. 401 Performance MiniLAB, p. 403 Applying Math, p. 404 Applying Skills, p. 406 Content Section Review, p. 406	🔦 Section Focus Transparency 💿 Virtual Labs CD-ROM 🎧 Guided Reading Audio Program 💿 Interactive Chalkboard CD-ROM 📼 Video Lab
MiniLAB: live frog, jar, water, magnifying glass	**Chapter *FAST FILE* Resources** Transparency Activity, p. 50 MiniLAB, p. 4 Lab Activity, pp. 11–15 Enrichment, p. 33 Reinforcement, p. 29 Directed Reading, p. 21	Portfolio Differentiated Instruction, p. 410 Performance MiniLAB, p. 410 Applying Skills, p. 411 Content Section Review, p. 411	🔦 Section Focus Transparency 💿 Virtual Labs CD-ROM 🎧 Guided Reading Audio Program 💿 Interactive Chalkboard CD-ROM
Lab: goldfish, aquarium, water, small fishnet, 600-mL beakers (3), ice, stirring rod, thermometer	**Chapter *FAST FILE* Resources** Transparency Activity, p. 51 Enrichment, p. 34 Reinforcement, p. 30 Transparency Activity, pp. 53–54 Directed Reading, pp. 21, 22 Lab Worksheet, pp. 7–8	Portfolio Differentiated Instruction, p. 413 Performance Applying Math, p. 417 Content Section Review, p. 417	🔦 Section Focus Transparency 🔦 Teaching Transparency 💿 Virtual Labs CD-ROM 🎧 Guided Reading Audio Program 💿 Interactive Chalkboard CD-ROM

End of Chapter Assessment

GLENCOE'S **ASSESSMENT** ADVANTAGE

Blackline Masters	Technology	Professional Series
Chapter *FAST FILE* Resources Chapter Review, pp. 41–42 Chapter Tests, pp. 43–46 **Standardized Test Practice, pp. 59–62**	📼 MindJogger Videoquiz 💿 Virtual Labs CD-ROM 💿 Exam*View*® Pro Testmaker 💿 TeacherWorks CD-ROM 💿 Interactive Chalkboard CD-ROM	**Performance Assessment in the Science Classroom (PASC)**

chapter 14 Fish, Amphibians, and Reptiles

Transparencies

Section Focus

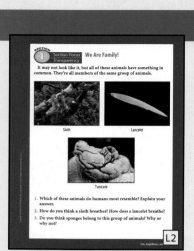

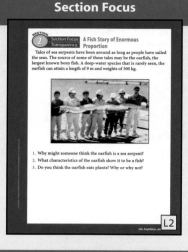

This is a representation of key blackline masters available in the Teacher Classroom Resources. See Resource Manager boxes within the chapter for additional information.

Key to Teaching Strategies

The following designations will help you decide which activities are appropriate for your students.

L1 Level 1 activities should be appropriate for students with learning difficulties.

L2 Level 2 activities should be within the ability range of all students.

L3 Level 3 activities are designed for above-average students.

ELL ELL activities should be within the ability range of English-Language Learners.

COOP LEARN Cooperative Learning activities are designed for small group work.

LS Multiple Learning Styles logos, as described on page 12T, are used throughout to indicate strategies that address different learning styles.

P These strategies represent student products that can be placed into a best-work portfolio.

PBL Problem-Based Learning activities apply real-world situations to learning.

Assessment

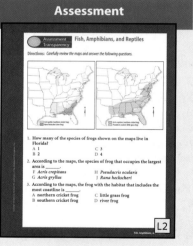

Teaching

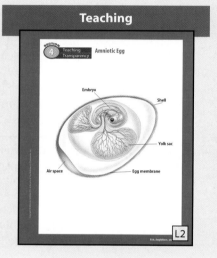

Hands-on Activities

Student Text Lab Worksheet

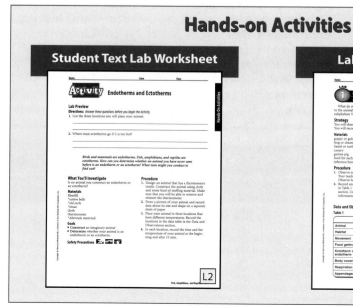

Laboratory Activities

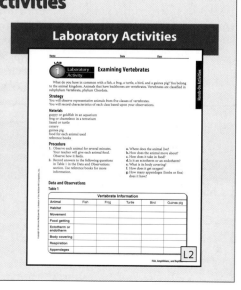

Resource Manager

Meeting Different Ability Levels

Content Outline

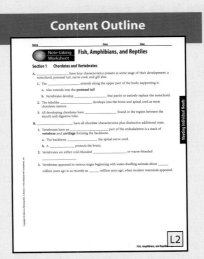

L2

Reinforcement

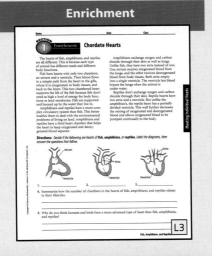

L2

Enrichment

L3

Directed Reading (English/Spanish)

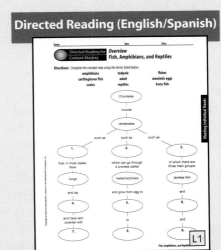

L1

Study Guide

L2

Reading Essentials

L1

Assessment

Test Practice Workbook

L2

Chapter Review

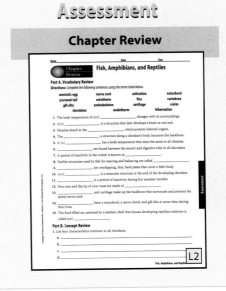

L2

Chapter Tests

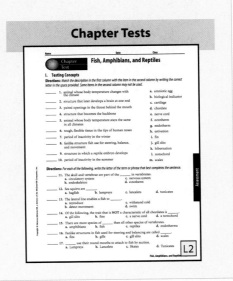

L2

Science Content Background

section 1
Chordates and Vertebrates
Chordate Characteristics

In Phylum *Chordata*, students are most aware of animals with backbones, such as fish and mammals, that belong to the subphylum *Vertebrata*. There are two other *Chordata* subphyla. The *Urochordata* includes sea squirts, which have a spongelike appearance. They are a very remote ancestor on the Chordata tree. Their larva, however, are similar in form to tadpoles. The *Cephalochordata* includes lancelets, which are fishlike in appearance and who spend most of their time buried in sand. In addition to having a notochord, chordates have a dorsal hollow nerve cord at some time during their life cycles.

Fish, amphibians, and reptiles are ectotherms, which means their temperature varies with their surroundings. The internal temperature of ectotherms fluctuates more than it does for endotherms. The advantage for ectotherms is they spend less energy maintaining a constant body temperature. The disadvantage is that these organisms are more sluggish at cooler temperatures. Other names for ectotherms are cold-blooded animals and poikilotherms.

Gail Shumway/FPG International

section 2
Fish
Fish Characteristics

Most fish have fins that occur in pairs. Fish breathe with gills and reproduce sexually, usually with external fertilization. Fish circulate blood in a closed system with a two-chambered heart, consisting of one atrium and one ventricle. The atrium receives blood from the body and pushes it to the ventricle. The ventricle pumps blood through the gills and then to the rest of the body. Some scientists define the fish heart as four-chambered. They include the area before the atrium and the area after the ventricle as chambers.

section 3
Amphibians
Amphibian Characteristics

Amphibians were the first land animals to evolve, and they developed adaptations that allow them to spend part of their life on land. Their three-chamber heart allows better circulation of oxygenated blood. This is necessary because walking as opposed to swimming uses more energy. Lungs and moist skin provide two methods for amphibians for the exchange of oxygen and carbon dioxide. Unlike fish and other vertebrates, most amphibians undergo a metamorphosis.

Teacher to Teacher
Jeff Remington
Palmyra Middle School
Palmyra, Pennsylvania

"I use Cartesian divers to demonstrate the concept of a swim bladder. Students pass them around and really seem to get the concept."

Jeff Remington

Salamanders

Having frogs and toads as the poster organisms for amphibians makes many people forget about salamanders, even though there is an abundance of species. In North America, there are more species of salamanders than in the rest of the world combined. Because they don't lose their tails as adults, they are sometimes mistaken for reptiles. Salamanders need to maintain moist skin for breathing. They lay their eggs in water, but the larva very much resemble the adult except they have gills.

Importance of Amphibians

There is concern about the declining numbers of amphibians and the possibility of extinctions. Among the species that are endangered are the San Marcos salamander *(Eurycea nana)*, Wyoming toad *(Bufo baxteri)*, and Mississippi gopher frog *(Rana capito sevosa)*.

Reptiles
Reptile Characteristics

Reptiles have adaptations for life away from moist environments. Their thick, dry skin is covered with scales to prevent water loss. They cannot absorb oxygen through their skin, so they have well-developed lungs for gas exchange. While most have three-chambered hearts, some reptiles evolved the more efficient four-chamber heart. Compared to amphibians, the legs of reptiles are located more directly under the animal. This increases the efficiency of movement on land. The reptile egg is an amniotic egg. It contains moisture and barriers to prevent moisture loss. It gets its name from the amnion, which is a membrane that contains fluid that cushions the embryo and prevents dehydration. So unlike the amphibian egg, the reptile egg can survive and develop in dry terrestrial environments. Without an external watery environment for sperm to swim to the egg, reptiles evolved the capability for internal fertilization.

Lizards come in a variety of forms. While most lizards eat insects, iguanas are herbivores. The largest lizard is the Komodo dragon, which can be ten feet long and two hundred pounds. Only a couple of lizards inject venom when biting. These are the Gila monster of the southwestern United States and the beaded lizard of Mexico.

Importance of Reptiles

The following turtles are endangered species: Kemp's Ridley Sea Turtle *(Lepidochelys kempii)* and Leatherback Sea Turtle *(Dermochelys coriacea).*

---

chapter content resources

Internet Resources

For additional content background, visit **life.msscience.com** to:
- access your book online
- find references to related articles in popular science magazines
- access Web links with related content background
- access current events with science journal topics

Print Resources

Fish and Amphibians (Discovery Channel Science) by Kathy Freely, Susan Wernert, Monique Peterson, Justine Ciovacco, Sharon Yates, Gareth Stevens, 2002

Herpetology: An Introductory Biology of Amphibians and Reptiles, Second Edition by George R. Zug, Laurie J. Vitt, Jonalee P. Caldwell, Academic Press, 2001

Amphibians: The World of Frogs, Toads, Salamanders, and Newts by Robert Hofrichter, Firefly Books, 2000

Fishes: A Field and Laboratory Manual on Their Structure, Identification, and Natural History by Gregor Cailliet, Milton Love, Alfred Ebeling, Waveland Press, 1996

chapter 14

Chapter Vocabulary

chordate, p. 394
notochord, p. 394
postanal tail, p. 394
nerve cord, p. 395
pharyngeal pouch, p. 395
endoskeleton, p. 395
cartilage, p. 395
vertebrate, p. 395
ectotherm, p. 397
endotherm, p. 397
fin, p. 399
scale, p. 399
hibernation, p. 407
estivation, p. 407
amniotic egg, p. 413

Science Journal Student responses will vary, but may include: fish live and breathe in water, amphibians change forms and live near water, and reptiles lay eggs and breathe air.

INTERACTIVE CHALKBOARD
with Image Bank

PowerPoint® Presentations

This CD-ROM is an editable Microsoft® PowerPoint® presentation that includes:
* a pre-made presentation for every chapter
* interactive graphics
* animations
* audio clips
* image bank
* all new section and chapter questions
* Standardized Test Practice
* transparencies
* pre-lab questions for all labs
* Foldables directions
* links to life.msscience.com

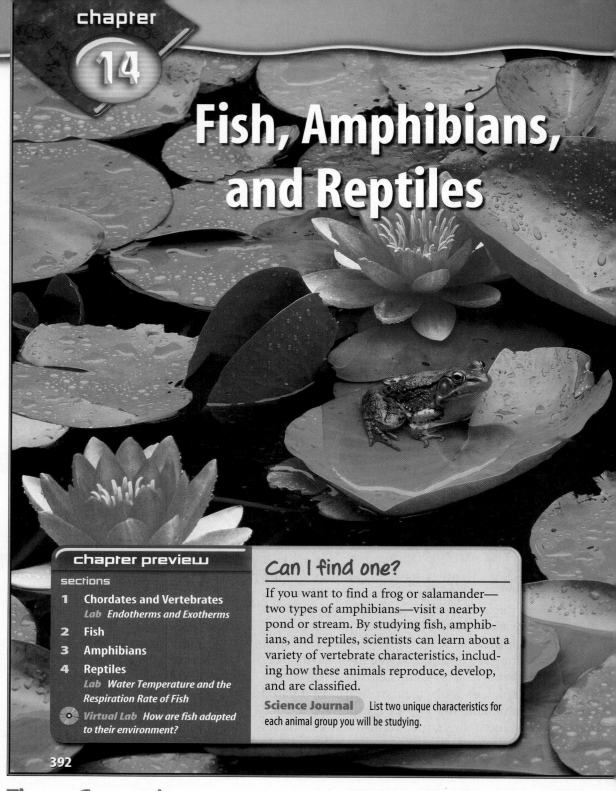

chapter 14

Fish, Amphibians, and Reptiles

chapter preview

sections

1 Chordates and Vertebrates
Lab Endotherms and Exotherms

2 Fish

3 Amphibians

4 Reptiles
Lab Water Temperature and the Respiration Rate of Fish

Virtual Lab How are fish adapted to their environment?

392

Can I find one?

If you want to find a frog or salamander—two types of amphibians—visit a nearby pond or stream. By studying fish, amphibians, and reptiles, scientists can learn about a variety of vertebrate characteristics, including how these animals reproduce, develop, and are classified.

Science Journal List two unique characteristics for each animal group you will be studying.

Theme Connection

Stability and Change The theme of stability and change is introduced in a discussion of chordates and vertebrates. The theme is developed through the discussion of adaptations that fish, amphibians, and reptiles have for living in their environments. The ecological importance of fish, amphibians, and reptiles is presented.

About the Photo

Bullfrogs The American Bullfrog, *Rana catesbeiana*, is one of the most well-known frogs due to its characteristic bass *jug-o-rum* sound. This call attracts females and marks territory. The bullfrog is native to the central and eastern United States and the southern portions of Ontario and Quebec. Bullfrogs are large, sometimes more than 6 inches. They range in color from dull green to dull gray to black.

Start-Up Activities

Snake Hearing

How much do you know about reptiles? For example, do snakes have eyelids? Why do snakes flick their tongues in and out? How can some snakes swallow animals that are larger than their own heads? Snakes don't have ears, so how do they hear? In this lab, you will discover the answer to one of these questions.

1. Hold a tuning fork by the stem and tap it on a hard piece of rubber, such as the sole of a shoe.

2. Hold it next to your ear. What, if anything, do you hear?

3. Tap the tuning fork again. Press the base of the stem firmly against your chin. In your Science Journal, describe what happens.

4. **Think Critically** Using the results from step 3, infer how a snake detects vibrations. In your Science Journal, predict how different animals can use vibrations to hear.

Preview this chapter's content and activities at life.msscience.com

---

FOLDABLES
Study Organizer

Fish, Amphibians, and Reptiles Make the following Foldable to help you organize information about the animals you will be studying.

STEP 1 **Fold** one piece of paper lengthwise into thirds.

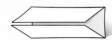

STEP 2 **Fold** the paper widthwise into fourths.

STEP 3 **Unfold,** lay the paper lengthwise, and draw lines along the folds.

STEP 4 **Label** your table as shown.

Fish	Amphibians	Reptiles

Make a Table As you read this chapter, complete the table describing characteristics of each type of animal.

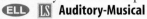

Chordates and Vertebrates

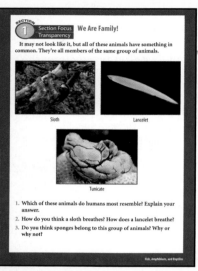

as you read

What You'll Learn

- List the characteristics of all chordates.
- Identify characteristics shared by vertebrates.
- Differentiate between ectotherms and endotherms.

Why It's Important

Humans are vertebrates. Other vertebrates play important roles in your life because they provide food, companionship, and labor.

⊙ Review Vocabulary
motor responses: responses that involve muscular movement

New Vocabulary
- chordate
- notochord
- postanal tail
- nerve cord
- pharyngeal pouch
- endoskeleton
- cartilage
- vertebrae
- ectotherm
- endotherm

Figure 1 Sea squirts get their name because when they're taken out of the ocean, they squirt water out of their body.
Determine *what you have in common with a sea squirt.*

Chordate Characteristics

During a walk along the seashore at low tide, you often can see jellylike masses of animals clinging to rocks. Some of these animals may be sea squirts, as shown in **Figure 1,** which is one of the many types of animals known as chordates (KOR dayts). **Chordates** are animals that have four characteristics present at some stage of their development—a notochord, postanal tail, nerve cord, and pharyngeal pouches.

Notochord All chordates have an internal **notochord** that supports the animal and extends along the upper part of its body, as shown in **Figure 2.** The notochord is flexible but firm because it is made up of fluid-filled cells that are enclosed in a stiff covering. The notochord also extends into the **postanal tail**—a muscular structure at the end of the developing chordate. Some chordates, such as fish, amphibians, reptiles, birds, and mammals, develop backbones that partly or entirely replace the notochord. They are called vertebrates. In some chordates, such as the sea squirt, other tunicates, and the lancelets, the notochord is kept into adulthood.

✓ Reading Check *What happens to the notochord as a bat develops?*

Nerve Cord Above the notochord and along the length of a developing chordate's body is a tubelike structure called the **nerve cord,** also shown in **Figure 2.** As most chordates develop, the front end of the nerve cord enlarges to form the brain and the remainder becomes the spinal cord. These two structures become the central nervous system that develops into complex systems for sensory and motor responses.

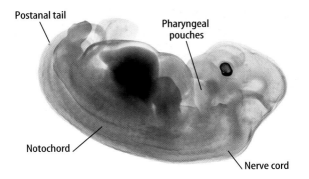

Postanal tail

Pharyngeal pouches

Notochord

Nerve cord

Pharyngeal Pouches All developing chordates have **pharyngeal pouches.** They are found in the region between the mouth and the digestive tube as pairs of openings to the outside. Many chordates have several pairs of pharyngeal pouches. Ancient invertebrate chordates used them for filter feeding. This is still their purpose in some living chordates such as lancelets. In fish, they have developed into internal gills where oxygen and carbon dioxide are exchanged. In humans, pharyngeal pouches are present only during embryonic development. However, one pair becomes the tubes that go from the ears to the throat.

Figure 2 At some time during its development, a chordate has a notochord, postanal tail, nerve cord, and pharyngeal pouches.

Figure 3 Vertebrae are separated by soft disks of cartilage.

Vertebrate Characteristics

Besides the characteristics common to all chordates, vertebrates have distinct characteristics. These traits set vertebrates apart from other chordates.

Structure All vertebrates have an internal framework called an **endoskeleton.** It is made up of bone and/or flexible tissue called **cartilage.** Your ears and the tip of your nose are made of cartilage. The endoskeleton provides a place for muscle attachment and supports and protects the organs. Part of the endoskeleton is a flexible, supportive column called the backbone, as shown in **Figure 3.** It is a stack of **vertebrae** alternating with cartilage. The backbone surrounds and protects the spinal nerve cord. Vertebrates also have a head with a skull that encloses and protects the brain.

Most of a vertebrate's internal organs are found in a central body cavity. A protective skin covers a vertebrate. Hair, feathers, scales, or horns sometimes grow from the skin.

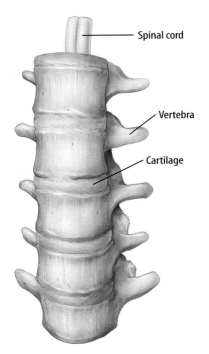

Spinal cord

Vertebra

Cartilage

Vertebrae column

SECTION 1 Chordates and Vertebrates **395**

Animal Performance Organize the class into seven groups. Assign each group one of the seven groups of vertebrates shown on this page. Give students time to research information about the kinds of animals in their group. Then have each group develop a game, poem, song, or short play that presents the information about the animals they researched. L2 ELL COOP LEARN IS
Interpersonal, Linguistic

Discussion

Jawless Fish Lampreys and hagfish are the only jawless fish that survive today. How can you explain the small number of species in this group? Possible answers: Without paired fins, they are not good swimmers. Without jaws, they are not good predators. When jaws and paired fins evolved, species with these characteristics were more successful and became dominant. L2

Teacher FYI

Chordata **Subphyla** The phylum *Chordata* includes three subphyla: *Urochordata* (tunicates), *Cephalochordata* (lancelets), and *Vertebrata*.

Visual Learning

Table 1 Have students make a circle graph from this data, showing what percentage of species belongs to each vertebrate group. L2 IS **Logical-Mathematical**

Table 1 Types of Vertebrates

Group	Estimated Number of Species	Examples	
Jawless fish	60	lamprey, hagfish	
Jawed cartilaginous fish	500 to 900	shark, ray, skate	
Bony fish	20,000	salmon, bass, guppy, sea horse, lungfish	
Amphibians	4,000	frog, toad, salamander	
Reptiles	7,970	turtle, lizard, snake, crocodile, alligator	
Birds	8,700	stork, eagle, sparrow, turkey, duck, ostrich	
Mammals	4,600	human, whale, bat, mouse, lion, cow, otter	

Differentiated Instruction

Challenge Have students list the characteristics of each vertebrate group. Which help contribute to the success of the group? Which keep the group from being more successful? L3

Active Reading

Learning Journal Have students draw a vertical line down each page of their Learning Journals. Have them record research notes, lecture notes, or vocabulary terms in the left column, and their responses to, interpretations of, questions about, or analyses in the right column. Direct students to write a Learning Journal related to chordates and vertebrates. L2

Vertebrate Groups Seven main groups of vertebrates are found on Earth today, as shown in **Table 1.** Vertebrates are either ectotherms or endotherms. Fish, amphibians, and reptiles are ectotherms, also known as cold-blooded animals. An **ectotherm** has an internal body temperature that changes with the temperature of its surroundings. Birds and mammals are endotherms, which sometimes are called warm-blooded animals. An **endotherm** has a nearly constant internal body temperature.

Vertebrate Origins Some vertebrate fossils, like the one in **Figure 4,** are of water-dwelling, armored animals that lived about 420 million years ago (mya). Lobe-finned fish appeared in the fossil record about 395 mya. The oldest known amphibian fossils date from about 370 mya. Reptile fossils have been found in deposits about 350 million years old. One well-known group of reptiles—the dinosaurs—first appeared about 230 mya.

In 1861, a fossil imprint of an animal with scales, jaws with teeth, claws on its front limbs, and feathers was found. The 150-million-year-old fossil was an ancestor of birds, and was named *Archaeopteryx* (ar kee AHP tuh rihks).

Mammal-like reptiles appeared about 235 mya. However, true mammals appeared about 190 mya, and modern mammals originated about 38 million years ago.

Figure 4 Placoderms were the first fish with jaws. These predatory fish were covered with heavy armor.

Discussion
Basking Ectotherms do not perspire or pant. How do they control body temperature? The temperature of an ectotherm changes with its surroundings. If an ectotherm becomes too cold, it moves to warmer surroundings. An example is a lizard on a rock in the Sun. If it becomes too warm, the ectotherm moves to cooler surroundings. L2

3 Assess

DAILY INTERVENTION

Check for Understanding
Linguistic Have students write a paragraph explaining why vertebrates are classified as chordates, but not all chordates are classified as vertebrates. L2 LS

Reteach
Fish and Cat Skeletons Provide a skeleton of a fish (ectothermic vertebrate) and a cat (endothermic vertebrate). Have students observe the skeletons and determine how they are similar and how they are different. L2 LS
Visual-Spatial

☑ Assessment

Oral Ask students to explain temperature control in ectotherms and endotherms, comparing the way energy is absorbed and used. In ectotherms heat energy is absorbed from sunlight, as opposed to chemical release of energy by digestion and respiration in endotherms. L2

---

section 1 review

Summary

Chordate Characteristics
- Chordates have four common characteristics at some point in their development: a notochord, postanal tail, nerve cord, and pharyngeal pouches.

Vertebrate Characteristics
- All vertebrates have an endoskeleton, a backbone, a head with a skull to protect the brain, internal organs in a central body cavity, and a protective skin.
- Vertebrates can be ectothermic or endothermic.
- There are seven main groups of vertebrates.

Self Check

1. **Explain** the difference between a vertebra and a notochord.

2. **Compare and contrast** some of the physical differences between ectotherms and endotherms.

3. **Think Critically** If the outside temperature decreases by 20°C, what will happen to a reptile's body temperature?

Applying Skills

4. **Concept Map** Construct a concept map using these terms: *chordates, bony fish, amphibians, cartilaginous fish, reptiles, birds, mammals, lancelets, tunicates, invertebrate chordates, jawless fish,* and *vertebrates*.

---

section 1 review

1. The notochord is made up of fluid-filled cells enclosed in a stiff covering; a vertebra is made of bone or cartilage.

2. The body temperature of an ectotherm changes with its surroundings. The body temperature of an endotherm remains the same regardless of its surroundings.

3. Its body temperature will decrease by about 20°.

4. Check students' concept maps to make sure they used all listed terms and classified organisms correctly.

▶ Real-World Question

Purpose Students construct a model animal and determine if it is an endotherm or an ectotherm.
L2 IS **Logical-Mathematical**

Process Skills observe and infer, construct, describe, compare

Time Required 45 minutes

▶ Procedure

Alternate Materials Students can use scraps of wool clothing, cotton balls, socks, shredded paper, or tissue paper for the stuffing.

Teaching Strategy Prepare locations in the classroom that have a wide range of temperatures such as near a heating vent or radiator, on a windowsill, and in a refrigerator.

Troubleshooting Students should use only one kind of stuffing so that their results are comparable with others.

▶ Conclude and Apply

1. Answers will vary.
2. If the temperature did not change dramatically, the model represents an endotherm. If the temperature did change dramatically, it is a model of an ectotherm.
3. Thicker "animals" should maintain the temperature of their inner core better than flat "animals."
4. Answers will vary.

Endotherms and Ectotherms

Birds and mammals are endotherms. Fish, amphibians and reptiles are ectotherms.

▶ Real-World Question

How can you determine whether an animal you have never seen before is an endotherm or an ectotherm? What tests might you conduct to find the answer?

Goals

■ **Construct** an imaginary animal.
■ **Determine** whether your animal is an endotherm or an ectotherm.

Materials

fiberfill	cloth
*cotton balls	thermometer
*old socks	*Alternate materials
*tissue	

Safety Precautions 🔥 ☁ 🧤 🗲

▶ Procedure

1. Design an animal that has a thermometer inside. Construct the animal using cloth and some kind of stuffing material. Make sure that you will be able to remove and reinsert the thermometer.
2. Draw a picture of your animal and record data about its size and shape.

Animal Temperature		
Location	**Beginning Time/ Temperature**	**Ending Time/ Temperature**
	Answers will vary.	

3. Copy the data table in your Science Journal.

4. Place your animal in three locations that have different temperatures. Record the locations in the data table.
5. In each location, record the time and the temperature of your animal at the beginning and after 10 min.

▶ Conclude and Apply

1. **Describe** your results. Did the animal's temperature vary depending upon the location?
2. Based on your results, is your animal an endotherm or an ectotherm? Explain.
3. **Compare** your results to those of others in your class. Were the results the same for animals of different sizes? Did the shape of the animal, such as one being flatter and another more cylindrical, matter?
4. Based on your results and information in the chapter, do you think your animal is most likely a bird, a mammal, a reptile, an amphibian, or a fish? Explain.

*C*ommunicating Your Data

Compare your conclusions with those of other students in your class. **For more help, refer to the** Science Skill Handbook.

398 CHAPTER 14 Fish, Amphibians, and Reptiles

✓ Assessment

Performance Have students build a second animal with an internal temperature opposite to the first. For example, if they first constructed an endotherm, ask them to construct an ectotherm and vice versa. Use **Performance Assessment in the Science Classroom,** p. 97. L2

*C*ommunicating Your Data

Encourage students to compare the shape and contents of their animals and discuss how differences in these variables affected their results. L2

section
2 Fish

Fish Characteristics

Did you know that more differences appear among fish than among any other vertebrate group? In fact, there are more species of fish than species of other vertebrate groups. All fish are ectotherms. They are adapted for living in nearly every type of water environment on Earth—freshwater and salt water. Some fish, such as salmon, spend part of their life in freshwater and part of it in salt water. Fish are found at varying depths, from shallow pools to deep oceans.

A streamlined shape, a muscular tail, and fins allow most fish to move rapidly through the water. **Fins** are fanlike structures attached to the endoskeleton. They are used for steering, balancing, and moving. Paired fins on the sides allow fish to move right, left, backward, and forward. Fins on the top and bottom of the body give the fish stability. Most fish secrete a slimy mucus that also helps them move through the water.

Most fish have scales. **Scales** are hard, thin plates that cover the skin and protect the body, similar to shingles on the roof of a house. Most fish scales are made of bone. **Figure 5** illustrates how they can be tooth shaped, diamond shaped, cone shaped, or round. The shape of the scales can be used to help classify fish. The age of some species can be estimated by counting the annual growth rings of the scales.

What You'll Learn
- **List** the characteristics of the three classes of fish.
- **Explain** how fish obtain food and oxygen and reproduce.
- **Describe** the importance and origin of fish.

Why It's Important
Fish are an important food source for humans as well as many other animals.

Review Vocabulary
streamline: formed to reduce resistance to motion through a fluid or air

New Vocabulary
- fin
- scale

1 Motivate

Bellringer

Section Focus Transparencies also are available on the Interactive Chalkboard CD-ROM. L2 ELL

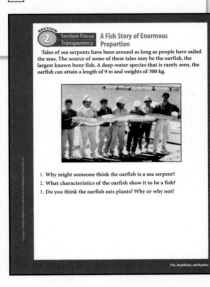

Tie to Prior Knowledge
Fish Characteristics Students will be familiar with fish. Many will have aquariums, some will have fished for recreation, and most will have eaten fish. Use their knowledge of fish to introduce fish characteristics. Most answers students give will relate to bony fish. L2

Activity
Wet Mounts Have each student make a wet mount of a cycloid or ctenoid fish scale to observe under low power with the microscope. After observing, have students draw what they see, and write a summary identifying the type of scale and estimating the age of the fish. L2 IS **Logical-Mathematical**

Figure 5 Four types of fish scales are shown here.

Sharks are covered with placoid scales such as these. Shark teeth are modified forms of these scales.

Lobe-finned fish and gars are covered by ganoid scales. These scales don't overlap like other fish scales.

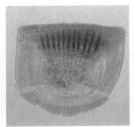
Ctenoid (TEN oyd) scales have a rough edge, which is thought to reduce drag as the fish swims through the water.

Cycloid scales are thin and overlap, giving the fish flexibility. These scales grow as the fish grows.

SECTION 2 Fish **399**

Section 2 Resource Manager

Chapter *FAST FILE* Resources
Transparency Activity, p. 49
Directed Reading for Content Mastery, p. 20
MiniLAB, p. 3
Enrichment, p. 32
Reinforcement, p. 28

Cultural Diversity, p. 7
Performance Assessment, p. 55
Physical Science Critical Thinking/Problem Solving, pp. 1, 23

Use an Analogy

House Shingles Show students a picture of shingles on a house. Explain that most fish are covered with scales arranged much like the shingles on a roof. Scales are firmly attached to the skin tissue from which they grow. In most fish species, the outer part of each scale overlaps the next scale, like shingles on a house. The exception are ganoid scales, found on lobe-finned fish. L2 LS
Logical-Mathematical

Activity

Jawless Fish Table Organize the class into groups of four. Have each group make a table comparing the characteristics of jawless fish, cartilaginous fish, and bony fish. They should compare body shapes and coverings, placement of fins, methods of feeding, sense organs, and any other characteristics they read about. L2 COOP LEARN
LS **Interpersonal**

Caption Answer

Figure 7 Fish breathe with gills—feathery filaments containing many tiny blood vessels. A fish takes water into its mouth and then it passes over the gills. There oxygen from the water is exchanged with the carbon dioxide in the blood.

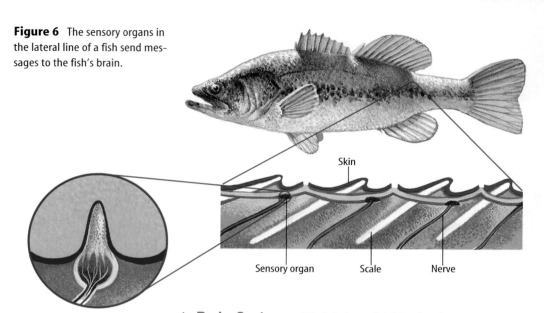

Figure 6 The sensory organs in the lateral line of a fish send messages to the fish's brain.

Skin

Sensory organ   Scale   Nerve

Body Systems All fish have highly developed sensory systems. Most fish have a lateral line system, as shown in **Figure 6.** A lateral line system is made up of a shallow, canal-like structure that extends along the length of the fish's body and is filled with sensory organs. The lateral line enables a fish to sense its environment and to detect movement. Some fish, such as sharks, also have a strong sense of smell. Sharks can detect blood in the water from several kilometers away.

Fish have a two-chambered heart in which oxygen-filled blood mixes with carbon dioxide-filled blood. A fish's blood isn't carrying as much oxygen as blood that is pumped through a three- or four-chambered heart.

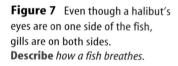

Figure 7 Even though a halibut's eyes are on one side of the fish, gills are on both sides. **Describe** *how a fish breathes.*

Gas Exchange Most fish have organs called gills for the exchange of carbon dioxide and oxygen. Gills are located on both sides of the fish's head and are made up of feathery gill filaments that contain many tiny blood vessels. When a fish takes water into its mouth, the water passes over the gills, where oxygen from the water is exchanged with carbon dioxide in the blood. The water then passes out through slits on each side of the fish. Many fish, such as the halibut in **Figure 7,** are able to take in water while lying on the ocean floor.

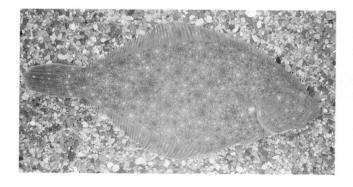

400   CHAPTER 14 Fish, Amphibians, and Reptiles

LAB DEMONSTRATION

Purpose to demonstrate water flow across a fish's gill
Materials guppy or goldfish, water, food coloring, clear container
Preparation Place guppy or goldfish in a clear container with an adequate amount of water.

Procedure Have students observe the fish as it swims, noting the opening and closing of its mouth and gill covers. Place a drop of food coloring in front of the fish's mouth.
Expected Outcome Students will see colored water come out of the fish's gills.

Assessment

How long did it take for colored water to come out of the gills? Answers will vary, but soon after the food coloring is added. What does the appearance of colored water indicate? That the water with food coloring flowed over the fish's gills before being expelled. L2

Figure 8 Fish obtain food in different ways.

A whale shark's mouth can open to 1.4 m wide.

Sawfish are rare. They use their toothed snouts to root out bottom fish to eat.

Parrot fish use their hard beaks to bite off pieces of coral.

Feeding Adaptations Some of the adaptations that fish have for obtaining food are shown in **Figure 8.** Some of the largest sharks are filter feeders that take in small animals as they swim. The archerfish shoots down insects by spitting drops of water at them. Even though some fish have strong teeth, most do not chew their food. They use their teeth to capture their prey or to tear off chunks of food.

Reproduction Fish reproduce sexually. Reproduction is controlled by sex hormones. The production of sex hormones is dependent upon certain environmental factors such as temperature, length of daylight, and availability of food.

Female fish release large numbers of eggs into the water. Males then swim over the eggs and release sperm. This behavior is called spawning. The joining of the egg and sperm cells outside the female's body is called external fertilization. Certain species of sharks and rays have internal fertilization and lay fertilized eggs. Some fish, such as guppies and other sharks, have internal fertilization but the eggs develop and hatch inside the female's body. After they hatch, they leave her body.

Some species do not take care of their young. They release hundreds or even millions of eggs, which increases the chances that a few offspring will survive to become adults. Fish that care for their young lay fewer eggs. Some fish, including some catfish, hold their eggs and young in their mouths. Male sea horses keep the fertilized eggs in a pouch until they hatch.

Electric eels produce a powerful electric shock that stuns their prey.

SECTION 2 Fish **401**

Use an Analogy

Airplane Wings Fish with paired fins use them the same way airplanes use wings and propellers to generate thrust, to direct the body up and down, and to change direction. L2

Fish Fats Accept all reasonable responses. Encourage students to use the Food Guide Pyramid as a guide for developing a healthful meal.

Career A dietician plans food and nutrition programs, and supervises the preparation and serving of meals. Part of their work is to prevent and treat illnesses by promoting healthy eating habits and suggesting diet modifications. Dieticians need at least a bachelor's degree in dietetics, food and nutrition, or a related area. Coursework generally includes chemistry, biochemistry, biology, microbiology, physiology, foods, and nutrition.

✔ Reading Check

Answer because of overfishing and the slow shark reproduction rate

Caption Answer

Figure 9 They are bottom feeders eating dead and dying fish and other marine organisms.

Types of Fish

Fish vary in size, shape, color, living environments, and other factors. Despite their diversity, fish are grouped into only three categories—jawless fish, jawed cartilaginous (kar tuh LA juh nuss) fish, and bony fish.

Jawless Fish

Lampreys, along with the hagfish in **Figure 9,** are jawless fish. Jawless fish have round, toothed mouths and long, tubelike bodies covered with scaleless, slimy skin. Most lampreys are parasites. They attach to other fish with their suckerlike mouth. They then feed by removing blood and other body fluids from the host fish. Hagfish feed on dead or dying fish and other aquatic animals.

Jawless fish have flexible endoskeletons made of cartilage. Hagfish live only in salt water, but some species of lamprey live in salt water and other species live in freshwater.

Jawed Cartilaginous Fish

Sharks, skates, and rays are jawed cartilaginous fish. These fish have endoskeletons made of cartilage like jawless fish. Unlike jawless fish, these fish have movable jaws that usually have well-developed teeth. Their bodies are covered with tiny scales that make their skins feel like fine sandpaper.

Sharks are top predators in many ocean food chains. They are efficient at finding and killing their food, which includes other fish, mammals, and some reptiles. Because of overfishing and the fact that shark reproduction is slow, shark populations are decreasing at an alarming rate.

✔ Reading Check *Why are shark populations decreasing?*

Fish Fats Many fish contain oil with omega-3 fatty acids, which seems to reverse the effects of too much cholesterol. A diet rich in fish that contain this oil might prevent the formation of fatty deposits in the arteries of humans. In your Science Journal, develop a menu for a meal that includes fish.

Figure 9 Hagfish have cartilaginous skeletons. They feed on marine worms, mollusks, and crustaceans, in addition to dead and dying fish.
Infer *how hagfish eat.*

Curriculum Connection

Language Arts Divide the class into groups. Assign each group a well-known shark—great white, bull, hammerhead, or nurse. Have each group research characteristics, feeding habits, and behavior of the sharks and report back to the class. L2 COOP LEARN **IS** **Interpersonal**

Figure 10 Bony fish come in many sizes, shapes, and colors. However, all bony fish have the same basic body structure.

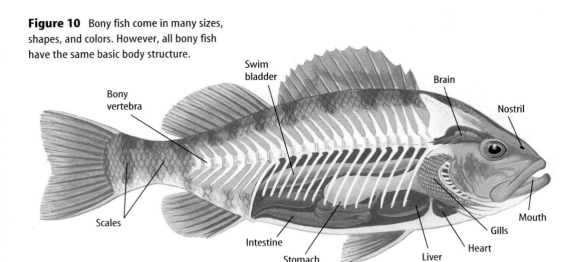

Labels: Bony vertebra, Swim bladder, Brain, Nostril, Scales, Intestine, Stomach, Liver, Heart, Gills, Mouth

Bony Fish

About 95 percent of all species of fish are bony fish. They have skeletons made of bone. The body structure of a typical bony fish is shown in **Figure 10.** A bony flap covers and protects the gills. It closes as water moves into the mouth and over the gills. When it opens, water exits from the gills.

 **INTEGRATE Physics** **Swim Bladder** An important adaptation in most bony fish is the swim bladder. It is an air sac that allows the fish to adjust its density in response to the density of the surrounding water. The density of matter is found by dividing its mass by its volume. If the density of the object is greater than that of the liquid it is in, the object will sink. If the density of the object is equal to the density of the liquid, the object will neither sink nor float to the surface. If the density of the object is less than the density of the liquid, the object will float on the liquid's surface.

The transfer of gases—mostly oxygen in deepwater fish and nitrogen in shallow-water fish—between the swim bladder and the blood causes the swim bladder to inflate and deflate. As the swim bladder fills with gases, the fish's density decreases and it rises in the water. When the swim bladder deflates, the fish's density increases and it sinks. Glands regulate the gas content in the swim bladder, enabling the fish to remain at a specific depth with little effort. Deepwater fish often have oil in their swim bladders rather than gases. Some bottom-dwelling fish and active fish that frequently change depth have no swim bladders.

Mini LAB

Modeling How Fish Adjust to Different Depths

Procedure
1. Fill a **balloon** with air.
2. Place it in a **bowl of water.**
3. Fill **another balloon** partially with water, then blow air into it until it is the same size as the air-filled balloon.
4. Place the second balloon in the bowl of water.

Analysis
1. Infer what structure these balloons model.
2. Compare where in the water (on the surface, or below the surface) two fish would be if they had swim bladders similar to the two balloons.

 Try at Home

Mini LAB

Purpose Students use a model to determine how fish use a swim bladder to control their depth. L1 ELL COOP LEARN IS **Kinesthetic and Interpersonal**

Materials 2 balloons, water, bowl

Teaching Strategies
• The bowl will need to be large enough to hold both balloons.
• Encourage students to experiment with different proportions of water and air in the balloon to simulate changes occurring within a fish's swim bladder.

Analysis
1. a swim bladder
2. A fish with a swim bladder filled with air would be near the surface; one with water and air would be farther beneath the surface.

Assessment

Process Ask students to infer the habitat of fish, such as blennies, that have no swim bladder. These fish are bottom dwellers. Use **Performance Assessment in the Science Classroom,** p. 89.

Try at Home

Fun Fact

The smallest freshwater fish is the dwarf pygmy goby, which measures 9 mm long. The largest living fish is the whale shark.

Differentiated Instruction

Challenge Have students research the different types of fishing such as fly-fishing, deep-sea fishing, spin-fishing, trolling, and down-rigging. If possible, have them interview persons who participate in these sports and report their finding to the class. L3

Cultural Diversity

Commercial Fishing Fish are a vital food source worldwide. Fishing is an important economic activity, and fish are part of the diet in many countries. Have students research the fishing industry in various countries and mark a world map to show where most commercial fishing occurs. L2 ELL IS **Visual-Spatial**

Freshwater Fish Have students research species of fish that live in the lakes and rivers of their state. Have them find or draw pictures of each species and make a bulletin board that illustrates where each species is found. L2

ELL **IS** **Visual-Spatial**

Fun Fact

A swim bladder works the same way a scuba diver's buoyancy compensator does. A scuba diver adds air to his or her compensator to rise, and releases air from the compensator to sink. Also, the diver may effect small changes in depth by inhaling or exhaling.

Discussion

Fish Bladders Bottom-dwelling fish often lack a swim bladder. What is the advantage of this? Swim bladders help fish maintain buoyancy. A bottom-dwelling fish would be at a disadvantage if it were buoyant. L2

Applying Math

National Math Standards
Correlation to Mathematics Objectives
1, 7

Teaching Strategy
Follow the steps in the example problem. Divide the mass of the fish by the volume of the fish.

Answers to Practice Problems
1. Divide the mass of the fish (215 g) by the volume (180 cm³). The fish will have a density of 1.19 g/cm³. The fish will sink in salt water because it is denser than the salt water.
2. The density of the fish is 1.023 g/cm³. The fish is a saltwater fish, because it is less dense than salt water and more dense than fresh water.

Figure 11 Coelacanths (SEE luh kanthz) have been found living in the Indian Ocean north of Madagascar.

Lobe-Finned Fish One of the three types of bony fish is the lobe-finned fish, as shown in **Figure 11**. Lobe-finned fish have fins that are lobelike and fleshy. These organisms were thought to have been extinct for more than 70 million years. But in 1938, some South African fishers caught a lobe-finned fish in a net. Several living lobe-finned fish have been studied since. Lobe-finned fish are important because scientists hypothesize that fish similar to these were the ancestors of the first land vertebrates—the amphibians.

Applying Math   Solve a One-Step Equation

DENSITY OF A FISH A freshwater fish has a mass of 645 g and a volume of 700 cm³. What is the fish's density, and will it sink or float in freshwater?

Solution

1. *This is what you know:*
   - density of freshwater = 1g/cm³
   - mass of fish = 645 g
   - volume of fish = 700 cm³

2. *This is the equation you need to use:*
   $$\frac{\text{mass of object (g)}}{\text{volume of object (cm}^3)} = \text{density of object (g/cm}^3)$$

3. *Substitute the known values:*
   $$\frac{645 \text{ g}}{700 \text{ cm}^3} = 0.921 \text{ g/cm}^3$$

4. *Check your answer:* Multiply 0.921 g/cm³ by 700 cm³. You should get 645 g. The fish will float in freshwater. Its density is less than that of freshwater.

Practice Problems

1. Calculate the density of a saltwater fish that has a mass of 215 g and a volume of 180 cm³. Will this fish float or sink in salt water? The density of ocean salt water is about 1.025 g/cm³.

2. A fish with a mass of 440 g and a volume of 430 cm³ floats in its water. Is it a freshwater fish or a saltwater fish?

For more practice, visit life.msscience.com/math_practice

404   CHAPTER 14 Fish, Amphibians, and Reptiles

Differentiated Instruction

Learning Disabled Have students make a mobile of the different types of fish mentioned in this section (jawless, cartilaginous, and bony). Beneath each type, have them write the fact they find most interesting about it. The same thing can be done with amphibians and reptiles. L2 **IS** **Kinesthetic and Visual-Spatial**

Curriculum Connection

Language Arts Read aloud poems about fish. Several can be found in John Hersey's book *Blues*. Others include "The Fish" by Elizabeth Bishop, "The Red Mullet" by Robert Penn Warren, "The Lung Fish" by John Ciardi, and "Pike" by Ted Hughes. Ask students how the poet used the fish in each poem. Have them find other poems about fish to share. L2

Figure 12 Australian lungfish are one of the six species of lungfish.
Identify *the unique adaptation of a lungfish.*

Lungfish A lungfish, as shown in **Figure 12,** has one lung and gills. This adaptation enables them to live in shallow waters that have little oxygen. The lung enables the lungfish to breathe air when the water evaporates. Drought conditions stimulate lungfish to burrow into the mud and cover themselves with mucus until water returns. Lungfish have been found along the coasts of South America and Australia.

Ray-Finned Fish Most bony fish have fins made of long, thin bones covered with skin. Ray-finned fish, like those in **Figure 13,** have a lot of variation in their body plans. Most predatory fish have long, flexible bodies, which enable them to pursue prey quickly. Many bottom fish have flattened bodies and mouths adapted for eating off the bottom. Fish with unusual shapes, like the sea horse and anglerfish, also can be found. Yellow perch, tuna, salmon, swordfish, and eels are ray-finned fish.

Figure 13 Bony fish have a diversity of body plans.

Most bony fish are ray-finned fish, like this rainbow trout.

Sea horses use their tails to anchor themselves to sea grass. This prevents the ocean currents from washing them away.

Anglerfish have a structure that looks like a lure to attract prey fish. When the prey comes close, the anglerfish quickly opens its mouth and captures the prey.

SECTION 2 Fish **405**

Reading Check

Answer They provide food, keep insect populations in check, keep plant growth from clogging waterways, and are kept in aquariums to admire. Fish farming and commercial fishing also are important to many economies.

Discussion

Fish Success Why are there more fish than any other kind of vertebrate? Answers may include that all life began in water and the water environment has undergone fewer changes than land environments. This reduced the risk of extinction because of the lack of ability to adapt to new conditions. L2

3 Assess

DAILY INTERVENTION

Check for Understanding

Linguistic Ask students to explain why fish are classified into three separate classes, whereas amphibians, reptiles, birds, and mammals are not. L2 LS

Reteach

Fish Classes Display pictures of the three classes of fish on the bulletin board. Have students place them in the appropriate class. Then have them examine the pictures and determine the similarities and differences in the three classes. L2 LS **Visual-Spatial**

Assessment

Process Have students use the results of the MiniLAB in this section to determine how a submarine is able to descend and ascend in the ocean. Use **Performance Assessment in the Science Classroom,** p. 89. L2

Figure 14 Lancelets are small, eel-like animals. They spend most of their time buried in the sand and mud at the bottom of the ocean.

Importance and Origin of Fish

Fish play a part in your life in many ways. They provide food for many animals, including humans. Fish farming and commercial fishing also are important to the U.S. economy. Fishing is a method of obtaining food as well as a form of recreation enjoyed by many people. Many fish eat large amounts of insect larvae, such as mosquitoes, which keeps insect populations in check. Some, such as grass carp, are used to keep the plant growth from clogging waterways. Captive fish are kept in aquariums for humans to admire their bright colors and exotic forms.

✔ **Reading Check** *How are fish helpful to humans?*

Most scientists agree that fish evolved from small, soft-bodied, filter-feeding organisms similar to present-day lancelets, shown in **Figure 14.** The earliest fossils of fish are those of jawless fish that lived about 450 million years ago. Fossils of these early fish usually are found where ancient streams emptied into the sea. This makes it difficult to tell whether these fish ancestors evolved in freshwater or in salt water.

Today's bony fish are probably descended from the first jawed fish called the acanthodians (a kan THOH dee unz). They appeared in the fossil record about 410 mya. Another group of ancient fish—the placoderms—appeared about 400 mya. For about 50 million years, placoderms dominated most water ecosystems then disappeared. Modern sharks and rays probably descended from the placoderms.

---

section 2 review

Summary

Fish Characteristics
- All fish have a streamlined shape, a muscular tail, fins, scales, well-developed sensory systems, and gills.
- All fish reproduce sexually and feed in many different ways.

Types of Fish
- There are three categories of fish: jawless fish, jawed cartilaginous fish, and bony fish.
- There are three types of bony fish: lobe-finned fish, lungfish, and ray-finned fish.

Self Check

1. **List** examples for each of the three classes of fish.
2. **Explain** how jawless fish and cartilaginous jawed fish take in food.
3. **Describe** the many ways that fish are important to humans.
4. **Think Critically** Female fish lay thousands of eggs. Why aren't lakes and oceans overcrowded with fish?

Applying Skills

5. **Concept Map** Make an events-chain concept map to show what must take place for the fish to rise from the bottom to the surface of the lake.

Science Online life.msscience.com/self_check_quiz

---

section 2 review

1. jawless fish—lamprey; cartilaginous fish—shark; bony fish—tuna
2. Jawless fish are parasites that attach to other fish. Cartilaginous fish are predators.
3. Possible answers: food, pets, controlling the growth of insect and plant pests
4. Many eggs are not fertilized; some eggs and young fish are eaten.
5. The sequence is as follows: A fish lying on the bottom of the lake transfers gases from the bloodstream into the swim bladder. As the swim bladder fills with gas, the fish rises in the water.

section 3

Amphibians

Amphibian Characteristics

The word *amphibian* comes from the Greek word *amphibios,* which means "double life." They are well named, because amphibians spend part of their lives in water and part on land. Frogs, toads, and the salamander shown in **Figure 15** are examples of amphibians. What characteristics do these animals have that allow them to live on land and in water?

Amphibians are ectotherms. Their body temperature changes when the temperature of their surroundings changes. In cold weather, amphibians become inactive and bury themselves in mud or leaves until the temperature warms. This period of inactivity during cold weather is called **hibernation.** Amphibians that live in hot, dry environments become inactive and hide in the ground when temperatures become too hot. Inactivity during the hot, dry months is called **estivation.**

> **Reading Check** *How are hibernation and estivation similar?*

Respiration Amphibians have moist skin that is smooth, thin, and without scales. They have many capillaries directly beneath the skin and in the lining of the mouth. This makes it possible for oxygen and carbon dioxide to be exchanged through the skin and the mouth lining. Amphibians also have small, simple, saclike lungs in the chest cavity for the exchange of oxygen and carbon dioxide. Some salamanders have no lungs and breathe only through their skin.

Figure 15 Salamanders often are mistaken for lizards because of their shape. However, like all amphibians, they have a moist, scaleless skin that requires them to live in a damp habitat.

as you read

What You'll Learn

- **Describe** the adaptations amphibians have for living in water and living on land.
- **List** the kinds of amphibians and the characteristics of each.
- **Explain** how amphibians reproduce and develop.

Why It's Important

Because amphibians are sensitive to changes in the environment, they can be used as biological indicators.

⊙ **Review Vocabulary**
habitat: place where an organism lives and that provides the types of food, shelter, moisture, and temperature needed for survival

New Vocabulary
- hibernation
- estivation

SECTION 3 Amphibians **407**

1 Motivate

Bellringer

Section Focus Transparencies also are available on the Interactive Chalkboard CD-ROM.
 L2 ELL

Tie to Prior Knowledge

Fish Adaptations Discuss the characteristics of lobe-finned fish. Show students a picture of a lobe-finned fish. Ask them what adaptations would be necessary for a fish to survive on land. L2

> **Reading Check**

Answer Both are periods of amphibian inactivity brought on by weather changes.

Section 3 Resource Manager

Chapter *FAST FILE* Resources
Transparency Activity, p. 50
Directed Reading for Content Mastery, p. 21
Enrichment, p. 33
Reinforcement, p. 29
MiniLAB, p. 4

Lab Activity, pp. 11–15
Life Science Critical Thinking/Problem Solving, p. 7

Discussion

Naming Amphibians *Amphibian* means "one who leads a double life." Why is this an appropriate name for amphibians? Many begin their lives as aquatic tadpoles and then live most of their adult lives on land. L2

Inquiry Lab

Frog Hibernation

Purpose to explore and observe amphibian reactions to changes in temperature L2

Possible Materials aquarium, water, mud, dirt, wire screen, frog, heat lamp, jar big enough for frog, shallow tub large enough to put aquarium or jar into, ice or cold water, thermometer

Estimated Time one class session

Teaching Strategies

• Students can design a terrarium for the frog, with mud on one side deep enough for the frog to burrow into and shallow water on the other end.

• Students can predict how the frog will react when the temperature is raised or lowered. They also can predict how they will see this reaction, perhaps by observing the throat.

• Students can raise the temperature by putting the terrarium under a heat lamp. They can lower the temperature by placing the frog in a jar and slowly lowering the temperature in a cold-water bath. They can observe hibernation by putting the terrarium in a cold-water bath.

• Allow students to explore other questions as they arise.

• Have students obtain your approval for their lab ideas to ensure the safety of both the students and the frog.

For additional inquiry activities, see *Science Inquiry Labs.*

Figure 16 Red-eyed tree frogs are found in forests of Central and South America. They eat a variety of foods, including insects and even other frogs.

Figure 17 Amphibians go through metamorphosis as they develop.

Circulation The three-chambered heart in amphibians is an important change from the circulatory system of fish. In the three-chambered heart, one chamber receives oxygen-filled blood from the lungs and skin, and another chamber receives carbon dioxide-filled blood from the body tissues. Blood moves from both of these chambers to the third chamber, which pumps oxygen-filled blood to body tissues and carbon dioxide-filled blood back to the lungs. Limited mixing of these two bloods occurs.

Reproduction Even though amphibians are adapted for life on land, they depend on water for reproduction. Because their eggs do not have a protective, waterproof shell, they can dry out easily, so amphibians must have water to reproduce.

Amphibian eggs are fertilized externally by the male. As the eggs come out of the female's body, the male releases sperm over them. In most species the female lays eggs in a pond or other body of water. However, many species have developed special reproductive adaptations, enabling them to reproduce away from bodies of water. Red-eyed tree frogs, like the ones in **Figure 16,** lay eggs in a thick gelatin on the underside of leaves that hang over water. After the tadpoles hatch, they fall into the water below, where they continue developing. The Sonoran Desert toad waits for small puddles to form in the desert during the rainy season. It takes tadpoles only two to 12 days to hatch in these temporary puddles.

After hatching, most young amphibians, like these tadpoles, do not look like adult forms.

Amphibian eggs are laid in a jellylike material to keep them moist.

408 CHAPTER 14 Fish, Amphibians, and Reptiles

Differentiated Instruction

Visually Impaired Use a model of a frog to help students locate and identify the function of different structures of amphibians. L2 IS **Kinesthetic**

Curriculum Connection

Language Arts Have students read "The Celebrated Jumping Frog of Calaveras County," written by Mark Twain while he lived in California. It appeared in the *New York Saturday Press* in November 1865. Every year, frog-jumping competitions are held in Calaveras County, California. Have students find out the distance frogs can jump. L2 IS **Linguistic**

Development Most amphibians go through a developmental process called metamorphosis (me tuh MOR fuh sus). Fertilized eggs hatch into tadpoles, the stage that lives in water. Tadpoles have fins, gills, and a two-chambered heart similar to fish. As tadpoles grow into adults, they develop legs, lungs, and a three-chambered heart. **Figure 17** shows this life cycle.

The tadpole of some amphibian species, such as salamanders, are not much different from the adult stage. Young salamanders look like adult salamanders, but they have external gills and usually a tail fin.

Frogs and Toads

Adult frogs and toads have short, broad bodies with four legs but no neck or tail. The strong hind legs are used for swimming and jumping. Bulging eyes and nostrils on top of the head let frogs and toads see and breathe while the rest of their body is submerged in water. On spring nights, males make their presence known with loud, distinctive croaking sounds. On each side of the head, just behind the eyes, are round tympanic membranes. These membranes vibrate somewhat like an eardrum in response to sounds and are used by frogs and toads to hear.

Most frog and toad tongues are attached at the front of their mouths. When they see prey, their tongue flips out and contacts the prey. The prey gets stuck in the sticky saliva on the tongue and the tongue flips back into the mouth. Toads and frogs eat a variety of insects, worms, and spiders, and one tropical species eats berries.

Science Online

Topic: Biological Indicators
Visit life.msscience.com for Web links to information about amphibians as biological indicators.

Activity What factors make amphibians good biological indicators?

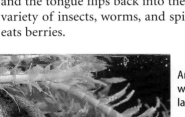

Amphibians go through metamorphosis, which means they change form from larval stage to adult.

Most adult amphibians are able to move about and live on land.

Frogs and Toads

Materials various photographs and models of different frogs and toads

Estimated Time 10 minutes

Procedure Have students look at the photographs and models to observe the differences between frogs and toads. They can sort them into groups, and also take note of the many types of frogs and toads. [L2]

Use an Analogy

Flypaper Tongues Explain that the tongue of a frog is very sticky, like the flypaper that is used to catch flies. This increases the ability of the frog to catch flying insects. [L1]

Activity

Frog Life Cycle Have students work in groups to prepare a poster showing the frog's life cycle. The poster should include drawings of each of the four stages of a frog's life cycle. Each stage should be explained with a paragraph. [L2] [IS] **Visual-Spatial and Linguistic**

IDENTIFYING Misconceptions

Toads and Warts Students may believe they can get warts from touching a toad. Explain that this is a myth which probably came about because many toads have bumpy, wartlike projections on their skin.

Differentiated Instruction

Challenge Have students write a report on the factors that may be contributing to the worldwide decline of frogs and other amphibians in recent years. [L3] [IS] **Linguistic**

Fun Fact

Is it a frog or a toad? Frogs have smooth, moist skin while toads have bumpy, dry skin. Frogs tend to have relatively longer hind legs than toads. This makes frogs capable of long leaps, while toads move in short hops. While toads return to water to lay their eggs, they can exist in drier terrestrial habitats than can frogs.

Mini LAB

Purpose Students observe frog adaptations. L1 IS **Visual-Spatial**

Materials one live frog in a jar for each student group, water, magnifying lens

Teaching Strategy Obtain references on amphibians for students to use in describing frog adaptations. Caution students to avoid moving the jar abruptly.

Analysis

1. bulging eyes and nostrils at the top of the head for seeing and breathing while in water, underside coloration for camouflage, webbed feet for swimming
2. strong legs for jumping, topside coloration for camouflage, wide mouth for capturing land insects

Assessment

Oral Ask students to list the metamorphic changes tadpoles undergo to adapt to life on land. Development of legs, lungs, wide mouth, and a digestive system designed for consuming insects instead of algae.

Mini LAB

Describing Frog Adaptations

Procedure

1. Carefully observe a **frog** in a **jar**. Notice the position of its legs as it sits. Record all of your observations in your **Science Journal.**
2. Observe its mouth, eyes, nostrils and ears.
3. Observe the color of its back and belly.
4. Return the frog to your teacher.

Analysis

1. Describe the adaptations the frog has for living in water.
2. What adaptations does it have for living on land?

Figure 18 Poison frogs are brightly colored to show potential predators that they are poisonous. Toxins from poison frogs have been used in hunting for centuries.

Salamanders

Most species of salamanders and newts live in North America. These amphibians often are mistaken for lizards because of their long, slender bodies. The short legs of salamanders and newts appear to stick straight out from the sides of their bodies.

Land-living species of salamanders and newts usually are found near water. These amphibians hide under leaf litter and rocks during the day to avoid the drying heat of the Sun. At night, they use their well-developed senses of smell and vision to find and feed on worms, crustaceans, and insects.

Many species of salamanders breed on land, where fertilization is internal. Aquatic species of salamanders and newts release and fertilize their eggs in the water.

Importance of Amphibians

Most adult amphibians are insect predators and are helpful in keeping some insect populations in check. They also are a source of food for other animals, including other amphibians. Some people consider frog legs a delicacy.

Poison frogs, like the one in **Figure 18,** produce a poison that can kill large animals. They also are known as poison dart frogs or poison arrow frogs. The toxin is secreted through their skin and can affect muscles and nerves of animals that come in contact with it. Native people of the Emberá Chocó in Colombia, South America, cover blowgun darts that they use for hunting with the poison of one species of these frogs. Researchers are studying the action of these toxins to learn more about how the nervous system works. Researchers also are using amphibians in regeneration studies in hopes of developing new ways of treating humans who have lost limbs or were born without limbs.

Differentiated Instruction

Learning Disabled Have students make flash cards of the vocabulary words in this chapter using an illustration, the phonetic spelling, and the definition of each word. L1 IS **Linguistic and Visual-Spatial**

Challenge Have students research the use of amphibians in regeneration studies and report their findings to the class. L3 IS **Linguistic** P

Biological Indicators Because they live on land and reproduce in water, amphibians are affected directly by changes in the environment, including pesticides and other pollution. Amphibians also absorb gases through their skin, making them susceptible to air pollutants. Amphibians, like the one in **Figure 19,** are considered to be biological indicators. Biological indicators are species whose overall health reflects the health of a particular ecosystem.

 **Reading Check** *What is a biological indicator?*

Origin of Amphibians The fossil record shows that ancestors of modern fish were the first vertebrates on Earth. For about 150 million years, they were the only vertebrates. Then as the climate changed and competition for food and space increased, some lobe-finned fish might have traveled across land searching for water as their ponds dried up. Fossil evidence shows that from these lobe-finned fish evolved aquatic animals with four limbs. Amphibians probably evolved from these aquatic animals about 350 mya.

Because competition on land from other animals was minimal, evolution favored the development of amphibians. Insects, spiders, and other invertebrates were an abundant source of food on land. Land was almost free of predators, so amphibians were able to reproduce in large numbers, and many new species evolved. For 100 million years or more, amphibians were the dominant land animals.

Figure 19 Beginning in 1995, deformed frogs such as this were found. Concerned scientists hypothesize that an increase in the number of deformed frogs could be a warning of environmental problems for other organisms.

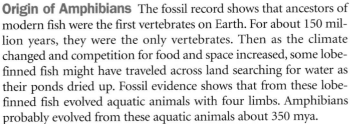

section 3 review

Summary

Amphibian Characteristics
- Amphibians have two phases of life—one in water and one on land.
- All amphibians have a three-chambered heart, reproduce in the water by laying eggs, and go through metamorphosis.

Types and Importance of Amphibians
- Frogs and toads have short, broad bodies, while salamanders have long, slender bodies.
- Amphibians are used for food, research, and are important as biological indicators.

Self Check

1. **List** the adaptations amphibians have for living in water and for living on land.
2. **Explain** how tadpole and frog hearts differ.
3. **Describe** two different environments where amphibians lay eggs.
4. **Think Critically** Why do you suppose frogs and toads seem to appear suddenly after a rain?

Applying Skills

5. **Concept Map** Make an events-chain concept map of frog metamorphosis. Describe each stage in your Science Journal.

 Science Online life.msscience.com/self_check_quiz

---

section 3 review

1. water: moist, smooth skin; bulging eyes and nostrils on top of the head; strong hind legs for swimming; land: lungs; strong skeleton; strong hind legs for jumping; moist, smooth skin

2. Tadpoles have a two-chambered heart; frogs have a three-chambered heart.
3. Possible answers: underside of leaves in rainforest, in ponds or lakes, on the back of the female

4. They hunt food when the air is moist.
5. egg→legless tadpole→tadpole with legs→young frog with developing legs→adult frog on land

---

Visual Learning

Figure 19 Have students compare this frog with a normal frog and list the differences.

Reading Check

Answer a species whose health reflects the health of their ecosystem

Discussion

Biological Indicators Why are amphibians considered to be biological indicators? They live on land, reproduce in water, and absorb gases from the air through their skin. They are sensitive to chemical changes on land, in water, and in the air. L2

3 Assess

DAILY INTERVENTION

Check for Understanding

Visual-Spatial Show pictures or slides of amphibians and have students identify each as a frog, toad, salamander, or caecilian. L1 LS

Reteach

Amphibian Traits Have students work in groups to create a game or a graphic that compares and contrasts the traits of the three amphibian groups. COOP LEARN L2 LS **Interpersonal**

Assessment

Performance Assess students' understanding of metamorphosis by having them prepare a poster to compare frog metamorphosis with insect metamorphosis. Use **Performance Assessment in the Science Classroom,** p. 145. L2

as you read

What You'll Learn

- **List** the characteristics of reptiles.
- **Determine** how reptile adaptations enable them to live on land.
- **Explain** the importance of the amniotic egg.

Why It's Important

Reptiles provide information about how body systems work during extreme weather conditions

Review Vocabulary
bask: to warm by continued exposure to heat

New Vocabulary
- amniotic egg

Figure 20 Skinks, like this northern blue-tongue skink, are one of the largest lizard families with around 800 species.

Reptile Characteristics

Reptiles are ectotherms with a thick, dry, waterproof skin. Their skin is covered with scales that help reduce water loss and protect them from injury. Even though reptiles are ectotherms, they are able to modify their internal body temperatures by their behavior. When the weather is cold, they bask in the Sun, which warms them. When the weather is warm and the Sun gets too hot, they move into the shade to cool down.

Reading Check *How are reptiles able to modify their body temperature?*

Some reptiles, such as turtles, crocodiles, and lizards, like the skink in **Figure 20,** move on four legs. Claws are used to dig, climb, and run. Reptiles, such as snakes and some lizards, move without legs.

Body Systems Scales on reptiles prevent the exchange of oxygen and carbon dioxide through the skin. Reptiles breathe with lungs. Even turtles and sea snakes that live in water must come to the surface to breathe.

The circulatory system of reptiles is more highly developed than that of amphibians. Most reptiles have a three-chambered heart with a partial wall inside the main chamber. This means that less mixing of oxygen-filled blood and carbon dioxide-filled blood occurs than in amphibians. This type of circulatory system provides more oxygen to all parts of the body. Crocodilians have a four-chambered heart that completely separates the oxygen-filled blood and the carbon dioxide-filled blood and keeps them from mixing.

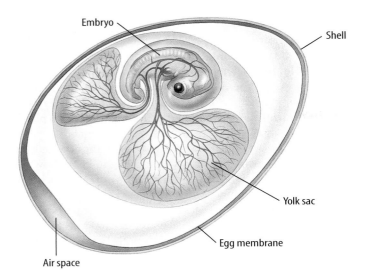

Embryo

Shell

Yolk sac

Egg membrane

Air space

Figure 21 The development of amniotic eggs enabled reptiles to reproduce on land.

Infer *how an amniotic egg helps reptiles be a more successful group.*

Amniotic Egg One of the most important adaptations of reptiles for living on land is the way they reproduce. Unlike the eggs of most fish and amphibians, eggs of reptiles are fertilized internally—inside the body of the female. After fertilization, the females of many reptiles lay eggs that are covered by tough, leathery shells. The shell prevents the eggs from drying out. This adaptation enables reptiles to lay their eggs on land.

The **amniotic egg** provides a complete environment for the embryo's development. **Figure 21** shows the structures in a reptilian egg. This type of egg contains membranes that protect and cushion the embryo and help it get rid of wastes. It also contains a large food supply—the yolk—for the embryo. Minute holes in the shell, called pores, allow oxygen and carbon dioxide to be exchanged. By the time it hatches, a young reptile looks like a small adult.

Reading Check *What is the importance of an amniotic egg?*

Types of Modern Reptiles

Reptiles live on every continent except Antarctica and in all the oceans except those in the polar regions. They vary greatly in size, shape, and color. Reticulated pythons, 10 m in length, can swallow small deer whole. Some sea turtles weigh more than 350 kg and can swim faster than humans can run. Three-horned lizards have movable eye sockets and tongues as long as their bodies. The three living groups of reptiles are lizards and snakes, turtles, and crocodilians.

Science Online

Visit life.msscience.com for Web links to recent news about the nesting sites of turtles.

Activity Name two conservation organizations that are giving the turtles a helping hand, and how they are doing it.

---

2 Teach

Caption Answer

Figure 21 It allowed reptiles to move onto land where there was less competition for food and mates.

Use Science Words

Word Meaning The word *reptile* comes from the Latin word *repere*, meaning "to crawl." Have students use the word in a sentence describing its meaning. [L2] [LS] **Linguistic**

Activity

Egg Parts Organize the class into groups of four. Give each group half of a hard-boiled chicken egg. Have students identify the three parts they observe, and tell the function of each. shell—protection, white—protects and cushions the embryo and gets rid of wastes, yolk—food supply for the embryo Explain to students that there is no embryo because commercial chicken eggs usually are not fertilized. [L2] COOP LEARN [LS] **Interpersonal and Kinesthetic**

Reading Check

Answer It enables the reptile to lay its eggs on land.

Differentiated Instruction

Challenge Have students research and report on a reptile in their state that is listed as threatened or endangered. Ask them to include information about the animal's history, reasons for the lower numbers, and actions being taken to help the species. [L3] [P]

Teacher FYI

Slitlike Pupils The shape of a reptile's pupil can indicate whether the animal is active during night or day. Many nocturnal reptiles have slitlike pupils, which indicate that they are active at night.

Venomous Snakes There are some 2,700 known species of snakes and only about 200 are venomous. The only venomous snakes in North America are the pit vipers and coral snakes. Pit vipers include rattlesnakes, water moccasins, and copperheads. Coral snakes can be recognized by their bright colors. Coral snakes and king snakes are often mistaken for one another.

Make a Model

Snake Swallowing Give each group of students plastic straws and a lump of soft clay. Ask them to find a way to move the clay through the straw to the center of the straw. (It can be moved by pinching the sides of the straw.) Use this to explain the muscular contractions of a snake to swallow and ingest food. ⬜L2 COOP LEARN ⬜ℕ **Interpersonal and Kinesthetic**

IDENTIFYING
Misconceptions

Rattlesnake Tail Students may think that the number of rattles on a rattlesnake's tail is the same as its age in years. However, a new rattle forms each time a snake molts, and molting can occur many times each year. Also, some rattles may break off during the year. Thus, there is no correlation between the number of rattles and the age of a snake.

Lizards and Snakes Some animals in the largest group of reptiles—the lizards and snakes like those shown in **Figure 22**—have a type of jaw not found in other reptiles, like the turtle also shown in **Figure 22.** The jaw has a special joint that unhinges and increases the size of their mouths. This enables them to swallow their prey whole. Lizards have movable eyelids, external ears, and legs with clawed toes on each foot. They feed on plants, other reptiles, insects, spiders, worms, and mammals.

Snakes have developed ways of moving without legs. They have poor hearing and most have poor eyesight. Recall how you could feel the vibrations of the tuning fork in the Launch Lab. Snakes do not hear sound waves in the air. They "hear" vibrations in the ground that are picked up by the lower jawbone and conducted to the bones of the snake's inner ear. From there, the vibrations are transferred to the snake's brain, where the sounds are interpreted.

Snakes are meat eaters. Some snakes wrap around and constrict their prey. Others inject their prey with venom. Many snakes feed on small mammals, and as a result, help control those populations.

Most snakes lay eggs after they are fertilized internally. In some species, eggs develop and hatch inside the female's body then leave her body shortly thereafter.

Figure 22 Examples of reptiles are shown below.

When frilled lizards are threatened, they flare out their collar. This behavior helps keep predators away.

Diamondback terrapins are one of the few species of turtles that live in brackish—slightly salty—water.

Rosy boas are one of only two species of boas found in the United States.

Cultural Diversity

Snakes In ancient Egypt, the poisonous asp was held in high esteem and its symbol is found in writings and artifacts. The Aztecs worshipped Quetzalcoatl, the mythical plumed serpent. In India, cobras were thought to be the reincarnated spirits of society's elite. Some cultures in Africa worship pythons. Have students find out how snakes are used in art or in celebrations in different cultures. ⬜L2

Curriculum Connection

History Have students research the impact hunting American alligators for their skin and meat had on the species early in the twentieth century. Ask them to find out what efforts were made to restore populations of these animals and the success of these efforts. ⬜L2

Turtles The only reptiles that have a two-part shell made of hard, bony plates are turtles. The vertebrae and ribs are fused to the inside of the top part of the shell. The muscles are attached to the lower and upper part of the inside of the shell. Most turtles can withdraw their heads and legs into the shell for protection against predators.

✔ **Reading Check** *What is the purpose of a turtle's shell?*

Turtles have no teeth but they do have powerful jaws with a beaklike structure used to crush food. They feed on insects, worms, fish, and plants. Turtles live in water and on land. Those that live on land are called tortoises.

Like most reptiles, turtles provide little or no care for their young. Turtles dig out a nest, deposit their eggs, cover the nest, and leave. Turtles never see their own hatchlings. Young turtles, like those in **Figure 23,** emerge from the eggs fully formed and live on their own.

Crocodilians Found in or near water in warm climates, crocodilians, such as crocodiles, gavials, and alligators, are similar in appearance. They are lizardlike in shape, and their backs have large, deep scales. Crocodilians can be distinguished from each other by the shape of their heads. Crocodiles have a narrow head with a triangular-shaped snout. Alligators have a broad head with a rounded snout. Gavials, as shown in **Figure 24,** have a very slender snout with a bulbous growth on the end. Crocodiles are aggressive and can attack animals as large as cattle. Alligators are less aggressive than crocodiles, and feed on fish, turtles, and waterbirds. Gavials primarily feed on fish. Crocodilians are among the world's largest living reptiles.

Crocodilians are some of the few reptiles that care for their young. The female guards the nest of eggs and when the eggs hatch, the male and female protect the young. A few crocodilian females have been photographed opening their nests in response to noises made by hatchlings. After the young hatch, a female carries them in her huge mouth to the safety of the water. She continues to keep watch over the young until they can protect themselves.

Figure 23 Most turtles are eaten shortly after they hatch. Only a few sea turtles actually make it into the ocean.

Figure 24 Indian gavials are one of the rarest crocodilian species on Earth. Adults are well adapted for capturing fish.

Visualizing Extinct Reptiles

Have students examine the pictures and read the captions. Then ask the following questions.

How did the shape of these reptiles help them catch food in their environment? Long, streamlined bodies enabled them to move quickly through the water to capture prey.

Why are these animals classified as reptiles and not fish? Possible answers: They have amniotic eggs that are internally fertilized. They can modify their internal body temperature by basking in the Sun.

Activity

Reptile Poems Have students write a poem about extinct reptiles. Research topics such as reptile characteristics, how long ago they lived on Earth, and the location where fossils have been found. Include interesting statistics. For example, *Temnodontosaurus*, a plesiosaur, had the largest eyes of any animal that has ever lived. L2

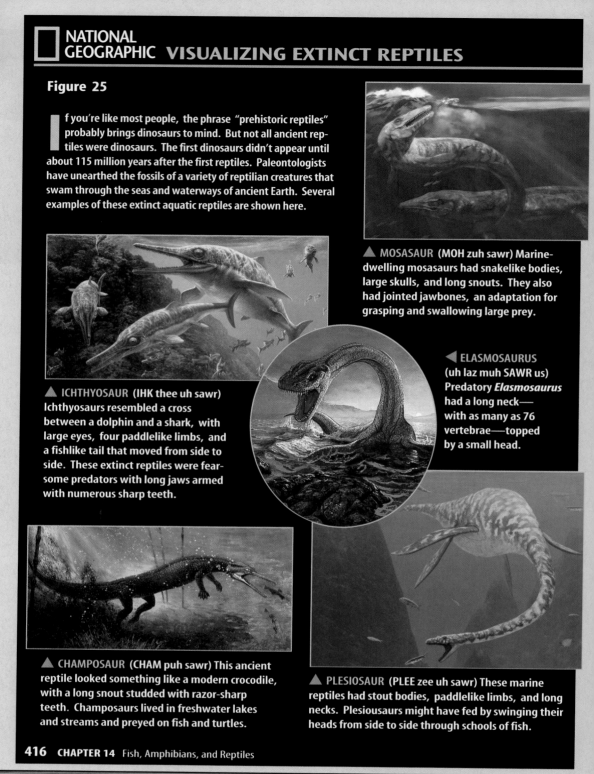

NATIONAL GEOGRAPHIC VISUALIZING EXTINCT REPTILES

Figure 25

If you're like most people, the phrase "prehistoric reptiles" probably brings dinosaurs to mind. But not all ancient reptiles were dinosaurs. The first dinosaurs didn't appear until about 115 million years after the first reptiles. Paleontologists have unearthed the fossils of a variety of reptilian creatures that swam through the seas and waterways of ancient Earth. Several examples of these extinct aquatic reptiles are shown here.

▲ **MOSASAUR** (MOH zuh sawr) Marine-dwelling mosasaurs had snakelike bodies, large skulls, and long snouts. They also had jointed jawbones, an adaptation for grasping and swallowing large prey.

▲ **ICHTHYOSAUR** (IHK thee uh sawr) Ichthyosaurs resembled a cross between a dolphin and a shark, with large eyes, four paddlelike limbs, and a fishlike tail that moved from side to side. These extinct reptiles were fearsome predators with long jaws armed with numerous sharp teeth.

◀ **ELASMOSAURUS** (uh laz muh SAWR us) Predatory *Elasmosaurus* had a long neck—with as many as 76 vertebrae—topped by a small head.

▲ **CHAMPOSAUR** (CHAM puh sawr) This ancient reptile looked something like a modern crocodile, with a long snout studded with razor-sharp teeth. Champosaurs lived in freshwater lakes and streams and preyed on fish and turtles.

▲ **PLESIOSAUR** (PLEE zee uh sawr) These marine reptiles had stout bodies, paddlelike limbs, and long necks. Plesiousaurs might have fed by swinging their heads from side to side through schools of fish.

416 CHAPTER 14 Fish, Amphibians, and Reptiles

Differentiated Instruction

Challenge Have students create an illustrated book of different types of extinct reptiles. Have students classify these animals. L3

The Importance of Reptiles

Reptiles are important predators in many environments. In farming areas, snakes eat rats and mice that destroy grains. Small lizards eat insects, and large lizards eat small animals that are considered pests.

Humans in many parts of the world eat reptiles and their eggs or foods that include reptiles, such as turtle soup. The number of reptile species is declining in areas where swamps and other lands are being developed for homes and recreation areas. Coastal nesting sites of sea turtles are being destroyed by development or are becoming unusable because of pollution. For years, many small turtles were collected in the wild and then sold as pets. People now understand that such practices disturb turtle populations. Today most species of turtles and their habitats are protected by law.

Origin of Reptiles Reptiles first appeared in the fossil record about 345 mya. The earliest reptiles did not depend upon water for reproduction. As a result, they began to dominate the land about 200 mya. Some reptiles even returned to the water to live, although they continued to lay their eggs on land. Dinosaurs—descendants of the early reptiles—ruled Earth during this era, then died out about 65 mya. Some of today's reptiles, such as the crocodilians, have changed little from their ancestors, some of which are illustrated in **Figure 25.**

A Changing Environment
Dinosaurs, reptiles that ruled Earth for 160 million years, died out about 65 million years ago. In your Science Journal, describe what changes in the environment could have caused the extinction of the dinosaurs.

---

section 4 review

Summary

Reptile Characteristics
- Reptiles are ectotherms with a thick, dry, waterproof skin that is covered with scales.
- Most have a three-chambered heart with a partial wall in the main chamber.
- Reptile young develop in an amniotic egg.

Types and Importance of Reptiles
- Lizards and snakes are the largest group of reptiles. Most lizards have legs, while snakes do not.
- Turtles have a two-part bony shell.
- Crocodilians are large reptiles and one of the few reptiles that care for their young.
- Reptiles are important predators. Some reptiles are food sources.

Self Check

1. **Describe** reptilian adaptations for living on land.
2. **Explain** how turtles differ from other reptiles.
3. **Infer** why early reptiles, including dinosaurs, were so successful as a group.
4. **Draw** the structure of an amniotic egg.
5. **Think Critically** Venomous coral snakes and some nonvenomous snakes have bright red, yellow, and black colors. How is this an advantage and a disadvantage to the nonvenomous snake?

Applying Math

6. **Solve One-Step Equations** *Brachiosaurus*, a dinosaur, was about 12 m tall and 22 m long. The average elephant is 3 m tall and 6 m long. How much taller and longer is the *Brachiosaurus* compared to an elephant?

---

section 4 review

1. a thick, dry, scaly waterproof skin; four legs with claws (except snakes and some lizards); three-chambered heart; lungs; amniotic egg
2. Turtles are covered with a hard shell on top and bottom. Most can withdraw into this shell for protection.
3. They did not depend on water for reproduction.
4. Drawing should resemble egg in **Figure 22.**
5. Predators think they are venomous snakes and leave them alone. Disadvantage: nonvenomous snakes may be killed because they are thought to be venomous.
6. The elephant is one-fourth the height of *Brachiosaurus,* and about one-third the length.

Design Your Own

◉ Real-World Question

Purpose Students design an experiment to determine the effect of water temperature on the respiration rate of fish. [L2]

[LS] **Visual-Spatial**

Process Skills design an experiment, form a hypothesis, observe and infer, communicate, compare, describe, graph, separate and control variables

Time Required two 30-minute class periods

Materials Large goldfish work best because their breathing is easily observed.

Safety Precautions Caution students not to handle the fish with their hands.

◉ Form a Hypothesis

Possible Hypothesis Students might predict a slowing respiration rate or no change with a decrease in temperature. Few students will hypothesize an increase in the rate.

◉ Test Your Hypothesis

Possible Procedures Students can place the fish in a large beaker of room-temperature water and record the respiration rate, the number of times the fish opens its mouth or gill covering in 20 seconds. Next, place the beaker into a large bowl filled with ice water. Measure the respiration rate each minute for 10 minutes. Allow the water in the beaker to return to room temperature before putting it into a hot-water bath. Measure the respiration rate.

Goals
- **Design** and carry out an experiment to measure the effect of water temperature on the rate of respiration of fish.
- **Observe** the breathing rate of fish.

Possible Materials
goldfish
aquarium water
small fishnet
600-mL beakers
container of ice water
stirring rod
thermometer
aquarium

Safety Precautions

Protect your clothing. Use the fishnet to transfer fish into beakers.

Water Temperature and the Respiration Rate of Fish

◉ Real-World Question

Imagine that last summer was hot with few storms. One day after many sunny, windless days, you noticed that a lot of dead fish were floating on the surface of your neighbor's pond. What might have caused these fish to die? How does water temperature affect the respiration rate of fish?

◉ Form a Hypothesis

Fish obtain oxygen from the water. State a hypothesis about how water temperature affects the respiration rate of fish.

◉ Test Your Hypothesis

Make a Plan

1. As a group, agree upon and write out a plan. You might make a plan that relates the amount of oxygen dissolved in water at different water temperatures and how this affects fish.

Alternative Inquiry Lab

Encourage Questions To extend this lab, make it an inquiry lab. Build on the experiences by encouraging your students to use what they have learned to brainstorm questions about a fish's breathing rate. Have each student choose one question to explore. Unsafe or impractical questions should be eliminated. Ask students to choose the materials they need to explore their questions. Students should have their plan approved before continuing. Conduct the experiments after all of the necessary materials have been gathered.

2. As a group, list the steps that you need to take to follow your plan. Be specific and describe exactly what you will do at each step. List your materials.

3. How will you measure the breathing rate of fish?

4. **Explain** how you will change the water temperature in the beakers. Fish respond better to a gradual change in temperature than an abrupt change. How will you measure the response of fish to changes in water temperature?

5. What data will your group collect? Prepare a data table in your Science Journal to record the data you collect. How many times will you run your experiment?

6. Read over your entire experiment to make sure the steps are in logical order. Identify any constants, variables, and controls.

Follow Your Plan

1. Make sure your teacher approves your setup and your plan before you start.

2. Carry out the experiment according to the approved plan.

3. While the experiment is going on, write down any observations that you make and complete the data table in your Science Journal.

◉ Analyze Your Data

1. **Compare** your results with the results of other groups in your class. Were the results similar?

2. **Infer** what you were measuring when you counted mouth or gill cover openings.

3. **Describe** how a decrease in water temperature affects respiration rate and behavior of the fish.

4. **Explain** how your results could be used to determine the kind of environment in which a fish can live.

◉ Conclude and Apply

1. **Explain** how fish can live in water that is totally covered by ice.

2. **Predict** what would happen to a fish if the water were to become very warm.

Communicating Your Data

Construct a graph of your data on poster board and share your results with your classmates.

Communicating Your Data

Encourage students to generate their graphs electronically.

✓ Assessment

Performance Have students research and report on the causes and effects of eutrophication. Eutrophication occurs when excess nutrients are added to the water from farms, lawns, and other sources. The nutrients cause an explosion of algae growth, and as the alga dies off, bacteria populations increase, depleting the water of oxygen and killing aquatic life. Use **Performance Assessment in the Science Classroom,** p. 159. L2

Teaching Strategies

• Placing a beaker with water and the fish into a large bowl of ice water will lower the temperature gradually without harming the fish.

• Allow water to return to room temperature before heating it.

• Heat fish's water gradually using a hot water bath.

Tie to Prior Knowledge Many students will be aware that fish have gills, but many will not know that a fish opening its mouth or gill covering indicates it is breathing.

Expected Outcomes The respiration rate of the fish should decrease and increase with a decrease and increase in water temperature, respectively.

◉ Analyze Your Data

Answers to Questions

1. Answers will vary, but results should be similar.

2. respiration rate

3. Respiration rate decreases and movement slows as temperature decreases.

4. Similar experiments could measure the temperature range in which various species of fish can breathe.

Error Analysis Students should compare their results and hypotheses and explain any differences in their data.

◉ Conclude and Apply

1. Ice is less dense than water, and a large body of water usually lies beneath the ice. The ice actually insulates the water, keeping the water temperature high enough for fish to breathe.

2. Warm water contains less oxygen, making it more difficult for a fish to breathe. Without enough dissolved oxygen, death could result.

Content Background

Explain that the use of venom by animals is either for subduing their prey, or for their own protection from predation. These organisms do not prey on humans, so attacks occur generally when an animal is surprised or finds itself threatened.

Discussion

Venom Controversies There are some uses of venom as medicinal treatments that are not generally accepted. *Apitherapy*, the use of bee venom for treatment of multiple sclerosis, is particularly controversial. Many people with this disease allow themselves to be stung by bees, reporting that they experience remission of their symptoms. The use of bee venom in this manner has not been approved by any federal agencies. Ask students to discuss whether people with life-changing diseases like MS should be permitted to use unproven and controversial techniques like this, and whether doctors should encourage or discourage their use. L2

Activity

Pretty Colors Most organisms that are venomous are brightly or elaborately colored. This is a protective measure, making it easier for a predator to associate the colors with distasteful or painful experiences. They are likely to avoid colored prey again. Have students look through magazines for pictures of such animals, and make a collage of organisms they think may be venomous. L2

TIME SCIENCE AND Society SCIENCE ISSUES THAT AFFECT YOU!

Bumble bee
Gila monster
Pit viper

Venom as Medicine

Hiss, rattle… Run! Just the sound of a snake sends most people on a sprint to escape what could be a painful bite. Why? The bites could contain venom, a toxic substance injected into prey or an enemy. Venom can harm—or even kill—the victim. Some venomous creatures use it to stun, kill, and digest their prey, while others use it as a means of protection.

Venom is produced by a gland in the body. Some fish use their sharp, bony spines to inject venom. Venomous snakes, such as pit vipers, have fangs. Venom passes through these hollow teeth into a victim's body. The Gila monster, the largest lizard in the United States, has enlarged, grooved teeth in its lower jaw through which its venom travels. It is one of only two species of venomous lizards.

Doctors and scientists have discovered a shocking surprise within this

sometimes deadly liquid. Oddly enough, the very same toxin that harms and weakens people can heal, too. In fact, doctors use the deadliest venom—that of some pit viper species—to treat certain types of heart attacks. Cobra venom has been used to soothe the effects of cancer, and other snake venoms reduce the spasms of epilepsy and asthma.

Some venoms also contain substances that help clot blood. Hemophiliacs—people whose blood will not clot naturally—rely on the medical benefits that venom-based medicines supply. Venoms also are used in biological research. For instance, venoms that affect the nervous system help doctors and researchers learn more about how nerves function.

It's still smart to steer clear of the rattle or the stinger—but it's good to know that the venom in them might someday help as many as it can hurt.

Research Besides venom, what other defenses do animals use to protect themselves or to subdue their prey? Explore how some animals that are native to your region use their built-in defenses.

Science Online
For more information, visit life.msscience.com/time

Research Animals use a number of strategies to attract prey or protect themselves. The viceroy butterfly resembles the monarch butterfly, which is distasteful to birds. Many insects avoid predation by blending with their environment. Other organisms, like the angler fish, have structures that attract their own prey closer to them.

Resources for Teachers and Students

Life on Earth: A Natural History, by David Attenborough, Little Brown & Company, 1981

Life on Earth: A Natural History Written and Hosted by David Attenborough, 1996, British Broadcasting Corporation and BBC Enterprises, Ltd. Available through Warner Home Video

Reviewing Main Ideas

Section 1 Chordates and Vertebrates

1. Chordates include lancelets, tunicates, and vertebrates. Chordates have a notochord, a nerve cord, pharyngeal pouches, and a postanal tail.

2. All vertebrates have an endoskeleton that includes a backbone and a skull that protects the brain.

3. An endotherm is an animal that has a nearly constant internal body temperature. An ectotherm has a body temperature that changes with the temperature of its environment.

Section 2 Fish

1. Fish are vertebrates that have a streamlined body, fins, gills for gas exchange, and a highly developed sensory system.

2. Fish are divided into three groups—jawless fish, jawed cartilaginous fish, and bony fish.

3. Bony fish, with scales and a swim bladder, have the greatest number of known fish species.

Section 3 Amphibians

1. The first vertebrates to live on land were the amphibians.

2. Amphibians have adaptations that allow them to live on land and in the water. The adaptations include moist skin, mucous glands, and lungs. Most amphibians are dependent on water to reproduce.

3. Most amphibians go through a metamorphosis from egg, to larva, to adult. During metamorphosis, legs develop, lungs replace gills, and the tail is lost.

Section 4 Reptiles

1. Reptiles are land animals with thick, dry, scaly skin. They lay amniotic eggs with leathery shells.

2. Turtles with tough shells, meat-eating crocodilians, and snakes and lizards make up the reptile groups.

3. Early reptiles were successful because of their adaptations to living on land.

Reviewing Main Ideas

Summary statements can be used by students to review the major concepts of the chapter.

Visualizing Main Ideas

See student page.

Visit life.msscience.com
/self_check_quiz
/interactive_tutor
/vocabulary_puzzlemaker
/chapter_review
/standardized_test

Assessment Transparency

For additional assessment questions, use the *Assessment Transparency* located in the transparency book.

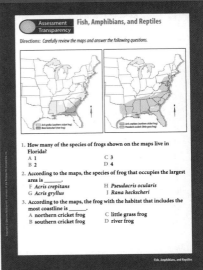

Visualizing Main Ideas

Copy and complete the concept map below that describes chordates.

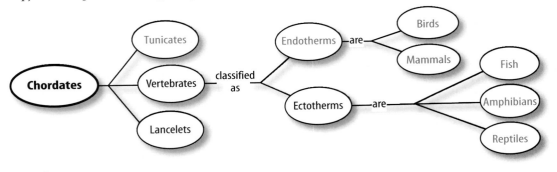

chapter 14 Review

Using Vocabulary

1. nerve cord
2. estivation
3. endotherms
4. ectotherms
5. cartilage
6. amniotic eggs
7. notochord

Checking Concepts

8. D	11. C	14. A
9. A	12. A	15. A
10. A	13. A	16. C

Thinking Critically

17. The populations of insects and other animals they eat might increase. Populations of their predators might decrease.

18. The skin of amphibians absorbs oxygen, as well as poisonous gases or chemicals in the area. They often show signs of environmental pollutants quickly. Because of this, amphibians can be considered biological indicators—species that reflect the condition of the environment.

19. They have a notochord, postanal tail, nerve cord, and gill slits in some stage of development.

20. All vertebrates have, at some time in their lives, a notochord that becomes the vertebrae in vertebrates, a postanal tail, a nerve cord, and gill slits. They also all have an endoskeleton.

Using Vocabulary

amniotic egg p. 413	hibernation p. 407
cartilage p. 395	nerve cord p. 395
chordate p. 394	notochord p. 394
ectotherm p. 397	pharyngeal pouch p. 395
endoskeleton p. 395	postanal tail p. 394
endotherm p. 397	scale p. 399
estivation p. 407	vertebrae p. 395
fin p. 399	

Fill in the blanks with the correct vocabulary word or words.

1. All chordates have a notochord, pharyngeal pouches, postanal tail, and a(n) _____.

2. The inactivity of amphibians during hot, dry weather is _____.

3. All animals with a constant internal temperature are _____.

4. Reptiles are _____ with scaly skin.

5. Jawless fish have skeletons made of a tough, flexible tissue called _____.

6. Reptiles lay _____.

7. The structure that becomes the backbone in vertebrates is the _____.

Checking Concepts

Choose the word or phrase that best answers the question.

8. Which animals have fins, scales, and gills?
   A) amphibians   C) reptiles
   B) crocodiles   D) fish

9. Which is an example of a cartilaginous fish?
   A) hagfish   C) perch
   B) tuna   D) goldfish

10. What fish group has the greatest number of species?
    A) bony   C) jawed cartilaginous
    B) jawless   D) amphibians

11. Which of these fish have gills and lungs?
    A) shark   C) lungfish
    B) ray   D) perch

12. Biological indicators include which group of ectothermic vertebrates?
    A) amphibians
    B) cartilaginous fish
    C) bony fish
    D) reptiles

Use the photo below to answer question 13.

13. Which kinds of reptiles are included with the animal above?
    A) snakes   C) turtles
    B) crocodiles   D) alligators

14. What term best describes eggs of reptiles?
    A) amniotic   C) jellylike
    B) brown   D) hard-shelled

15. Vertebrates that have lungs and moist skin belong to which group?
    A) amphibians   C) reptiles
    B) fish   D) lizards

16. How can crocodiles be distinguished from alligators?
    A) care of the young
    B) scales on the back
    C) shape of the head
    D) habitats in which they live

 Science Online life.msscience.com/vocabulary_puzzlemaker

Use the Exam*View*® Pro Testmaker CD-ROM to:
- create multiple versions of tests
- create modified tests with one mouse click for inclusion students
- edit existing questions and add your own questions
- build tests aligned with state standards using built-in State Curriculum Tags
- change English tests to Spanish with one mouse click and vice versa

Thinking Critically

17. Infer Populations of frogs and toads are decreasing in some areas. What effects could this decrease have on other animal populations?

18. Explain why some amphibians are considered to be biological indicators.

19. Compare and contrast the ways tunicates and lancelets are similar to humans.

20. Describe the physical features common to all vertebrates.

21. Compare and contrast endotherms and ectotherms.

22. Explain how the development of the amniotic egg led to the success of early reptiles.

23. Communicate In your Science Journal, sequence the order in which these structures appeared in evolutionary history, then explain what type of organism had this adaptation and the advantage it provided: skin has mucous glands; skin has scales; dry, scaly skin.

24. Compare and Contrast Copy and complete this chart that compares the features of some vertebrate groups.

Vertebrate Groups

Feature	Fish	Amphibians	Reptiles
Heart	Two-chambered	Three-chambered	Three-chambered
Respiratory organ(s)	Gills	Skin and two lungs	Two lungs
Reproduction requires water	yes	yes	no

25. Explain how a fish uses its swim bladder.

26. Identify and Manipulate Variables and Controls Design an experiment to find out the effect of water temperature on frog egg development.

27. Classify To what animal group does an animal with a two-chambered heart belong?

28. Identify why it is necessary for a frog to live in a moist environment.

Performance Activities

29. Conduct a Survey Many people are wary of reptiles. Write questions about reptiles to find out how people feel about these animals. Give the survey to your classmates, then graph the results and share them with your class.

30. Display Cut out pictures of fish from magazines and mount them on poster board. Letter the names of each fish on 3-in × 5-in cards. Have your classmates try to match the names of the fish with their pictures. To make this activity more challenging, use only the scientific names of each fish.

Applying Math

Use the table below to answer questions 31 and 32.

Fish Species

Kinds of Fish	Number of Species
Jawless	45
Jawed cartilaginous	500
Bony	20,000

31. Fish Species Make a circle graph of the species of fish in the table above.

32. Fish Percentages What percent of fish species is bony fish? Jawed cartilaginous? Jawless?

Thinking Critically

21. Endotherms maintain a constant body temperature while an ectotherm's body temperature changes with the environment.

22. The amniotic egg provides the developing embryo with protection from drying out and being eaten. An adequate supply of food is also provided. Reptile eggs can be laid anywhere on land, thus freeing reptiles from a reliance on water for reproduction.

23. Scales are present in fish, allowing them to move in water; skin with mucus glands is present in amphibians, which began to live on land; dry, scaly skin developed in reptiles that lived on land.

24. See student page.

25. By taking in or releasing gases, it raises and lowers itself in the water.

26. Students should design experiments with a control—a set temperature—and groups with higher or lower temperatures as the variables.

27. The animal is most likely a fish.

28. It allows exchange of oxygen and carbon dioxide within the environment.

Performance Activities

29. Student graphs will vary according to their survey audience. Use **PASC**, p. 107.

30. Students should find matching scientific names that describe the characteristics of each fish chosen. Use **PASC**, p. 145.

Applying Math

National Math Standards

5, 6

31. Students should find that 350° represents bony fish, 8.6° represents cartilagenous jawed fish, and about 0.8° represents jawless fish.

32. 97.3% are bony fish, 2.4% are cartilagenous jawed fish, and 0.22% are jawless fish

---

Assessment Resources

Reproducible Masters

Chapter *Fast File* Resources
 Chapter Review, pp. 41–42
 Chapter Tests, pp. 43–46
 Assessment Transparency Activity, p. 55

Glencoe Science Web site
 Chapter Review Test
 Standardized Test Practice

Glencoe Technology

 Assessment Transparency
 Exam*View*® Pro Testmaker
 MindJogger Videoquiz
 Interactive Chalkboard

Answer Sheet A practice answer sheet can be found at life.msscience.com/answer_sheet.

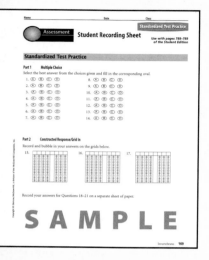

S A M P L E

Part 1 | Multiple Choice

Record your answers on the answer sheet provided by your teacher or on a sheet of paper.

1. What are fins attached to?
   A. ectoskeleton   C. endoskeleton
   B. notochord   D. spine

2. How many chambers does a fish heart contain, and does it carry more or less oxygen than other types of hearts?
   A. two, less   C. three, less
   B. four, less   D. four, more

Use the photo below to answer question 3.

3. What type of fish is shown in this picture?
   A. bony
   B. jawed cartilaginous
   C. large-mouth bass
   D. jawless

4. How do amphibians exchange carbon dioxide and oxygen?
   A. lungs only   C. gills only
   B. lungs and skin   D. lungs and gills

5. How do frogs and toads hear?
   A. eardrum
   B. tympanic membrane
   C. skin
   D. tongue

6. Fish and amphibians do not have this type of egg so they must reproduce near water.
   A. external   C. porous
   B. membranous   D. amniotic

Use the photos below to answer questions 7 and 8.

7. What is the developmental process shown in this diagram?
   A. metamorphosis
   B. respiration
   C. ectotherm
   D. asexual reproduction

8. Where does this transition take place?
   A. land to air   C. water to land
   B. air to land   D. land to water

9. What is one way to distinguish a crocodile from an alligator?
   A. the shape of the snout
   B. number of eggs in nest
   C. size of teeth
   D. placement of nostrils

10. What are turtles missing that all other reptiles have?
    A. hair
    B. three-chambered heart
    C. teeth
    D. shelled eggs

Test-Taking Tip

Marking on Tests Be sure to ask if it is okay to mark in the test booklet when taking the test, but make sure you mark all of the answers on your answer sheet.

Question 6 Cross out answers you know are wrong or circle answers you know are correct. This will help you narrow your choices.

424 STANDARDIZED TEST PRACTICE

Part 2 | Short Response

11. The lateral line system is a system of sensory organs that extend along the body. They detect movement and sense the environment.

12. Fish have feathery gill filaments that contain many tiny blood vessels for gas exchange when water passes over the gills.

13. When the swim bladder fills the fish, it becomes less dense, rising to a higher depth. When it empties, the fish becomes more dense and falls to a deeper depth.

14. Hibernation is a period of inactivity in cold weather and estivation is a period of inactivity in hot weather.

15. An amphibian heart changes from 2-chambered to 3-chambered and lungs replace gills.

16. construction, pollution, and habitat destruction

17. fewer offspring produced receive greater care

18. through vibrations in the ground that are picked up by the lower jawbone

19. ectothermic, modify their body temperature by behavior

20. The front end becomes the brain and the remainder becomes the spinal cord.

Part 2 | Short Response/Grid In

Record your answers on the answer sheet provided by your teacher or on a sheet of paper.

Use the illustration below to answer question 11.

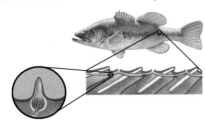

11. Describe the body system of the fish shown in this diagram. Why is it important to the fish?

12. What organs do fish have for the exchange of carbon dioxide and oxygen? How does the exchange take place?

13. How does a fish's swim bladder regulate its depth in water?

14. What is the difference between hibernation and estivation?

15. As an amphibian goes through metamorphosis, how do their heart and lungs change?

16. What is one possible reason for the decline in the number of reptiles in swamps and coastal areas?

17. What is the relationship between the number of young produced and the amount of care given by the parents in fish, amphibians, and reptiles?

18. How do snakes hear?

19. Are reptiles endothermic or ectothermic? Can reptiles modify their body temperature?

20. During chordate development, what structures originate from the nerve chord?

Part 3 | Open Ended

Record your answers on a sheet of paper.

21. Describe the composition and function of fish scales.

22. How did amphibians evolve and why were they the dominant land animals for a period of time?

23. Compare and contrast the circulatory systems of fish, amphibians, and reptiles. Which system provides the most oxygenated blood to the organs?

Use the illustration below to answer question 24.

24. Explain the composition and significance of the structure in this diagram.

25. Discuss the structure of a turtle's shell and what other body parts are attached to it.

26. What are two classifications of how organisms regulate body temperature? How does regulation of body temperature help to determine the climate in which an organism is found?

27. What are pharyngeal pouches and what animal group has them at some point during development? How has their function changed over time?

25. It is a two-part shell made of hard bony plates. The vertebrae and ribs are fused to the inside top and muscles are attached to the inside of both parts of the shell.

26. Ectotherm and endotherm; ectotherms' body temperatures change with their surroundings and they tend to live in warmer climates, and endotherms have a constant internal body temperature and can live in any environment.

27. All chordates have pharyngeal pouches at some point in development. They were used by ancient invertebrates for filter feeding, and this is still their purpose in some chordates. In fish they develop into gills and in humans they are only present during embryonic development.

Rubrics

For more help evaluating open-ended assessment questions, see the rubric on p. 10T.

Science Online life.msscience.com/standardized_test

Part 3 | Open Ended

21. They cover and protect the body of fish, most are made of bone and are tooth shaped, diamond shaped, cone shaped or round.

22. Lobe-finned fish had lungs and bony fins allowing them to survive a trip across land when resources became scarce. On land, insects and spiders were abundant with very little competition or predation so the amphibian became a dominant species.

23. All have hearts that pump oxygenated blood to the organs and tissues for gas exchange. Fish have a 2-chambered heart that allows for mixing of oxygenated and deoxygenated blood. Amphibians have a 3-chambered heart for less mixing of the blood. Most efficient for providing oxygenated blood to the organs is the reptilian 3-chambered heart with a partial wall.

24. The structure shown in this diagram is a backbone, a stack of vertebrae alternating with cartilage. It surrounds and protects the spinal nerve cord.

Section/Objectives	Standards		Labs/Features
Chapter Opener	**National**	**State/Local**	**Launch Lab:** Bird Gizzards, p. 427 **Foldables,** p. 427
	See pp. 16T–17T for a Key to Standards.		
Section 1 Birds ⏱ 2 sessions 📦 1 block 1. **Identify** the characteristics of birds. 2. **Identify** the adaptations birds have for flight. 3. **Explain** how birds reproduce and develop.	National Content Standards: UCP.1–UCP.5, A.1, A.2, C.1–C.5		**Integrate Astronomy,** p. 429 **MiniLAB:** Modeling Feather Function, p. 430 **Integrate Social Studies,** p. 431 **Science Online,** p. 432 **Visualizing Birds,** p. 434
Section 2 Mammals ⏱ 3 sessions 📦 1.5 blocks 4. **Identify** the characteristics of mammals and explain how they have enabled mammals to adapt to different environments. 5. **Distinguish** among monotremes, marsupials, and placentals. 6. **Explain** why many species of mammals are becoming threatened or endangered.	National Content Standards: UCP.1–UCP.3, UCP.5, A.1, A.2, F.1		**MiniLAB:** Inferring How Blubber Insulates, p. 438 **Applying Science:** Does a mammal's heart rate determine how long it will live?, p. 439 **Science Online,** p. 441 **Lab:** Mammal Footprints, p. 445 **Lab:** Bird Counts, pp. 446–447 **Science Stats:** Eggciting Facts, p. 448

Lab Materials	Reproducible Resources	Section Assessment	Technology
Launch Lab: cracked corn, sunflower seeds, nuts, or other seeds; gravel; old sock	**Chapter FAST FILE Resources** Foldables Worksheet, p. 15 Directed Reading Overview, p. 17 Note-taking Worksheets, pp. 29–31	GLENCOE'S **ASSESSMENT** ADVANTAGE	Teacher**Works** includes: • Interactive Teacher Edition • Lesson Planner with calendar • Access to all program blacklines • Correlations to standards • Web links
MiniLAB: alcohol thermometers (2), polyester fiber or cotton, plastic bags (2), container of cold water, Science Journal *Need materials?* Contact Science Kit at 1-800-828-7777 or www.sciencekit.com on the Internet.	**Chapter FAST FILE Resources** Transparency Activity, p. 40 MiniLAB, p. 3 Lab Activity, pp. 9–10 Enrichment, p. 27 Reinforcement, p. 25 Directed Reading, p. 18 Transparency Activity, pp. 43–44 **Home and Community Involvement,** p. 27 **Earth Science Critical Thinking/ Problem Solving,** p. 12 **Life Science Critical Thinking/ Problem Solving,** pp. 12, 13	**Portfolio** Science Journal, p. 431 Assessment, p. 427 **Performance** MiniLAB, p. 430 Applying Skills, p. 435 **Content** Section Review, p. 435	Section Focus Transparency Teaching Transparency Virtual Labs CD-ROM Guided Reading Audio Program Interactive Chalkboard CD-ROM
MiniLAB: self-sealing plastic bags (2), vegetable shortening, ice water **Lab:** diagram of mammal footprints **Lab:** Internet and other sources of information on birds	**Chapter FAST FILE Resources** Transparency Activity, p. 41 MiniLAB, p. 4 Lab Activity, pp. 11–14 Enrichment, p. 28 Reinforcement, p. 26 Directed Reading, pp. 19, 20 Lab Worksheets, pp. 5–6, 7–8 **Lab Management and Safety,** p. 37 **Mathematics Skill Activities,** p. 7 **Cultural Diversity,** p. 9	**Portfolio** Assessment, p. 447 **Performance** MiniLAB, p. 438 Applying Science, p. 439 Applying Math, p. 448 Applying Math, p. 444 **Content** Section Review, p. 444	Section Focus Transparency Virtual Labs CD-ROM Guided Reading Audio Program Interactive Chalkboard CD-ROM Video Lab

End of Chapter Assessment

GLENCOE'S **ASSESSMENT** ADVANTAGE

Blackline Masters	Technology	Professional Series
Chapter FAST FILE Resources Chapter Review, pp. 33–34 Chapter Tests, pp. 35–38 **Standardized Test Practice,** pp. 63–66	MindJogger Videoquiz Virtual Labs CD-ROM Exam*View*® Pro Testmaker TeacherWorks CD-ROM Interactive Chalkboard CD-ROM	**Performance Assessment in the Science Classroom (PASC)**

Transparencies

Section Focus

SECTION 1 Section Focus Transparency **A Long Flight**

Albatrosses are among the largest flying birds. They are able to ride the ocean winds in such a way that they can stay aloft for hours without flapping their wings. Albatrosses spend between five and ten years at sea before returning to shore to mate for the first time.

1. Describe the albatross pictured. How is it similar to other birds?
2. What might albatrosses eat?
3. What body characteristics enable birds to fly?

L2

SECTION 2 Section Focus Transparency **Romp with the Otters**

Sea otters are playful marine mammals. One of the few nonprimates to use tools, sea otters often balance rocks on their stomachs to crack open shellfish. This once endangered species is now protected and increasing in numbers.

1. What other mammals live in the ocean?
2. How are otters and fish similar? How are they different?
3. How do otters and humans compare physically?

L2

This is a representation of key blackline masters available in the Teacher Classroom Resources. See Resource Manager boxes within the chapter for additional information.

Key to Teaching Strategies

The following designations will help you decide which activities are appropriate for your students.

L1 Level 1 activities should be appropriate for students with learning difficulties.

L2 Level 2 activities should be within the ability range of all students.

L3 Level 3 activities are designed for above-average students.

ELL ELL activities should be within the ability range of English-Language Learners.

COOP LEARN Cooperative Learning activities are designed for small group work.

LS Multiple Learning Styles logos, as described on page 12T, are used throughout to indicate strategies that address different learning styles.

P These strategies represent student products that can be placed into a best-work portfolio.

PBL Problem-Based Learning activities apply real-world situations to learning.

Assessment

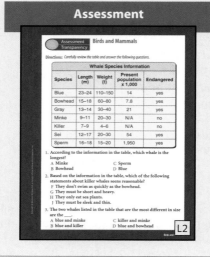

Assessment Transparency **Birds and Mammals**

Directions: Carefully review the table and answer the following questions.

Whale Species Information

Species	Length (m)	Weight (t)	Present population x 1,000	Endangered
Blue	23–24	110–150	14	yes
Bowhead	15–18	60–80	7.8	yes
Gray	13–14	30–40	21	yes
Minke	9–11	20–30	N/A	no
Killer	7–9	4–6	N/A	no
Sei	12–17	20–30	54	yes
Sperm	16–18	15–20	1,950	yes

1. According to the information in the table, which whale is the longest?
   A Minke   C Sperm
   B Bowhead   D Blue
2. Based on the information in the table, which of the following statements about killer whales seems reasonable?
   F They don't swim as quickly as the bowhead.
   G They must be short and heavy.
   H They only eat sea plants.
   I They must be sleek and thin.
3. The two whales listed in the table that are the most different in size are the _____.
   A blue and minke   C killer and minke
   B blue and killer   D blue and bowhead

L2

Teaching

SECTION 1 Teaching Transparency **Hollow Bones of Birds**

Tail A bird does not have a bony tail.

Sternum The sternum has a structure called a keel, which is where flight muscles attach.

L2

Hands-on Activities

Student Text Lab Worksheet

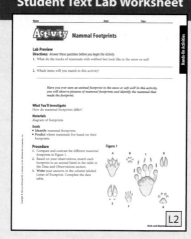

Activity Mammal Footprints

Lab Preview
Directions: Answer these questions before you begin the Activity.
1. What do the tracks of mammals with webbed feet look like in the snow or soil?

2. Which items will you match in this activity?

Have you ever seen an animal footprint in the snow or soft soil? In this activity, you will observe pictures of mammal footprints and identify the mammal that made the footprint.

What You'll Investigate
How do mammal footprints differ?

Materials
diagram of footprints

Goals
• **Identify** mammal footprints.
• **Predict** where mammals live based on their footprints.

Procedure
1. Compare and contrast the different mammal footprints in Figure 1.
2. Based on your observations, match each footprint to an animal listed in the table in the Data and Observations section.
3. **Write** your answers in the column labeled Letter of Footprint. Complete the data table.

Figure 1

L2

Laboratory Activities

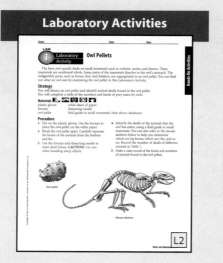

LAB 1 Laboratory Activity **Owl Pellets**

The barn owl usually feeds on small mammals such as rodents, moles, and shrews. These mammals are eaten whole. Some parts of the mammals dissolve in the owl's stomach. The indigestible parts, such as bones, hair, and feathers, are regurgitated in an owl pellet. You can find out what an owl eats by examining the owl pellet in this Laboratory Activity.

Strategy
You will dissect an owl pellet and identify animal skulls found in the owl pellet.
You will complete a table of the numbers and kinds of prey eaten by owls.

Materials
plastic gloves   white sheet of paper
forceps   dissecting needle
owl pellet   field guide to small mammals (that shows skeletons)

Procedure
1. Put on the plastic gloves. Use the forceps to place the owl pellet on the white paper.
2. Break the owl pellet apart. Carefully separate the bones of the animals from the feathers and fur.
3. Use the forceps and dissecting needle to clean skull bones. **CAUTION:** Use care when handling sharp objects.
4. Identify the skulls of the animals that the owl has eaten, using a field guide to small mammals. You can also refer to the mouse skeleton below to help you determine which are leg bones, which are ribs, and so on. Record the number of skulls of different animals in Table 1.
5. Make a class record of the kinds and numbers of animals found in the owl pellets.

Owl pellet

Mouse skeleton

L2

Meeting Different Ability Levels

Content Outline

L2

Reinforcement

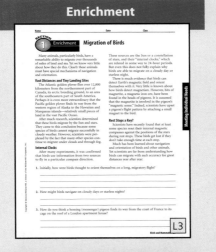

L2

Enrichment

L3

Directed Reading (English/Spanish)

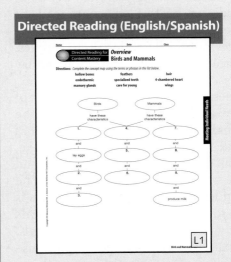

L1

Study Guide

Features
• Contains a study guide page for each section of the chapter
• Reviews key concepts
• Includes answer pages

L2

Reading Essentials

Reading Essentials for Glencoe Science
An Interactive Student Workbook

Features
• Condensed core content
• Actively involves students in reading
• Reinforces key vocabulary

L1

Assessment

Test Practice Workbook

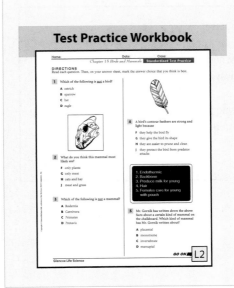

L2

Chapter Review

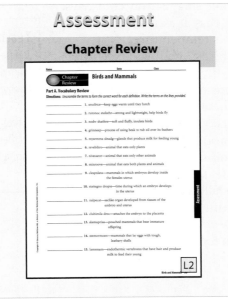

L2

Chapter Tests

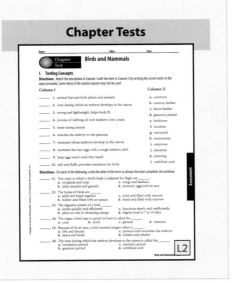

L2

Science Content Background

Steve Lucas/International Stock

section 1 Birds
Bird Characteristics

As opposed to amphibians and reptiles, birds and mammals are endotherms—their bodies maintain a nearly constant internal body temperature. This has two advantages—metabolic functions work optimally at certain temperature ranges, and maintaining a warm temperature prevents endotherms from being sluggish on cold days. The disadvantage is that it can take a lot of energy to maintain this temperature.

If you observe birds, you will see their preening behavior, which involves smoothing feathers and spreading oil from the uropygial gland located at the base of their tails. The oil conditions the feathers, and smoothing feathers keeps them in their proper locations and in the proper shape. Sticky oil from oil spills hurts sea birds because their feathers get stuck in the wrong positions. This allows cold water to contact their skin, resulting in the birds needing more energy to stay warm. In cold areas or places without enough food, this can cause death to the birds.

Body Systems
Examinations of bird hearts reveal another way birds (and mammals) are different from all amphibians and most reptiles. Birds have a four-chambered heart. This is a more efficient pump because oxygenated and deoxygenated blood don't mix.

The Importance of Birds
Fossil evidence suggests that birds may have evolved from a group of dinosaurs. The scales on birds' feet and legs suggest their reptilian origins. In addition, birds' feathers are made of a protein called keratin, which is the same material that makes up reptile scales. Like reptiles, birds reproduce by internal fertilization and lay amniotic eggs.

Bird species are threatened by the actions of people. For example, the introduction of the brown tree snake onto the island of Guam has caused the loss of many bird species. The snake, which reproduces rapidly, climbs into trees and eats the eggs and chicks of many birds. The snake can find its way into airplanes and thus is easily spread to other islands. Nonflying birds are especially vulnerable to introduced animals. For example, about a century ago a lighthouse keeper's cat killed all the species of nonflying birds on one of New Zealand's islands.

Teacher to Teacher
Jeff Remington
Palmyra Middle School
Palmyra, Pennsylvania

"I pass around contour feathers, down feathers, and courtship feathers to have students determine form and function through inquiry."

Jeff Remington

---

section 2

Mammals

Characteristics of Mammals

Like the scales of reptiles and the feathers of birds, mammal hair is made of keratin. Hair helps these endotherms retain body heat. At times it is necessary to lose heat. Sweating and panting are two mechanisms that allow cooling of the body through evaporation of sweat from the skin or moisture from the lungs.

Body Systems

Herbivores generally have longer digestive systems than carnivores and omnivores. Many plant products, such as starches and fruits, are easy to digest. However, when a diet includes eating large amounts of leaves, large amounts of cellulose must be digested. Large molars start the digestive process by grinding the leaves into smaller pieces. Then the food moves slowly through the long digestive system where it is broken down.

While amphibians, reptiles, and birds all have red blood cells, those of mammals differ in that they don't have a nucleus in their mature state. This allows more room in the cells for hemoglobin to carry oxygen. The biconcave shape of mammalian red blood cells give them more surface area to absorb oxygen.

Types of Mammals

Mammals are thought to have evolved from a group of ancient reptiles called therapsids. These animals had both reptilian and mammalian characteristics.

chapter content resources

Internet Resources

For additional content background, visit **life.msscience.com** to:
- access your book online
- find references to related articles in popular science magazines
- access Web links with related content background
- access current events with science journal topics

Print Resources

Animal Life, Copper Beech Books, 2002

A Field Guide to the Birds of Eastern and Central North America by Roger Tory Peterson, Houghton Mifflin Co; 5th edition, 2002

Building a Backyard Bird Habitat by Scott Shalaway, Satckpole Books, 2000

The Encyclopedia of Mammals by David W. MacDonald, Checkmark Books, 1995

Jeff Rotman/Stone

Chapter Vocabulary

contour feather, p. 430
down feather, p. 430
endotherm, p. 430
preening, p. 430
mammal, p. 436
mammary gland, p. 436
omnivore, p. 437
carnivore, p. 437
herbivore, p. 437
monotreme, p. 440
marsupial, p. 440
placental, p. 441
gestation period, p. 441
placenta, p. 441
umbilical cord, p. 441

Science Journal Student answers will vary. Similar—warm-blooded; live on every continent on Earth; give parental care. Different—birds have feathers; mammals have hair or fur; birds lay eggs and most mammals do not; most birds fly, most mammals do not

INTERACTIVE CHALKBOARD with Image Bank

PowerPoint® Presentations

This CD-ROM is an editable Microsoft® PowerPoint® presentation that includes:
- a pre-made presentation for every chapter
- interactive graphics
- animations
- audio clips
- image bank
- all new section and chapter questions
- Standardized Test Practice
- transparencies
- pre-lab questions for all labs
- Foldables directions
- links to life.msscience.com

Birds and Mammals

chapter preview

sections

1 Birds

2 Mammals
  Lab Mammal Footprints
  Lab Bird Counts
  Virtual Lab How are birds adapted to their habitat?

More Alike than Not!

Birds and mammals have adaptations that allow them to live on every continent and in every ocean. Some of these animals have adapted to withstand the coldest or hottest conditions. These adaptations help to make these animal groups successful.

Science Journal List similar characteristics of a mammal and a bird. What characteristics are different?

426

Theme Connection

Stability and Change A discussion of the adaptations of birds to life in the air and on land reinforces the steps in the evolution of different species that have moved from water to land environments. The theme of stability and change is continued in the discussion of mammal characteristics and origins. Both birds and mammals have developed homeostatic mechanisms for living on land.

About the Photo

In Harmony Birds and mammals often live together in harmony and interact. Birds will often eat insects that are parasites on a mammal. In return, the mammal is parasite-free!

Start-Up Activities

Bird Gizzards

You may have observed a variety of animals in your neighborhood. Maybe you have watched birds at a bird feeder. Birds don't chew their food because they don't have teeth. Instead, many birds swallow small pebbles, bits of eggshells, and other hard materials that go into the gizzard—a muscular digestive organ. Inside the gizzard, they help grind up the seeds. The lab below models the action of a gizzard.

1. Place some cracked corn, sunflower seeds, nuts or other seeds, and some gravel in an old sock.
2. Roll the sock on a hard surface and tightly squeeze it.
3. Describe the appearance of the seeds after rolling.
4. **Think Critically** Describe in your Science Journal how a bird's gizzard helps digest the bird's food.

Preview this chapter's content and activities at life.msscience.com

Birds and Mammals Make the following Foldable to help you organize information about the behaviors of birds and mammals.

STEP 1 **Fold** one piece of paper widthwise into thirds.

STEP 2 **Fold** down 2.5 cm from the top. (Hint: From the tip of your index finger to your middle knuckle is about 2.5 cm.)

STEP 3 **Fold** the rest into fifths.

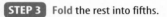

STEP 4 **Unfold,** lay the paper lengthwise, and draw lines along the folds. **Label** your table as shown.

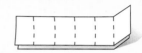

	Birds	Mammals
Habitats		
Diet		
Movement		
Body Systems		
Young		

Make a Table As you read the chapter, complete the table describing the behaviors of birds and mammals.

427

Birds

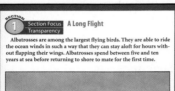

as you read

What You'll Learn
- **Identify** the characteristics of birds.
- **Identify** the adaptations birds have for flight.
- **Explain** how birds reproduce and develop.

Why It's Important
Most birds demonstrate structural and behavioral adaptations for flight.

⟲ Review Vocabulary
thrust: for an object moving through air, the horizontal force that pushes or pulls the object forward

New Vocabulary
- contour feather
- down feather
- endotherm
- preening

Bird Characteristics

Birds are versatile animals. Geese have been observed flying at an altitude of 9,000 m, and penguins have been seen underwater at a depth of 543 m. An ostrich might weigh 155,000 g, while a hummingbird might weigh only 2 g. Some birds can live in the tropics and others can live in polar regions. Their diets vary and include meat, fish, insects, fruit, seeds, and nectar. Birds have feathers and scales and they lay eggs. Which of these characteristics is unique to birds?

Bird Eggs Birds lay amniotic (am nee AH tihk) eggs with hard shells, as shown in **Figure 1.** This type of egg provides a moist, protective environment for the developing embryo. The hard shell is made of calcium carbonate, the same chemical that makes up seashells, limestone, and marble. The egg is fertilized internally before the shell forms around it. The female bird lays one or more eggs usually in some type of nest, also shown in **Figure 1.** A group of eggs is called a clutch. One or both parents may keep the eggs warm, or incubate them, until they hatch. The length of time for incubation varies from species to species. The young are cared for by one or both parents.

Figure 1 This robin's round nest is built of grasses and mud in a tree.

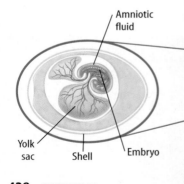

Amniotic fluid

Yolk sac

Shell

Embryo

428 CHAPTER 15

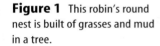

Figure 2 The hollow bones of birds are an adaptation for flight.
Infer *what advantages thin cross braces provide.*

Sternum The sternum has a structure called a keel, which is where flight muscles attach.

Tail A bird does not have a bony tail.

Leg bone

Hollow leg bone

Flight Adaptations People have always been fascinated by the ability of birds to fly. Flight in birds is made possible by their almost hollow but strong skeleton, wings, feathers, strong flight muscles, and an efficient respiratory system. Well-developed senses, especially eyesight, and tremendous amounts of energy also are needed for flight.

Hollow Bones One adaptation that birds have for flight is a unique internal skeleton, as shown in **Figure 2.** Many bones of some birds are joined together. This provides more strength and more stability for flight. Most bones of birds that fly are almost hollow. These bones have thin cross braces inside that also strengthen the bones. The hollow spaces inside of the bones are filled with air.

☑ Reading Check *What features strengthen a bird's bones?*

A large sternum, or breastbone, supports the powerful chest muscles needed for flight. The last bones of the spine support the tail feathers, which play an important part in steering and balancing during flight and landing.

INTEGRATE Astronomy

Star Navigation Many theories have been proposed about how birds navigate at night. Some scientists hypothesize that star positions help night-flying birds find their way. Research the location of the North Star. In your Science Journal, infer how the North Star might help birds fly at night.

SECTION 1 Birds **429**

Differentiated Instruction

Learning Disabled Ask students to draw or take pictures of different birds found around school or their homes. They should identify the birds and start a bird diary. Have them note the time of day they saw each bird, its location, and any other interesting observations. L2 IS **Visual-Spatial and Linguistic**

Fun Fact

Bird eggs come in a variety of sizes. Some hummingbird eggs are as small as a pea; some ostrich eggs are larger than softballs!

---

2 Teach

Caption Answer
Figure 2 They give the bones strength and support.

Quick Demo
Bird Behavior
Materials live bird
Estimated Time 10 minutes
Procedure If someone in the class has a pet bird (canary, parakeet, parrot), ask that student to bring the bird to class so its characteristics and behavior may be observed. L1 IS **Visual-Spatial**

INTEGRATE Astronomy

Star Navigation The North Star is located very close to the northern celestial pole, making its position appear relatively fixed. It is one of the brightest stars in the night sky. Because of this, it can be used in navigation.

☑ Reading Check

Answer Many bones are joined; cross braces within hollow bones add strength.

Activity

Flaps per Minute Organize the class into pairs. Have one student keep time and count while the other holds his or her arms straight out and flaps them up and down. See how many times a student can flap his or her arms in one minute and how long it takes for the student to tire. Explain that just as our leg muscles are well developed for walking, the chest muscles of most birds are well developed for flying. L1 IS **Kinesthetic**

Mini LAB

Purpose to discover the function of down feathers L2 LS
Kinesthetic

Materials two alcohol thermometers, polyester fiber or cotton, two plastic bags, container of cold water, Science Journal

Teaching Strategy Check that students thoroughly cover the bulb of the thermometer.

Analysis

1. the thermometer without fiber or cotton
2. down feathers

Assessment

Oral Ask students to infer if the amount of down feathers would be different for bird species in different environments. Use **Performance Assessment in the Science Classroom,** p. 89.

✔ **Reading Check**

Answer To help maintain a constant body temperature

Virtual Labs

Bird Adaptations *How are birds adapted to their habitat?*

Mini LAB

Modeling Feather Function

Procedure

1. Wrap **polyester fiber** or **cotton** around the bulb of an **alcohol thermometer.** Place it into a **plastic bag.** Record its temperature in your **Science Journal.**
2. Place a second **alcohol thermometer** into a **plastic bag** and record its temperature.
3. Simultaneously submerge the thermometers into a **container** of **cold water,** keeping the top of each bag above the water's surface.
4. After 2 min, record the temperature of each thermometer.

Analysis

1. Which thermometer had the greater change in temperature?
2. Infer the type of feather that the fiber or cotton models.

Feathers Birds are the only animals that have feathers. Their bodies are covered with two main types of feathers—contour feathers and down feathers. Strong, lightweight **contour feathers** give a bird its coloring and smooth shape. These are also the feathers that a bird uses when flying. The contour feathers on the wings and tail help the bird steer and keep it from spinning out of control.

Have you ever wondered how ducks can swim in a pond on a freezing cold day and keep warm? Soft, fluffy **down feathers** provide an insulating layer next to the skin of adult birds and cover the bodies of young birds. Birds are **endotherms,** meaning they maintain a constant body temperature. Feathers help birds maintain their body temperature, and grow in much the same way as your hair grows. Each feather grows from a microscopic pit in the skin called a follicle (FAH lih kul). When a feather falls out, a new one grows in its place. As shown in **Figure 3,** the shaft of a feather has many branches called barbs. Each barb has many branches called barbules that give the feather strength.

✔ **Reading Check** *Why are some young birds covered with down feathers?*

A bird has an oil gland located just above the base of its tail. Using its bill or beak, a bird rubs oil from the gland over its feathers in a process called **preening.** The oil conditions the feathers and helps them last longer.

Figure 3 Down feathers help keep birds warm. Contour feathers are the feathers used for flight, and the feathers that cover the body.

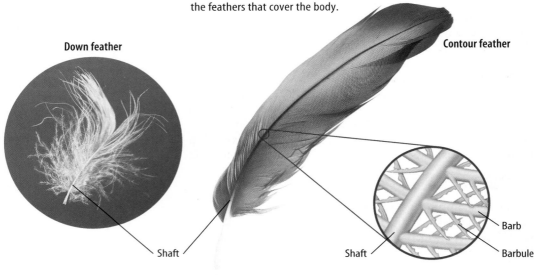

Down feather

Contour feather

Shaft

Shaft

Barb

Barbule

Visual Learning

Figure 3 What differences do you see between down feathers and contour feathers? Contour feathers are larger, with a more rigid shaft, and the barbs are hooked together. Down feathers are smaller, fluffier, and softer. The hairlike filaments are not hooked together, and the shaft is very flexible.

✔ Active Reading

Reflective Journal Have students divide sheets of paper into several columns. Have them record their thoughts about an activity under headings such as *What I did, What I learned, What questions I have, What surprised me,* and *Overall response.* Have students write a Reflective Journal entry for the MiniLAB on this page. L2

Figure 4 Wings provide an upward force called lift for birds and airplanes.
Describe *how birds are able to fly.*

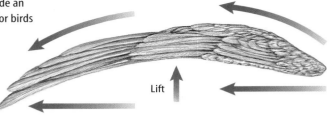

Lift

Bald eagles are able to soar for long periods of time because their wings have a large surface area to provide lift.

This glider gets lift from its wings the same way a bald eagle gets lift.

Wings Although not all birds fly, most wings are adapted for flight. Wings are attached to powerful chest muscles. By flapping its wings, a bird attains thrust to go forward and lift to stay in the air. Its wings move up and down, as well as back and forth.

The shape of a bird's wings helps it fly. The wings are curved on top and flat or slightly curved on the bottom. Humans copied this shape to make airplane wings, as shown in **Figure 4.** When a bird flies, air moves more slowly across the bottom than across the top of its wings. Slow-moving air has greater pressure than fast-moving air, resulting in an upward push called lift. The amount of lift depends on the total surface area of the wing, the speed at which air moves over the wing, and the angle of the wing to the moving air. Once birds with large wings, such as vultures, reach high altitudes, they can soar and glide for a long time without having to beat their wings.

Wings also serve important functions for birds that don't fly. Penguins are birds that use their wings to swim underwater. Ostriches use their wings in courtship and to maintain their balance while running or walking.

Bird Pests Some birds have become pests in urban areas. Research to learn what birds are considered pests in urban areas, what effect they have on the urban environment, and what measures are taken to reduce the problems they create. Build a bulletin board showing your results.

SECTION 1 Birds **431**

Science Online

Topic: Homing Pigeons

Visit life.msscience.com for Web links to information about homing pigeons.

Activity Name two past uses for homing pigeons, and write an advertisement for a new use in the future.

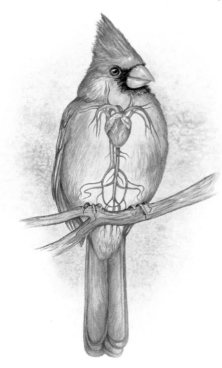

Figure 5 A bird's blood is circulated quickly so enough oxygen-filled blood is carried to the bird's muscles.

Body Systems

Whether they fly, swim, or run, most birds are extremely active. Their body systems are adapted for these activities.

Digestive System Because flying uses large amounts of energy, birds need large amounts of high energy foods, such as nuts, seeds, nectar, insects, and meat. Food is broken down quickly in the digestive system to supply this energy. In some birds, digestion can take less than an hour—for humans digestion can take more than a day.

From a bird's mouth, unchewed food passes into a digestive organ called the crop. The crop stores the food until it absorbs enough moisture to move on. The food enters the stomach where it is partially digested before it moves into the muscular gizzard. In the gizzard, food is ground and crushed by small stones and grit that the bird has swallowed. Digestion is completed in the intestine, and then the food's nutrients move into the bloodstream.

Respiratory System Body heat is generated when energy in food is combined with oxygen. A bird's respiratory system efficiently obtains oxygen, which is needed to power flight muscles and to convert food into energy. Birds have two lungs. Each lung is connected to balloonlike air sacs that reach into different parts of the body, including some of the bones. Most of the air inhaled by a bird passes into the air sacs behind the lungs. When a bird exhales, air with oxygen passes from these air sacs into the lungs. Air flows in only one direction through a bird's lungs. Unlike other vertebrates, birds receive air with oxygen when they inhale and when they exhale. This provides a constant supply of oxygen for the flight muscles.

Circulatory System A bird's circulatory system consists of a heart, arteries, capillaries, and veins, as shown in **Figure 5.** Their four-chambered heart is large compared to their body. On average, a sparrow's heart is 1.68 percent of its body weight. The average human heart is only 0.42 percent of the human's body weight. Oxygen-filled blood is kept separate from carbon dioxide-filled blood as both move through a bird's heart and blood vessels. A bird's heart beats rapidly—an active hummingbird's heart can beat more than 1,000 times per minute.

432 CHAPTER 15 Birds and Mammals

Owl

Hummingbird

The Importance of Birds

Birds play important roles in nature. Some are sources of food and raw materials, and others are kept as pets. Some birds, like the owl in **Figure 6,** help control pests, such as destructive rodents. Barn swallows and other birds help keep insect populations in check by eating them. Some birds, like the hummingbird in **Figure 6,** are pollinators for many flowers. As they feed on the flower's nectar, pollen collects on their feathers and is deposited on the next flower they visit. Other birds eat fruits, then their seeds are dispersed in the birds' droppings. Seed-eating birds help control weeds. Birds can be considered pests when their populations grow too large. In cities where large numbers of birds roost, their droppings can damage buildings. Some droppings also can contain microorganisms that can cause diseases in humans.

Uses of Birds Humans have hunted birds for food and fancy feathers for centuries. Eventually, wild birds such as chickens and turkeys were domesticated and their meat and eggs became a valuable part of human diets. Feathers are used in mattresses and pillows because of their softness and ability to be fluffed over and over. Down feathers are good insulators. Even bird droppings, called guano (GWAH noh), are collected from seabird colonies and used as fertilizer.

Parakeets, parrots, and canaries often are kept as pets because many sing or can be taught to imitate sounds and human voices. Most birds sold as pets are bred in captivity, but some wild birds still are collected illegally, which threatens many species.

Figure 6 In nature, some birds, like the owl on the left, help control pests. Others, like the hummingbird above, pollinate flowers. **Identify** *other important uses of birds.*

Visualizing Birds

Have students examine the pictures and read the captions. Then ask the following questions:

How does the shape of the heron's beak help it catch food in its environment? The beak is long and helps it scoop up fish.

Why do seed-eating birds need grasping claws? They need to be able to hook onto tree limbs or hold on to tree bark.

What other adaptation do you think birds of prey must have besides sharp beaks and grasping claws? They must be able to see well so they can spot and track prey, and to fly fast so they can catch prey.

Activity

Bird Statistics Have students research bird statistics, naming the birds with the following characteristics:

- Tallest and heaviest: ostrich
- Largest wingspan: Andean condor, albatross, marabou stork
- Earliest known: Archaeopteryx
- Smallest: hummingbird of Cuba
- Fastest: swift
- Fastest diver: peregrine falcon
- Fastest swimmer: penguin
- Largest eyes: ostrich

Have students list in a table or on the board other interesting statistics found. L2

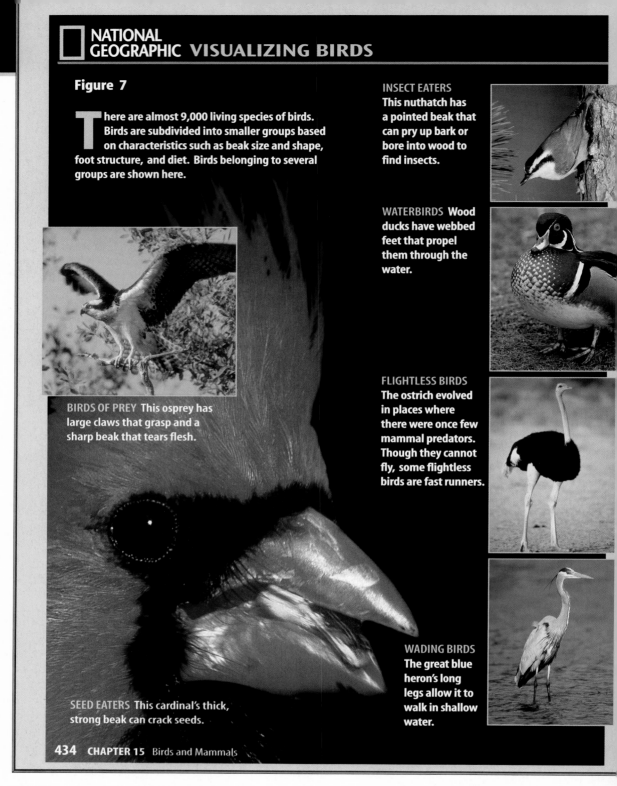

NATIONAL GEOGRAPHIC VISUALIZING BIRDS

Figure 7

There are almost 9,000 living species of birds. Birds are subdivided into smaller groups based on characteristics such as beak size and shape, foot structure, and diet. Birds belonging to several groups are shown here.

INSECT EATERS This nuthatch has a pointed beak that can pry up bark or bore into wood to find insects.

WATERBIRDS Wood ducks have webbed feet that propel them through the water.

FLIGHTLESS BIRDS The ostrich evolved in places where there were once few mammal predators. Though they cannot fly, some flightless birds are fast runners.

WADING BIRDS The great blue heron's long legs allow it to walk in shallow water.

BIRDS OF PREY This osprey has large claws that grasp and a sharp beak that tears flesh.

SEED EATERS This cardinal's thick, strong beak can crack seeds.

434 CHAPTER 15 Birds and Mammals

Differentiated Instruction

Challenge Have students consider birds adapted to extreme environments, such as penguins or roadrunners. Have students draw conclusions about the adaptations that allow these birds to survive, then confirm their conclusions with research. L3

Teacher FYI

Extinction More than 80 species of birds have become extinct in the last 300 years. Causes of extinction include habitat destruction; collecting bird parts such as feathers, beaks, and talons; illegal pet trade; competition from introduced species; and toxic effects of pesticides, oil spills, and chemical dumping.

Origin of Birds Birds, like those in **Figure 7,** have some characteristics of reptiles, including scales on their feet and legs. Scientists learn about the origins of most living things by studying their fossils; however, few fossils of birds have been found. Some scientists hypothesize that birds developed from reptiles millions of years ago.

Archaeopteryx (ar kee AHP tuh rihks)—a birdlike fossil—is about 150 million years old. Although it is not known that *Archaeopteryx* was a direct ancestor of modern birds, evidence shows that it had feathers and wings similar to modern birds. However, it had solid bones, teeth, a long bony tail, and clawed front toes, like some reptiles.

In 1991 in Texas, scientists discovered a fossil that had hollow bones and a well-developed sternum with a keel. *Protoavis* (proh toh AY vihs) lived about 225 million years ago. No fossil feathers were found with *Protoavis*. Scientists do not know if it was an ancestor of modern birds or a type of ground-living dinosaur. **Figure 8** shows an artist's idea of what *Archaeopteryx* and *Protoavis* may have looked like.

Figure 8 The first *Archaeopteryx* fossil was found more than 100 years ago. *Archaeopteryx,* to the left, is considered a link between reptiles and birds. *Protoavis,* below, may be an ancestor of birds.

Discussion

Bird Fossils Why are fewer bird fossils found in the fossil record than those of reptiles and mammals? Their small, lightweight bones often disintegrate or are crushed before they can become fossils.

3 Assess

DAILY INTERVENTION

Check for Understanding

Visual-Spatial Have students work together to develop a plan showing how the area near your school can be made into a more favorable habitat for a specific species of bird. L1 COOP LEARN IS

Reteach

Bird Survival How does the diversity of birds help them survive? Because birds have different adaptations for different environments, they can live all over the world. If they all lived in one place, there would not be enough food or shelter. L2 IS **Logical-Mathematical**

Assessment

Performance Assess students' abilities to compare and contrast birds native to your area by having them examine pictures that show the birds' beaks and feet. Students can make a model of a hypothetical bird's feet, and describe their bird's lifestyle. Use **Performance Assessment in the Science Classroom,** p.123. L2 P

---

 section 1 review

Summary

Bird Characteristics

- Birds are feathered vertebrates. Females lay hard-shelled amniotic eggs, which hatch after an incubation period.
- Most birds are capable of flight, due to a hollow strong skeleton, wings, feathers, strong flight muscles, and efficient body systems.

Body Systems

- Birds have no teeth, but grind food in their gizzard.
- Birds take in oxygen while inhaling and exhaling, which provides more oxygen for flight.

Importance of Birds

- Birds pollinate plants, are a food source, keep pest populations low, and are used commercially.

Self Check

1. **Describe** the type of feather that helps birds maintain their body temperature.
2. **Sequence** Make a network-tree concept map about birds using the following terms: *birds, beaks, hollow bones, wings, eggs, adaptations for flight, feathers,* and *air sacs.*
3. **Think Critically** Hypothesize why most birds eat nuts, berries, insects, nectar, or meat, but not grass and leaves.

Applying Skills

4. **Venn Diagram** Draw a Venn diagram to compare and contrast the characteristics of birds that fly and birds that do not fly.
5. **Communicate** Many expressions mention birds, such as "proud as a peacock" and "wise as an owl." Make a list of several of these expressions and then decide which are accurate.

---

section 1 review

1. Down feathers provide insulation that helps a bird maintain its body temperature.
2. The network-tree should begin with birds, then adaptations for flight (include lightweight bones, feathers, air sacs). Eggs, beaks, and wings should be level with adaptations for flight.
3. Because birds need so much energy, they eat high-energy foods such as nuts and berries.
4. Have students work in pairs to compare diagrams and check answers.
5. Possible answers: "Water off a duck's back" and "eagle eyes" are accurate. Others such as "eats like a bird," "wise as an owl," "happy as a lark," and "crazy as a loon" are inaccurate.

as you read

What You'll Learn

- **Identify** the characteristics of mammals and explain how they have enabled mammals to adapt to different environments.
- **Distinguish** among monotremes, marsupials, and placentals.
- **Explain** why many species of mammals are becoming threatened or endangered.

Why It's Important

Mammals, including humans, have many characteristics in common.

Review Vocabulary
gland: a cell or group of cells that releases fluid

New Vocabulary
- mammal
- mammary gland
- omnivore
- carnivore
- herbivore
- monotreme
- marsupial
- placental
- gestation period
- placenta
- umbilical cord

Figure 9 Mammals, such as this moose, care for their young after they are born.
Explain how mammals feed their young.

Characteristics of Mammals

You probably can name dozens of mammals, but can you list a few of their common characteristics? **Mammals** are endothermic vertebrates that have hair and produce milk to feed their young, as shown in **Figure 9**. Like birds, mammals care for their young. Mammals can be found almost everywhere on Earth. Each mammal species is adapted to its unique way of life.

Skin and Glands Skin covers and protects the bodies of all mammals. A mammal's skin is an organ that produces hair and in some species, horns, claws, nails, or hooves. The skin also contains different kinds of glands. One type of gland found in all mammals is the mammary gland. Female mammals have **mammary glands** that produce milk for feeding their young. Oil glands produce oil that lubricates and conditions the hair and skin. Sweat glands in some species remove wastes and help keep them cool. Many mammals have scent glands that secrete substances that can mark their territory, attract a mate, or be a form of defense.

Figure 10 Mammals have teeth that are shaped specifically for the food they eat.

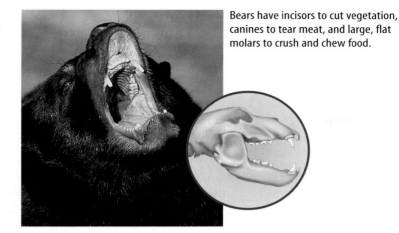

Bears have incisors to cut vegetation, canines to tear meat, and large, flat molars to crush and chew food.

A tiger easily can tear away the flesh of an animal because of large, sharp canine teeth and strong jaw muscles.

A horse's back teeth, called molars, are large. **Infer** *how a horse chews.*

Teeth Notice that each mammal in **Figure 10** has different kinds of teeth. Almost all mammals have specialized teeth. Scientists can determine a mammal's diet by examining its teeth. Front teeth, called incisors, bite and cut. Sometimes the teeth next to the incisors, called canine teeth, are well developed to grip and tear. Premolars and molars at the back of the mouth shred, grind, and crush. Animals, like the bear in **Figure 10,** and humans, have all four kinds of teeth. They eat plants and other animals, so they are called **omnivores.** A **carnivore,** like the tiger in **Figure 10,** has large canine teeth and eats only the flesh of other animals. **Herbivores,** such as the horse in **Figure 10,** eat only plants. Their large premolars and molars grind the tough fibers in plants.

SECTION 2 Mammals   **437**

Differentiated Instruction

Learning Disabled Display a wall map of the world. Ask students to affix drawings and magazine pictures of mammals to the map to show where each mammal is commonly found. Students can visit a local zoo to take pictures of mammals to add to the map. L1 LS **Visual-Spatial**

Teacher FYI

Mutualism Some birds and mammals have developed unique mutualistic relationships. Ostriches and gazelles feed near each other. Both watch for predators and can alert each other to an approaching predator. Their visual abilities differ, so each benefits from the other species' watchfulness.

2 Teach

Caption Answer
Figure 10 Horses use molars for grinding grasses.

Quick Demo
Mammal Behavior
Materials live mammal pet, such as a gerbil, hamster, or guinea pig
Estimated Time 10 minutes
Procedure If someone in your class has a pet gerbil, hamster, or guinea pig, have that student bring the pet to class for a day. Have students observe its characteristics and behavior and record their observations. L1 LS **Visual-Spatial**

Activity

Animal Teeth Obtain models or pictures that show the teeth of mammals that eat different foods. A veterinarian might be a source of these models. Have students identify the incisors, canines, premolars, and molars on each model. L2 LS **Visual-Spatial**

IDENTIFYING Misconceptions

Humans as Mammals Students may not think of themselves as mammals. To help them realize that humans are classified as mammals, list the specific characteristics of mammals on the chalkboard. Include *endothermic, hair, mammary glands, oil glands, sweat glands, specialized teeth,* and *well-developed body systems* in the list. Invite volunteers to circle each characteristic possessed by humans.

Mini LAB

Purpose Students model how fat insulates an animal. L1
ELL **LS** **Kinesthetic**

Materials two self-sealing plastic bags, vegetable shortening, bowl of ice water

Teaching Strategy Have students hold the hand in the blubber mitten under the ice water, and time how long it takes for the cold to penetrate. Point out that real blubber insulates from cold indefinitely.

Analysis
1. the hand that is bare
2. Blubber is an insulator—it traps air and protects against cold.

Assessment

Performance Ask students to design and carry out an experiment comparing the insulating properties of polyester batting and plastic foam peanuts. Use **Performance Assessment in the Science Classroom,** p. 95.
P

Try at Home

Caption Answer

Figure 11 Plants contain materials that are harder to digest than meats.

Mini LAB

Inferring How Blubber Insulates

Procedure 🖐

1. Fill a **self-sealing plastic bag** about one-third full with **vegetable shortening.**
2. Turn another self-sealing plastic bag inside out. Carefully place it inside the bag with the shortening so that you are able to seal one bag to the other. This is a blubber mitten.
3. Put your hand in the blubber mitten and place it in **ice water** for 5 s. Remove the blubber mitten when finished.
4. Put your bare hand in the same bowl of ice water for 5 s.

Analysis
1. Which hand seemed colder?
2. Infer how a layer of blubber provides protection against cold water.

Try at Home

Figure 11 Herbivores, like this elk, have four-chambered stomachs and long intestinal tracts that contain microorganisms, which help break down the plant material.
Explain *why herbivores need a longer digestive system than carnivores.*

Hair All adult mammals have hair on their bodies. It may be thick fur that covers all or part of the animal's body, or just a few hairs around the mouth. Fur traps air and helps keep the animal warm. Whiskers located near the mouth help many mammals sense their environments. Whales have almost no hair. They rely on a thick layer of fat under their skin, called blubber, to keep them warm. Porcupine quills and hedgehog spines are modified hairs that offer protection from predators.

Body Systems

The body systems of mammals are adapted to their activities and enable them to survive in many environments.

Mammals have four-chambered hearts that pump oxygen-filled blood directly throughout the body in blood vessels. Mammals have lungs made of millions of microscopic sacs. These sacs increase the lungs' surface area, allowing a greater exchange of carbon dioxide and oxygen.

A mammal's nervous system consists of a brain, spinal cord, and nerves. In mammals, the part of the brain involved in learning, problem solving, and remembering is larger than in other animals. Another large part of the mammal brain controls its muscle coordination.

The digestive systems of mammals vary according to the kinds of food they eat. Herbivores, like the one shown in **Figure 11,** have long digestive tracts compared to carnivores because plants take longer to digest than meat.

Stomach | Small intestine | Large intestine

LAB DEMONSTRATION

Purpose to compare mammal hair

Materials samples of mammal hair (from humans, dogs, cats, gerbils, horses, and so on); glycerin, projecting microscope, microscope slides, cover slips

Preparation Place a drop of glycerin on each slide, add the animal hair, then the coverslip.

Procedure Project the hairs under low and high power. Students should draw what they see and write brief descriptions.

Expected Outcome Students observe differences in the hair of different mammals.

Assessment

How are the hairs of various mammals alike? All mammal hairs have layers and are covered by lines, blocks, or surface scales. How are they different? The layers have different thicknesses and different shaped lines cutting through, or no lines at all.

Reproduction and Caring for Young All mammals reproduce sexually. Most mammals give birth to live young after a period of development inside the female reproductive organ called the uterus. Many mammals are nearly helpless, and sometimes even blind, when they are born. They can't care for themselves for the first several days or even years. If you've seen newborn kittens or human babies, you know they just eat, sleep, grow, and develop. However, the young of some mammals, such as antelope, deer, and elephants, are well developed at birth and are able to travel with their constantly moving parents. These young mammals usually can stand by the time they are a few minutes old. Marine mammals, such as the whales, shown in **Figure 12,** can swim as soon as they are born.

 *Is a house cat or a deer more developed at birth?*

During the time that young mammals are dependent on their female parent's milk, they learn many of the skills needed for their survival. Defensive skills are learned while playing with other young of their own kind. Other skills are learned by imitating adults. In many mammal species only females raise the young. Males of some species, such as wolves and humans, help provide shelter, food, and protection for their young.

Figure 12 When a whale is born, the female whale must quickly push the newborn whale to the water's surface to breathe. Otherwise, the newborn whale will drown.

Applying Science

Does a mammal's heart rate determine how long it will live?

Some mammals live long lives, but other mammals live for only a few years. Do you think that a mammal's life span might be related to how fast its heart beats? Use your ability to interpret a data table to answer this question.

Identifying the Problem
The table on the right lists the average heart rates and life spans of several different mammals. Heart rate is recorded as the number of heartbeats per minute, and life span is recorded as the average maximum years. When you examine the data, look for a relationship between the two variables.

Mammal Heart Rates and Life Spans		
Mammal	**Heart Rate (beats/min)**	**Life Span (years)**
Mouse	400	2
Large dog	80	15
Bear	40	15–20
Elephant	25	75

Solving the Problem
1. Infer how heart rate and life span are related in mammals.
2. Humans have heart rates of about 70 beats per minute. Some humans may live for more than 100 years. Is this consistent with the data in the table? Explain.

Figure 13 A duck-billed platypus is a mammal, yet it lays eggs. **Explain** *why the duck-billed platypus is classified as a mammal.*

Figure 14 Opossums are the only marsupials found in North America. A joey, or young kangaroo, returns to its mother's pouch when danger is near.

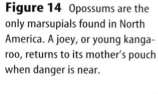

Opossums

A joey with its mother

Types of Mammals

Mammals are classified into three groups based on how their young develop. The three mammal groups are monotremes (MAH nuh treemz), marsupials (mar SEW pee ulz), and placentals (pluh SEN tulz).

Monotremes The duck-billed platypus, shown in **Figure 13,** is a monotreme. **Monotremes** are mammals that lay eggs with leathery shells. The female incubates the eggs for about ten days. After the young hatch, they nurse by licking the female's skin and hair where milk oozes from the mammary glands. Monotreme mammary glands do not have nipples.

Marsupials Many of the mammals that are classified as marsupials live in Australia, New Guinea, or South America. Only one type of marsupial, the opossum, lives in North America. **Marsupials** give birth to immature young that usually crawl into an external pouch on the female's abdomen. However, not all marsupials have pouches. Whether an immature marsupial is in a pouch or not, it instinctively crawls to a nipple. It stays attached to the nipple and feeds until it is developed. In pouched marsupials, the developed young return to the pouch for feeding and protection. Examples of marsupials are kangaroos and opossums, as shown in **Figure 14,** wallabies, koalas, bandicoots, and Tasmanian devils.

Placentals In **placentals,** embryos completely develop inside the female's uterus. The time during which the embryo develops in the uterus is called the **gestation period.** Gestation periods range from 16 days in hamsters to 650 days in elephants. Placentals are named for the **placenta,** an organ that develops from tissues of the embryo and tissues that line the inside of the uterus. The placenta absorbs oxygen and food from the mother's blood. An umbilical cord connects the embryo to the placenta, as shown in **Figure 15.** Several blood vessels make up the umbilical cord. Blood in the **umbilical cord** transports food and oxygen from the placenta to the embryo and removes waste products from the embryo. The female parent's blood doesn't mix with the embryo's blood. Examples of placentals are shown in **Table 1** on the following two pages.

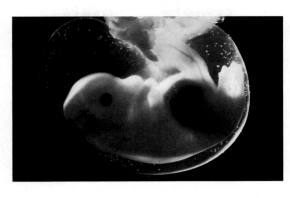

Figure 15 An unborn mammal receives nutrients and oxygen through the umbilical cord. **Compare and contrast** *placental, marsupial, and monotreme development.*

✔ **Reading Check** *How does an embryo receive the things it needs to grow?*

Some placental groups include unusual animals such as the manatee shown in **Figure 16.** Dugongs and manatees are aquatic mammals. They have no back legs, and their front legs are modified into flippers. Another group includes small, rabbit-like animals called hyraxes that have hooves and molars for grinding vegetation. The aardvark is the only member of its group. Aardvarks have tubelike teeth and dig termites for food. Many Southeast Asian islands are home to members of a group that includes gliding lemurs. Pangolins, another group of placentals, look like anteaters covered with scales.

Figure 16 A manatee swims slowly below the surface of the water.

Science⬤nline

Topic: Manatee Habitats
Visit life.msscience.com for Web links to recent news or magazine articles about manatees and their habitats.

Activity Create a pamphlet about the manatees' habitat, their threats, and what people can do to help them.

✔ **Reading Check**

Answer The umbilical cord transports food and oxygen from the placenta to the embryo.

Discussion

Mammal Gestation Is there a connection between the size of mammals and their gestation periods? Generally, the gestation periods of larger species are longer than those of smaller species. An exception to this rule are tigers, lions, and other large cats, who have average gestation period of 3.5 months, shorter than that of a domestic sheep.

Caption Answer

Figure 15 Placentals develop inside the uterus of the mother; marsupials develop a short time in the uterus, followed by development in a pouch; monotremes develop inside an egg.

SECTION 2 Mammals **441**

Curriculum Connection

Geography Mammals first appeared during the Jurassic period and diversified during the Cenozoic Era. Monotremes and marsupials developed in Australia and South America; placentals dominated North America. When North and South America joined, placentals spread southward. Australia remained separate and has a diverse population of monotremes and marsupials. Have students locate these areas on a world map. L1

Differentiated Instruction

Challenge Have students research and report on gestation periods of mammals and the average number of offspring born to different species. Some gestation periods are: opossum—12 days; hamster—16 to 37 days; mouse—20 to 30 days; rabbit—30 days; dog—53 to 71 days; cat—52 days; guinea pig—63 days; human—266 days; cow—238 days; horse—340 days; giraffe—453 to 464 days; and Asian elephant—609 to 760 days. L3

Make a Model

Placentals Mobile Have students make a mobile that shows the orders of placentals they have studied. [L1] **ELL** [IS] **Kinesthetic**

Activity

Listing Placentals Have students keep records of every placental they see for a period of three days. Then have them classify the mammals according to order. [L2] [IS] **Logical-Mathematical**

Discussion

Retractable Claws In what ways do retractable claws help lions and other cats to survive? They use their claws to climb trees and hold prey. The claws can be retracted, enabling the animals to walk and run faster.

Camel Humps Students may think that camels store water in their humps. In reality, the humps contain fat, which provides energy and, when oxidized, can manufacture water. This fat helps camels survive in the desert where food and water are scarce.

Table 1 Placentals

Order	Examples		Major Characteristics
Rodentia (roh DEN chuh)	beavers, mice, rats, squirrels		one pair of chisel-like front teeth adapted for gnawing; incisors grow throughout life; herbivores
Chiroptera (ki RAHP tuh ruh)	bats		front limbs adapted for flying; active at night; different species feed on fruit, insects, fish, or other bats
Insectivora (ihn sek TIH vuh ruh)	moles, shrews, hedgehogs		small; feed on insects, earthworms, and other small animals; most have long skulls and narrow snouts; high metabolic rate
Carnivora (kar NIH vuh ruh)	cats, dogs, bears, foxes, raccoons		long, sharp canine teeth for tearing flesh; most are predators, some are omnivores
Primates (PRI maytz)	apes, monkeys, humans		arms with grasping hands and opposable thumbs; eyes are forward facing; large brains; omnivores
Artiodactyla (ar tee oh DAHK tih luh)	deer, moose, pigs, camels, giraffes, cows		hooves with an even number of toes; most are herbivores with large, flat molars; complex stomachs and intestines

---

Differentiated Instruction

Challenge Have students discuss the definition of "intelligence." Then explain that dolphins are surpassed in cerebrum-to-body mass ratio only by humans and chimpanzees. Have students research current studies investigating the intelligence of dolphins and share their findings in an oral report to the class. They should include a definition of intelligence in their reports. [L3]

Teacher FYI

Hibernating Animals Examples of hibernating mammals include certain bats, echidnas, chipmunks, and woodchucks. Most scientists do not consider bears to be true hibernators because their body temperature drops only slightly. Bears go into a state called *torpor*.

Order	Examples		Major Characteristics
Cetacea (sih TAY shuh)	whales, dolphins, porpoises		one or two blowholes on top of the head for breathing; forelimbs are modified into flippers; teeth or baleen
Lagomorpha (la guh MOR fuh)	rabbits, hares, pikas		some with long hind legs adapted for jumping and running; one pair of large, upper incisors; one pair of small, peglike incisors
Pinnipedia (pih nih PEE dee uh)	sea lions, seals, walruses		marine carnivores; limbs modified for swimming
Edentata (ee dehn TAH tuh)	anteaters, sloths, armadillos		eat insects and other small animals; most are toothless or have tiny, peglike teeth
Perissodactyla (puh ris oh DAHK tih luh)	horses, zebras, tapirs, rhinoceroses		hooves with an odd number of toes; skeletons adapted for running; herbivores with large, grinding molars
Proboscidea (proh boh SIH dee uh)	elephants		a long nose called a trunk; herbivores; upper incisor teeth grow to form tusks; thick, leathery skin

IDENTIFYING Misconceptions

Elephants v. Whales Some students may think that elephants are the largest animals living today. It is true that elephants are the largest *land* animals. However, many whale species are much larger than the largest elephants. The largest elephants weigh 6,000 kg (13,000 pounds). The largest whales weigh 135,000 kg (300,000 pounds). Blue whales are the largest whales and in fact are the largest animal to have ever lived—much larger than dinosaurs, a misconception some students may have.

Visual Learning

Table 1 Look at this table and name each animal's order. Which mammals are plant-eaters with legs adapted for running and jumping? *Lagomorpha* Which order has hooves with one or three toes and skeletons adapted for running? *Perissodactyla* Which order has blowholes for breathing? *Cetacea* Which mammals have front limbs adapted for flying and are most active at night? *Chiroptera* Which mammals have long, sharp canine teeth for tearing flesh? *Carnivora* L2

Text Question Answer
Answers may include advocating stricter hunting laws, changing to a vegetarian diet, and recycling.

DAILY INTERVENTION

Check for Understanding
Logical-Mathematical Label 3-in × 5-in cards with mammal characteristics. Have each student take a card, read the characteristics aloud, and classify the mammal described as a monotreme, marsupial, or placental. L1 LS

Reteach
Mammal Success Have students debate which type of mammalian reproductive pattern is most successful. All strategies are successful, as they enable the species to survive. However, because the young of placental mammals are more developed when born, they may have a better chance of surviving. Accept all reasonable answers. L3

☑ Assessment

Performance Have students make a model of a hypothetical mammal and explain how it is adapted to its environment. Use **Performance Assessment in the Science Classroom,** p. 123. L3

Importance of Mammals

Mammals, like other organisms, are important in maintaining a balance in the environment. Carnivores, such as lions, help control populations of other animals. Bats help pollinate flowers and control insects. Other mammals pick up plant seeds in their fur and distribute them. However, mammals and other animals are in trouble today. As millions of wildlife habitats are destroyed for shopping centers, recreational areas, housing, and roads, many mammals are left without food, shelter, and space to survive. Because humans have the ability to reason, they have a responsibility to learn that their survival is related closely to the survival of all mammals. What can you do to protect the mammals in your community?

Figure 17 The *Dvinia* was an ancestor of ancient mammals.

Origin of Mammals About 65 million years ago, dinosaurs and many other organisms became extinct. This opened up new habitats for mammals, and they began to branch out into many different species. Some of these species gave rise to modern mammals. Today, more than 4,000 species of mammals have evolved from animals similar to the one in **Figure 17,** which lived about 200 million years ago.

---

section 2 review

Summary

Characteristics of Mammals
- Mammals have mammary glands, hair covering all or part of the body, and teeth specialized to the foods they eat.
- A mammal's body systems are well-adapted to the environment it lives in.

Types of Mammals
- There are three types of mammals: monotremes, which lay eggs; marsupials, which give birth to immature young that are nursed until developed, usually in a pouch; and placentals, which completely develop inside the female.

Importance of Mammals
- Mammals help maintain a balance in the environment. They are a food source, pollinators, and used commercially.

Self Check

1. **Describe** five characteristics of mammals and explain how they allow mammals to survive in different environments.
2. **Compare and contrast** birds and mammals.
3. **Describe** the differences between herbivores, carnivores, and omnivores.
4. **Classify** the following animals into the three mammal groups: whales, koalas, horses, elephants, opossums, kangaroos, rabbits, bats, bears, platypuses, and monkeys.
5. **Think Critically** How have humans contributed to the decrease in many wildlife populations?

Applying Math

6. **Solve One-Step Equations** The tallest land mammal is the giraffe at 5.6 m. Calculate your height in meters, and determine how many of you it would take to be as tall as the giraffe.

Science online life.msscience.com/self_check_quiz

---

section 2 review

1. hair, four-chambered hearts, well-developed lungs, relatively large brains, and functional mammary glands; these characteristics allow them to adapt to many environments
2. similar: endothermic, reproduce sexually, have an endoskeleton; mammals have hair, mammary glands, and most produce live young; birds have feathers and wings and lay eggs
3. Herbivores eat only plants and have front teeth for nipping and large molars for grinding. They have a longer digestive tract to aid in digestion. Carnivores eat only flesh and have sharp canine teeth for tearing.

Omnivores eat plants and flesh, and have both molars and canines.
4. placental—horses, elephants, rabbits, bats, bears, monkeys, whales; marsupials—koalas, opossums, kangaroos; monotremes—platypuses
5. Answers will vary, but may include hunting and deforestation.
6. Answers will vary.

Mammal F🐾🐾tprints

Have you ever seen an animal footprint in the snow or soft soil? In this lab, you will observe pictures of mammal footprints and identify the mammal that made the footprint.

▶ Real-World Question

How do mammal footprints differ?

Goals
- **Identify** mammal footprints.
- **Predict** where mammals live based on their footprints.

Materials
diagram of footprints

▶ Procedure

1. Copy the following data table in your Science Journal.

Identifying Mammal Footprints

Animal	Letter of Footprint	Traits of Footprint
Bear	C	
Beaver	A	
Cougar	G	
Coyote	B	Answers
Deer	D	will
Moose	E	vary.
Raccoon	F	

2. Compare and contrast the different mammal footprints in the above diagram.

3. Based on your observations, match each footprint to an animal listed in the first column of the data table.

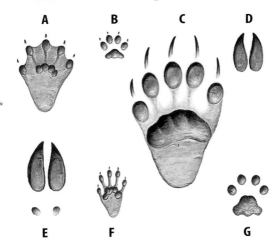

A   B   C   D

E   F   G

4. **Write** your answers in the column labeled *Letter of Footprint*. Complete the data table.

▶ Conclude and Apply

1. Which mammals have hoofed feet?
2. Which mammals have clawed toes?
3. Which mammals have webbed feet?
4. **Explain** how the different feet are adapted to the areas in which these different mammals live.
5. What are the differences between track **B** and track **E**? How does that help you identify the track?

*C*ommunicating
Your Data

Compare your conclusions with those of other students in your class. **For more help, refer to the Science Skill Handbook.**

LAB   445

---

*C*ommunicating
Your Data

Students should discuss why their conclusions did or did not agree. They can cite their references to support their arguments.

▶ Real-World Question

Purpose Students observe how mammal footprints differ. [L2] COOP LEARN [N] **Naturalist**

Process Skills observe, predict, compare and contrast, infer

Time Required 50 minutes

▶ Procedure

Teaching Strategy Have students use reference materials to help them identify the footprints. Students may think that cougars do not have claws because claws don't show in the footprint. Point out that cougars have retractable claws that they use for capturing prey and climbing. Use this as an opportunity to talk about how making a simple visual observation may be misleading and that collecting further data is sometimes necessary to reach the right conclusion.

▶ Conclude and Apply

1. deer, moose
2. coyote, bear, raccoon, beaver
3. beaver
4. Beavers use their webbed feet to swim. Deer and moose live in open, flat areas where hooves help them run. Coyotes, bears, and raccoons use their claws to dig; bears and raccoons climb trees.
5. B is an animal with paw pads and claws. E is an animal with split hooves. The size and shape of the prints help you identify the animal that left them.

▶ Real-World Question

Purpose

Internet Students use Internet sites that can be accessed through life.msscience.com/internet_lab.

Non-Internet Sources Collect materials about local birds from nature centers. Then they will observe birds in their neighborhoods.

Time Required one week to one month

▶ Make a Plan

Preparation

Internet To run through the steps that the students will follow, visit life.msscience.com/internet_lab.

Non-Internet Collect field guides and other materials about birds found in your area.

▶ Follow Your Plan

Teaching Strategies

- Have field guides handy for students to use near the place where they conduct their bird observations.
- Allow class time for students to build their feeders and make their observations.
- Have students devise a table for recording data.

LAB Use the Internet

Bird Counts

▶ Real-World Question

What is the most common bird in your neighborhood? Think about the types of birds that you observe around your neighborhood. What types of food do they eat? Do all birds come to a bird feeder? Form a hypothesis about the type of bird that you think you will see most often at your bird feeder.

Goals
- **Research** how to build a bird feeder and attract birds to it.
- **Observe** the types of birds that visit your feeder.
- **Identify** the types of birds that you observe at your bird feeder.
- **Graph** your results and then communicate them to other students.

Data Source
Science Online

Visit life.msscience.com/ internet_lab for Web links to more information about how to build a bird feeder, hints on bird-watching, and data from other students who do this lab.

Safety Precautions

▶ Make a Plan

1. **Research** general information about how to attract and identify birds. Determine where you will make your observations.

Cardinal

2. **Search** reference sources to find out how to build a bird feeder. Do all birds eat the same types of seeds?

3. **Select** the type of feeder you will build and the seed you will use based on your research.

4. What variables can you control in this lab? Do seasonal changes, length of time, or weather conditions affect your observations?

5. What will you do to identify the birds that you do not know?

▶ Follow Your Plan

1. Make sure your teacher approves your plan before you start.

2. **Record** your data in your Science Journal each time you make an observation of the birds at your bird feeder.

American Goldfinch

Alternative Inquiry Lab

Real-World Connection To make this Lab an Inquiry Lab, give the students more personal investment into the problem by connecting it to the real world. Tell the students that they are ornithologists, scientists who study birds, studying the changes in the bird population in the local area. What kinds of birds are found in your area? Has the landscape changed and, if so, has that affected the bird population? It is important that they collect as much accurate information as possible. The data collected will help other scientists understand more about birds. Encourage them to research how ornithologists conduct their bird counts and to research and look for rare or endangered bird species from your area. L3

⊙ Analyze Your Data

1. **Write** a description of where you placed your feeder and when you made your bird observations.
2. **Record** the total number of birds you observed each day.
3. **Record** the total number of each type of bird species you observed each day.
4. **Graph** your data using a line graph, a circle graph, or a bar graph.

Black-capped Chickadee

⊙ Conclude and Apply

1. **Interpret Data** What type of bird was most common to your feeder?
2. **Explain** if all of your classmates' data agree with yours. Why or why not?
3. **Review** your classmates' data and determine if the location of bird observations affected the number of birds observed.
4. **Infer** if the time of day affected the number of birds observed. Explain.
5. **Infer** Many birds eat great numbers of insects. What might humans do to maintain a healthy environment for birds?

Birds at a feeder

𝒞ommunicating Your Data

Find this lab using the link below. Post your data in the table provided. **Compare** your data to those of other students. Combine your data with those of other students and plot the combined data on a map to recognize patterns in bird populations.

Science⊙nline
life.msscience.com/internet_lab

LAB 447

⊙ Analyze Your Data

1. Students should include information about nearby structures, bushes, and trees.
2. Answers will vary.
3. Answers will vary.
4. Students may wish to make a bar graph summarizing the number of birds observed each day. Line graphs of individual species observed could also be devised. Circle graphs could be made to represent the percentage of each species observed over the course of the activity.

⊙ Conclude and Apply

1. Answers will vary. Have students describe birds' appearances in their journals.
2. Answers will vary. Data may vary because of the amount of time spent observing birds.
3. Location will likely affect the number of birds observed.
4. More birds may be observed during morning hours.
5. Possible answer: by reducing amounts of insecticides used

✓ Assessment

Portfolio Have students make a field guide for the birds they observed. In their guides, they should describe markings, beak shape, types of food eaten, and other unique characteristics of the observed birds. Use **Performance Assessment in the Science Classroom,** p. 165. L2 P

𝒞ommunicating Your Data

Have students prepare a written report that describes their findings. Include information such as days and times of observation, weather conditions, and numbers of birds counted. If they combine their data with other classes, have them add conclusions about the density and location of bird populations.

Content Background

Bird eggs have many adaptations that help them survive until they hatch. For example, the color of bird's eggs helps to camouflage the eggs to avoid predation. The shape of a particular species' eggs can give clues about where the nests are found. Eggs with a pointed end are common in birds that nest on ledges. These eggs tend to roll in circles when disturbed, keeping the eggs from rolling off the ledge. Other eggs have a texture that is adapted to the environment in which they are found. For example, certain species of ducks lay eggs with a greasy, water-repellent coating.

Discussion

Ostrich Eggs Why must ostrich eggs be able to support a weight equal to that of an adult human? Students should infer that the ostrich that sits on the eggs to incubate them weighs about the same amount as a human adult.

Activity

Incubation Periods Have students work in pairs to research the incubation period of the eggs of four different species of birds. Students should display their findings in a bar graph and share their graphs with the class. [L2]

Applying Math

Answer 4

Eggciting Facts

Did you know...

...The ostrich lays the biggest egg of all birds now living. Its egg is 15 cm to 20 cm long and 10 cm to 15 cm wide. The volume of the ostrich egg is about equal to 24 chicken eggs. It can have a mass from approximately 1 kg to a little more than 2 kg. The shell of an ostrich egg is 1.5 mm thick and can support the weight of an adult human.

...The bird that lays the smallest egg is the hummingbird. Hummingbird eggs are typically 1.3 cm long and 0.8 cm wide. The smallest hummingbird egg on record was less than 1 cm long and weighed 0.36 g.

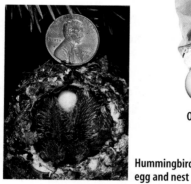

Ostrich egg

Hummingbird egg and nest

Elephant Bird/Vouron Patra
(*Aepyornis maximus*)

Ostrich egg

Elephant bird egg

...The elephant bird, extinct within the last 1,000 years, laid an egg that was seven times larger than an ostrich egg. These eggs weighed about 12 kg. They were 30 cm long and could hold up to 8.5 L of liquid. It could hold the equivalent of 12,000 hummingbird eggs.

Applying Math
How many elephant bird eggs would it take to equal a dog weighing 48 kg?

Graph It

Go to life.msscience.com/science_stats and research the egg length of an American robin, a house sparrow, a bald eagle, and a Canada goose. Make a bar graph of this information.

Graph It

Have students use graph paper to make their graphs as accurate as possible. Have students research the size of these birds and make a graph of their relative sizes. Have the students determine if there is a correlation between the size of the bird and the size of the eggs it produces. [L2]

Reviewing Main Ideas

Section 1   Birds

1. Birds are endothermic animals that are covered with feathers and lay eggs.

2. Adaptations that enable most birds to fly include wings; feathers; a strong, light-weight skeleton; and efficient body systems.

3. Birds lay eggs enclosed in hard shells. All birds' eggs are incubated until they hatch.

Section 2   Mammals

1. Mammals are endothermic animals with fur or hair.

2. Mammary glands of female mammals can produce milk.

3. Mammals have teeth that are specialized for eating certain foods. Herbivores eat plants, carnivores eat meat, and omnivores eat plants and meat.

4. There are three groups of mammals. Monotremes lay eggs. Most marsupials have pouches for the development of their young. Placental offspring develop within a uterus and are nourished through a placenta.

5. Mammals are important in maintaining balance in the environment.

Visualizing Main Ideas

Copy and complete the following concept map on mammals.

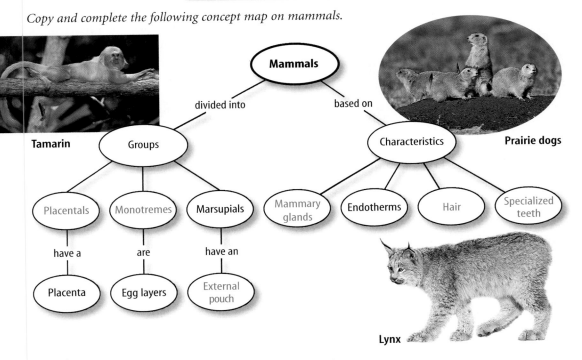

Tamarin

Prairie dogs

Lynx

Reviewing Main Ideas

Summary statements can be used by students to review the major concepts of the chapter.

Visualizing Main Ideas

See student page.

Visit life.msscience.com
/self_check_quiz
/interactive_tutor
/vocabulary_puzzlemaker
/chapter_review
/standardized_test

Assessment Transparency

For additional assessment questions, use the *Assessment Transparency* located in the transparency book.

Assessment

Assessment Transparency   Birds and Mammals

Directions: *Carefully review the table and answer the following questions.*

Whale Species Information				
Species	Length (m)	Weight (t)	Present population x 1,000	Endangered
Blue	23–24	110–150	14	yes
Bowhead	15–18	60–80	7.8	yes
Gray	13–14	30–40	21	yes
Minke	9–11	20–30	N/A	no
Killer	7–9	4–6	N/A	no
Sei	12–17	20–30	54	yes
Sperm	16–18	15–20	1,950	yes

1. According to the information in the table, which whale is the longest?
   A Minke   C Sperm
   B Bowhead   D Blue

2. Based on the information in the table, which of the following statements about killer whales seems reasonable?
   F They don't swim as quickly as the bowhead.
   G They must be short and heavy.
   H They only eat sea plants.
   J They must be sleek and thin.

3. The two whales listed in the table that are the most different in size are the ___.
   A blue and minke   C killer and minke
   B blue and killer   D blue and bowhead

Birds and Mammals

Using Vocabulary

1. Omnivores eat both plants and animals; carnivores eat other animals; herbivores eat plants.

2. Contour feathers are used for flight. Down feathers help insulate birds.

3. Monotremes lay eggs; marsupials give birth to immature offspring that develop in their mother's pouch.

4. The umbilical cord attaches the embryo to the placenta, a saclike organ that absorbs oxygen and food from the female's blood.

5. Endotherms maintain a constant body temperature. Mammals are endotherms.

6. Placentals are mammals in which the embryo develops inside the uterus of the female. Monotremes lay eggs.

7. A mammal is an endothermic vertebrate with hair and mammary glands that produce milk to feed its young.

8. A mammal that eats both plants and other animals is an omnivore.

9. Endotherms maintain a constant body temperature. Birds are endotherms that are covered with down feathers to conserve warmth.

10. Preening is an activity that keeps the feathers in the correct place as well as conditioning them. Down feathers provide insulation.

Checking Concepts

11. A	16. A
12. D	17. C
13. C	18. A
14. C	19. C
15. C	20. B

Using Vocabulary

carnivore p. 437	marsupial p. 440
contour feather p. 430	monotreme p. 440
down feather p. 430	omnivore p. 437
endotherm p. 430	placenta p. 441
gestation period p. 441	placental p. 441
herbivore p. 437	preening p. 430
mammal p. 436	umbilical cord p. 441
mammary gland p. 436	

Explain the difference between the vocabulary words in each of the following sets.

1. omnivore—carnivore—herbivore

2. contour feather—down feather

3. monotreme—marsupial

4. placenta—umbilical cord

5. endotherm—mammal

6. placental—monotreme

7. mammary gland—mammal

8. mammal—omnivore

9. endotherm—down feather

10. preening—down feather

Checking Concepts

Choose the word or phrase that best answers the question.

11. Which of the following birds has feet adapted for moving on water?
    A) duck   C) owl
    B) oriole   D) rhea

12. Birds do NOT use their wings for which of the following activities?
    A) flying   C) balancing
    B) swimming D) eating

13. Which of these mammals lay eggs?
    A) carnivores   C) monotremes
    B) marsupials   D) placentals

14. Birds use which of the following organs to crush and grind their food?
    A) crop   C) gizzard
    B) stomach   D) small intestine

15. Which of the following mammals is classified as a marsupial?
    A) cat   C) kangaroo
    B) human   D) camel

Use the photo below to answer question 16.

16. What are mammals with pouches, like the koala pictured above, called?
    A) marsupials   C) placentals
    B) monotremes   D) chiropterans

17. Which of the following have mammary glands without nipples?
    A) marsupials   C) monotremes
    B) placentals   D) omnivores

18. Teeth that are used for tearing food are called what?
    A) canines   C) molars
    B) incisors D) premolars

19. Bird eggs do NOT have which of the following structures?
    A) hard shells   C) placentas
    B) yolks   D) membranes

20. Which of the following animals eat only plant materials?
    A) carnivores   C) omnivores
    B) herbivores   D) endotherms

 Science Online life.msscience.com/vocabulary_puzzlemaker

Use the ExamView® Pro Testmaker CD-ROM to:
- create multiple versions of tests
- create modified tests with one mouse click for inclusion students
- edit existing questions and add your own questions
- build tests aligned with state standards using built-in State Curriculum Tags
- change English tests to Spanish with one mouse click and vice versa

Thinking Critically

21. **Compare and contrast** bird and mammal reproduction.

22. **Classify** You are a paleontologist studying fossils. One fossil appears to have hollow bones, a keeled breastbone, and a short, bony tail. How would you classify it?

23. **Explain** which type of bird, a duck or an ostrich, would have lighter bones.

24. **List** the features of birds that allow them to be fully adapted to life on land.

25. **Concept Map** Copy and complete this concept map about birds.

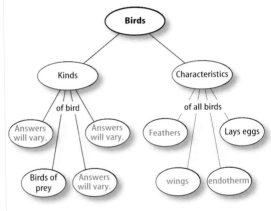

26. **Describe** A mammal's teeth are similar in size and include all four types of teeth. What kind of mammal has teeth like this?

27. **Classify** You discover three new species of placentals, with the following traits. Using **Table 1** in this chapter, place each placental into the correct order.
Placental 1 swims and eats meat.
Placental 2 flies and eats fruit.
Placental 3 runs on four legs and hunts.

 Science Online life.msscience.com/chapter_review

28. **Classify** Group the following mammals as herbivore, carnivore, or omnivore: bear, tiger, opossum, raccoon, mouse, rabbit, seal, and ape.

29. **Compare and contrast** the teeth of herbivores, carnivores, and omnivores. How are their types of teeth adapted to their diets?

Performance Activities

30. **Song with Lyrics** Create a song about bird adaptations for flight by changing the words to a song that you know. Include in your song as many adaptations as possible.

Applying Math

Use the graph below to answer questions 31 and 32.

Record of Canada Geese	
Year	Number of Geese
1996	550
1997	600
1998	575
1999	750
2000	825

31. **Number of Geese** This table is a record of the approximate number of Canada geese that wintered at a midwestern wetland area over a five-year time period. Construct a line graph from these data.

32. **Population Increase** What percent increase occurred in the Canada goose population between 1996 and 2000? What percent increase occurred each year?

CHAPTER REVIEW 451

Thinking Critically

21. Both reproduce sexually; birds lay and incubate eggs; most mammals give birth to live young after a period of development in the uterus.

22. as a bird

23. Ducks have lighter bones than ostriches; ostriches do not fly but ducks do.

24. The amniotic egg and specialized beaks, feet, and wings allow birds to live on land.

25. See student page.

26. an omnivore

27. Mammal 1: *Pinnipedia;* Mammal 2: *Chiroptera;* Mammal 3: *Carnivora*

28. herbivores: rabbit, mouse; carnivores: tiger, seal; omnivores: raccoon, ape, bear, opossum

29. herbivores: large incisors for cutting off blades of grass, molars to grind plants; carnivores: small incisors, large canine teeth to grip and tear food; omnivores: canines, incisors, and molars to feed on both plants and animals

Performance Activities

30. Songs may be simple as long as the lyrics discuss bird adaptations for flight. Use **Performance Assessment in the Science Classroom,** p.151.

Applying Math

National Math Standards
1, 5, 9

31. Graphs should show a slight increase, then slight decrease, followed by a steady, sharp increase.

32. Between 1996 and 2000 there was a 50% increase. 1996 to 1997 there was a 9% increase, 1997 to 1998 there was a 4% decrease, 1998 to 1999 there was a 30% increase, and 1999 to 2000 there was a 10% increase.

✔ Assessment   Resources

Reproducible Masters
Chapter *Fast File* **Resources**
   Chapter Review, pp. 33–34
   Chapter Tests, pp. 35–38
   Assessment Transparency Activity, p. 45
Glencoe Science Web site
   Chapter Review Test
   Standardized Test Practice

Glencoe Technology
   Assessment Transparency
   Exam*View*® Pro Testmaker
   MindJogger Videoquiz
   Interactive Chalkboard

FAST FILE

Answer Sheet A practice answer sheet can be found at life.msscience.com/answer_sheet.

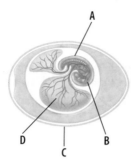

S A M P L E

Part 1 | Multiple Choice

1. A
2. B
3. B
4. D
5. D
6. C
7. C
8. A
9. B

Part 1 | Multiple Choice

Record your answers on the answer sheet provided by your teacher or on a sheet of paper.

Use the illustration below to answer questions 1–2.

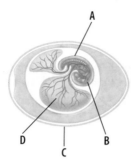

1. Which letter represents amniotic fluid?
   A. A   **C.** C
   B. B   **D.** D

2. Which letter represents a developing embryo?
   A. A   **C.** C
   B. B   **D.** D

3. Which of the following features is an adaptation that allows birds to fly?
   A. a gizzard
   B. bones that are almost hollow
   C. a crop
   D. a four-chambered heart

4. Which of the following is a monotreme?
   A. a penguin   **C.** a kangaroo
   B. an eagle   **D.** a platypus

5. What is a characteristic that sets mammals apart from birds?
   A. They help pollinate flowers.
   B. They have a four-chambered heart.
   C. They have special glands that produce milk for feeding their young.
   D. They have a special skeleton that is lightweight but strong.

Use the illustration below to answer questions 6–7.

6. What part of the mammal's body is indicated by 1–4 in the diagram?
   A. small intestine   **C.** stomach
   B. large intestine   **D.** gizzard

7. Which animals have this type of digestive system?
   A. carnivorous birds
   B. carnivorous mammals
   C. herbivorous mammals
   D. birds that eat only nuts and seeds

8. What is the significance of *Archaeopteryx*?
   A. It was the first birdlike fossil found.
   B. It represents the direct ancestor of birds.
   C. It was probably a ground-living dinosaur with wings.
   D. It is the oldest birdlike fossil.

9. What is the unique characteristic of a marsupial?
   A. They all live in Australia.
   B. Their young develop in a pouch.
   C. They lay eggs.
   D. They provide milk for their young.

452 STANDARDIZED TEST PRACTICE

Part 2 | Short Response/Grid In

10. keel, feathers, bones that are almost hollow

11. the animal maintains a nearly constant body temperature

12. flight, shape, color

13. insulation

14. the crop stores food while it absorbs moisture; the gizzard grinds up food

15. Birds are able to receive oxygen when they inhale and when they exhale.

16. horns, nails, hooves, hair

17. monotremes—platypus; marsupial—opossum; placental—humans

Part 2 | Short Response/Grid In

Record your answers on the answer sheet provided by your teacher or on a sheet of paper.

10. What are two examples of body features that enable birds to fly?

11. What does it mean if an animal is an endotherm?

Use the photos below to answer questions 12 and 13.

12. What is the purpose of feather B?

13. What is the purpose of feather A?

14. In a bird's digestive system, what purpose do the crop and gizzard serve?

15. What adaptation in birds provides a constant supply of oxygen for the flight muscles?

16. Give two examples of special structures produced by the skin of mammals.

17. Give the names of the three groups of mammals based on how their young develop. Give an example of each one.

Test-Taking Tip

Essay Organization For essay questions, spend a few minutes listing and organizing the main points that you plan to discuss. Make sure to do all of this work on your scratch paper, not on the answer sheet.

Question 18 List the characteristics that you want to discuss in one column, and the advantage in flight in another column.

 Science Online life.msscience.com/standardized_test

Part 3 | Open Ended

Record your answers on a sheet of paper.

18. Describe the physical characteristics of birds' bones that make flight possible.

19. Compare the barbs of a contour feather with those of a down feather.

20. Describe the function of wings in flightless birds such as penguins and ostriches.

21. Explain how feathers help a bird fly.

Use the illustration below to answer questions 22 and 23.

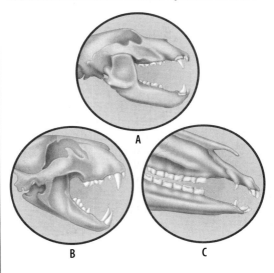

22. How can you tell that diagram C does NOT represent a carnivore? What can you tell about the diet of the animal that would have the type of teeth shown in diagram C?

23. What can you say about the diets of the animals represented by the teeth shown in diagrams A and B?

STANDARDIZED TEST PRACTICE 453

Rubrics

The following rubrics are sample scoring devices for short response and open-ended questions.

Short Response

Points	Description
2	The student demonstrates a thorough understanding of the science of the task. The response may contain minor flaws that do not detract from the demonstration of a thorough understanding.
1	The student has provided a response that is only partially correct.
0	The student has provided a completely incorrect solution or no response at all.

Open Ended

Points	Description
4	The student demonstrates a thorough understanding of the science of the task. The response may contain minor flaws that do not detract from the demonstration of a thorough understanding.
3	The student demonstrates an understanding of the science of the task. The response is essentially correct and demonstrates an essential but less than thorough understanding of the science.
2	The student demonstrates only a partial understanding of the science of the task. Although the student may have used the correct approach to a solution or may have provided a correct solution, the work lacks an essential understanding of the underlying science concepts.
1	The student demonstrates a very limited understanding of the science of the task. The response is incomplete and exhibits many flaws.
0	The student provides a completely incorrect solution or no response at all.

Part 3 | Open Ended

18. Birds' bones are almost hollow and have cross braces that add strength.

19. The barbs of down feathers are soft and have very few barbules. Contour feathers have many barbules to keep the barbs aligned and thus, give the feather strength.

20. penguins—swimming; ostriches —courtship and maintaining balance when walking or running

21. Air moves more slowly across the bottom than across the top of the wings creating more pressure lifting upward.

22. There are no large, sharp canines. The size and number of molars indicate that the animal is an herbivore.

23. The animal in diagram B eats more meat, and the animal in diagram A probably eats both meat and vegetation.

Section/Objectives	Standards		Labs/Features
Chapter Opener	**National**	**State/Local**	**Launch Lab:** How do animals communicate?, p. 455 **Foldables,** p. 455
	See pp. 16T–17T for a Key to Standards.		
Section 1 **Types of Behavior** ⏱ 2 sessions 📦 1 block 1. **Identify** the differences between innate and learned behavior. 2. **Explain** how reflexes and instincts help organisms survive. 3. **Identify** examples of imprinting and conditioning.	National Content Standards: UCP.1–UCP.4, A.1, A.2, C.3, C.5		**Integrate Health,** p. 457 **Science Online,** p. 459 **MiniLAB:** Observing Conditioning, p. 460
Section 2 **Behavioral Interactions** ⏱ 3 sessions 📦 1.5 blocks 4. **Explain** why behavioral adaptations are important. 5. **Describe** how courtship behavior increases reproductive success. 6. **Explain** the importance of social behavior and cyclic behavior.	National Content Standards: UCP.1–UCP.4, A.1, A.2, C.2, C.4, C.5, G.3		**MiniLAB:** Demonstrating Chemical Communication, p. 465 **Integrate History,** p. 466 **Visualizing Bioluminescence,** p. 467 **Science Online,** p. 468 **Applying Science:** How can you determine which animals hibernate?, p. 469 **Lab:** Observing Earthworm Behavior, p. 471 **Lab:** Animal Habitats, p. 472 **Oops! Accidents in Science:** Going to the Dogs, p. 474

Lab Materials	Reproducible Resources	Section Assessment	Technology
Launch Lab: Science Journal, various objects	**Chapter FAST FILE Resources** Foldables Worksheet, p. 15 Directed Reading Overview, p. 17 Note-taking Worksheets, pp. 29–31	*GLENCOE'S ASSESSMENT ADVANTAGE*	TeacherWorks includes: • Interactive Teacher Edition • Lesson Planner with calendar • Access to all program blacklines • Correlations to standards • Web links
MiniLAB: photos of different foods and landscapes *Need materials? Contact Science Kit at 1-800-828-7777 or www.sciencekit.com on the Internet.*	**Chapter FAST FILE Resources** Transparency Activity, p. 40 MiniLAB, p. 3 Enrichment, p. 27 Reinforcement, p. 25 Directed Reading, p. 18 Lab Activity, pp. 9–11 Transparency Activity, pp. 43–44 **Home and Community Involvement,** p. 44	**Portfolio** Reteach, p. 461 **Performance** MiniLAB, p. 460 Applying Skills, p. 461 **Content** Section Review, p. 461	Section Focus Transparency Teaching Transparency Virtual Labs CD-ROM Guided Reading Audio Program Interactive Chalkboard CD-ROM
MiniLAB: sample of perfume, air freshener, or flavoring oil **Lab:** scissors, shoe box with lid, flashlight, tape, paper, moist paper towels, earthworms, timer **Lab:** poster board, markers or colored pencils, materials to make a scale model	**Chapter FAST FILE Resources** Transparency Activity, p. 41 MiniLAB, p. 4 Enrichment, p. 28 Reinforcement, p. 26 Directed Reading, pp. 19, 20 Lab Worksheet, pp. 5–6, 7–8 Lab Activity, pp. 13–14 **Reading and Writing Skill Activities,** p. 5 **Lab Management and Safety,** p. 43	**Portfolio** Cultural Diversity, p. 467 Curriculum Connection, p. 468 **Performance** MiniLAB, p. 465 Applying Science, p. 469 **Content** Applying Math, p. 470 Section Review, p. 470	Section Focus Transparency Virtual Labs CD-ROM Guided Reading Audio Program Interactive Chalkboard CD-ROM Video Lab

End of Chapter Assessment

Blackline Masters	Technology	Professional Series
Chapter FAST FILE Resources Chapter Review, pp. 33–34 Chapter Tests, pp. 35–38 **Standardized Test Practice,** pp. 67–70	MindJogger Videoquiz Virtual Labs CD-ROM ExamView® Pro Testmaker TeacherWorks CD-ROM Interactive Chalkboard CD-ROM	**Performance Assessment in the Science Classroom (PASC)**

Transparencies

Section Focus

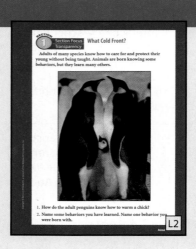

SECTION 1 Section Focus Transparency — **What Cold Front?**

Adults of many species know how to care for and protect their young without being taught. Animals are born knowing some behaviors, but they learn many others.

1. How do the adult penguins know how to warm a chick?
2. Name some behaviors you have learned. Name one behavior you were born with.

L2

SECTION 2 Section Focus Transparency — **Jump Back!**

The snow leopard, which is sometimes called an ounce, is on the endangered species list. Found mainly in the mountains of Asia, the snow leopard tends to live alone. Though snow leopards are solitary animals, they still must interact with other snow leopards as well as with other species.

1. How would you describe this animal's behavior?
2. What are some ways the snow leopard might interact with other animals?

L2

This is a representation of key blackline masters available in the Teacher Classroom Resources. See Resource Manager boxes within the chapter for additional information.

Key to Teaching Strategies

The following designations will help you decide which activities are appropriate for your students.

L1 Level 1 activities should be appropriate for students with learning difficulties.

L2 Level 2 activities should be within the ability range of all students.

L3 Level 3 activities are designed for above-average students.

ELL ELL activities should be within the ability range of English-Language Learners.

COOP LEARN Cooperative Learning activities are designed for small group work.

LS Multiple Learning Styles logos, as described on page 12T, are used throughout to indicate strategies that address different learning styles.

P These strategies represent student products that can be placed into a best-work portfolio.

PBL Problem-Based Learning activities apply real-world situations to learning.

Assessment

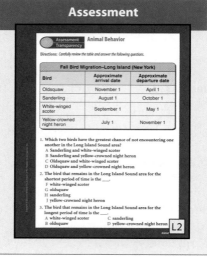

Assessment Transparency — **Animal Behavior**

Directions: Carefully review the table and answer the following questions.

Fall Bird Migration–Long Island (New York)

Bird	Approximate arrival date	Approximate departure date
Oldsquaw	November 1	April 1
Sanderling	August 1	October 1
White-winged scoter	September 1	May 1
Yellow-crowned night heron	July 1	November 1

1. Which two birds have the greatest chance of not encountering one another in the Long Island Sound area?
   A Sanderling and white-winged scoter
   B Sanderling and yellow-crowned night heron
   C Oldsquaw and white-winged scoter
   D Oldsquaw and yellow-crowned night heron
2. The bird that remains in the Long Island Sound area for the shortest period of time is the ___.
   F white-winged scoter
   G oldsquaw
   H sanderling
   J yellow-crowned night heron
3. The bird that remains in the Long Island Sound area for the longest period of time is the ___.
   A white-winged scoter   C sanderling
   B oldsquaw   D yellow-crowned night heron

L2

Teaching

Teaching Transparency — **Problem Solving**

L2

Hands-on Activities

Student Text Lab Worksheet

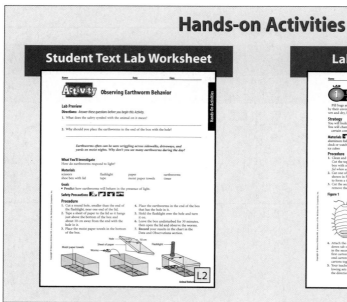

Activity — Observing Earthworm Behavior

Lab Preview
Directions: Answer these questions before you begin this activity.
1. What does the safety symbol with the animal on it mean?

2. Why should you place the earthworms in the end of the box with the hole?

Earthworms often can be seen wriggling across sidewalks, driveways, and yards on moist nights. Why don't you see many earthworms during the day?

What You'll Investigate
How do earthworms respond to light?

Materials
scissors   flashlight   paper
shoe box with lid tape   moist paper towels   earthworms
                                                                  timer
Goals
• Predict how earthworms will behave in the presence of light.

Safety Precautions

Procedure
1. Cut a round hole, smaller than the end of the flashlight, near one end of the lid.
2. Tape a sheet of paper to the lid so it hangs just above the bottom of the box and about 10 cm away from the end with the hole in it.
3. Place the moist paper towels in the bottom of the box.
4. Place the earthworms in the end of the box that has the hole in it.
5. Hold the flashlight over the hole and turn it on.
6. Leave the box undisturbed for 30 minutes, then open the lid and observe the worms.
7. Record your results in the chart in the Data and Observations section.

L2

Laboratory Activities

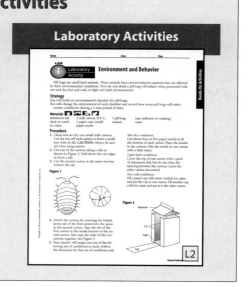

LAB 1 Laboratory Activity — **Environment and Behavior**

Pill bugs are small land animals. These animals have certain behavior patterns that are affected by their environmental conditions. How do you think a pill bug will behave when presented with wet and dry, hot and cold, or light and dark environments?

Strategy
You will build an environmental chamber for pill bugs.
You will change the environment of each chamber and record how many pill bugs will select certain conditions during a 5-min period of time.

Materials
aluminum foil   2 milk cartons (0.5-L)   5 pill bugs   tape (adhesive or masking)
clock or watch   2 paper cups (small)   scissors   water
ice cubes   paper towels

Procedure
1. Clean and air dry two small milk cartons. Cut the top off each carton to form a small box with no lid. CAUTION: Always be careful when using scissors.
2. Cut one of the cartons along a side as shown in Figure 2. Fold down the cut edges to form a tab.
3. Cut the second carton in the same way but remove the tab.

Figure 1

Wet-dry conditions
Cut about four or five paper towels to fit the bottom of each carton. Place the towels in the cartons. Wet the towels in one carton with a little water.
Light-dark conditions
Cover the top of one carton with a piece of aluminum foil, but do not close the opening between the cartons. Leave the other carton uncovered.
Hot-cold conditions
Fill a paper cup with some crushed ice cubes and put the cup in one carton. Fill another cup with hot water and put it in the other carton.

Figure 2

4. Attach the cartons by inserting the folded down tab of the first carton in the space in the second carton. Tape the tabs of the first carton to the inside bottom of the second carton. Also tape the sides of the two cartons together. See Figure 3.
5. Your teacher will assign you one of the following sets of conditions to study. Follow the directions for that set of conditions only.

L2

Resource Manager

Meeting Different Ability Levels

Content Outline

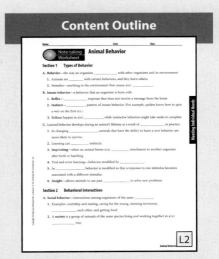

Note-taking Worksheet — Animal Behavior

L2

Reinforcement

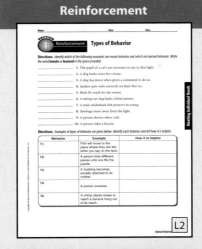

Reinforcement — Types of Behavior

L2

Enrichment

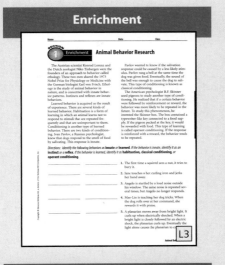

Enrichment — Animal Behavior Research

L3

Directed Reading (English/Spanish)

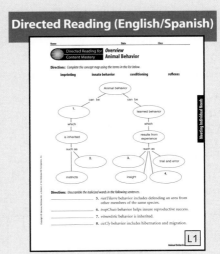

Directed Reading for Content Mastery — Overview Animal Behavior

L1

Study Guide

Study Guide

Features
- Contains a study guide page for each section of the chapter
- Reviews key concepts
- Includes answer pages

L2

Reading Essentials

Reading Essentials for Glencoe Science
An Interactive Student Workbook

Features
- Condensed core content
- Actively involves students in reading
- Reinforces key vocabulary

L1

Assessment

Test Practice Workbook

L2

Chapter Review

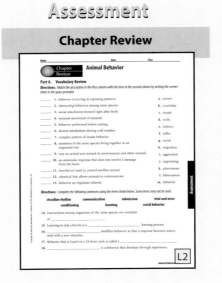

Chapter Review — Animal Behavior

L2

Chapter Tests

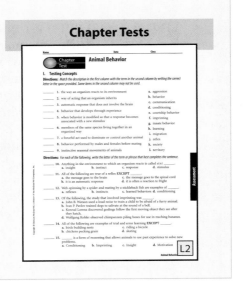

Chapter Test — Animal Behavior

L2

Science Content Background

Types of Behavior

Ethology

The scientific study of animal behavior in an organism's natural environment is called ethology. Konrad Z. Lorenz, a founder of ethology, studied the behavior of birds and developed a theory of animal behavior that stressed its inherited aspects. Lorenz and two other ethologists—Karl von Frisch of Austria, who studied bee communication, and Nikolaas Tinbergen of the Netherlands, who studied gull and fish behavior—received the 1973 Nobel prize for their work.

Early ethologists thought that most behaviors were instinctual. In contrast, psychologists thought that the environment modified instinctual behavior and that learning was more important. Today, ideas from both groups are combined in studies of animal behavior.

Innate Behavior

Innate behavior often also is called instinctive behavior. It is triggered by a specific environmental stimulus that causes a behavior called a fixed action pattern. Although innate behaviors are inherited, the environment plays a role in the development of them. For example, young toads instinctively flick their tongues at all dark objects, a fixed action pattern. If it catches a bee and is stung, it learns to avoid bees.

Learned Behavior

It is sometimes difficult to distinguish between innate behavior and learned behavior. Learned behaviors and innate behaviors involve neural and often hormonal mechanisms. The complexity of an animal's brain and nervous system is genetically determined. Animals with more complex brains receive more input from experience and exhibit learned behavior. Though learning is not instinctive, it can be automatic. For example, people learn how to use eating utensils. After a while, this action does not require conscious thought.

Habituation is learning to tune out unimportant stimuli. When animals ignore unimportant stimuli they conserve energy to deal with relevant stimuli. A person may ignore constant noises, such as traffic outside a window.

Imprinting

Goats, sheep, and the Alaskan fur seals are imprinted during the first few minutes after the birth of their offspring to recognize the offspring by their odor. The mother will accept any young that they smell during this critical period and reject any young that they did not smell.

Trial and Error

Trial-and-error learning also is called operant conditioning. Animals repeat behaviors that result in positive stimuli and avoid behaviors that result in negative stimuli. For example, bears soon learn by trial and error that they will catch a fish by remaining quiet rather than splashing about in the water. The toad that learned to avoid bees learned by trial and error.

Teacher to Teacher

Jeff Remington
Palmyra Middle School
Palmyra, Pennsylvania

"As a follow-up to the pupil dilation activity, I ask students if each of their eyes is independent in regard to that reflex. Students are unsure. To investigate, students partner again in a darkened room. Students get a penlight and an index card. One student holds an index card between their eyes while the other student shines the pen light on only one eye. Students find that both eyes respond even though only one is stimulated."

Jeff Remington

---

section 2 Social Behavior

Animal Societies

Some animal societies are organized into dominance hierarchies, such as a pecking order within a society of chickens. Animals with a high rank in the hierarchy usually have access to more food and thus have more reproductive success. The young of these dominant animals will have some of the same characteristics that helped their parents survive. If food is scarce, animals lower in the hierarchy die and the population is reduced to a number the habitat can support.

In many animal societies, reproduction occurs at the same time within the group. Having many young in a population at once ensures that some will survive to adulthood. Ethologists think that this type of behavior is more common when members of a group are related.

A group of animals is more likely to be successful in finding food than an individual alone. Some animals, like wolves and hyenas, hunt in groups so they can more easily corner prey.

Territorial Behavior

Dominant individuals are usually more successful in defending a territory. Because only individuals with territories mate, genes of the best-adapted individuals are likely to pass on to the next generation. Some territories are only large enough for mating. Other larger territories help ensure an adequate food supply for offspring.

Sound Communication

Whales "sing," and dolphins emit clicking noises that can travel more than 100 kilometers underwater. Elephants emit low-frequency sounds called infrasound. These sounds are in the same sound range as earthquakes and cannot be heard by humans. Elephants emit these sounds as warnings and female elephants "sing" at this frequency to attract mates.

Migration

Animals use a variety of navigational devices to find their way. Honeybees use polarized light. Birds use the Sun during the day or the stars at night, much as humans use a compass and map.

Brandon D. Cole/Corbis

chapter content resources

Internet Resources

For additional content background, visit
life.msscience.com to:

- access your book online
- find references to related articles in popular science magazines
- access Web links with related content background
- access current events with science journal topics

Print Resources

Guide to Bird Behavior, by Donald Stokes, Little Brown and Company, 2002

Measuring Behavior, by Paul Martin and Patrick Bateson, Cambridge University Press, 1993

chapter 16

Chapter Vocabulary

behavior, p. 456
innate behavior, p. 457
reflex, p. 457
instinct, p. 458
imprinting, p. 459
conditioning, p. 460
insight, p. 461
social behavior, p. 462
society, p. 463
aggression, p. 464
courtship behavior, p. 465
pheromone, p. 465
cyclic behavior, p. 468
hibernation, p. 469
migration, p. 470

Science Journal Animals may call, sing, leave scent marks, or display to other animals to indicate the territory is occupied.

with Image Bank

PowerPoint® Presentations

This CD-ROM is an editable Microsoft® PowerPoint® presentation that includes:
• a pre-made presentation for every chapter
• interactive graphics
• animations
• audio clips
• image bank
• all new section and chapter questions
• Standardized Test Practice
• transparencies
• pre-lab questions for all labs
• Foldables directions
• links to life.msscience.com

chapter 16

Animal Behavior

chapter preview

sections

1 Types of Behavior

2 Behavioral Interactions
  Lab Observing Earthworm Behavior
  Lab Animal Habitats
  Virtual Lab How do mealworms behave in response to various stimuli?

Why do animals fight?

Animals often defend territories from other members of the same species. Fighting is usually a last resort to protect a territory that contains food, shelter, and potential mates.

Science Journal What other behaviors might an animal use to signal that a territory is occupied?

454

Theme Connection

Stability and Change Survival of a species is dependent upon the ability of its members to respond to changes in the environment by changing either themselves or their behaviors. Complex patterns of behavior have evolved in animals to help them successfully compete in a variety of environments.

About the Photo

Wolf Packs These wolves were photographed in Montana. Wolves are social animals that live in packs. Sometimes, fights break out when wolves from one pack cross into the territory of another pack, or when a wolf is trying to improve its rank in the pack.

454 CHAPTER 16 Animal Behavior

Start-Up Activities

How do animals communicate?

One way humans communicate is by speaking. Other animals communicate without the use of sound. For example, a gull chick pecks at its parent's beak to get food. Try the lab below to see if you can communicate without speaking.

1. Form groups of students. One at a time, have each student choose an object and describe that object using gestures.

2. The other students observe and try to identify the object that is being described.

3. **Think Critically** In your Science Journal, describe how you and the other students were able to communicate without speaking to one another.

Preview this chapter's content and activities at
life.msscience.com

Behavior As you study behaviors, make the following Foldable to help you find the similarities and differences between the behaviors of two animals.

STEP 1 Fold a vertical sheet of paper in half from top to bottom.

STEP 2 Fold in half from side to side with the fold at the top.

STEP 3 Unfold the paper once. Cut only the fold of the top flap to make two tabs.

STEP 4 Turn the paper vertically and label the front tabs as shown.

> Observed Behaviors of Animal 1
> Observed Behaviors of Animal 2

Read and Write Before you read the chapter, choose two animals to compare. As you read the chapter, list the behaviors you learn about Animal 1 and Animal 2 under the appropriate tab.

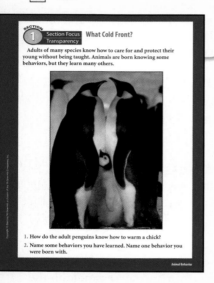

Tie to Prior Knowledge

Communication Ask students to define the term *communication.* Have them explain how they communicate with their pets and other animals. Invite volunteers to describe how a pet communicates with its owner. L1

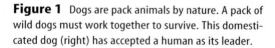

as you read

What You'll Learn

- **Identify** the differences between innate and learned behavior.
- **Explain** how reflexes and instincts help organisms survive.
- **Identify** examples of imprinting and conditioning.

Why It's Important

Innate behavior helps you survive on your own.

Review Vocabulary

salivate: to secrete saliva in anticipation of food

New Vocabulary

- behavior
- innate behavior
- reflex
- instinct
- imprinting
- conditioning
- insight

Figure 1 Dogs are pack animals by nature. A pack of wild dogs must work together to survive. This domesticated dog (right) has accepted a human as its leader.

Behavior

When you come home from school, does your dog run to meet you? Your dog barks and wags its tail as you scratch behind its ears. Sitting at your feet, it watches every move you make. Why do dogs do these things? In nature, dogs are pack animals that generally follow a leader. They have been living with people for about 12,000 years. Domesticated dogs treat people as part of their own pack, as shown in **Figure 1.**

Animals are different from one another in their behavior. They are born with certain behaviors, and they learn others. **Behavior** is the way an organism interacts with other organisms and its environment. Anything in the environment that causes a reaction is called a stimulus. A stimulus can be external, such as a rival male entering another male's territory; or internal, such as hunger or thirst. You are the stimulus that causes your dog to bark and wag its tail. Your dog's reaction to you is a response.

456 CHAPTER 16 Animal Behavior

Section 1 Resource Manager

Chapter *FAST FILE* Resources

Transparency Activity, pp. 40, 43–44

Directed Reading for Content Mastery, pp. 17, 18

Note-taking Worksheets, pp. 29–31

Enrichment, p. 27

Lab Activity, pp. 9–11

Reinforcement, p. 25

MiniLAB, p. 3

Home and Community Involvement, p. 44

Cliff swallows build nests out of mud.

Hummingbirds build delicate cup-shaped nests on branches of trees.

Figure 2 Bird nests come in different sizes and shapes. This male weaverbird is knotting the ends of leaves together to secure the nest.

Innate Behavior

A behavior that an organism is born with is called an **innate behavior.** These types of behaviors are inherited. They don't have to be learned.

Innate behavior patterns occur the first time an animal responds to a particular internal or external stimulus. For birds like the swallows and the hummingbird in **Figure 2** building a nest is innate behavior. When it's time for the female weaverbird to lay eggs, the male weaverbird builds an elaborate nest, also shown in **Figure 2.** Although a young male's first attempt may be messy, the nest is constructed correctly.

The behavior of animals that have short life spans is mostly innate behavior. Most insects do not learn from their parents. In many cases, the parents have died or moved on by the time the young hatch. Yet every insect reacts innately to its environment. A moth will fly toward a light, and a cockroach will run away from it. They don't learn this behavior. Innate behavior allows animals to respond instantly. This quick response often means the difference between life and death.

Reflexes The simplest innate behaviors are reflex actions. A **reflex** is an automatic response that does not involve a message from the brain. Sneezing, shivering, yawning, jerking your hand away from a hot surface, and blinking your eyes when something is thrown toward you are all reflex actions.

In humans a reflex message passes almost instantly from a sense organ along the nerve to the spinal cord and back to the muscles. The message does not go to the brain. You are aware of the reaction only after it has happened. Your body reacts on its own. A reflex is not the result of conscious thinking.

INTEGRATE Health

Reflex A tap on a tendon in your knee causes your leg to straighten. This is known as the knee-jerk reflex. Abnormalities in this reflex tell doctors of a possible problem in the central nervous system. Research other types of reflexes and write a report about them in your Science Journal.

Activity

Animal Communication Play an audiotape of animal communication sounds—whales, wolves, birds, or pet sounds. Why do animals need to communicate with one another? Possible answers: to warn, to locate food, to court Can you identify the message sent by any of these sounds? Students may distinguish some repeated sounds. How could you determine the message? Observe the animals in their natural habitats and note what other animals do upon hearing each sound. L2

Discussion

Ancient Survival How was the survival of ancient people dependent on their knowledge of animal behavior? They had to know the habits and behavior of animals in order to hunt and fish for food and to train animals to do work.

Fun Fact

Behaviors are more likely to be innate in animals that develop without parental care.

INTEGRATE Health

Reflex Many vital body processes, such as breathing, heartbeat, diameter of blood vessels, and sweat gland secretions, are reflex actions.

Research Have students investigate how else behavior can influence their health.

Differentiated Instruction

Visually and Hearing Impaired Chirping is an innate behavior of crickets. Place crickets in an aquarium with moist soil and lettuce. Have hearing-impaired students observe the crickets through magnifying lenses to note how chirping is produced. Visually impaired students can listen to the chirps and estimate the room's temperature (°F) using this method: Count the number of chirps in 14 s, add 40. L2 IS **Auditory-Musical**

Challenge Many students will find animal communication interesting. Have them research and design a project that involves tape-recording and analyzing animal sounds. L3 IS **Auditory-Musical**

Figure 3 Spiders, like this orb weaver spider, know how to spin webs as soon as they hatch.

Figure 4 As they grow older, these quail chicks will learn which organisms to avoid.
Describe *why it is important for young quail to react the same toward all organisms.*

Instincts An **instinct** is a complex pattern of innate behavior. Spinning a web like the one in **Figure 3** is complicated, yet spiders spin webs correctly on the first try. Unlike reflexes, instinctive behaviors can take weeks to complete. Instinctive behavior begins when the animal recognizes a stimulus and continues until all parts of the behavior have been performed.

✓ Reading Check *What is the difference between a reflex and an instinct?*

Learned Behavior

All animals have innate and learned behaviors. Learned behavior develops during an animal's lifetime. Animals with more complex brains exhibit more behaviors that are the result of learning. However, the behavior of insects, spiders, and other arthropods is mostly instinctive behavior. Fish, reptiles, amphibians, birds, and mammals all learn. Learning is the result of experience or practice.

Learning is important for animals because it allows them to respond to changing situations. In changing environments, animals that have the ability to learn a new behavior are more likely to survive. This is especially important for animals with long life spans. The longer an animal lives, the more likely it is that the environment in which it lives will change.

Learning also can modify instincts. For example, grouse and quail chicks, shown in **Figure 4,** leave their nests the day they hatch. They can run and find food, but they can't fly. When something moves above them, they instantly crouch and keep perfectly still until the danger has passed. They will crouch without moving even if the falling object is only a leaf. Older birds have learned that leaves will not harm them, but they freeze when a hawk moves overhead.

458   CHAPTER 16 Animal Behavior

🔬 LAB DEMONSTRATION

Figure 5 When feeding chicks in captivity, puppets of adult condors are used so the chicks don't learn to associate humans with food.

Imprinting Learned behavior includes imprinting, trial and error, conditioning, and insight. Have you ever seen young ducks following their mother? This is an important behavior because the adult bird has had more experience in finding food, escaping predators, and getting along in the world. **Imprinting** occurs when an animal forms a social attachment, like the condor in **Figure 5,** to another organism within a specific time period after birth or hatching.

Konrad Lorenz, an Austrian naturalist, developed the concept of imprinting. Working with geese, he discovered that a gosling follows the first moving object it sees after hatching. The moving object, whatever it is, is imprinted as its parent. This behavior works well when the first moving object a gosling sees is an adult female goose. But goslings hatched in an incubator might see a human first and become imprinted on that human. Animals that become imprinted toward animals of another species have difficulty recognizing members of their own species.

Trial and Error Can you remember when you learned to ride a bicycle? You probably fell many times before you learned how to balance on the bicycle. After a while you could ride without having to think about it. You have many skills that you learned through trial and error, such as feeding yourself and tying your shoes, as shown in **Figure 6.**

Behavior that is modified by experience is called trial-and-error learning. Many animals learn by trial and error. When baby chicks first try to feed themselves, they peck at many stones before they get any food. As a result of trial and error, they learn to peck only at food particles.

Science Online

Topic: Captive Breeding
Visit life.msscience.com for Web links to information about captive breeding.

Activity Identify and describe techniques used to raise captive species and introduce them into the wild.

Figure 6 Were you able to tie your shoes on the first attempt? **List** *other things you do every day that require learning.*

SECTION 1 Types of Behavior **459**

Activity

Puzzle Sections Separate a large puzzle into six sections. Place the disassembled pieces for each section in a paper bag. Divide the class into six groups, each with one of the bags. Have groups work together to reassemble the sections. Then, have students combine the sections to complete the puzzle. Ask students what type of behavior they demonstrated. learned L2   ELL   COOP LEARN

Caption Answer

Figure 6 Possible answers: reading, writing, brushing teeth, using the telephone, walking

Virtual Labs

Mealworms *How do mealworms behave in response to various stimuli?*

Differentiated Instruction

English-Language Learners Have students draw symbols on one side of a card and a vocabulary word on the other side. Pair students up and have them show the symbol and vocabulary word to their partner. Have students guess the vocabulary word from the symbol. This is an example of trial-and-error learning.

Visual Learning

Figure 5 The use of puppets of adult condors ensures that expected imprinting occurs. Predict what would likely occur if puppets of adult geese had been used to feed the condor chicks. Because of imprinting, the chicks would form a social attachment to adult geese instead of to adult condors. L2

IS Logical-Mathematical

Mini LAB

Observing Conditioning

Procedure

1. Obtain several **photos of different foods and landscapes** from your teacher.
2. Show each picture to a classmate for 20 s.
3. Record how each photo made your partner feel.

Analysis

1. How did your partner feel after looking at the photos of food?
2. What effect did the landscape pictures have on your partner?
3. Infer how advertising might condition consumers to buy specific food products.

Figure 7 In Pavlov's experiment, a dog was conditioned to salivate when a bell was rung. It associated the bell with food.

Conditioning Do you have an aquarium in your school or home? If you put your hand above the tank, the fish probably will swim to the top of the tank, expecting to be fed. They have learned that a hand shape above them means food. What would happen if you tapped on the glass right before you fed them? Soon the fish probably will swim to the top of the tank if you just tap on the glass. Because they are used to being fed after you tap on the glass, they associate the tap with food.

Animals often learn new behaviors by conditioning. In **conditioning,** behavior is modified so that a response to one stimulus becomes associated with a different stimulus. There are two types of conditioning. One type introduces a new stimulus before the usual stimulus. Russian scientist Ivan P. Pavlov performed experiments using this type of conditioning. He knew that the sight and smell of food made hungry dogs secrete saliva. Pavlov added another stimulus. He rang a bell before he fed the dogs. The dogs began to connect the sound of the bell with food. Then Pavlov rang the bell without giving the dogs food. They salivated when the bell was rung even though he did not give them food. The dogs, like the one in **Figure 7,** were conditioned to respond to the bell.

In the second type of conditioning, the new stimulus is given after the affected behavior. Getting an allowance for doing chores is an example of this type of conditioning. You do your chores because you want to receive your allowance. You have been conditioned to perform an activity that you may not have done if you had not been offered a reward.

✔ **Reading Check** *How does conditioning modify behavior?*

Cultural Diversity

Hunting The lifestyle and survival of hunting cultures revolved around the responses of hunted animals. Have students select a Native American nation and read about its relationship with the animals it depended upon. Ask students to report on animal behaviors that were important to the cultures, such as when salmon swam upriver to spawn (Northwestern nations) or patterns of bison herd movement (Plains nations).

Teacher FYI

Conditioning Conditioning is very common in the animal kingdom. For example, birds learn to avoid certain brightly colored caterpillars that have a bad taste. Birds associate the color pattern with the bad taste. Other species of caterpillars who mimic the appearance of the bad-tasting organisms also benefit from this conditioning, as birds will avoid them also.

Insight How does learned behavior help an animal deal with a new situation? Suppose you have a new math problem to solve. Do you begin by acting as though you've never seen it before, or do you use what you have learned previously in math to solve the problem? If you use what you have learned, then you have used a kind of learned behavior called insight. **Insight** is a form of reasoning that allows animals to use past experiences to solve new problems. In experiments with chimpanzees, as shown in **Figure 8,** bananas were placed out of the chimpanzees' reach. Instead of giving up, they piled up boxes found in the room, climbed them, and reached the bananas. At some time in their lives, the chimpanzees must have solved a similar problem. The chimpanzees demonstrated insight during the experiment. Much of adult human learning is based on insight. When you were a baby, you learned by trial and error. As you grow older, you will rely more on insight.

Figure 8 This illustration shows how chimpanzees may use insight to solve problems.

section 1 review

Summary

Behavior
- Animals are born with certain behaviors, while other behaviors are learned.
- A stimulus is anything in the environment that causes a reaction.

Innate and Learned Behaviors
- Innate behaviors are those behaviors an organism inherits, such as reflexes and instincts.
- Learned behavior allows animals to respond to changing situations.
- Imprinting, trial and error, conditioning, and insight are examples of learned behavior.

Self Check

1. **Compare and contrast** a reflex and an instinct.
2. **Compare and contrast** imprinting and conditioning.
3. **Think Critically** Use what you know about conditioning to explain how the term *mouthwatering food* might have come about.

Applying Skills

4. **Use a Spreadsheet** Make a spreadsheet of the behaviors in this section. Sort the behaviors according to whether they are innate or learned behaviors. Then identify the type of innate or learned behavior.

section 1 review

1. reflex: automatic response, doesn't involve brain; instinct: complex pattern of innate behavior
2. Imprinting occurs when an animal forms a social attachment to another organism within a specific time period after birth or hatching. Conditioning occurs when a response

to one stimulus becomes associated with a different stimulus.
3. The response to the stimulus of food is the production of saliva. Upon conditioning, the sight, smell, or thought of food can cause the production of saliva.

4. innate: reflexes and instincts; learned: imprinting, trial and error, conditioning, and insight; An example should be provided for each.

Teacher FYI

Insight Much of human learning is based on insight. Babies first learn by trial and error. As they grow older, they rely on insight. Solving problems is an example of using insight.

3 Assess

DAILY INTERVENTION

Check for Understanding

Logical-Mathematical Place the words *Innate Behavior* on one side of the board and *Learned Behavior* on the other side. Have students write secondary headings of reflex, instinct, imprint, trial-and-error, conditioning, and insight under the appropriate heading. Ask students to give an example of each behavior.

Reteach

Vocabulary Concept Map Have students make a concept map using all vocabulary terms in this section. L2 IN **Visual-Spatial** P

☑ Assessment

Portfolio Have students write a paragraph in their Science Journals describing the type of learning that occurs when crows in a farmer's field do not react to a scarecrow that has been in place for a month. Use **Performance Assessment in the Science Classroom,** p. 99. L2

Behavioral Interactions

Bellringer

Section Focus Transparencies also are available on the Interactive Chalkboard CD-ROM.

L2 ELL

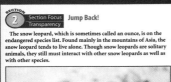

SECTION 2 Section Focus Transparency Jump Back!

The snow leopard, which is sometimes called an ounce, is on the endangered species list. Found mainly in the mountains of Asia, the snow leopard tends to live alone. Though snow leopards are solitary animals, they still must interact with other snow leopards as well as with other species.

1. How would you describe this animal's behavior?
2. What are some ways the snow leopard might interact with other animals?

Animal Behavior

Tie to Prior Knowledge

Territorial Behavior Students will be familiar with aggressive and territorial behaviors of pets and other animals. Discuss familiar examples of territorial displays and threatening behaviors.

✓ Reading Check

Answer It provides advantages for survival of the species.

---

as you read

What You'll Learn
- **Explain** why behavioral adaptations are important.
- **Describe** how courtship behavior increases reproductive success.
- **Explain** the importance of social behavior and cyclic behavior.

Why It's Important
Organisms must be able to communicate with each other to survive.

⊙ Review Vocabulary
nectar: a sweet liquid produced in a plant's flower that is the main raw material of honey

New Vocabulary
- social behavior
- society
- aggression
- courtship behavior
- pheromone
- cyclic behavior
- hibernation
- migration

Figure 9 When several zebras are close together, their stripes make it difficult for predators to pick out one individual.

Instinctive Behavior Patterns

Complex interactions of innate behaviors between organisms result in many types of animal behavior. For example, courtship and mating within most animal groups are instinctive ritual behaviors that help animals recognize possible mates. Animals also protect themselves and their food sources by defending their territories. Instinctive behavior, just like natural hair color, is inherited.

Social Behavior

Animals often live in groups. One reason, shown in **Figure 9,** is that large numbers provide safety. A lion is less likely to attack a herd of zebras than a lone zebra. Sometimes animals in large groups help keep each other warm. Also, migrating animal groups are less likely to get lost than animals that travel alone.

Interactions among organisms of the same species are examples of **social behavior.** Social behaviors include courtship and mating, caring for the young, claiming territories, protecting each other, and getting food. These inherited behaviors provide advantages that promote survival of the species.

✓ Reading Check *Why is social behavior important?*

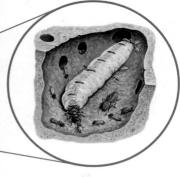

Figure 10 Termites built this large mound in Australia. The mound has a network of tunnels and chambers for the queen termite to deposit eggs into.

Societies Insects such as ants, bees, and the termites shown in **Figure 10,** live together in societies. A **society** is a group of animals of the same species living and working together in an organized way. Each member has a certain role. Usually a specific female lays eggs, and a male fertilizes them. Workers do all the other jobs in the society.

Some societies are organized by dominance. Wolves usually live together in packs. A wolf pack has a dominant female. The top female controls the mating of the other females. If plenty of food is available, she mates and then allows the others to do so. If food is scarce, she allows less mating. During such times, she is usually the only one to mate.

Territorial Behavior

Many animals set up territories for feeding, mating, and raising young. A territory is an area that an animal defends from other members of the same species. Ownership of a territory occurs in different ways. Songbirds sing, sea lions bellow, and squirrels chatter to claim territories. Other animals leave scent marks. Some animals, like the tiger in **Figure 11,** patrol an area and attack other animals of the same species who enter their territory. Why do animals defend their territories? Territories contain food, shelter, and potential mates. If an animal has a territory, it will be able to mate and produce offspring. Defending territories is an instinctive behavior. It improves the survival rate of an animal's offspring.

Figure 11 A tiger's territory may cover several miles. It will confront any other tiger who enters it. **Explain** *what may be happening in this photo.*

Visual Learning

Figure 11 What other animals defend their territories? Possible answers: songbirds, sea lions, squirrels

Make a Model

Social Animals Have students work in groups of three to make a model of animals with social behavior, such as honeybees, hornets, ants, beavers, or wolves. Ask them to identify the members of the group modeled and explain their roles. L2

Discussion

Roaring Some male lions roar to compete for mates. Roaring takes a lot of strength. How might roaring prevent a fight between two males? The roar's intensity illustrates the strength of a male. A weaker male will likely leave the area rather than fight.

Caption Answer

Figure 11 One tiger may have entered into the other tiger's territory.

Inquiry Lab

Observing Territory Behavior

Purpose To explore territory behavior, have students design an experiment to elicit a response from an animal in a territory.

Possible Materials tape player and bird song tape

Estimated Time 1 class session

Teaching Strategies

• Students can play a song of a resident bird during the spring to elicit a response from the bird.

• Students could place two territorial fish of the same species in an aquarium, place food on one end and observe their behavior.

• Be cautious of which animals are experimented on since some animals such as dogs could attack, some species may not be territorial, and some species may be territorial at certain times of the year.

• Allow students to explore other questions that arise. L2

For additional inquiry activities, see *Science Inquiry Labs.*

Figure 12 Young wolves roll over and make themselves as small as possible to show their submission to adult wolves.

Figure 13 During the waggle dance, if the food source is far from the hive, the dance takes the form of a figure eight. The angle of the waggle is equal to the angle from the hive between the Sun and nectar source.

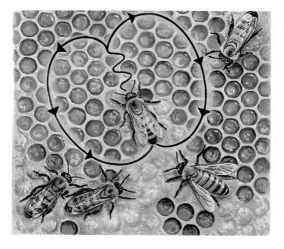

Aggression Have you ever watched as one dog approached another dog that was eating a bone? What happened to the appearance of the dog with the bone? Did its hair on its back stick up? Did it curl its lips and make growling noises? This behavior is called aggression. **Aggression** is a forceful behavior used to dominate or control another animal. Fighting and threatening are aggressive behaviors animals use to defend their territories, protect their young, or to get food.

Many animals demonstrate aggression. Some birds let their wings droop below their tail feathers. It may take another bird's perch and thrust its head forward in a pecking motion as a sign of aggression. Cats lay their ears flat, arch their backs, and hiss.

Submission Animals of the same species seldom fight to the death. Teeth, beaks, claws, and horns are used for killing prey or for defending against members of a different species.

To avoid being attacked and injured by an individual of its own species, an animal shows submission. Postures that make an animal appear smaller often are used to communicate surrender. In some animal groups, one individual is usually dominant. Members of the group show submissive behavior toward the dominant individual. This stops further aggressive behavior by the dominant animal. Young animals also display submissive behaviors toward parents or dominant animals, as shown in **Figure 12.**

Communication

In all social behavior, communication is important. Communication is an action by a sender that influences the behavior of a receiver. How do you communicate with the people around you? You may talk, make noises, or gesture like you did in this chapter's Launch Lab. Honeybees perform a dance, as shown in **Figure 13,** to communicate to other bees in the hive the location of a food source. Animals in a group communicate with sounds, scents, and actions. Alarm calls, chemicals, speech, courtship behavior, and aggression are forms of communication.

464 CHAPTER 16 Animal Behavior

Figure 14 This male Emperor of Germany bird of paradise attracts mates by posturing and fanning its tail.

List other behaviors animals use to attract mates.

Caption Answer
Figure 14 Examples include fireflies that use bioluminescence to attract mates, birds that sing, and many species that release pheromones.

Teacher FYI

Woodpeckers' Courtship Courtship patterns are complex innate behaviors. The ranges of two types of woodpeckers overlap in a narrow region of Texas. Despite similarities in appearance and behavior, they do not interbreed because they use different cues in recognizing mates.

Courtship Behavior A male bird of paradise, shown in **Figure 14,** spreads its tail feathers and struts. A male sage grouse fans its tail, fluffs its feathers, and blows up its two red air sacs. These are examples of behavior that animals perform before mating. This type of behavior is called **courtship behavior.** Courtship behaviors allow male and female members of a species to recognize each other. These behaviors also stimulate males and females so they are ready to mate at the same time. This helps ensure reproductive success.

In most species the males are more colorful and perform courtship displays to attract a mate. Some courtship behaviors allow males and females to find each other across distances.

INTEGRATE Chemistry **Chemical Communication** Ants are sometimes seen moving single file toward a piece of food. Male dogs frequently urinate on objects and plants. Both behaviors are based on chemical communication. The ants have laid down chemical trails that others of their species can follow. The dog is letting other dogs know he has been there. In these behaviors, the animals are using chemicals called pheromones (FER uh mohnz) to communicate. A chemical that is produced by one animal to influence the behavior of another animal of the same species is called a **pheromone.** They are powerful chemicals needed only in small amounts. They remain in the environment so that the sender and the receiver can communicate without being in the same place at the same time. They can advertise the presence of an animal to predators, as well as to the intended receiver of the message.

Males and females use pheromones to establish territories, warn of danger, and attract mates. Certain ants, mice, and snails release alarm pheromones when injured or threatened.

Mini LAB

Demonstrating Chemical Communication

Procedure
1. Obtain a **sample of perfume or air freshener.**
2. Spray it into the air to leave a scent trail as you move around the house or apartment to a hiding place.
3. Have someone try to discover where you are by following the scent of the substance.

Analysis
1. What was the difference between the first and last room you were in?
2. Would this be an efficient way for humans to communicate? Explain.

Try at Home

Mini LAB

Purpose to observe a method of chemical communication

Materials perfume, air freshener, or flavoring oil

Teaching Strategy Have students choose a strong scent with a pleasant odor. Be certain students are not allergic to the scent.

Analysis
1. The scent would be stronger in the last room.
2. Yes; a person could be located by the scent.

Assessment

Oral How do law enforcement officers help trained dogs pick up the scent of a missing person? They have the dog smell an object that belonged to the missing person. L2

Try at Home

Teacher FYI

Pheromones Ants make a "pheromone trail" from their nest to food sources for other ants to follow. Some female insects give off pheromones that attract males. Scientists have developed artificial pheromones for use in pest control. Traps contain the female pheromones, which attract the males.

Behavioral Warnings Some animals are very sensitive to changes in the environment that precede violent natural events, such as earthquakes, hurricanes, typhoons, and other storms. In China, people have learned that unusual panicky behavior by certain animals may signal an imminent earthquake. Have students research this behavior and how it can benefit people. [L2]

IDENTIFYING Misconceptions

Adaptive Traits Some students may think individual organisms evolve a structure or behavior in order to respond to their environments. In reality, traits pre-exist that may help an animal adapt. The animals that survive pass the traits to offspring. For example, if a population of flies is sprayed with a deadly chemical, some may already have a genetic makeup that causes them to be resistant to the chemical. As a result, they survive and pass the trait on to their offspring.

INTEGRATE History

Morse Code Another ship must be in the line of sight to decode the message, improving the security of the message. It allows ships to maintain radio silence to avoid detection.

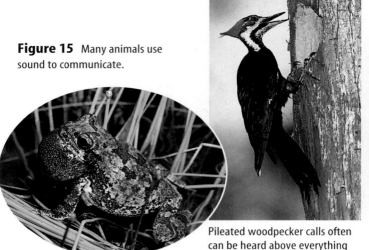

Figure 15 Many animals use sound to communicate.

Frogs often croak loud enough to be heard far away.

Pileated woodpecker calls often can be heard above everything else in the forest.

Howler monkeys got their name because of the sounds they make.

INTEGRATE History

Morse Code Samuel B. Morse created a code in 1838 using numbers to represent letters. His early work led to Morse code. Naval ships today still use Morse code to communicate with each other using huge flashlights mounted on the ships' decks. In your Science Journal, write what reasons you believe that Morse code is still used by the Navy.

Sound Communication Male crickets rub one forewing against the other forewing. This produces chirping sounds that attract females. Each cricket species produces several calls that are different from other cricket species. These calls are used by researchers to identify different species. Male mosquitoes have hairs on their antennae that sense buzzing sounds produced by females of their same species. The tiny hairs vibrate only to the frequency emitted by a female of the same species.

Vertebrates use a number of different forms of sound communication. Rabbits thump the ground, gorillas pound their chests, beavers slap the water with their flat tails, and frogs, like the one in **Figure 15,** croak. Do you think that sound communication in noisy environments is useful? Seabirds that live where waves pound the shore rather than in some quieter place must rely on visual signals, not sound, for communication.

Light Communication Certain kinds of flies, marine organisms, and beetles have a special form of communication called bioluminescence. Bioluminescence, shown in **Figure 16,** is the ability of certain living things to give off light. This light is produced through a series of chemical reactions in the organism's body. Probably the most familiar bioluminescent organisms in North America are fireflies. These insects are not flies, but beetles. The flash of light that is produced on the underside of the last abdominal segments is used to locate a prospective mate. Each species has its own characteristic flashing. Males fly close to the ground and emit flashes of light. Females must flash an answer at exactly the correct time to attract males.

Differentiated Instruction

Challenge Have students use encyclopedias and other resources to find out what environmental factors might trigger an animal's urge to hibernate. Examples include decreasing temperature, shorter day length, and weather conditions. [L3]

Science Journal

Animal Entertainers Animals often perform in circus acts. Have students research and write reports on animals as entertainers. Have students consider whether the behaviors of animals such as dolphins, birds, and elephants should be modified for entertainment.

NATIONAL GEOGRAPHIC VISUALIZING BIOLUMINESCENCE

Figure 16

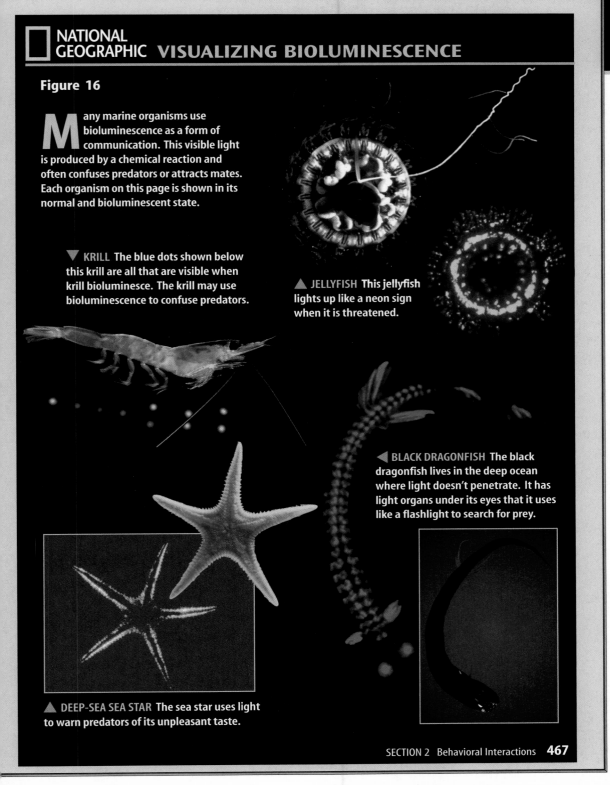

Many marine organisms use bioluminescence as a form of communication. This visible light is produced by a chemical reaction and often confuses predators or attracts mates. Each organism on this page is shown in its normal and bioluminescent state.

▼ **KRILL** The blue dots shown below this krill are all that are visible when krill bioluminesce. The krill may use bioluminescence to confuse predators.

▲ **JELLYFISH** This jellyfish lights up like a neon sign when it is threatened.

◄ **BLACK DRAGONFISH** The black dragonfish lives in the deep ocean where light doesn't penetrate. It has light organs under its eyes that it uses like a flashlight to search for prey.

▲ **DEEP-SEA SEA STAR** The sea star uses light to warn predators of its unpleasant taste.

NATIONAL GEOGRAPHIC

Visualizing Bioluminescence

Have students examine the pictures and read the captions. Then ask the following questions.

During which times are organisms bioluminescent? Possible answers: Organisms that live near the surface are bioluminescent at night. Organisms that live in the deep sea, where there is no light, can use bioluminescence all the time.

Explain how bioluminescence can be used to attract prey. Possible answer: Prey organisms are attracted to the light, which is often coming from the mouthparts or a fleshy lure of the predator. As the unsuspecting prey approaches to investigate, it nears the mouth and is gobbled up.

Activity

Bioluminescent Animals Have students find examples of land animals that are bioluminescent and record where in the world they can be found living. Students can make a simple map of the world and draw in the representative bioluminescent animals found in different locations. Possible answers: fireflies are found east of the continental divide in the U.S., a type of beetle larvae called railroad worms is found in Central and South America, glowworms, which are fly larvae, can be found in caves in New Zealand, and land snails in Malaysia. Other bioluminescent land animals include some types of earthworms, centipedes, and millipedes. L2

Cultural Diversity

Adapting to the Environment People who live in desert areas often wear loose-fitting, light-weight, light-colored garments that reflect sunlight and heat. They may live in tents that enable them to take advantage of the smallest breezes. A tundra, rain forest, or deciduous forest would call for different cultural adaptations. Students can make posters that show the food, shelter, and clothing of different cultures. L2 IN **Kinesthetic** P

Differentiated Instruction

Challenge Have students investigate why there are almost no bioluminescent animals found in freshwater. Possible answer: Scientists hypothesize that the different chemical composition of freshwater may account for the lack of bioluminescence. Some essential chemical may be missing in the freshwater that will not allow the reaction to proceed. L3

Figure 17 Barn owls usually sleep during the day and hunt at night.
Identify *the type of behavior the owl is exhibiting.*

Uses of Bioluminescence Many bioluminescent animals are found deep in oceans where sunlight does not reach. The ability to produce light may serve several functions. One species of fish dangles a special luminescent organ in front of its mouth. This lures prey close enough to be caught and eaten. Deep-sea shrimp secrete clouds of a luminescent substance when disturbed. This helps them escape their predators. Patterns of luminescence on an animal's body may serve as marks of recognition similar to the color patterns of animals that live in sunlit areas.

Cyclic Behavior

Why do most songbirds rest at night while some species of owls rest during the day? Some animals like the owl in **Figure 17** show regularly repeated behaviors such as sleeping in the day and feeding at night.

A **cyclic behavior** is innate behavior that occurs in a repeating pattern. It often is repeated in response to changes in the environment. Behavior that is based on a 24-hour cycle is called a circadian rhythm. Most animals come close to this 24-hour cycle of sleeping and wakefulness. Experiments show that even if animals can't tell whether it is night or day, they continue to behave in a 24-hour cycle.

Animals that are active during the day are diurnal (dy UR nul). Animals that are active at night are nocturnal. Owls are nocturnal. They have round heads, big eyes, and flat faces. Their flat faces reflect sound and help them navigate at night. Owls also have soft feathers that make them almost silent while flying.

✔ Reading Check *What is a diurnal behavior?*

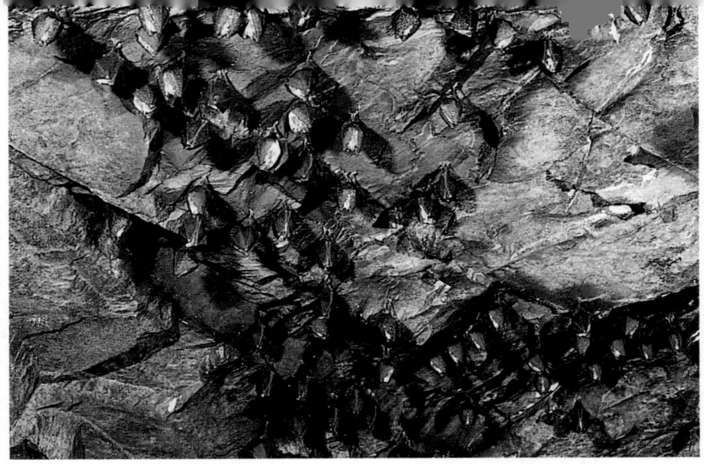

Hibernation Some cyclic behaviors also occur over long periods of time. **Hibernation** is a cyclic response to cold temperatures and limited food supplies. During hibernation, an animal's body temperature drops to near that of its surroundings, and its breathing rate is greatly reduced. Animals in hibernation, such as the bats in **Figure 18,** survive on stored body fat. The animal remains inactive until the weather becomes warm in the spring. Some mammals and many amphibians and reptiles hibernate.

Animals that live in desertlike environments also go into a state of reduced activity. This period of inactivity is called estivation. Desert animals sometimes estivate due to extreme heat, lack of food, or periods of drought.

Figure 18 Many bats find a frost-free place like this abandoned coal mine to hibernate for the winter when food supplies are low.

Applying Science

How can you determine which animals hibernate?

Many animals hibernate in the winter. During this period of inactivity, they survive on stored body fat. While they are hibernating, they undergo several physical changes. Heart rate slows down and body temperature decreases. The degree to which the body temperature decreases varies among animals. Scientists disagree about whether some animals truly hibernate or if they just reduce their activity and go into a light sleep. Usually, a true hibernator's body temperature will decrease significantly while it is hibernating.

Average Body Temperatures of Hibernating Animals

Animal	Normal Body Temperature (°C)	Hibernating Body Temperature (°C)
Woodchuck	37	3
Squirrel	32	4
Grizzly bear	32–37	27–32
Whippoorwill	40	18
Hoary marmot	37	10

Identifying the Problem

The table on the right shows the difference between the normal body temperature and the hibernating body temperature of several animals. What similarities do you notice?

Solving the Problem

1. Which animals would you classify as true hibernators and which would you classify as light sleepers? Explain.
2. Some animals such as snakes and frogs also hibernate. Why would it be difficult to record their normal body temperature?

Applying Science

Answers

1. The woodchuck, squirrel, hoary marmot, and whippoorwill are "true hibernators" because their body temperatures decrease significantly during hibernation. The grizzly bear is a "light sleeper." It does not undergo significant physical changes during its period of inactivity.
2. Cold-blooded animals' body temperatures adapt to their surroundings, and therefore are in a constant state of change depending on the environment. If these animals were to be included on the chart, the physical environment would also need to be included.

Fun Fact

Woodchucks in hibernation breathe once every five to six minutes.

Active Reading

Pair of Pairs This strategy encourages students as partners to respond to a question. They brainstorm together, recording on one paper their ideas. After a few minutes, they combine with another pair and share responses. Finally, groups of four share responses. Have students use the Pair of Pairs strategy on the Think Critically question in this Section Review. L2

Curriculum Connection

Social Studies Have each student research a different migrating animal and summarize his or her findings in a poster. Posters should indicate where the animal spends winters and summers, the distance between the two areas, and the animal's breeding location. Encourage students to include pictures of the animals, contrasting their appearance in summer and winter. L2 P

Check for Understanding

Visual-Spatial More than 100 million monarch butterflies migrate from Canada and the eastern United States to Mexico every fall. Gray whales migrate from the Bering Sea to the coastal region of California. Have students trace these routes and others on a map or globe. L1 LS

Reteach

Pick a Card Label 3-in × 5-in cards with examples of social behavior, territorial behavior, communication, and cyclic behavior. Ask students to choose a card, classify the type of behavior, and provide reasons for their responses. L2

✓ Assessment

Content Have pairs of students make a multimedia presentation that explains social behavior, territorial behavior, communication, or cyclic behavior. Use **Performance Assessment in the Science Classroom,** p. 145. L2

Figure 19 Many monarch butterflies travel from the United States to Mexico for the winter.

Migration Instead of hibernating, many animals move to new locations when the seasons change. This instinctive seasonal movement of animals is called **migration.** Most animals migrate to find food or to reproduce in environments that are more favorable for the survival of offspring. Many bird species fly for hours or days without stopping. The blackpoll warbler flies more than 4,000 km, nearly 90 hours nonstop from North America to its winter home in South America. Monarch butterflies, shown in **Figure 19,** can migrate as far as 2,900 km. Gray whales swim from arctic waters to the waters off the coast of northern Mexico. After the young are born, they make the return trip.

---

section 2 review

Summary

Instinctive Behavior Patterns
- Instinctive behavior patterns are inherited.
- Courtship and mating are instinctive for most animal groups.

Social and Territorial Behaviors
- Interactions among organisms of a group are examples of social behavior.
- Many animals protect a territory for feeding, mating, and raising young.

Communication and Cyclic Behavior
- Species can communicate with each other using behavior, chemicals, sound, or bioluminescence.
- Cyclic behaviors occur in response to environmental changes.

Self Check

1. **Describe** some examples of courtship behavior and how this behavior helps organisms survive.
2. **Identify** and **explain** two reasons that animals migrate.
3. **Compare** and **contrast** hibernation and migration.
4. **Think Critically** Suppose a species of frog lives close to a loud waterfall. It often waves a bright blue foot in the air. What might the frog be doing?

Applying Math

5. **Solve One-Step Equations** Some cicadas emerge from the ground every 17 years. The population of one type of caterpillar peaks every five years. If the peak cycle of the caterpillars and the emergence of cicadas coincided in 1990, in what year will they coincide again?

470 CHAPTER 16 Animal Behavior

 Science Online life.msscience.com/self_check_quiz

---

section 2 review

1. Answers will vary. These behaviors help ensure reproductive success.
2. to find food and to reproduce in a favorable environment for offspring
3. An animal that hibernates stays in the same place and becomes inactive until environmental conditions become favorable. An animal that migrates moves to a location with favorable conditions.
4. Possible answer: signalling other frogs, either to attract a mate or to defend its territory
5. Since 17 and 5 are prime numbers, the cycles will again coincide in 17 × 5, or 85 years from 1990; 1990 + 85 = 2075.

Observing Earthworm Behavior

Earthworms can be seen at night wriggling across wet sidewalks and driveways. Why don't you see many earthworms during the day?

▶ Real-World Question

How do earthworms respond to light?

Goals
■ **Predict** how earthworms will behave in the presence of light.

Materials

scissors	paper
shoe box with lid	moist paper towels
flashlight	earthworms
tape	timer

Safety Precautions

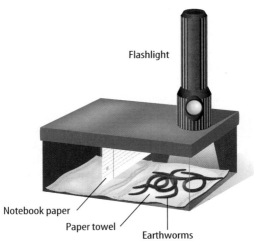

Flashlight

Notebook paper

Paper towel

Earthworms

▶ Procedure

1. Cut a round hole, smaller than the end of the flashlight, near one end of the lid.

2. Tape a sheet of paper to the lid so it hangs just above the bottom of the box and about 10 cm away from the end with the hole in it.

3. Place the moist paper towels in the bottom of the box.

4. Place the earthworms in the end of the box that has the hole in it.

5. Hold the flashlight over the hole and turn it on.

6. Leave the box undisturbed for 30 minutes, then open the lid and observe the worms.

7. **Record** the results of your experiment in your Science Journal.

▶ Conclude and Apply

1. **Identify** which direction the earthworms moved when the light was turned on.

2. **Infer** Based on your observations, what can you infer about earthworms?

3. **Explain** what type of behavior the earthworms exhibited.

4. **Predict** where you would need to go to find earthworms during the day.

Communicating Your Data

Write a story that describes a day in the life of an earthworm. List activities, dangers, and problems an earthworm might face. Include a description of its habitat. **For more help, refer to the** Science Skill Handbook.

Communicating Your Data

Students should base their story on their knowledge of earthworms and their habitat.

▶ Real-World Question

Purpose Students observe earthworm responses to light. L2 LS **Kinesthetic**

Process Skills observe and infer, recognize cause and effect

Time Required 45 minutes

Safety Precautions Caution students to wash their hands after handling earthworms.

▶ Procedure

Teaching Strategy Have students keep their hands moist while handling earthworms. Remind them to handle worms gently.

▶ Conclude and Apply

1. away from the light
2. Earthworms prefer darkness to light.
3. Innate behavior; the earthworms instinctively move away from the light and toward the darkened area.
4. in the soil

☑ Assessment

Process Have students use their observations to list what they think an earthworm needs to survive. soil, darkness, moisture Use **Performance Assessment in the Science Classroom,** p. 89. L2

LAB · Model and Invent

◉ Real-World Question

Purpose Students research information about animals in their natural habitats, and then design and build a model of a habitat that supports the survival of that animal. ☐L2☐ ☐LS☐
Logical-Mathematical

Process Skills make models, research information, predict, collect data, measure in SI, recognize cause and effect, interpret data, communicate, use proportions

Time Required one to two weeks

Possible Materials Provide basic materials for making models such as modeling clay, scrap paper, scissors, and glue. Encourage reusing and recycling by having students bring in scrap materials from home.

Safety Precautions Discuss the dangers of any materials being used, such as sharp scissors or glue with strong fumes.

◉ Make a Model

Possible Procedures Direct students to think about the types of animals with which they are familiar. What types of food do they eat? What kind of environment do they need to survive? Have students discuss and research other types of animals that could live in the same environments. Provide reference materials or allow students to use library resources and the Internet.

Goals
■ **Research** the natural habitat and basic needs of one animal.
■ **Design** and model an appropriate zoo, animal park, or aquarium environment for this animal. Working cooperatively with your classmates, design an entire zoo or animal park.

Possible Materials
poster board
markers or colored pencils
materials that can be used to make a scale model

Animal Habitats

◉ Real-World Question

Zoos, animal parks, and aquariums are safe places for wild animals. Years ago, captive animals were kept in small cages or behind glass windows. Almost no attempt was made to provide natural habitats for the animals. People who came to see the animals could not observe the animal's normal behavior. Now, most captive animals are kept in exhibit areas that closely resemble their natural habitats. These areas provide suitable environments for the animals so that they can interact with members of their same species and have healthier, longer lives. What types of environments are best suited for raising animals in captivity? How can the habitats provided at an animal park affect the behavior of animals?

◉ Make a Model

1. Choose an animal to research. Find out where this animal is found in nature. What does it eat? What are its natural predators? Does it exhibit unique territorial, courtship, or other types of behavior? How is this animal adapted to its natural environment?

2. **Design** a model of a proposed habitat in which this animal can live successfully. Don't forget to include all of the things, such as shelter, food, and water, that your animal will need to survive. Will there be any other organisms in the habitat?

3. **Research** how zoos, animal parks, or aquariums provide habitats for animals. Information may be obtained by contacting scientists who work at zoos, animal parks, and aquariums.

4. **Present** your design to your class in the form of a poster, slide show, or video. Compare your proposed habitat with that of the animal's natural environment. Make sure you include a picture of your animal in its natural environment.

◉ Test Your Model

1. Using all of the information you have gathered, create a model exhibit area for your animal.

2. Indicate what other plants and animals may be present in the exhibit area.

◉ Analyze Your Data

1. **Decide** whether all of the animals studied in this lab can coexist in the same zoo or wildlife preserve.

2. **Analyze** problems that might exist in your design. Suggest some ways you might want to improve your design.

◉ Conclude and Apply

1. **Interpret Data** Using the information provided by the rest of your classmates, design an entire zoo or aquarium that could include the majority of animals studied.

2. **Predict** which animals could be grouped together in exhibit areas.

3. **Determine** how large your zoo or wildlife preserve needs to be. Which animals require a large habitat?

Communicating Your Data

Give an oral presentation to another class on the importance of providing natural habitats for captive animals. **For more help, refer to the Science Skill Handbook.**

LAB 473

Content Background

Dogs can be trained to help people in many capacities. Many police departments have special K-9 units. The dogs in these units are specially trained to help the officer in a variety of ways, including searching for people or finding drugs. Dogs are often used in search and rescue after disasters such as earthquakes or avalanches. Guide dogs for the visually impaired learn that things like curbs and moving cars are dangerous and that they must stop for these in order to warn their master. The dogs are also trained to be aware of and lead their masters around things like trees and low-hanging obstructions such as signs and awnings. Even though the dog can walk underneath such obstacles, a person could be injured if they had no warning.

Discussion

Patrol Dogs Arrange for a patrol dog and its handler to come to the classroom. Before the guests arrive, have students make a list of questions for the officer. Questions can be about the acquisition of the dogs, information on the training procedures, at-home handling, or retiring a patrol dog.

Activity

Helper Animals Have students investigate other capacities in which dogs can help people. Students can also research any other animals that help or have helped people in the past, such as carrier pigeons or capuchin monkeys. Students should make a poster showing their results. They could act out a story as a skit. L2

Going to the Dogs

A simple and surprising stroll showed that dogs really are humans' best friends

You've probably seen visually impaired people walking with their trusted "seeing-eye" dogs. Over 85 years ago, a doctor and his patient discovered this canine ability entirely by accident!

Near the end of World War I in Germany, Dr. Gerhard Stalling and his dog strolled with a patient—a German soldier who had been blinded—around hospital grounds.

A dog safely guides its owner across a street.

While they were walking, the doctor was called away. A few moments later, the doctor returned but the dog and the soldier were gone! Searching the paths frantically, Dr. Stalling made an astonishing discovery. His pet had led the soldier safely around the hospital grounds. Inspired by what his dog could do, Dr. Stalling set up the first school in the world dedicated to training dogs as guides.

German shepherds make excellent guide dogs.

German shepherds, golden retrievers, and Labrador retrievers seem to make the best guide dogs. They learn hand gestures and simple commands to lead visually impaired people safely across streets and around obstacles. This is what scientists call "learned behavior." Animals gain learned behavior through experience. But, a guide dog doesn't just learn to respond to special commands; it also must learn when *not* to obey. If its human owner urges the dog to cross the street and the dog sees that a car is approaching, the dog refuses because it has learned to disobey the command. This trait, called "intelligent disobedience," ensures the safety of the owner and the dog—a sure sign that dogs are still humans' best friends.

Write Lead a blindfolded partner around the classroom. Help your partner avoid obstacles. Then trade places. Write in your Science Journal about your experience leading and being led.

Science Online
For more information, visit life.msscience.com/oops

Resources for Teachers and Students

Dogs With Jobs, by Merrily Weisbord and Kim Kachanoff, Pocket Books, 2000

Working Dogs: Tales from Animal Planet's K-9 to 5 World, by Colleen Needles and Kit Carlson, Discovery Books, 2000

A Dog's Gotta Do What A Dog's Gotta Do: Dogs at Work, by Marilyn Singer, Henry Holt and Company, Inc., 2000

Reviewing Main Ideas

Section 1   Types of Behavior

1. Behavior that an animal has when it's born is innate behavior. Other animal behaviors are learned through experience.

2. Reflexes are simple innate behaviors. An instinct is a complex pattern of innate behavior.

3. Learned behavior includes imprinting, in which an animal forms a social attachment immediately after birth.

4. Behavior modified by experience is learning by trial and error.

5. Conditioning occurs when the response to one stimulus becomes associated with another. Insight is the ability to use past experiences to solve new problems.

Section 2   Behavioral Interactions

1. Behavioral adaptations such as defense of territory, courtship behavior, and social behavior help species of animals survive and reproduce.

2. Courtship behaviors allow males and females to recognize each other and prepare to mate.

3. Interactions among members of the same species are social behaviors.

4. Communication among organisms occurs in several forms, including chemical, sound, and light.

5. Cyclic behaviors are behaviors that occur in repeating patterns. Animals that are active during the day are diurnal. Animals that are active at night are nocturnal.

Visualizing Main Ideas

Copy and complete the following concept map on types of behavior.

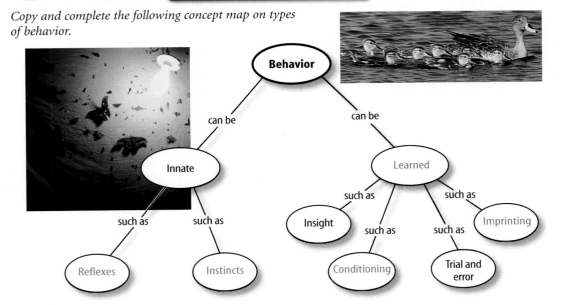

Science Online   life.msscience.com/interactive_tutor

CHAPTER STUDY GUIDE   475

Reviewing Main Ideas

Summary statements can be used by students to review the major concepts of the chapter.

Visualizing Main Ideas

See student page.

Science Online

Visit life.msscience.com
  /self_check_quiz
  /interactive_tutor
  /vocabulary_puzzlemaker
  /chapter_review
  /standardized_test

Assessment Transparency

For additional assessment questions, use the *Assessment Transparency* located in the transparency book.

Using Vocabulary

1. Conditioning is the modification of established behaviors. Imprinting is the formation of a new behavior. Both are learned behaviors.

2. Not all innate behaviors are social behaviors, but all social behaviors are innate behaviors.

3. Instinct is an innate behavior, and insight is a learned behavior. Both can be complex patterns of behavior.

4. Social behavior is an innate behavior. The social behaviors within an animal population form a society.

5. Instinct: complex pattern of innate behavior; reflex: simple innate behavior.

6. Hibernation is a period of inactive behavior, and migration is the seasonal movement of an animal or animal populations. Both are cyclic behaviors.

7. Courtship behavior is a social behavior between males and females of a species. Chemicals called pheromones usually stimulate courtship behavior.

8. All migrations are cyclic behaviors, but not all cyclic behaviors are migrations.

9. Aggression is just one of the many types of social behaviors.

10. Behavior is the interaction of one organism with another organism. Some behaviors are learned and others are instinctive. Reflex is the simplest innate behavior.

Checking Concepts

11. A	16. C
12. B	17. A
13. C	18. C
14. D	19. A
15. C	

Using Vocabulary

aggression p. 464	insight p. 461
behavior p. 456	instinct p. 458
conditioning p. 460	migration p. 470
courtship behavior p. 465	pheromone p. 465
cyclic behavior p. 468	reflex p. 457
hibernation p. 469	social behavior p. 462
imprinting p. 459	society p. 463
innate behavior p. 457	

Explain the differences between the pairs of vocabulary words given below. Then explain how the words are related.

1. conditioning—imprinting

2. innate behavior—social behavior

3. insight—instinct

4. social behavior—society

5. instinct—reflex

6. hibernation—migration

7. courtship behavior—pheromone

8. cyclic behavior—migration

9. aggression—social behavior

10. behavior—reflex

Checking Concepts

Choose the word or phrase that best answers the question.

11. What is an instinct an example of?
   A) innate behavior
   B) learned behavior
   C) imprinting
   D) conditioning

12. What is an area that an animal defends from other members of the same species called?
   A) society   C) migration
   B) territory   D) aggression

13. Which animals depend least on instinct and most on learning?
   A) birds   C) mammals
   B) fish   D) amphibians

14. What is a spider spinning a web an example of?
   A) conditioning   C) learned behavior
   B) imprinting   D) an instinct

15. What is a forceful act used to dominate or control another called?
   A) courtship   C) aggression
   B) reflex   D) hibernation

16. What is an organized group of animals doing specific jobs called?
   A) community   C) society
   B) territory   D) circadian rhythm

17. What is the response of inactivity and slowed metabolism that occurs during cold conditions?
   A) hibernation   C) migration
   B) imprinting   D) circadian rhythm

18. Which of the following is a reflex?
   A) writing   C) sneezing
   B) talking   D) riding a bicycle

Use the photo below to answer question 19.

19. The photo above is an example of what type of communication?
   A) light communication
   B) sound communication
   C) chemical communication
   D) cyclic behavior

Science Online   life.msscience.com/vocabulary_puzzlemaker

Use the ExamView® Pro Testmaker CD-ROM to:

- create multiple versions of tests
- create modified tests with one mouse click for inclusion students
- edit existing questions and add your own questions
- build tests aligned with state standards using built-in State Curriculum Tags
- change English tests to Spanish with one mouse click and vice versa

Thinking Critically

20. Explain the type of behavior involved when the bell rings at the end of class.

21. Describe the advantages and disadvantages of migration as a means of survival.

22. Explain how a habit, such as tying your shoes, is different from a reflex.

23. Explain how behavior increases an animal's chance for survival using one example.

24. Infer Hens lay more eggs in the spring when the number of daylight hours increases. How can farmers use this knowledge of behavior to their advantage?

25. Record Observations Make observations of a dog, cat, or bird for a week. Record what you see. How did the animal communicate with other animals and with you?

26. Classify Make a list of 25 things that you do regularly. Classify each as an innate or learned behavior. Which behaviors do you have more of?

27. Concept Map Copy and complete the following concept map about communication. Use these words: *sound, chirping, biolumi-nescence,* and *buzzing.*

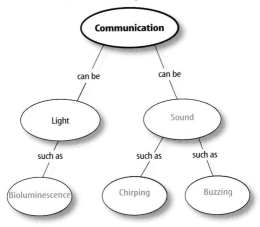

Performance Activities

28. Poster Draw a map showing the migration route of monarch butterflies, gray whales, or blackpoll warblers.

Applying Math

Use the graphs below to answer question 29.

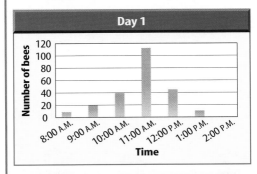

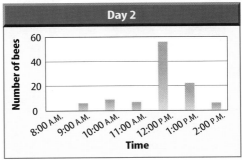

29. Bee Foraging Bees were trained to forage from 1:00 P.M. to 2:30 P.M. in New York and then were flown to California. The graphs above show the number of bees looking for food during the first two days in California. What was the difference in peak activity from day 1 to day 2? Was there a difference in the proportion of bees active during peak hours?

30. Bird Flight A blackpoll warbler flies 4,000 km nonstop from North America to South America in about 90 hours. What is its rate of speed?

 Science Online life.msscience.com/chapter_review

CHAPTER REVIEW 477

Thinking Critically

20. Leaving the room when the bell rings is a conditioned learned response.

21. Migration allows organisms to survive changes in weather. Some organisms may not survive the long, stressful journey.

22. A habit is a learned behavior that has become automatic. A reflex is an innate behavior.

23. Behaviors that help obtain food, are protective, or are defensive help organisms survive.

24. A farmer can artificially lengthen the amount of "daylight" hens are exposed to by using lights, which stimulate the hens to lay more eggs.

25. Answers will be determined by the animal the student observes.

26. Possible answers may include: innate—sneezing, yawning, hiccups, jerking your hand away from something hot; learned—tying shoes, reading, writing, solving problems, riding a bike. Learned behaviors are probably more numerous.

27. See student page.

Performance Activities

28. Maps should indicate both spring and fall migration routes. Use **Performance Assessment in the Science Classroom,** p. 145.

Applying Math

National Math Standards
1, 5, 9
29. Peak activity occurred one hour later on day 2. Day 1 equals 48% and day 2 equals 53%.

30. 44.4 km/h

✔ Assessment Resources

Reproducible Masters
Chapter *Fast File* Resources
Chapter Review, pp. 33–34
Chapter Tests, pp. 35–38
Assessment Transparency Activity, p. 45
Glencoe Science Web site
Chapter Review Test
Standardized Test Practice

Glencoe Technology
Assessment Transparency
Exam*View*® Pro Testmaker
MindJogger Videoquiz
Interactive Chalkboard

FAST FILE

Answer Sheet A practice answer sheet can be found at life.msscience.com/answer_sheet.

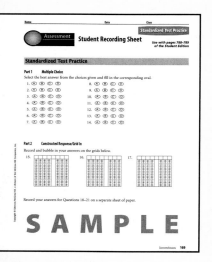

S A M P L E

1. D
2. B
3. A
4. D
5. C
6. B
7. A

Part 1 | Multiple Choice

Record your answers on the answer sheet provided by your teacher or on a sheet of paper.

1. Which of the following is true about innate behaviors?
  A. They are learned behaviors.
  B. They are observed in only some animals.
  C. They are the result of conscious thought.
  D. They include reflexes.

2. A spider spinning its web is an example of a(n)
  A. reflex.
  C. imprinting.
  B. instinct.
  D. conditioning.

Use the illustration below to answer questions 3 and 4.

3. The illustration above describes what kind of learned behavior?
  A. conditioning
  B. trial and error
  C. imprinting
  D. insight

4. Which of the following best describes this learned behavior?
  A. The dog learns to salivate when presented with food.
  B. The dog learns to eat only if the bell is rung.
  C. The dog is conditioned to stop salivating when a bell is rung.
  D. The dog is conditioned to salivate when a bell is rung.

5. Which of the following is an example of territorial behavior?
  A. A honeybee performs a waggle dance when it returns to the hive.
  B. A peacock fans his tail while approaching a peahen.
  C. A mountain goat charges and attacks an unfamiliar mountain goat.
  D. A group of bats remain in hibernation for the winter.

Use the photo below to answer questions 6 and 7.

6. The male wolf lying on its back is displaying what kind of behavior to the other male wolf?
  A. aggressive behavior
  B. submissive behavior
  C. cyclic behavior
  D. courtship behavior

7. Which of the following statements best describes the behavior of the wolf that is standing?
  A. The wolf is displaying its dominance over the wolf on the ground.
  B. The wolf is displaying courtship behavior to the other wolf.
  C. The wolf is using bioluminescence to communicate with the other wolf.
  D. The wolf is watching the other wolf perform the waggle dance.

478 STANDARDIZED TEST PRACTICE

Part 2 | Short Response/Grid In

8. Possible answer: An innate behavior in hummingbirds could be its attraction to certain flowers.

9. Reflexes are simpler and more automatic.

10. insight learning

11. past experience in solving a similar problem

12. Young children learn mostly by trial-and-error, not insight, because they have limited experiences.

13. Possible answers: getting food, caring for young, defending territory, protecting others, mating

14. to avoid being attacked or hurt by an animal of its own species

Part 2 | Short Response/Grid In

Record your answers on the answer sheet provided by your teacher or on a sheet of paper.

8. Give an example of an innate behavior in a hummingbird.

9. Which is simpler and more automatic, instincts or reflexes?

Use the illustration below to answer questions 10 and 11.

10. What type of learning is shown above?

11. What is required in order for an animal to use this type of learning to solve a problem?

12. Could a young child solve a problem using insight? Why or why not?

13. Give three examples of social behaviors.

14. Why might an animal be submissive to another animal?

Test-Taking Tip

Compare and Contrast Make sure each part of the question is answered when listing discussion points. For example, if the question asks you to compare and contrast, make sure you list both similarities and differences.

Part 3 | Open Ended

Record your answers on a sheet of paper.

15. Compare and contrast the innate behaviors of animals with short life spans and animals with long life spans.

16. Give three examples of ways bioluminescence is used for communication.

17. Explain the difference between a diurnal animal and a nocturnal animal. Give an example of each.

18. Compare and contrast hibernation and estivation.

Use the photo below to answer questions 19 and 20.

19. Explain the type of behavior that is shown above.

20. How is this behavior related to why zoos feed newborn condors with hand puppets that look like adult condors?

21. A male antelope approaches a female antelope during the breeding season. Is the male antelope responding to an external stimulus, an internal stimulus, or both? Explain.

19. The picture is showing imprinting in birds. After hatching, newborn ducklings will follow the first moving object they see.

20. Since newborn condors imprint on the first moving object they see after hatching, it is important that a condor not a human hand feed condor chicks hatched in zoos.

21. The male antelope is responding to both: an internal stimulus—the need to breed; and an external stimulus—the female antelope.

Rubrics

For more help evaluating open-ended assessment questions, see the rubric on p. 10T.

Part 3 | Open Ended

15. Animals with short life spans show mostly innate behavior. Because their lives are short, they do not have time to learn from their parents or other animals like them. Animals with long life spans have innate and learned behaviors. The learned behaviors develop over the animal's lifetime.

16. Answers might include fireflies flash their undersides to attract a mate; jellyfish use bioluminescence to protect themselves when threatened; fish that live in the deep ocean use bioluminescence to find prey.

17. A diurnal animal is active during the day. A nocturnal animal is active during the night. Most owls are nocturnal animals. Butterflies are diurnal.

18. Hibernation is a response to cold temperatures and limited food supplies. Estivation is a response to dry or hot conditions, and limited food supplies.

Unit Contents

 Investigating Disease and Prevention investigates five different diseases and science through history. Students will choose one disease to study further, and then create a time line of discoveries that help prevent the spread of disease.

How are
Chickens & Rice
Connected?

480

PROJECT
CRISS℠

Study Skills

Cooperative Team Research Cooperative team assignments are a reliable means of involving every student. Break into cooperative teams and assign each member of the team a human body system. Each should research the system, its function, and any diseases associated with that system. Team members come back together to share information and draft a group report.

NATIONAL GEOGRAPHIC

Back in the 1800s, a mysterious disease called beriberi affected people in certain parts of Asia. One day, a doctor in Indonesia noticed some chickens staggering around, a symptom often seen in people with beriberi. It turned out that the chickens had been eating white rice—the same kind of rice that was being eaten by human beriberi sufferers. White rice has had the outer layers, including the bran, removed. When the sick chickens were fed rice that still had its bran, they quickly recovered. It turned out that the same treatment worked for people with beriberi! Research eventually showed that rice bran contains a vitamin, B_1, which is essential for good health. Today, white rice usually is "vitamin-enriched" to replace B_1 and other nutrients lost in processing.

unit ⚡ projects

Visit **life.msscience.com/unit_project** to find project ideas and resources. Projects include:

- **History** Contribute to a class "remedy journal" with interesting, out-dated medical treatments, and how techniques have improved.
- **Technology** Investigate rare and interesting medical conditions, including their history, characteristics, and treatments. Present a colorful poster with photos and information for class display.
- **Model** Research and create a menu that includes vitamin-rich foods. Prepare a sample and a recipe card for a class food fair.
- **WebQuest** Understand the *History of Disease Prevention,* and how science has progressed through history. Become acquainted with famous scientists and learn how healthy lifestyles prevent disease.

unit ⚡ projects

History Have students investigate unusual, old-fashioned, or native-culture medicines and treatments practiced throughout history. After writing a one-page summary about their historical medicine or treatment, the ailment associated with it, and any connection to modern medicine, have the class compile an alphabetical "medical remedy" journal to share.

Technology Have students explore an assigned disease or syndrome. Research should include a paragraph on each of the following topics: discovered by whom and when, symptoms, diagnosis, therapy, medications, inherited or how contracted and where, and a photo, chart, or other visual. Information may be displayed in a poster or brochure and presented to the class.

Model Ask students to conduct research to discover the role vitamin B_1 (or another specific vitamin) plays in body functions and to find out the recommended daily allowance (RDA) of this vitamin. Have students make a list of foods that are rich in their chosen vitamin, then create a menu for a full day's meals (breakfast, lunch, and dinner), making sure that each meal contains at least one food from their list. Class presentations of their new vitamin knowledge might include a student-chef food fair with recipe cards available.

Additional Resources For more information, resources, and assessment rubrics, visit life.msscience.com/unit_project

NATIONAL GEOGRAPHIC   How Are Chickens & Rice Connected?

Deficiencies of vitamin B_1 affect many human systems. This vitamin allows cells to use many other nutrients. When B_1 is deficient, blood vessels expand in an attempt to deliver more blood and more nutrients to cells. This, in turn, leads to increased work for the heart. Each body system must perform its functions in order for the other systems to do so.

All vertebrates share a common body plan and similar organ systems. Observations of animals in nature and in the laboratory provide valuable clues for an understanding of human health and biology.

Section/Objectives	Standards		Labs/Features
Chapter Opener	**National**	**State/Local**	**Launch Lab:** Effects of Muscles on Movement , p. 483 **Foldables,** p. 483
	See pp. 16T–17T for a Key to Standards.		
Section 1 The Skeletal System ⏱ 2 sessions 🔲 1 block 1. **Identify** five functions of the skeletal system. 2. **Compare and contrast** movable and immovable joints.	National Content Standards: UCP.1–UCP.3, UCP.5, A.1, A.2, C.1, C.2, C.5, F.1		**Science Online,** p. 486 **Applying Math:** Volume of Bones, p. 487
Section 2 The Muscular System ⏱ 2 sessions 🔲 1 block 3. **Identify** the major function of the muscular system. 4. **Compare** and contrast the three types of muscles. 5. **Explain** how muscle action results in the movement of body parts.	National Content Standards: UCP.1–UCP.3, UCP.5, A.1, A.2, B.2, B.3, C.1–C.3, C.5, F.1		**Science Online,** p. 491 **Visualizing Human Body Levers,** p. 492 **MiniLAB:** Comparing Muscle Activity, p. 494
Section 3 The Skin ⏱ 3 sessions 🔲 1.5 blocks 6. **Distinguish** between the epidermis and dermis of the skin. 7. **Identify** the skin's functions. 8. **Explain** how skin protects the body from disease and how it heals itself.	National Content Standards: UCP.1–UCP.3, UCP.5, A.1, A.2, B.3, C.1–C.3, C.5, F.1, G.1, G.2		**Integrate Career,** p. 497 **MiniLAB:** Recognizing Why You Sweat, p. 498 **Integrate Chemistry,** p. 499 **Lab:** Measuring Skin Surface, p. 501 **Lab:** Similar Skeletons, p. 502 **Oops! Accidents in Science:** First Aid Dolls, p. 504

Lab Materials	Reproducible Resources	Section Assessment	Technology
Launch Lab: table and chair	**Chapter *Fast File* Resources** Foldables Worksheet, p. 17 Directed Reading Overview, p. 19 Note-taking Worksheets, pp. 33–36	GLENCOE'S ASSESSMENT ADVANTAGE	**Teacher**Works includes: • Interactive Teacher Edition • Lesson Planner with calendar • Access to all program blacklines • Correlations to standards • Web links
	Chapter *Fast File* Resources Transparency Activity, p. 46 Enrichment, p. 30 Reinforcement, p. 27 Directed Reading, p. 20 Lab Activity, pp. 9–11 **Life Science Critical Thinking/ Problem Solving,** p. 14 **Mathematics Skill Activities,** p. 17	Portfolio Visual Learning, p. 486 Performance Applying Math, p. 487 Applying Skills, p. 489 Content Challenge, p. 488 Section Review, p. 489	Section Focus Transparency Virtual Labs CD-ROM Guided Reading Audio Program Interactive Chalkboard CD-ROM
MiniLAB: book, table, meterstick *Need materials?* Contact Science Kit at 1-800-828-7777 or www.sciencekit.com on the Internet.	**Chapter *Fast File* Resources** Transparency Activity, p. 47 MiniLAB, p. 3 Enrichment, p. 31 Reinforcement, p. 28 Directed Reading, p. 20 Transparency Activity, pp. 49–50 Lab Activity, pp. 13–16 **Home and Community Involvement,** p. 49	Portfolio Reteach, p. 495 Performance MiniLAB, p. 494 Applying Skills, p. 495 Content Challenge, p. 492 Section Review, p. 495	Section Focus Transparency Teaching Transparency Virtual Labs CD-ROM Guided Reading Audio Program Interactive Chalkboard CD-ROM
MiniLAB: magnifying lens, clear plastic sandwich bag, tape **Lab:** large sheets of newspaper (10), scissors, tape, meterstick or ruler **Lab:** diagrams of a variety of mammal skeletons	**Chapter *Fast File* Resources** Transparency Activity, p. 48 MiniLAB, p. 4 Enrichment, p. 32 Reinforcement, p. 29 Directed Reading, pp. 21, 22 Lab Worksheet, pp. 5–6, 7–8 **Cultural Diversity,** p. 15 **Lab Management and Safety,** p. 67	Portfolio Visual Learning, p. 498 Performance MiniLAB, p. 498 Applying Math, p. 500 Content Challenge, p. 499 Section Review, p. 500	Section Focus Transparency Virtual Labs CD-ROM Guided Reading Audio Program Interactive Chalkboard CD-ROM Video Lab

End of Chapter Assessment

GLENCOE'S ASSESSMENT ADVANTAGE

Blackline Masters	Technology	Professional Series
Chapter *Fast File* Resources Chapter Review, pp. 39–40 Chapter Tests, pp. 41–44 **Standardized Test Practice,** pp. 71–74	MindJogger Videoquiz Virtual Labs CD-ROM Exam*View*® Pro Testmaker TeacherWorks CD-ROM Interactive Chalkboard CD-ROM	**Performance Assessment in the Science Classroom (PASC)**

Transparencies

Section Focus

Section Focus Transparency 1 — Cloud Catchers

If you've ever watched a skyscraper being built, you may have noticed the first part to go up is the metal frame that supports the building. After the skyscraper is completed, the frame usually cannot be seen.

1. What is the function of the frame in the picture?
2. How is the function of this metal frame similar to your "frame"?

L2

Section Focus Transparency 2 — No Sweat

Just after World War II, an English neurosurgeon named Sir Ludwig Guttman organized a competition for people in wheelchairs. Today, opportunities exist for everyone to participate in a variety of sports and recreation at all levels.

1. Name a body system that helps people to move.
2. What do hitting a tennis ball and a heartbeat have in common? How are they different?

L2

Section Focus Transparency 3 — A Matter of Perception

You might be able to identify a sculpture of a goose by looking at it, but how might you identify it if you couldn't see it? This man is using his sense of touch to identify and investigate the sculpture.

1. What are some functions of the skin?
2. What role is skin playing in studying the sculpture?
3. How does a blind person read?

L2

This is a representation of key blackline masters available in the Teacher Classroom Resources. See Resource Manager boxes within the chapter for additional information.

Key to Teaching Strategies

The following designations will help you decide which activities are appropriate for your students.

L1 Level 1 activities should be appropriate for students with learning difficulties.

L2 Level 2 activities should be within the ability range of all students.

L3 Level 3 activities are designed for above-average students.

ELL ELL activities should be within the ability range of English-Language Learners.

COOP LEARN Cooperative Learning activities are designed for small group work.

LS Multiple Learning Styles logos, as described on page 12T, are used throughout to indicate strategies that address different learning styles.

P These strategies represent student products that can be placed into a best-work portfolio.

PBL Problem-Based Learning activities apply real-world situations to learning.

Assessment

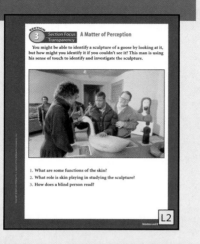

Assessment Transparency — Structure and Movement

Directions: Carefully review the tables and answer the following questions.

Results of Strength Test		
Name	Age	Push-ups
Mr. Vincent	35	23
Mr. Steinberg	68	23
Mr. Johnson	22	16

Results of Strength Test Age (years)					
Rank	20–29	30–39	40–49	50–59	60 +
High	45 +	35 +	30 +	25 +	20 +
Average	35–44	25–34	20–29	15–24	10–19
Below average	20–34	15–24	12–19	8–14	5–9
Low	0–19	0–14	0–11	0–7	0–4

1. According to the results of this experiment, Mr. Johnson has a ranking of ___.
   A high   C below average
   B average   D low
2. A reasonable hypothesis based on Table B is that when we age our muscles ___.
   F become stronger   H become weaker
   G become larger   J change color

L2

Teaching

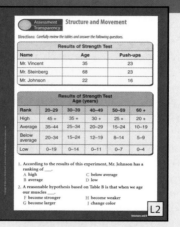

Teaching Transparency 1 — Human Bones

(labels: Humerus, Periosteum, Spongy bone, Marrow cavity, Compact bone, Artery, Vein, Bone cells, Blood vessels and nerves, Haversian system, Spongy bone, Blood vessels, Compact bone)

L2

Hands-on Activities

Student Text Lab Worksheet

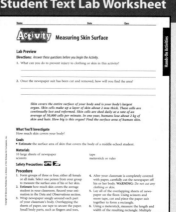

Activity — Measuring Skin Surface

Lab Preview
Directions: Answer these questions before you begin the Activity.

1. What can you do to prevent injury to clothing or skin in this activity?

2. Once the newspaper suit has been cut and removed, how will you find the area?

Skin covers the entire surface of your body and is your body's largest organ. Skin cells make up a layer of skin about 2 mm thick. These cells are continually lost and reformed. Skin cells are shed daily at a rate of an average of 50,000 cells per minute. In one year, humans lose about 2 kg of skin and hair. How big is this organ? Find the surface area of human skin.

What You'll Investigate
How much skin covers your body?

Goals
• **Estimate** the surface area of skin that covers the body of a middle-school student.

Materials
10 large sheets of newspaper   tape
scissors   meterstick or ruler

Safety Precautions

Procedure
1. Form groups of three or four, either all female or all male. Select one person from your group to measure the surface area of his or her skin.
2. **Estimate** how much skin covers the average student in your classroom. Record your estimation in the Data and Observations section.
3. Wrap newspaper snugly around each part of your classmate's body. Overlapping the sheets of paper, use tape to secure the paper. Small body parts, such as fingers and toes, do not need to be wrapped individually. Cover entire hands and feet.
4. After your classmate is completely covered with paper, carefully cut the newspaper off his or her body. **WARNING:** *Do not cut any clothing or skin.*
5. Lay all of the overlapping sheets of newspaper on the floor. Using scissors and more tape, cut and piece the paper back together to form a rectangle.
6. Using a meterstick, measure the length and width of the resulting rectangle. Multiply these two measurements to get an estimate of the surface area of your classmate's skin.

L2

Laboratory Activities

Laboratory Activity — Analyzing Bones

The skeletal system provides support for the body and protection for internal organs. In order to provide these functions, bones must be hard and strong. Scientists have discovered that the element calcium is responsible for making bones strong. Adding calcium to a bone can make it stronger, while removing calcium will make the bone weak and brittle. The amount of calcium in bones can change over time. Certain types of hard physical exercise and work can result in a gain of calcium to bones, while certain diseases and diets can result in a loss of calcium from bones.

Strategy
You will test the hardness of chicken bones before and after soaking them in different liquids. You will hypothesize which solutions will remove calcium from bones and test your hypothesis.

Materials
hydrogen peroxide
water
vinegar
a liquid chosen by the student
4 beakers or jars
chicken leg bones (boiled and cleaned)
forceps
CAUTION: *Wear gloves throughout this experiment. Do not taste, eat, or drink any materials used in the lab. Inform your teacher if you come into contact with any chemicals.*

Procedure
1. Four liquids will be tested for their effects on bones. Three of these liquids are listed in Table 1. You should choose a fourth liquid to test (lemon juice, fruit juices, soft drinks, milk, and so forth). Have your choice approved by your teacher and then record the type of liquid in Table 1 in Data and Observations.
2. Make a hypothesis about the effects each liquid will have on the strength of chicken bones. Write your hypothesis in Table 1.
3. Check the hardness of a chicken bone by gently twisting and bending the bone. Be careful not to crack or break the bone. Write your observations on the lines provided in the Data and Observations section.
4. Fill each beaker with one of the liquids. Label the beakers with your name and the kind of liquid.
5. Place a bone in each beaker of liquid. After 10 min, observe the bones and record in Table 2 any changes that you see.
6. After 48–72 h, use forceps to remove the bones from the liquids. Rinse the bones with water and observe them carefully.
7. Retest the bones for hardness by twisting and bending. Record the results of the test in the Results column of Table 1.

L2

Resource Manager

Meeting Different Ability Levels

Content Outline

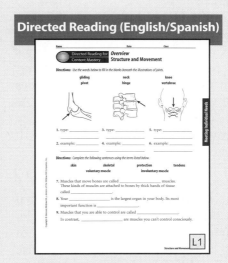

L2

Reinforcement

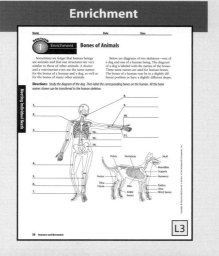

L2

Enrichment

L3

Directed Reading (English/Spanish)

L1

Study Guide

Study Guide

Features
• Contains a study guide page for each section of the chapter
• Reviews key concepts
• Includes answer pages

L2

Reading Essentials

Reading Essentials for Glencoe Science
An Interactive Student Workbook

Features
• Condensed core content
• Actively involves students in reading
• Reinforces key vocabulary

L1

Assessment

Test Practice Workbook

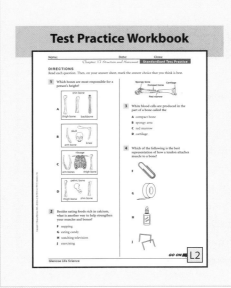

L2

Chapter Review

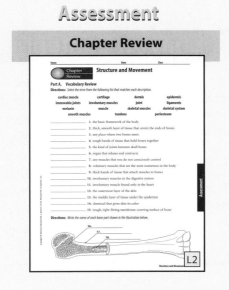

L2

Chapter Tests

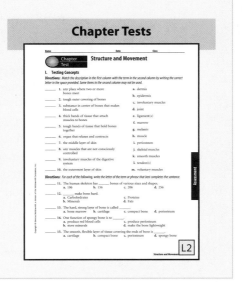

L2

Science Content Background

 The Skeletal System

Human Skeletons

Humans have endoskeletons—skeletons inside the body. The skeleton consists of the appendicular skeleton and the axial skeleton. The appendicular skeleton is made up of arm and leg bones and the girdler that attaches them to the body. The axial skeleton is made up of the skull, backbone, ribs, and breastbone.

 The Muscular System

Muscle Contractions

The contraction of a muscle cell involves a chemical called acetylcholine, which is released by the ends of the motor neurons. This action sends an impulse over the surface and into the interior of the muscle fiber. Calcium ions are released, which results in muscle contraction.

 **The Skin**

The skin is stretchable, tough, and selectively permeable. The epidermis is only about 30 to 60 cells thick. The dermis varies from 1 to 3 mm in thickness. The surface area of the skin is nearly 1.2 m^2 for an adolescent.

The Dermis

The dermis has two layers. The upper papillary layer is composed of connective tissue and has many small blood vessels and nerves. The folding of this layer produces ridges on the skin's surface, including fingerprints. The lower reticular layer is made of dense connective tissue with many collagen fibers. This layer also contains the sweat glands, oil glands, and hair follicles.

Sweat Glands

Sweat glands can be found in large numbers on the hands, feet, chest, and neck. Perspiration is similar to weak urine. The oil (sebaceous) glands secrete an oil composed of fats, salts, proteins, and water that lubricates the skin and reduces evaporation of water from the skin's surface. As the oil and sweat mix on the skin's surface, they form a protective layer that inhibits the growth of harmful bacteria and fungi.

Hair

The hair follicles produce masses of epidermal cells that are pushed up through the follicle. These cells then flatten and die. The amount of melanin in the cells gives hair its color. Because hair comes from the skin, it is considered an appendage of the skin.

chapter content resources

Internet Resources
For additional content background, visit
life.msscience.com to:
- access your book online
- find references to related articles in popular science magazines
- access Web links with related content background
- access current events with science journal topics

Print Resources
Biology (6th Edition), by Neil A. Campbell, Jane B. Reece, Pearson Benjamin Cummings Publishing, 2001
Human Anatomy & Physiology (5th Edition), by Elaine N. Marieb, Pearson Benjamin Cummings Publishing Company, 2000
Principles of Human Physiology, by William J. Germann, Cindy L. Stanfield, Pearson Benjamin Cummings Publishing, 2001

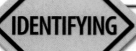

IDENTIFYING ▷ Misconceptions

Find Out What Students Think

Students may think that . . .

The muscular system is unrelated to other body systems.
When asked about the structure and function of muscles, most students tend to think only about the importance of muscles in movement. Often they don't understand the importance of muscles in the functioning of other systems or the role of the nervous system in controlling the muscular system.

Discussion

Ask students to explain what muscles do. Most will note the importance of muscles in gross motor movement. Record their responses on the board or on the overhead projector. Then ask students to consider other roles muscles play in the body. For example, shivering is a result of muscle contractions. These contractions release heat, which helps warm the body. Have students speculate on other processes that might depend on the movement of muscles. L2

Promote Understanding

Activity

Show students how to take a pulse by lightly placing two fingers on the major artery on the neck and counting the number of pulses in 6 seconds. By adding a zero to this number, the number of beats per minute (heart rate) can be determined. A similar process can be used to determine the respiration rate. L2

• Have students determine and record their at-rest pulse and respiration rates.

• Have those who are able exercise vigorously for 30 seconds. You might have students jump up and down or jog in place.

• When you call time, again have students determine and record their pulse and respiration rates.

Have students compare their at-rest and after-exercise pulse and respiration rates. Emphasize that the data they have collected illustrate that the muscular system is related to both the circulatory and respiratory systems. As muscle activity increased, so too did pulse and respiration rate. Remind students that increased breathing brings needed oxygen into the body

and expels waste carbon dioxide. The increase in heart rate quickly moves this oxygen to working muscles. Explain that it is the nervous system that causes these increased rates. As the nervous system senses a buildup of carbon dioxide and other waste products in muscle cells, it causes the body to increase breathing and heart rate.

As an extension, discuss with students how muscles support other systems. An example of this would be muscles aiding in digestion by moving food and undigested material through the digestive track.

Summing

Ask students to describe activities that would cause heart rate to increase. If necessary, ask students what happens to their heart rates when they are frightened. Again point out the connections between the muscular system and the cardiovascular and nervous systems. L2

Assess

After completing the chapter, see *Identifying Misconceptions* in the Study Guide at the end of the chapter.

Chapter Vocabulary

Science Journal Student responses will vary, but may be creative. It would be impossible for humans to exist without structure and movement.

INTERACTIVE CHALKBOARD with Image Bank

PowerPoint® Presentations

This CD-ROM is an editable Microsoft® PowerPoint® presentation that includes:

- a pre-made presentation for every chapter
- interactive graphics
- animations
- audio clips
- image bank
- all new section and chapter questions
- Standardized Test Practice
- transparencies
- pre-lab questions for all labs
- Foldables directions
- links to life.msscience.com

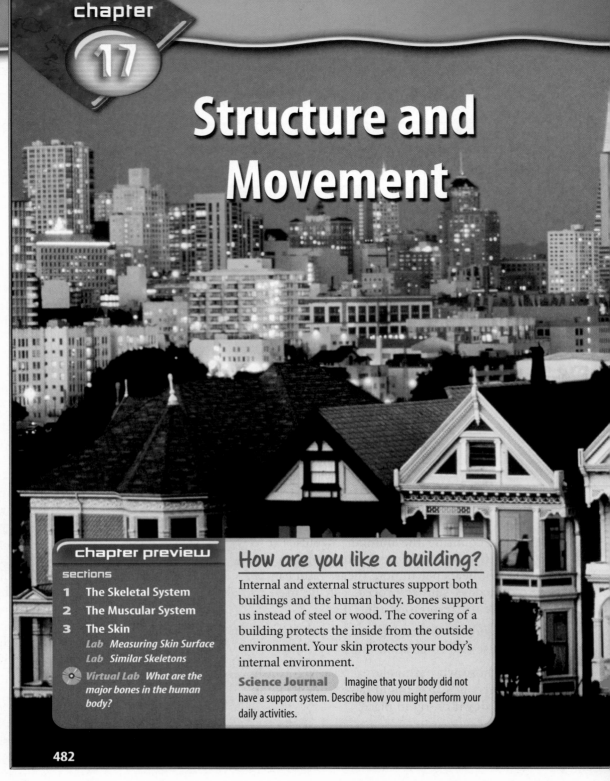

Structure and Movement

chapter preview

sections

1 The Skeletal System
2 The Muscular System
3 The Skin
  Lab Measuring Skin Surface
  Lab Similar Skeletons
  Virtual Lab What are the major bones in the human body?

How are you like a building?

Internal and external structures support both buildings and the human body. Bones support us instead of steel or wood. The covering of a building protects the inside from the outside environment. Your skin protects your body's internal environment.

Science Journal Imagine that your body did not have a support system. Describe how you might perform your daily activities.

482

Theme Connection

Energy When the skeletal and muscular systems work to produce movement, energy is used and work is done. Food is processed by the digestive system and converted into glucose. The chemical energy in glucose is used by muscles and transformed into mechanical energy.

About the Photo

Structure If a building's structural support was severely damaged, the building would collapse. The importance of the skeleton and skin in the human body can be compared to the structural framework and external structure of a building.

Start-Up Activities

Effect of Muscles on Movement

The expression "Many hands make light work" is also true when it comes to muscles in your body. In fact, hundreds of muscles and bones work together to bring about smooth, easy movement. Muscle interactions enable you to pick up a penny or lift a 10-kg weight.

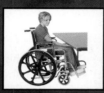

1. Sit on a chair at an empty table and place the palm of one hand under the edge of the table.

2. Push your hand up against the table. Do not push too hard.

3. Use your other hand to feel the muscles located on both sides of your upper arm, as shown in the photo.

4. Next, place your palm on the top of the table and push down. Again, feel the muscles in your upper arm.

5. **Think Critically** Describe in your Science Journal how the different muscles in your upper arm were working during each movement.

Study Organizer

Structure and Movement Without skin, muscle and bone each of us would be a formless mass. Make the following Foldable to help you understand the function of skin, muscle and bone in structure and movement.

STEP 1 Fold a sheet of paper in half lengthwise. Make the back edge about 5 cm longer than the front edge.

STEP 2 Turn the paper so the fold is on the bottom. Then, fold it into thirds.

STEP 3 Unfold and cut only the top layer along both folds to make three tabs. Label the Foldable as shown.

Read and Write As you read this chapter, write the functions that skin, muscle, and bone each have in structure and movement.

Preview this chapter's content and activities at
life.msscience.com

Purpose Use the Launch Lab to introduce students to muscles.
L2 ELL COOP LEARN LS
Kinesthetic

Preparation Clear tables of anything that could spill or break before students begin the lab.

Materials table, chair

Teaching Strategy Inform students that they will learn more about the muscular and skeletal systems as they read the chapter. This lab may also be done by student pairs.

Think Critically

Possible answers: When pushing up on the table, the top of the upper arm muscles feel hard. When pushing down, the muscles on the back of the upper arm feel hard.

Assessment

Process Ask students to observe and decide where the largest muscles in their bodies are located. The largest muscles are located where they can move the limbs and other large parts of the body, such as the buttocks. Use **Performance Assessment in the Science Classroom,** p. 89.
L2

 Dinah Zike
Study Organizer **Study Fold**

Student preparation materials for this Foldable are available in the **Chapter FAST FILE Resources.**

483

The Skeletal System

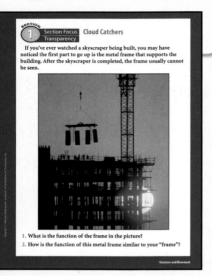

Living Bones

Often in a horror movie, a mad scientist works frantically in his lab while a complete human skeleton hangs silently in the corner. When looking at a skeleton, you might think that bones are dead structures made of rocklike material. Although these bones are no longer living, the bones in your body are very much alive. Each is a living organ made of several different tissues. Like all the other living tissues in your body, bone tissue is made of cells that take in nutrients and use energy. Bone cells have the same needs as other body cells.

Functions of Your Skeletal System All the bones in your body make up your **skeletal system,** as shown in **Figure 1.** It is the framework of your body and has five major functions.

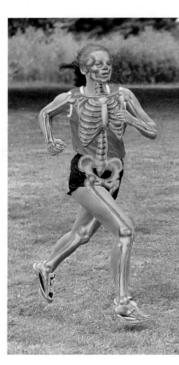

Figure 1 The 206 bones of the human body are connected, forming a framework called the skeleton.

1. The skeleton gives shape and support to your body.

2. Bones protect your internal organs. For example, ribs surround the heart and lungs, and the skull encloses the brain.

3. Major muscles are attached to bone and help them move.

4. Blood cells are formed in the center of many bones in soft tissue called red marrow.

5. Major quantities of calcium and phosphorous compounds are stored in the skeleton for later use. Calcium and phosphorus make bones hard.

484 CHAPTER 17 Structure and Movement

Bone Structure

Several characteristics of bones are noticeable. The most obvious are the differences in their sizes and shapes. The shapes of bones are inherited. However, a bone's shape can change when the attached muscles are used.

Looking at bone through a magnifying glass will show you that it isn't smooth. Bones have bumps, edges, round ends, rough spots, and many pits and holes. Muscles and ligaments attach to some of the bumps and pits. In your body blood vessels and nerves enter and leave through the holes. Internal characteristics, how a bone looks from the inside, and external characteristics, how the same bone looks from the outside, are shown in **Figure 2.**

A living bone's surface is covered with a tough, tight-fitting membrane called the **periosteum** (per ee AH stee um). Small blood vessels in the periosteum carry nutrients into the bone. Cells involved in the growth and repair of bone also are found in the periosteum. Under the periosteum are two different types of bone tissue—compact bone and spongy bone.

Compact Bone Directly under the periosteum is a hard, strong layer called compact bone. Compact bone gives bones strength. It has a framework containing deposits of calcium phosphate. These deposits make the bone hard. Bone cells and blood vessels also are found in this layer. This framework is living tissue and even though it's hard, it keeps bone from being too rigid, brittle, or easily broken.

Figure 2 Bone is made of layers of living tissue. Compact bone is arranged in circular structures called Haversian systems—tiny, connected channels through which blood vessels and nerve fibers pass.

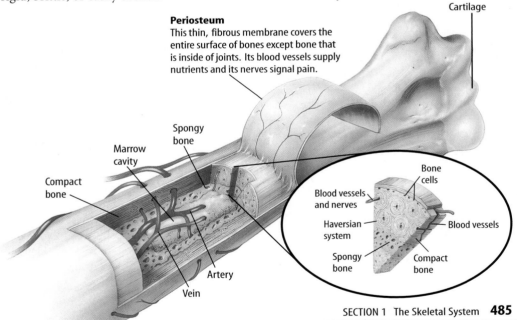

Periosteum
This thin, fibrous membrane covers the entire surface of bones except bone that is inside of joints. Its blood vessels supply nutrients and its nerves signal pain.

Cartilage

Spongy bone

Marrow cavity

Compact bone

Artery

Vein

Blood vessels and nerves

Bone cells

Haversian system

Blood vessels

Spongy bone

Compact bone

SECTION 1 The Skeletal System   **485**

Quick Demo

Building Columns

Materials 4-in × 6-in index cards, tape, books

Estimated Time 10 minutes

Procedure Construct one rectangular column and one cylindrical tube. Stand the structures on a flat surface and balance books on top of each one. Have students predict which structure collapses first. Relate this strength to the long, round bones of the human body. L2

Use Science Words

Word Usage Have students find nonscientific meanings of the use of the word *skeleton*. Refer to such idioms as *skeleton outline*, *skeleton crew*, and *skeleton structure*. L2

Teacher FYI

Osteoporosis A condition in which bones become porous and thin, resulting in reduced bone mass is osteoporosis. Factors that increase the risk of this condition include being female, being Caucasian, having chronic low calcium intake, lacking exercise, being underweight, and smoking.

Differentiated Instruction

English-Language Learners Ask students to interview a physician to find out what the most common fractures are, and how they occur. Have the students give an oral presentation to the class about what they have learned.

Curriculum Connection

Health Fractures are breaks or cracks in bones. When the broken bone isn't completely separated, it is called a greenstick fracture. Complete fractures occur when the broken bone is completely separated, but the broken ends do not pierce the skin. Compound, or open, fractures occur when the ends of the broken bone pierce the skin. Have students find out how each type of fracture is treated. L2

Activity

Elastic Bones Have students place dry, clean chicken bones in jars of 5% white vinegar for several days. Then have them remove the bones and examine them. Have students wash their hands after handling any chicken bones. Students should note how the mineral salts have dissolved, leaving only elastic tissue. Have them compare how the bone originally felt with how it feels now. [L2]

  **Visual-Spatial**

✔ Reading Check

Answer a smooth, thick, flexible layer of tissue at the ends of bones

IDENTIFYING Misconceptions

Bone Formation Students may think that the cartilage of a fetus hardens into bone. Explain that the fibrous part of cartilage calcifies over time, and eventually osteocytes begin to be produced, replacing cartilage cells.

Visual Learning

Figure 3 Have students make an events chain concept map of the process depicted in this figure. [L2] [P]

Caption Answer

Figure 3 osteoblasts

Science Online

Topic: Bone Fractures
Visit life.msscience.com for Web links to information about new techniques for treating bone fractures.

Activity Describe one of these new techniques in your Science Journal.

Figure 3 Cartilage is replaced slowly by bone as solid tissue grows outward. Over time, the bone reshapes to include blood vessels, nerves, and marrow. **Describe** *the type of bone cell that builds up bone.*

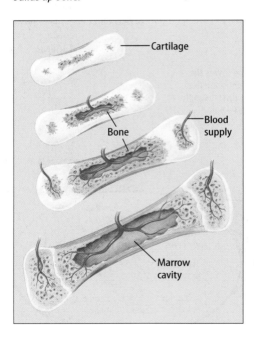

Spongy Bone Spongy bone is located toward the ends of long bones such as those in your thigh and upper arm. Spongy bone has many small, open spaces that make bones lightweight. If all your bones were completely solid, you'd have greater mass. In the centers of long bones are large openings called cavities. These cavities and the spaces in spongy bone are filled with a substance called marrow. Some marrow is yellow and is composed of fat cells. Red marrow produces red blood cells at an incredible rate of 2 million to 3 million cells per second.

Cartilage The ends of bones are covered with a smooth, slippery, thick layer of tissue called **cartilage.** Cartilage does not contain blood vessels or minerals. Nutrients are delivered to cartilage by nearby blood vessels. Cartilage is flexible and important in joints because it acts as a shock absorber. It also makes movement easier by reducing friction that would be caused by bones rubbing together. Cartilage can be damaged because of disease, injury, or years of use. People with damaged cartilage experience pain when they move.

✔ Reading Check *What is cartilage?*

Bone Formation

Although your bones have some hard features, they have not always been this way. Months before your birth, your skeleton was made of cartilage. Gradually the cartilage broke down and was replaced by bone, as illustrated in **Figure 3.** Bone-forming cells called osteoblasts (AHS tee oh blasts) deposit the minerals calcium and phosphorus in bones, making the bone tissue hard. At birth, your skeleton was made up of more than 300 bones. As you developed, some bones fused, or grew together, so that now you have only 206 bones.

Healthy bone tissue is always being formed and re-formed. Osteoblasts build up bone. Another type of bone cell, called an osteoclast, breaks down bone tissue in other areas of the bone. This is a normal process in a healthy person. When osteoclasts break bone down, they release calcium and phosphorus into the bloodstream. This process maintains the elements calcium and phosphorus in your blood at about the levels they need to be. These elements are necessary for the working of your body, including the movement of your muscles.

Differentiated Instruction

Visually Impaired Have students gently manipulate their ears and the ends of their noses and note the flexibility. Discuss the advantages of these body extremities being flexible and strong. The resiliency of this material makes it difficult to break these body parts. [L1]

Joints

What will you do during your lunch break today? You may sit at a table, pick up a sandwich, bite off a piece of a carrot and chew it, and walk to class. All of these motions are possible because your skeleton has joints.

Anyplace where two or more bones come together is a **joint.** The bones making up healthy joints are kept far enough apart by a thin layer of cartilage so that they do not rub against each other as they move. The bones are held in place at these joints by a tough band of tissue called a **ligament.** Many joints, such as your knee, are held together by more than one ligament. Muscles move bones by moving joints.

Applying Math   Calculate Volume

VOLUME OF BONES The Haversian systems found in the cross section of your bones are arranged in long cylinders. This cylindrical shape allows your bones to withstand great pressure. Estimate the volume of a bone that is 36 cm long and is 7 cm in diameter.

Solution

1 *This is what you know:* The bone has a shape of a cylinder whose height, h, measures 36 cm and whose diameter is 7.0 cm.

2 *This is what you need to find out:* What is the volume of the cylinder?

3 *This is the procedure you need to use:*
- Volume = $\pi \times (\text{radius})^2 \times \text{height}$, or $V = \pi \times r^2 \times h$
- A radius is one-half the diameter $\left(\frac{1}{2} \times 7 \text{ cm}\right)$, so
  $r = 3.5$ cm, $h = 36$ cm, and $\pi = 3.14$.
- Substitute in known values and solve.
  $3.14 \times (3.5 \text{ cm})^2 \times 36 \text{ cm} = 1{,}384.74 \text{ cm}^3$
- The volume of the bone is approximately $1{,}384.74 \text{ cm}^3$.

4 *Check your answer:* Divide your answer by 3.14 and then divide that number by $(3.5)^2$. This number should be the height of the bone.

Practice Problems

1. Estimate the volume of a bone that has a height of 12 cm and a diameter of 2.4 cm.

2. If a bone has a volume of 314 cm³ and a diameter of 4 cm, what is its height?

For more practice, visit life.msscience.com/ math_practice

Teacher FYI

Arthroscopic Surgery During arthroscopic surgery, an arthroscope (surgical instrument used to visually examine the interior of a joint) is inserted through an incision and the surgeon looks around inside the joint. Repair of the joint is done through the incision by means of instruments designed to be used with the arthroscope.

Curriculum Connection

Language Arts Have students look up *periosteum* and *osteoblast* in the dictionary. Have volunteers explain how the root of the word reflects its meaning. The root word *osteo* means "bone"; the root word *peri* means "surrounding"; the root word *blast* means "bud" or "germ." The periosteum surrounds the bone; the osteoblasts are bone-forming cells. L2 🔲 **Linguistic**

Make a Model

Ligaments Use two cardboard paper towel tubes and rubber bands to model how ligaments hold bones together at a joint. L2 ⬛ 🔲 **Visual-Spatial**

Applying Math

National Math Standards
Correlation to Mathematics Objectives
1
Use equations to determine time from average speed and distance measurements.

Teaching Strategy
Use division to find unit rates and ratios in proportional relationships such as speed, density, price, and recipes.

Answers to Practice Problems
1. 54 cm³
2. 25 cm

Use an Analogy

Lubricants Moving parts of machines require protection from friction. Lubricants such as oil and grease and other coatings serve to reduce the wear of the parts. Moving parts of the body at bone joints have spaces between the bones. These spaces have lubricants called synovial fluids and sacs of fluids—the bursae and synovial sheaths—to reduce friction between bone surfaces.

Teacher **FYI**

Forming Skull Joints The joints between the bones of the skull are called sutures. In an infant, the bones are held together by fibrous connective tissue and there is some flexibility between the bones. In later years, the tissue is replaced by bone and the skull becomes a hard, solid protective case for the brain.

Discussion

Importance of Joints If your hand had no joints, how would this affect you? Possible answer: You would not be able to pick up, hold, or turn objects.

Immovable Joints Refer to **Figure 4** as you learn about different types of joints. Joints are broadly classified as immovable or movable. An immovable joint allows little or no movement. The joints of the bones in your skull and pelvis are classified as immovable joints.

Movable Joints All movements, including somersaulting and working the controls of a video game, require movable joints. A movable joint allows the body to make a wide range of motions. There are several types of movable joints—pivot, ball and socket, hinge, and gliding. In a pivot joint, one bone rotates in a ring of another bone that does not move. Turning your head is an example of a pivot movement.

A ball-and-socket joint consists of a bone with a rounded end that fits into a cuplike cavity on another bone. A ball-and-socket joint provides a wider range of motion than a pivot joint does. That's why your legs and arms can swing in almost any direction.

A third type of joint is a hinge joint. This joint has a back-and-forth movement like hinges on a door. Elbows, knees, and fingers have hinge joints. Hinge joints have a smaller range of motion than the ball-and-socket joint. They are not dislocated as easily, or pulled apart, as a ball-and-socket joint can be.

A fourth type of joint is a gliding joint in which one part of a bone slides over another bone. Gliding joints also move in a back-and-forth motion and are found in your wrists and ankles and between vertebrae. Gliding joints are used the most in your body. You can't write a word, use a joystick, or take a step without using a gliding joint.

Figure 4 When a basketball player shoots a ball, several types of joints are in action.
Describe *other activities that use several types of joints.*

Skull

Immovable joints

Shoulder

Ball-and-socket joint

Vertebrae

Gliding joint

Arm

Pivot joint

Knee

Hinge joint

488 CHAPTER 17 Structure and Movement

Science Journal

Mechanical Joints at Home Have students make lists in their Science Journals of mechanical joints found at and around the home that are similar to joints found in the body. Examples include: door hinge—elbow; swivel chair—wrist; and wind vane—skull on vertebra. L2 **IS** **Visual-Spatial**

Differentiated Instruction

Challenge Have students write a brief report on the hyoid bone located in the anterior part of the neck. It is the only bone in the body that is not part of a joint with another bone. L3

Moving Smoothly When you rub two pieces of chalk together, their surfaces begin to wear away, and they get reshaped. Without the protection of the cartilage at the end of your bones, they also would wear away at the joints. Cartilage helps make joint movement easier. It reduces friction and allows bones to slide more easily over each other. Shown in **Figure 5,** pads of cartilage, called disks, are located between the vertebrae in your back. They act as a cushion and prevent injury to your spinal cord. A fluid that comes from nearby blood vessels also lubricates the joint.

✅ **Reading Check** *Why is cartilage important?*

Common Joint Problems Arthritis is the most common joint problem. The term *arthritis* describes more than 100 different diseases that can damage the joints. About one out of every seven people in the United States suffers from arthritis. All forms of arthritis begin with the same symptoms: pain, stiffness, and swelling of the joints.

Two types of arthritis are osteoarthritis and rheumatoid arthritis. Osteoarthritis results when cartilage breaks down because of years of use. Rheumatoid arthritis is an ongoing condition in which the body's immune system tries to destroy its own tissues.

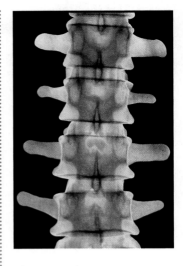

Figure 5 A colored X ray of the human backbone shows disks of cartilage between the vertebrae.

✅ **Reading Check**

Answer Cartilage makes joint movement easier by reducing friction that allows bones to slide more easily over each other.

3 Assess

DAILY INTERVENTION

Check for Understanding

Intrapersonal If your hand had no joints, how would this affect you? Possible answer: You would not be able to pick up, hold, or turn objects. L2

Reteach

Bones Bring in the leg and wing bones of cooked chicken or turkey and allow students to examine the ends of the bones for cartilage. Have them note the smooth and slippery surface that facilitates movement, but also notice the firmness needed for support. L2 **ELL** **IS**

Visual-Spatial

✅ **Assessment**

Oral Have students infer the functions of a fluid-filled cavity between two cartilage surfaces. The cavity cushions the cartilage and keeps the surfaces from rubbing against each other. Use **Performance Assessment in the Science Classroom,** p. 89. L2

---

section 1 review

Summary

Living Bones
- The skeletal system is the framework of your body and has five major functions.

Bone Structure
- A tough membrane called the periosteum covers a bone and supplies nutrients to it.
- Compact bone is hard bone located directly under the periosteum.
- Spongy bone is lightweight and located toward the ends of long bones.
- Cartilage covers the ends of bones and acts as a shock absorber.

Bone Formation
- Osteoblasts are bone-forming cells and osteoclasts are cells that break down bone.
- A joint is anyplace where two or more bones come together.
- Ligaments are tough bands of tissue that hold bones together at joints.

Self Check

1. **List** the five major functions of the skeletal system.
2. **Name** and give an example of both a movable joint and an immovable joint.
3. **Explain** the functions of cartilage in your skeletal system.
4. **Describe** ligaments.
5. **Think Critically** A thick band of bone forms around a broken bone as it heals. In time, the thickened band disappears. Explain how this extra bone can disappear over time.

Applying Skills

6. **Make and Use Tables** Use a table to classify the bones of the human body as follows: *long, short, flat,* or *irregular.*
7. **Use graphics software** to make a circle graph that shows how an adult's bones are distributed: *29 skull bones, 26 vertebrae, 25 ribs, four shoulder bones, 60 arm and hand bones, two hip bones,* and *60 leg and feet bones.*

---

section 1 review

1. gives shape and support; protects internal organs; provides place for muscle attachment; produces blood cells; stores minerals
2. movable joint: base of skull, shoulder, hip, elbow, knee, finger, wrist, and ankle; immovable joint: skull and pelvis
3. provides padding; also provides shape for ears and nose
4. tough bands of tissue that hold bones in place
5. Osteoclasts break down the extra bone material.
6. Have students work in pairs to compare their classification tables.
7. Circle graph should show these approximate percentages: skull–14% (50°), vertebral column–13% (47°), rib cage–12% (43°), shoulder–2% (7°), arms and hands–29% (104°), hip–1% (4°), legs and feet–29% (104°).

The Muscular System

as you read

What You'll Learn

- **Identify** the major function of the muscular system.
- **Compare and contrast** the three types of muscles.
- **Explain** how muscle action results in the movement of body parts.

Why It's Important

The muscular system is responsible for how you move and the production of heat in your body. Muscles also give your body its shape.

Review Vocabulary

bone: dense, calcified tissue of the skeleton, that is moved by muscles

New Vocabulary

- muscle
- voluntary muscle
- involuntary muscle
- skeletal muscle
- tendon
- cardiac muscle
- smooth muscle

Movement of the Human Body

The golfer looks down the fairway and then at the golf ball. With intense concentration and muscle coordination, the golfer swings the club along a graceful arc and connects with the ball. The ball sails through the air, landing inches away from the flag. The crowd applauds. A few minutes later, the golfer makes the final putt and wins the tournament. The champion has learned how to use controlled muscle movement to bring success.

Muscles help make all of your daily movements possible. **Figure 6** shows which muscles connect some of the bones in your body. A **muscle** is an organ that can relax, contract, and provide the force to move your body parts. In the process, energy is used and work is done. Imagine how much energy the more than 600 muscles in your body use each day. No matter how still you might try to be, some muscles in your body are always moving. You're breathing, your heart is beating, and your digestive system is working.

Figure 6 Your muscles come in many shapes and sizes. Even simple movements require the coordinated use of several muscles. The muscles shown here are only those located directly under the skin. Beneath these muscles are middle and deep layers of muscles.

490   CHAPTER 17 Structure and Movement

Figure 7 Facial expressions generally are controlled by voluntary muscles. It takes only 13 muscles to smile, but 43 muscles to frown.

Muscle Control Your hand, arm, and leg muscles are voluntary. So are the muscles of your face, shown in **Figure 7.** You can choose to move them or not move them. Muscles that you are able to control are called **voluntary muscles.** In contrast, **involuntary muscles** are muscles you can't control consciously. They go on working all day long, all your life. Blood gets pumped through blood vessels, and food is moved through your digestive system by the action of involuntary muscles.

Reading Check *What is a body activity that is controlled by involuntary muscles?*

Your Body's Simple Machines—Levers

Your skeletal system and muscular system work together when you move, in the same way that the parts of a bicycle work together when it moves. A machine, such as a bicycle, is any device that makes work easier. A simple machine does work with only one movement, like a hammer. The hammer is a type of simple machine called a lever, which is a rod or plank that pivots or turns about a point. This point is called a fulcrum. The action of muscles, bones, and joints working together is like a lever. In your body, bones are rods, joints are fulcrums, and contraction and relaxation of muscles provide the force to move body parts. Levers are classified into three types—first-class, second-class, and third-class. Examples of the three types of levers that are found in the human body are shown in **Figure 8.**

Science Online

Topic: Joint Replacement
Visit life.msscience.com for Web links to recent news or magazine articles about replacing diseased joints.

Activity Make a list in your Science Journal of the most commonly replaced joints.

SECTION 2 The Muscular System **491**

Visualizing Human Body Levers

Have students examine the pictures and read the captions. Then ask the following questions.

Which type of lever moves the load in the opposite direction of the effort force? First-class levers move the load in a direction opposite to the effort force.

How could the tennis racquet in the picture be thought of as an extension of a lever arm? If the fulcrum is the shoulder and the load is the tennis ball being struck, then the player's arm and racquet together form the lever arm.

Activity

Finding Levers Have students work in small groups to conduct a search through the classroom, or, if possible, the school building for first-, second- and third-class levers. Have each group prepare a visual to list the different examples of levers they found. Have the students include a diagram of one of the examples. L2

Quick Demo

Classes of Levers

Materials 2-inch thick piece of foam (or other material to simulate the brake pedal of car)

Estimated Time 10 minutes

Procedure Demonstrate the three classes of levers by movements of the foot: first-class—press down on the piece of foam with the ball of the foot to simulate pressing on the brake pedal of a car; second-class—rise up on tiptoe; third-class—rise up on heels.

Figure 8

All three types of levers—first-class, second-class, and third-class—are found in the human body. In the photo below, a tennis player prepares to serve a ball. As shown in the accompanying diagrams, the tennis player's stance demonstrates the operation of all three classes of levers in the human body.

▲ Fulcrum
▼ Effort force
■ Load

FIRST-CLASS LEVER The fulcrum lies between the effort force and the load. This happens when the tennis player uses his neck muscles to tilt his head back.

THIRD-CLASS LEVER The effort force is between the fulcrum and the load. This happens when the tennis player flexes the muscles in his arm and shoulder.

SECOND-CLASS LEVER The load lies between the fulcrum and the effort force. This happens when the tennis player's calf muscles lift the weight of his body up on his toes.

492

Differentiated Instruction

Challenge There are other examples of levers within the human body. Have students research to find out which parts of the human ear work as a lever, and write a paragraph explaining their findings to the class. L3

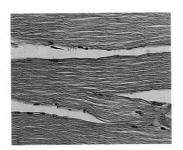

A Skeletal muscles move bones. The muscle tissue is striated, and attached to bone.

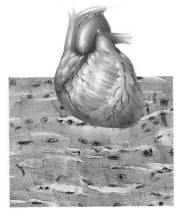

B Cardiac muscle is found only in the heart. The muscle tissue has striations.

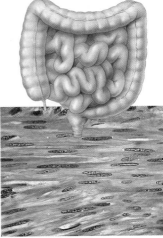

C Smooth muscle is found in many of your internal organs, such as the digestive tract. This muscle tissue is nonstriated.

Figure 9 The three types of muscle tissue are skeletal muscle, cardiac muscle, and smooth muscle.

Classification of Muscle Tissue

All the muscle tissue in your body is not the same. The three types of muscles are skeletal, smooth, and cardiac. The muscles that move bones are **skeletal muscles.** They are more common than other muscle types and are attached to bones by thick bands of tissue called **tendons.** When viewed under a microscope, skeletal muscle cells are striated (STRI ay tud), and appear striped. You can see the striations in **Figure 9A.** Skeletal muscles are voluntary muscles. You choose when to walk or when not to walk. Skeletal muscles tend to contract quickly and tire more easily than involuntary muscles do.

The remaining two types of muscles are shown in **Figures 9B** and **9C. Cardiac muscle** is found only in the heart. Like skeletal muscle, cardiac muscle is striated. This type of muscle contracts about 70 times per minute every day of your life. **Smooth muscles** are found in your intestines, bladder, blood vessels, and other internal organs. They are nonstriated, involuntary muscles that slowly contract and relax. Internal organs are made of one or more layers of smooth muscles.

Visual Learning

Figure 9 Have students study the photographs and illustrations of each muscle type. Then ask riddle-type questions and have students identify which muscle type (or types) you are describing. For example: I have striations and am attached to bones. What am I? skeletal muscle I have no striations. What am I? smooth muscle L2

Fun Fact

You have the same number of muscle fibers now as when you were born. Muscle fibers grow in length and width, but not in number.

Teacher FYI

Muscle Contraction Structures within muscle fibers contain thick filaments of the protein myosin and thin filaments of the protein actin. When a muscle is activated, the chemical adenosine triphosphate (ATP) is broken down, resulting in the release of large amounts of energy. The energy causes the actin and myosin filaments to slide over each other and the muscle contracts.

 LAB DEMONSTRATION

Purpose to observe the coordinated work of muscle pairs

Materials chart of arm muscles

Procedure Have students feel the muscles in their upper arms as they pump their lower arms out and back. Have them use the chart of arm muscles to determine which upper arm muscles are involved.

Expected Outcome Students should note that the biceps and triceps are involved in the action.

Assessment

Which muscle contracted to bring the forearm closer to the shoulder? The biceps contracted. Which muscle relaxed to allow this action? The triceps relaxed. L2

Mini LAB

Purpose Students feel the effects of muscle fatigue. L1

ELL IS **Kinesthetic**

Materials book, table, meterstick

Teaching Strategy Students can work with a family member. One person can do the activity while the other holds the meterstick vertically.

Analysis

1. Arm muscles become tired after a relatively short period of activity, heart muscles work continuously.
2. Heart muscles do not tire, but work continuously throughout one's life.

Assessment

Oral Have students infer why muscle contractions of the heart must be rhythmic. Use **Performance Assessment in the Science Classroom,** p. 89. L1

IDENTIFYING Misconceptions

Muscular System Some students think that the muscular system is unrelated to other body systems. Refer to page F at the beginning of this chapter for teaching strategies that address this misconception.

✔ **Reading Check**

Answer With increased muscle activity, individual muscle cells become larger.

Figure 10 **A** When the flexor (hamstring) muscles of your thigh contract, the lower leg is brought toward the thigh. **B** When the extensor (quadriceps) muscles contract, the lower leg is straightened.
Describe *the class of lever shown to the right.*

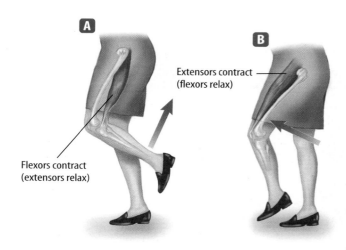

Extensors contract (flexors relax)

Flexors contract (extensors relax)

Mini LAB

Comparing Muscle Activity

Procedure
1. Hold a light **book** in your outstretched hand over a dining or kitchen **table.**
2. Lift the book from this position to a height of 30 cm from the table 20 times.

Analysis
1. Compare your arm muscle activity to the continuous muscle activity of the heart.
2. Infer whether heart muscles become tired.

Working Muscles

How do muscles allow you to move your body? You move because pairs of skeletal muscles work together. When one muscle of a pair contracts, the other muscle relaxes, or returns to its original length, as shown in **Figure 10.** Muscles always pull. They never push. When the muscles on the back of your upper leg contract, they shorten and pull your lower leg back and up. When you straighten your leg, the back muscles lengthen and relax, and the muscles on the front of your upper leg contract. Compare how the muscles of your legs work with how the muscles of your arms work.

Changes in Muscles Over a period of time, muscles can become larger or smaller, depending on whether or not they are used. Skeletal muscles that do a lot of work, such as those in your writing hand, become strong and large. For example, many soccer and basketball players have noticeably larger, defined leg muscles. Muscles that are given regular exercise respond quickly to stimuli. Some of this change in muscle size is because of an increase in the number of muscle cells. However, most of this change in muscle size is because individual muscle cells become larger.

In contrast, if you participate only in nonactive pastimes such as watching television or playing computer games, your muscles will become soft and flabby and will lack strength. Muscles that aren't exercised become smaller in size. When someone is paralyzed, his or her muscles become smaller due to lack of exercise.

✔ **Reading Check** *How do muscles increase their size?*

Cultural Diversity

Acupuncture Acupuncture originated in China more than 2,500 years ago. It is the system of inserting thin needles into the skin at specific body points. Acupuncture has been used to treat a variety of disorders. Have students find out some modern uses of acupuncture. Possible answers: to anesthetize patients for surgery, to cure disease, to relieve pain, to improve health L2

Differentiated Instruction

Visually Impaired Have students use their hand to feel the muscle contraction of muscles in their thigh when the lower leg is brought toward the thigh and when the lower leg is straightened. Have sighted students use **Figure 10** to name the muscles as they are touched.

How Muscles Move Your muscles need energy to contract and relax. Your blood carries energy-rich molecules to your muscle cells where the chemical energy stored in these molecules is released. As the muscle contracts, this released energy changes to mechanical energy (movement) and thermal energy (heat), as shown in **Figure 11.** When the supply of energy-rich molecules in a muscle is used up, the muscle becomes tired and needs to rest. During this resting period, your blood supplies more energy-rich molecules to your muscle cells. The heat produced by muscle contractions helps keep your body temperature constant.

Figure 11 Chemical energy is needed for muscle activity. During activity, chemical energy supplied by food is changed into mechanical energy (movement) and thermal energy (heat).

section 2 review

Summary

Movement of the Human Body
- Muscles are organs that relax, contract, and provide force to move your body parts.

Classification of Muscle Tissue
- Skeletal muscles are striated muscles that move bones.
- Cardiac muscles are striated muscles which are found only in the heart.
- Smooth muscles are found in your internal organs and are nonstriated muscles.

Working Muscles
- Muscles always pull and when one muscle of a pair contracts, the other muscle relaxes.
- Chemical energy is needed for muscle activity.

Self Check

1. **Describe** the function of muscles.
2. **Compare and contrast** the three types of muscle tissue.
3. **Name** the type of muscle tissue found in your heart.
4. **Describe** how a muscle attaches to a bone.
5. **Think Critically** What happens to your upper-arm muscles when you bend your arm at the elbow?

Applying Skills

6. **Concept Map** Using a concept map, sequence the activities that take place when you bend your leg at the knee.
7. **Communicate** Write a paragraph in your Science Journal about the three forms of energy involved in a muscle contraction.

section 2 review

1. movement
2. Skeletal (voluntary) and cardiac (involuntary) have striations; smooth muscle (involuntary) has no striations.
3. cardiac
4. Thick bands of tissue called tendons attach muscles to bones.
5. Muscles in the front (biceps) contract, while muscles in the back (triceps) relax.
6. The muscles on the underside of your thigh contract, and the bottom part of your leg is drawn toward the thigh. At the same time, the muscles on the top of the thigh relax and lengthen.
7. Entries should list the three forms of energy as chemical, mechanical, and thermal. It is the thermal energy of muscle contractions that helps maintain the constant body heat of warm-blooded animals.

section 3
The Skin

as you read

What You'll Learn

- **Distinguish** between the epidermis and dermis of the skin.
- **Identify** the skin's functions.
- **Explain** how skin protects the body from disease and how it heals itself.

Why It's Important

Skin plays a vital role in protecting your body.

⟳ Review Vocabulary

vitamin: an inorganic nutrient needed by the body in small quantities for growth, disease prevention, and/or regulation of body functions

New Vocabulary

- epidermis
- dermis
- melanin

Your Largest Organ

What is the largest organ in your body? When you think of an organ, you might imagine your heart, stomach, lungs, or brain. However, your skin is the largest organ of your body. Much of the information you receive about your environment comes through your skin. You can think of your skin as your largest sense organ.

Skin Structures

Skin is made up of three layers of tissue—the epidermis, the dermis, and a fatty layer—as shown in **Figure 12.** Each layer of skin is made of different cell types. The **epidermis** is the outer, thinnest layer of your skin. The epidermis's outermost cells are dead and water repellent. Thousands of epidermal cells rub off every time you take a shower, shake hands, blow your nose, or scratch your elbow. New cells are produced constantly at the base of the epidermis. These new cells move up and eventually replace those that are rubbed off.

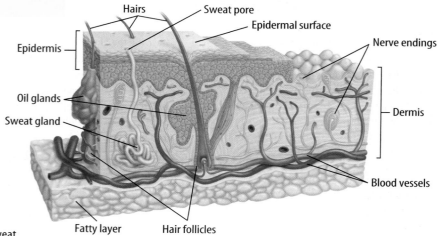

Figure 12 Hair, sweat glands, and oil glands are part of your body's largest organ, the skin.

496 CHAPTER 17 Structure and Movement

Melanin Cells in the epidermis produce the chemical melanin (MEL uh nun). **Melanin** is a pigment that protects your skin and gives it color. The different amounts of melanin produced by cells result in differences in skin color, as shown in **Figure 13.** When your skin is exposed to ultraviolet rays, melanin production increases and your skin becomes darker. Lighter skin tones have less protection from the Sun. Such skin burns more easily and may be more susceptible to skin cancer.

Other Skin Layers The **dermis** is the layer of cells directly below the epidermis. This layer is thicker than the epidermis and contains many blood vessels, nerves, muscles, oil and sweat glands, and other structures. Below the dermis is a fatty region that insulates the body. This is where much of the fat is deposited when a person gains weight.

Skin Functions

Your skin is not only the largest organ of your body, it also carries out several major functions, including protection, sensory response, formation of vitamin D, regulation of body temperature, and ridding the body of wastes. The most important function of the skin is protection. The skin forms a protective covering over the body that prevents physical and chemical injury. Some bacteria and other disease-causing organisms cannot pass through the skin as long as it is unbroken. Glands in the skin secrete fluids that can damage or destroy some bacteria. The skin also slows down water loss from body tissues.

Specialized nerve cells in the skin detect and relay information to the brain, making the skin a sensory organ, too. Because of these cells, you are able to sense the softness of a cat, the sharpness of a pin, or the heat of a frying pan.

INTEGRATE
Career

Mountain Climber Research the effects of ultraviolet radiation on skin. Mountain climbers risk becoming severely sunburned even in freezing temperatures due to increased ultraviolet (UV) radiation. Research other careers that increase your risk of sunburn. Record your answers in your Science Journal.

Figure 13 Melanin gives skin and eyes their color. The more melanin that is present, the darker the color is. This pigment provides protection from damage caused by harmful UV rays.

SECTION 3 The Skin **497**

Teacher FYI

Losing Epidermis Dandruff flakes are batches of old epidermal cells that are being shed from the surface of the scalp. Batches of the dead cells may harbor bacteria. Scratching the scalp accelerates the formation of new cells to replace the cells that are flaking away.

Differentiated Instruction

Learning Disabled Have students pat a wet cotton ball onto their wrists. Then have them gently blow on the wet surface. The evaporation removes body heat. Relate this experience to the evaporation of perspiration from the skin during hot weather. L1

INTEGRATE
Career

Mountain Climber At higher altitudes the atmosphere is thinner and fewer of the Sun's ultraviolet rays are blocked. Therefore, the skin is exposed to more harmful radiation.

Research Have students name a variety of careers that have an increased risk of sunburn. Ask students what people in these careers can do to reduce their risk of sunburn.

Use an Analogy

Human Body's Thermostat The hypothalamus in the brain acts like a thermostat on a furnace. A furnace's thermostat senses the temperature of the air and turns the furnace on and off to maintain a constant temperature in a home. The hypothalamus receives temperature readings from the skin and relays messages to body parts to maintain a constant temperature.

Activity

Animal Thermoregulation Have students find out how various animals thermoregulate (maintain or regulate their body temperature). Students might investigate dogs panting, elephants fanning ears, and desert lizards escaping into burrows.

Quick Demo

Layers of Skin

Materials glass slide of human skin, microscope

Estimated Time 10 minutes

Procedure Have students look at a slide of human skin to get an idea of the appearance of cells in the different layers and the thickness of the different layers.

Figure 14 Normal human body temperature is about 37°C. Temperature varies throughout the day. The highest body temperature is reached at about 11 A.M. and the lowest at around 4 A.M. At 43°C (109.5°F) internal bleeding results, causing death.

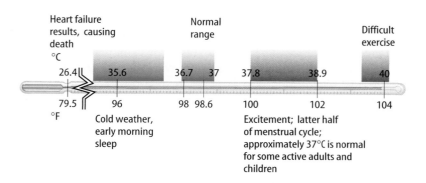

Mini LAB

Recognizing Why You Sweat

Procedure

1. Examine the epidermis and the pores of your skin using a **magnifying lens.**
2. Place a **clear-plastic sandwich bag** on your hand. Use tape to seal the bag around your wrist. **WARNING:** *Do not wrap the tape too tightly.*
3. Quietly study your **text** for 10 min, then look at your hand. Remove the bag.
4. Describe what happened to your hand while it was inside the bag.

Analysis

1. Identify what formed inside the bag. Where did this substance come from?
2. Why does this substance form even when you are not active?

Vitamin D Formation Another important function of skin is the formation of vitamin D. Small amounts of this vitamin are produced in the presence of ultraviolet light from a fatlike molecule in your epidermis. Vitamin D is essential for good health because it helps your body absorb calcium into your blood from food in your digestive tract.

Heat and Waste Exchange Humans can withstand a limited range of body temperatures, as shown in **Figure 14.** Your skin plays an important role in regulating your body temperature. Blood vessels in the skin can help release or hold heat. If the blood vessels expand, or dilate, blood flow increases and heat is released. In contrast, less heat is released when the blood vessels constrict. Think of yourself after running—are you flushed red or pale and shivering?

The adult human dermis has about 3 million sweat glands. These glands help regulate the body's temperature and excrete wastes. When the blood vessels dilate, pores open in the skin that lead to the sweat glands. Perspiration, or sweat, moves out onto the skin. Heat transfers from the body to the sweat on the skin. Eventually, this sweat evaporates, removing the heat and cooling the skin. This system eliminates excess heat produced by muscle contractions.

✔ Reading Check *What are two functions of sweat glands?*

As your cells use nutrients for energy, they produce wastes. Such wastes, if not removed from your body, can act as poisons. In addition to helping regulate your body's temperature, sweat glands release water, salt, and other waste products. If too much water and salt are released by sweating during periods of extreme heat or physical exertion, you might feel light-headed or may even faint.

Visual Learning

✔ Active Reading

Skin Injuries and Repair

Your skin often is bruised, scratched, burned, ripped, and exposed to harsh conditions like cold and dry air. In response, the skin produces new cells in its epidermis and repairs tears in the dermis. When the skin is injured, disease-causing organisms can enter the body rapidly. An infection often results.

Bruises Bruises are common, everyday events. Playing sports or working around your house often results in minor injuries. What is a bruise and how does your body repair it?

When you have a bruise, your skin is not broken but the tiny blood vessels underneath the skin have burst. Red blood cells from these broken blood vessels leak into the surrounding tissue. These blood cells then break down, releasing a chemical called hemoglobin. The hemoglobin gradually breaks down into its components, called pigments. The color of these pigments causes the bruised area to turn shades of blue, red, and purple, as shown in **Figure 15.** Swelling also may occur. As the injury heals, the bruise eventually turns yellow as the pigment in the red blood cells is broken down even more and reenters the bloodstream. After all of the pigment is absorbed into the bloodstream, the bruise disappears and the skin looks normal again.

Reading Check *What is the source of the yellow color of a bruise that is healing?*

Cuts Any tear in the skin is called a cut. Blood flows out of the cut until a clot forms over it. A scab then forms, preventing bacteria from entering the body. Cells in the surrounding blood vessels fight infection while the skin cells beneath the scab grow to fill the gap in the skin. In time, the scab falls off, leaving the new skin behind. If the cut is large enough, a scar may develop because of the large amounts of thick tissue fibers that form.

The body generally can repair bruises and small cuts. What happens when severe burns, some diseases, and surgeries result in injury to large areas of skin? Sometimes, not enough skin cells are left that can divide to replace this lost layer. If not treated, this can lead to rapid water loss from skin and muscle tissues, leading to infection and possible death. Skin grafts can prevent such problems. What are skin grafts?

SECTION 3 The Skin **499**

INTEGRATE Chemistry

Acidic Skin Oil and sweat glands in your skin cause the skin to be acidic. With a pH between 3 and 5, the growth of potential disease-causing microorganisms on your skin is reduced. What does pH mean? What common substances around your home have a pH value similar to that of your skin? Research to find these answers and then record them in your Science Journal.

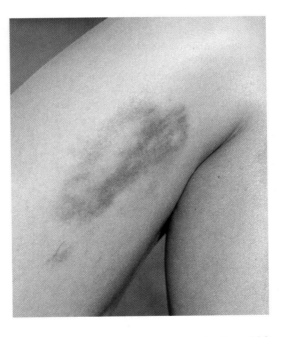

Figure 15 Bruising occurs when capillaries and other tiny blood vessels beneath the skin burst.

INTEGRATE Chemistry

Acidic Skin pH is a symbol for the measure of acidity or alkalinity of a solution. Substances with pH similar to that of your skin are apples, bananas, cherries, oranges, grapes, and tomatoes.

Reading Check

Answer the breakdown of pigment in red blood cells

Inquiry Lab

Protective Oils

Purpose to explore and observe what happens to your skin when its oil-rich protective film that locks moisture inside the skin and prevents bacteria and other infections is removed

Possible Materials dish soap, moisturizing hand soap, rubbing alcohol, baby oil, dye, non-latex gloves

Estimated Time 1 class session

Teaching Strategies

• Students can wash one hand with dish soap (while wearing a glove on the other hand) and wash the other hand with a moisturizing soap.

• Students can observe what happens when baby oil is applied to the back of one hand, while rubbing alcohol is applied to the back of the other hand.

• Students can predict what happens when a dye is applied to the hand that was treated with baby oil, versus the hand that was treated with rubbing alcohol

• Allow students to explore other questions that arise.

For additional inquiry activities, see *Science Inquiry Labs.*

Differentiated Instruction

Challenge Have students do research to find out about the use of artificial skin for burn victims. Have them write a report about the properties of the artificial skin that helps the patient heal. Artificial skin is a combination of human skin cells and biodegradable polymers. Currently used in treatment of severe burns, artificial skin provides an interactive bandage that covers the wound until a real skin graft can be grown. L3

Teacher FYI

Skin Allergies Contact with certain plants such as poison ivy, poison oak, and poison sumac may produce an inflammation of the skin due to an allergic reaction to the plants. The skin becomes red and itchy, and small blisters develop. Scratching the affected area will cause the blisters to open and may allow infections to develop.

Acne Among teenagers, acne is a common skin disorder. It starts when excess oil combines with dead skin cells to clog pores. Bacterial infection within the pore can cause a red, inflamed pimple, a blackhead, or a white, pus-filled pimple. Rupture of the pimple may cause the bacteria to infect nearby follicles. About 80% of teenagers suffer from acne.

3 Assess

DAILY INTERVENTION

Check for Understanding
Coop Learn Have students find out what happens to the skin when it is sunburned. They should write a list of ways to prevent damage to the skin from the sun or from other sources. L1

Reteach
Skin Functions Have students prepare an outline of skin functions correlated with the skin layers. L2

✓ Assessment

Content Have students make a concept map to describe the steps the body goes through as it heals a cut. Use **Performance Assessment in the Science Classroom**, p. 161. L2

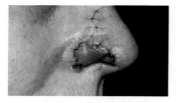
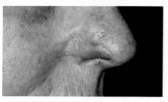

Figure 16 A cancerous growth was removed from the nose of a 69-year-old woman. A piece of skin removed from her scalp was grafted onto her nose to replace the lost skin (top). The skin graft is healing after only one month (bottom).

Skin Grafts Pieces of skin that are cut from one part of a person's body and then moved to the injured or burned area where there is no skin are called skin grafts. This skin graft is kept alive by nearby blood vessels and soon becomes part of the surrounding skin. Successful skin grafts, shown in **Figure 16,** must be taken from the victim's own body or possibly an identical twin. Skin transplants from other sources are rejected in about three weeks.

What can be done for severe burn victims who have little healthy skin left? Since the 1880s, doctors have used the skin from dead humans, called cadavers, to treat such burns temporarily. However, the body usually rejects this skin, so it must be replaced continually until the burn heals.

A recent advancement in skin repair uses temporary grafts from cadavers to prevent immediate infections, while scientists grow large sheets of epidermis from small pieces of the burn victim's healthy skin. After 19 to 21 days, the cadaver skin patch is removed and the new epidermis is applied. With new technologies, severe cases of skin loss or damage that cannot be repaired may no longer be fatal.

---

section 3 review

Summary

Skin Structures
- The epidermis is the thinnest, outermost layer of skin.
- The dermis is the thick layer below the epidermis. It contains blood vessels, nerves, muscles, oil, and sweat glands.
- Melanin is a pigment that protects your skin and gives it color.

Skin Functions
- Your skin provides protection, and eliminates body wastes.

Skin Injuries and Repair
- A bruise is caused by tiny broken blood vessels underneath the skin.
- When you cut your skin, blood flows out of the cut until a clot forms, causing a scab to protect against bacteria.
- Skin grafts can be made from a cadaver or a victim's healthy skin to repair the epidermis.

Self Check

1. **Compare and contrast** the epidermis and dermis.
2. **List** five of the major functions of the body's largest organ, skin.
3. **Explain** how skin helps prevent disease in the body.
4. **Describe** one way in which doctors are able to repair severe skin damage from burns, injuries, or surgeries.
5. **Think Critically** Why is a person who has been severely burned in danger of dying from loss of water?

Applying Math

6. **Solve One-Step Equations** The skin of eyelids is about 0.5 mm thick. On the soles of your feet, skin is up to 0.4 cm thick. How many times thicker is the skin on the soles of your feet compared to your eyelids?
7. **Calculate** The outermost layers of your skin are replaced every 27 days. How many times per year are your outermost layers of skin replaced?

500 CHAPTER 17 Structure and Movement

Science Online life.msscience.com/self_check_quiz

---

section 3 review

1. epidermis—thin outer layer of the skin, contains melanin; dermis—under the epidermis, is thicker, contains many blood vessels, nerves, and sweat glands
2. protects, regulates body temperature, excretes wastes, serves as sensory organ, forms vitamin D
3. As long as it is unbroken, skin prevents pathogens from entering the body. Glands in the skin secrete fluids that destroy bacteria.
4. A graft of skin from another part of the person's body is moved to the injured area. The graft eventually becomes part of the surrounding skin.
5. The person has lost the skin's protection from loss of water.
6. 8 times
7. 13.5 times

Measuring Skin Surface

Skin covers the entire surface of your body and is your body's largest organ. Skin cells make up a layer of skin about 2 mm thick. These cells are continually lost and re-formed. Skin cells are shed daily at a rate of an average of 50,000 cells per minute. In one year, humans lose about 2 kg of skin and hair. How big is this organ? Find the surface area of human skin.

Real-World Question

How much skin covers your body?

Goal
■ **Estimate** the surface area of skin that covers the body of a middle-school student.

Materials
10 large sheets   tape
   of newspaper   meterstick or ruler
scissors

Safety Precautions

Procedure

1. Form groups of three or four, either all female or all male. Select one person from your group to measure the surface area of his or her skin.

2. **Estimate** how much skin covers the average student in your classroom. In your Science Journal, record your estimation.

3. Wrap newspaper snugly around each part of your classmate's body. Overlap sheets of paper and use tape to secure them. Cover entire hands and feet. Small body parts, such as fingers and toes, do not need to be wrapped individually. **WARNING:** *Do not cover face. May cause suffocation.*

4. After your classmate is completely covered with paper, carefully cut the newspaper off his or her body. **WARNING:** *Do not cut any clothing or skin.*

5. Lay all of the overlapping sheets of newspaper on the floor. Using scissors and more tape, cut and piece the paper suit together to form a rectangle.

6. Using a meterstick, measure the length and width of the resulting rectangle. Multiply these two measurements for an estimate of the surface area of your classmate's skin.

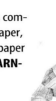

Conclude and Apply

1. Was your estimation correct? Explain.

2. How accurate are your measurements of your classmate's skin surface area? How could your measurements be improved?

3. **Calculate** the skin's volume using 2 mm as the average skin thickness and your calculated surface area from this lab.

Communicating Your Data

Make a table of all data. Find the average area for male groups and then for female groups. Discuss the differences. **For more help, refer to the** Math Skill Handbook.

Real-World Question

Purpose Students will estimate the surface area of skin covering a middle school student. L2

Process Skills collect data, predict, measure in SI, analyze results, draw conclusions

Time Required 40 minutes

Safety Precautions Students should use care when cutting the newspaper model off of the student.

Procedure

Teaching Strategy Provide printless paper if possible, so the ink does not rub off onto students.

Conclude and Apply

1. Answers will vary.
2. Measurements are estimates only. Improvement suggestions will vary.
3. Answers will vary.

Assessment

Performance Today scientists are researching methods for producing synthetic skin. This is especially important for burn victims that lose large portions of their skin. Research this topic and report to your class the results of your search. Use **Performance Assessment in the Science Classroom,** p. 143. L2

Communicating Your Data

Students may want to use a spreadsheet program to record their results.

▶ Real-World Question

Purpose

Internet Students use Internet sites that can be accessed through life.msscience.com/internet_lab.

Students can post their findings on the site and get information from other schools around the country about similar skeletal structures among humans and other mammals. L2

Process Skills collect data, identify, write, compare and contrast, infer, describe.

Time Required two days

▶ Make a Plan

Preparation

Internet To run through the steps that the students will follow, visit life.msscience.com/internet_lab.

Non-Internet Sources Collect books about mammals. Find realistic models of different mammals to display in the classroom.

LAB Use the Internet

Similar Skeletons

Goals
- **Identify** a skeletal structure in the human body.
- **Write** a list of mammals with which you are familiar.
- **Compare** the identified human skeletal structure to a skeletal structure in each of the mammals.
- **Determine** if the mammal skeletal structure that you selected is similar to the human skeletal structure you identified.
- **Describe** how the mammal skeletal structure is similar to or different from the skeletal structure in a human.

Data Source

Science Online

Visit life.msscience.com/internet_lab for Web links to more information about skeletal structures, and for data collected by other students.

▶ Real-World Question

Humans and other mammals share many similar characteristics, including similar skeletal structures. Think about all the different types of mammals you have seen or read about. Tigers, dogs, and household cats are meat-eating mammals. Whales and dolphins live in water. Primates, which include gorillas, chimpanzees, and humans, can walk on two legs. Mammals live in different environments, eat different types of food, and even look different, but they all have hair, possess the ability to maintain fairly constant body temperatures, and have similar skeletal structures. Which skeletal structures are similar among humans and other mammals? How many bones do you have in your hand? What types of bones are they? Do other mammals have similar skeletal structures? Form a hypothesis about the skeletal structures that humans and other mammals have in common.

▶ Make a Plan

1. Choose a specific part of the human skeletal structure to study, such as your hand, foot, skull, leg, or arm.

Alternative Inquiry Lab

Tail Wagging Make this Lab an Inquiry Lab by building on the experience. Encourage your students to use what they have learned to explain why some mammal skeletons have tails, and others do not. Ask students to do research to find out if human skeletons exhibit any evidence of a tail. Have student groups each choose one question to explore.

2. **List** four to six different mammals.

3. Do these mammals possess skeletal structures similar to the human skeleton? Remember, the mammals' skeletons can be similar to that of the human, but the structures can have different functions.

4. **Compare and contrast** the mammal and human skeletal structures. Are the types of bone similar? Is the number of bones the same? Where are these structures located?

◉ Follow Your Plan

1. Make sure your teacher approves your plan before you start.

2. Visit the link below to post your data.

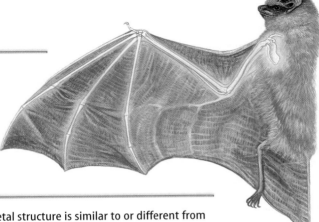

◉ Analyze Your Data

1. **Describe** how each mammal's skeletal structure is similar to or different from the human skeletal structure you chose.

2. **Record** your data in the data table provided on the Web site.

◉ Conclude and Apply

1. Visit the link below and compare your data to that of other students. Do other students agree with your conclusions?

2. Do the structures studied have similar functions in the human and the mammals you researched?

Communicating Your Data

Find this lab using the link below. Post your data in the table provided. Compare your data with that posted by other students.

Science Online
life.msscience.com/internet_lab

LAB 503

◉ Follow Your Plan

Teaching Strategies

- Have students focus on similar features among humans and mammals. Encourage them to think about human hands, feet, legs, and arms. L2
- Have students determine which mammals have similar limb structures to humans.

Troubleshooting While students can compare mammal skeletal structure to skeletal structure for other non-mammals, be sure to have students compare human skeletal structures to other mammals to draw comparisons.

◉ Analyze Your Data

1. Answers will vary. Have students compare specific human bones to specific mammal bones to determine whether they are alike or different.

2. Answers will vary. Students should describe how a particular skeletal structure, such as a foot, is similar between a human and a mammal. To do this, they might describe the function of that structure in humans and for that mammal.

◉ Conclude and Apply

Answers will be individualized and often based on the student's opinion of his or her research. Look for depth and quality of research performed.

☑ Assessment

Content Have students make drawings of the skeletal structures they investigated. Make separate drawings for the human structure and the mammal's structure. Have them label the bones and other physical features in both drawings. Use **Performance Assessment in the Science Classroom,** p. 127. L2

Communicating Your Data

Have students use a word processing program to create a two-column table describing how the human structure and the mammal structure are similar or different. Include descriptions of the labels that are featured on students' drawings of skeletal structures. L2

Content Background

Improving the look, function, and comfort of artificial body parts, or prostheses, is a constant concern for the scientists who develop them. Innovations include myoelectric arms, which are powered by batteries and remaining arm muscles. Bionics connect a prosthesis with the brain through a combination of computer sensors in the prosthesis and nerve cells in the remainder of the limb. Bionics allow limited reactions to some stimuli. Special limbs, such as a sprinting leg, have also been developed for individuals who have lost a limb and wish to participate in sports.

Discussion

Handy Joints Imagine the steps involved with selecting your lunch in the school cafeteria, paying for it, and eating it. How would artificial fingers without flexible joints make these tasks difficult? How would a flexible finger help? *Possible answers: Difficulty in picking up trays and food, difficulty holding and sorting money and holding eating utensils. In every case, flexibility in the finger would make these tasks easier.*

Activity

Prostheses Organize the class into several groups. Each group should research innovations and uses of prostheses in a certain time period: ancient times, the 1800s, 1900–1950, 1950–present, the future. Each group should report their findings to the class.

First Aid Dolls

A fashion doll is doing her part for medical science! It turns out that the plastic joints that make it possible for one type of doll's legs to bend make good joints in prosthetic (artificial) fingers for humans.

Jane Bahor (photo at right) works at Duke University Medical Center in Durham, North Carolina. She makes lifelike body parts for people who have lost legs, arms, or fingers. A few years ago, she met a patient named Jennifer Jordan, an engineering student who'd lost a finger. The artificial finger that Bahor made looked real, but it couldn't bend. She and Jordan began to discuss the problem.

"If only the finger could bend like a doll's legs bend," said Bahor. "It would be so much more useful to you!"

Jordan's eyes lit up. "That's it!" Jordan said. The engineer went home and borrowed one of her sister's dolls. Returning with it to Bahor's office, she and Bahor did "surgery." They operated on the fashion doll's legs and removed the knee joints from their vinyl casings.

"It turns out that the doll's knee joints flexed the same way that human finger joints do," says Bahor. "We could see that using these joints would allow patients more use and flexibility with their 'new' fingers."

Holding On

The new, fake, flexible fingers can bend in the same way that a doll's legs bend. A person can use his or her other hand to bend and straighten the joint. When the joint bends, it makes a sound similar to a cracking knuckle.

Being able to bend prosthetic fingers allows wearers to hold a pen, pick up a cup, or grab a steering wheel. These are tasks that were impossible before the plastic knee joints were implanted in the artificial fingers. "We've even figured out how to insert three joints in each finger, so that now its wearer can almost make a fist," adds Bahor. Just like the doll's legs, the prosthetic fingers stay bent until the wearer straightens them.

Bahor removes a knee joint from a doll. The joint will soon be in a human's prosthetic finger!

Invent Choose a "problem" you can solve. Use what Bahor calls "commonly found materials" to solve the problem. Then make a model or a drawing of the problem-solving device.

Science online

For more information, visit life.mssience.com/oops

Invent Direct students to solve a problem that will impact their everyday lives—something that is important to them. Display everyday items that might be used to solve problems and could provide ideas to students. Instruct students that they are not limited to using display items.

Resources for Teachers and Students

"Rebuilding the Body," by Alexander Newman, *National Geographic World*, February 2000

"Lending a Helping Leg," by Diane Martindale, *Scientific American*, May 2000

"Barbie Lends a Leg," by Sharon Guynup, *Science World*, Sept. 2000

chapter **Study Guide** **17**

Reviewing Main Ideas

Section 1 The Skeletal System

1. Bones are living structures that protect, support, make blood, store minerals, and provide for muscle attachment.

2. The skull and pelvic joints in adults do not move and are classified as immovable.

3. Movable joints move freely, and include pivot, hinge, ball-and-socket, and gliding joints.

Section 2 The Muscular System

1. Skeletal muscle is voluntary and moves bones. Smooth muscle is involuntary and controls movement of internal organs. Cardiac muscle is involuntary and located only in the heart.

2. Muscles contract—they pull, not push, to move body parts.

3. Skeletal muscles work in pairs—when one contracts, the other relaxes.

Section 3 The Skin

1. The epidermis has dead cells on its surface. Melanin is produced in the epidermis. Cells at the base of the epidermis produce new skin cells. The dermis is the inner layer where nerves, sweat and oil glands, and blood vessels are located.

2. The functions of skin include protection, reduction of water loss, production of vitamin D, and maintenance of body temperature.

3. Glands in the epidermis produce substances that destroy bacteria.

4. Severe damage to skin, including injuries and burns, can lead to infection and death if it is not treated.

Visualizing Main Ideas

Copy and complete the following concept map on body movement.

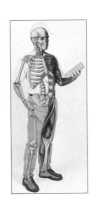

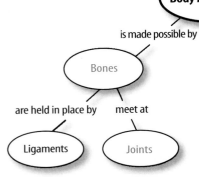

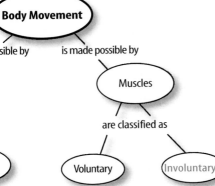

Body Movement

is made possible by — is made possible by

Bones — Muscles

are held in place by — meet at — are classified as

Ligaments — Joints — Voluntary — Involuntary

Science nline life.msscience.com/interactive_tutor

CHAPTER STUDY GUIDE 505

Reviewing Main Ideas

Summary statements can be used by students to review the major concepts of the chapter.

Visualizing Main Ideas

See student page.

Visit life.msscience.com
/self_check_quiz
/interactive_tutor
/vocabulary_puzzlemaker
/chapter_review
/standardized_test
/field_guide

Assessment Transparency

For additional assessment questions, use the *Assessment Transparency* located in the transparency book.

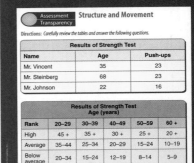

Assessment

Assessment Transparency **Structure and Movement**

Directions: *Carefully review the tables and answer the following questions.*

Results of Strength Test

Name	Age	Push-ups
Mr. Vincent	35	23
Mr. Steinberg	68	23
Mr. Johnson	22	16

Results of Strength Test Age (years)

Rank	20–29	30–39	40–49	50–59	60 +
High	45 +	35 +	30 +	25 +	20 +
Average	35–44	25–34	20–29	15–24	10–19
Below average	20–34	15–24	12–19	8–14	5–9
Low	0–19	0–14	0–11	0–7	0–4

1. According to the results of this experiment, Mr. Johnson has a ranking of ___.
   A high   C below average
   B average   D low

2. A reasonable hypothesis based on Table B is that when we age our muscles ___.
   F become stronger   H become weaker
   G become larger   J change color

Structure and Movement

Identifying Misconceptions

Assess

Procedure Group students in pairs. Have one student carefully strike the knee of the second student. Have students note the strength of the reaction as measured by the height of the jerk. Then tell one student of the pair to lock his or her right and left hands together and pull. Have the other student strike the other's knee and measure the strength of the reflex. The strength of the reflex should be greater this time.

Expected Outcome Students should understand the interaction of the muscular system with other systems and be able to cite examples of other interactions.

Using Vocabulary

1. periosteum
2. skeletal system
3. epidermis
4. tendons
5. cardiac muscle
6. ligaments
7. muscles
8. voluntary muscles

Checking Concepts

9. A	13. D	17. B
10. D	14. B	18. C
11. A	15. C	19. D
12. A	16. C	

Thinking Critically

20. If there is not enough exposure to sunlight, not enough vitamin D is produced.

21. the severity and size of the burn and the general health of the patient

Using Vocabulary

cardiac muscle p. 493	muscle p. 490
cartilage p. 486	periosteum p. 485
dermis p. 497	skeletal muscle p. 493
epidermis p. 496	skeletal system p. 484
involuntary muscle p. 491	smooth muscle p. 493
joint p. 487	tendon p. 493
ligament p. 487	voluntary muscle p. 491
melanin p. 497	

Match the definitions with the correct vocabulary word.

1. tough outer covering of bone
2. internal framework of the body
3. outer layer of skin
4. thick band of tissue that attaches muscle to a bone
5. muscle found only in the heart
6. a tough band of tissue that holds two bones together
7. organ that can relax and contract to aid in the movement of the body
8. a muscle that you control

Checking Concepts

Choose the word or phrase that best answers the question.

9. Which of the following is the most solid form of bone?
   A) compact   C) spongy
   B) periosteum   D) marrow

10. Where are blood cells made?
   A) compact bone   C) cartilage
   B) periosteum   D) marrow

11. Where are minerals stored?
   A) bone   C) muscle
   B) skin   D) blood

12. What are the ends of bones covered with?
   A) cartilage   C) ligaments
   B) tendons   D) muscle

13. Where are immovable joints found in the human body?
   A) at the elbow   C) in the wrist
   B) at the neck   D) in the skull

14. What kind of joints are the knees, toes, and fingers?
   A) pivot   C) gliding
   B) hinge   D) ball and socket

15. Which vitamin is made in the skin?
   A) A   C) D
   B) B   D) K

16. Where are dead skin cells found?
   A) dermis   C) epidermis
   B) marrow   D) periosteum

17. Which of the following is found in bone?
   A) iron   C) vitamin D
   B) calcium   D) vitamin K

18. Which of the following structures helps retain fluids in the body?
   A) bone   C) skin
   B) muscle   D) a joint

Use the illustration below to answer question 19.

19. Where would this type of muscle tissue be found in your body?
   A) heart   C) stomach
   B) esophagus   D) leg

Science Online life.msscience.com/vocabulary_puzzlemaker

Use the ExamView® Pro Testmaker CD-ROM to:

- create multiple versions of tests
- create modified tests with one mouse click for inclusion students
- edit existing questions and add your own questions
- build tests aligned with state standards using built-in State Curriculum Tags
- change English tests to Spanish with one mouse click and vice versa

Thinking Critically

20. Explain why skin might not be able to produce enough vitamin D.

21. List what factors a doctor might consider before choosing a method of skin repair for a severe burn victim.

22. Explain what a lack of calcium would do to bones.

23. Concept Map Copy and complete the following concept map that describes the types and functions of bone cells.

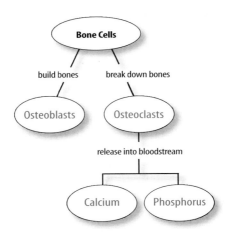

24. Name the function of your lower lip's skin that changes when a dentist gives you novocaine before filling a bottom tooth. Why?

25. Draw Conclusions The joints in the skull of a newborn baby are flexible, but those of a teenager have fused together and are immovable. Conclude why the infant's skull joints are flexible.

26. Predict what would happen if a person's sweat glands didn't produce sweat.

27. Compare and contrast the functions of ligaments and tendons.

 Science online life.msscience.com/chapter_review

28. Form a Hypothesis Your body has about 3 million sweat glands. Make a hypothesis about where these sweat glands are on your body. Are they distributed evenly throughout your body?

Performance Activities

29. Display Research the differences among first-, second-, and third-degree burns. A local hospital's burn unit or a fire department are possible sources of information about burns. Display pictures of each type of burn and descriptions of treatments on a three-sided, free-standing poster.

Applying Math

30. Bone Volume Estimate the volume of a hand bone that is 7 cm long and is 1.5 cm in diameter.

Use the graph below to answer question 31.

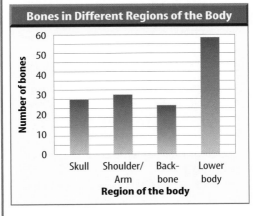

31. Bone Quantity The total number of bones in the human body is 206. Approximately what percentage of bones is located in the backbone?

A) 2%   C) 50%

B) 12%   D) 75%

Thinking Critically

22. Bones lacking calcium become too flexible and misshapen. They also break more easily.

23. See student page.

24. Novocaine numbs the nerves so your skin can no longer sense stimuli such as pressure or pain. Novocaine numbs nerves in the dermis.

25. Accept all reasonable answers. Flexible joints are thought to be helpful during the birthing process.

26. The person would not be able to maintain a constant body temperature or release certain wastes through the skin.

27. Ligaments hold bones in place at joints. Tendons attach muscle to bones.

28. Possible answer: Sweat glands are not evenly distributed on the skin. This is known because when a person exercises, more sweat is found in some areas (face, underarms) than others.

Performance Activities

29. First-degree burns involve only the epidermis; second-degree burns involve the epidermis and dermis; and third-degree burns extend beyond the dermis into the muscle and bone. **Use Performance Assessment in the Science Classroom,** p. 145.

Applying Math

National Math Standards

1, 5

30. 12.4cm³

31. B

✔ Assessment Resources

📁 Reproducible Masters

Chapter *Fast File* Resources
Chapter Review, pp. 39–40
Chapter Tests, pp. 41–44
Assessment Transparency Activity, p. 51

Glencoe Science Web site
Chapter Review Test
Standardized Test Practice

Glencoe Technology

🖋 Assessment Transparency
⊕ Exam*View*® Pro Testmaker
💻 MindJogger Videoquiz
⊙ Interactive Chalkboard

FAST FILE

Answer Sheet A practice answer sheet can be found at life.msscience.com/answer_sheet.

Part 1 Multiple Choice

1. C
2. C
3. B
4. D
5. A
6. C
7. C
8. B
9. B

Part 1 Multiple Choice

Record your answers on the answer sheet provided by your teacher or on a sheet of paper.

1. Which type of muscle tends to contract quickly and tire more easily?
   A. cardiac muscle   C. skeletal muscle
   B. bladder   D. smooth muscle

Use the table below to answer questions 2 and 3.

Number of Bicycle Deaths per Year		
Year	Male	Female
1996	654	107
1997	712	99
1998	658	99
1999	656	94
2000	605	76

Data from Insurance Institute for Highway Safety

2. If 99% of the people who die in bicycle accidents were not wearing helmets, to the nearest whole number, how many people who died in 1998 were wearing bicycle helmets?
   A. 7   C. 8
   B. 6   D. 9

3. Which year had the greatest total number of bicycle deaths?
   A. 1996   C. 1998
   B. 1997   D. 1999

4. Which of the following is NOT released by sweat glands?
   A. water   C. waste products
   B. salt   D. oil

Test-Taking Tip

Ease Nervousness Stay calm during the test. If you feel yourself getting nervous, close your eyes and take five slow, deep breaths.

Use the illustration below to answer questions 5 and 6.

Ball-and-socket joint

Pivot joint

Gliding joint

Hinge joint

5. Which type of joint do your elbows have?
   A. hinge   C. ball-and-socket
   B. gliding   D. pivot

6. Which type of joint allows your legs and arms to swing in almost any direction?
   A. hinge   C. ball-and-socket
   B. gliding   D. pivot

7. What is the name of the pigment that gives your skin color?
   A. hemoglobin   C. melanin
   B. keratin   D. calcium

8. What does the periosteum do?
   A. connects bones together
   B. covers the surface of bones
   C. produces energy
   D. makes vitamin D

9. Which type of muscle is found in the intestines?
   A. skeletal muscle
   B. smooth muscle
   C. cardiac muscle
   D. tendon

508 STANDARDIZED TEST PRACTICE

Part 2 Short Response/Grid In

10. $300 - 206 = 94$

11. $1/7 = 14\%$

12. Voluntary muscles can be consciously controlled. Involuntary muscles are muscles that cannot be controlled consciously.

13. first-class lever

14. The fulcrum is between the effort force and the load.

15. Heat produced by muscle contractions helps to keep body temperature constant.

16. When the skin is exposed to ultraviolet rays, melanin production increases and the skin becomes darker

Record your answers on the answer sheet provided by your teacher or on a sheet of paper.

10. At birth, your skeleton had approximately 300 bones. As you developed, some bones fused together. Now you have 206 bones. How many fewer bones do you have now?

11. One in seven people in the United States suffers from arthritis. Calculate the percentage of people that suffer from arthritis.

12. Explain the difference between voluntary and involuntary muscles.

Use the illustration below to answer questions 13 and 14.

13. What type of lever is shown in the photo?

14. Where is the fulcrum?

15. How do muscles help maintain body temperature?

16. Explain what happens when your skin is exposed to ultraviolet rays.

Record your answers on a sheet of paper.

17. Compare and contrast compact and spongy bone.

18. Explain how bone cells help maintain homeostasis.

19. Describe the changes that occur in muscles that do a lot of work. Compare these muscles to the muscles of a person who only does inactive pastimes.

Use the illustration below to answer questions 20 and 21.

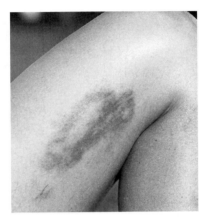

20. Identify the injury in the photograph. Describe the sequence of events from the time of injury until the injury disappears.

21. Contrast the injury in the photograph with a cut. Explain why a cut needs to be cleaned but the injury in the photograph does not.

22. What might happen to your body temperature if blood vessels in the skin did not contain smooth muscle?

into the surrounding tissue. These blood cells break down and release hemoglobin. As the hemoglobin gradually breaks down into its component pigments, the color of the bruise changes from blue to red to purple to yellow. Finally the pigment reenters the bloodstream, the bruise disappears, and the skin looks normal again.

20. In a bruise, the skin is not broken, only tiny blood vessels underneath the skin have burst. In a cut, the skin is torn. Blood flows out until a clot forms. Then a scab covers the cut, preventing bacteria from entering the injury. A cut must be cleaned because the skin surface is broken and bacteria could enter the wound. Because the skin is not broken in a bruise, bacteria cannot enter through the skin injury.

21. Blood vessels in the skin can help release or hold heat. Without smooth muscle in the walls, the blood vessels could not change their diameter, that is, they could not constrict (muscle contracts) or dilate (muscle relaxes). When the blood vessels expand or dilate, blood flow increases and heat is released. When you are cold, blood vessels constrict and less heat is released.

Rubrics

For more help evaluating open-ended assessment questions, see the rubric on p. 10T.

17. Compact bone is located directly under the periosteum. Compact bone is a hard, strong layer of bone. Compact bones contain deposits of calcium and phosphate that make the bone hard. Bone cells and blood vessels are also found in this layer. Spongy bone is located toward the ends of long bones. It has many small, open spaces that make bones lightweight. Spongy bone contains marrow. Some marrow is fat. Red marrow makes blood cells.

18. Healthy bone is always being formed and re-formed. As bone is broken down by osteoclasts, calcium and phosphorus deposited in the bone are released into the bloodstream. This process maintains the correct levels of calcium and phosphorus in the blood. Calcium and phosphorus are necessary for the working of the body, including muscle movement.

19. This injury is a bruise. When the skin is bruised, tiny blood vessels underneath the skin have burst. Red blood cells from these vessels leak

Section/Objectives	Standards		Labs/Features
	National	**State/Local**	
Chapter Opener	See pp. 16T–17T for a Key to Standards.		**Launch Lab:** Model the Digestive Tract, p. 511 **Foldables,** p. 511
Section 1 Nutrition ⏱ 2 sessions 📦 1 block 1. **Distinguish** among the six classes of nutrients. 2. **Identify** the importance of each type of nutrient. 3. **Explain** the relationships between diet and health.	National Content Standards: UCP.1, UCP.2, A.1, A.2, B.3, C.1, C.3, C.5, F.1		**Science Online,** p. 514 **MiniLAB:** Comparing the Fat Content of Foods, p. 515 **Applying Science:** Is it unhealthy to snack between meals? p. 516 **Visualizing Vitamins,** p. 517 **Integrate Social Studies,** p. 519 **Lab:** Identifying Vitamin C Content, p. 522
Section 2 The Digestive System ⏱ 3 sessions 📦 1.5 block 4. **Distinguish** the differences between mechanical digestion and chemical digestion. 5. **Identify** the organs of the digestive system and what takes place in each. 6. **Explain** how homeostasis is maintained in digestion.	National Content Standards: UCP.1, A.1, A.2, B.1, B.3, C.1, C.3, C.5, F.1, G.1, G.2		**Science Online,** p. 526 **MiniLAB:** Modeling Absorption in the Small Intestine, p. 528 **Integrate Environment,** p. 529 **Lab:** Particle Size and Absorption, p. 530 **Science and Society:** Eating Well, p. 532

Lab Materials	Reproducible Resources	Section Assessment	Technology
Launch Lab: index cards, marker, masking tape, meterstick	**Chapter _Fast File_ Resources** Foldables Worksheet, p. 17 Directed Reading Overview, p. 19 Note-taking Worksheets, pp. 31–33	GLENCOE'S ASSESSMENT ADVANTAGE	Teacher**Works** includes: • Interactive Teacher Edition • Lesson Planner with calendar • Access to all program blacklines • Correlations to standards • Web links
MiniLAB: 3 potato chips, pretzels, peanuts; small cubes of fruits, cheese, vegetables, meat; brown grocery bag **Lab:** 4 test tubes, test-tube rack, masking tape, 13 wooden stirrers, graduated cylinder, 2% tincture of iodine, dropper, cornstarch, triple-beam balance, weighing paper, water, glass-marking pencil, 4 types of orange juice in dropper bottles	**Chapter _Fast File_ Resources** Transparency Activity, p. 42 MiniLAB, p. 3 Enrichment, p. 29 Reinforcement, p. 27 Directed Reading, p. 20 Lab Worksheet, pp. 5–6 Lab Activity, pp. 9–11 Transparency Activity, pp. 45–46 **Cultural Diversity,** pp. 6, 23 **Mathematics Skill Activities,** p. 47 **Life Science Critical Thinking/ Problem Solving,** pp. 15, 16 **Performance Assessment in the Science Classroom,** p. 66	**Portfolio** Science Journal, p. 516 **Performance** MiniLAB, p. 515 Applying Science, p. 516 Applying Skills, p. 521 **Content** Section Review, p. 521	Section Focus Transparency Teaching Transparency Virtual Labs CD-ROM Guided Reading Audio Program Interactive Chalkboard CD-ROM Video Lab
MiniLAB: smooth cotton cloth (25 × 25 cm), cotton terry cloth (25 × 25 cm), bowl, water, measuring cup, 2 containers **Lab:** 3 beakers or jars, 3 thermometers, sugar granules, mortar and pestle, triple-beam balance, stirring rod, sugar cubes, weighing paper, warm water, stopwatch	**Chapter _Fast File_ Resources** Transparency Activity, p. 43 MiniLAB, p. 4 Enrichment, p. 30 Reinforcement, p. 28 Directed Reading, pp. 21, 22 Lab Worksheet, pp. 7–8 Lab Activity, pp. 13–15 **Lab Management and Safety,** p. 52 **Home and Community Involvement,** p. 41	**Portfolio** Science Journal, p. 526 Reteach, p. 529 **Performance** MiniLAB, p. 528 Applying Skills, p. 529 **Content** Section Review, p. 529	Section Focus Transparency Virtual Labs CD-ROM Guided Reading Audio Program Interactive Chalkboard CD-ROM

End of Chapter Assessment

GLENCOE'S ASSESSMENT ADVANTAGE

Blackline Masters	Technology	Professional Series
Chapter _Fast File_ Resources Chapter Review, pp. 35–36 Chapter Tests, pp. 37–40 **Standardized Test Practice,** pp. 75–78	MindJogger Videoquiz Virtual Labs CD-ROM Exam*View*® Pro Testmaker TeacherWorks CD-ROM Interactive Chalkboard CD-ROM	**Performance Assessment in the Science Classroom (PASC)**

Transparencies

Section Focus

This is a representation of key blackline masters available in the Teacher Classroom Resources. See Resource Manager boxes within the chapter for additional information.

Key to Teaching Strategies

The following designations will help you decide which activities are appropriate for your students.

L1 Level 1 activities should be appropriate for students with learning difficulties.

L2 Level 2 activities should be within the ability range of all students.

L3 Level 3 activities are designed for above-average students.

ELL ELL activities should be within the ability range of English-Language Learners.

COOP LEARN Cooperative Learning activities are designed for small group work.

LS Multiple Learning Styles logos, as described on page 12T, are used throughout to indicate strategies that address different learning styles.

P These strategies represent student products that can be placed into a best-work portfolio.

PBL Problem-Based Learning activities apply real-world situations to learning.

Assessment

Teaching

Hands-on Activities

Student Text Lab Worksheet

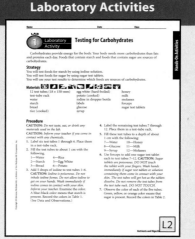

Laboratory Activities

Resource Manager

Meeting Different Ability Levels

Content Outline
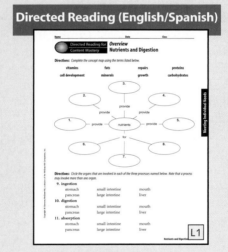

Reinforcement
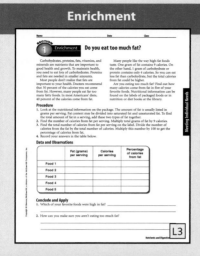

Enrichment

Directed Reading (English/Spanish)
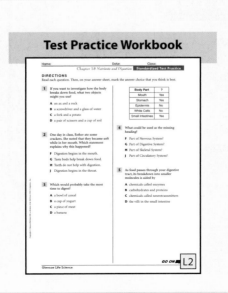

Study Guide
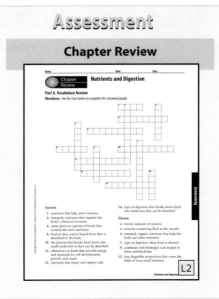

Reading Essentials

Assessment

Test Practice Workbook

Chapter Review

Chapter Tests
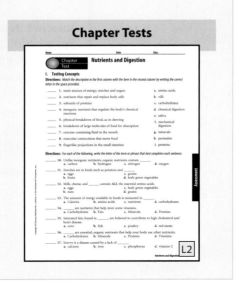

Science Content Background

section 1 Nutrition

Calorie Needs

The rate at which the body consumes energy when at rest is termed the basal metabolic rate. The basal metabolic rate and the physical activity metabolic rate are two of the factors that help determine the number of Calories a person's body requires each day. Other factors include age, body mass, size, sex, endocrine gland activity, and external temperature.

Energy Sources

Carbohydrates and proteins supply about four Calories per gram, and fats supply about nine Calories per gram. Excess sugar is stored in the liver and muscles in the form of glycogen. When energy is required, a series of activities involving the brain, nerves, and adrenal glands brings about the conversion of glycogen to glucose. The amino acids of protein can be converted into carbohydrates, and then these can be utilized as a source of energy. Excess fat stored in the body can oxidize and release energy. This reaction produces a great deal of heat as a waste product.

Vitamins

The role of vitamins as nutrients was not recognized until the early 1900s. During the early years of research, each new vitamin that was identified was given a letter designation. This method proved to be inadequate to correctly classify the substances. Vitamins then were called by their chemical names. Niacin is an example of a vitamin that goes by its chemical name rather than a letter designation.

section 2 The Digestive System

Digestion

The process of transforming foods into usable nutrients is called digestion. This extracellular process takes place in the digestive system, specifically in the stomach and small intestine. Enzymes that serve as catalysts for chemical reactions often require precise environmental conditions, including the proper temperature, pH, and substrate, to be active. For example, the enzyme pepsin, which is found in the stomach, is only active in a medium having a pH of 1.5 to 2.2 and only helps digest proteins.

chapter content resources

Internet Resources

For additional content background, visit **life.msscience.com** to:

- access your book online
- find references to related articles in popular science magazines
- access Web links with related content background
- access current events with science journal topics

Print Resources

Contemporary Nutrition, by Gordon M. Wardlaw, McGraw-Hill, 2000

The Digestive System, by Carol Ballard, Heinemann Library, 2002

The Human Body for Every Kid, by Janice VanCleave, Wiley, John & Sons, Incorporated, 1995

IDENTIFYING ▷ Misconceptions

Find Out What Students Think

Students may think that . . .

Energy comes directly from the food they eat.
Students often think that digestion is a process in which usable energy is released directly from food. Many students do not understand that food must be broken down in the digestive tract into other substances before it is transported to various parts of the body where it can be used to make new substances or broken down for energy release.

Discussion
Have students describe the process of digestion, including what happens to the food they eat, where it goes, and how it is used. Record their ideas on the board or on the overhead projector next to an outline of the digestive system. Keep track of misconceptions, but do not attempt to correct them at this time.

Promote Understanding

Activity

Preparation Prepare a 0.1% starch solution by heating 1 mL soluble starch in 1 L water. Prepare a 0.2% diastase solution by dissolving 2 mL diastase in 1 L water. (Diastase can be purchased from most biological supply houses.)

Procedure Students simulate the digestion of starch in the body. Starch is found in foods such as crackers, rice, and potatoes.

- Have students place two drops of starch solution on each end of a clean glass slide. (One of the sets of drops will serve as a control.)

John Paul Endress/The Stock Market

- Have students add two drops of dilute Lugol's solution to each of the sets of drops. Both sets of drops should turn a pale blue.

- Add one drop of the diastase solution to one of the sets of drops. The diastase will cause the blue of the solution to disappear.

Ask students why the color disappeared. After some discussion, explain that the changes they observed are similar to the way starch is affected by amylase in the body. Starches are broken down into simple sugars and then transported to different parts of the body where they are used. Emphasize that simple sugars also may be reassembled in the liver and stored as glycogen, or they may be converted into fat molecules and stored throughout the body.

As an extension, have students brainstorm a list of other foods that are broken down and then used to make new substances. For example, proteins can be broken down into amino acids, which are then assembled in the cells to form new proteins.

Assess

After completing the chapter, see *Identifying Misconceptions* in the Study Guide at the end of the chapter.

Chapter Vocabulary

nutrient, p. 512
protein, p. 513
amino acid, p. 513
carbohydrate, p. 514
fat, p. 515
vitamin, p. 516
mineral, p. 518
food group, p. 520
digestion, p. 523
mechanical digestion, p. 523
chemical digestion, p. 523
enzyme, p. 524
peristalsis, p. 526
chyme, p. 527
villi, p. 528

Science Journal Student responses should include some or all of the following: mouth, esophagus, stomach, small intestine, large intestine, rectum, and anus.

INTERACTIVE CHALKBOARD with Image Bank

PowerPoint® Presentations

This CD-ROM is an editable Microsoft® PowerPoint® presentation that includes:

- a pre-made presentation for every chapter
- interactive graphics
- animations
- audio clips
- image bank
- all new section and chapter questions
- Standardized Test Practice
- transparencies
- pre-lab questions for all labs
- Foldables directions
- links to life.msscience.com

Nutrients and Digestion

chapter preview

sections

1 Nutrition
Lab Identifying Vitamin C Content

2 The Digestive System
Lab Particle Size and Absorption

Virtual Lab How can you design a healthful diet?

Intestinal Landscape

This photo may look like a pile of potatoes, but it is a close-up of your small intestine. The wall of the small intestine has many fingerlike projections that soak up substances from digested food. The small intestine is just one of many organs that make up your digestive system.

Science Journal Make a list of all the organs you think are part of your digestive system.

510

Theme Connection

Energy Energy is a major theme of this chapter. Nutrients contain chemical energy. During digestion, complex food molecules are broken down into simpler forms that body cells can use for metabolism. This process transforms chemical energy into thermal and mechanical energy.

About the Photo

Absorption The inner surface of the small intestine forms many fingerlike projections called villi. On the tip of each villus are thousands of hair-like projections called microvilli. The combination of villi and microvilli increases the absorptive surface area of the small intestine over 6,000 times.

Start-Up Activities

Model the Digestive Tract

Imagine taking a bite of your favorite food. When you eat, your body breaks down food to release energy. How long does it take?

Organs of the Digestive System		
Organ	Length	Time
Mouth	8 cm	5 s to 30 s
Pharynx and esophagus	25 cm	10 s
Stomach	16 cm	2 h to 4 h
Small intestine	4.75 m	3 h
Large intestine	1.25 m	2 days

1. Make a label for each of the digestive organs listed here. Include the organ's name, length, and the time it takes for food to pass through it.
2. Working with a partner, place a piece of masking tape that is 6.5 m long on the classroom floor.
3. Beginning at one end of the tape, and in the same order as they are listed in the table, mark the length for each organ. Place each label next to its section.
4. **Think Critically** In your Science Journal, suggest reasons why food spends a different amount of time in each organ.

Nutrients in Foods Make the following Foldable to help you organize foods based on the nutrients that they contain.

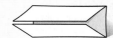 **STEP 1** **Fold** the top of a vertical piece of paper down and the bottom up to divide the paper into thirds. Then, **fold** the paper in half from top to bottom.

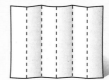

STEP 2 **Turn** the paper horizontally, **unfold and label** the six columns as follows: *Proteins, Carbohydrates, Lipids, Water, Vitamins,* and *Minerals.*

Read for Main Ideas As you read the chapter, list foods you eat that provide each of these nutrients in the proper columns.

 Preview this chapter's content and activities at life.msscience.com

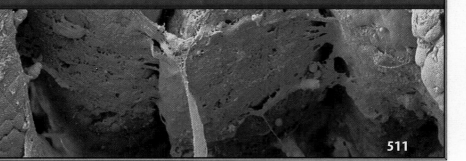

Purpose Use the Launch Lab to introduce students to the digestive system. L2 COOP LEARN IS
Visual-Spatial

Preparation Find an area where students can work undisturbed during the activity.

Materials index cards, marking pens, masking tape, meterstick or measuring tape

Teaching Strategies
• Explain that the length of time food spends in the digestive tract varies among individuals and can depend on health conditions.
• After the complete length of the digestive system has been marked off, encourage students to infer how something that long can fit inside their bodies.

Think Critically
The amount of digestion time depends on the type of food. Different foods undergo different chemical processes as they are digested.

Assessment
Process Have students predict what symptoms an infant might exhibit if a birth defect caused a constriction in a portion of the digestive tract. Use **Performance Assessment in the Science Classroom,** p. 93.

FOLDABLES Dinah Zike
Study Organizer Study Fold

Student preparation materials for this Foldable are available in the Chapter *FAST FILE* Resources.

511

Nutrition

Tie to Prior Knowledge

Balanced Diet Have students discuss what they know about eating a "balanced" diet.

---

as you read

What You'll Learn

- **Distinguish** among the six classes of nutrients.
- **Identify** the importance of each type of nutrient.
- **Explain** the relationship between diet and health.

Why It's Important

You can make healthful food choices if you know what nutrients your body uses daily.

Review Vocabulary

molecule: the smallest particle of a substance that retains the properties of the substance and is composed of one or more atoms

New Vocabulary

- nutrient
- fat
- protein
- vitamin
- amino acid
- mineral
- carbohydrate
- food group

Why do you eat?

You're listening to a favorite song on the radio, maybe even singing along. Then all of a sudden, the music stops. You examine the radio to see what happened. The batteries died. You hunt for more batteries and quickly put in the new ones. In the same way that the radio needs batteries to work, you need food to carry out your daily activities—but not just any food. When you are hungry, you probably choose food based on taste and the amount of time you have to eat it. However, as much as you don't want to admit it, the nutritional value of the food you choose is more important than the taste. A chocolate-iced donut might be tasty and quick to eat, yet it provides few of the nutrients your body needs. **Nutrients** (NEW tree unts) are substances in foods that provide energy and materials for cell development, growth, and repair.

Energy Needs Your body needs energy for every activity that it performs. Muscle activities such as the beating of your heart, blinking your eyes, and lifting your backpack require energy. How much energy you need depends on several factors, such as body mass, age, and activity level. This energy comes from the foods you eat. The amount of energy available in food is measured in Calories. A Calorie (Cal) is the amount of heat necessary to raise the temperature of 1 kg of water 1°C. As shown in **Figure 1,** different foods contain different numbers of Calories. A raw carrot may have 30 Cal. This means that when you eat a carrot, your body has 30 Cal of energy available to use. A slice of cheese pizza might have 170 Cal, and one hamburger might have 260 Cal. The number of Calories varies due to the kinds of nutrients a food provides.

Figure 1 Foods vary in the number of Calories they contain. A hamburger has the same number of Calories as 8.5 average-sized carrots.

512 CHAPTER 18 Nutrients and Digestion

Section 1 Resource Manager

Chapter *FAST FILE* Resources

Transparency Activity, pp. 42, 45–46

Directed Reading for Content Mastery, pp. 19, 20

MiniLAB, p. 3

Enrichment, p. 29

Reinforcement, p. 27

Lab Worksheet, pp. 5–6

Lab Activity, pp. 9–11

Note-taking Worksheets, pp. 31–33

Life Science Critical Thinking/Problem Solving, pp. 15, 16

Performance Assessment in the Science Classroom, p. 66

Classes of Nutrients

Six kinds of nutrients are available in food—proteins, carbohydrates, fats, vitamins, minerals, and water. Proteins, carbohydrates, vitamins, and fats all contain carbon and are called organic nutrients. In contrast, inorganic nutrients, such as water and minerals, do not contain carbon. Foods containing carbohydrates, fats, and proteins need to be digested or broken down before your body can use them. Water, vitamins, and minerals don't require digestion and are absorbed directly into your bloodstream.

Figure 2 Meats, poultry, eggs, fish, peas, beans, and nuts are all rich in protein.

Proteins Your body uses proteins for replacement and repair of body cells and for growth. **Proteins** are large molecules that contain carbon, hydrogen, oxygen, nitrogen and sometimes sulfur. A molecule of protein is made up of a large number of smaller units, or building blocks, called **amino acids.** In **Figure 2** you can see some sources of proteins. Different foods contain different amounts of protein, as shown in **Figure 3.**

Your body needs only 20 amino acids in various combinations to make the thousands of proteins used in your cells. Most of these amino acids can be made in your body's cells, but eight of them cannot. These eight are called essential amino acids. They have to be supplied by the foods you eat. Complete proteins provide all of the essential amino acids. Eggs, milk, cheese, and meat contain complete proteins. Incomplete proteins are missing one or more of the essential amino acids. If you are a vegetarian, you can get all of the essential amino acids by eating a wide variety of protein-rich vegetables, fruits, and grains.

540 Calories
10 g protein

280 Calories
16 g protein

186 Calories
15 g protein

Figure 3 The amount of protein in a food is not the same as the number of Calories in the food. A taco has nearly the same amount of protein as a slice of pizza, but it usually has about 100 fewer Calories.

SECTION 1 Nutrition **513**

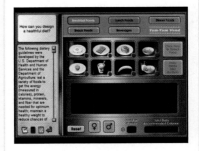

Figure 4 These foods contain carbohydrates that provide energy for all the things that you do. **List** *the carbohydrates that you've eaten today.*

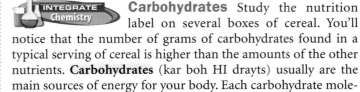

Carbohydrates Study the nutrition label on several boxes of cereal. You'll notice that the number of grams of carbohydrates found in a typical serving of cereal is higher than the amounts of the other nutrients. **Carbohydrates** (kar boh HI drayts) usually are the main sources of energy for your body. Each carbohydrate molecule is made of carbon, hydrogen, and oxygen atoms. Energy holds the atoms together. When carbohydrates are broken down in the presence of oxygen in your cells, this energy is released for use by your body.

Three types of carbohydrates are sugar, starch, and fiber, as shown in **Figure 4.** Sugars are called *simple carbohydrates.* You're probably most familiar with table sugar. However, fruits, honey, and milk also contain forms of sugar. Your cells break down glucose, a simple sugar. The other two types of carbohydrates—starch and fiber—are called *complex carbohydrates.* Starch is found in potatoes and foods made from grains such as pasta. Starches are made up of many simple sugars in long chains. Fiber, such as cellulose, is found in the cell walls of plant cells. Foods like whole-grain breads and cereals, beans, peas, and other vegetables and fruits are good sources of fiber. Because different types of fiber are found in foods, you should eat a variety of fiber-rich plant foods. You cannot digest fiber, but it is needed to keep your digestive system running smoothly.

Nutritious snacks can help your body get the nutrients it needs, especially when you are growing rapidly and are physically active. Choose snacks that provide nutrients such as complex carbohydrates, proteins, and vitamins, as well as fiber. Foods high in sugar and fat can have lots of Calories that supply energy, but they provide only some of the nutrients your body needs.

514 CHAPTER 18 Nutrients and Digestion

Figure 5 Fat is stored in certain cells in your body. The cytoplasm and nucleus are pushed to the edge of the cell by the fat deposits.

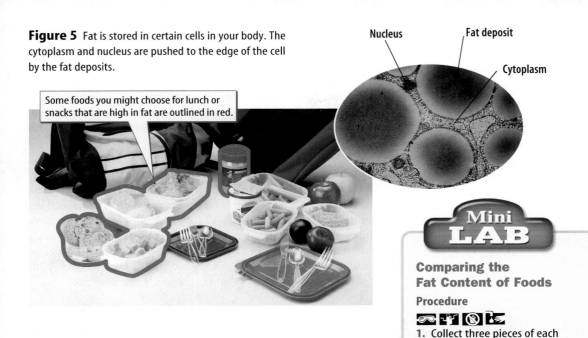

Nucleus   Fat deposit

Cytoplasm

Some foods you might choose for lunch or snacks that are high in fat are outlined in red.

Fats

Fats The term fat has developed a negative meaning for some people. However, **fats,** also called lipids, are necessary because they provide energy and help your body absorb vitamins. Fat tissue cushions your internal organs. A major part of every cell membrane is made up of fat. A gram of fat can release more than twice as much energy as a gram of carbohydrate can. During the digestion process, fat is broken down into smaller molecules called fatty acids and glycerol (GLIH suh rawl). Because fat is a good storage unit for energy, excess energy from the foods you eat is converted to fat and stored for later use, as shown in **Figure 5.**

Reading Check *Why is fat a good storage unit for energy?*

Fats are classified as unsaturated or saturated based on their chemical structure. Unsaturated fats are usually liquid at room temperature. Vegetable oils as well as fats found in seeds are unsaturated fats. Saturated fats are found in meats, animal products, and some plants and are usually solid at room temperature. Although fish contains saturated fat, it also has some unsaturated fats that your body needs. Saturated fats have been associated with high levels of blood cholesterol. Your body makes cholesterol in your liver. Cholesterol is part of the cell membrane in all of your cells. However, a diet high in cholesterol may result in deposits forming on the inside walls of blood vessels. These deposits can block the blood supply to organs and increase blood pressure. This can lead to heart disease and strokes.

Mini LAB

Comparing the Fat Content of Foods

Procedure

1. Collect three pieces of each of the following foods: **potato chips; pretzels; peanuts;** and **small cubes of fruits, cheese, vegetables, and meat.**
2. Place the food items on a piece of **brown grocery bag.** Label the paper with the name of each food. Do not taste the foods.
3. Allow foods to sit for 30 min.
4. Remove the items, properly dispose of them, and observe the paper.

Analysis

1. Which items left a translucent (greasy) mark? Which left a wet mark?
2. How are the foods that left a greasy mark on the paper alike?
3. Use this test to determine which other foods contain fats. A greasy mark means the food contains fat. A wet mark means the food contains a lot of water.

Discussion

Milk Is milk the perfect food? Milk does supply many nutrients but it is not a perfect food, as it lacks certain essential vitamins and minerals. **IS Interpersonal**

Applying Science

Answers

1. Of the snack foods listed, pretzels are the lowest in fat. Other snack foods could be brought into the classroom to compare their fat contents. Students can discuss the difference between fried and baked snacks, and healthier alternatives to their favorite snack foods.

2. Most frozen pizzas are prepared using cheese and pepperoni, which are both high in fat. Ways to make pizza healthier include preparing it fresh at home using low-fat cheese, homemade tomato sauce, turkey pepperoni, and a variety of fresh vegetables.

IDENTIFYING Misconceptions

Vitamin Consumption Students may have the notion that if vitamins are good for you, more is better. Some vitamins should not be taken in high doses. An excess of vitamin A can cause liver and skin problems. Too much vitamin D can cause an imbalance of blood calcium, resulting in digestive, urinary, and nervous system disorders.

Vitamins Organic nutrients needed in small quantities for growth, regulating body functions, and preventing some diseases are called **vitamins.** For instance, your bone cells need vitamin D to use calcium, and your blood needs vitamin K in order to clot.

Most foods supply some vitamins, but no food has them all. Some people feel that taking extra vitamins is helpful, while others feel that eating a well-balanced diet usually gives your body all the vitamins it needs.

Vitamins are classified into two groups, as shown in **Figure 6.** Some vitamins dissolve easily in water and are called water-soluble vitamins. They are not stored by your body so you have to take them daily. Other vitamins dissolve only in fat and are called fat-soluble vitamins. These vitamins are stored by your body. Although you eat or drink most vitamins, some are made by your body. Vitamin D is made when your skin is exposed to sunlight. Some vitamin K and two of the B vitamins are made with the help of bacteria that live in your large intestine.

Applying Science

Is it unhealthy to snack between meals?

Most children eat three meals each day accompanied by snacks in between. Grabbing a bite to eat to satisfy you until your next meal is a common occurrence in today's society, and 20 percent of our energy and nutrient needs comes from snacking. While it would be best to select snacks consisting of fruits and vegetables, most children prefer to eat a bag of chips or a candy bar. Although these quick snacks are highly convenient, many times they are high in fat, as well.

Identifying the Problem

The table on the right lists several snack foods that are popular among adolescents. They are listed alphabetically, and the grams of fat per individual serving is shown. As you examine the chart, can you conclude which snacks would be a healthier choice based on their fat content?

Solving the Problem

1. Looking at the data, what can you conclude about the snack foods you eat? What other snack foods do you eat that are not listed on the chart? How do you think they compare in nutritional value? Which snack foods are healthiest?

2. Pizza appears to be the unhealthiest choice on the chart because of the amount of the fat it contains. Why do you think pizza contains so much fat? List at least three ways to make pizza a healthier snack food.

Fat in Snack Foods

One Serving	Fat (g)
Candy bar	12
Frozen pizza	30
Ice cream	8
Potato chips	10
Pretzels	1

516   CHAPTER 18 Nutrients and Digestion

Differentiated Instruction

Challenge Have students research and report on a particular vitamin deficiency. Their reports should include information about how the vitamin was discovered, the symptoms of a deficiency, and foods that are high in the vitamin. Have students work together to present their findings on a "Vitamins for Good Health" bulletin board. **L3** COOP LEARN **IS Linguistic**

Science Journal

Taking Your Vitamins Have students write a paragraph about why it might be a disadvantage to substitute vitamin pills for a proper diet. Their entries should indicate an understanding that other nutrients besides vitamins are needed for maintaining health. A well-balanced diet supplies the range of needed vitamins. **L2 IS Logical-Mathematical P**

Figure 6

Vitamins come in two groups—water soluble, which should be replaced daily, and fat soluble, which can be stored in the body. The sources and benefits of both groups are shown below.

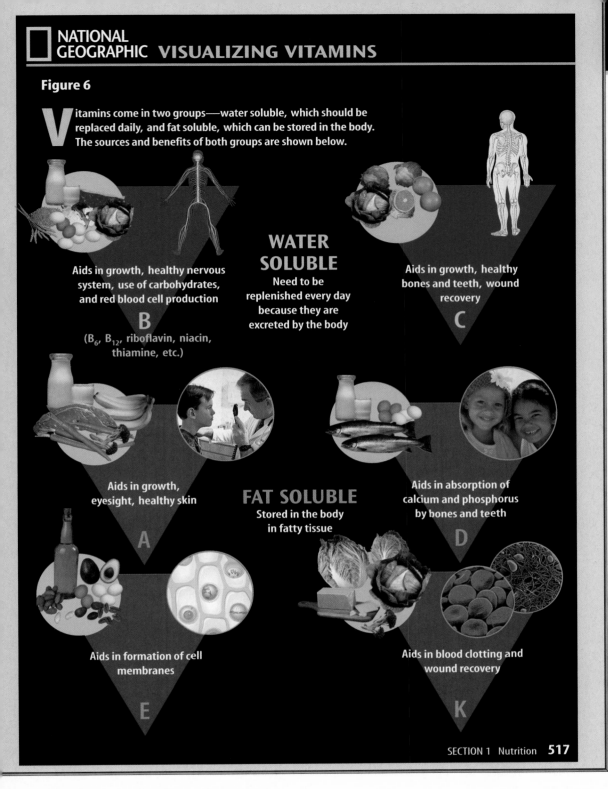

WATER SOLUBLE
Need to be replenished every day because they are excreted by the body

Aids in growth, healthy nervous system, use of carbohydrates, and red blood cell production
B
(B_6, B_{12}, riboflavin, niacin, thiamine, etc.)

Aids in growth, healthy bones and teeth, wound recovery
C

Aids in growth, eyesight, healthy skin
A

FAT SOLUBLE
Stored in the body in fatty tissue

Aids in absorption of calcium and phosphorus by bones and teeth
D

Aids in formation of cell membranes
E

Aids in blood clotting and wound recovery
K

SECTION 1 Nutrition **517**

Visualizing Vitamins

Have students examine the pictures and read the captions. Then ask the following questions.

Why is it important to eat foods containing vitamin K? A deficiency can lead to excessive bleeding when you are injured and it may take longer for the wound to heal.

What role does vitamin D have in healthy bones? It aids in the absorption of calcium, which is a necessary component of bone tissue.

Activity
Vitamin Needs Have students define the following terms: *beriberi*, *rickets*, *scurvy*, *pellagra*, *night blindness*. Be sure to have students include which vitamin is deficient in each condition and how the deficiency affects the body. L2

Differentiated Instruction

Challenge Have students research the dangers of vitamin overdose. What effects can high doses of vitamins such as A, C, or E have on the body? Have students answer the question: Why do the Inuit people choose not to eat polar bear liver?

Possible answer: Polar bear liver contains a high amount of vitamin A. As much as 12 times the minimum daily requirement of vitamin A can be found in one gram of polar bear liver. Ingestion of too much vitamin A results in a host of ailments and can even be deadly. L3

Minerals Inorganic nutrients—nutrients that lack carbon and regulate many chemical reactions in your body—are called **minerals.** Your body uses about 14 minerals. Minerals build cells, take part in chemical reactions in cells, send nerve impulses throughout your body, and carry oxygen to body cells. In **Figure 7,** you can see how minerals can get from the soil into your body. Of the 14 minerals, calcium and phosphorus are used in the largest amounts for a variety of body functions. One of these functions is the formation and maintenance of bone. Some minerals, called trace minerals, are required only in small amounts. Copper and iodine usually are listed as trace minerals. Several minerals, what they do, and some food sources for them are listed in **Table 1.**

✔ Reading Check   *Why is copper considered a trace mineral?*

Figure 7 The roots of the wheat take in phosphorus from the soil. Then the mature wheat is harvested and used in bread and cereal. Your body gets phosphorus when you eat the cereal.

Phosphorus   Wheat being harvested

Table 1 Minerals		
Mineral	**Health Effect**	**Food Sources**
Calcium	strong bones and teeth, blood clotting, muscle and nerve activity	dairy products, eggs, green leafy vegetables, soy
Phosphorus	strong bones and teeth, muscle contraction, stores energy	cheese, meat, cereal
Potassium	balance of water in cells, nerve impulse conduction, muscle contraction	bananas, potatoes, nuts, meat, oranges
Sodium	fluid balances in tissues, nerve impulse conduction	meat, milk, cheese, salt, beets, carrots, nearly all foods
Iron	oxygen is transported in hemoglobin by red blood cells	red meat, raisins, beans, spinach, eggs
Iodine (trace)	thyroid activity, metabolic stimulation	seafood, iodized salt

518   CHAPTER 18 Nutrients and Digestion

Figure 8 About two-thirds of your body water is located within your body cells. Water helps maintain the cells' shapes and sizes. The water that is lost through perspiration and respiration must be replaced.

Water Loss	
Method of Loss	Amount (mL/day)
Exhaled air	350
Feces	150
Skin (mostly as sweat)	500
Urine	1,500

Water Have you ever gone on a bike ride on a hot summer day without a bottle of water? You probably were thirsty and maybe you even stopped to get some water. Water is important for your body. Next to oxygen, water is the most important factor for survival. Different organisms need different amounts of water to survive. You could live for a few weeks without food but for only a few days without water because your cells need water to carry out their work. Most of the nutrients you have studied in this chapter can't be used by your body unless they are carried in a solution. This means that they have to be dissolved in water. In cells, chemical reactions take place in solutions.

The human body is about 60 percent water by weight. About two thirds of your body water is located in your body cells. Water also is found around cells and in body fluids such as blood. As shown in **Figure 8,** your body loses water as perspiration. When you exhale, water leaves your body as water vapor. Water also is lost every day when your body gets rid of wastes. To replace water lost each day, you need to drink about 2 L of liquids. However, drinking liquids isn't the only way to supply cells with water. Most foods have more water than you realize. An apple is about 80 percent water, and many meats are 90 percent water.

INTEGRATE Social Studies

Salt Mines The mineral halite is processed to make table salt. In the United States, most salt comes from underground mines. Research to find the locations of these mines, then label them on a map.

Use an Analogy

Water Loss Perspiration of water from the body is like the transpiration of water from plants. In both animals and plants, excessive water loss can have profoundly negative effects on the health of the organism.

Discussion

Sources of Water What are other sources of water in your diet in addition to drinking water? Other sources include fruits and vegetables. Water is also a by-product of the breakdown of molecules in the process of respiration.

INTEGRATE Social Studies

Salt Mines Salt-producing regions in the United States are found in New York, Ohio, Michigan, Louisiana, Texas, and Kansas.

Research Have students research the different methods used to mine salt. Does the mining method depend on location? Students can use their maps to compare the type of method used with the location of the mines in the United States. L2

LAB DEMONSTRATION

Purpose to measure the water content of food

Materials pan balance, 250-mL beaker, sliced celery, tray

Preparation Use the pan balance to find the mass of the beaker.

Procedure Fill the beaker with celery and find its mass. Spread the celery on the tray to dry for 2 or 3 days. Again mass the celery.

Expected Outcome Students should find that dried celery has a mass much less than fresh celery. Have them calculate the percentage of celery that is water.

Assessment

Why was the beaker massed when empty? so its mass could be subtracted from the mass of the beaker and celery Infer how much water might be in other fresh vegetables. Answers will vary. Leafy vegetables have more water than hard vegetables such as broccoli.

Food Pyramids Have students work together to make a three-dimensional display of the food pyramid using packages of representative food items. L2 ELL COOP LEARN IS Kinesthetic

Inquiry Lab

Comparing Snacks

Purpose To explore and observe the effects of snacks on hunger, have students design activities to compare a variety of foods.

Possible Materials variety of fruits, chocolate, soft candies

Estimated Time 10 minutes for each of four class sessions

Teaching Strategies

• Students can predict and then observe the effects on hunger of eating different types of snack food.

• Students can compare the effects on hunger of different amounts of snack foods.

• Allow students to explore other questions that arise.

For additional inquiry activities, see *Science Inquiry Labs.*

Caption Answer

Figure 9 from the fats, oils, and sweets group at the top of the pyramid

Why do you get thirsty? Your body is made up of systems that operate together. When your body needs to replace lost water, messages are sent to your brain that result in a feeling of thirst. Drinking water satisfies your thirst and usually restores the body's homeostasis (hoh mee oh STAY sus). Homeostasis is the regulation of the body's internal environment, such as temperature and amount of water. When homeostasis is restored, the signal to the brain stops and you no longer feel thirsty.

Food Groups

Because no naturally occurring food has every nutrient, you need to eat a variety of foods. Nutritionists have developed a simple system, called the food pyramid, shown in **Figure 9,** to help people select foods that supply all the nutrients needed for energy and growth.

Foods that contain the same type of nutrient belong to a **food group.** Foods have been divided into five groups—bread and cereal, vegetable, fruit, milk, and meat. The recommended daily amount for each food group will supply your body with the nutrients it needs for good health. Using the food pyramid to make choices when you eat will help you maintain good health.

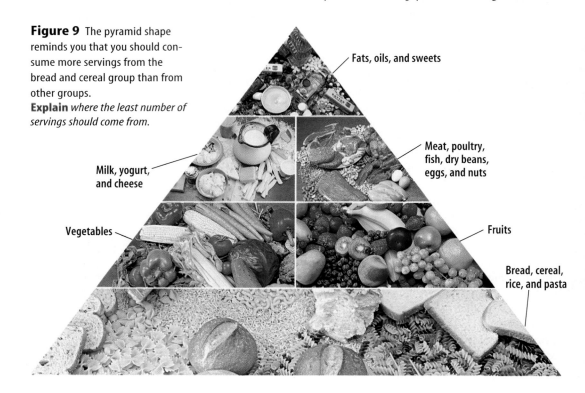

Figure 9 The pyramid shape reminds you that you should consume more servings from the bread and cereal group than from other groups.
Explain *where the least number of servings should come from.*

Fats, oils, and sweets

Meat, poultry, fish, dry beans, eggs, and nuts

Milk, yogurt, and cheese

Vegetables

Fruits

Bread, cereal, rice, and pasta

520 CHAPTER 18 Nutrients and Digestion

Cultural Diversity

Diet and Disease Certain cultures have diets that contain little animal fat. Such diets typically result in low intake of cholesterol. These diets may include large amounts of vegetables, fruits, and grains. People of Asia have a lower incidence of heart disease than people in the United States, possibly as a result of having a diet that is lower in fat.

Differentiated Instruction

English-Language Learners Bring a sample school lunch to class. Ask students to list, on a sheet of paper, the foods provided and the food groups they represent. L2

Daily Servings Each day you should eat six to eleven servings from the bread and cereal group, three to five servings from the vegetable group, two to four servings from the fruit group, two to three servings from the milk group, and two to three servings from the meat group. Only small amounts of fats, oils, and sweets should be consumed.

The size of a serving is different for different foods. For example, a slice of bread or one ounce of ready-to-eat cereal is a bread and cereal-group serving. One cup of raw leafy vegetables or one-half cup of cooked or chopped raw vegetables make a serving from the vegetable group. One medium apple, banana, or orange is a fruit serving. A serving from the milk group can be one cup of milk or yogurt. Two ounces of cooked lean meat or one egg is a serving from the meat group.

Food Labels The nutritional facts found on all packaged foods make it easier to make healthful food choices. These labels, as shown in **Figure 10,** can help you plan meals that supply the daily recommended amounts of nutrients and meet special dietary requirements (for example, a low-fat diet).

Figure 10 The information on a food label can help you decide what to eat.

Nutrition Facts	
Serving Size 1 Meal	

Amount Per Serving	
Calories 330	Calories from Fat 60

	% Daily Value*
Total Fat 7g	**10%**
Saturated Fat 3.5g	**17%**
Polyunsaturated Fat 1g	
Monounsaturated Fat 2.5g	
Cholesterol 35mg	**12%**
Sodium 460mg	**19%**
Total Carbohydrate 52g	**18%**
Dietary Fiber 6g	**24%**
Sugars 17g	
Protein 15g	

Vitamin A 15%	•	Vitamin C 70%
Calcium 4%	•	Iron 10%

* Percent Daily Values are based on a 2,000 calorie diet. Your daily values may be higher or lower depending on your calorie needs.

		Calories	2,000	2,500
Total Fat	Less than		65g	80g
Sat Fat	Less than		20g	25g
Cholesterol	Less than		300mg	300mg
Sodium	Less than		2,400mg	2,400mg
Total Carbohydrate			300g	375g
Dietary Fiber			25g	30g

---

section 1 review

Summary

Why do you eat?
- Food provides the energy for your body.

Classes of Nutrients
- The nutrients in food fall into six classes.
- Organic nutrients—proteins, vitamins, fats, and carbohydrates—contain carbon.
- Inorganic nutrients—water and minerals—do not contain carbon.

Food Groups
- Foods are divided into groups based on the type of nutrient in the foods.
- The five food groups are bread and cereal, vegetable, fruit, milk, and meat.

Self Check

1. **List** the six classes of nutrients. Give one example of a food source for each class.
2. **Describe** a major function of each class of nutrient.
3. **Discuss** how food choices can positively and negatively affect your health.
4. **Explain** the importance of water in the body.
5. **Think Critically** What foods from each food group would provide a balanced breakfast? Explain.

Applying Skills

6. **Interpret Data** Nutritional information can be found on the labels of most foods. Interpret the labels found on three different types of food products.

---

section 1 review

1. carbohydrates: bread; proteins: fish; fats: butter; vitamins: fruit; minerals: vegetables; water: juice
2. carbohydrates: source of energy; proteins: growth of cells; fats: source of energy; vitamins: growth;
   minerals: nerve activity; water: enables chemical reactions to occur
3. Student answers will vary. Accept all correct responses.
4. dissolves and carries nutrients, removes wastes, enables chemical reactions to occur
5. Students should be able to support their answers with information from **Figure 9.**
6. Have pairs of students compare their interpretations.

Activity

Food Labels Have students read the labels of canned and packaged foods. Discuss the major sources of various nutrients in the foods they eat each day. [L2]
LS Logical-Mathematical

3 Assess

DAILY INTERVENTION

Check for Understanding
Visual-Spatial Have students research unique sources of proteins and carbohydrates used in different countries. Make labels with the food names and place them in the proper locations on a world map. Examples include amaranth in South America and Africa and taro root in the Pacific Islands. [L3]

Reteach
Food Flash Cards Have students make flash cards with names of fruits or vegetables. On the reverse side, have them identify the major vitamin content of each food. Students can test each other using the flash cards. [L1]
LS Visual-Spatial

✓ Assessment

Performance Assess students' abilities to make and use tables by having them use **Figure 8** to determine how much water (in liters) is lost through the skin. Use **Performance Assessment in the Science Classroom,** p. 109.

⊙ Real-World Question

Purpose Students test orange juices for vitamin C content. ⌷L2⌷
ELL COOP LEARN

Process Skills observe, measure, predict, interpret data, experiment, communicate, compare and contrast

Time Required 50 minutes

Safety Precautions Remind students not to consume any substances used in the lab.

⊙ Procedure

Teaching Strategy Have students practice making uniform drops using water before they begin adding drops of iodine to the test tubes. Remind students to rinse test tubes after each trial.

Troubleshooting Warn students not to mix up the test-solution droppers as they are preparing the test tubes.

⊙ Conclude and Apply

1. Answers should reflect student results.
2. Results may vary because of freshness, exposure to heat or air, and amount of vitamin C added.

Identifying Vitamin C Content

Vitamin C is found in many fruits and vegetables. Oranges have a high vitamin C content. Try this lab to test which orange juice has the highest vitamin C content.

⊙ Real-World Question

Which orange juice contains the most vitamin C?

Goals
■ **Observe** the vitamin C content of different orange juices.

Materials
test tubes (4)	2% tincture of iodine
*paper cups	dropper
test-tube rack	cornstarch
masking tape	triple-beam balance
wooden stirrers (13)	weighing paper
graduated cylinder	water (50 mL)
*graduated container	glass-marking pencil

dropper bottles (4) containing:
(1) freshly squeezed orange juice
(2) orange juice made from frozen concentrate
(3) canned orange juice
(4) dairy carton orange juice
*Alternate materials

Safety Precautions

WARNING: *Do not taste any of the juices. Iodine is poisonous, can stain skin and clothing, and is an irritant that can cause damage if it comes in contact with your eyes. Notify your teacher if a spill occurs.*

Sample Data

Juice	Trial 1	2	3	Average
	Drops of Iodine Needed to Change Color			
1 Fresh juice	8	7	8	8
2 Frozen juice	7	8	8	8
3 Canned juice	6	6	6	6
4 Carton juice	4	3	4	4

⊙ Procedure

1. Copy the data table shown above.
2. Label four test tubes as shown in the table above and place them in the test-tube rack.
3. **Measure** and pour 5 mL of juice from each bottle into its labeled test tube.
4. **Measure** 0.3 g of cornstarch, then put it in a container. Slowly mix in 50 mL of water until the cornstarch completely dissolves.
5. Add 5 mL of the cornstarch solution to each of the four test tubes. Stir well.
6. Add iodine to test tube 1, one drop at a time. Stir after each drop. Record the number of drops needed to change the juice to purple. The more vitamin C, the more drops needed.
7. Repeat step 6 with test tubes 2, 3, and 4.
8. Empty and clean the test tubes. Repeat steps 3 through 7 two more times, then average your results.

⊙ Conclude and Apply

1. **Compare and contrast** the amount of vitamin C in the orange juices tested.
2. **Infer** why the amount of vitamin C varied.

✔ Assessment

Performance To further assess students' abilities to identify vitamin C content, have them test water in which shredded lettuce or shredded cabbage cores have been soaked overnight. Use **Performance Assessment in the Science Classroom,** p. 97.

Communicating Your Data

Have students check the labels of the containers to see how much vitamin C each claims to contain. Have students use a spreadsheet program to enter the comparison between their tests and the information on the labels.

The Digestive System

Functions of the Digestive System

You are walking through a park on a cool, autumn afternoon. Birds are searching in the grass for insects. A squirrel is eating an acorn. Why are the animals so busy? Like you, they need food to supply their bodies with energy. Food is processed in your body in four stages—ingestion, digestion, absorption, and elimination. Whether it is a piece of fruit or an entire meal, all the food you eat is treated to the same processes in your body. As soon as food enters your mouth, or is ingested as shown in **Figure 11,** breakdown begins. **Digestion** is the process that breaks down food into small molecules so that they can be absorbed and moved into the blood. From the blood, food molecules are transported across the cell membrane to be used by the cell. Unused molecules pass out of your body as wastes.

Digestion is mechanical and chemical. **Mechanical digestion** takes place when food is chewed, mixed, and churned. **Chemical digestion** occurs when chemical reactions occur that break down large molecules of food into smaller ones.

Figure 11 Humans have to chew solid foods before swallowing them, but snakes have adaptations that allow them to swallow their food whole.

as you read

What You'll Learn
- **Distinguish** the differences between mechanical digestion and chemical digestion.
- **Identify** the organs of the digestive system and what takes place in each.
- **Explain** how homeostasis is maintained in digestion.

Why It's Important
The processes of the digestive system make the food you eat available to your cells.

🔎 Review Vocabulary
bacteria: one-celled organism without membrane-bound organelles

New Vocabulary
- digestion
- mechanical digestion
- chemical digestion
- enzyme
- peristalsis
- chyme
- villi

Bellringer

Section Focus Transparencies also are available on the Interactive Chalkboard CD-ROM.

L2 ELL

Tie to Prior Knowledge

Digestion Remind students that one feature of living things is that they use energy. Discuss with students that food is the source of energy for cell activities, but that it must be processed into usable molecules. This is the function of the digestive system.

Section 2 Resource Manager

Chapter *FAST FILE* Resources
Transparency Activity, p. 43
Directed Reading for Content Mastery, pp. 21, 22
MiniLAB, p. 4
Enrichment, p. 30
Reinforcement, p. 28

Lab Worksheet, pp. 7–8
Lab Activity, pp. 13–15
Lab Management and Safety, p. 52
Home and Community Involvement, p. 41

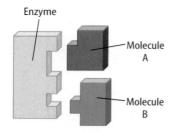
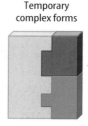
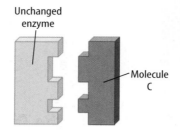

The surface shape of an enzyme fits the shape of specific molecules that take part in the reaction.

The enzyme and the molecules join and the reaction occurs between the two molecules.

Following the reaction, the enzyme and the new molecule separate. The enzyme is not changed by the reaction. The resulting new molecule has a new chemical structure.

Quick Demo

Meat Tenderizers

Meat tenderizers often contain the enzyme papain, which is made from papaya juice.

Materials meat tenderizer, two small cubes of beef, sugar, oven, plastic fork

Estimated Time 15 minutes

Procedure Sprinkle some meat tenderizer on a small cube of beef. On another cube of beef, sprinkle some sugar. Heat both pieces in an oven at 250°F until brown. When cooled, have students examine both pieces and probe with a plastic fork to compare tenderness.

Use Science Words

Word Meaning The names of many enzymes are designated with the suffix -ase. For example, the enzyme that is responsible for the conversion of sucrose is called *sucrase.* Have students determine the enzymes for lactose (lactase), lipids (lipase), and amylose (amylase).

Caption Answer

Figure 12 It is free to join with another molecule in another reaction.

✓ Reading Check

Answer Enzymes speed up the rate of chemical digestion.

Figure 12 Enzymes speed up the rate of certain body reactions. During these reactions, the enzymes are not used up or changed in any way.
Explain *what happens to the enzyme after it separates from the new molecule.*

Enzymes

Chemical digestion is possible only because of enzymes (EN zimez). An **enzyme** is a type of protein that speeds up the rate of a chemical reaction in your body. One way enzymes speed up reactions is by reducing the amount of energy necessary for a chemical reaction to begin. If enzymes weren't there to help, the rate of chemical reactions would slow down. Some might not even happen at all. As shown in **Figure 12,** enzymes work without being changed or used up.

Enzymes in Digestion Many enzymes help you digest carbohydrates, proteins, and fats. Amylase (AM uh lays) is an enzyme produced by glands near the mouth. This enzyme helps speed up the breakdown of complex carbohydrates, such as starch, into simpler carbohydrates—sugars. In your stomach, the enzyme pepsin aids the chemical reactions that break down complex proteins into less complex proteins. In your small intestine, a number of other enzymes continue to speed up the breakdown of proteins into amino acids.

The pancreas, an organ on the back side of the stomach, releases several enzymes through a tube into the small intestine. Some of these enzymes continue to aid the process of starch breakdown that started in the mouth. The resulting sugars are turned into glucose and are used by your body's cells. Different enzymes from the pancreas are involved in the breakdown of fats into fatty acids. Others help in the reactions that break down proteins.

✓ Reading Check
What is the role of enzymes in the chemical digestion of food?

Teacher FYI

Enzyme Interactions Nearly every bodily chemical reaction involves enzymes. There is an intricate relationship among enzymes, vitamins, and minerals. Often enzymes cannot function in the absence of specific vitamins or minerals.

Differentiated Instruction

Visually Impaired and Learning Disabled Cut from foam-core board pairs of shapes that fit together as shown in **Figure 12.** Mix up several pairs, and have students find the enzyme for each molecule by matching the shapes. Compare the matching of shapes to a key fitting in a lock or pieces of a puzzle fitting together. L1 IS **Kinesthetic**

Other Enzyme Actions Enzyme-aided reactions are not limited to the digestive process. Enzymes also help speed up chemical reactions responsible for building your body. They are involved in the energy production activities of your muscle and nerve cells. Enzymes also aid in the blood-clotting process. Without enzymes, the chemical reactions of your body would not happen. In fact, you would not exist.

Organs of the Digestive System

Your digestive system has two parts—the digestive tract and the accessory organs. The major organs of your digestive tract—mouth, esophagus (ih SAH fuh guhs), stomach, small intestine, large intestine, rectum, and anus—are shown in **Figure 13.** Food passes through all of these organs. The tongue, teeth, salivary glands, liver, gallbladder, and pancreas, also shown in **Figure 13,** are the accessory organs. Although food doesn't pass through them, they are important in mechanical and chemical digestion. Your liver, gallbladder, and pancreas produce or store enzymes and chemicals that help break down food as it passes through the digestive tract.

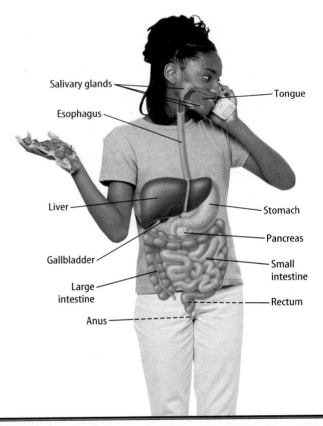

Figure 13 The human digestive system can be described as a tube divided into several specialized sections. If stretched out, an adult's digestive system is 6 m to 9 m long.

Salivary glands
Esophagus
Liver
Gallbladder
Large intestine
Anus
Tongue
Stomach
Pancreas
Small intestine
Rectum

IDENTIFYING Misconceptions

Peristalsis Students may think that peristalsis cannot occur in the "weightless" environment of a spacecraft. Because peristalsis is an action controlled by muscles, the lack of gravity does not affect swallowing and the movement of food through the digestive system.

Fun Fact

Birds have a specialized stomach chamber, the gizzard, that contains small stones. These stones aid in grinding food—a process that is needed in the absence of teeth.

Figure 14 About 1.5 L of saliva are produced each day by salivary glands in your mouth. **Describe** *what happens in your mouth when you think about a food you like.*

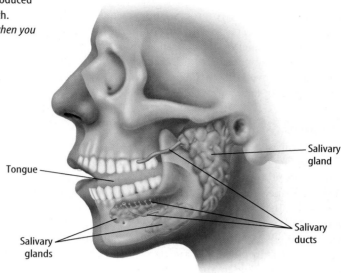

Tongue

Salivary gland

Salivary ducts

Salivary glands

Science Online

Topic: The Stomach
Visit life.msscience.com for Web links to information about the role of the stomach during digestion.

Activity Research to find out how antacids provide relief from stomach discomfort.

The Mouth Mechanical and chemical digestion begin in your mouth. Mechanical digestion happens when you chew your food with your teeth and mix it with your tongue. Chemical digestion begins with the addition of a watery substance called saliva (suh LI vuh). As you chew, your tongue moves food around and mixes it with saliva. Saliva is produced by three sets of glands near your mouth, as shown in **Figure 14.** Although saliva is mostly water, it also contains mucus and an enzyme that aids in the breakdown of starch into sugar. Food mixed with saliva becomes a soft mass and is moved to the back of your mouth by your tongue. It is swallowed and passes into your esophagus. Now ingestion is complete, but the process of digestion continues.

The Esophagus Food moving into the esophagus passes over the epiglottis (ep uh GLAH tus). This structure automatically covers the opening to the windpipe to prevent food from entering it, otherwise you would choke. Your esophagus is a muscular tube about 25 cm long. It takes about 4 s to 10 s for food to move down the esophagus to the stomach. No digestion takes place in the esophagus. Mucous glands in the wall of the esophagus keep the food moist. Smooth muscles in the wall move food downward with a squeezing action. These waves of muscle contractions, called **peristalsis** (per uh STAHL sus), move food through the entire digestive tract.

526 CHAPTER 18 Nutrients and Digestion

Science Journal

Cavities Have interested students research information about the relationship between sugars in the mouth and cavity-causing bacteria. Have them record in their journals information on the formation of tooth cavities. Some students might like to include diagrams showing the stages of tooth decay. L2 LS **Linguistic** P

The Stomach The stomach, shown in **Figure 15,** is a muscular bag. When empty, it is somewhat sausage shaped with folds on the inside. As food enters from the esophagus, the stomach expands and the folds smooth out. Mechanical and chemical digestion take place in the stomach. Mechanically, food is mixed in the stomach by peristalsis. Chemically, food is mixed with enzymes and strong digestive solutions, such as hydrochloric acid solution, to help break it down.

Specialized cells in the walls of the stomach release about 2 L of hydrochloric acid solution each day. The acidic solution works with the enzyme pepsin to digest protein. The acidic solution has another important purpose—it destroys bacteria that are present in the food. The stomach also produces mucus, which makes food more slippery and protects the stomach from the strong, digestive solutions. Food moves through your stomach in 2 hours to 4 hours and is changed into a thin, watery liquid called **chyme** (KIME). Little by little, chyme moves out of your stomach and into your small intestine.

✔ **Reading Check** *Why isn't your stomach digested by the acidic digestive solution?*

Figure 15 A band of muscle is at the entrance of the stomach to control the entry of food from the esophagus. Muscles at the end of the stomach control the flow of the partially digested food into the first part of the small intestine.

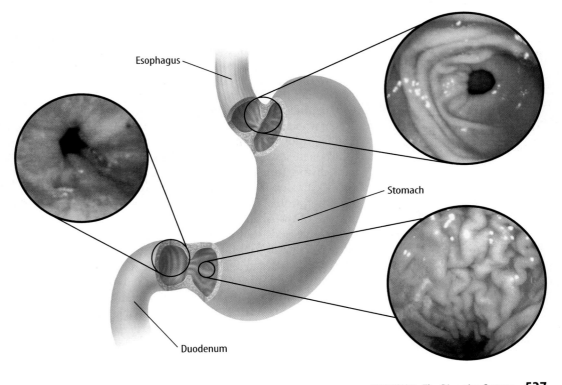

Esophagus

Stomach

Duodenum

Comparison Have students place a spoonful of cooking oil in a glass of warm water. Tell students to add a quarter-spoonful of dishwashing detergent to the glass, then stir. Have students note how the oil is separated into tiny droplets. Relate this to the action of bile on fats in the small intestine. L2

✔ **Reading Check**

Answer It is protected by a mucous coating.

Visual Learning

Figure 15 Why do you think it is important for the entrance and exit of the stomach to be controlled by strong muscles? Possible answer: The muscles at the entrance to the stomach keep partially digested food and stomach acids from moving back into the esophagus. The muscle at the exit of the stomach allows only chyme to leave the stomach, keeping larger food particles in the stomach for further digestion.

Teacher FYI

The Small Intestine The amount of time needed for food undergoing digestion to move through the small intestine is between one and six hours. The small intestine is subdivided into three parts: the duodenum, jejunum, and ileum. Most digestion occurs in the duodenum and most absorption of nutrients takes place in the duodenum and the jejunum. Vitamin B_{12} and bile salts are absorbed in the ileum.

Active Reading

Metacognition Journal In this strategy, each student analyzes his or her own thought processes. Have students divide the paper in half. On the left, have them record what they have learned about a topic. On the right, have them record the reason they learned it. Have students write a Metacognition Journal about the digestive system.

Figure 16 The person would lose weight because not as many nutrients could be absorbed by the body; the surface area involved in the process would be reduced.

Mini LAB

Purpose Students model how villi increase absorption area.
L1 ELL LS **Kinesthetic**

Materials 2 bowls, measuring cup, water, 2 containers, one piece 25-cm × 25-cm smooth cotton cloth, one piece 25-cm × 25-cm cotton terry cloth

Teaching Strategy Cloths should be wrung out completely.

Analysis

1. The terry cloth will absorb more water.
2. The terry cloth's surface of threads is similar to the small intestine's surface of villi.

Assessment

Process Have students compare the absorption of various other cloths and observe differences in their surfaces. Use **Performance Assessment in the Science Classroom,** p. 89.

Try at Home

Figure 16 Hundreds of thousands of densely packed villi give the impression of a velvet cloth surface. If the surface area of your villi could be stretched out, it would cover an area the size of a tennis court.
Infer *what would happen to a person's weight if the number of villi were drastically reduced. Why?*

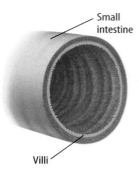
Small intestine

Villi

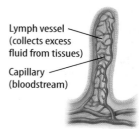
Lymph vessel (collects excess fluid from tissues)
Capillary (bloodstream)

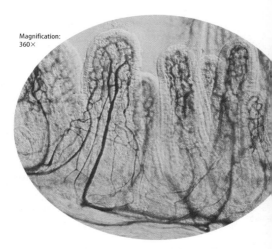
Magnification: 360×

Mini LAB

Modeling Absorption in the Small Intestine

Procedure

1. Place one piece of smooth **cotton cloth** (about 25 cm × 25 cm) and a similar-sized piece of **cotton terry cloth** into a **bowl of water.**
2. Soak each for 30 s.
3. Remove the cloths and drain for 1 minute.
4. Wring out each cloth into different containers. Measure the amount of water collected in each.

Analysis

1. Which cloth absorbed the most water?
2. How does the surface of the terry cloth compare to the internal surface of the small intestine?

Try at Home

The Small Intestine Your small intestine is small in diameter, but it measures 4 m to 7 m in length. As chyme leaves your stomach, it enters the first part of your small intestine, called the duodenum (doo AH duh num). Most digestion takes place in your duodenum. Here, a greenish fluid from the liver, called bile, is added. The acid from the stomach makes large fat particles float to the top of the liquid. Bile breaks up the large fat particles, similar to the way detergent breaks up grease.

Chemical digestion of carbohydrates, proteins, and fats occurs when a digestive solution from the pancreas is mixed in. This solution contains bicarbonate ions and enzymes. The bicarbonate ions help neutralize the stomach acid that is mixed with chyme. Your pancreas also makes insulin, a hormone that allows glucose to pass from the bloodstream into your cells.

Absorption of food takes place in the small intestine. Look at the wall of the small intestine in **Figure 16.** The wall has many ridges and folds that are covered with fingerlike projections called **villi** (VIH li). Villi increase the surface area of the small intestine so that nutrients in the chyme have more places to be absorbed. Peristalsis continues to move and mix the chyme. The villi move and are bathed in the soupy liquid. Nutrients move into blood vessels within the villi. From here, blood transports the nutrients to all cells of your body. Peristalsis continues to force the remaining undigested and unabsorbed materials slowly into the large intestine.

Differentiated Instruction

Challenge Have students demonstrate the chemical process involved in neutralizing an acid. First, have them use litmus paper to test a vinegar solution (5 mL in 100 mL water) and a baking soda solution (5 mL in 100 mL water). After the two solutions are combined, have students again test to show that the combined solution is no longer acidic or basic. Note: The reaction will produce bubbles of carbon dioxide gas. L3

The Large Intestine When the chyme enters the large intestine, it is still a thin, watery mixture. The main job of the large intestine is to absorb water from the undigested mass. This keeps large amounts of water in your body and helps maintain homeostasis. Peristalsis usually slows down in the large intestine. The chyme might stay there for as long as three days. After the excess water is absorbed, the remaining undigested materials become more solid. Muscles in the rectum, which is the last section of the large intestine, and the anus control the release of semisolid wastes from the body in the form of feces (FEE seez).

Bacteria Are Important

Many types of bacteria live in your body. Bacteria live in many of the organs of your digestive tract including your mouth and large intestine. Some of these bacteria live in a relationship that is beneficial to the bacteria and to your body. The bacteria in your large intestine feed on undigested material like cellulose. In turn, bacteria make vitamins you need—vitamin K and two B vitamins. Vitamin K is needed for blood clotting. The two B vitamins, niacin and thiamine, are important for your nervous system and for other body functions. Bacterial action also converts bile pigments into new compounds. The breakdown of intestinal materials by bacteria produces gas.

INTEGRATE Environment

Bacteria The species of bacteria that live in your large intestine are adapted to their habitat. What do you think would happen to the bacteria if their environment were to change? How would this affect your large intestine? Discuss your ideas with a classmate and write your answers in your Science Journal.

INTEGRATE Environment

Bacteria If the environment changed, the bacteria might die, preventing the decomposition of undigested material and the manufacture of certain vitamins.

---

section 2 review

Summary

Functions of the Digestive System
- To process food, your body must ingest, digest, absorb, and eliminate it.

Enzymes
- Enzymes aid the chemical reactions of digestion.

Organs of the Digestive System
- The mouth, esophagus, stomach, small intestine, large intestine, rectum, and anus are the major organs of this system.
- The digestive system also has accessory organs that are important to mechanical and chemical digestion.

Bacteria Are Important
- Bacteria help break down intestinal materials and make vitamins.

Self Check

1. **Compare and contrast** mechanical digestion and chemical digestion.
2. **Explain** how activities in the large intestine help maintain homeostasis.
3. **Describe** the function of each of the organs in the digestive tract.
4. **Explain** how the accessory organs aid digestion.
5. **Think Critically** A cracker contains starch. Explain why a cracker begins to taste sweet after it is in your mouth for five minutes without being chewed.

Applying Skills

6. **Recognize Cause and Effect** What would happen to some of the nutrients in chyme if the pancreas did not secrete its solution into the small intestine?

---

section 2 review

1. Mechanical digestion—cutting and grinding by teeth, tongue and peristalsis move food; chemical digestion—the chemical breakdown of food into usable nutrients.
2. Water is removed from wastes and returned to the body.
3. mouth—mechanical and chemical digestion; esophagus—moistens food; stomach—mechanical and chemical digestion; small intestine—chemical digestion and food absorption; large intestine—water absorption; rectum and anus—release wastes
4. liver produces digestive juices and bile that breaks up fat particles; pancreas produces digestive juices
5. Starch is broken down into simple sugars by saliva.
6. Chyme would remain acidic in the digestive tract, possibly causing damage.

BENCH TESTED

Real-World Question

Purpose Students will observe the relationship between particle size and rate of dissolving. L2
ELL **IS** **Naturalist**

Process Skills observe and infer, communicate, recognize cause and effect, separate and control variables, interpret data, compare and contrast

Time Required 50 minutes

Procedure

Safety Precautions Remind students not to taste, eat, or drink any materials used in the lab.

Teaching Strategy

Troubleshooting Be sure the water temperature and amount of water is the same in each beaker.

Analyze Your Data

Expected Outcome Most student lab results will show that the ground sugar particles were the quickest to dissolve.

LAB

Goals
- **Compare** the dissolving rates of different sized particles.
- **Predict** the dissolving rate of sugar particles larger than sugar cubes.
- **Predict** the dissolving rate of sugar particles smaller than particles of ground sugar.
- Using the lab results, infer why the body must break down and dissolve food particles.

Materials
250-mL beakers or jars (3)
thermometers (3)
sugar granules
mortar and pestle
triple-beam balance
stirring rod
sugar cubes
weighing paper
warm water
stopwatch

Safety Precautions

WARNING: *Do not taste, eat, or drink any materials used in the lab.*

Particle Size and Absorption

Real-World Question

Before food reaches the small intestine, it is digested mechanically in the mouth and the stomach. The food mass is reduced to small particles. You can chew an apple into small pieces, but you would feed applesauce to a small child who didn't have teeth. What is the advantage of reducing the size of the food material? How does reducing the size of food particles aid the process of digestion?

Procedure

1. Copy the data table below into your Science Journal.

Dissolving Time of Sugar Particles

Size of Sugar Particles	Mass	Time Until Dissolved
Sugar cube		Answers will vary.
Sugar granules		
Ground sugar particles		

2. Place a sugar cube into your mortar and grind up the cube with the pestle until the sugar becomes powder.
3. Using the triple-beam balance and weighing paper, measure the mass of the powdered sugar from your mortar. Using separate sheets of weighing paper, measure the mass of a sugar cube and the mass of a sample of the granular sugar. The masses of the powdered sugar, sugar cube, and granular sugar should be approximately equal to each other. Record the three masses in your data table.
4. Place warm water into the three beakers. Use the thermometers to be certain the water in each beaker is the same temperature.

530 CHAPTER 18 Nutrients and Digestion

Alternative Inquiry Lab

Absorption Rate Students may further investigate absorption rate by determining if factors other than particle size, such as temperature, affect the rate of dissolution. Students can predict the results and then design an experiment to test their hypothesis.

5. Place the sugar cube in a beaker, the pow-dered sugar in a second beaker, and the granular sugar in the third beaker. Place all the sugar samples in the beakers at the same time and start the stopwatch when you put the sugar samples in the beaker.

6. Stir each sample equally.

7. **Measure** the time it takes each sugar sample to dissolve and record the times in your data table.

◉ *Analyze Your Data*

1. **Identify** the experiment's constants and variables.

2. **Compare** the rate at which the sugar samples dissolved. What type of sugar dissolved most rapidly? Which was the slowest to dissolve?

◉ *Conclude and Apply*

1. **Predict** how long it would take sugar particles larger than the sugar cubes to dissolve. Predict how long it would take sugar particles smaller than the powdered sugar to dissolve.

2. **Infer and explain** the reason why small particles dissolve more rapidly than large particles.

3. **Infer** why you should thoroughly chew your food.

4. **Explain** how reducing the size of food particles aids the process of digestion.

*C*ommunicating
Your Data

Write a news column for a health maga-zine explaining to health-conscious people what they can do to digest their food better.

LAB 531

*C*ommunicating
Your Data

Articles should emphasize the idea that smaller parti-cles of food will digest more easily than larger food par-ticles. Chewing food thoroughly speeds up the digestion process. To be used by the body, foods must be broken down into nutrients. Once digested, the blood carries these nutrients to all the cells of the body.

TIME

Content Background

Early studies of food by nutritionists and food scientists were steeped in the food traditions of the culture from which they came. For instance, food scientists from the West believed a diet high in protein was essential for good health.

Then, in 1991, the U.S. Department of Agriculture introduced a food pyramid that emphasizes grains and a carbohydrate-rich diet. Some nutritionists believe it is still culturally specific to Americans. Thus, some groups have taken the U.S. food pyramid and adapted it to reflect the culture and foodways of different regions and countries.

Discussion

Proper Diets Why might Western nutritionists suggest that Indian women eat more meat and eggs? Possible answer: The U.S. and European diets were based on consuming animal products and foods high in protein.

Investigate the Issue

Ask students to think about the foods they eat every day. Explain to students that different cultural, age, ethnic, and even family groups have distinct food traditions. Give students the following examples of food traditions: Asian-American students might consume a largely plant-based diet with rice being served at most meals. Share with the class an example of a food tradition in your own family. Then, ask students to name a food tradition or food item that they believe is unique to their family or ethnic or cultural group.

TIME SCIENCE AND Society

SCIENCE ISSUES THAT AFFECT YOU!

Eating Well

Does the same diet work for everyone?

Growing up in India in the first half of the twentieth century, R. Rajalakshmi (RAH jah lok shmee) saw many people around her who did not get enough food. Breakfast for a poor child might have been a cup of tea. Lunch might have consisted of a slice of bread. For dinner, a child might have eaten a serving of rice with a small piece of fish. This type of diet, low in calories and nutrients, produced children who were often sick and died young.

Good Diet, Wrong Place

R. Rajalakshmi studied biochemistry and nutrition at universities in India and in Canada. In the 1960s, she was asked to help manage a program to improve nutrition in her country. At that time, North American and European nutritionists suggested foods that were common and worked well for people who lived in these nations.

Thanks to R. Rajalakshmi and other nutritionists, many children in India are eating well and staying healthy.

For example, they told poor Indian women to eat more meat and eggs and drink more orange juice. But Rajalakshmi knew this advice was useless in a country such as India. People there didn't eat such foods. They weren't easy to find. And for the poor, such foods were too expensive.

The Proper Diet for India

Rajalakshmi knew that for the program to work, it had to fit Indian culture. So she decided to restructure the nutrition program. She first found out what healthy middle class people in India ate. She took note of the nutrients available in those foods. Then she looked for cheap, easy-to-find foods that would provide the same nutrients.

Rajalakshmi created a balanced diet of cheap, locally grown fruits, vegetables, and grains. Legumes (plants related to peas and peanuts), vegetables, and an Indian food called dhokla (DOH kluh) were basics. Dhokla is made of grains, legumes, and leafy vegetables. The grains and legumes provided protein, and the vegetables added vitamins and minerals.

Rajalakshmi's ideas were thought unusual in the 1960s. For example, she insisted that a diet without meat could provide all major nutrients. Now we know she was right. But it took persistence to get others to accept her diet about 40 years ago. Because of Rajalakshmi's program, Indian children almost doubled their food intake. And many children who would have been hungry and ill grew healthy and strong.

Report Choose a continent and research what foods are native to that area. Share your findings with your classmates and compile a list of the foods and where they originated. Using the class list, mark the origins of the different foods on a world map.

Science online
For more information, visit life.msscience.com/time

Report Have students research a specific region, such as a continent, and compile a list of foods that are common there. After students write their lists on the board, direct students to note the differences in diets. Which cultures have a mostly plant-based diet and which have a mostly meat-based diet? What might be the reasons for the difference?

Resources for Teachers and Students

American Food Habits in Historical Perspective by Elain N. McIntosh, Ph.D., R.D. Praeger, 1995

Food and Culture: a Reader. Routledge, 1997

Reviewing Main Ideas

Section 1 Nutrition

1. Proteins, carbohydrates, fats, vitamins, minerals, and water are the six nutrients found in foods.

2. Carbohydrates provide energy, proteins are needed for growth and repair, and fats store energy and cushion organs. Vitamins and minerals regulate functions. Water makes up about 60 percent of your body's mass and is used for a variety of homeostatic functions.

3. Health is affected by the combination of foods that make up a diet.

Section 2 The Digestive System

1. Mechanical digestion breaks down food through chewing and churning.

2. Enzymes and other chemicals aid chemical digestion.

3. Digestion breaks down food into substances that cells can absorb and use. Carbohydrates break down into simple sugars; proteins into amino acids; and fats into fatty acids and glycerol.

4. Food is ingested in the mouth. Digestion occurs in the mouth, stomach, and small intestine, with absorption occurring in the small and large intestines. Wastes are excreted through the anus.

5. The accessory digestive organs move and cut up food and supply digestive enzymes and other chemicals, such as bile, needed for digestion.

6. The large intestine absorbs water, which helps the body maintain homeostasis.

Visualizing Main Ideas

Copy and complete the following table indicating good sources of vitamins and minerals.

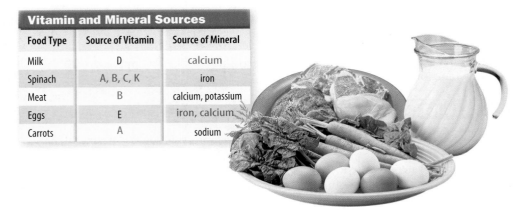

Vitamin and Mineral Sources

Food Type	Source of Vitamin	Source of Mineral
Milk	D	calcium
Spinach	A, B, C, K	iron
Meat	B	calcium, potassium
Eggs	E	iron, calcium
Carrots	A	sodium

Science Online life.msscience.com/interactive_tutor

CHAPTER STUDY GUIDE 533

Reviewing Main Ideas

Summary statements can be used by students to review the major concepts of the chapter.

Visualizing Main Ideas

See student page.

Visit life.msscience.com
/self_check_quiz
/interactive_tutor
/vocabulary_puzzlemaker
/chapter_review
/standardized_test
/field_guide

Assessment Transparency

For additional assessment questions, use the *Assessment Transparency* located in the transparency book.

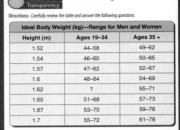

Assessment

Assessment Transparency — **Nutrients and Digestion**

Directions: *Carefully review the table and answer the following questions.*

Ideal Body Weight (kg)—Range for Men and Women		
Height (m)	Ages 19–34	Ages 35 +
1.52	44–58	49–62
1.54	46–60	50–65
1.57	47–62	52–67
1.6	48–64	54–69
1.62	?	55–71
1.65	51–68	57–73
1.67	53–70	59–76
1.7	55–72	61–78

1. Based on the information in the table, which of the following should the ideal weight range be for somebody who is 1.62 m tall and 27 years old?
   A 53–66   B 49–62   C 50–66   D 48–71

2. These data were collected by studying many different people. If everything remains the same, what would be a healthy weight for someone who is 1.7 m tall and 50 years old?
   F 55   G 59   H 72   J 80

3. A reasonable hypothesis using the table is that when we are younger ___.
   A our legs and arms weigh more
   B we usually weigh more
   C our weight never changes
   D we usually weigh less

Nutrients and Digestion

◆ Identifying Misconceptions

Assess

Use this assessment as follow-up to the F page at the beginning of this chapter.

Materials test tubes, starch solution, Lugol's solution, saliva (collected safely)

Procedure Take two large test tubes and add to each some of the starch solution and Lugol's solution. Add saliva to one of the tubes. Explain that saliva contains an enzyme, amylase. (The danger of using body fluids in experiments should be stressed to students.) The blue color in the tube with the saliva should disappear. Ask students what they think happened to the blue color.

Expected Outcome Students should be able to explain that the enzyme helped digest the starch.

Using Vocabulary

1. Peristalsis
2. villi
3. amino acids
4. chyme
5. Digestion
6. carbohydrates
7. Minerals
8. food group
9. Mechanical digestion
10. vitamin

Checking Concepts

11. D
12. C
13. B
14. A
15. D
16. C
17. B
18. A
19. B

Using Vocabulary

amino acid p. 513	mechanical
carbohydrate p. 514	digestion p. 523
chemical digestion p. 523	mineral p. 518
chyme p. 527	nutrient p. 512
digestion p. 523	peristalsis p. 526
enzyme p. 524	protein p. 513
fat p. 515	villi p. 528
food group p. 520	vitamin p. 516

Fill in the blanks with the correct vocabulary word or words.

1. _____ is the muscular contractions of the esophagus.
2. The _____ increase the surface area of the small intestine.
3. The building blocks of proteins are _____.
4. The liquid product of digestion is called _____.
5. _____ is the breakdown of food.
6. Your body's main source of energy is _____.
7. _____ are inorganic nutrients.
8. Pears and apples belong to the same _____.
9. _____ is when food is chewed and mixed.
10. A(n) _____ is a nutrient needed in small quantities for growth and for regulating body functions.

Checking Concepts

Choose the word or phrase that best answers the question.

11. In which organ is water absorbed?
    A) liver
    B) esophagus
    C) small intestine
    D) large intestine

12. What beneficial substances are produced by bacteria in the large intestine?
    A) fats
    B) minerals
    C) vitamins
    D) proteins

13. Which organ makes bile?
    A) gallbladder
    B) liver
    C) stomach
    D) small intestine

14. Where in humans does most chemical digestion occur?
    A) duodenum
    B) stomach
    C) liver
    D) large intestine

15. Which of these organs is an accessory organ?
    A) mouth
    B) stomach
    C) small intestine
    D) liver

16. Which vitamin is found most abundantly in citrus fruits?
    A) A
    B) B
    C) C
    D) K

17. Where is hydrochloric acid solution added to the food mass?
    A) mouth
    B) stomach
    C) small intestine
    D) large intestine

18. Which of the following is in the same food group as yogurt and cheese?

A)

C)

B)

D)

19. Which organ produces enzymes that help in digestion of proteins, fats, and carbohydrates?
    A) mouth
    B) pancreas
    C) large intestine
    D) gallbladder

Science Online life.mssience.com/vocabulary_puzzlemaker

Use the Exam*View*® Pro Testmaker CD-ROM to:
- create multiple versions of tests
- create modified tests with one mouse click for inclusion students
- edit existing questions and add your own questions
- build tests aligned with state standards using built-in State Curriculum Tags
- change English tests to Spanish with one mouse click and vice versa

Thinking Critically

Use the figure below to answer question 20.

Nutrition Facts
Serving Size 1 Meal

Amount Per Serving	
Calories 330 Calories from Fat 60	

	% Daily Value*
Total Fat 7g	**10%**
Saturated Fat 3.5g	**17%**
Polyunsaturated Fat 1g	
Monounsaturated Fat 2.5g	
Cholesterol 35mg	**12%**
Sodium 460mg	**19%**
Total Carbohydrate 52g	**18%**
Dietary Fiber 6g	**24%**
Sugars 17g	
Protein 15g	

Vitamin A 15%	•	Vitamin C 70%
Calcium 4%	•	Iron 10%

* Percent Daily Values are based on a 2,000 calorie diet. Your daily values may be higher or lower depending on your calorie needs.

	Calories	2,000	2,500
Total Fat	Less than	65g	80g
Sat Fat	Less than	20g	25g
Cholesterol	Less than	300mg	300mg
Sodium	Less than	2,400mg	2,400mg
Total Carbohydrate		300g	375g
Dietary Fiber		25g	30g

20. **Explain** how the information on the food label above can help you make healthful food choices.

21. **Infer** Food does not enter your body until it is absorbed into the blood. Explain why.

22. **Discuss** the meaning of the familiar statement "You are what you eat." Base your answer on your knowledge of food groups and nutrients.

23. **Explain** Bile's action is similar to that of soap. Use this information to explain how bile works on fats.

24. **Compare and contrast** the three types of carbohydrates—sugar, starch, and fiber.

Performance Activities

25. **Project** Research the ingredients used in antacid medications. Identify the compounds used to neutralize the excess stomach acid. Note the time, and then place an antacid tablet in a glass of vinegar—an acid. Using pH paper, check when the acid is neutralized. Record the time it took for the antacid to neutralize the vinegar. Repeat this procedure with different antacids. Compare your results.

Applying Math

26. **Villi Surface Area** The surface area of the villi in your small intestine is comparable to the area of a tennis court. A tennis court measures 11.0 m by 23.8 m. What is the area of a tennis court—and the surface area of the small intestine's villi—in square meters?

Use the table below to answer question 27.

Recommended Dietary Allowances

Nutrient	Percent U.S. RDA
Protein	2
Vitamin A	20
Vitamin C	25
Vitamin D	15
Calcium (Ca)	less than 2
Iron (Fe)	25
Zinc (Zn)	15
Total fat	5
Saturated fat	3
Cholesterol	0
Sodium	3

27. **Nutrients** A product nutrient label is shown above. Make a bar graph of this information.

Thinking Critically

20. This information can help you plan meals that supply the daily recommended amounts of nutrients and meet special dietary requirements.

21. As food passes through the digestive tract it is broken down into smaller pieces, eventually reaching the molecular level. These molecules are absorbed by the blood, transported to body cells, and used as an energy source.

22. If we eat nutritious food, the body will have good building blocks to use. A poor diet will not supply good building blocks.

23. Bile breaks down fats into smaller droplets, which have an increased surface area; this allows digestion to occur more quickly and easily.

24. Sugar—simple carbohydrate, dissolves in water, tastes sweet; starch and fiber—complex carbohydrates, do not dissolve in water; fiber absorbs water, starch does not.

Performance Activities

25. Common ingredients in antacids include sodium bicarbonate, calcium carbonate, ranitidine hydrochloride, and famotidine. Use **Performance Assessment in the Science Classroom,** p. 115.

Applying Math

National Math Standards
1, 4, 5, 6, 9

26. $11.0 \text{ m} \times 23.8 \text{ m} = 261.8 \text{ m}^2$

27. Check student graphs to ensure consistency with data provided.

☑ **Assessment** **Resources**

📁 **Reproducible Masters**

Chapter *Fast File* Resources
Chapter Review, pp. 35–36
Chapter Tests, pp. 37–40
Assessment Transparency Activity, p. 47

Glencoe Science Web site
Chapter Review Test
Standardized Test Practice

Glencoe Technology
🖌 Assessment Transparency
💿 Exam*View*® Pro Testmaker
📼 MindJogger Videoquiz
💿 Interactive Chalkboard

FAST FILE

Answer Sheet A practice answer sheet can be found at life.msscience.com/answer_sheet.

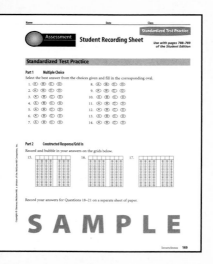

S A M P L E

Part 1 Multiple Choice

1. C	4. D
2. C	5. B
3. A	6. D

Part 2 Short Response

7. Organic nutrients, like proteins, carbohydrates, fats, and vitamins, contain carbon; inorganic nutrients, like minerals and water, do not contain carbon.

Part 1 Multiple Choice

Record your answers on the answer sheet provided by your teacher or on a sheet of paper.

1. How many amino acids are required by your body?
   - **A.** 5
   - **B.** 12
   - **C.** 20
   - **D.** 50

Use the illustration below to answer questions 2 and 3.

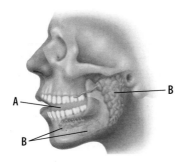

2. How does the organ labeled "A" help break down food?
   - **A.** produces enzymes
   - **B.** produces saliva
   - **C.** moves food around
   - **D.** produces mucus

3. Which of the following is produced by the organs labeled "B"?
   - **A.** saliva
   - **B.** bile
   - **C.** hydrochloric acid
   - **D.** chyme

Test-Taking Tip

Using Tables Concentrate on what the question is asking from a table, not all the information in the table.

Question 4 Look in the column titled *DV (Daily Values)* to find what the question asks, then follow the row to the *Item* column to find the answer.

Use the table below to answer questions 4 and 5.

Nutrition Facts of Vanilla Ice Cream		
Item	**Amount**	**DV (Daily Values)**
Serving Size	112 g	0
Calories	208	0
Total Fat	19 g	29%
Saturated Fat	11 g	55%
Cholesterol	0.125 g	42%
Sodium	0.90 g	4%
Total Carbohydrates	22 g	7%
Fiber	0 g	0%
Sugars	22 g	n/a
Protein	5 g	n/a
Calcium	0.117 g	15%
Iron	n/a	0%

4. According to the table above, which mineral has the greatest DV?
   - **A.** sodium
   - **B.** cholesterol
   - **C.** iron
   - **D.** calcium

5. If you had two servings of this vanilla ice cream, how many grams of saturated fat and Daily Value (DV) percentage would you eat?
   - **A.** 11 g, 110%
   - **B.** 22 g, 110%
   - **C.** 21 g, 55%
   - **D.** 5.5 g, 110%

6. Which of the following is the correct sequence of the organs of the digestive tract?
   - **A.** mouth, stomach, esophagus, small intestine, large intestine
   - **B.** esophagus, mouth, stomach, small intestine, large intestine
   - **C.** mouth, esophagus, small intestine, stomach, large intestine
   - **D.** mouth, esophagus, stomach, small intestine, large intestine

---

8. teen playing soccer; More water is being lost through the skin (sweat).

9. teen playing soccer; An active person needs more food energy to meet the increased demand for energy.

10. eggs, milk, cheese, and meat

11. Bile breaks up the large fat particles.

12. An essential amino acid is one that cannot be made by the body's cells.

13. These bacteria make vitamin K and two B vitamins, niacin and thiamine. They also convert bile pigments into new compounds.

14. Fats are a good storage unit for energy, help the body absorb vitamins, and cushion internal organs.

15. Enzymes help speed up reactions responsible for building the body, are involved in energy releasing activities of muscles and nerve cells, and aid in blood clotting.

16. $540 \div 180 = 3$

Part 2 | Short Response/Grid In

Record your answers on the answer sheet provided by your teacher or on a sheet of paper.

7. Explain the difference between organic and inorganic nutrients. Name a class of nutrients for each.

Use the photos below to answer questions 8 and 9.

8. During the activity shown above, which of the two teens is losing more body water? Why?

9. Based on the activity shown above, which teen may need more food energy (Calories)? Why?

10. Name three food sources that contain complete proteins.

11. How does bile help in digestion?

12. What is meant by an "essential amino acid"?

13. How do bacteria that live in the large intestine help your body?

14. Explain the importance of fats in the body.

15. Enzymes play an important role in the digestive process. But enzyme-aided reactions are also involved in other body systems. Give an example of how enzymes are used by the body in a way that does not involve the digestive system.

16. A taco has 180 Calories (Cal) and an ice cream sundae has 540 Cal. How many tacos could you eat to equal the number of Calories in the ice cream sundae?

Part 3 | Open Ended

Record your answers on a sheet of paper.

17. Explain what might happen to a child who is deficient in vitamin D. What foods should be eaten to prevent a deficiency in vitamin D?

18. Certain bacteria that do not normally live in the body can make toxins that affect intestinal absorption. Explain what might happen if these bacteria were present in the small and large intestines.

Use the illustration below to answer questions 19 and 20.

19. Identify the food group shown at the base of the food pyramid. Explain why the greatest number of servings should come from this group.

20. Identify the food group at the top of the pyramid. Explain why the least number of servings should come from this group.

21. Antibiotics may be given to help a person fight off a bacterial infection. If a person is taking antibiotics, what might happen to the normal bacteria living in the large intestine? How would this affect the body?

22. Sometimes the esophagus can be affected by a disease in which peristalsis is not normal and the band of muscle at the entrance to the stomach does not work properly. What do you think would happen to food that the person swallowed?

20. The food group at the top of the pyramid is fats, oils, and sweets. The least number of servings should come from this group because they may have lots of Calories that supply energy, but provide only some of the nutrients that the body needs.

21. Antibiotics kill the bacteria that cause the infection, but may also kill some of the bacteria normally in the large intestine. These bacteria produce vitamins and break down intestinal materials, so vitamin production and bacterial breakdown may not occur or may be reduced.

22. The person would have difficulty swallowing food, and, because the muscle at the stomach entrance is not working properly, undigested food could go back up the esophagus.

Rubrics

For more help evaluating open-ended assessment questions, see the rubric on p. 10T.

Part 3 | Open Ended

17. Vitamin D helps bones and teeth absorb calcium and phosphorus, which makes them hard. A child with vitamin D deficiency would not have hard bones and teeth. Good food sources of vitamin D are fortified milk, butter, eggs, fish liver oil, and sunshine on the skin.

18. These bacteria affect intestinal absorption, which would affect absorption of food and water. Water would not be reabsorbed into the body through the intestines, affecting homeostasis. All the nutrients from the food may not be absorbed. Excess food and water in the bowel would cause diarrhea.

19. The food group at the base of the pyramid is the bread, cereal, rice, and pasta group. The greatest number of servings should come from this group because these foods are carbohydrates, which are the main sources of energy for the body.

Section/Objectives	Standards		Labs/Features
Chapter Opener	National	State/Local	**Launch Lab:** Comparing Circulatory and Road Systems, p. 539 **Foldables,** p. 539 A data-collection lab using Probeware technology can be found in the **Probeware Lab Manual,** pp. 5–8
	See pp. 16T–17T for a Key to Standards.		
Section 1 The Circulatory System 🕐 3 sessions 📦 1.5 blocks 1. **Compare and contrast** arteries, veins, and capillaries. 2. **Explain** how blood moves through the heart. 3. **Identify** the functions of the pulmonary and systemic circulation systems.	National Content Standards: UCP.1–UCP.3, UCP.5, A.1, A.2, C.1, C.3, C.5		**MiniLAB:** Inferring How Hard the Heart Works, p. 541 **Integrate Physics,** p. 545 **Visualizing Atherosclerosis,** p. 546 **Science Online,** p. 547 **Lab:** The Heart as a Pump, p. 549
Section 2 Blood 🕐 2 sessions 📦 1 block 4. **Identify** the parts and functions of blood. 5. **Explain** why blood types are checked before a transfusion. 6. **Give examples** of diseases of blood.	National Content Standards: UCP.1–UCP.3, UCP.5, A.1, A.2, C.1, C.3, C.5		**Science Online,** p. 551 **MiniLAB:** Modeling Scab Formation, p. 552 **Integrate History,** p. 554 **Applying Science:** Will there be enough blood donors?, p. 554
Section 3 The Lymphatic System 🕐 2 sessions 📦 1 block 7. **Describe** the functions of the lymphatic system. 8. **Identify** where lymph comes from. 9. **Explain** how lymph organs help fight infections.	National Content Standards: UCP.1–UCP.5, A.1, A.2, C.1, C.3, C.5, G.1, G.3		**Lab:** Blood Type Reactions, p. 558 **Science and History:** Have a Heart, p. 560

Lab Materials	Reproducible Resources	Section Assessment	Technology
Launch Lab: a city, county, or state map; Science Journal	**Chapter *FAST FILE* Resources** Foldables Worksheet, p. 17 Directed Reading Overview, p. 19 Note-taking Worksheets, pp. 33–37	GLENCOE'S ASSESSMENT ADVANTAGE	Teacher**Works** includes: • Interactive Teacher Edition • Lesson Planner with calendar • Access to all program blacklines • Correlations to standards • Web links
MiniLAB: bowl of water, stopwatch or clock **Lab:** watch or clock with second hand *Need materials?* Contact Science Kit at 1-800-828-7777 or www.sciencekit.com on the Internet.	**Chapter *FAST FILE* Resources** Transparency Activity, p. 46 MiniLAB, p. 3 Enrichment, p. 30 Reinforcement, p. 27 Directed Reading, p. 20 Lab Worksheet, pp. 5–6 Lab Activities, pp. 9–12, 13–16 Transparency Activity, pp. 49–50 **Home and Community Involvement,** p. 26	Portfolio Assessment, p. 548 Performance MiniLAB, p. 541 Applying Skills, p. 548 Content Section Review, p. 548 Challenge, p. 546	Section Focus Transparency Teaching Transparency Virtual Labs CD-ROM Guided Reading Audio Program Interactive Chalkboard CD-ROM
MiniLAB: gauze, aluminum foil, liquid bandage solution, dropper, water	**Chapter *FAST FILE* Resources** Transparency Activity, p. 47 MiniLAB, p. 4 Enrichment, p. 31 Reinforcement, p. 28 Directed Reading, p. 20 **Mathematics Skill Activities,** p. 33 **Cultural Diversity,** p. 18	Portfolio Challenge, p. 552 Performance MiniLAB, p. 552 Applying Math, p. 555 Content Section Review, p. 555	Section Focus Transparency Virtual Labs CD-ROM Guided Reading Audio Program Interactive Chalkboard CD-ROM
Lab: simulated blood (10 mL low-fat milk and 10 mL water plus red food coloring), lemon juice, water, droppers, small paper cups, marking pen, 10-mL graduated cylinder	**Chapter *FAST FILE* Resources** Transparency Activity, p. 48 Enrichment, p. 32 Reinforcement, p. 29 Directed Reading, pp. 21, 22 Lab Worksheet, pp. 7–8 **Lab Management and Safety,** p. 69	Portfolio Check for Understanding, p. 557 Performance Applying Skills, p. 557 Content Section Review, p. 557	Section Focus Transparency Virtual Labs CD-ROM Guided Reading Audio Program Interactive Chalkboard CD-ROM Video Lab Probeware Lab

End of Chapter Assessment

Blackline Masters	Technology	Professional Series
Chapter *FAST FILE* Resources Chapter Review, pp. 39–40 Chapter Tests, pp. 41–44 Standardized Test Practice, pp. 79–82	MindJogger Videoquiz Virtual Labs CD-ROM Exam*View*® Pro Testmaker TeacherWorks CD-ROM Interactive Chalkboard CD-ROM	**Performance Assessment in the Science Classroom (PASC)**

Transparencies

Section Focus

Section Focus Transparency

How to Relax in Traffic

Venice is a city in Italy that includes over one hundred islands. Because there's so much water, Venetians use canals instead of streets for transportation. There is a main canal, called the Grand Canal, and many smaller canals branching off the main canal.

1. If you compared the canals in Venice to blood vessels, what would the water represent?
2. What might the gondolas represent?

L2

Section Focus Transparency

A Friend in Need

Do you know someone who has participated in a blood drive? During a blood drive, people are asked to donate blood that will be used to treat sick or injured people. The blood collected by blood banks saves many lives each year.

1. What is the purpose of a blood bank?
2. Who do you think should or should not donate blood?

L2

Section Focus Transparency

Here I Come to Save the Day!

This image shows a cell from the immune system at work. A white blood cell is devouring an invading organism. The only part of the organism that can be seen is at the lower right portion of the photo. It is being sucked into the tube-like extension of the colorful white blood cell.

1. Describe what is happening to the invading organism.
2. What purpose do you think white blood cells serve?

L2

This is a representation of key blackline masters available in the Teacher Classroom Resources. See Resource Manager boxes within the chapter for additional information.

Key to Teaching Strategies

The following designations will help you decide which activities are appropriate for your students.

- **L1** Level 1 activities should be appropriate for students with learning difficulties.

- **L2** Level 2 activities should be within the ability range of all students.

- **L3** Level 3 activities are designed for above-average students.

- **ELL** ELL activities should be within the ability range of English-Language Learners.

- **COOP LEARN** Cooperative Learning activities are designed for small group work.

- **LS** Multiple Learning Styles logos, as described on page 12T, are used throughout to indicate strategies that address different learning styles.

- **P** These strategies represent student products that can be placed into a best-work portfolio.

- **PBL** Problem-Based Learning activities apply real-world situations to learning.

Assessment

Assessment Transparency

Circulation

Directions: Carefully review the table and answer the following questions.

Regional HIV/AIDS Statistics, December 1998

Region	Individuals living with AIDS/HIV	Individuals newly infected HIV	Women with HIV (%)
South and Southeast Asia	6,700,000	1,200,000	25
Western Europe	500,000	30,000	20
North America	890,000	44,000	20
Sub-Saharan Africa	22,500,000	4,000,000	50
Latin America	1,400,000	160,000	20

1. According to the table, which region has the most people infected and living with AIDS/HIV?
   A Latin America   C North America
   B South & Southeast Asia   D Sub-Saharan Africa
2. According to the table, in which region is 75 percent of the HIV-infected population male?
   F Western Europe   H South & Southeast Asia
   G Sub-Saharan Africa   J North America
3. The total world population of individuals living with HIV/AIDS is 33.4 million. Approximately what percentage of these individuals live in the Sub-Sahara African region?
   A 5%   B 10%   C 70%   D 100%

L2

Teaching

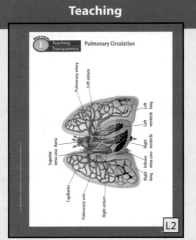

Teaching Transparency

Pulmonary Circulation

L2

Hands-on Activities

Student Text Lab Worksheet

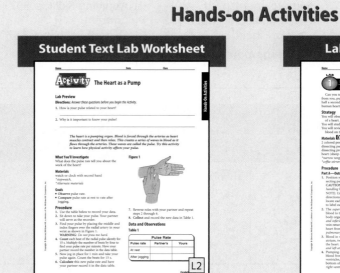

Activity The Heart as a Pump

L2

Laboratory Activities

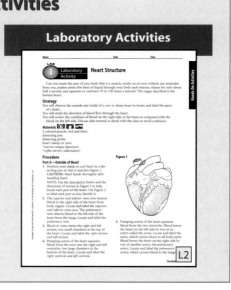

Laboratory Activity

Heart Structure

L2

Resource Manager

Meeting Different Ability Levels

Content Outline
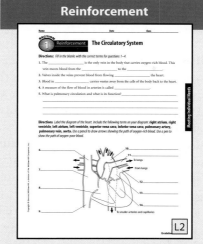

Reinforcement
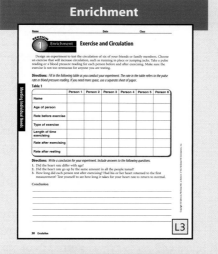

Enrichment

Directed Reading (English/Spanish)
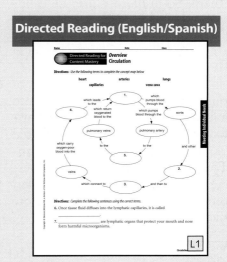

Study Guide

Reading Essentials

Assessment

Test Practice Workbook
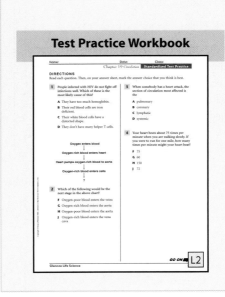

Chapter Review
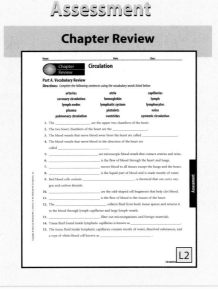

Chapter Tests
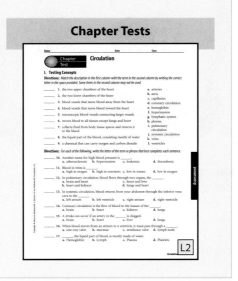

Science Content Background

section 1 The Circulatory System

How Materials Move Through the Body

In 1628, William Harvey published his findings, which indicated that blood in the human body follows "a motion as it were in a circle." Pumped by the heart, the blood moved through arteries into the body and returned to the heart via the veins. However, it was still a mystery how the blood made its way from the arteries, through tissues, and into the veins. Not until the invention of the microscope was it discovered that minute vessels, the capillaries, made the connection.

The Heart

The heart is a muscular organ that lies in the thoracic cavity between the lungs. It is enclosed by a protective sac of fibrous tissue, the pericardium.

The initiation of the heartbeat originates within the heart muscle. The sinoatrial node is a modified piece of cardiac muscle tissue located near the superior vena cava. An impulse for this node spreads to the atria of the heart, causing them to contract. Another node (atrioventricular) receives the signal and then transmits it to the ventricles, causing them to contract.

The first human heart transplant was conducted in 1967. The first permanent artificial heart was implanted in 1982, but the patient lived for only three months afterward. In July 2001, a self-contained, battery-powered, titanium and plastic heart was implanted into a man, who lived for thirteen months afterward.

Hank Morgan/Photo Researchers, Inc.

Blood Vessels

A cross section of arteries and veins shows that the walls have three layers. The inner lining of the vessels is covered with two types of tissue; one of these is a network of elastic connective tissue. The middle layer is smooth muscle and elastic tissue. The outer layer is collagenous connective tissue. The middle layer in veins is less developed than it is in arteries, and therefore collapses more easily. Capillaries have walls only one cell thick. This allows materials to diffuse through them. So numerous are the capillaries in the body that most cells are less than one-fourth of a millimeter from a capillary.

Blood Pressure

The pressure in the blood vessels is the result of a greater amount of blood being pumped into the arteries than can be absorbed by the arterioles and capillaries. Blood pressure is measured in millimeters of mercury with a sphygmomanometer. The person taking the blood pressure is listening for the flow of blood to be cut off and then return to normal while taking note of the respective pressures.

Teacher to Teacher

Edward G. Ezrailson, Ph.D.
Science Consultant
Spring, TX

"The discussion of the circulatory system provides an opportunity to integrate the sciences. Supernovas are known to produce elements found in nature. The iron bound to hemoglobin came from deep space in this manner when the planets were formed."

Edward G. Ezrailson, Ph.D.

section 2

Blood
A Liquid Tissue

The liquid component of blood, plasma, is a complex solution of organic and inorganic substances dissolved in water. Blood is about 90 percent water and eight percent proteins. The remaining two percent is made up of dissolved substances such as electrolytes, gases, and nutrients. Blood characteristics such as pH and sugar content are precisely controlled by the body. The pH of blood is slightly alkaline, and serious problems can occur if the pH changes only slightly. Because blood supplies for transfusions often are in short supply, synthetic substitutes for blood or blood parts are being developed.

section 3

The Lymphatic System
Understanding Tissue Fluid

The lymphatic system can be thought of as a branch of the circulatory system. Lymph is blood plasma that has diffused and filtered from the blood capillaries into the spaces between cells. Often the lymph in these spaces is referred to as intercellular or interstitial fluid. Like blood plasma, lymph consists mainly of water, some dissolved substances, and white blood cells called lymphocytes.

Lymph from the interstitial spaces passes through lymph capillaries, larger lymph vessels, lymph nodes, and lymph glands before entering a vein. Lymph is not under great pressure; therefore, external forces are needed to cause it to flow. Gravity plays a role in the movement of lymph above the heart. Other forces include the contraction of smooth muscles in the larger lymphatic vessels, the contraction of skeletal muscles, and the movements of breathing muscles. Backflow of lymph is prevented by valves in the large lymph vessels.

When skin is subjected to continued friction or pressure, a blow, or heat, the blood capillaries

Charles Gupton/The Stock Market

dilate. Lymph accumulates in the injured area, and a liquid-filled blister is formed under the skin. If there is poor circulation in a region of the body, lymph may collect and cause a swelling called edema.

chapter content resources

Internet Resources
For additional content background, visit
life.msscience.com to:
- access your book online
- find references to related articles in popular science magazines
- access Web links with related content background
- access current events with science journal topics

Print Resources
Biology (6th Edition), by Neil A. Campbell, Jane B. Reece, Pearson Benjamin Cummings Publishing, 2001
Human Anatomy & Physiology (5th Edition), by Elaine N. Marieb, Pearson Benjamin Cummings Publishing, 2000
Principles of Human Physiology, by William J. Germann, Cindy L. Stanfield; Pearson Benjamin Cummings Publishing, 2001

chapter 19

Chapter Vocabulary

atrium, p. 541
ventricle, p. 541
coronary circulation, p. 541
pulmonary circulation, p. 542
systemic circulation, p. 543
artery, p. 544
vein, p. 544
capillary, p. 545
plasma, p. 550
hemoglobin, p. 551
platelet, p. 551
lymph, p. 556
lymphatic system, p. 556
lymphocyte, p. 556
lymph node, p. 556

Science Journal Student responses may vary, but may include questions about blood, the heart, and lungs.

PowerPoint® Presentations

This CD-ROM is an editable Microsoft® PowerPoint® presentation that includes:

- a pre-made presentation for every chapter
- interactive graphics
- animations
- audio clips
- image bank
- all new section and chapter questions
- Standardized Test Practice
- transparencies
- pre-lab questions for all labs
- Foldables directions
- links to life.msscience.com

chapter 19

Circulation

chapter preview

sections

1 The Circulatory System
Lab The Heart as a Pump

2 Blood

3 The Lymphatic System
Lab Blood Type Reactions

Virtual Lab What factors affect the likelihood of hypertension?

What does a highway have to do with circulation?

Think of this interchange as a simplified way to visualize how your blood travels through your body. Your complex circulatory system also plays an important role in protecting you from disease.

Science Journal Infer how the circulatory system provides your body with the nutrients it needs to stay healthy?

538

Theme Connection

Stability and Change The circulatory system is a good example of a system that functions to maintain stability and respond to changes in human life processes.

About the Photo

Transportation Systems Highway interchanges, like this one in England, are used in the same way that the circulatory system uses blood vessels. There are about 40 billion microscopic capillaries and they constitute the majority of the body's 100,000 miles of vessels. The circumference of Earth at the equator is about 25,000 miles. If all of the blood vessels in one adult were laid end to end, they would circle the equator four times.

Start-Up Activities

Comparing Circulatory and Road Systems

If you look at an aerial view of a road system, as shown in the photograph, you see roads leading in many directions. These roads provide a way to carry people and goods from one place to another. Your circulatory system is like a road system. Just as roads are used to transport goods to homes and factories, your blood vessels transport substances throughout your body.

1. Look at a map of your city, county, or state.
2. Identify roads that are interstates, as well as state and county routes, using the map key.
3. Plan a route to a destination that your teacher describes. Then plan a different return trip.
4. Draw a diagram in your Science Journal showing your routes to and from the destination.
5. **Think Critically** If the destination represents your heart, what do the routes represent? Draw a comparison between a blocked road on your map and a clogged artery in your body.

FOLDABLES
Study Organizer

Circulation Your body is supplied with nutrients by blood circulating through your blood vessels. Make the following Foldable to help you organize information about circulation.

STEP 1 **Fold** a sheet of paper in half lengthwise. Make the back edge about 5 cm longer than the front edge.

STEP 2 **Turn** the paper so the fold is on the bottom. Then, **fold** it into thirds.

STEP 3 **Unfold and cut** only the top layer along both folds to make three tabs. **Label** the top of the page *Circulation*, and label the three tabs *Pulmonary, Coronary,* and *Systemic.*

Read and Write As you read the chapter, write about each section under its tab.

Science Online
Preview this chapter's content and activities at life.mscience.com

539

The Circulatory System

as you read

What You'll Learn

- **Compare and contrast** arteries, veins, and capillaries.
- **Explain** how blood moves through the heart.
- **Identify** the functions of the pulmonary and systemic circulation systems.

Why It's Important

Your body's cells depend on the blood vessels to bring nutrients and remove wastes.

🔍 Review Vocabulary

heart: organ that circulates blood through your body continuously

New Vocabulary

- atrium
- ventricle
- coronary circulation
- pulmonary circulation
- systemic circulation
- artery
- vein
- capillary

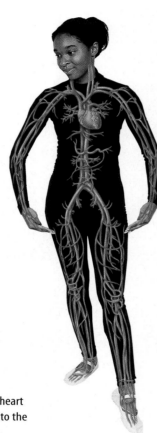

Figure 1 The blood is pumped by the heart to all the cells of the body and then back to the heart through a network of blood vessels.

How Materials Move Through the Body

It's time to get ready for school, but your younger sister is taking a long time in the shower. "Don't use up all the water," you shout. Water is carried throughout your house in pipes that are part of the plumbing system. The plumbing system supplies water for all your needs and carries away wastes. Just as you expect water to flow when you turn on the faucet, your body needs a continuous supply of oxygen and nutrients and a way to remove wastes. In a similar way materials are moved throughout your body by your cardiovascular (kar dee oh VAS kyuh lur) system. It includes your heart, kilometers of blood vessels, and blood.

Blood vessels carry blood to every part of your body, as shown in **Figure 1.** Blood moves oxygen and nutrients to cells and carries carbon dioxide and other wastes away from the cells. Sometimes blood carries substances made in one part of the body to another part of the body where these substances are needed. Movement of materials into and out of your cells occurs by diffusion (dih FYEW zhun) and active transport. Diffusion occurs when a material moves from an area where there is more of it to an area where there is less of it. Active transport is the opposite of diffusion. Active transport requires an input of energy from the cell, but diffusion does not.

The Heart

Your heart is an organ made of cardiac muscle tissue. It is located behind your breastbone, called the sternum, and between your lungs. Your heart has four compartments called chambers. The two upper chambers are called the right and left **atriums** (AY tree umz). The two lower chambers are called the right and left **ventricles** (VEN trih kulz). During one heartbeat, both atriums contract at the same time. Then, both ventricles contract at the same time. A one-way valve separates each atrium from the ventricle below it. The blood flows only in one direction from an atrium to a ventricle, then from a ventricle into a blood vessel. A wall prevents blood from flowing between the two atriums or the two ventricles. This wall keeps blood rich in oxygen separate from blood low in oxygen. If oxygen-rich blood and oxygen-poor blood were to mix, your body's cells would not get all the oxygen they need.

Scientists have divided the circulatory system into three sections—coronary circulation, pulmonary (PUL muh ner ee) circulation, and systemic circulation. The beating of your heart controls blood flow through each section.

Coronary Circulation Your heart has its own blood vessels that supply it with nutrients and oxygen and remove wastes. **Coronary** (KOR uh ner ee) **circulation,** as shown in **Figure 2,** is the flow of blood to and from the tissues of the heart. When the coronary circulation is blocked, oxygen and nutrients cannot reach all the cells of the heart. This can result in a heart attack.

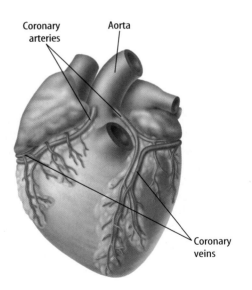

Coronary arteries

Aorta

Coronary veins

Figure 2 Like the rest of the body, the heart receives the oxygen and nutrients that it needs from the blood. The blood also carries away wastes from the heart's cells. On the diagram, you can see the coronary arteries, which nourish the heart.

Mini LAB

Inferring How Hard the Heart Works

Procedure

1. Make a fist and observe its size, which is approximately the size of your heart.
2. Place your fist in a **bowl of water.** Then clench and unclench your fist to cause water to squirt out between your thumb and forefinger.
3. Continue the squeezing action for 3 min. Determine the number of squeezes per minute.

Analysis

1. State how many times you squeezed your fist in 1 min. A resting heart beats approximately 70 times per minute.
2. What can you do when the muscles of your hand and arm get tired? Explain why cardiac muscle does not get tired.

Try at Home

Quick Demo
The Heart
Materials a beef heart
Estimated Time 10 minutes
Procedure Have students examine the heart. Draw attention to the thick, muscular walls of the ventricles, which are necessary to provide a lifetime of pumping action.

Use Science Words
Word Origins The body's largest artery is the aorta. The name has its origin in the Greek word *aorte*, meaning "to raise or lift." Discuss why this is an appropriate word for this vessel. The aorta rises from the top of the heart.

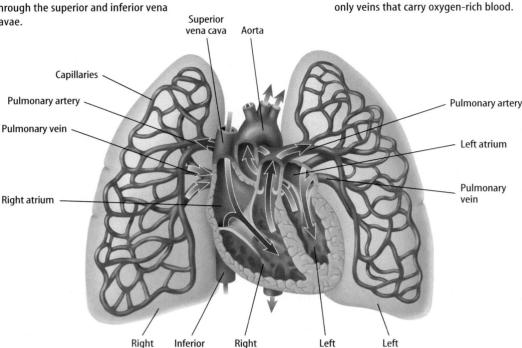

Blood, high in carbon dioxide and low in oxygen, returns from the body to the heart. It enters the right atrium through the superior and inferior vena cavae.

Oxygen-rich blood travels from the lungs through the pulmonary veins and into the left atrium. The pulmonary veins are the only veins that carry oxygen-rich blood.

The right atrium contracts, forcing the blood into the right ventricle. When the right ventricle contracts, the blood leaves the heart and goes through the pulmonary arteries to the lungs. The pulmonary arteries are the only arteries that carry blood that is high in carbon dioxide.

The left atrium contracts and forces the blood into the left ventricle. The left ventricle contracts, forcing the blood out of the heart and into the aorta.

Figure 3 Pulmonary circulation moves blood between the heart and lungs.

Pulmonary Circulation
The flow of blood through the heart to the lungs and back to the heart is **pulmonary circulation.** Use **Figure 3** to trace the path blood takes through this part of the circulatory system. The blood returning from the body through the right side of the heart and to the lungs contains cellular wastes. The wastes include molecules of carbon dioxide and other substances. In the lungs, gaseous wastes diffuse out of the blood, and oxygen diffuses into the blood. Then the blood returns to the left side of the heart. In the final step of pulmonary circulation, the oxygen-rich blood is pumped from the left ventricle into the aorta (ay OR tuh), the largest artery in your body. Next, the oxygen-rich blood flows to all parts of your body.

542 CHAPTER 19 Circulation

Active Reading

Double Bubble Map This strategy uses two bubble maps to compare concepts. Each cluster has qualities that are unique to that idea. In the middle, connecting ideas are similar to both cluster ideas. This technique helps students list common qualities before writing or discussing a topic. Have students design a Double Bubble Map about the circulatory system. [L2]

Sample map:

- from heart to body and back to heart
- oxygen provided to cells
- wastes removed from cells
- Pulmonary circulation
- Pumped by heart
- Systemic circulation
- from heart to lungs and back to heart
- wastes removed in lungs
- oxygen added

Systemic Circulation Oxygen-rich blood moves to all of your organs and body tissues, except the heart and lungs, by **systemic circulation,** and oxygen-poor blood returns to the heart. Systemic circulation is the largest of the three sections of your circulatory system. **Figure 4** shows the major arteries (AR tuh reez) and veins (VAYNZ) of the systemic circulation system. Oxygen-rich blood flows from your heart in the arteries of this system. Then nutrients and oxygen are delivered by blood to your body cells and exchanged for carbon dioxide and wastes. Finally, the blood returns to your heart in the veins of the systemic circulation system.

✓ **Reading Check** *What are the functions of the systemic circulation system in your body?*

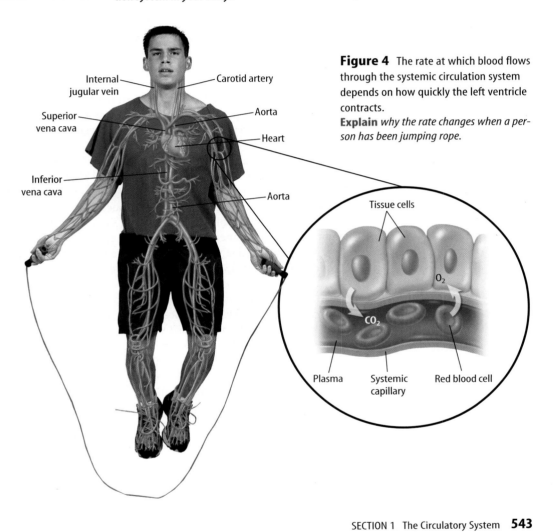

Figure 4 The rate at which blood flows through the systemic circulation system depends on how quickly the left ventricle contracts.
Explain *why the rate changes when a person has been jumping rope.*

Labels: Internal jugular vein · Carotid artery · Superior vena cava · Aorta · Heart · Inferior vena cava · Aorta · Tissue cells · O_2 · CO_2 · Plasma · Systemic capillary · Red blood cell

Caption Answer

Figure 4 The rate increases in order to supply oxygen and remove carbon dioxide and wastes that build up, because of your muscles increasing their activity.

Use Science Words

Word Meaning Have students compare the architectural meaning of the word *atrium* with its biological meaning. In architectural use, the word atrium refers to an entrance hall or open court. In biological terms, the atrium is the entrance chamber that receives blood from the body.

Teacher FYI

Coronary Arteries Cardiac muscles do not directly absorb nutrients and oxygen from the blood that flows through the chambers of the heart. The right and left coronary arteries that branch off the aorta near its origin from the left ventricle supply nutrients and oxygen and remove wastes. In addition, the right coronary artery also supplies the sinoatrial and atrioventricular nodes responsible for coordinating the heartbeat.

Differentiated Instruction

Visually Impaired Provide visually impaired students with a three-dimensional model of the heart and lungs. Have students trace with their fingers both pulmonary and coronary circulations. As they trace the flow of blood, have a sighted peer identify major vessels and chambers of the heart. L1 **Kinesthetic**

Activity

Capillary Walls Have students prepare a brief report on how the one-cell thick capillary walls are held together and why a covering would not be practical. A cementing material holds the cells together. A covering would not easily allow materials to pass in and out of the walls. [L2] [IS]
Logical-Mathematical

✔ Reading Check

Answer Arteries and veins have walls consisting of three layers of tissue. Arteries move blood away from the heart; veins move blood to the heart. Veins have valves that keep blood from flowing backward.

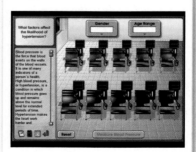
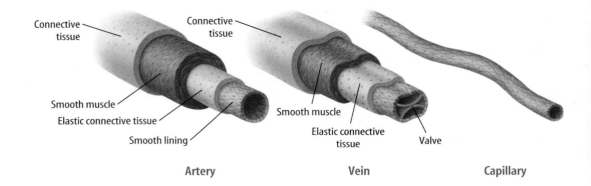

Figure 5 The structures of arteries, veins, and capillaries are different. Valves in veins prevent blood from flowing backward. Capillaries are much smaller. Capillary walls are only one cell thick.

Connective tissue
Connective tissue
Smooth muscle
Elastic connective tissue
Smooth lining
Artery

Smooth muscle
Elastic connective tissue
Valve
Vein

Capillary

Blood Vessels

In the middle 1600s, scientists proved that blood moves in one direction in a blood vessel, like traffic on a one-way street. They discovered that blood moves by the pumping of the heart and flows from arteries to veins. But, they couldn't explain how blood gets from arteries to veins. Using a new invention of that time, the microscope, scientists discovered capillaries (KAP uh ler eez), the connection between arteries and veins.

Arteries As blood is pumped out of the heart, it travels through arteries, capillaries, and then veins. **Arteries** are blood vessels that carry blood away from the heart. Arteries, shown in **Figure 5,** have thick, elastic walls made of connective tissue and smooth muscle tissue. Each ventricle of the heart is connected to an artery. The right ventricle is connected to the pulmonary artery, and the left ventricle is attached to the aorta. Every time your heart contracts, blood is moved from your heart into arteries.

Veins The blood vessels that carry blood back to the heart are called **veins,** as shown in **Figure 5.** Veins have one-way valves that keep blood moving toward the heart. If blood flows backward, the pressure of the blood against the valves causes them to close. The flow of blood in veins also is helped by your skeletal muscles. When skeletal muscles contract, the veins in these muscles are squeezed and help blood move toward the heart. Two major veins return blood from your body to your heart. The superior vena cava returns blood from your head and neck. Blood from your abdomen and lower body returns through the inferior vena cava.

✔ **Reading Check** *What are the similarities and differences between arteries and veins?*

Science Journal

Blood Vessels Have students write brief descriptions in their own words of arteries, veins, and capillaries. Ask them to write a paragraph contrasting these three types of blood vessels. [L2] [IS]
Linguistic

Capillaries Arteries and veins are connected by microscopic blood vessels called **capillaries,** as shown in **Figure 5.** The walls of capillaries are only one cell thick. You can see capillaries when you have a bloodshot eye. They are the tiny red lines you see in the white area of your eye. Nutrients and oxygen diffuse into body cells through the thin capillary walls. Waste materials and carbon dioxide diffuse from body cells into the capillaries.

Blood Pressure

If you fill a balloon with water and then push on it, the pressure moves through the water in all directions, as shown in **Figure 6.** Your circulatory system is like the water balloon. When your heart pumps blood through the circulatory system, the pressure of the push moves through the blood. The force of the blood on the walls of the blood vessels is called blood pressure. This pressure is highest in arteries and lowest in veins. When you take your pulse, you can feel the waves of pressure. This rise and fall of pressure occurs with each heartbeat. Normal resting pulse rates are 60 to 100 heartbeats per minute for adults, and 80 to 100 beats per minute for children.

Measuring Blood Pressure Blood pressure is measured in large arteries and is expressed by two numbers, such as 120 over 80. The first number is a measure of the pressure caused when the ventricles contract and blood is pushed out of the heart. This is called the systolic (sihs TAH lihk) pressure. Then, blood pressure drops as the ventricles relax. The second number is a measure of the diastolic (di uh STAH lihk) pressure that occurs as the ventricles fill with blood just before they contract again.

Controlling Blood Pressure Your body tries to keep blood pressure normal. Special nerve cells in the walls of some arteries sense changes in blood pressure. When pressure is higher or lower than normal, messages are sent to your brain by these nerve cells. Then messages are sent by your brain to raise or lower blood pressure—by speeding up or slowing the heart rate for example. This helps keep blood pressure constant within your arteries. When blood pressure is constant, enough blood reaches all organs and tissues in your body and delivers needed nutrients to every cell.

INTEGRATE Physics

Blood Pressure Some molecules of nutrients are forced through capillary walls by the force of blood pressure. What is the cause of the pressure? Discuss your answer with a classmate. Then write your answer in your Science Journal.

Figure 6 When pressure is exerted on a fluid in a closed container, the pressure is transmitted through the liquid in all directions. Your circulatory system is like a closed container.

Water-filled balloon

INTEGRATE Physics

Blood Pressure Blood pressure, a force produced by the pumping action of the heart, is exerted by the blood against the walls of the blood vessels. Blood pressure tends to force fluids into capillaries at their artery end (where blood pressure is higher); osmosis tends to force water out of capillaries at their venous end (where blood pressure is lower).

Fun Fact

Systolic pressure is the peak pressure of blood flow caused by the contraction of the ventricles. Diastolic pressure is the low pressure of blood flow produced when the heart relaxes.

Teacher FYI

Pressure The term *pressure* is used in discussions of fluids such as gases and liquids. Pressure is produced when a force is applied to a fluid. The greater the force, the greater the pressure on the fluid, and the smaller the volume it takes up. Usually, the volume of a gas decreases by one-half when the pressure doubles. The volume of liquids changes less dramatically.

Visualizing Atherosclerosis

Have students examine the pictures and read the captions. Then ask the following questions.

How do you think a person with restricted arteries would feel while lifting a heavy object? Possible answers: short of breath, difficulty breathing, dizzy, lightheaded, tiring quickly, chest pain.

How do medicines that thin the blood help a person who is suffering from atherosclerosis? Possible answer: The thinner blood will be able to pass more easily through a restricted passage.

IDENTIFYING Misconceptions

Cholesterol The main component of fatty deposits, atheroma, in arteries is cholesterol, a steroid lipid. Some students will assume that any cholesterol is unhealthy. The liver produces cholesterol, it is a component of nerve cells, and it is involved in the synthesis of certain hormones. Normal levels of cholesterol are essential for good health.

Use an Analogy

Lime Deposits The buildup of fatty deposits in the walls of arteries is similar to the buildup of lime deposits in plumbing pipes. In both cases, the pathway is narrowed and the flow is reduced. If possible, show students an old pipe that is full of this type of deposit.

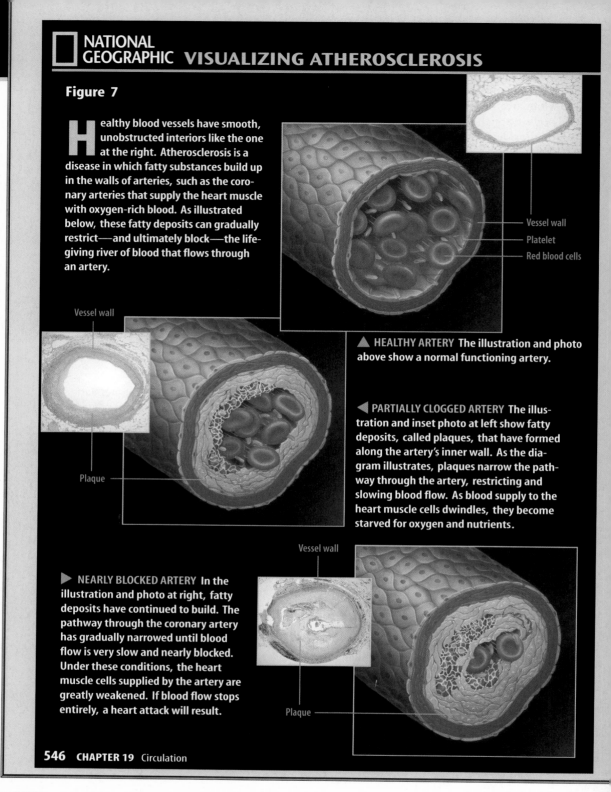

VISUALIZING ATHEROSCLEROSIS

Figure 7

Healthy blood vessels have smooth, unobstructed interiors like the one at the right. Atherosclerosis is a disease in which fatty substances build up in the walls of arteries, such as the coronary arteries that supply the heart muscle with oxygen-rich blood. As illustrated below, these fatty deposits can gradually restrict—and ultimately block—the life-giving river of blood that flows through an artery.

Vessel wall
Platelet
Red blood cells

Vessel wall
Plaque

▲ **HEALTHY ARTERY** The illustration and photo above show a normal functioning artery.

◄ **PARTIALLY CLOGGED ARTERY** The illustration and inset photo at left show fatty deposits, called plaques, that have formed along the artery's inner wall. As the diagram illustrates, plaques narrow the pathway through the artery, restricting and slowing blood flow. As blood supply to the heart muscle cells dwindles, they become starved for oxygen and nutrients.

Vessel wall

▶ **NEARLY BLOCKED ARTERY** In the illustration and photo at right, fatty deposits have continued to build. The pathway through the coronary artery has gradually narrowed until blood flow is very slow and nearly blocked. Under these conditions, the heart muscle cells supplied by the artery are greatly weakened. If blood flow stops entirely, a heart attack will result.

Plaque

546 CHAPTER 19 Circulation

Differentiated Instruction

Challenge Have students find statistics on atherosclerosis, and graph the data. This can include percentages in categories such as age, race, gender, countries, or other characteristics that may be associated with the condition. L3

Cardiovascular Disease

Any disease that affects the cardiovascular system—the heart, blood vessels, and blood—can seriously affect the health of your entire body. People often think of cancer and automobile accidents as the leading causes of death in the United States. However, heart disease is the leading cause of death, when you factor in all age groups.

Atherosclerosis One leading cause of heart disease is called atherosclerosis (ah thuh roh skluh ROH sus). In this condition, shown in **Figure 7,** fatty deposits build up on arterial walls. Eating foods high in cholesterol and saturated fats can cause these deposits to form. Atherosclerosis can occur in any artery in the body, but deposits in coronary arteries are especially serious. If a coronary artery is blocked, a heart attack can occur. Open heart surgery may then be needed to correct the problem.

Hypertension Another condition of the cardiovascular system is called hypertension (HI pur TEN chun), or high blood pressure. **Figure 8** shows the instruments used to measure blood pressure. When blood pressure is higher than normal most of the time, extra strain is placed on the heart. The heart must work harder to keep blood flowing. One cause of hypertension is atherosclerosis. A clogged artery can increase pressure within the vessel. The walls become stiff and hard, like a metal pipe. The artery walls no longer contract and dilate easily because they have lost their elasticity.

Heart Failure Heart failure results when the heart cannot pump blood efficiently. It might be caused when heart muscle tissue is weakened by disease or when heart valves do not work properly. When the heart does not pump blood properly, fluids collect in the arms, legs, and lungs. People with heart failure usually are short of breath and tired.

 **Reading Check** *What is heart failure?*

Figure 8 Blood pressure is measured in large arteries using a blood pressure cuff and stethoscope.

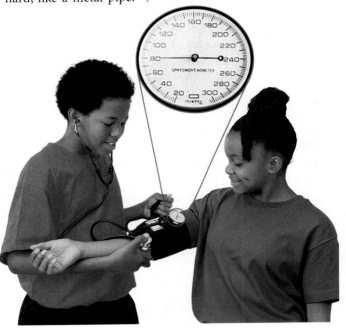

Science Online

Topic: Cardiovascular Disease
Visit life.msscience.com for Web links to recent news or magazine articles about cardiovascular disease.

Activity In your Science Journal, list five steps you can take to lead a healthy life style.

Inquiry Lab

Testing Physical Fitness

Purpose To test physical fitness, have students measure their heart rates before, during, and after exercise, until their heart rates return to normal.

Possible Materials stopwatch, jump rope, or access to steps

Estimated Time 1 class session

Teaching Strategies
• Have students stand for 2 minutes and then measure their heart rate.
• Students can predict their maximum heart rate and level of fitness. Have students measure their heart rate immediately after jumping rope or climbing stairs for 120 s.
• Have students continue exercising an additional 120 s, and then monitor their heart rate and measure the amount of time required for their heart rate to return to normal. During recovery, students should remain standing and relatively still.
• Have students research what their different heart rates indicate about their fitness.
• Allow students to explore other questions that arise.

For additional inquiry activities, see *Science Inquiry Labs.*

 **Reading Check**

Answer Heart failure occurs when the heart cannot pump blood efficiently.

SECTION 1 The Circulatory System **547**

 LAB DEMONSTRATION

Purpose to compare the flow of liquid through an open tube and a partially blocked tube

Materials two 10-cm pieces of plastic tubing, dropper, mineral oil, modeling clay, tweezers

Preparation Be sure there is enough clay to impede but not stop the flow of oil.

Procedure Insert a dropperful of oil into the tubing. Squeeze the oil through the tubing. Observe the amount of oil that comes out. Compare this to the amount of oil that comes out of a clay-clogged tube.

Expected Outcome Students will observe less oil escaping from the clogged tube.

Assessment

How does this demonstrate what happens in clogged arteries? The clay represents deposits that may collect on the walls of arteries. Blood flow in these tubes is slower, and blocked tubes can carry less blood than unblocked tubes.

Figure 9 Nicotine, present in tobacco, contracts blood vessels and causes the body to release hormones that raise blood pressure. **Name** *another substance that raises blood pressure.*

Preventing Cardiovascular Disease Having a healthy lifestyle is important for the health of your cardiovascular system. The choices you make to maintain good health may reduce your risk of future serious illness. Regular checkups, a healthful diet, and exercise are part of a heart-healthy lifestyle.

Many diseases, including cardiovascular disease, can be prevented by following a good diet. Choose foods that are low in salt, sugar, cholesterol, and saturated fats. Being overweight is associated with heart disease and high blood pressure. Large amounts of body fat force the heart to pump faster.

Learning to relax and having a regular program of exercise can help prevent tension and relieve stress. Exercise also strengthens the heart and lungs, helps in controlling cholesterol, tones muscles, and helps lower blood pressure.

Another way to prevent cardiovascular disease is to not smoke. Smoking causes blood vessels to contract, as shown in **Figure 9,** and makes the heart beat faster and harder. Smoking also increases carbon monoxide levels in the blood. Not smoking helps prevent heart disease and a number of respiratory system problems, too.

section 1 review

Summary

Cardiovascular System
- Coronary circulation is the flow of blood to and from the tissues of the heart.
- Pulmonary circulation is the flow of blood through the heart, to the lungs, and back to the heart.
- Oxygen-rich blood is moved to all tissues and organs of the body, except the heart and lungs, by systemic circulation.

Blood Vessels
- Arteries carry blood away from the heart.
- Veins carry blood back to the heart.
- Arteries and veins are connected by capillaries.

Blood Pressure
- The force of the blood on the walls of the blood vessels is called blood pressure.

Cardiovascular Disease
- Atherosclerosis occurs when fatty deposits build up on arterial walls.
- High blood pressure is called hypertension.

Self Check

1. **Compare and contrast** the structure of the three types of blood vessels.
2. **Explain** the pathway of blood through the heart.
3. **Contrast** pulmonary and systemic circulation. Identify which vessels carry oxygen-rich blood.
4. **Explain** how exercise can help prevent heart disease.
5. **Think Critically** What waste product builds up in blood and cells when the heart is unable to pump blood efficiently?

Applying Skills

6. **Concept Map** Make an events-chain concept map to show pulmonary circulation beginning at the right atrium and ending at the aorta.
7. **Use a Database** Research diseases of the circulatory system. Make a database showing what part of the circulatory system is affected by each disease. Categories should include the organs and vessels of the circulatory system.

 Science online life.msscience.com/self_check_quiz

section 1 review

1. Arteries have thick walls. Veins have valves. Capillary walls are only one cell thick.
2. right atrium, right ventricle, lungs, left atrium, left ventricle
3. Pulmonary circulation transports blood through the heart and to the lungs and back to the heart; veins carry oxygen-rich blood. Systemic circulation transports blood to all parts of the body and back to the heart; arteries carry oxygen-rich blood.
4. It strengthens the heart and lungs, helps control cholesterol, and lowers blood pressure.
5. carbon dioxide
6. Map should show blood moving in this order: right atrium, right ventricle, pulmonary artery, lungs, pulmonary vein, left atrium, left ventricle, aorta.
7. Sample entries: atherosclerosis—arteries; myocardial infarction—heart; leukemia—white blood cells

The Heart as a Pump

The heart is a pumping organ. Blood is forced through the arteries as heart muscles contract and then relax. This creates a series of waves in blood as it flows through the arteries. These waves are called the pulse. Try this lab to learn how physical activity affects your pulse.

◉ Real-World Question

What does the pulse rate tell you about the work of the heart?

Goals

- **Observe** pulse rate.
- **Compare** pulse rate at rest to rate after jogging.

Materials

watch or clock with a second hand
*stopwatch
*Alternate materials

Pulse Rate

Pulse Rate	Partner's	Yours
At rest	about 70	about 70
After jogging	Answers will vary.	Answers will vary.

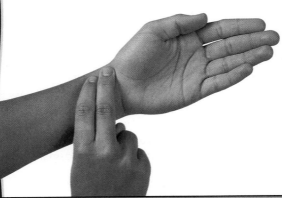

◉ Procedure

1. Make a table like the one shown. Use it to record your data.
2. Sit down to take your pulse. Your partner will serve as the recorder.
3. Find your pulse by placing your middle and index fingers over the radial artery in your wrist as shown in the photo. **WARNING:** *Do not press too hard.*
4. **Count** each beat of the radial pulse silently for 15 s. Multiply the number of beats by four to find your pulse rate per minute. Have your partner record the number in the data table.
5. Now jog in place for 1 min and take your pulse again. Count the beats for 15 s.
6. **Calculate** this new pulse rate and have your partner record it in the data table.
7. Reverse roles with your partner and repeat steps 2 through 6.
8. **Collect** and record the new data.

◉ Conclude and Apply

1. **Describe** why the pulse rate changes.
2. **Infer** what causes the pulse rate to change.
3. **Explain** why the heart is a pumping organ.

ℭommunicating Your Data

Record the class average for pulse rate at rest and after jogging. Compare the class averages to your data. **For more help, refer to the** Science Skill Handbook.

LAB **549**

ℭommunicating Your Data

Prepare a graph of the class data and include the class average. Compare the data from your class with those of another class in your school. L2

◉ Real-World Question

Purpose Students measure radial pulse rate and interpret their data. L2 **ELL** COOP LEARN **IS** Logical-Mathematical

Process Skills interpret data, communicate, make and use graphs, use numbers, infer

Time Required 30–40 minutes

Safety Precautions Caution students not to press too hard. Students with heart conditions should not jog.

Teaching Strategies

- Encourage all students to perform some activity to increase their heart rate unless medically unadvisable. Suggest that these students be the timekeeper and recorder for a pair of students.
- Students should count their pulses silently and then report results to the recorder.
- Explain that the reason for multiplying by four is to obtain the pulse rate for one minute ($15 \text{ s} \times 4 = 60 \text{ s}$ or one min).

◉ Conclude and Apply

1. Pulse rate increases as they jog.
2. Greater muscle activity requires the heart to pump more blood (and thus more oxygen) to the muscles.
3. The heart pumps blood to the body to meet all of its needs—both when at rest and when active.

☑ Assessment

Performance Have students design another activity that will result in an increased pulse rate (i.e., dancing or shooting baskets). Have them do the activity and gather and interpret their data. Use **PASC,** p. 95.

Bellringer

Section Focus Transparencies also are available on the Interactive Chalkboard CD-ROM.

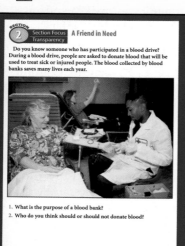

SECTION 2 Section Focus Transparency **A Friend in Need**

Do you know someone who has participated in a blood drive? During a blood drive, people are asked to donate blood that will be used to treat sick or injured people. The blood collected by blood banks saves many lives each year.

1. What is the purpose of a blood bank?
2. Who do you think should or should not donate blood?

Tie to Prior Knowledge

Blood Volume Fill five 1-L plastic soft drink bottles with red-colored water. Explain to students that this volume of water represents the 5 L of blood in an adult.

Text Question Answer

Blood could be referred to as the tissue of life because it carries oxygen and nutrients to your cells. It also carries waste products to your kidneys to be removed and helps fight infections and heal wounds.

---

section 2 Blood

as you read

What You'll Learn
- **Identify** the parts and functions of blood.
- **Explain** why blood types are checked before a transfusion.
- **Give examples** of diseases of blood.

Why It's Important
Blood plays a part in every major activity of your body.

⚙ Review Vocabulary
blood vessels: Structures that include arteries, veins, and capillaries, which transport blood

New Vocabulary
- plasma
- hemoglobin
- platelet

Functions of Blood

You take a last, deep, calming breath before plunging into a dark, vessel-like tube. The water transports you down the slide much like the way blood carries substances to all parts of your body. Blood has four important functions.

1. Blood carries oxygen from your lungs to all your body cells. Carbon dioxide diffuses from your body cells into your blood. Your blood carries carbon dioxide to your lungs to be exhaled.

2. Blood carries waste products from your cells to your kidneys to be removed.

3. Blood transports nutrients and other substances to your body cells.

4. Cells and molecules in blood fight infections and help heal wounds.

Anything that disrupts or changes these functions affects all the tissues of your body. Can you understand why blood is sometimes called the tissue of life?

Parts of Blood

As shown in **Figure 10,** blood is a tissue made of plasma (PLAZ muh), platelets (PLAYT luts), and red and white blood cells. Blood makes up about eight percent of your body's total mass. If you weigh 45 kg, you have about 3.6 kg of blood moving through your body. The amount of blood in an adult would fill five 1-L bottles.

Plasma The liquid part of blood is mostly water and is called **plasma.** It makes up more than half the volume of blood. Nutrients, minerals, and oxygen are dissolved in plasma and carried to cells. Wastes from cells are also carried in plasma.

55% — Plasma

White blood cells

45% — Red blood cells

Figure 10 The blood in this graduated cylinder has separated into its parts. Each part plays a key role in body functions.

550 CHAPTER 19 Circulation

Section 2 Resource Manager

Chapter FAST FILE Resources
Transparency Activity, p. 47
Directed Reading for Content Mastery, p. 20
MiniLAB, p. 4
Enrichment, p. 31

Reinforcement, p. 28
Mathematics Skill Activities, p. 33
Cultural Diversity, p. 18

Blood Cells A cubic millimeter of blood has about five million red blood cells. These disk-shaped blood cells, shown in **Figure 11,** are different from other cells in your body because they have no nuclei. They contain **hemoglobin** (HEE muh gloh bun), which is a molecule that carries oxygen and carbon dioxide, and made of an iron compound that gives blood its red color. Hemoglobin carries oxygen from your lungs to your body cells. Then it carries some of the carbon dioxide from your body cells back to your lungs. The rest of the carbon dioxide is carried in the cytoplasm of red blood cells and in plasma. Red blood cells have a life span of about 120 days. They are made at a rate of 2 million to 3 million per second in the center of long bones like the femur in your thigh. Red blood cells wear out and are destroyed at about the same rate.

In contrast to red blood cells, a cubic millimeter of blood has about 5,000 to 10,000 white blood cells. White blood cells fight bacteria, viruses, and other invaders of your body. Your body reacts to invaders by increasing the number of white blood cells. These cells leave the blood through capillary walls and go into the tissues that have been invaded. Here, they destroy bacteria and viruses and absorb dead cells. The life span of white blood cells varies from a few days to many months.

Circulating with the red and white blood cells are platelets. **Platelets** are irregularly shaped cell fragments that help clot blood. A cubic millimeter of blood can contain as many as 400,000 platelets. Platelets have a life span of five to nine days.

Science Online

Topic: White Blood Cells
Visit life.msscience.com for Web links to information about types of human white blood cells and their functions.

Activity Write a brief summary describing how white blood cells destroy bacteria and viruses in your Science Journal.

Figure 11 Red blood cells supply your body with oxygen, and white blood cells and platelets have protective roles.

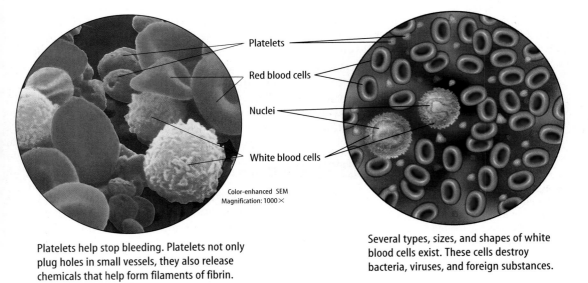

Platelets

Red blood cells

Nuclei

White blood cells

Color-enhanced SEM
Magnification: 1000×

Platelets help stop bleeding. Platelets not only plug holes in small vessels, they also release chemicals that help form filaments of fibrin.

Several types, sizes, and shapes of white blood cells exist. These cells destroy bacteria, viruses, and foreign substances.

SECTION 2 Blood **551**

2 Teach

Make a Model
Clay Blood Cells Have students make models of red and white blood cells from modeling clay. Encourage students to make the models to scale in order to reinforce concepts about the relative sizes, shapes, and colors of the cells. L2 IN **Visual-Spatial**

Use an Analogy
Amoebas Have students view a film clip of amoeba activity to draw an analogy to white blood cell movement and ingestion. L2

Discussion
Blood Platelets How do blood platelets function in maintaining homeostasis when the skin is cut? Platelets form clots to help prevent further blood loss. L2

Quick Demo
Living Blood
Materials students, contained area of space, chairs with wheels
Estimated Time 15 minutes
Procedure Assign student groups to represent red blood cells, white blood cells and platelets. Use chairs with wheels like plasma, to carry cells and platelets. Create a hole in the contained area, allowing some red and white blood cells to escape. Have the platelets try to clog the hole by holding hands. Draw attention to the fact that blood is a living tissue, which must be maintained.

Cultural Diversity

Seaweed Soup It is a tradition for Korean mothers to eat seaweed soup for the first month after giving birth. Koreans believe that seaweed soup cleanses the blood and increases milk production. Seaweeds have generous amounts of calcium and minerals required to maintain healthy bones, which produce blood cells.

Differentiated Instruction

English-Language Learners Have students find out what *CPR* stands for, analyze the parts of the words to determine their meanings, and then describe this technique to their classmates. CPR stands for cardiopulmonary resuscitation. Cardio = heart; pulmonary = lungs; resuscitation = to revive. CPR is an emergency procedure that includes clearing air passages, mouth-to-mouth resuscitation, and heart massage. L2

Mini LAB

Purpose Students use a model to discover how a scab forms.
L2 ELL IS **Visual-Spatial**

Materials 5-cm × 5-cm square of gauze, aluminum foil, liquid bandage solution, dropper, water

Teaching Strategy Explain that the gauze represents the fibers formed in the clotting process.

Analysis

1. The water soaks into the untreated gauze but not into the treated area.
2. The treated area is like a scab because it forms a covering that prevents leakage of liquids and protects the area underneath it.

Assessment

Process Have students use cotton cloth and white glue to make another model of scab formation and repeat the water drop test. Use **Performance Assessment in the Science Classroom,** p. 123.

Discussion

Hemophilia Why would relatively minor cuts and bruises be hazardous to a person with hemophilia? Even minor cuts and bruises would cause major bleeding problems that could result in death.

Reading Check

Answer platelets, clotting factors, and fibrin

Figure 12 When the skin is damaged, a sticky blood clot seals the leaking blood vessel. Eventually, a scab forms to protect the wound from further damage and allow it to heal.

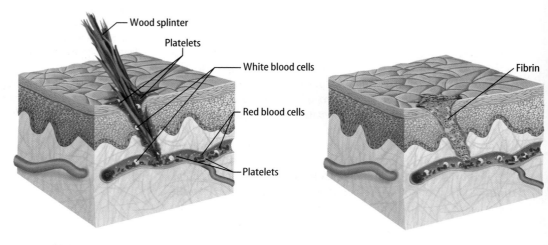

- Wood splinter
- Platelets
- White blood cells
- Red blood cells
- Platelets
- Fibrin

Mini LAB

Modeling Scab Formation

Procedure

1. Place a 5-cm × 5-cm square of **gauze** on a piece of **aluminum foil.**
2. Place several drops of a **liquid bandage solution** onto the gauze and let it dry. Keep the liquid bandage away from eyes and mouth.
3. Use a **dropper** to place one drop of **water** onto the area of the liquid bandage. Place another drop of water in another area of the gauze.

Analysis

1. Compare the drops of water in both areas.
2. Describe how the treated area of the gauze is like a scab.

Blood Clotting

You're running with your dog in a park, when all of a sudden you trip and fall down. Your knee starts to bleed, but the bleeding stops quickly. Already the wounded area has begun to heal. Bleeding stops because platelets and clotting factors in your blood make a blood clot that plugs the wounded blood vessels. A blood clot also acts somewhat like a bandage. When you cut yourself, platelets stick to the wound and release chemicals. Then substances called clotting factors carry out a series of chemical reactions. These reactions cause threadlike fibers called fibrin (FI brun) to form a sticky net, as shown in **Figure 12.** This net traps escaping blood cells and plasma and forms a clot. The clot helps stop more blood from escaping. After the clot is in place and becomes hard, skin cells begin the repair process under the scab. Eventually, the scab is lifted off. Bacteria that might get into the wound during the healing process are destroyed by white blood cells.

✔ Reading Check *What blood components help form blood clots?*

Most people will not bleed to death from a minor wound, such as a cut or scrape. However, some people have a genetic condition called hemophilia (hee muh FIH lee uh). Their plasma lacks one of the clotting factors that begins the clotting process. A minor injury can be a life threatening problem for a person with hemophilia.

552   CHAPTER 19 Circulation

Differentiated Instruction

Challenge Have students find out about the role of vitamin K, prothrombin, calcium ions, thrombin, fibrinogen, and fibrin in the mechanism of blood clotting. Suggest they use this information to draw a labeled diagram showing the sequence of events and the components involved in this process. L3 IS **Linguistic** P

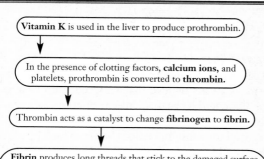

Vitamin K is used in the liver to produce prothrombin.

In the presence of clotting factors, **calcium ions,** and platelets, prothrombin is converted to **thrombin.**

Thrombin acts as a catalyst to change **fibrinogen** to **fibrin.**

Fibrin produces long threads that stick to the damaged surface of the blood vessel and form the webbing of the clot, trapping blood cells and platelets, which strengthen the clot.

Table 1 Blood Types

Blood Type	Antigen	Antibody
A	A	Anti-B
B	B	Anti-A
AB	A, B	None
O	None	Anti-B Anti-A

Blood Types

Blood clots stop blood loss quickly in a minor wound, but a person with a serious wound might lose a lot of blood and need a blood transfusion. During a blood transfusion, a person receives donated blood or parts of blood. The medical provider must be sure that the right type of blood is given. If the wrong type is given, the red blood cells will clump together. Then, clots form in the blood vessels and the person could die.

The ABO Identification System People can inherit one of four types of blood: A, B, AB, or O, as shown in **Table 1.** Types A, B, and AB have chemical identification tags called antigens (AN tih junz) on their red blood cells. Type O red blood cells have no antigens.

Each blood type also has specific antibodies in its plasma. Antibodies are proteins that destroy or neutralize substances that do not belong in or are not part of your body. Because of these antibodies, certain blood types cannot be mixed. This limits blood transfusion possibilities as shown in **Table 2.** If type A blood is mixed with type B blood, the type A antibodies determine that type B blood does not belong there. The type A antibodies cause the type B red blood cells to clump. In the same way, type B antibodies cause type A blood to clump. Type AB blood has no antibodies, so people with this blood type can receive blood from A, B, AB, and O types. Type O blood has both A and B antibodies.

Reading Check *Why are people with type O blood called universal donors?*

Table 2 Blood Transfusion Options

Type	Can Receive	Can Donate To
A	O, A	A, AB
B	O, B	B, AB
AB	all	AB
O	O	all

SECTION 2 Blood **553**

Visual Learning

Table 1 and Table 2 After students have studied the information in these tables, have them explain why people with blood type AB are sometimes called universal recipients. These people can receive all blood types. L2

Teacher FYI

Indicator Serums To determine the blood type of an individual, suspensions of the person's red blood cells are mixed separately with different serums. Each serum has a known, particular antibody. When a serum causes agglutination of blood cells, it indicates that the cells contain the antigen with which that specific antibody agglutinates. This reaction identifies the blood type of the individual.

Fun Fact

The first known blood transfusion was conducted in the seventeenth century by French physician Jean Baptiste Denis, who infused sheep's blood into the patient.

Reading Check

Answer People with type O blood are able to give blood to people with all other blood types.

Curriculum Connection

Health Some cultures consider blood to be a necessary part of their diet. Others use it in the preparation of certain foods (blood sausage). Have students find out what nutrients are supplied by blood. usually sodium and iron L2

Research Have students research the pros and cons of artificial blood that scientists are developing. Ask students to find out which areas of the world would most benefit from the use of artificial blood.

✔ Reading Check

Answer If someone with Rh− blood receives a transfusion from someone with Rh+ blood, the results could be fatal.

Applying Science

Answers

1. There would be 54 possible donors. Type B, Rh+ blood can be transfused with Type B, Rh+ (9%); Type B, Rh− (1%); Type O, Rh+ (37%); and Type O, Rh− (7%).

2. Type O, Rh− would be most at risk as this population can receive only Type O, Rh− blood. In an average sample of 100 people, only 7 would match this blood type.

Activity

Blood Transfusions Have students research how blood transfusion experiments started in the early 1800s. The first successful blood transfusion was performed in the seventeenth century by a French physician, Jean Baptiste Denis. He used lamb's blood. His second attempt was unsuccessful and the patient died. L2

Blood Transfusions The first blood transfusions took place in the 1600s and were from animal to animal, and then from animal to human. In 1818, James Blundell, a British obstetrician, performed the first successful transfusion of human blood to a patient for the treatment of hemorrhage.

The Rh Factor Another chemical identification tag in blood is the Rh factor. The Rh factor also is inherited. If the Rh factor is on red blood cells, the person has Rh-positive (Rh+) blood. If it is not present, the person's blood is called Rh-negative (Rh−). If an Rh− person receives a blood transfusion from an Rh+ person, he or she will produce antibodies against the Rh factor. These antibodies can cause Rh+ cells to clump. Clots then form in the blood vessels and the person could die.

When an Rh− mother is pregnant with an Rh+ baby, the mother might make antibodies to the child's Rh factor. Close to the time of birth, Rh antibodies from the mother can pass from her blood into the baby's blood. These antibodies can destroy the baby's red blood cells. If this happens, the baby must receive a blood transfusion before or right after birth. At 28 weeks of pregnancy and immediately after the birth, an Rh− mother can receive an injection that blocks the production of antibodies to the Rh+ factor. These injections prevent this life-threatening situation. To prevent deadly results, blood groups and Rh factor are checked before transfusions and during pregnancies.

✔ Reading Check   *Why is it important to check Rh factor?*

Applying Science

Will there be enough blood donors?

Successful human blood transfusions began during World War II. This practice is much safer today due to extensive testing of the donated blood prior to transfusion. Health care professionals have determined that each blood type can receive certain other blood types as illustrated in **Table 2.**

Blood Type Distribution

	Rh+(%)	Rh−(%)
O	37	7
A	36	6
B	9	1
AB	3	1

Identifying the Problem

The table on the right lists the average distribution of blood types in the United States. The data are recorded as percents, or a sample of 100 people. By examining these data and the data in **Table 2,** can you determine safe donors for each blood type? Recall that people with Rh− blood cannot receive a transfusion from an Rh+ donor.

Solving the Problem

1. If a Type B, Rh+ person needs a blood transfusion, how many possible donors are there?

2. Frequently, the supply of donated blood runs low. Which blood type and Rh factor would be most affected in such a shortage? Explain your answer.

554   CHAPTER 19 Circulation

Teacher ▐FYI▌

Rhesus Monkeys The original research regarding the Rh factor was done with blood cells from rhesus monkeys. The antigen found was named using the first two letters of the word *rhesus.* Treatment for the Rh problem, *erythroblastosis fetalis,* includes blood transfusions and exposure to fluorescent light.

Differentiated Instruction

Challenge Explain to students that if the blood type of the donor and recipient are the same, it is not always true that a blood transfusion is absolutely safe. Have students research reasons for this and write a report. A number of other blood factors can cause harmful reactions. Also, repeated transfusions of even the same blood type may eventually cause agglutination. This is because there are other antigens on red blood cells besides the A and B antigens. L3

Diseases of Blood

Because blood circulates to all parts of your body and performs so many important functions, any disease of the blood is a cause for concern. One common disease of the blood is anemia (uh NEE mee uh). In this disease of red blood cells, body tissues can't get enough oxygen and are unable to carry on their usual activities. Anemia has many causes. Sometimes, anemia is caused by the loss of large amounts of blood. A diet lacking iron or certain vitamins also might cause anemia. In addition, anemia can be the result of another disease or a side effect of treatment for a disease. Still other types of anemia are inherited problems related to the structure of the red blood cells. Cells from one such type of anemia, sickle-cell anemia, are shown in **Figure 13.**

Leukemia (lew KEE mee uh) is a disease in which one or more types of white blood cells are made in excessive numbers. These cells are immature and do not fight infections well. They fill the bone marrow and crowd out the normal cells. Then not enough red blood cells, normal white blood cells, and platelets can be made. Types of leukemia affect children or adults. Medicines, blood transfusions, and bone marrow transplants are used to treat this disease. If the treatments are not successful, the person eventually will die from related complications.

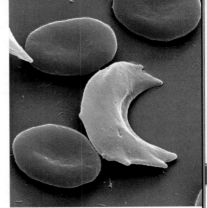

Color-enhanced TEM Magnification: 7400×

Figure 13 Persons with sickle-cell anemia have misshapened red blood cells. The sickle-shaped cells clog the capillaries of a person with this disease. Oxygen cannot reach tissues served by the capillaries, and wastes cannot be removed. **Describe** *how this damages the affected tissues.*

section 2 review

Summary

Parts of Blood
- Plasma is made mostly of water, with nutrients, minerals, and oxygen dissolved in it.
- Red blood cells contain hemoglobin, which carries oxygen and carbon dioxide.
- White blood cells control infections and viruses.
- Blood clotting factors and platelets help blood to clot.

Blood Types
- People can inherit one of four types of blood and an Rh factor.
- Type A, B, and AB blood all have antigens. Type O blood has no antigens.

Diseases of Blood
- Anemia is a disease of red blood cells.
- Leukemia is a disease that produces immature white blood cells that don't fight infections.

Self Check

1. **List** the four functions of blood in the body.
2. **Infer** why blood type and Rh factor are checked before a transfusion.
3. **Interpret Data** Look at the data in **Table 2** about blood group interactions. To which group(s) can blood type AB donate blood, and which blood type(s) can AB receive blood from?
4. **Think Critically** Think about the main job of your red blood cells. If red blood cells couldn't deliver oxygen to your cells, what would be the condition of your body tissues?

Applying Math

5. **Use Percentages** Find the total number of red blood cells, white blood cells, and platelets in 1 mm³ of blood. Calculate what percentage of the total each type is.

 life.msscience.com/self_check_quiz

section 2 review

1. carries oxygen to cells and removes carbon dioxide; carries wastes to kidneys; transports nutrients from the digestive system to cells; has materials to fight infections and heal wounds
2. to prevent blood cells from clumping
3. only to another person with AB blood type; A, B, and O
4. Wastes would build up and become toxic.
5. In a cubic millimeter of blood, there are over 5 million red blood cells, 5,000 to 10,000 white blood cells, and 400,000 platelets. Thus blood is approximately 92.5% red blood cells, 0.09–0.18% white blood cells, and 7.4% platelets.

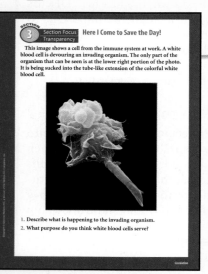
as you read

What You'll Learn
- **Describe** functions of the lymphatic system.
- **Identify** where lymph comes from.
- **Explain** how lymph organs help fight infections.

Why It's Important
The lymphatic system helps protect you from infections and diseases.

🔍 Review Vocabulary
smooth muscles: muscles found in your internal organs and digestive track

New Vocabulary
- lymph
- lymphatic system
- lymphocyte
- lymph node

Functions of the Lymphatic System

You're thirsty so you turn on the water faucet and fill a glass with water. The excess water runs down the drain. In a similiar way, your body's excess tissue fluid is removed by the lymphatic (lihm FA tihk) system. The nutrient, water, and oxygen molecules in blood diffuse through capillary walls to nearby cells. Water and other substances become part of the tissue fluid that is found between cells. This fluid is collected and returned to the blood by the lymphatic system.

After tissue fluid diffuses into the lymphatic capillaries it is called **lymph** (LIHMF). Your **lymphatic system,** as shown in **Figure 14,** carries lymph through a network of lymph capillaries and larger lymph vessels. Then, the lymph drains into large veins near the heart. No heartlike structure pumps the lymph through the lymphatic system. The movement of lymph depends on the contraction of smooth muscles in lymph vessels and skeletal muscles. Lymphatic vessels, like veins, have valves that keep lymph from flowing backward. If the lymphatic system is not working properly, severe swelling occurs because the tissue fluid cannot get back to the blood.

In addition to water and dissolved substances, lymph also contains **lymphocytes** (LIHM fuh sites), a type of white blood cell. Lymphocytes help your body defend itself against disease-causing organisms.

 **Reading Check** *What are the differences and similarities between lymph and blood?*

Lymphatic Organs

Before lymph enters the blood, it passes through lymph nodes, which are bean-shaped organs of varying sizes found throughout the body. **Lymph nodes** filter out microorganisms and foreign materials that have been taken up by lymphocytes. When your body fights an infection, lymphocytes fill the lymph nodes. The lymph nodes become warm, reddened, and tender to the touch. After the invaders are destroyed, the redness, warmth, and tenderness in the lymph nodes goes away.

Section 3 Resource Manager

Chapter *FAST FILE* Resources
Transparency Activity, p. 48
Enrichment, p. 32
Reinforcement, p. 29
Directed Reading for Content Mastery, pp. 21, 22

Lab Worksheet, pp. 7–8
Lab Management and Safety, p. 69

Besides lymph nodes, the tonsils, the thymus, and the spleen are important lymphatic organs. Tonsils are in the back of your throat and protect you from harmful microorganisms that enter through your mouth and nose. Your thymus is a soft mass of tissue located behind the sternum. It makes lymphocytes that travel to other lymph organs. The spleen is the largest lymphatic organ. It is located behind the upper-left part of the stomach and filters the blood by removing worn out and damaged red blood cells. Cells in the spleen take up and destroy bacteria and other substances that invade your body.

A Disease of the Lymphatic System

HIV is a deadly virus. When HIV enters a person's body, it attacks and destroys lymphocytes called helper T cells that help make antibodies to fight infections. This affects a person's immunity to some diseases. Usually, the person dies from these dieseases, not from the HIV infection.

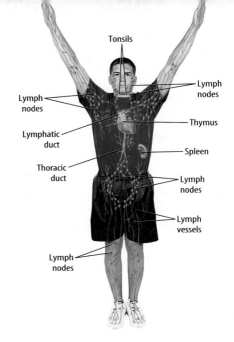

Figure 14 The lymphatic system is connected by a network of vessels.
Describe *how muscles help move lymph.*

section 3 review

Summary

Functions of the Lymphatic System

- Fluid is collected and returned from the body tissues to the blood by the lymphatic system.
- After fluid from tissues diffuses into the lymphatic capillaries it is called lymph.
- Lymphocytes are a type of white blood cell that helps your body defend itself against disease.

Lymphatic Organs

- Lymph nodes filter out microorganisms and foreign materials taken up by lymphocytes.
- The tonsils, thymus, and spleen also protect your body from harmful microorganisms that enter through your mouth and nose.

A Disease of the Lymphatic System

- HIV destroys helper T cells that help make antibodies to fight infections.

Self Check

1. **Describe** where lymph comes from and how it gets into the lymphatic capillaries.
2. **Explain** how lymphatic organs fight infection.
3. **Sequence** the events that occur when HIV enters the body.
4. **Think Critically** When the amount of fluid in the spaces between cells increases, so does the pressure in these spaces. What do you infer will happen?

Applying Skills

5. **Concept Map** The circulatory system and the lymphatic system work together in several ways. Make a concept map comparing the two systems.
6. **Communicate** An infectious microorganism enters your body. In your Science Journal, describe how the lymphatic system protects the body against the microorganism.

Caption Answer
Figure 14 As skeletal muscles contract, they force lymph to move within the lymph vessels.

3 Assess

DAILY INTERVENTION

Check for Understanding

Logical-Mathematical Have students construct a table to compare the functions of lymph nodes, the thymus, and the spleen. L2 P

Reteach

Breast Cancer Explain why lymph nodes are sometimes examined to determine the extent of breast cancer. Nodes along the side of the chest and under the arm filter lymph that drains from the breast. The lymph nodes are examined for cancer cells. If present, further treatments are recommended.

☑ Assessment

Performance Ask students to do research and write about the functions of macrophages. Macrophages engulf foreign materials and probably alter them to initiate the immune response. Use **Performance Assessment in the Science Classroom,** p. 159. L2

section 3 review

1. from tissue fluids; by absorption and diffusion
2. Nodes filter out microorganisms and foreign materials; tonsils protect the mouth and throat from germs; thymus makes lymphocytes; spleen removes and recycles old red blood cells and destroys bacteria.
3. It attacks helper T-cells.
4. Diffusion of fluid into the lymphatic capillaries will increase.
5. Cardiovascular: vessels connect heart to body and transport food and gases; Lymphatic: vessels connect lymph nodes to body, transport lymph, return fluid to blood, fight pathogens.
6. Journal entries should reflect the roles of the lymph nodes, lymphocytes, and the spleen in providing protection against microorganisms.

⊙ Real-World Question

Purpose Students determine how different blood types react when mixed. L2 **ELL**

IS Naturalist P

Process Skills design an experiment, form a hypothesis, observe and infer, communicate, recognize cause and effect, separate and control variables, interpret data

Time Required 50 minutes

Materials For simulated blood, mix 10 mL of lowfat milk with 10 mL of water and add 2 or 3 drops of red food coloring. The lemon juice and water are used as antigens. Also needed are droppers, small paper cups, a marking pen, and a graduated cylinder.

⊙ Form a Hypothesis

Possible Hypothesis Most students' hypotheses will reflect that there will be clumping when some blood types are mixed.

⊙ Test Your Hypothesis

Possible Procedures

- Mark four paper cups with blood type names A, B, AB, and O.
- Add 5 mL simulated blood to each cup.
- Use the lemon juice as antigen A for blood types B and O. Add 2 to 3 drops of lemon juice to cups B and O. Clumping occurs.
- Use water as antigen A for blood types A and AB. Add 2 to 3 drops to cups A and AB. No clumping occurs.

Design Your Own

Blood Type Reactions

Goals
- **Design** an experiment that simulates the reactions between different blood types.
- **Identify** which blood types can donate to which other blood types.

Possible Materials
simulated blood (10 mL low-fat milk and 10 mL water plus red food coloring)
lemon juice as antigen A (for blood types B and O)
water as antigen A (for blood types A and AB)
droppers
small paper cups
marking pen
10-mL graduated cylinder

Safety Precautions
WARNING: *Do not taste, eat, or drink any materials used in the lab.*

⊙ Real-World Question

Human blood can be classified into four main blood types—A, B, AB, and O. These types are determined by the presence or absence of antigens on the red blood cells. After blood is collected into a transfusion bag, it is tested to determine the blood type. The type is labeled clearly on the bag. Blood is refrigerated to keep it fresh and available for transfusion. What happens when two different blood types are mixed?

⊙ Form a Hypothesis

Based on your reading and observations, state a hypothesis about how different blood types will react to each other.

Alternative Inquiry Lab

Extend the Activity Make this lab an Inquiry Lab by building on the experience. Encourage your students to use what they have learned to brainstorm questions about easing the ongoing problem of blood supply shortages. Have student groups each choose one question to explore. Ask them to list the materials and do the research they need to explore their questions. Unsafe or impractical questions should be eliminated. Students could develop a marketing plan or education program to recruit more blood donors. Conduct the experiments after all of the necessary materials and research have been gathered.

▶ Test Your Hypothesis

Make a Plan

1. As a group, agree upon the hypothesis and decide how you will test it. Identify the results that will confirm the hypothesis.

2. **List** the steps you must take and the materials you will need to test your hypothesis. Be specific. Describe exactly what you will do in each step.

3. **Prepare** a data table like the one at the right in your Science Journal to record your observations.

4. Reread the entire experiment to make sure all steps are in logical order.

5. **Identify** constants and variables. Blood type O will be the control.

Blood Type Reactions	
Blood Type	**Clumping (Yes or No)**
A	No
B	Yes
AB	No
O	Yes

Follow Your Plan

1. While doing the experiment, record your observations and complete the data table in your Science Journal.

▶ Analyze Your Data

1. **Compare** the reactions of each blood type (A, B, AB, and O) when antigen A was added to the blood.

2. **Observe** where clumping took place.

3. **Compare** your results with those of other groups.

4. What was the control factor in this experiment?

5. What were your variables?

▶ Conclude and Apply

1. Did the results support your hypothesis? Explain.

2. **Predict** what might happen to a person if other antigens are not matched properly.

3. What would happen in an investigation with antigen B added to each blood type?

𝒞ommunicating Your Data

Write a brief report on how blood is tested to determine blood type. **Describe** why this is important to know before receiving a blood transfusion. **For more help, refer to the** Science Skill Handbook.

LAB 559

Teaching Strategy Instruct students to look for curdling of the milk in the simulated blood as it reacts with the acidic lemon juice. This represents the "clumping" of blood cells.

▶ Analyze Your Data

Expected Outcomes Clumping will occur when the lemon juice antigen is mixed with blood types B and O. No clumping will occur when the water antigen is mixed with blood types A and AB.

Answers to Questions

1. Blood types B and O clumped when lemon juice antigen A was added. Blood types A and AB did not clump when water antigen A was added.

2. Clumping took place in cups with B and O blood types.

3. Students' results should be similar to those of other groups.

4. The control in this experiment was the blood solution and the amount of each antigen added to the blood.

5. The variable was the type of antigen solution used.

Error Analysis Have students compare their results with their hypotheses and explain any differences that might have occurred.

▶ Conclude and Apply

1. Answers will be determined by student hypotheses.

2. Clumping of blood cells could result.

3. Clumping would occur with blood types A and O and not with blood types B and AB.

✓ Assessment

Oral Have students explain why persons with blood type O can donate to anyone but can receive only from a person with blood type O. Type O has no A or B antigens and has antibodies A and B. L2

𝒞ommunicating Your Data

Have students do online or library research to find information on how blood is checked before a transfusion is given.

Content Background

Medieval and early Renaissance medicine in Europe was dominated by the theories of Galen, a Roman physician. Galen taught that there were two types of blood and separate circulatory systems, venous and arterial. It was believed that blood was manufactured in the liver and delivered to veins. The blood received air from the lungs and was carried to the heart by the pulmonary vein, which also took "sooty vapours" back to be expelled by the lungs. Oxygenated blood supposedly seeped from the right to the left side of the heart and became arterial blood that was then consumed by the body.

Renaissance doctors began to question this theory when Arab medical texts became available in the West. Pulmonary circulation and the function of the lungs were described in the 1200s.

Harvey correctly described the circulatory system in 1628. Harvey also discovered that the volume of blood exiting the heart could not be replaced by the daily intake of food and water.

Discussion

Theory of Circulation What did Harvey do to develop his theory of circulation that is still done in medical research today? Possible answer: He used animals for his early observations and applied his findings to humans.

Historical Significance

Harvey's discovery and theory were based on the observations of his predecessors and measurable phenomenon to construct a result that others could reproduce. He had developed a scientific method. Investigation, as opposed to traditional authority, was a defining aspect of the Renaissance that led to modern scientific practices.

Have a Heart

Dr. Daniel Hale Williams was a pioneer in open-heart surgery.

People didn't always know where blood came from or how it moved through the body

"Ouch!" You prick your finger, and when blood starts to flow out of the cut, you put on a bandage. But if you were a scientist living long ago, you might have also asked yourself some questions: How did your blood get to the tip of your finger? And why and how does it flow through (and sometimes out of!) your body?

As early as the 1500s, a Spanish scientist named Miguel Serveto (mee GEL • ser VE toh) asked that question. His studies led him to the theory that blood circulated throughout the human body, but he didn't know how or why.

About 100 years later, William Harvey, an English doctor, explored Serveto's idea. Harvey studied animals to develop a theory about how the heart and the circulatory system work.

Harvey hypothesized, from his observations of animals, that blood was pumped from the heart throughout the body, and that it returned to the heart and recirculated. He published his ideas in 1628 in his famous book, *On the Motion of the Heart and Blood in Animals.* His theories were correct, but many of Harvey's patients left him. His patients thought his ideas were ridiculous. His theories were correct, and over time, Harvey's book became the basis for all modern research on heart and blood vessels.

Medical Pioneer

More than two centuries later, another pioneer stepped forward and used Harvey's ideas to change the science frontier again. His name was Dr. Daniel Hale Williams. In 1893, Williams used what he knew about heart and blood circulation to become a new medical pioneer. He performed the first open-heart surgery by removing a knife from the heart of a stabbing victim. He stitched the wound to the fluid-filled sac surrounding the heart, and the patient lived several more years. In 1970, the U.S. recognized Williams by issuing a stamp in his honor.

Report Identify a pioneer in science or medicine who has changed our lives for the better. Find out how this person started in the field, and how they came to make an important discovery. Give a presentation to the class.

science online

For more information, visit life.msscience.com/time

Report Divide students into teams and assign each an organ of the body. Each team will research that organ and prepare a presentation that compares its functions as they were known before the Renaissance with what is known today. The results can be presented as individual team reports or compiled into a pamphlet or bulletin board presentation. L2

Resources for Teachers and Students

The Greatest Benefit to Mankind: A Medical History of Humanity by Roy Porter. New York: W. W. Norton, 1998

Medicine: An Illustrated History by Albert S. Lyons and R. Joseph Petrucelli, II. New York: Harry N. Abrams, Inc., 1978

"William Harvey" by Frederick G. Kilgour, *Scientific American,* June 1952

Reviewing Main Ideas

Section 1 The Circulatory System

1. Arteries carry blood away from the heart. Capillaries allow the exchange of nutrients, oxygen, and wastes in cells. Veins return blood to the heart.

2. Carbon-dioxide-rich blood enters the right atrium, moves to the right ventricle, and then goes to the lungs through the pulmonary artery. Oxygen-rich blood returns to the left atrium, moves to the left ventricle, and then leaves through the aorta.

3. Pulmonary circulation is the path of blood between the heart and lungs. Circulation through the rest of the body is called systemic circulation. Coronary circulation is the flow of blood to tissues of the heart.

Section 2 Blood

1. Plasma carries nutrients, blood cells, and other substances.

2. Red blood cells carry oxygen and carbon dioxide, platelets form clots, and white blood cells fight infection.

3. A, B, AB, and O blood types are determined by the presence or absence of antigens on red blood cells.

4. Anemia is a disease of red blood cells, in which not enough oxygen is carried to the body's cells.

5. Leukemia is a disease where one or more types of white blood cells are present in excessive numbers. These cells are immature and do not fight infection well.

Section 3 The Lymphatic System

1. Lymph structures filter blood, produce white blood cells that destroy bacteria and viruses, and destroy worn out blood cells.

2. HIV attacks helper T cells, which are a type of lymphocyte. The person is unable to fight infections well.

Visualizing Main Ideas

Copy and complete this concept map on the functions of the parts of the blood.

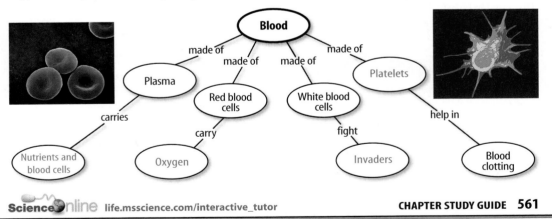

Reviewing Main Ideas

Summary statements can be used by students to review the major concepts of the chapter.

Visualizing Main Ideas

See student page.

Visit **life.msscience.com**
/self_check_quiz
/interactive_tutor
/vocabulary_puzzlemaker
/chapter_review
/standardized_test

Assessment Transparency

For additional assessment questions, use the *Assessment Transparency* located in the transparency book.

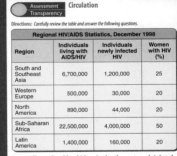

Using Vocabulary

1. coronary circulation (or veins)
2. lymphatic system
3. Hemoglobin
4. Platelets
5. capillaries
6. pulmonary circulation
7. Lymphatic system or Lymphocytes
8. systemic circulation
9. Arteries
10. ventricles

Checking Concepts

11. B	16. C
12. C	17. D
13. A	18. D
14. C	19. A
15. A	

Thinking Critically

20. Oxygen-rich blood: aorta, coronary arteries, left atrium, left ventricle; carbon dioxide-filled blood: coronary veins, inferior vena cava, right atrium, right ventricle, superior vena cava

21. All three blood vessels transport blood. Capillaries are only one cell thick; arteries have three layers; veins have valves. Veins carry blood to the heart; arteries carry blood away from the heart; capillaries link veins to arteries.

Using Vocabulary

artery p. 544
atrium p. 541
capillary p. 545
coronary circulation p. 541
hemoglobin p. 551
lymph p. 556
lymph node p. 556
lymphatic system p. 556

lymphocyte p. 556
plasma p. 550
platelet p. 551
pulmonary circulation p. 542
systemic circulation p. 543
vein p. 544
ventricle p. 541

Fill in the blanks with the correct vocabulary word(s).

1. The _____ carries blood to the heart.

2. The _____ transports tissue fluid through a network of vessels.

3. _____ is the chemical in red blood cells.

4. _____ are cell fragments.

5. The smallest blood vessels are called the _____.

6. The flow of blood to and from the lungs is called _____.

7. _____ helps protect your body against infections.

8. The largest section of the circulatory system is the _____.

9. _____ are blood vessels that carry blood away from the heart.

10. The two lower chambers of the heart are called the right and left _____.

Checking Concepts

Choose the word or phrase that best answers the question.

11. Where does the exchange of food, oxygen, and wastes occur?
    A) arteries
    B) capillaries
    C) veins
    D) lymph vessels

12. What is circulation to all body organs called?
    A) coronary
    B) pulmonary
    C) systemic
    D) organic

13. Where is blood under greatest pressure?
    A) arteries
    B) capillaries
    C) veins
    D) lymph vessels

14. Which cells fight off infection?
    A) red blood
    B) bone
    C) white blood
    D) nerve

15. Of the following, which carries oxygen in blood?
    A) red blood cells
    B) platelets
    C) white blood cells
    D) lymph

16. What is required to clot blood?
    A) plasma
    B) oxygen
    C) platelets
    D) carbon dioxide

17. What kind of antigen does type O blood have?
    A) A
    B) B
    C) A and B
    D) no antigen

Use the figure below to answer question 18.

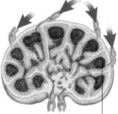

Lymphocytes

18. What is the bean-shaped organ above that filters out microorganisms and foreign materials taken up by lymphocytes?
    A) kidney
    B) lymph
    C) lung
    D) lymph node

19. What is the largest filtering lymph organ?
    A) spleen
    B) thymus
    C) tonsil
    D) node

 life.msscience.com/vocabulary_puzzlemaker

Use the Exam*View*® Pro Testmaker CD-ROM to:
• create multiple versions of tests
• create modified tests with one mouse click for inclusion students
• edit existing questions and add your own questions
• build tests aligned with state standards using built-in State Curriculum Tags
• change English tests to Spanish with one mouse click and vice versa

Thinking Critically

20. Identify the following as having oxygen-rich or carbon dioxide-filled blood: *aorta, coronary arteries, coronary veins, inferior vena cava, left atrium, left ventricle, right atrium, right ventricle,* and *superior vena cava.*

21. Compare and contrast the three types of blood vessels.

22. Compare and contrast the life spans of the red blood cells, white blood cells, and platelets.

23. Describe the sequence of blood clotting from the wound to forming a scab.

24. Compare and contrast the functions of arteries, veins, and capillaries.

25. Concept Map Copy and complete the events-chain concept map showing how lymph moves in your body.

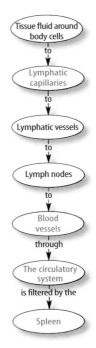

Tissue fluid around body cells

to

Lymphatic capillaries

to

Lymphatic vessels

to

Lymph nodes

to

Blood vessels

through

The circulatory system

is filtered by the

Spleen

26. Explain how the lymphatic system works with the cardiovascular system.

27. Infer why cancer of the blood cells or lymph nodes is hard to control.

28. Explain why a pulse is usually taken at the neck or wrist, when arteries are distributed throughout the body.

Performance Activities

29. Poster Prepare a poster illustrating heart transplants. Include an explanation of why the patient is given drugs that suppress the immune system and describe the patient's life after the operation.

30. Scientific Illustrations Prepare a drawing of the human heart and label its parts.

Applying Math

Use the table below to answer question 31.

Gender and Heart Rate	
Sex	**Pulse/Minute**
Male 1	72
Male 2	64
Male 3	65
Female 1	67
Female 2	84
Female 3	74

31. Heart Rates Using the table above, find the average heart rate of the three males and the three females. Compare the two averages.

32. Blood Mass Calculate how many kilograms of blood is moving through your body, if blood makes up about eight percent of your body's total mass and you weigh 38 kg.

 Science Online life.msscience.com/chapter_review

CHAPTER REVIEW 563

Thinking Critically

22. red blood cells—120 days; white blood cells—a few days to several months; platelets—5 to 9 days

23. Student responses should match **Figure 12.**

24. All transport blood. Arteries carry blood away from the heart. Veins carry blood to the heart. Capillaries connect arteries and veins.

25. See student page.

26. The lymphatic system, much like the cardiovascular system, carries fluid away from body tissues and returns it to your circulatory system through veins. The lymphatic system collects tissue fluid and returns it to the blood.

27. Blood and lymph move throughout the entire body.

28. The arteries there are close to the skin, so the pulse can be easily felt.

Performance Activities

29. Drugs are given to prevent the body from rejecting the transplant (an antigen). Patients must avoid conditions that will bring them into contact with germs while their immune systems are suppressed. Use **Performance Assessment in the Science Classroom,** p. 145.

30. Compare student drawings to the illustration of the heart in **Figure 2.** Use **Performance Assessment in the Science Classroom,** p. 127.

Applying Math

National Math Standards
1, 5, 9

31. males = 67; females = 75; In general, males' heart rates are lower than females'.

32. 3 Kg

☑ Assessment   Resources

Reproducible Masters
Chapter *Fast File* Resources
  Chapter Review, pp. 39–40
  Chapter Tests, pp. 41–44
  Assessment Transparency Activity, p. 51
Glencoe Science Web site
  Chapter Review Test
  Standardized Test Practice

Glencoe Technology
  ♣ Assessment Transparency
  ⚫ Exam*View*® Pro Testmaker
  ▭ MindJogger Videoquiz
  ⚫ Interactive Chalkboard

FAST FILE

Answer Sheet A practice answer sheet can be found at life.msscience.com/answer_sheet.

Part 1 Multiple Choice

1. C	**6.** B
2. A	**7.** C
3. D	**8.** A
4. A	**9.** B
5. A	**10.** D

Part 2 Short Response

11. 2,000,000/sec × 60 sec/min × 60 min/hr = 7,200,000,000

12. 400,000 ÷ 10,000 = 40; 40 times more platelets than white blood cells

13. If type A blood is given to a type O person, the antibodies in type A blood would cause type O red blood cells to clump.

14. A is the pulmonary artery. Blood in the pulmonary artery could not get to the lungs to get rid of carbon dioxide and wastes and take on oxygen. The body would not be supplied with enough oxygen and waste gas would not be completely removed.

Part 1 Multiple Choice

Record your answers on the answer sheet provided by your teacher or on a sheet of paper.

1. Which of the following is a function of blood?
   A. carry saliva to the mouth
   B. excrete salts from the body
   C. transport nutrients and other substances to cells
   D. remove lymph from around cells

Use the table below to answer questions 2 and 3.

Results from Ashley's Activities			
Activity	**Pulse Rate (beats/min)**	**Body Temperature**	**Degree of Sweating**
1	80	98.6°F	None
2	90	98.8°F	Minimal
3	100	98.9°F	Little
4	120	99.1°F	Moderate
5	150	99.5°F	Considerable

2. Which of the following activities caused Ashley's pulse to be less than 100 beats per minute?
   A. Activity 2   C. Activity 4
   B. Activity 3   D. Activity 5

3. A reasonable hypothesis based on these data, is that during Activity 2, Ashley was probably
   A. sprinting   C. sitting down
   B. marching   D. walking slowly

4. Which of the following activities contributes to cardiovascular disease?
   A. smoking   C. sleeping
   B. jogging   D. balanced diet

5. Where does blood low in oxygen enter first?
   A. right atrium   C. left ventricle
   B. left atrium   D. right ventricle

6. Which of the following is an artery?
   A. left ventricle   C. superior vena cava
   B. aorta   D. inferior vena cava

7. Which of the following is NOT a part of the lymphatic system?
   A. lymph nodes   C. heartlike structure
   B. valves   D. lymph capillaries

Use the table below to answer questions 8 and 9.

Blood Cell Counts (per 1 mm³)			
Patient	**Red Blood Cells**	**White Blood Cells**	**Platelets**
Normal	3.58–4.99 million	3,400– 9,600	162,000– 380,000
Mrs. Stein	3 million	8,000	400,000
Mr. Chavez	5 million	7,500	50,000

8. What problem might Mrs. Stein have?
   A. low oxygen levels in tissues
   B. inability to fight disease
   C. poor blood clotting
   D. irregular heart beat

9. If Mr. Chavez cut himself, what might happen?
   A. minimal bleeding
   B. prolonged bleeding
   C. infection
   D. quick healing

10. Which lymphatic organ protects your body from harmful microorganisms that enter through your mouth?
    A. spleen   C. node
    B. thymus   D. tonsils

Test-Taking Tip

Don't Stray During the test, keep your eyes on your own paper. If you need to rest them, close them or look up at the ceiling.

15. B is the coronary circulation. If the coronary circulation is blocked, oxygen and nutrients cannot reach all the cells in the heart. This can result in a heart attack.

16. Capillaries have thin walls—one cell layer thick—so that nutrients and oxygen can diffuse into body cells from capillaries and waste materials and carbon dioxide can diffuse from body cells into capillaries. If capillaries were thick walled, then diffusion could not take place through their walls.

17. A person with hemophilia lacks one of the clotting factors that begin the clotting process. Bleeding in a cut would not stop quickly. If the cut was severe, the bleeding might become life threatening.

18. In leukemia, immature white blood cells crowd out the normal cells in the bone marrow. Thus not enough red blood cells, normal white blood cells and platelets can be made. The counts of these cells in the blood could be decreased.

Part 2 | **Short Response/Grid In**

Record your answers on the answer sheet provided by your teacher or on a sheet of paper.

11. If red blood cells are made at the rate of 2 million per second in the center of long bones, how many red blood cells are made in one hour?

12. If a cubic milliliter of blood has 10,000 white blood cells and 400,000 platelets, how many times more platelets than white blood cells are present in a cubic milliliter of blood?

13. What would happen if type A blood was given to a person with type O blood?

Use the illustration below to answer questions 14 and 15.

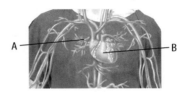

14. What might happen if there was a blood clot blocking vessel "A"?

15. What might happen if there was a blood clot blocking vessel "B"?

16. Why don't capillaries have thick, elastic walls?

17. Why would a cut be dangerous for a person with hemophilia?

18. Why would a person with leukemia have low numbers of red blood cells, normal white blood cells, and platelets in the blood?

Part 3 | **Open Ended**

Record your answers on a sheet of paper.

Use the illustration below to answer questions 19 and 20.

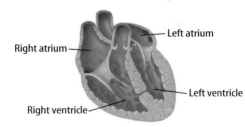

Right atrium — Left atrium — Left ventricle — Right ventricle

19. What is wrong with this heart? How do you know?

20. The left ventricle pumps blood under higher pressure than the right ventricle does. In which direction would you predict blood would flow through the hole in the heart? Compare the circulation in this heart with that of a normal heart.

21. What are some ways to prevent cardiovascular disease?

22. Compare and contrast diffusion and active transport.

23. Describe the role of the brain in blood pressure homeostasis. Why is this important?

24. Thrombocytopenia is a condition in which the number of platelets in the blood is decreased. Hemophilia is a genetic condition where blood plasma lacks one of the clotting factors. Compare how a small cut would affect a person with thrombocytopenia and someone with hemophilia.

the other way around. The oxygen level in the blood in the right ventricle would be higher than normal.

21. Some ways to prevent cardiovascular disease include having a healthy lifestyle, regular checkups, a healthful diet, and exercise. Not smoking is an important way to prevent cardiovascular disease.

22. Both processes move materials into and out of cells. Diffusion occurs when a material moves from an area where there is more of it to an area where there is less of it. Active transport moves a material from an area where there is less of it to an area where there is more of it. Active transport requires energy, but diffusion does not.

23. Special nerve cells in the walls of some arteries sense changes in blood pressure. When blood pressure is higher or lower than normal, messages are sent to your brain by these nerve cells. Then messages are sent by your brain to raise or lower blood pressure—by speeding up or slowing the heart rate. This keeps blood pressure constant in the arteries. Constant blood pressure ensures that enough blood reaches all organs and tissues in the body and nutrients are delivered to every cell.

24. Platelets help clot blood. They are the first step in the clotting process. They stick to the wound and release chemicals. If platelets were decreased, blood would not clot as quickly. The person might have bleeding that did not stop quickly. In hemophilia, one of the clotting factors is absent which begins the clotting process. Bleeding will not stop quickly; a minor injury could be a life-threatening problem.

Part 3 | **Open Ended**

19. There is a hole in the heart where there should not be one, between the two ventricles. Normally there is a wall between the two ventricles without a hole, as can be seen in the illustration of the heart and lungs in this chapter.

20. In a normal heart, blood returning from the body enters the right side

of the heart. This blood contains wastes—carbon dioxide and other substances. The blood is pumped through the right atrium into the right ventricle and then to the lungs through the pulmonary artery. Then blood rich in oxygen returns from the lungs to the left atrium and into the left ventricle.

Oxygen-rich blood then leaves the heart to go the body. In this heart, there is a hole between the ventricles which allows the blood in both ventricles to mix. Because the left ventricle is under more pressure than the right ventricle, blood will flow through the hole from the left ventricle to the right ventricle, not

Rubrics

For more help evaluating open-ended assessment questions, see the rubric on p. 10T.

Section/Objectives	Standards		Labs/Features
	National	**State/Local**	
Chapter Opener	See pp. 16T–17T for a Key to Standards.		**Launch Lab:** Effect of Activity on Breathing, p. 567 **Foldables,** p. 567 A data-collection lab using Probeware technology can be found in the **Probeware Lab Manual,** pp. 13–15
Section 1 The Respiratory System ⏱ 2 sessions 📦 1 block 1. **Describe** the functions of the respiratory system. 2. **Explain** how oxygen and carbon dioxide are exchanged in the lungs and in tissues. 3. **Identify** the pathway of air in and out of the lungs. 4. **Explain** the effects of smoking on the respiratory system.	National Content Standards: UCP.1–UCP.3, UCP.5, A.1, A.2, C.1, C.3		**Integrate Earth Science,** p. 569 **Science Online,** p. 571 **MiniLAB:** Comparing Surface Area, p. 572 **Visualizing Abdominal Thrusts,** p. 573 **Science Online,** p. 574
Section 2 The Excretory System ⏱ 3 sessions 📦 1.5 blocks 5. **Distinguish** between the excretory and urinary systems. 6. **Describe** how the kidneys work. 7. **Explain** what happens when urinary organs don't work.	National Content Standards: UCP.1–UCP.3, UCP.5, A.1, A.2, C.1, C.3, G.3		**MiniLAB:** Modeling Kidney Function, p. 579 **Applying Science:** How does your body gain and lose water?, p. 580 **Integrate Social Studies,** p. 581 **Lab:** Kidney Structure, p. 583 **Lab:** Simulating the Abdominal Thrust Maneuver, p. 584 **Science and History:** Overcoming the Odds, p. 587

Glencoe Exclusive!
TeacherWorks™
All-In-One Planner and Resource Center

Lab Materials	Reproducible Resources	Section Assessment	Technology
Launch Lab: stopwatch or clock with second hand, calculator	**Chapter _FAST FILE_ Resources** Foldables Worksheet, p. 15 Directed Reading Overview, p. 17 Note-taking Worksheets, pp. 29–31	**GLENCOE'S ASSESSMENT ADVANTAGE**	**Teacher Works** includes: • Interactive Teacher Edition • Lesson Planner with calendar • Access to all program blacklines • Correlations to standards • Web links
MiniLAB: bathroom-tissue cardboard tube, bowl, marbles, calculator	**Chapter _FAST FILE_ Resources** Transparency Activity, p. 40 MiniLAB, p. 3 Enrichment, p. 27 Reinforcement, p. 25 Directed Reading, p. 18 Lab Activity, pp. 9–12, 13–14 **Performance Assessment in the Science Classroom,** p. 48 **Reading and Writing Skill Activities,** p. 39 **Life Science Critical Thinking/ Problem Solving,** p. 17	Portfolio Activity, p. 571 Performance MiniLAB, p. 572 Applying Skills, p. 576 Content Section Review, p. 576	Section Focus Transparency Virtual Labs CD-ROM Guided Reading Audio Program Interactive Chalkboard CD-ROM
MiniLAB: 3 cups, soil, fine gravel, water, funnel, small piece of wire screen, filter paper **Lab:** large animal kidney, scalpel, magnifying lens, disposable gloves **Lab:** cardboard tube, paper, clay, bicycle pump, sports bottle, scissors *Need materials?* Contact Science Kit at 1-800-828-7777 or www.sciencekit.com on the Internet.	**Chapter _FAST FILE_ Resources** Transparency Activity, p. 41 MiniLAB, p. 4 Enrichment, p. 28 Reinforcement, p. 26 Directed Reading, pp. 19, 20 Lab Worksheet, pp. 5–6, 7–8 Transparency Activity, pp. 43–44 **Lab Management and Safety,** p. 77 **Mathematics Skill Activities,** p. 1 **Home and Community Involvement,** p. 40	Portfolio MiniLAB Assessment, p. 579 Performance MiniLAB, p. 579 Applying Science, p. 580 Applying Math, p. 582 Content Section Review, p. 582	Section Focus Transparency Teaching Transparency Virtual Labs CD-ROM Guided Reading Audio Program Interactive Chalkboard CD-ROM Video Lab Probeware Lab

GLENCOE'S ASSESSMENT ADVANTAGE End of Chapter Assessment		
Blackline Masters	**Technology**	**Professional Series**
Chapter _FAST FILE_ Resources Chapter Review, pp. 33–34 Chapter Tests, pp. 35–38 **Standardized Test Practice,** pp. 83–86	MindJogger Videoquiz Virtual Labs CD-ROM ExamView® Pro Testmaker TeacherWorks CD-ROM Interactive Chalkboard CD-ROM	**Performance Assessment in the Science Classroom (PASC)**

Transparencies

Section Focus

Strange Creature from Above

Scuba diving is an activity that requires special equipment that allows you to breathe while underwater. The word scuba actually stands for self-contained underwater breathing apparatus. This equipment is needed because, unlike fish, people breathe oxygen as a gas in air.

1. What special equipment is required for scuba diving?
2. What do the bubbles in this picture indicate?
3. How do people and fish differ in the way they get oxygen?

L2

Liquid Wastes

Have you ever thought of your skin as an organ that rids your body of waste? You probably perspire most heavily when you exercise. Perspiration is a liquid waste given off by the body.

1. How is perspiring helpful to the body?
2. Why is it important to drink plenty of fluids before, during, and after periods of intense physical activity?
3. What other body system is involved with the removal of liquid wastes?

L2

This is a representation of key blackline masters available in the Teacher Classroom Resources. See Resource Manager boxes within the chapter for additional information.

Key to Teaching Strategies

The following designations will help you decide which activities are appropriate for your students.

L1 Level 1 activities should be appropriate for students with learning difficulties.

L2 Level 2 activities should be within the ability range of all students.

L3 Level 3 activities are designed for above-average students.

ELL ELL activities should be within the ability range of English-Language Learners.

COOP LEARN Cooperative Learning activities are designed for small group work.

LS Multiple Learning Styles logos, as described on page 12T, are used throughout to indicate strategies that address different learning styles.

P These strategies represent student products that can be placed into a best-work portfolio.

PBL Problem-Based Learning activities apply real-world situations to learning.

Assessment

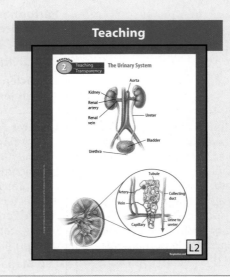

Respiration and Excretion

Directions: *Carefully review the graph and answer the following questions.*

Percentage of Cigarette Smokers, Organized by Gender 1965–1990 (Selected Years)

1. Between which two years did the percentage of female smokers decrease the most?
   A 1965 and 1974   C 1979 and 1983
   B 1974 and 1979   D 1988 and 1990
2. A reasonable conclusion is that between the years 1965 and 1990 ____.
   F a greater percentage of women quit smoking
   G a greater percentage of men quit smoking
   H more women smoked than men
   J it is more difficult for men to quit smoking
3. From the information in the graph, which statement would best describe the number of smokers in 1991?
   A More people probably smoked.
   B More women than men probably smoked.
   C Fewer people probably smoked.
   D There were no more smokers.
4. Which year had the highest difference in percentages between men and women?
   F 1965   G 1974   H 1979   J 1988

L2

Teaching

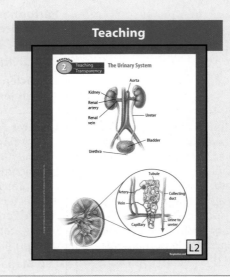

The Urinary System

L2

Hands-on Activities

Student Text Lab Worksheet

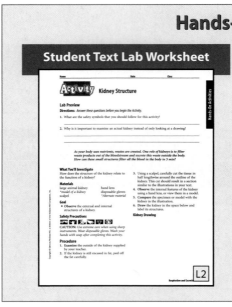

Activity Kidney Structure

Lab Preview
Directions: *Answer these questions before you begin the Activity.*

1. What are the safety symbols that you should follow for this activity?

2. Why is it important to examine an actual kidney instead of only looking at a drawing?

L2

Laboratory Activities

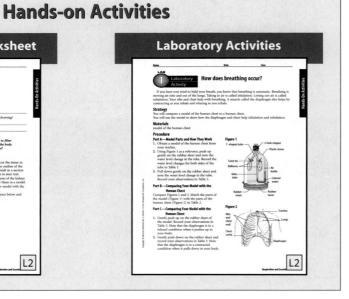

Laboratory Activity How does breathing occur?

L2

Meeting Different Ability Levels

Content Outline

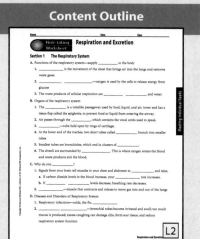

L2

Reinforcement

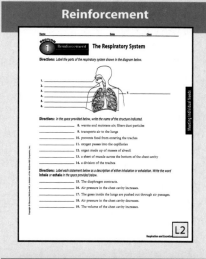

L2

Enrichment

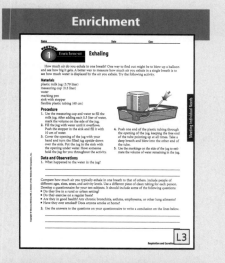

L3

Directed Reading (English/Spanish)

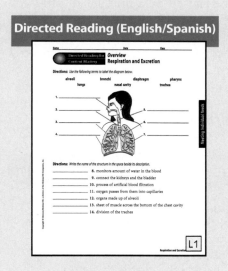

L1

Study Guide

Study Guide

Features
- Contains a study guide page for each section of the chapter
- Reviews key concepts
- Includes answer pages

L2

Reading Essentials

Reading Essentials for Glencoe Science
An Interactive Student Workbook

Features
- Condensed core content
- Actively involves students in reading
- Reinforces key vocabulary

L1

Assessment

Test Practice Workbook

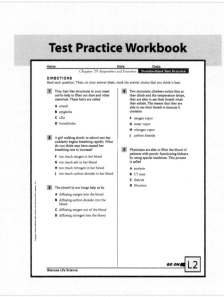

L2

Chapter Review

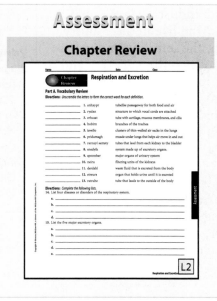

L2

Chapter Tests

L2

Science Content Background

section 1

The Respiratory System
Functions of the Respiratory System

In order to function, cells need nutrients, which must be oxidized in order to release energy. The process of obtaining energy from nutrients is called cellular respiration. In respiration the most commonly used carbohydrate is glucose. The oxidation of glucose produces water and carbon dioxide, and releases energy.

$$C_6H_{12}O_6 + 6O_2 \rightarrow 6H_2O + 6CO_2 + energy$$

Obtaining oxygen and removing carbon dioxide are the major functions of the respiratory system. These processes occur in two successive phases of functioning—breathing and transporting gases. In order to effectively exchange the gases involved in respiration, a large surface area is required. There are 300 million to 400 million alveoli in each lung. The air sacs of both lungs have a total surface area of about 93 m^2, nearly 50 times the total surface area of the skin.

The Lungs

Lungs are pink at birth, but as a person ages, they become gray and mottled from tiny particles breathed in with the air. Usually people who live in cities and industrial areas have darker lungs than those who live in the country.

In the adult human, the left lung is divided into two sections, or lobes—the superior and the inferior. The right lung is somewhat larger than the left lung and is divided into three lobes—the superior, middle, and inferior. The two lungs are separated by an area which contains the heart, trachea, esophagus, and blood vessels.

The movement of air in and out of the lungs is possible due to three factors: the ability of the thoracic cavity to change size, the elasticity of the lung tissue, and the difference in pressure between the lungs and chest.

Diseases and Disorders of the Respiratory System

Many diseases and disorders affect the health of the human respiratory system and interfere with its effectiveness. Allergies affect so many people that pollen counts of the atmosphere are reported in the media. The worst allergens include the pollen of wind-pollinated trees, grasses, and ragweed, and air pollutants.

Pneumonia is the term used to describe any condition that results in alveoli filling up with fluid. It can be caused by a number of different factors, including chemicals, bacteria, viruses, or fungi. Blood infections, chronic alcoholism, inhalation of fluids into the lungs, or even prolonged bed rest can predispose a person to infection of the lungs by microorganisms. Chronic smoking has the potential to promote emphysema and lung cancer.

chapter content resources

Internet Resources
For additional content background, visit
life.msscience.com to:
- access your book online
- find references to related articles in popular science magazines
- access Web links with related content background
- access current events with science journal topics

Print Resources
Biology (6th Edition), by Neil A. Campbell, Jane B. Reece, Pearson Benjamin Cummings Publishing, 2001

Human Anatomy & Physiology (5th Edition), by Elaine N. Marieb, Pearson Benjamin Cummings Publishing Company, 2000

Principles of Human Physiology, by William J. Germann, Cindy L. Stanfield; Pearson Benjamin Cummings Publishing, 2001

section 2

The Excretory System

The Urinary System

The metabolic processes of the body produce waste products. The respiratory system rids the body of carbon dioxide and other waste gases. The digestive system eliminates solid wastes. The urinary system removes a variety of dissolved salts and nitrogenous wastes from the blood and lymph systems.

The major organs of the urinary system are a pair of bean-shaped structures called kidneys, each of which is approximately 10 cm long and 5 cm wide. They weigh about 170 g each. The functioning unit of the kidney is the nephron. All of the blood in the body flows through the kidneys about once every five minutes.

Urine

Urea and uric acid are wastes from the metabolism of proteins. The straw color of fresh urine is due to a pigment called urochrome. The average pH of urine is approximately 6.0, making it slightly acidic.

The urinary system also functions in maintaining the homeostasis of body fluids and electrolytes and keeps the levels of acids and bases in proper balance. All of this provides for the uniform composition of the blood components.

Urinary Disease and Disorders

Urinary tract infections are common, second only to respiratory infections. Normally urine is sterile. An infection occurs when microbes, usually bacteria from the digestive tract, adhere to the opening of the urethra and begin to multiply. Most urinary tract infections can be traced to one type of colon bacteria, *Escherichia coli (E. coli)*. Often the bacteria move from the urethra to the bladder causing a bladder infection. Such infections are usually treated with specific antibacterial drugs.

Teacher to Teacher

Jeff Remington
Palmyra Middle School
Palmyra, PA

"To show students that water vapor is released in the cellular respiration equation, I invert a dry glass beaker for a few seconds over a lit Bunsen burner. The inside of the beaker instantly fogs and becomes wet from the flame. It is a discrepant event but shows students when you burn an organic compound such as sugar or methane, water vapor is produced. Jet fuel is a carbon compound as well. Hence, you see water vapor trails behind jets in the sky as they respire."

Jeff Remington

Greg Vaughn/Tom Stack & Associates

Chapter Vocabulary

pharynx, p. 570
larynx, p. 571
trachea, p. 571
bronchi, p. 571
alveoli, p. 571
diaphragm, p. 572
emphysema, p. 575
asthma, p. 576
urinary system, p. 577
urine, p. 578
kidney, p. 578
nephron, p. 579
ureter, p. 580
bladder, p. 580
urethra, p. 580

Science Journal Student responses may vary, but may include questions about breathing harder or faster, and questions about perspiring.

INTERACTIVE CHALKBOARD
with Image Bank

PowerPoint® Presentations

This CD-ROM is an editable Microsoft® PowerPoint® presentation that includes:
- a pre-made presentation for every chapter
- interactive graphics
- animations
- audio clips
- image bank
- all new section and chapter questions
- Standardized Test Practice
- transparencies
- pre-lab questions for all labs
- Foldables directions
- links to life.msscience.com

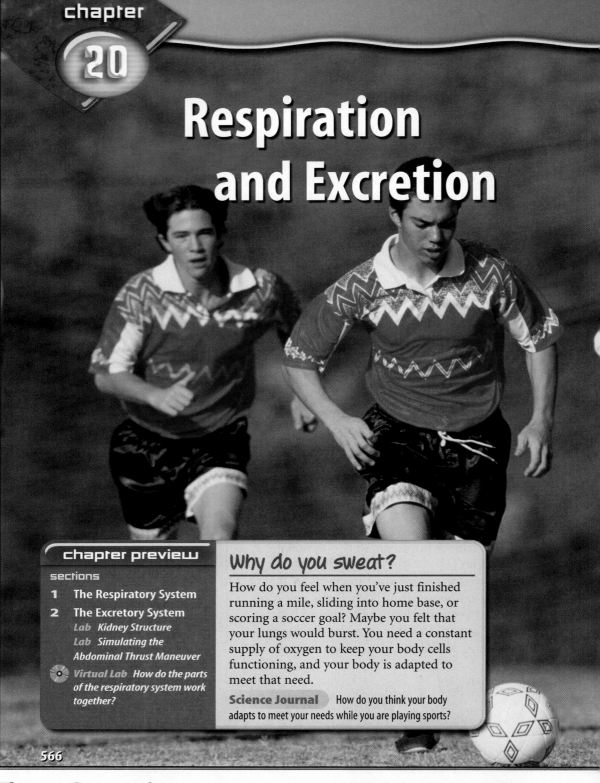

Respiration and Excretion

chapter preview

sections

1 The Respiratory System

2 The Excretory System
    Lab Kidney Structure
    Lab Simulating the Abdominal Thrust Maneuver

    Virtual Lab How do the parts of the respiratory system work together?

Why do you sweat?

How do you feel when you've just finished running a mile, sliding into home base, or scoring a soccer goal? Maybe you felt that your lungs would burst. You need a constant supply of oxygen to keep your body cells functioning, and your body is adapted to meet that need.

Science Journal How do you think your body adapts to meet your needs while you are playing sports?

566

Theme Connection

Energy Energy transformation is a central theme in this text. Human cells require oxygen in order to utilize nutrients and provide energy for cellular activities. Chemical energy is transformed into thermal and mechanical energy.

About the Photo

Increased Respiration During heavy exercise, respiration increases about 20 times. Rapid delivery of oxygen and fast removal of waste and heat is required. The cardiovascular and respiratory systems deliver oxygen and fuel, and remove waste and heat. More heat can be removed by the skin through evaporation.

Start-Up Activities

Effect of Activity on Breathing

Your body can store food and water, but it cannot store much oxygen. Breathing brings oxygen into your body. In the following lab, find out about one factor that can change your breathing rate.

1. Put your hand on the side of your rib cage. Take a deep breath. Notice how your rib cage moves out and upward when you inhale.

2. Count the number of breaths you take for 15 s. Multiply this number by four to calculate your normal breathing rate for 1 min.

3. Repeat step 2 two more times, then calculate your average breathing rate.

4. Do a physical activity described by your teacher for 1 min and repeat step 2 to determine your breathing rate now.

5. Time how long it takes for your breathing rate to return to normal.

6. **Think Critically** Explain how breathing rate appears to be related to physical activity.

Preview this chapter's content and activities at life.msscience.com

 Respiration and Excretion

Make the following Foldable to help you identify what you already know, what you want to know, and what you learned about respiration.

STEP 1 Fold a vertical sheet of paper from side to side. Make the front edge about 1.25 cm shorter than the back edge.

STEP 2 Turn lengthwise and **fold** into thirds.

STEP 3 Unfold and cut only the top layer along both folds to make three tabs.

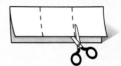

STEP 4 Label each tab.

Know | Want | Learned

Read and Write Before you read the chapter, write what you already know about respiration under the left tab of your Foldable, and write questions about what you'd like to know under the center tab. After you read the chapter, list what you learned under the right tab.

567

The Respiratory System

as you read

What You'll Learn
- **Describe** the functions of the respiratory system.
- **Explain** how oxygen and carbon dioxide are exchanged in the lungs and in tissues.
- **Identify** the pathway of air in and out of the lungs.
- **Explain** the effects of smoking on the respiratory system.

Why It's Important
Your body's cells depend on your respiratory system to supply oxygen and remove carbon dioxide.

Review Vocabulary
lungs: saclike respiratory organs that function with the heart to remove carbon dioxide from blood and provide it with oxygen

New Vocabulary
- pharynx
- larynx
- trachea
- bronchi
- alveoli
- diaphragm
- emphysema
- asthma

Functions of the Respiratory System

Can you imagine an astronaut walking on the Moon without a space suit or a diver exploring the ocean without scuba gear? Of course not. You couldn't survive in either location under those conditions because you need to breathe air. Earth is surrounded by a layer of gases called the atmosphere (AT muh sfihr). You breathe atmospheric gases that are closest to Earth. As shown in **Figure 1,** oxygen is one of those gases.

For thousands of years people have known that air, food, and water are needed for life. However, the gas in the air that is necessary for life was not identified as oxygen until the late 1700s. At that time, a French scientist experimented and discovered that an animal breathed in oxygen and breathed out carbon dioxide. He measured the amount of oxygen that the animal used and the amount of carbon dioxide produced by its bodily processes. After his work with animals, the French scientist used this knowledge to study the way that humans use oxygen. He measured the amount of oxygen that a person uses when resting and when exercising. These measurements were compared, and he discovered that more oxygen is used by the body during exercise.

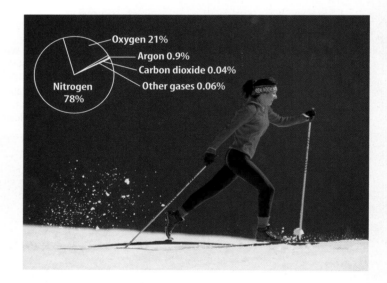

Figure 1 Air, which is needed by most organisms, is only 21 percent oxygen.

568 CHAPTER 20 Respiration and Excretion

Section 1 Resource Manager

Chapter *FAST FILE* Resources
Transparency Activity, p. 40
Note-taking Worksheets, pp. 29–31
MiniLAB, p. 3
Enrichment, p. 27
Reinforcement, p. 25
Directed Reading for Content Mastery, pp. 17, 18

Lab Activity, pp. 9–12, 13–14
Performance Assessment in the Science Classroom, p. 48
Reading and Writing Skill Activities, p. 39
Life Science Critical Thinking/Problem Solving, p. 17

Figure 2 Several processes are involved in how the body obtains, transports, and uses oxygen.

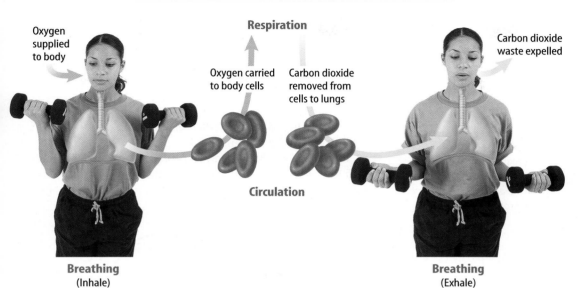

$$C_6H_{12}O_6 \; + \; 6O_2 \; \longrightarrow \; 6CO_2 \; + \; 6H_2O \; + \; Energy$$

Glucose + Oxygen ⟶ Carbon + Water + Energy
dioxide

Oxygen supplied to body

Respiration

Oxygen carried to body cells

Carbon dioxide removed from cells to lungs

Carbon dioxide waste expelled

Circulation

Breathing
(Inhale)

Breathing
(Exhale)

Breathing and Respiration

People often confuse the terms *breathing* and *respiration*. Breathing is the movement of the chest that brings air into the lungs and removes waste gases. The air entering the lungs contains oxygen. It passes from the lungs into the circulatory system because there is less oxygen in the blood than in cells of the lungs. Blood carries oxygen to individual cells. At the same time, the digestive system supplies glucose from digested food to the same cells. The oxygen delivered to the cells is used to release energy from glucose. This chemical reaction, shown in the equation in **Figure 2,** is called cellular respiration. Without oxygen, this reaction would not take place. Carbon dioxide and water molecules are waste products of cellular respiration. They are carried back to the lungs in the blood. Exhaling, or breathing out, eliminates waste carbon dioxide and some water molecules.

✔ **Reading Check** *What is respiration?*

INTEGRATE Earth Science

Water Vapor The amount of water vapor in the atmosphere varies from almost none over deserts to nearly four percent in tropical rain forest areas. This means that every 100 molecules that make up air include only four molecules of water. In your Science Journal, infer how breathing dry air can stress your respiratory system.

INTEGRATE Earth Science

Water Vapor Breathing dry air can irritate nasal and throat passages.

✔ **Reading Check**

Answer A cellular chemical reaction in which glucose and oxygen combine and produce CO_2 and H_2O with the release of energy.

Quick Demo
Pig Lungs
Materials pig lungs
Estimated Time 10 minutes
Procedure Obtain pig lungs from a meat-packing house or biological supply company for students to examine. Lead a discussion on why lungs aren't heavy. Lungs are composed of alveoli, which are hollow. L2

Activity
Carbon Dioxide Reaction Limewater is made by mixing 1.5 g calcium hydroxide with 1 L of distilled water. Allow it to stand overnight and filter it before using. Have students blow through a straw into a test tube one-fourth full of limewater. Note the change from a clear liquid to a cloudy liquid. This indicates the presence of carbon dioxide. L1 LS **Kinesthetic**

Teacher FYI
Nasal Cavities Sinuses are air-filled cavities in the cranial bones that open into the nasal cavity. The cavities act as resonant chambers and affect the sound of our speech.

Differentiated Instruction

Challenge An opera singer's ability to be heard over an orchestra in a large auditorium for an extended period of time is a result of breath control. Breath control enables singers to sustain a long musical phrase, and change volume for dramatic effect. Invite students who have studied voice or a wind instrument to perform for the class and demonstrate their breathing techniques. L3 ELL LS **Auditory-Musical**

Text Question Answer
The food or drink has gotten into your airway.

Caption Answer
Figure 3 It can be cleaned, warmed, and moistened before moving to the pharynx.

Make a Model
Balloon Music Blow up a balloon and stretch the opening into a narrow slit. Explain to students that the balloon represents a lung and its neck is the trachea. Stretch the slit to make it longer and release a bit to make it shorter, noting the changes in pitch. Correlate the higher-pitched sounds and tighter stretch with the shorter vocal cords of females and the lower-pitched sounds and looser stretch with the longer vocal cords of males.

Use an Analogy
Trapping Dust The nasal cavity traps air particles just as a dust mask traps dust and pollen from the air.

Virtual Labs

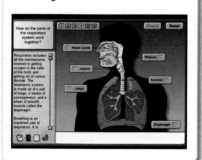

Respiratory System *How do parts of the respiratory system work together?*

Organs of the Respiratory System
The respiratory system, shown in **Figure 3,** is made up of structures and organs that help move oxygen into the body and waste gases out of the body. Air enters your body through two openings in your nose called nostrils or through the mouth. Fine hairs inside the nostrils trap dust from the air. Air then passes through the nasal cavity, where it gets moistened and warmed by the body's heat. Glands that produce sticky mucus line the nasal cavity. The mucus traps dust, pollen, and other materials that were not trapped by nasal hairs. This process helps filter and clean the air you breathe. Tiny, hairlike structures, called cilia (SIH lee uh), sweep mucus and trapped material to the back of the throat where it can be swallowed.

Pharynx Warmed, moist air then enters a tubelike passageway used by food, liquid, and air called the **pharynx** (FER ingks). At the lower end of the pharynx is a flap of tissue called the epiglottis (eh puh GLAH tus). When you swallow, your epiglottis folds down to prevent food or liquid from entering your airway. The food enters your esophagus instead. If you began to choke, what do you think has happened?

Figure 3 Air can enter the body through the nostrils and the mouth.
Explain *the advantages of having air enter through the nostrils.*

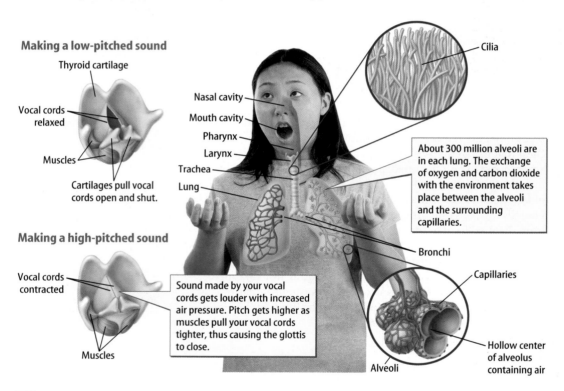

Making a low-pitched sound
Thyroid cartilage
Vocal cords relaxed
Muscles
Cartilages pull vocal cords open and shut.

Making a high-pitched sound
Vocal cords contracted
Sound made by your vocal cords gets louder with increased air pressure. Pitch gets higher as muscles pull your vocal cords tighter, thus causing the glottis to close.
Muscles

Nasal cavity
Mouth cavity
Pharynx
Larynx
Trachea
Lung

Cilia

About 300 million alveoli are in each lung. The exchange of oxygen and carbon dioxide with the environment takes place between the alveoli and the surrounding capillaries.

Bronchi
Capillaries
Hollow center of alveolus containing air
Alveoli

570 CHAPTER 20 Respiration and Excretion

Curriculum Connection
Health The pharynx serves as the passageway of food into the esophagus and air into the trachea. The epiglottis is a small flap of tissue that normally closes over the tracheal opening when food is swallowed. Sometimes food or liquid gets past the epiglottis and goes into the trachea, triggering the choking reflex. Ask students to discuss ways to prevent choking. L2 **LS** **Logical-Mathematical**

Differentiated Instruction
Challenge A person can experience oxygen deficiency in carbon monoxide poisoning. Have students research how carbon monoxide impairs the delivery of oxygen to tissues. Prepare a chart to show how to avoid carbon monoxide poisoning in the home. L3

Larynx and Trachea Next, the air moves into your larynx (LER ingks). The **larynx** is the airway to which two pairs of horizontal folds of tissue, called vocal cords, are attached as shown in **Figure 3.** Forcing air between the cords causes them to vibrate and produce sounds. When you speak, muscles tighten or loosen your vocal cords, resulting in different sounds. Your brain coordinates the movement of the muscles in your throat, tongue, cheeks, and lips when you talk, sing, or just make noise. Your teeth also are involved in forming letter sounds and words.

From the larynx, air moves into the **trachea** (TRAY kee uh), which is a tube about 12 cm in length. Strong, C-shaped rings of cartilage prevent the trachea from collapsing. The trachea is lined with mucous membranes and cilia, as shown in **Figure 3,** that trap dust, bacteria, and pollen. Why must the trachea stay open all the time?

Bronchi and the Lungs Air is carried into your lungs by two short tubes called **bronchi** (BRAHN ki) (singular, *bronchus*) at the lower end of the trachea. Within the lungs, the bronchi branch into smaller and smaller tubes. The smallest tubes are called bronchioles (BRAHN kee ohlz). At the end of each bronchiole are clusters of tiny, thin-walled sacs called **alveoli** (al VEE uh li). Air passes into the bronchi, then into the bronchioles, and finally into the alveoli. Lungs are masses of alveoli arranged in grapelike clusters. The capillaries surround the alveoli like a net, as shown in **Figure 3.**

The exchange of oxygen and carbon dioxide takes place between the alveoli and capillaries. This easily happens because the walls of the alveoli (singular, *alveolus*) and the walls of the capillaries are each only one cell thick, as shown in **Figure 4.** Oxygen moves through the cell membranes of the alveoli and then through the cell membranes of the capillaries into the blood. There the oxygen is picked up by hemoglobin (HEE muh gloh bun), a molecule in red blood cells, and carried to all body cells. At the same time, carbon dioxide and other cellular wastes leave the body cells. The wastes move through the cell membranes of the capillaries. Then they are carried by the blood. In the lungs, waste gases move through the cell membranes of the capillaries and through the cell membranes of the alveoli. Then waste gases leave the body during exhalation.

Alveolus

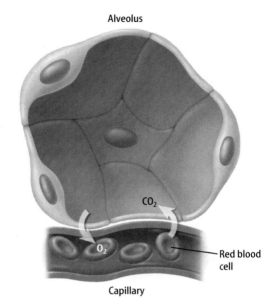

Red blood cell

Capillary

Figure 4 The thin capillary walls allow gases to be exchanged easily between the alveoli and the capillaries.

Science Online

Topic: Speech

Visit life.msscience.com for Web links to information about how speech sounds are made.

Activity In your Science Journal, describe the changes in the position of your lips and tongue when you say each letter of the alphabet.

SECTION 1 The Respiratory System **571**

Text Question Answer
If the trachea collapsed, it would be difficult or impossible to breathe.

Use Science Words
Word Origin *Alvearium* is the Latin word for "beehive." Think about the internal structure of the beehive and relate this to the air cells of the lungs, the alveoli. L2

Activity
Humidifying Air Have students research how dry air taken in through the nostrils has about 100% humidity by the time it reaches the alveoli. Have them report on why this is important. L2 P

Fun Fact

During one minute, while the body is at rest, approximately 12.5 mL of oxygen per kg of body weight are used by body cells; an equal amount of carbon dioxide is produced.

Discussion
Carbon Monoxide Poisoning How does carbon monoxide impair the delivery of oxygen to tissues? CO displaces O_2 in blood and deprives organs and tissues of oxygen, causing suffocation. What are the symptoms of carbon monoxide poisoning? headache, fatigue, dizziness, drowsiness, nausea, vomiting, confusion, muscle weakness, and loss of consciousness What steps can be taken to decrease the chances of carbon monoxide poisoning? proper ventilation, maintain equipment and appliances, CO monitors, yearly furnace checks, prohibit use of gasoline-powered equipment in poorly ventilated areas

---

Cultural Diversity

Living at High Altitudes People living at high altitudes must deal with a slightly reduced pull of gravity, gas molecules that are spread out in the air, and a reduced pressure gradient. Have students research how the bodies of people native to high altitudes have adapted to these changes. Possible answers: number of red blood cells and amount of hemoglobin increase; increase in the number of small blood vessels. L3

Differentiated Instruction

Learning Disabled Have students place their fingers on the front of their necks, tilt their heads backward, and gently move their fingers up and down. Tell students that the ridges they feel are the rings of cartilage around the trachea. L1 LS
Kinesthetic

Mini LAB

Purpose Students observe the increased surface area provided by alveoli. L2 ELL

LS Logical-Mathematical

Materials bathroom-tissue cardboard tube, marbles, bowl, calculator

Teaching Strategy Gently shake the tube when half-full of marbles to settle them and avoid gaps.

Analysis

1. Answers will vary depending on stacking techniques, but will usually indicate a more than twofold increase in the surface area when using marbles.

2. The marbles represent the alveoli.

3. More gas can be exchanged because there is greater surface area within the same space.

Assessment

Performance Have students calculate the surface area of a cube that is 10 cm × 5 cm × 2 cm and compare this with the surface area of one hundred 1-cm × 1-cm × 1-cm cubes that have the same volume as the larger cube. Use **Performance Assessment in the Science Classroom,** p. 101.

Reading Check

Answer It helps move gases into and out of the body.

Mini LAB

Comparing Surface Area

Procedure

1. Stand a **bathroom-tissue cardboard tube** in an **empty bowl.**
2. Drop **marbles** into the tube, filling it to the top.
3. Count the number of marbles used.
4. Repeat steps 2 and 3 two more times. Calculate the average number of marbles needed to fill the tube.
5. The tube's inside surface area is approximately 161.29 cm^2. Each marble has a surface area of approximately 8.06 cm^2. Calculate the surface area of the average number of marbles.

Analysis

1. Compare the inside surface area of the tube with the surface area of the average number of marbles needed to fill the tube.
2. If the tube represents a bronchus, what do the marbles represent?
3. Using this model, explain what makes gas exchange in the lungs efficient.

Figure 5 Your lungs inhale and exhale about 500 mL of air with an average breath. This increases to 2,000 mL of air per breath when you do strenuous activity.

Why do you breathe?

Signals from your brain tell the muscles in your chest and abdomen to contract and relax. You don't have to think about breathing to breathe, just like your heart beats without you telling it to beat. Your brain can change your breathing rate depending on the amount of carbon dioxide present in your blood. As carbon dioxide increases, your breathing rate increases. When there is less carbon dioxide in your blood, your breathing rate decreases. You do have some control over your breathing—you can hold your breath if you want to. Eventually, though, your brain will respond to the buildup of carbon dioxide in your blood. The brain's response will tell your chest and abdomen muscles to work automatically, and you will breathe whether you want to or not.

Inhaling and Exhaling Breathing is partly the result of changes in air pressure. Under normal conditions, a gas moves from an area of high pressure to an area of low pressure. When you squeeze an empty, soft-plastic bottle, air is pushed out. This happens because air pressure outside the top of the bottle is less than the pressure you create inside the bottle when you squeeze it. As you release your grip on the bottle, the air pressure inside the bottle becomes less than it is outside the bottle. Air rushes back in, and the bottle returns to its original shape.

Your lungs work in a similar way to the squeezed bottle. Your **diaphragm** (DI uh fram) is a muscle beneath your lungs that contracts and relaxes to help move gases into and out of your lungs. **Figure 5** illustrates breathing.

Reading Check *How does your diaphragm help you breathe?*

When a person is choking, a rescuer can use abdominal thrusts, as shown in **Figure 6,** to save the life of the choking victim.

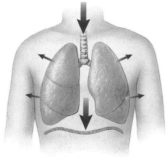

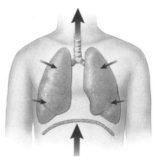

Inhale   **Exhale**

Visual Learning

Figure 5 The position of the diaphragm during the process of inhaling and expanding is shown. Compare this process with the squeezing of the plastic bottle discussed in the text.

Figure 6

When food or other objects become lodged in the trachea, airflow between the lungs and the mouth and nasal cavity is blocked. Death can occur in minutes. However, prompt action by someone can save the life of a choking victim. The rescuer uses abdominal thrusts to force the victim's diaphragm up. This decreases the volume of the chest cavity and forces air up in the trachea. The result is a rush of air that dislodges and expels the food or other object. The victim can breathe again. This technique is shown at right and should only be performed in emergency situations.

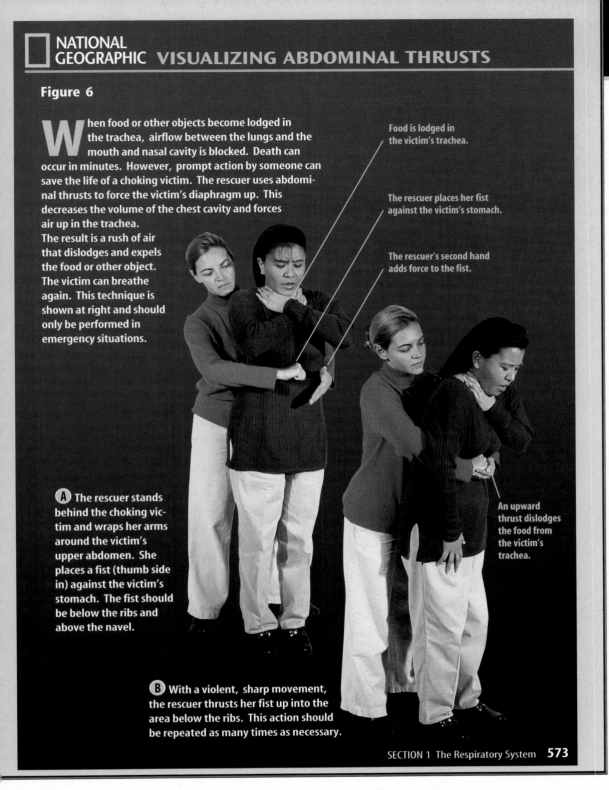

Food is lodged in the victim's trachea.

The rescuer places her fist against the victim's stomach.

The rescuer's second hand adds force to the fist.

An upward thrust dislodges the food from the victim's trachea.

A The rescuer stands behind the choking victim and wraps her arms around the victim's upper abdomen. She places a fist (thumb side in) against the victim's stomach. The fist should be below the ribs and above the navel.

B With a violent, sharp movement, the rescuer thrusts her fist up into the area below the ribs. This action should be repeated as many times as necessary.

Visualizing Abdominal Thrusts

Have students examine the pictures and read the captions. Then ask the following questions.

Why should abdominal thrusts only be performed in emergencies, and never performed on other people for practice or for fun? Abdominal thrusts could cause injury if performed on a person who is not choking.

Why is it important that the rescuer's fist be located below the ribs of the choking victim? The fist must be below the diaphragm in order for an upward force to be applied to the diaphragm. A fist located on the rib cage or breastbone could cause injury to the victim.

Activity

Memory Device Have students work in small groups to develop a mnemonic, or memory, device that will allow them to quickly and accurately remember the steps of proper abdominal thrusts to save a choking victim. L2

Visual Learning

Figure 6 Review the theory of how abdominal thrusts work. This maneuver is often called the Heimlich maneuver. Abdominal thrusts lift the diaphragm and force enough air from the lungs to create an artificial cough. The cough is intended to move and expel an obstructing foreign body from an airway.

Differentiated Instruction

English-Language Learners Have students practice their communication skills by pretending to call the emergency number to contact the local rescue squad. Students can take turns being the operator who asks vital questions and the bystander who reports the choking incident. L1

Curriculum Connection

Health Arrange a visit to a Red Cross center or have a health specialist come to school and demonstrate how to use abdominal thrusts and cardiopulmonary resuscitation (CPR) to revive a person who is not breathing. Ask students to find out where CPR training is available in their area. L2

Attack of Viral Particles

Purpose to compare the effect of different quantities of inhaled virus or bacteria particles on the cells of the respiratory system

Possible Materials dominoes, large marbles

Estimated Time 1 class session

Teaching Strategies

• Students can set up the dominoes, which represent respiratory cells, so that when the dominoes fall, a cascade of events is triggered.

• Students can designate specific areas of dominoes to represent different areas of the respiratory system. Designate the large marbles as bacteria or virus particles.

• Students can drop one or two marbles on the dominoes to demonstrate what happens when you breathe in a small quantity of particles, acquired from dirty hands or contaminated surface areas.

• Students can drop several marbles on the dominoes to demonstrate what happens when you breathe in large quantities of particles, acquired from a sneeze or cough.

• Allow students to explore other questions that arise.

For additional inquiry activities, see *Science Inquiry Labs.*

✓ Reading Check

Answer all parts, but usually the upper part, from the nose to the pharynx

---

Table 1 Smokers' Risk of Death from Disease	
Disease	**Smokers' Risk Compared to Nonsmokers' Risk**
Lung cancer	23 times higher for males, 11 times higher for females
Chronic bronchitis and emphysema	5 times higher
Heart disease	2 times higher

Diseases and Disorders of the Respiratory System

INTEGRATE Environment

If you were asked to list some of the things that can harm your respiratory system, you probably would put smoking at the top. As you can see in **Table 1,** many serious diseases are related to smoking. The chemical substances in tobacco—nicotine and tars—are poisons and can destroy cells. The high temperatures, smoke, and carbon monoxide produced when tobacco burns also can injure a smoker's cells. Even if you are a nonsmoker, inhaling smoke from tobacco products—called secondhand smoke—is unhealthy and has the potential to harm your respiratory system. Smoking, polluted air, coal dust, and asbestos (as BES tus) have been related to respiratory problems such as bronchitis (brahn KI tus), emphysema (em fuh SEE muh), asthma (AZ muh), and cancer.

Respiratory Infections Bacteria, viruses, and other microorganisms can cause infections that affect any of the organs of the respiratory system. The common cold usually affects the upper part of the respiratory system—from the nose to the pharynx. The cold virus also can cause irritation and swelling in the larynx, trachea, and bronchi. The cilia that line the trachea and bronchi can be damaged. However, cilia usually heal rapidly. A virus that causes influenza, or flu, can affect many of the body's systems. The virus multiplies in the cells lining the alveoli and damages them. Pneumonia is an infection in the alveoli that can be caused by bacteria, viruses, or other microorganisms. Before antibiotics were available to treat these infections, many people died from pneumonia.

✓ Reading Check
What parts of the respiratory system are affected by the cold virus?

> **Science Online**
>
> **Topic: Second-Hand Smoke**
> Visit life.msscience.com for Web links to information about the health concerns of second-hand smoke.
>
> **Activity** Make a poster to teach younger students about the dangers of second-hand smoke.

574 CHAPTER 20 Respiration and Excretion

LAB DEMONSTRATION

Purpose to compare how tar affects cilia function

Materials toothbrush, water, black pepper, molasses, newspaper

Preparation Cover work area with newspaper.

Procedure Wet the toothbrush bristles (cilia) and sprinkle them with pepper (dust). Run a finger over the bristles five times. Wash the toothbrush and repeat the process using molasses (tar) instead of water.

Expected Outcome Students will see how tar prevents cilia from moving.

Assessment

Why do foreign particles need to be removed from the bronchial tubes? Particles can irritate tissues, and bacteria can cause infections. In addition to preventing normal cilia action, why are tars dangerous? They are poisonous. [L2]

Chronic Bronchitis When bronchial tubes are irritated and swell, and too much mucus is produced, a disease called bronchitis develops. Sometimes, bacterial infections occur in the bronchial tubes because the mucus there provides nearly ideal conditions for bacteria to grow. Antibiotics are effective treatments for this type of bronchitis.

Many cases of bronchitis clear up within a few weeks, but the disease sometimes lasts for a long time. When this happens, it is called chronic (KRAH nihk) bronchitis. A person who has chronic bronchitis must cough often to try to clear the excess mucus from the airway. However, the more a person coughs, the more the cilia and bronchial tubes can be harmed. When cilia are damaged, they cannot move mucus, bacteria, and dirt particles out of the lungs effectively. Then harmful substances, such as sticky tar from burning tobacco, build up in the airways. Sometimes, scar tissue forms and the respiratory system cannot function properly.

Emphysema A disease in which the alveoli in the lungs enlarge is called **emphysema** (em fuh SEE muh). When cells in the alveoli are reddened and swollen, an enzyme is released that causes the walls of the alveoli to break down. As a result, alveoli can't push air out of the lungs, so less oxygen moves into the bloodstream from the alveoli. When blood becomes low in oxygen and high in carbon dioxide, shortness of breath occurs. Some people with emphysema require extra oxygen as shown in **Figure 7.** Because the heart works harder to supply oxygen to body cells, people who have emphysema often develop heart problems, as well.

Figure 7 Lung diseases can have major effects on breathing.

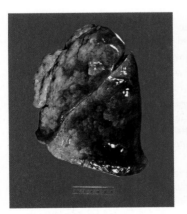

A normal, healthy lung can exchange oxygen and carbon dioxide effectively.

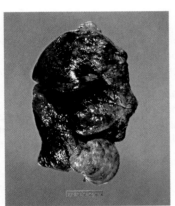

A diseased lung carries less oxygen to body cells.

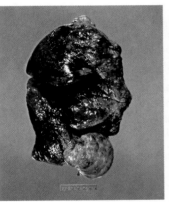

Emphysema may take 20 to 30 years to develop.

SECTION 1 The Respiratory System **575**

✓ **Reading Check**

Answer The air passages will become irritated, and cancer cells may develop and destroy healthy lung tissue.

DAILY INTERVENTION

Check for Understanding

Linguistic Have students write a paragraph describing why air moves into the lungs when the ribs move upward and the diaphragm moves downward. This action reduces air pressure within the chest cavity, and the higher external air pressure causes air to rush into the lungs. L2

Reteach

Pressure Use a lung demonstration apparatus to illustrate how the downward movement of the diaphragm causes reduced pressure within the chest cavity. L2

✓ Assessment

Process Have students use a chart of the respiratory system to describe the passage of air into and out of the lungs. Use **Performance Assessment in the Science Classroom,** p. 143. L2

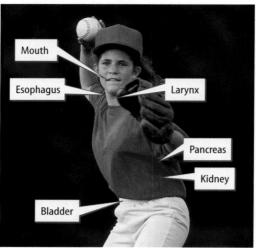

Figure 8 More than 85 percent of all lung cancer is related to smoking. Smoking also can play a part in the development of cancer in other body organs indicated above.

Lung Cancer The third leading cause of death in men and women in the United States is lung cancer. Inhaling the tar in cigarette smoke is the greatest contributing factor to lung cancer. Tar and other ingredients found in smoke act as carcinogens (kar SIH nuh junz) in the body. Carcinogens are substances that can cause an uncontrolled growth of cells. In the lungs, this is called lung cancer. As represented in **Figure 8,** smoking also has been linked to the development of cancers of the esophagus, mouth, larynx, pancreas, kidney, and bladder.

✓ **Reading Check** *What happens to the lungs of people who begin smoking?*

Asthma Shortness of breath, wheezing, or coughing can occur in a lung disorder called **asthma.** When a person has an asthma attack, the bronchial tubes contract quickly. Inhaling medicine that relaxes the bronchial tubes is the usual treatment for an asthma attack. Asthma is often an allergic reaction. An allergic reaction occurs when the body overreacts to a foreign substance. An asthma attack can result from breathing certain substances such as cigarette smoke or certain plant pollen, eating certain foods, or stress in a person's life.

section ① review

Summary

Functions of the Respiratory System

- Breathing brings air into the lungs and removes waste gases.
- Cellular respiration converts oxygen and glucose to carbon dioxide, water, and energy.

Organs of the Respiratory System

- Air is carried into the lungs by bronchi.
- Bronchioles are smaller branches of bronchi, and at the ends of these are alveoli.

Diseases and Disorders of the Respiratory System

- Emphysema is a disease that causes the alveoli to enlarge.
- Lung cancer occurs when carcinogens cause an uncontrolled growth of cells.

Self Check

1. **Describe** the main function of the respiratory system.
2. **Explain** how oxygen, carbon dioxide, and other waste gases are exchanged in the lungs and body tissues.
3. **Identify** how air moves into and out of the lungs.
4. **Think Critically** How is the work of the digestive and circulatory systems related to the respiratory system?

Applying Skills

5. **Research Information** Nicotine in tobacco is a poison. Using library references, find out how nicotine affects the body.
6. **Communicate** Use references to find out about lung disease common among coal miners, stonecutters, and sandblasters. Find out what safety measures are required now for these trades. In your Science Journal, write a paragraph about these safety measures.

576 CHAPTER 20 Respiration and Excretion

 Science Online life.msscience.com/self_check_quiz

section ① review

1. supply oxygen and remove carbon dioxide
2. Oxygen, carbon dioxide, and waste gases are exchanged by diffusion into and out of the blood.
3. movement of the diaphragm and rib cage; differences in pressure

4. digestive system—provides food for cell respiration; circulatory system—transports oxygen for food breakdown and carries respiration waste products to the lungs for expulsion

5. Nicotine causes blood vessels to constrict, resulting in increased blood pressure. It also causes nausea, headaches, and gastric upset.
6. Students answers will vary.

The Excretory System

Functions of the Excretory System

It's your turn to take out the trash. You carry the bag outside and put it in the trash can. The next day, you bring out another bag of trash, but the trash can is full. When trash isn't collected, it piles up. Just as trash needs to be removed from your home to keep it livable, your body must eliminate wastes to remain healthy. Undigested material is eliminated by your large intestine. Waste gases are eliminated through the combined efforts of your circulatory and respiratory systems. Some salts are eliminated when you sweat. These systems function together as parts of your excretory system. If wastes aren't eliminated, toxic substances build up and damage organs. If not corrected, serious illness or death occurs.

The Urinary System

The **urinary system** rids the blood of wastes produced by the cells. **Figure 9** shows how the urinary system functions as a part of the excretory system. The urinary system also controls blood volume by removing excess water produced by body cells during respiration.

as you read

What You'll Learn
- **Distinguish** between the excretory and urinary systems.
- **Describe** how the kidneys work.
- **Explain** what happens when urinary organs don't work.

Why It's Important
The urinary system helps clean your blood of cellular wastes.

Review Vocabulary
blood: tissue that transports oxygen, nutrients, and waste materials throughout your body

New Vocabulary
- urinary system
- urine
- kidney
- nephron
- ureter
- bladder
- urethra

Figure 9 The excretory system includes other body systems.

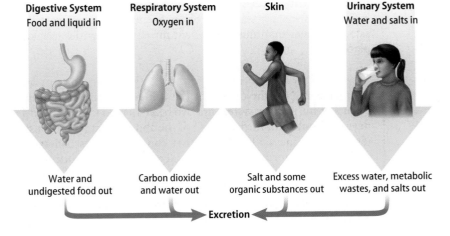

Digestive System	Respiratory System	Skin	Urinary System
Food and liquid in	Oxygen in		Water and salts in
Water and undigested food out	Carbon dioxide and water out	Salt and some organic substances out	Excess water, metabolic wastes, and salts out

Excretion

1 Motivate

INTERACTIVE CHALKBOARD
PowerPoint® Presentations

Bellringer

Section Focus Transparencies also are available on the Interactive Chalkboard CD-ROM.

L2 ELL

SECTION 2 Section Focus Transparency — Liquid Wastes

Have you ever thought of your skin as an organ that rids your body of waste? You probably perspire most heavily when you exercise. Perspiration is a liquid waste given off by the body.

1. How is perspiring helpful to the body?
2. Why is it important to drink plenty of fluids before, during, and after periods of intense physical activity?
3. What other body system is involved with the removal of liquid wastes?

Tie to Prior Knowledge

Filters Remind students of how the filter on a coffeemaker works. Only liquid is allowed to flow through. Explain that, in a similar way, the urinary system acts as a filter.

Section 2 Resource Manager

Chapter FAST FILE Resources
Transparency Activity, pp. 41, 43–44
MiniLAB, p. 4
Enrichment, p. 28
Reinforcement, p. 26
Directed Reading for Content Mastery, pp. 19, 20

Lab Worksheet, pp. 5–6, 7–8
Lab Management and Safety, p. 77
Mathematics Skill Activities, p. 1
Home and Community Involvement, p. 40

Activity

Urine Composition Have students do research and construct a circle graph to illustrate the composition of urine. water = 95%, urea = 2%, sodium chloride = 1%, other substances = 2% L3 IS **Visual-Spatial**

Visual Learning

Figure 10 Have students study this figure and make a sequencing concept map. Student maps should outline each step in the process by which the human body determines how much urine to excrete. L2

✔ Reading Check

Answer by increasing and decreasing the amount of wastewater excreted

Quick Demo

Diffusion

Materials cellophane bags, container of water, colored sugar solution, container of sugar solution, colored pure water

Estimated Time 15 minutes

Procedure Set up a diffusion experiment using a cellophane bag with a colored sugar solution placed in a container of water. To demonstrate diffusion in the other direction, place a cellophane bag of colored pure water into a container of sugar solution.

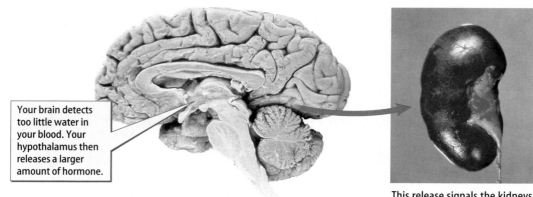

Your brain detects too little water in your blood. Your hypothalamus then releases a larger amount of hormone.

This release signals the kidneys to return more water to your blood and decrease the amount of urine excreted.

Figure 10 The amount of urine that you eliminate each day is determined by the level of a hormone that is produced by your hypothalamus.

Regulating Fluid Levels To stay in good health, the fluid levels within the body must be balanced and normal blood pressure must be maintained. An area in the brain, the hypothalamus (hi poh THA luh mus), constantly monitors the amount of water in the blood. When the brain detects too much water in the blood, the hypothalamus releases a lesser amount of a specific hormone. This signals the kidneys to return less water to the blood and increase the amount of wastewater, called **urine,** that is excreted. **Figure 10** indicates how the body reacts when too little water is in the blood.

✔ Reading Check
How does the urinary system control the volume of water in the blood?

A specific amount of water in the blood is also important for the movement of gases and excretion of solid wastes from the body. The urinary system also balances the amounts of certain salts and water that must be present for all cell activities to take place.

Organs of the Urinary System Excretory organs is another name for the organs of the urinary system. The main organs of the urinary system are two bean-shaped **kidneys.** Kidneys are located on the back wall of the abdomen at about waist level. The kidneys filter blood that contains wastes collected from cells. In approximately 5 min, all of the blood in your body passes through the kidneys. The red-brown color of the kidneys is due to their enormous blood supply. In **Figure 11,** you can see that blood enters the kidneys through a large artery and leaves through a large vein.

578 CHAPTER 20 Respiration and Excretion

Curriculum Connection

Math Calculate the ratio of body weight to amount of urine excreted. If an 11-kg child excretes 600 mL, what would you expect a 45-kg adult to excrete? 2,455 mL The amount is actually only about 1500 mL. The amount excreted by children is greater in proportion to their weight. L2 IS **Logical-Mathematical**

Teacher FYI

Body Homeostasis Filtering waste from the circulatory system is essential to maintaining life. The urinary system regulates the concentration and volume of blood by removing and restoring selected amounts of water and chemicals. Any change in the normal functioning of the urinary system represents a health threat.

Filtration in the Kidney The kidney, as shown in **Figure 11A**, is a two-stage filtration system. It is made up of about 1 million tiny filtering units called **nephrons** (NEF rahnz), which are shown in **Figure 11B.** Each nephron has a cuplike structure and a tube-like structure called a duct. Blood moves from a renal artery to capillaries in the cuplike structure. The first filtration occurs when water, sugar, salt, and wastes from the blood pass into the cuplike structure. Left behind in the blood are red blood cells and proteins. Next, liquid in the cuplike structure is squeezed into a narrow tubule. Capillaries that surround the tubule perform the second filtration. Most of the water, sugar, and salt are reabsorbed and returned to the blood. These collection capillaries merge to form small veins, which merge to form a renal vein in each kidney. Purified blood is returned to the main circulatory system. The liquid left behind flows into collecting tubules in each kidney. This wastewater, or urine, contains excess water, salts, and other wastes that are not reabsorbed by the body. An average-sized person produces about 1 L of urine per day.

Figure 11 The urinary system removes wastes from the blood and includes the kidneys, the bladder, and the connecting tubes.

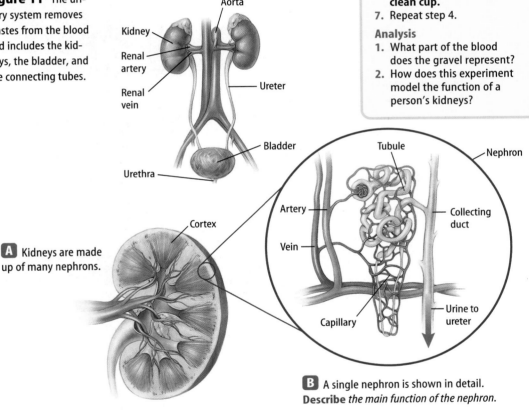

A Kidneys are made up of many nephrons.

B A single nephron is shown in detail. **Describe** *the main function of the nephron.*

Mini LAB

Modeling Kidney Function

Procedure
1. Mix a small amount of **soil** and **fine gravel** with **water** in a **clean cup.**
2. Place the **funnel** into a **second cup.**
3. Place a small piece of **wire screen** in the funnel.
4. Carefully pour the mud-water-gravel mixture into the funnel. Let it drain.
5. Remove the screen and replace it with a piece of **filter paper.**
6. Place the funnel in **another clean cup.**
7. Repeat step 4.

Analysis
1. What part of the blood does the gravel represent?
2. How does this experiment model the function of a person's kidneys?

Mini LAB

Purpose Students model and observe the function of a kidney. [L2] [IS] **Kinesthetic**

Materials soil (2 T), fine gravel (1 T), 8-ounce plastic cups (3), funnel, wire screen, filter paper, tap water

Teaching Strategy Students may work in pairs to cut down on the amount of materials needed.

Troubleshooting Moisten the filter paper before filtering the dirty water so that the paper adheres to the funnel.

Analysis
1. the blood cells and proteins
2. This experiment modeled the two-stage filtration process of the kidneys. The filter removes dirt and particles, like a nephron, which filters wastes from the blood.

Assessment

Portfolio Have students make a labeled drawing of the urinary system. Have them place arrows on the diagrams to show the flow of fluids through the nephrons to the bladder and then out of the body. Use **Performance Assessment in the Science Classroom,** p. 127. [L2] [P]

Caption Answer

Figure 11B to filter blood

Active Reading

Synthesis Journal In this strategy, students reflect on a project, a paper, or a performance in light of their own experiences and plan for personal application. Have each student divide a piece of paper into three sections. Have them record *What I did, What I learned,* and *How I can use it.* Have students write a Synthesis Journal entry for the MiniLAB. [L2]

Fun Fact

Protozoans are complete organisms (most are one-celled) that ingest food, digest food, expel waste, and breathe without the benefit of separate organs such as those that humans have.

Urine Collection and Release The urine in each collecting tubule drains into a funnel-shaped area of each kidney that leads to the ureter (YOO ruh tur). **Ureters** are tubes that lead from each kidney to the bladder. The **bladder** is an elastic, muscular organ that holds urine until it leaves the body. The elastic walls of the bladder can stretch to hold up to 0.5 L of urine. When empty, the bladder looks wrinkled and the cells lining the bladder are thick. When full, the bladder looks like an inflated balloon and the cells lining the bladder are stretched and thin. A tube called the **urethra** (yoo REE thruh) carries urine from the bladder to the outside of the body.

Applying Science

How does your body gain and lose water?

Your body depends on water. Without water, your cells could not carry out their activities and body systems could not function. Water is so important to your body that your brain and other body systems are involved in balancing water gain and water loss.

Identifying the Problem

Table A shows the major sources by which your body gains water. Oxidation of nutrients occurs when energy is released from nutrients by your body's cells. Water is a waste product of these reactions. **Table B** lists the major sources by which your body loses water. The data show you how daily gain and loss of water are related.

Solving the Problem

1. What is the greatest source of water gained by your body?
2. Explain how the percentages of water gained and lost would change in a person who was working in extremely warm temperatures. In this case, what organ of the body would be the greatest contributor to water loss?

Table A

Major Sources by Which Body Water is Gained		
Source	Amount (mL)	Percent
Oxidation of nutrients	250	10
Foods	750	30
Liquids	1,500	60
Total	2,500	100

Table B

Major Sources by Which Body Water is Lost		
Source	Amount (mL)	Percent
Urine	1,500	60
Skin	500	20
Lungs	350	14
Feces	150	6
Total	2,500	100

580 CHAPTER 20 Respiration and Excretion

Differentiated Instruction

Challenge Adult kidneys weigh only about 170 g each. The kidneys of an average adult process about 1,600 L of liquid per day, most of which is recycled. Have students calculate how many liters an adult's kidneys process in a year, in a decade, and in 75 years. 584,000 L; 5,840,000 L; 43,800,000 L ☐L3 ☐IS **Logical-Mathematical**

Curriculum Connection

Health Small stones made up of precipitated minerals such as uric acid or calcium salts may form in the kidneys. These kidney stones may move into the ureter and can cause severe pain. Drinking large quantities of water can help prevent the formation of the stones. Ask students to investigate what foods may contribute to the formation of kidney stones. ☐L2

Other Organs of Excretion

Large amounts of liquid wastes are lost every day by your body in other ways, as shown in **Figure 12.** The liver also filters the blood to remove wastes. Certain wastes are converted to other substances. For example, excess amino acids are changed to a chemical called urea (yoo REE uh) that is excreted in urine. Hemoglobin from broken-down red blood cells becomes part of bile, which is the digestive fluid from the liver.

Urinary Diseases and Disorders

What happens when someone's kidneys don't work properly or stop working? Waste products that are not removed build up and act as poisons in body cells. Water that normally is removed from body tissues accumulates and causes swelling of the ankles and feet. Sometimes these fluids also build up around the heart, causing it to work harder to move blood to the lungs.

Without excretion, an imbalance of salts occurs. The body responds by trying to restore this balance. If the balance isn't restored, the kidneys and other organs can be damaged. Kidney failure occurs when the kidneys don't work as they should. This is always a serious problem because the kidneys' job is so important to the rest of the body.

Infections caused by microorganisms can affect the urinary system. Usually, the infection begins in the bladder. However, it can spread and involve the kidneys. Most of the time, these infections can be cured with antibiotics.

Because the ureters and urethra are narrow tubes, they can be blocked easily in some disorders. A blockage of one of these tubes can cause serious problems because urine cannot flow out of the body properly. If the blockage is not corrected, the kidneys can be damaged.

 **Reading Check** *Why is a blocked ureter or urethra a serious problem?*

Detecting Urinary Diseases Urine can be tested for any signs of a urinary tract disease. A change in the urine's color can suggest kidney or liver problems. High levels of glucose can be a sign of diabetes. Increased amounts of a protein called albumin (al BYOO mun) indicate kidney disease or heart failure. When the kidneys are damaged, albumin can get into the urine, just as a leaky water pipe allows water to drip.

Figure 12 On average, the volume of water lost daily by exhaling is a little more than the volume of a soft-drink can. The volume of water lost by your skin each day is about the volume of a 20-ounce soft-drink bottle.

INTEGRATE Social Studies

Desalination Nearly 80 percent of Earth's surface is covered by water. Ninety-seven percent of this water is salt water. Humans cannot drink salt water. Desalination is a process that removes salt from salt water making it safe for human consumption. Research to learn which countries use desalination as a source of drinking water. Mark the countries' locations on a world map.

Use Science Words

Word Origin *Urina* is the Latin word for urine. It is the root for many words associated with the urinary system. Ask students to find words with this root and explain their meaning. Possible answers: uric acid—a chemical found in urine; urinal—a toilet L2

3 Assess

DAILY INTERVENTION

Check for Understanding

Logical-Mathematical What happens to the dissolved nutrients in the blood that pass through the kidneys? They are filtered out, but later returned to the blood.

Reteach

Liquid Wastes Have students prepare a basic diagram of the sequence involved in the processing of liquid wastes in the body. L2 **IS** **Visual-Spatial**

✓ Assessment

Portfolio Provide students with a diagram of the circulatory, respiratory, and excretory systems. Have them construct concept maps from these diagrams. Use **Performance Assessment in the Science Classroom**, p. 161. L2 **IS** **Visual-Spatial, Logical-Mathematical**

Figure 13 A dialysis machine can replace or help with some of the activities of the kidneys in a person with kidney failure. Like the kidney, the dialysis machine removes wastes from the blood.

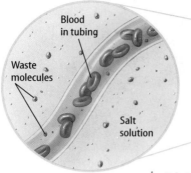
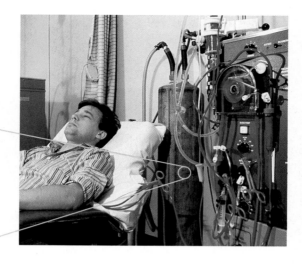

Blood in tubing

Waste molecules

Salt solution

Dialysis A person who has only one kidney still can live normally. The remaining kidney increases in size and works harder to make up for the loss of the other kidney. However, if both kidneys fail, the person will need to have his or her blood filtered by an artificial kidney machine in a process called dialysis (di AH luh sus), as shown in **Figure 13.**

---

section 2 review

Summary

The Urinary System

- The urinary system rids the blood of wastes produced by your cells.
- The hypothalamus monitors and regulates the amount of water in the blood.
- Nephrons are tiny filtering units in the kidneys that remove water, sugar, salt, and wastes from blood.
- Urine from the kidneys drains into the ureter, then into the bladder, and is carried outside the body by the urethra.

Urinary Diseases and Disorders

- Waste products that are not removed build up and act as poisons in your cells.
- If both kidneys fail, your blood will need to be filtered using a process called dialysis.
- Urine can be tested for kidney and liver problems, heart failure, and diabetes.

Self Check

1. **Explain** how the kidneys remove wastes and keep fluids and salts in balance.
2. **Describe** what happens when the urinary system does not function properly.
3. **Compare** the excretory system and urinary system.
4. **Concept Map** Using a network-tree concept map, compare the excretory functions of the kidneys and the lungs.
5. **Think Critically** Explain why reabsorption of certain materials in the kidneys is important to your health.

Applying Math

6. **Solve One-Step Equations** In approximately 5 min, all 5 L of blood in the body pass through the kidneys. Calculate the average rate of flow through the kidneys in liters per minute.

---

section 2 review

1. Kidneys filter the blood to remove wastes, sugar, water, and salt. Necessary amounts of water, sugar, and salt are returned to the blood.
2. Waste products not removed cause the destruction of cells. Fluids not removed from body tissues cause swellings in the extremities and buildup of fluids around the heart. Salts are in imbalance in body fluids, which can lead to organ damage.
3. excretory system—includes all systems that rid the body of wastes; urinary system—consists of organs that produce urine as waste
4. Many of the substances are needed by the body to maintain homeostasis.
5. Wastes in blood are carried to the lungs, which remove water and carbon dioxide, and to the kidneys, which remove water and excess salts, and other wastes.
6. 1 liter per minute rate of flow

LAB

Kidney Structure

As your body uses nutrients, wastes are created. One role of the kidneys is to filter waste products out of the bloodstream and excrete this waste outside the body. How can these small structures filter all the blood in the body in 5 min?

▶ Real-World Question

How does the structure of the kidney relate to the function of a kidney?

Goals

■ **Observe** the external and internal structures of a kidney.

Materials

large animal kidney
*model of a kidney
scalpel
magnifying lens
disposable gloves
dissecting tray
*Alternate materials

Safety Precautions

WARNING: *Use extreme care when using sharp instruments. Wear disposable gloves. Wash your hands with soap after completing this lab.*

▶ Procedure

1. **Examine** the outside of the kidney supplied by your teacher.
2. If the kidney still is encased in fat, peel off the fat carefully.
3. Using a scalpel, carefully cut the tissue in half lengthwise around the outline of the kidney. This cut should result in a section similar to the illustration on this page.

4. **Observe** the internal features of the kidney using a magnifying lens, or view these features in a model.
5. **Compare** the specimen or model with the kidney in the illustration.
6. **Draw** the kidney in your Science Journal and label its structures.

▶ Conclude and Apply

1. What part makes up the cortex of the kidney? Why is this part red?
2. **Describe** the main function of nephrons.
3. The medulla of the kidney is made up of a network of tubules that come together to form the ureter. What is the function of this network of tubules?
4. How can the kidney be compared to a portable water-purifying system?

Communicating Your Data

Compare your conclusions with those of other students in your class. **For more help, refer to the** Science Skill Handbook.

LAB 583

Communicating Your Data

Students should discuss why their conclusions did or did not agree. They can prepare a listing of references that support their findings. L2

▶ Real-World Question

Purpose Students examine the structures in a kidney and relate each structure to its function. L2 IS **Kinesthetic**

Process Skills observe and infer, interpret scientific illustrations, compare and contrast

Time Required 50 minutes

Safety Precautions Caution students about using sharp objects.

Teaching Strategies

• You may wish to have some kidneys remain intact.
• Other kidneys may be already sliced longitudinally.
• Kidneys can be reused.

Troubleshooting Demonstrate proper techniques for scalpel usage.

▶ Conclude and Apply

1. Nephrons; the color is caused by the blood in the nephrons.
2. to filter blood within the kidneys
3. The network of tubules moves the fluid from the kidney to the bladder so it can be excreted.
4. Both are filtering mechanisms.

✓ Assessment

Oral Have students describe the evidence that two kidneys are more than enough to take care of excretory functions. Possible answer: people who have only one kidney are still able to function normally. L2

Real-World Question

Purpose Students model a blocked trachea and demonstrate how the abdominal thrust maneuver is used to remove the blockage. **L2** **IS** **Kinesthetic**

Process Skills record observations, make models, analyze results, recognize cause and effect, draw conclusions

Time Required 40 minutes

Make a Model

Discussion Tell students that the trachea is a tube that carries air from the mouth to the lungs. This passageway is the only normal path for air to flow into the lungs. What might happen if this passage were blocked? The oxygen supply would be cut off, and the person would die within a few minutes. Explain that the abdominal thrust maneuver is a simple method of removing a blockage from this passageway.

Possible Materials paper towel roll tube or other tube, paper, clay, bellows, bicycle pump, sports bottle, scissors

Safety Precautions Caution students to use care with scissors.

LAB Model and Invent

Simulating the Abdominal Thrust Maneuver

Goals
- **Construct** a model of the trachea with a piece of food stuck in it.
- **Demonstrate** what happens when the abdominal thrust maneuver is performed on someone.
- **Predict** another way that air could get into the lungs if the food could not be dislodged with an abdominal thrust maneuver.

Possible Materials
paper towel roll or other tube
paper (wadded into a ball)
clay
bicycle pump
sports bottle
scissors

Safety Precautions

Always be careful when you use scissors.

Real-World Question

Have you ever taken a class in CPR or learned about how to help a choking victim? Using the abdominal thrust maneuver, or Heimlich maneuver, is one way to remove food or another object that is blocking someone's airway. What happens internally when the maneuver is used? What can you use to make a model of the trachea? How can you simulate what happens during an abdominal thrust maneuver using your model?

Make a Model

1. **List** the materials that you will need to construct your model. What will represent the trachea and a piece of food or other object blocking the airway?

2. How can you use your model to simulate the effects of an abdominal thrust maneuver?

3. **Suggest** a way to get air into the lungs if the food could not be dislodged. How would you simulate this method in your model?

Alternative Inquiry Lab

Extend the Activity Make this Lab an Inquiry Lab by building on the experience. Encourage your students to use what they have learned to brainstorm questions about what to do if the airway is blocked by water, in the case of a drowning victim. Have student groups each choose 1 question to explore. Ask them to list the materials they need to explore their questions. Unsafe or impractical questions should be eliminated. Students should have their plans for their additional experiments approved before continuing. Conduct the experiments after all of the necessary materials have been gathered. **L2**

4. **Compare** your plans for the model and the abdominal thrust maneuver simulation with those of other students in your class. Discuss why each of you chose the plans and materials that you did.

5. Make sure your teacher approves your plan and materials for your model before you start.

Test the Model

1. **Construct** your model of a trachea with an object stuck in it. Make sure that air cannot get through the trachea if you try blowing softly through it.

2. Simulate what happens when an abdominal thrust maneuver is used. Record your observations. Was the object dislodged? How hard was it to dislodge the object?

3. Replace the object in the trachea. Use your model to simulate how you could get air into the lungs if an abdominal thrust maneuver did not remove the object. Is it easy to blow air through your model now?

4. Model a crushed trachea. Is it easy to blow air through the trachea in this case?

Analyze Your Data

1. **Describe** how easy it was to get air through the trachea in each step in the Make the Model section above. Include any other observations that you made as you worked with your model.

2. Think about what you did to get air into the trachea when the object could not be dislodged with an abdominal thrust maneuver. How could this be done to a person? Do you know what this procedure is called?

Conclude and Apply

Explain why the trachea has cartilage around it to protect it. What might happen if it did not?

ommunicating Your Data

Explain to your family or friends what you have learned about how the abdominal thrust maneuver can help choking victims.

LAB **585**

TIME

Content Background

Samuel Kountz was born in extreme poverty in an all-black town in Arkansas in 1930. His grandmother was born a slave. He became the first African American to be accepted to the University of Arkansas Medical School.

While interning at Stanford, Kountz discovered that large amounts of the steroid methyl-prednisolone given to the patient after the transplant operation helped to reverse the rejection of the new organ. Kountz was a man of many achievements, and received several awards during his career.

Discussion

Kidney Rejection What did Kountz discover was the reason kidneys were being rejected after transplant surgeries? Possible answer: The patient's cells attacked and destroyed the small blood vessels of the transplanted kidney, thus, the kidney would die from lack of blood-supplied oxygen.

Historical Significance

Kountz's work also had a significant impact on other transplant surgeries, because other transplant procedures were associated with similar rejection problems.

The first successful kidney transplant without the use of immunosuppressive drugs was performed in 1954, because the donor was the recipient's twin. Organ rejection can be lessened when the donor is a sibling or other family member.

As a prelude to the Research activity, have students create a time line of transplant history starting from the early 1900s. Have students use poster board and ask them to include photographs and illustrations that illustrate transplant history. L2

IS Visual-Spatial

Overcoming the Odds

Guts and determination helped one pioneering doctor to save the lives of thousands

O vercoming the odds is a challenge that many people face. Dr. Samuel Lee Kountz, Jr. had the odds stacked against him. Thanks to his determination he beat them.

Dr. Kountz was interested in kidney transplants, a process that was still brand new in the 1950s. For many patients, a kidney transplant added months or a year to one's life. But then a patient's body would reject the kidney, and the patient would die. Dr. Kountz was determined to see that kidney transplants saved lives and kept patients healthy for years.

A donated organ is on its way to save a life.

Fixing the Problem

Kountz discovered the root of the problem—why and how a patient's body rejected the transplanted kidney. He discovered that the patient's cells attacked and destroyed the small blood vessels of the transplanted kidney. So the new kidney would die from lack of blood-supplied oxygen. From this, doctors knew when to give patients the right kinds of drugs, so that their bodies could overcome the rejection process.

In 1959, Kountz performed the first successful kidney transplant. He went on to develop a procedure to keep body organs healthy for up to 60 hours after being taken from a donor. He also set up a system of organ donor cards through the National Kidney Foundation. And in his career, Dr. Kountz transplanted more than 1,000 kidneys himself—and paved the way for thousands more.

Research What kinds of medical breakthroughs has the last century brought? Locate an article that explains either a recent advance in medicine or the work that doctors and medical researchers are doing. Share your findings with your class.

Science online
For more information, visit life.msscience.com/time

Research First, ask students to focus on one part of medicine or one specialization in medicine that interests them. If a student is interested in the brain, suggest a search for an article about neurological advancements in medicine. Suggest avenues that are available for your students to successfully fulfill research in whatever interests they present for this project.

Resources for Teachers and Students

"The Black Surgeon in the Twentieth Century: A Tribute to Samuel L. Kountz," by Claude Organ. *Journal of the National Medical Association*, (September, 1978)

Understanding Kidney Transplantation by Edith T. Oberley and Neal R. Glass. Thomas; Springfield, Ill. 1987

Reviewing Main Ideas

Section 1 — The Respiratory System

1. The respiratory system brings oxygen into the body and removes carbon dioxide.

2. Inhaled air passes through the nasal cavity, pharynx, larynx, trachea, bronchi, and into the alveoli of the lungs.

3. Breathing brings air into the lungs and removes waste gases.

4. The chemical reaction in the cells that needs oxygen to release energy from glucose is called cellular respiration.

5. The exchange of oxygen and carbon dioxide between aveoli and capillaries, and between capillaries and body cells, happens by the process of diffusion.

6. Smoking causes many problems throughout the respiratory system, including chronic bronchitis, emphysema, and lung cancer.

Section 2 — The Excretory System

1. The kidneys are the major organs of the urinary system. They filter wastes from all of the blood in the body.

2. The first stage of kidney filtration occurs when water, sugar, salt, and wastes from the blood pass into the cuplike part of the nephron. The capillaries surrounding the tubule part of the nephron perform the second filtration, returning most of the water, sugar, and salt to the blood.

3. The urinary system is part of the excretory system. The skin, lungs, liver, and large intestine are also excretory organs.

4. Urine can be tested for signs of urinary tract disease and other diseases.

5. A person who has only one kidney still can live normally. When kidneys fail to work, an artificial kidney can be used to filter the blood in a process called dialysis.

Visualizing Main Ideas

Copy and complete the following table on the respiratory and excretory systems.

Human Body Systems	Respiratory System	Excretory System
Major Organs	lungs	kidneys, lungs, large intestine, skin, liver
Wastes Eliminated	carbon dioxide, water vapor	water, salts, toxins
Disorders	chronic bronchitis, emphysema, lung cancer, asthma	builldup of waste, infections

Science Online   life.msscience.com/interactive_tutor

CHAPTER STUDY GUIDE   587

---

chapter Study Guide **20**

Reviewing Main Ideas

Summary statements can be used by students to review the major concepts of the chapter.

Visualizing Main Ideas

See student page.

Visit life.msscience.com
/self_check_quiz
/interactive_tutor
/vocabulary_puzzlemaker
/chapter_review
/standardized_test

Assessment Transparency

For additional assessment questions, use the *Assessment Transparency* located in the transparency book.

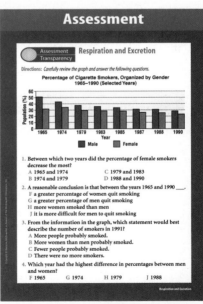

Assessment

Respiration and Excretion

Directions: Carefully review the graph and answer the following questions.

Percentage of Cigarette Smokers, Organized by Gender 1965–1990 (Selected Years)

1. Between which two years did the percentage of female smokers decrease the most?
   A 1965 and 1974   C 1979 and 1983
   B 1974 and 1979   D 1988 and 1990

2. A reasonable conclusion is that between the years 1965 and 1990 ___.
   F a greater percentage of women quit smoking
   G a greater percentage of men quit smoking
   H more women smoked than men
   J it is more difficult for men to quit smoking

3. From the information in the graph, which statement would best describe the number of smokers in 1991?
   A More people probably smoked.
   B More women than men probably smoked.
   C Fewer people probably smoked.
   D There were no more smokers.

4. Which year had the highest difference in percentages between men and women?
   F 1965   G 1974   H 1979   J 1988

chapter 20 Review

Using Vocabulary

1. Both are structures of the respiratory system.
2. Urine is stored in the bladder until it can be eliminated from the body.
3. Both are structures in the passageway leading to the esophagus.
4. The ureter carries urine to the bladder, and the urethra carries urine away from the bladder.
5. Alveoli are structures in the lungs that are damaged by the disease emphysema.
6. A nephron is the filtering unit of the kidney.
7. The urethra is a tube that carries urine away from the bladder.
8. Asthma is a disorder that causes the bronchi to contract.
9. The kidney filters blood and discharges liquid wastes, called urine.
10. Both are structures of the respiratory system.

Checking Concepts

11. B 16. D
12. C 17. B
13. A 18. A
14. A 19. C
15. B 20. C

Thinking Critically

21. Small objects can be sucked into and block their small windpipes, causing the child to choke.
22. Having many air sacs increases the surface area for gas exchange.
23. Tars coat cilia, making them less flexible and unable to move particles out of the lungs; alveoli lose elasticity, decreasing the total surface area of the lungs available for gas exchange; carcinogens cause the growth of cancerous cells in lung tissue.

chapter 20 Review

Using Vocabulary

asthma p.576
bladder p.580
bronchi p.571
diaphragm p.572
emphysema p.575
kidney p.578
larynx p.571
nephron p.579
pharynx p.570
trachea p.571
ureter p.580
urethra p.580
urinary system p.577
urine p.578

For each set of vocabulary words below, explain the relationship that exists.

1. alveoli—bronchi
2. bladder—urine
3. larynx—pharynx
4. ureter—urethra
5. alveoli—emphysema
6. nephron—kidney
7. urethra—bladder
8. asthma—bronchi
9. kidney—urine
10. diaphragm—alveoli

Checking Concepts

Choose the word or phrase that best answers the question.

11. When you inhale, which of the following contracts and moves down?
A) bronchioles C) nephrons
B) diaphragm D) kidneys

12. Air is moistened, filtered, and warmed in which of the following structures?
A) larynx C) nasal cavity
B) pharynx D) trachea

13. Exchange of gases occurs between capillaries and which of the following structures?
A) alveoli C) bronchioles
B) bronchi D) trachea

14. Which of the following is a lung disorder that can occur as an allergic reaction?
A) asthma C) atherosclerosis
B) cancer D) emphysema

15. When you exhale, which way does the rib cage move?
A) up C) out
B) down D) stays the same

16. Which of the following conditions does smoking worsen?
A) arthritis C) excretion
B) respiration D) emphysema

17. In the illustration to the right, what is the name of the organ labeled A?
A) kidneys
B) bladder
C) ureter
D) urethra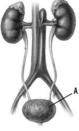

18. What are the filtering units of the kidneys?
A) nephrons C) neurons
B) ureters D) alveoli

19. Approximately 1 L of water is lost per day through which of the following?
A) sweat C) urine
B) lungs D) large intestine

20. Which of the following substances is not reabsorbed by blood after it passes through the kidneys?
A) salt C) wastes
B) sugar D) water

588 CHAPTER REVIEW

 Science Online life.msscience.com/vocabulary_puzzlemaker

Use the ExamView® Pro Testmaker CD-ROM to:
- create multiple versions of tests
- create modified tests with one mouse click for inclusion students
- edit existing questions and add your own questions
- build tests aligned with state standards using built-in State Curriculum Tags
- change English tests to Spanish with one mouse click and vice versa

588 CHAPTER REVIEW

Thinking Critically

21. Explain why certain foods, such as peanuts, can cause choking in small children.

22. Infer why it is an advantage to have lungs with many smaller air sacs instead of having just two large sacs, like balloons.

23. Explain the damage to cilia, alveoli, and lungs from smoking.

24. Describe what happens to the blood if the kidneys stop working.

25. Explain why it is often painful when small, solid particles called kidney stones, pass into the ureter.

Use the table below to answer question 26.

Materials Filtered by the Kidneys

Substance Filtered in Urine	Amount Moving Through Kidney	Amount Excreted
Water	125 L	1 L
Salt	350 g	10 g
Urea	1 g	1 g
Glucose	50 g	0 g

26. Interpret Data Study the data above. How much of each substance is reabsorbed into the blood in the kidneys? What substance is excreted completely in the urine?

27. Recognize Cause and Effect Discuss how lack of oxygen is related to lack of energy.

28. Form a hypothesis about the number of breaths a person might take per minute in each of these situations: sleeping, exercising, and standing on top of Mount Everest. Give a reason for each hypothesis.

 Science Online life.msscience.com/chapter_review

Performance Activities

29. Questionnaire and Interview Prepare a questionnaire that can be used to interview a health specialist who works with lung cancer patients.

Applying Math

30. Lung Capacity Make a circle graph of total lung capacity using the following data:
- volume of air in a normal inhalation or exhalation = 500 mL
- volume of additional air that can be inhaled forcefully after a normal inhalation = 3,000 mL
- volume of additional air that can be exhaled forcefully after a normal expiration = 1,100 mL
- volume of air still left in the lungs after all the air that can be exhaled has been forcefully exhaled = 1,200 mL

Use the table below to answer question 31.

Death Rates in Industry

Industry	Number of Deaths (1999)	Current Smokers (2000)
Construction	3336	37.4%
Eating and drinking places	907	39.7%
Engineering and science	55	18.7%
Mining	327	32.6%
Railroads	385	24.8%
Trucking service	1004	33.2%

31. Lung Cancer Deaths The table above shows the number of lung cancer deaths and the percentage of smokers for specified industries. How many times higher are the death rates for the construction industry than for the eating-and-drinking-places industry?

CHAPTER REVIEW 589

Thinking Critically

24. If the kidneys stopped working, blood would accumulate waste products from the body's organs. These wastes would act as poisons, and the person would need immediate medical care.

25. Kidney stones in the ureter extend and block the tube and cause severe pain. Infections may also occur.

26. Water: 124 L; salt: 340 g; glucose: 50 g; all urea is excreted.

27. Cells need oxygen to break down food and release energy.

28. Possible answers: Sleeping—breathing rate is low because less respiration is occurring; exercising—breathing rate would increase to get oxygen to the muscles; on Mount Everest—breathing rate would increase because less oxygen is present.

Performance Activities

29. Students should prepare questionnaires and conduct interviews. Use **Performance Assessment in the Science Classroom,** p. 91.

Applying Math

National Math Standards
5

30. Check student graphs for accuracy: 500 mL = 9% of circle (32°); 3,000 mL = 52% (187°); 1,100 mL = 19% (68°); 1,200 mL = 21% (76°).

31. 3.7 times; Construction workers breathe in a lot of particulate matter.

✓ Assessment   Resources

📁 Reproducible Masters
Chapter *Fast File* Resources
Chapter Review, pp. 33–34
Chapter Tests, pp. 35–38
Assessment Transparency Activity, p. 45
Glencoe Science Web site
Chapter Review Test
Standardized Test Practice

Glencoe Technology
🖋 Assessment Transparency
⊚ Exam*View*® Pro Testmaker
▭ MindJogger Videoquiz
⊚ Interactive Chalkboard

FAST FILE

Answer Sheet A practice answer sheet can be found at life.msscience.com/answer_sheet.

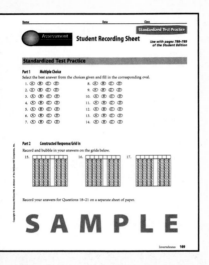

S A M P L E

Part 1 | Multiple Choice

1. A
2. C
3. D
4. B
5. C
6. C
7. A

Part 1 | Multiple Choice

Record your answers on the answer sheet provided by your teacher or on a sheet of paper.

1. Which of the following diseases is caused by smoking?
   A. lung cancer
   B. diabetes
   C. dialysis
   D. bladder infection

Use the table below to answer questions 2 and 3.

Major Sources by Which Body Water is Lost		
Source	**Amount per day (mL)**	**Percent**
Urine	1,500	60
Skin	500	20
Lungs	350	14
Feces	150	6
Total	2,500	100

2. If the amount of body water lost in the urine increased by 500 mL, what percent of the total body water lost would now be lost in the urine?
   A. 60%
   B. 75%
   C. 67%
   D. 66%

3. If a person had diarrhea, which source of body water loss would increase?
   A. urine
   B. lungs
   C. skin
   D. feces

4. The movement of the chest that brings air into the lungs and removes waste gases is called
   A. oxidation.
   B. breathing.
   C. respiration.
   D. expiration.

5. What traps dust, pollen, and other materials in your nose?
   A. glands
   B. vocal cords
   C. nasal hairs and mucus
   D. epiglottis

Use the illustration below to answer question 6.

6. What is the structure shown above and to what body system does it belong?
   A. capillary—circulatory
   B. alveolus—respiratory
   C. nephron—urinary
   D. ureter—excretory

7. What is the correct order of steps in the abdominal thrust maneuver?
   A. Rescuer stands behind victim and wraps arms around victim's upper abdomen; rescuer places fist against victim's stomach; rescuer thrusts fist up into area below ribs; rescuer repeats action as many times as necessary.
   B. Rescuer places fist against victim's stomach; rescuer thrusts fist up into area below ribs; rescuer stands behind victim and wraps arms around victim's upper abdomen; rescuer repeats action as many times as necessary.
   C. Rescuer places fist against victim's stomach; rescuer thrusts fist up into area below ribs; rescuer repeats action as many times as necessary.
   D. Rescuer stands in front of victim; rescuer places fist against victim's stomach; rescuer thrusts fist up into area below ribs; rescuer repeats action as needed.

590 STANDARDIZED TEST PRACTICE

Part 2 | Short Response/Grid In

8. $0.50 + 0.50 + 0.55 + 0.32 = 1.87$; $1.87 \div 4 = 0.47$ L

9. Mr. Stoler

10. Day 3

11. Mr. Stoler

12. nicotine and tars

13. In some people, plant pollen can cause asthma. Because asthma can be an allergic reaction, people who are allergic to certain plant pollen can have an asthma attack.

14. It allows oxygen to diffuse out of alveoli and carbon dioxide to diffuse into alveoli. If the alveoli were thick walled, diffusion could not take place as easily.

15. Energy is released from glucose through respiration. The oxygen delivered to the cells is used to release energy from glucose. Water and carbon dioxide also are produced.

Part 2 | Short Response/Grid In

Record your answers on the answer sheet provided by your teacher or on a sheet of paper.

Use the paragraph and table below to answer questions 8–11.

For one week, research scientists collected and accurately measured the amount of body water lost and gained per day for four different patients. The following table lists results from their investigation.

Body Water Gained (+) and Lost (−)				
Person	Day 1 (L)	Day 2 (L)	Day 3 (L)	Day 4 (L)
Mr. Stoler	+0.15	+0.15	−0.35	+0.12
Mr. Jemma	−0.01	0.00	−0.20	−0.01
Mr. Lowe	0.00	+0.20	−0.28	+0.01
Mr. Cheng	−0.50	−0.50	−0.55	−0.32

8. What was Mr. Cheng's average daily body water loss for the 4 days shown in the table?

9. Which patient had the greatest amount of body water gained on days 1 and 2?

10. According to the data in the table, on which day was the temperature in each patient's hospital room probably the hottest?

11. Which patient had the highest total gain in body water over the 4-day period?

12. What chemical substances in tobacco can destroy cells?

13. What effect can plant pollen have on the respiratory system?

14. Why do alveoli have thin walls?

15. How is energy released from glucose? What also is produced?

Part 3 | Open Ended

Record your answers on a sheet of paper.

16. Explain the role of cilia in the respiratory system. Give an example of a disease in which cilia are damaged. What effects does this damage have on the respiratory system?

Use the table below to answer questions 17–19.

Urine Test Results				
Test Items	Normal Results	Mrs. Beebe	Mrs. Chavez	Mrs. Jelton
Glucose	Absent	High	Absent	Absent
Albumin	Absent	Absent	Absent	Absent
Urine volume per 24 hours	1 L	1 L	1 L	0.5 L

17. Mrs. Jelton's urine tests were done when outside temperatures had been higher than 35°C for several days. When Mrs. Jelton came to Dr. Marks' office after the urine test, he asked her about the amount of liquid that she had been drinking. Infer why Dr. Marks asked this question.

18. Assuming that Mrs. Jelton is healthy, form a hypothesis that would explain what had happened.

19. Dr. Marks called another patient to come in for more testing. Who was it? How do you know?

Test-Taking Tip

Understand Symbols Be sure you understand all symbols on a table or graph before attempting to answer any questions about the table or graph.

Questions 21–23. Notice that the unit of volume is in liters (L).

signals the kidneys to return more water to the blood and decrease the amount of urine excreted. If Mrs. Jelton was taking in a normal amount of water, then she might be losing more water from perspiration. She should drink more water to replace the extra water lost by sweating.

18. Dr. Marks called Mrs. Beebe. Mrs. Beebe had glucose in the urine. Glucose normally is not excreted in the urine in large amounts. Dr. Marks wanted to find out if Mrs. Beebe had diabetes.

19. The liver filters the blood to remove wastes. Some wastes are converted to other substances. Excess amino acids are changed to urea (which is excreted by the kidneys). Hemoglobin from broken down red blood cells becomes part of bile, the digestive fluid from the liver. The skin removes some salts and organic substances from the body through perspiration. The skin also removes water.

Rubrics

For more help evaluating open-ended assessment questions, see the rubric on p. 10T.

Part 3 | Open Ended

16. Cilia remove mucus, bacteria, and dirt particles from the respiratory system. Chronic bronchitis is a disease in which the cilia are damaged. (Although cilia are damaged in the common cold, cilia damage usually heals quickly in this disease.) If the cilia do not remove these materials, they build up in the airways and the airways cannot work properly.

17. Mrs. Jelton produced less urine in one day than an average-sized person usually does. Dr. Marks wanted to find out why. Since Mrs. Jelton did not have any disease that might affect the amount of urine produced, the decrease in the amount of urine was a response of her body to a decrease in body water. When the brain detects too little water in the blood, the hypothalamus releases a larger amount of hormone. This

Section/Objectives	Standards		Labs/Features
Chapter Opener	**National**	**State/Local**	**Launch Lab:** How quick are your responses?, p. 593 **Foldables,** p. 593
	See pp. 16T–17T for a Key to Standards.		
Section 1 The Nervous System 🕐 2 sessions 📦 1 block 1. **Describe** the basic structure of a neuron and how an impulse moves across a synapse. 2. **Compare** the central and peripheral nervous systems. 3. **Explain** how drugs affect the body.	National Content Standards: UCP.1, UCP.2, UCP.3, UCP.5, A.1, A.2, C.1, C.3, C.5, F.1, G.3		**Integrate History,** p. 595 **Visualizing Nerve Impulse Pathways,** p. 596 **Integrate Chemistry,** p. 598 **Science Online,** p. 599 **Science Online,** p. 601 **Lab:** Improving Reaction Time, p. 603
Section 2 The Senses 🕐 3 sessions 📦 1.5 blocks 4. **List** the sensory receptors in each sense organ. 5. **Explain** what type of stimulus each sense organ responds to and how. 6. **Explain** why healthy senses are needed.	National Content Standards: UCP.1, UCP.2, UCP.3, UCP.5, A.1, A.2, C.1, C.3, C.5		**Integrate Astronomy,** p. 606 **MiniLAB:** Observing Balance Control, p. 608 **Science Online,** p. 609 **Applying Math:** Speed of Sound, p. 609 **MiniLAB:** Comparing Sense of Smell, p. 610 **Lab:** Skin Sensitivity, p. 612 **Science and Language Arts:** Sula, p. 614

Lab Materials	Reproducible Resources	Section Assessment	Technology
Launch Lab: safety goggles, chair, sheet of discarded paper	**Chapter FAST FILE Resources** Foldables Worksheet, p. 17 Directed Reading Overview, p. 19 Note-taking Worksheets, pp. 31–33	GLENCOE'S ASSESSMENT ADVANTAGE	**TeacherWorks** includes: • Interactive Teacher Edition • Lesson Planner with calendar • Access to all program blacklines • Correlations to standards • Web links
Lab: metric ruler	**Chapter FAST FILE Resources** Transparency Activity, p. 42 Lab Worksheet, pp. 5–6 Enrichment, p. 29 Reinforcement, p. 27 Directed Reading, p. 20 Transparency Activity, pp. 45–46 Lab Activity, pp. 9–12 **Reading and Writing Skill Activities,** p. 17 **Life Science Critical Thinking/ Problem Solving,** pp. 2, 18 **Mathematics Skill Activities,** p. 9	Portfolio Science Journal, p. 595 Assessment, p. 602 Performance Applying Skills, p. 602 Content Section Review, p. 602	🖐 Section Focus Transparency 🖐 Teaching Transparency 💿 Virtual Labs CD-ROM 🎧 Guided Reading Audio Program 💿 Interactive Chalkboard CD-ROM 📼 Video Lab
MiniLAB: 2 narrow strips of paper, tape **MiniLAB:** samples of different foods, colognes, or household products; cotton balls; blindfold **Lab:** 3-in × 5-in index card, toothpicks, tape, metric ruler *Need materials?* Contact Science Kit at 1-800-828-7777 or www.sciencekit.com on the Internet.	**Chapter FAST FILE Resources** Lab Worksheet, pp. 7–8 Enrichment, p. 30 Reinforcement, p. 28 Directed Reading, pp. 21, 22 Transparency Activity, p. 43 Lab Activity, pp. 13–16 MiniLAB, pp. 3, 4 **Home and Community Involvement,** p. 28 **Performance Assessment in the Science Classroom,** p. 66 **Lab Management and Safety,** p. 65	Portfolio Reteach, p. 611 Performance MiniLAB, p. 608 Applying Math, p. 609 MiniLAB, p. 610 Applying Skills, p. 611 Content Section Review, p. 611	🖐 Section Focus Transparency 💿 Virtual Labs CD-ROM 🎧 Guided Reading Audio Program 💿 Interactive Chalkboard CD-ROM

GLENCOE'S ASSESSMENT ADVANTAGE — End of Chapter Assessment

Blackline Masters	Technology	Professional Series
Chapter FAST FILE Resources Chapter Review, pp. 35–36 Chapter Tests, pp. 37–40 **Standardized Test Practice,** pp. 87–90	📼 MindJogger Videoquiz 💿 Virtual Labs CD-ROM 💿 ExamView® Pro Testmaker 💿 TeacherWorks CD-ROM 💿 Interactive Chalkboard CD-ROM	**Performance Assessment in the Science Classroom (PASC)**

Transparencies

Section Focus

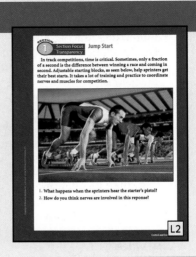

SECTION 1 Section Focus Transparency Jump Start

In track competitions, time is critical. Sometimes, only a fraction of a second is the difference between winning a race and coming in second. Adjustable starting blocks, as seen below, help sprinters get their best starts. It takes a lot of training and practice to coordinate nerves and muscles for competition.

1. What happens when the sprinters hear the starter's pistol?
2. How do you think nerves are involved in this reponse?

L2

SECTION 2 Section Focus Transparency Life in the Balance

One of the attractions of a circus is the skilled performers. Walking on a tightrope requires a keen sense of balance and years of practice and training. Can you see this performer's feet on the wire?

1. What sort of shoes is the performer wearing? Why?
2. What senses do you think help us maintain balance?

L2

This is a representation of key blackline masters available in the Teacher Classroom Resources. See Resource Manager boxes within the chapter for additional information.

Key to Teaching Strategies

The following designations will help you decide which activities are appropriate for your students.

L1 Level 1 activities should be appropriate for students with learning difficulties.

L2 Level 2 activities should be within the ability range of all students.

L3 Level 3 activities are designed for above-average students.

ELL ELL activities should be within the ability range of English-Language Learners.

COOP LEARN Cooperative Learning activities are designed for small group work.

LS Multiple Learning Styles logos, as described on page 12T, are used throughout to indicate strategies that address different learning styles.

P These strategies represent student products that can be placed into a best-work portfolio.

PBL Problem-Based Learning activities apply real-world situations to learning.

Assessment

Assessment Transparency Control and Coordination

Directions: Carefully review the table and answer the following questions.

Reaction Experiment Results		
Students	**Distance of catch (cm)**	**Reaction time (s)**
Dorothea	5	0.10
Billy	10	0.13
Hans	15	0.16
Sandra	20	?
Martha	25	0.22
Leo	30	0.25

1. According to the information in the table, the student with the lowest reaction time is ___.
   A Leo C Hans
   B Billy D Dorothea
2. Based on the relationship between catch distance and reaction time, which is most likely Sandra's reaction time?
   F 0.10 s H 0.19 s
   G 0.18 s I 0.21 s
3. Eleanor, another student, is asked to participate in the experiment. Her reaction time was determined to be 0.23 seconds. Based on the information in the table, Eleanor's catch distance would be ___.
   A 31.15 cm C 24.25 cm
   B 26.67 cm D 21.67 cm

L2

Teaching

SECTION 1 Teaching Transparency The Brain

L2

Hands-on Activities

Student Text Lab Worksheet

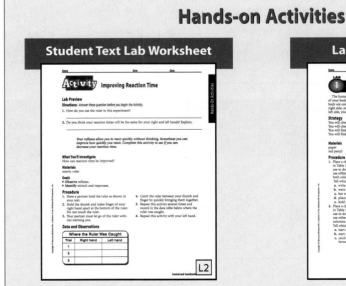

Activity Improving Reaction Time

Lab Preview
Directions: Answer these question before you begin the Activity.

1. How do you use the ruler in this experiment?

2. Do you think your reaction times be the same for your right and left hand? Explain.

Your reflexes allow you to react quickly without thinking. Sometimes you can improve how quickly you react. Complete this activity to see if you can decrease your reaction time.

What You'll Investigate
How can reaction time be improved?

Materials
metric ruler

Goals
• Observe reflexes.
• Identify stimuli and responses.

Procedure
1. Have a partner hold the ruler as shown in your text.
2. Hold the thumb and index finger of your right hand apart at the bottom of the ruler. Do not touch the ruler.
3. Your partner must let go of the ruler without warning you.
4. Catch the ruler between your thumb and finger by quickly bringing them together.
5. Repeat this several times and record in the data table below where the ruler was caught.
6. Repeat this activity with your left hand.

Data and Observations

Where the Ruler Was Caught		
Trial	**Right hand**	**Left hand**
1		
2		
3		

L2

Laboratory Activities

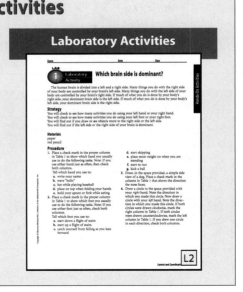

LAB 1 Laboratory Activity Which brain side is dominant?

The human brain is divided into a left and a right side. Many things you do with the right side of your body are controlled by your brain's left side. Many things you do with the left side of your body are controlled by your brain's right side. If much of what you do is done by your body's right side, your dominant brain side is the left side. If much of what you do is done by your body's left side, your dominant brain side is the right side.

Strategy
You will check to see how many activities you do using your left hand or your right hand.
You will check to see how many activities you do using your left foot or your right foot.
You will find out if you draw or see objects more to the right side or the left side.
You will find out if the left side or the right side of your brain is dominant.

Materials
paper
red pencil

Procedure
1. Place a check mark in the proper column in Table 1 to show which hand you usually use to do the following tasks. Note: If you use either hand just as often, then check both columns.
   Tell which hand you use to:
   a. write your name
   b. wave "hello"
   c. bat while playing baseball
   d. place on top when folding your hands
   e. hold your spoon or fork while eating
2. Place a check mark in the proper column in Table 1 to show which foot you usually use to do the following tasks. Note: If you use either foot just as often, check both columns.
   Tell which foot you use to:
   a. start down a flight of stairs
   b. start up a flight of stairs
   c. catch yourself from falling as you lean forward
   d. start skipping
   e. place most weight on when you are standing
   f. start to run
   g. kick a ball
3. Draw, in the space provided, a simple side view of a dog. Place a check mark in the column in Table 1 that shows the direction the nose faces.
4. Draw a circle in the space provided with your right hand. Note the direction in which you made this circle. Now draw a circle with your left hand. Note the direction in which you made this circle. If both circles were drawn clockwise, mark the right column in Table 1. If both circles were drawn counterclockwise, mark the left column in Table 1. If you drew one circle in each direction, check both columns.

L2

Resource Manager

Meeting Different Ability Levels

Content Outline

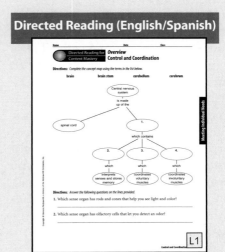

L2

Reinforcement

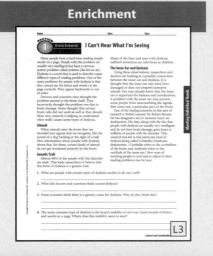

L2

Enrichment

L3

Directed Reading (English/Spanish)

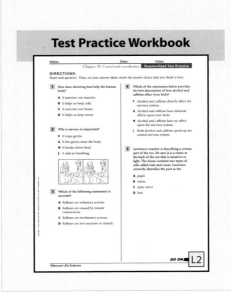

L1

Study Guide

Study Guide

Features
• Contains a study guide page for each section of the chapter
• Reviews key concepts
• Includes answer pages

L2

Reading Essentials

Reading Essentials for Glencoe Science
An Interactive Student Workbook

Features
• Condensed core content
• Actively involves students in reading
• Reinforces key vocabulary

L1

Assessment

Test Practice Workbook

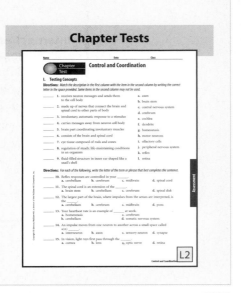

L2

Chapter Review

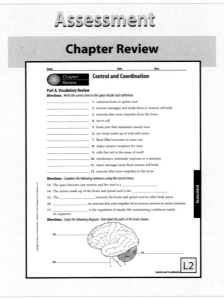

L2

Chapter Tests

L2

Science Content Background

section 1

The Nervous System
Nerve Cells

Specialized receptor cells respond to specific stimuli from various parts of the body. These stimuli produce a self-propagating wave of negative charges that is transmitted to the central nervous system via peripheral nerves. The nerve impulse travels at a rate of approximately 120 m/s. The brain and spinal cord of the central nervous system interpret the stimuli information. Appropriate responses are sent via nerves to the various body parts, which react to the stimulus. The response is a coordinated, integrated action that maintains homeostasis within the body.

section 2

The Senses
Hearing and Taste

The sensory receptors for the senses of hearing, equilibrium, and taste are specialized. Each type is found in only one place, or pair of places, in the body. Vibrations in the air with frequencies between about 16,000 and 20,000 cycles-per-second can be detected as a sound by your ears. Hair cells within the inner ear are found in the organ of Corti. The hair cells' responses to the vibrations are converted to electrical signals. Sensory hair cells help maintain balance by responding to movements of liquids and of the tiny bits of calcium carbonate called otoliths in the labyrinth canals. Taste buds, located on small projections called papillae on the tongue, the soft palate, and the walls of the pharynx, are sensitive to substances dissolved in liquids. Specialized taste cells within the taste buds function as receptors.

Understanding the Eye

At the back of the human eye is a layer called the retina that contains photosensitive cells. These cells contain pigments that, when exposed to sufficient light, change their shape and break into two parts. This stimulates the nerve cell attached to the photoreceptor, which sends a signal down the optic nerve and into the back of the brain. For humans to see an object, therefore, light must strike the object and be reflected toward the eye. The light energy must have a wavelength between 380 nm and 760 nm in order to stimulate the photoreceptive pigments in the retina.

chapter content resources

Internet Resources
For additional content background, visit
life.msscience.com to:
- access your book online
- find references to related articles in popular science magazines
- access Web links with related content background
- access current events with science journal topics

Print Resources
Biology (6th Edition), by Neil A. Campbell, Jane B. Reece, Pearson Benjamin Cummings Publishing, 2001
Human Anatomy & Physiology (5th Edition), by Elaine N. Marieb, Pearson Benjamin Cummings Publishing, 2000
Principles of Human Physiology, by William J. Germann, Cindy L. Stanfield; Pearson Benjamin Cummings Publishing, 2001

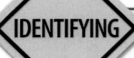 **IDENTIFYING** **Misconceptions**

Find Out What Students Think

Students may think that . . .

Human eyes "see" by sending rays toward an object.

Students seldom understand the link between light and sight. Light is often viewed as a substance that fills a space, as in "the room was filled with light." Students' everyday experiences with light do not reveal the nature of light as wave energy. Student models of how vision works range from no connection between the eye and the object it sees to believing that the eyes themselves send out beams of light or some other energy to illuminate the object and allow sight. Some students may even conclude that it is possible to see in total darkness if they think that the eye provides its own source of illumination. The experience of seeing animal eyes "glow" at night may support this. Very few students have experienced total darkness, so they are confident in their abilities to see in the dark. They know their eyes "get used" to, or adapt to, semidarkness, allowing limited vision. Even if students are exposed to total darkness, the conclusion they draw may be that they will be able to see once their eyes "get used" to the dark.

Activity

After identifying the parts of the eye, sketch a diagram of an eye on one end of the board and an object at the other end. Ask students to draw a diagram that explains how the eye is able to "see" the object. Students should label all parts of their diagram to make their explanations clear. L2

Promote Understanding

Demonstration

Materials shoe box, sharp knife, cardboard tube (about 5 cm long), black electrician's tape, flashlight, black spray paint, small object

Preparation Cut a hole in the box top. Tape a flashlight over the hole. Seal the edges with tape. Cut a peephole in one box end. Tape the cardboard tube over the hole. Paint the inside of the box black. Place an object inside and replace the lid.

Procedure

- Have students look in the box with the light off and describe what they can see. They should see nothing. Have students turn the flashlight on and look in the box again. The object is now visible.

- On the board, sketch a picture of the box with the object inside. Show how light comes from the flashlight and illuminates the object. Light reflected from the object reaches the eye and stimulates the retina, allowing the viewer to see the object. L2

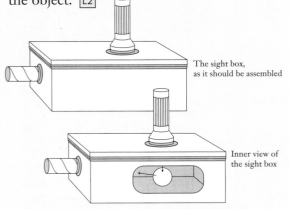

The sight box, as it should be assembled

Inner view of the sight box

Assess

After completing the chapter, see *Identifying Misconceptions* in the Study Guide at the end of the chapter.

Chapter Vocabulary

homeostasis, p. 595
neuron, p. 595
dendrite, p. 595
axon, p. 595
synapse, p. 597
central nervous system, p. 597
peripheral nervous system,
   p. 597
cerebrum, p. 598
cerebellum, p. 598
brain stem, p. 598
reflex, p. 601
retina, p. 605
cochlea, p. 608
olfactory cell, p. 609
taste bud, p. 610

Science Journal   Student
responses may vary, but may
include questions about hearing
and reaction time.

INTERACTIVE CHALKBOARD
with Image Bank

PowerPoint® Presentations

This CD-ROM is an editable
Microsoft® PowerPoint®
presentation that includes:

* a pre-made presentation for
  every chapter
* interactive graphics
* animations
* audio clips
* image bank
* all new section and chapter
  questions
* Standardized Test Practice
* transparencies
* pre-lab questions for all labs
* Foldables directions
* links to life.msscience.com

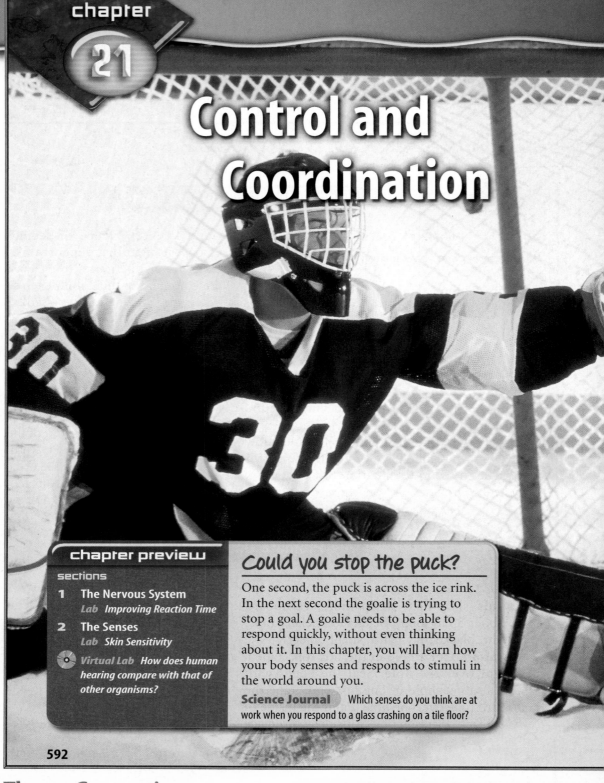

Control and Coordination

chapter preview

sections

1 The Nervous System
   Lab Improving Reaction Time

2 The Senses
   Lab Skin Sensitivity

⊙ *Virtual Lab How does human
   hearing compare with that of
   other organisms?*

592

Could you stop the puck?

One second, the puck is across the ice rink.
In the next second the goalie is trying to
stop a goal. A goalie needs to be able to
respond quickly, without even thinking
about it. In this chapter, you will learn how
your body senses and responds to stimuli in
the world around you.

Science Journal   Which senses do you think are at
work when you respond to a glass crashing on a tile floor?

Theme Connection

Stability and Change The stimulus-response action
of the nervous system helps maintain the stable
environment necessary for the healthy functioning of the body.

About the Photo

Don't Blink It takes 0.3 seconds for a single blink of
the eye, with an average of 2.8 seconds between
blinks. There are 100 billion neurons in the human
brain, and the typical neuron has 1,000 to 10,000
synapses. Your hand has 1,300 nerve endings per
square inch. A hockey goalie's senses must be finely
tuned to stop his opponent from scoring.

Start-Up Activities

How quick are your responses?

If the weather is cool, you might put on a jacket. If you see friends, you might call out to them. You also might pick up a crying baby. Every second of the day you react to different sights, sounds, and smells in your environment. You control some of these reactions, but others take place in your body without thought. Some reactions protect you from harm. 👓

1. Wearing safety goggles, sit on a chair 1 m away from a partner.
2. Ask your partner to toss a wadded-up piece of paper at your face without warning you.
3. Switch positions and repeat the activity.
4. **Think Critically** Describe in your Science Journal how you reacted to the ball of paper being thrown at you. Explain how your anticipation of being hit altered your body's response.

 **Preview this chapter's content and activities at** life.msscience.com

---

FOLDABLES
Study Organizer

Senses Your body is constantly responding to stimuli around you. Make the following Foldable to help you understand your five senses.

STEP 1 Collect three sheets of paper and layer them about 1.25 cm apart vertically. Keep the edges level.

STEP 2 Fold up the bottom edges of the paper to form six equal tabs.

STEP 3 Crease the fold, and then staple along the fold. **Label** the tabs *Five Senses, Vision, Hearing, Smell, Taste,* and *Touch*.

Read and Write As you read the chapter, write what you learn about each of your senses under the appropriate tab.

593

INTERACTIVE CHALKBOARD
PowerPoint® Presentations

Bellringer

Section Focus Transparencies also are available on the Interactive Chalkboard CD-ROM.

L2 ELL

SECTION
1 Section Focus Transparency Jump Start

In track competitions, time is critical. Sometimes, only a fraction of a second is the difference between winning a race and coming in second. Adjustable starting blocks, as seen below, help sprinters get their best starts. It takes a lot of training and practice to coordinate nerves and muscles for competition.

1. What happens when the sprinters hear the starter's pistol?
2. How do you think nerves are involved in this reponse?

Control and Coordination

Tie to Prior Knowledge

Muscle Actions Have students brainstorm a list of muscle actions that are out of their conscious control. Lists might include blinking or heartbeat. Explain that these actions occur as the body responds to stimuli.
L1

Caption Answer

Figure 1 Sights, sounds, odors, tastes; accept reasonable answers.

---

as you read

What You'll Learn

■ **Describe** the basic structure of a neuron and how an impulse moves across a synapse.
■ **Compare** the central and peripheral nervous systems.
■ **Explain** how drugs affect the body.

Why It's Important

Your body is able to react to your environment because of your nervous system.

🔊 **Review Vocabulary**

response: a reaction to a specific stimulus

New Vocabulary

● homeostasis
● neuron
● dendrite
● axon
● synapse
● central nervous system
● peripheral nervous system
● cerebrum
● cerebellum
● brain stem
● reflex

Figure 1 Stimuli are everywhere and all the time, even when you're with your friends.
List the types of stimuli present at this party.

How the Nervous System Works

After doing the dishes and finishing your homework, you settle down in your favorite chair and pick up that mystery novel you've been trying to finish. Only three pages to go . . . Who did it? Why did she do it? Crash! You scream. What made that unearthly noise? You turn around to find that your dog's wagging tail has just swept the lamp off the table. Suddenly, you're aware that your heart is racing and your hands are shaking. After a few minutes though, your breathing returns to normal and your heartbeat is back to its regular rate. What's going on?

Responding to Stimuli The scene described above is an example of how your body responds to changes in its environment. Any internal or external change that brings about a response is called a stimulus (STIHM yuh lus). Each day, you're bombarded by thousands of stimuli, as shown in **Figure 1.** Noise, light, the smell of food, and the temperature of the air are all stimuli from outside your body. Chemical substances such as hormones are examples of stimuli from inside your body. Your body adjusts to changing stimuli with the help of your nervous system.

Section 1 Resource Manager

Chapter *FAST FILE* Resources
Transparency Activity, pp. 42, 45–46
Directed Reading for Content Mastery, pp. 19, 20
Note-taking Worksheets, pp. 31–33
Lab Worksheet, pp. 5–6
Enrichment, p. 29

Lab Activity, pp. 9–12
Reinforcement, p. 27
Reading and Writing Skill Activities, p. 17
Life Science Critical Thinking/Problem Solving, pp. 2, 18
Mathematics Skill Activities, p. 9

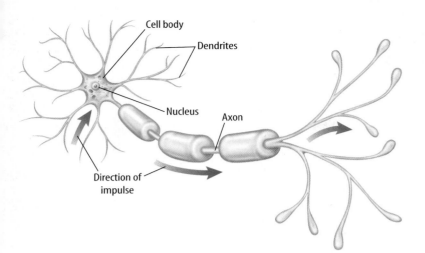

Cell body

Dendrites

Nucleus

Axon

Direction of impulse

Figure 2 A neuron is made up of a cell body, dendrites, and axons.

Explain *how the branching of the dendrites allows for more impulses to be picked up by the neuron.*

Homeostasis It's amazing how your body handles all these stimuli. Control systems maintain steady internal conditions. The regulation of steady, life-maintaining conditions inside an organism, despite changes in its environment, is called **homeostasis.** Examples of homeostasis are the regulation of your breathing, heartbeat, and digestion. Your nervous system is one of several control systems used by your body to maintain homeostasis.

Nerve Cells

The basic functioning units of the nervous system are nerve cells, or **neurons** (NOOR ahnz). As shown in **Figure 2,** a neuron is made up of a cell body and branches called dendrites and axons. Any message carried by a neuron is called an impulse. **Dendrites** receive impulses from other neurons and send them to the cell body. **Axons** (AK sahns) carry impulses away from the cell body. Notice the branching at the end of the axon. This allows the impulses to move to many other muscles, neurons, or glands.

Types of Nerve Cells Your body has sensory receptors that produce electrical impulses and respond to stimuli, such as changes in temperature, sound, pressure, and taste. Three types of neurons—sensory neurons, motor neurons, and interneurons—transport impulses. Sensory neurons receive information and send impulses to the brain or spinal cord, where interneurons relay these impulses to motor neurons. Motor neurons then conduct impulses from the brain or spinal cord to muscles or glands throughout your body.

INTEGRATE History

Multiple Sclerosis In 1868, Jean Martin Charcot, a neurology professor in Paris, was the first to scientifically describe, document, and name the disease multiple sclerosis. It was named because of the many scars found widely dispersed throughout the central nervous system. Research to find out the symptoms of multiple sclerosis.

2 Teach

Caption Answer

Figure 2 Each neuron can receive impulses from several different sensory receptors because of the branched dendrites.

Quick Demo

Nerve Impulses

Materials students, schoolyard or athletic field

Estimated Time 15 minutes

Procedure Position two students 100 meters apart. Use this visual representation to illustrate the distance that some nerve impulses travel in one second. L2

Discussion

Sensory Neurons What would happen if all your sensory neurons stopped working? Your brain would stop receiving stimuli from inside and outside your body, making it impossible to maintain homeostasis. L2

INTEGRATE History

Multiple Sclerosis Symptoms vary, but include abnormal fatigue, loss of balance and muscle coordination, slurred speech, vision problems, tremors, stiffness, and bladder problems.

Research Have students research a variety of medical treatments, including alternative medical treatments, that are used to help ease the symptoms of multiple sclerosis.

Fun Fact

The structure of an axon of a neuron can change when used. More and better connections with other neurons result from learning. Schoolwork helps neurons make connections.

Science Journal

Nerve Analogy Have students write a paragraph in their Science Journals that explains how a nerve is similar to a wire going from a controlling switch (stimulus) to a light bulb (response). Possible response: The switch receives a stimulus, which travels along the wire. The bulb responds to the stimulus by lighting up. L2

LS **Linguistic** P

Visualizing Nerve Impulse Pathways

Have students examine the pictures and read the captions. Then ask the following questions.

What would happen if an interneuron could not perform its function? Possible answer: There would be no connection between the sensory neuron and the motor neuron. The nerve impulse may not be passed on.

What are the differences between a sensory neuron and a motor neuron? Possible answer: Sensory neurons detect internal or external stimuli and transfer impulses to the spinal cord or brain. Motor neurons respond to stimuli from the spinal cord or brain and carry impulses back out to muscles.

Activity

Model Neurons Have students make a model of a neuron. Students can use yarn and markers on construction paper to model and label the different parts of a neuron including the dendrites, the cell body, and the axon. Students can also show the direction of impulse transmission. Dendrites receive an impulse from another neuron and pass it on to the cell body. The axon carries the impulse to the next neuron. L2

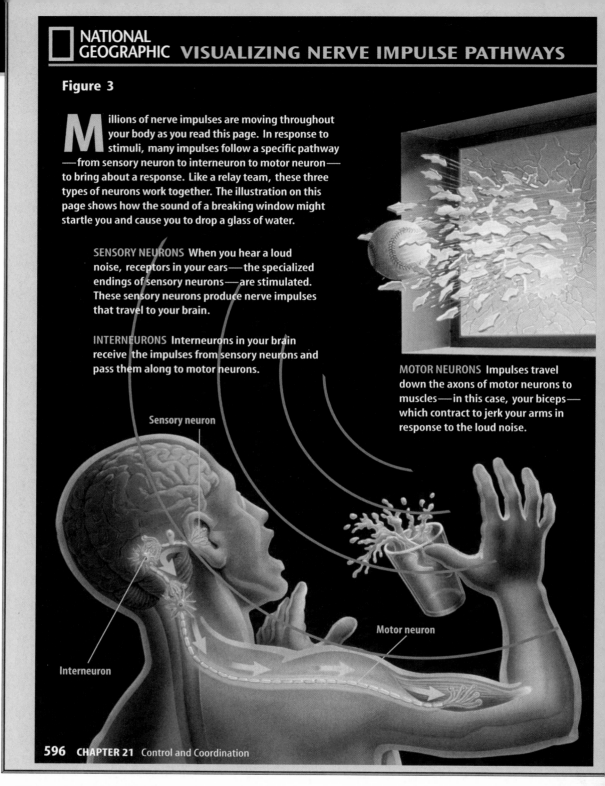

NATIONAL GEOGRAPHIC VISUALIZING NERVE IMPULSE PATHWAYS

Figure 3

Millions of nerve impulses are moving throughout your body as you read this page. In response to stimuli, many impulses follow a specific pathway —from sensory neuron to interneuron to motor neuron— to bring about a response. Like a relay team, these three types of neurons work together. The illustration on this page shows how the sound of a breaking window might startle you and cause you to drop a glass of water.

SENSORY NEURONS When you hear a loud noise, receptors in your ears—the specialized endings of sensory neurons—are stimulated. These sensory neurons produce nerve impulses that travel to your brain.

INTERNEURONS Interneurons in your brain receive the impulses from sensory neurons and pass them along to motor neurons.

MOTOR NEURONS Impulses travel down the axons of motor neurons to muscles—in this case, your biceps—which contract to jerk your arms in response to the loud noise.

Sensory neuron

Interneuron

Motor neuron

596 CHAPTER 21 Control and Coordination

Differentiated Instruction

Challenge Have students research the differences between myelinated neurons and unmyelinated neurons. Students should determine which type of nerve impulse conduction each has. They can present their results on a poster. L3

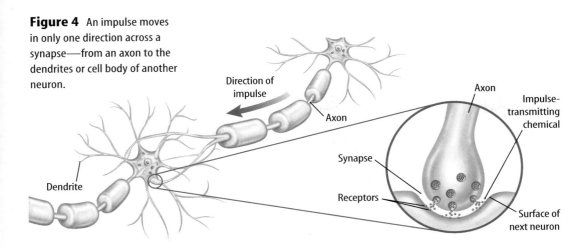

Figure 4 An impulse moves in only one direction across a synapse—from an axon to the dendrites or cell body of another neuron.

Direction of impulse

Axon

Axon

Impulse-transmitting chemical

Synapse

Receptors

Surface of next neuron

Dendrite

Synapses

In a relay race, the first runner sprints down the track with a baton in his or her hand. As the runner rounds the track, he or she hands the baton off to the next runner. The two runners never physically touch each other. The transfer of the baton signals the second runner to continue the race.

As shown in **Figure 3,** your nervous system works in a similar way. Like the runners in a relay race, neurons don't touch each other. How does an impulse move from one neuron to another? To move from one neuron to the next, an impulse crosses a small space called a **synapse** (SIH naps). In **Figure 4,** note that when an impulse reaches the end of an axon, the axon releases a chemical. This chemical flows across the synapse and stimulates the impulse in the dendrite of the next neuron. Your neurons are adapted in such a way that impulses move in only one direction. An impulse moves from neuron to neuron just like a baton moves from runner to runner in a relay race. The baton represents the chemical at the synapse.

The Central Nervous System

Figure 5 shows the organs of the central nervous system (CNS) and the peripheral (puh RIH fuh rul) nervous system (PNS). The **central nervous system** is made up of the brain and spinal cord. The **peripheral nervous system** is made up of all the nerves outside the CNS. These nerves include those in your head, called cranial nerves, and the nerves that come from your spinal cord, called spinal nerves. The peripheral nervous system connects the brain and spinal cord to other body parts. Sensory neurons send impulses to the brain or spinal cord.

Figure 5 The brain and spinal cord (yellow) form the central nervous system (CNS). All other nerves (green) are part of the peripheral nervous system (PNS).

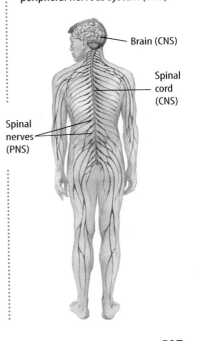

Brain (CNS)

Spinal cord (CNS)

Spinal nerves (PNS)

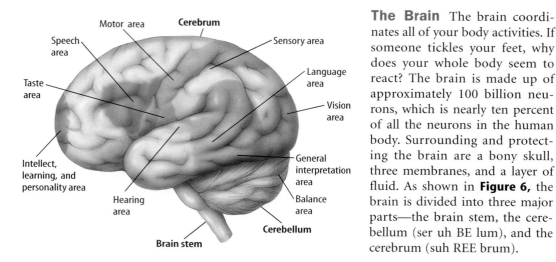

Figure 6 Different areas of the brain control specific body activities.
Describe the three major parts of the brain, and their functions.

INTEGRATE Chemistry

Impulses Acetylcholine (uh see tul KOH leen) is a chemical produced by neurons, which carries an impulse across a synapse to the next neuron. After the impulse is started, the acetylcholine breaks down rapidly. In your Science Journal, hypothesize why the breakdown of acetylcholine is important.

The Brain The brain coordinates all of your body activities. If someone tickles your feet, why does your whole body seem to react? The brain is made up of approximately 100 billion neurons, which is nearly ten percent of all the neurons in the human body. Surrounding and protecting the brain are a bony skull, three membranes, and a layer of fluid. As shown in **Figure 6,** the brain is divided into three major parts—the brain stem, the cerebellum (ser uh BE lum), and the cerebrum (suh REE brum).

Cerebrum Thinking takes place in the **cerebrum,** which is the largest part of the brain. This also is where impulses from the senses are interpreted, memory is stored, and movements are controlled. The outer layer of the cerebrum, called the cortex, is marked by many ridges and grooves. These structures increase the surface area of the cortex, allowing more complex thoughts to be processed. **Figure 6** shows some of the motor and sensory tasks that the cortex controls.

Reading Check *What major activity takes place within the cerebrum?*

Cerebellum Stimuli from the eyes and ears and from muscles and tendons, which are the tissues that connect muscles to bones, are interpreted in the **cerebellum.** With this information, the cerebellum is able to coordinate voluntary muscle movements, maintain muscle tone, and help maintain balance. A complex activity, such as riding a bike, requires a lot of coordination and control of your muscles. The cerebellum coordinates your muscle movements so that you can maintain your balance.

Brain Stem At the base of the brain is the **brain stem.** It extends from the cerebrum and connects the brain to the spinal cord. The brain stem is made up of the midbrain, the pons, and the medulla (muh DUH luh). The midbrain and pons act as pathways connecting various parts of the brain with each other. The medulla controls involuntary actions such as heartbeat, breathing, and blood pressure. The medulla also is involved in such actions as coughing, sneezing, swallowing, and vomiting.

Visual Learning

Figure 6 Have students describe how the brain is protected. Hair, skin, skull bones, membranes, and fluids protect the brain. L2

Differentiated Instruction

Visually Impaired and Learning Disabled Have students make a model of the brain from papier-mâché or craft foam. Have them paint each part a different color and label the areas of activity. These models can then be used by visually impaired and learning disabled students for study. L1 IS **Kinesthetic**

The Spinal Cord Your spinal cord, illustrated in **Figure 7,** is an extension of the brain stem. It is made up of bundles of neurons that carry impulses from all parts of the body to the brain and from the brain to all parts of your body. The adult spinal cord is about the width of an adult thumb and is about 43 cm long.

The Peripheral Nervous System

Your brain and spinal cord are connected to the rest of your body by the peripheral nervous system. The PNS is made up of 12 pairs of nerves from your brain called cranial nerves and 31 pairs from your spinal cord called spinal nerves. Spinal nerves are made up of bundles of sensory and motor neurons bound together by connective tissue. For this reason, a single spinal nerve can have impulses going to and from the brain at the same time. Some nerves contain only sensory neurons, and some contain only motor neurons, but most nerves contain both types of neurons.

Somatic and Autonomic Systems The peripheral nervous system has two major divisions. The somatic system controls voluntary actions. It is made up of the cranial and spinal nerves that go from the central nervous system to your skeletal muscles. The autonomic system controls involuntary actions—those not under conscious control—such as your heart rate, breathing, digestion, and glandular functions. These two divisions, along with the central nervous system, make up your body's nervous system.

Science Online

Topic: Nervous System
Visit life.msscience.com for Web links to information about the nervous system.

Activity In your Science Journal, make a brochure outlining recent medical advances.

Figure 7 A column of vertebrae, or bones, protects the spinal cord. The spinal cord is made up of bundles of neurons that carry impulses to and from all parts of the body, similar to a telephone cable.

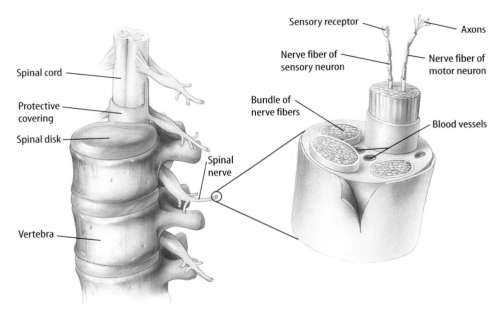

Sensory receptor

Axons

Nerve fiber of sensory neuron

Nerve fiber of motor neuron

Spinal cord

Bundle of nerve fibers

Protective covering

Blood vessels

Spinal disk

Spinal nerve

Vertebra

IDENTIFYING Misconceptions

Alcohol Is a Depressant Alcohol is often perceived as a stimulant because it initially makes a person feel more energetic. However, alcohol actually slows down the actions of the central nervous system.

Make a Model

Protecting Vertebrae Have students make a model of the vertebral column and spinal cord by stringing 33 thread spools on a thin rope. Use circular pieces of foam rubber for the disks between the vertebrae. Have students note how the cord (rope) is protected. The spools (vertebrae) protect the rope (spinal cord); vertebrae are cushioned by the foam rubber. L2

Differentiated Instruction

Challenge Have an interested student interview a pediatrician to find out which motor reflexes a child is born with. A partial list includes gag reflex, blink reflex, pain avoidance reflex, shivering in response to cold, sucking reflex, and swallowing reflex. L3

Curriculum Connection

History In the latter part of the eighteenth century, scientists investigated animals that were able to produce an electric shock such as the electric eel. These investigations led to research on the effects of electricity on nerves and the muscular contractions that could be produced. Have students research the results of such investigations and share their findings. L3

Discussion

Preventing Injury Have students discuss other types of reflex responses to stimuli that prevent injury to the body. Examples include holding hands over the ear when there are loud noises and rapid upward foot movement when stepping on a sharp object. L2

Discussion

Head Injuries What kinds of accidents at home might cause head injuries? Possible answers: slipping in the bathtub or falling off a ladder

Use Science Words

Word Origin When the brain is damaged, paralysis can result. Quadriplegics are individuals whose arms and legs are paralyzed. The word *quadriplegic* has its roots in the Latin word *quadra*, meaning "four," and the Greek word *plege*, meaning "stroke." How is this combination of words appropriate for its definition? A stroke can cause paralysis of all four limbs. Have students research the word origin of hemiplegia. Hemiplegia is total or partial paralysis of one side of the body (hemi = half). L2

Caption Answer

Figure 8 to prevent serious injuries and loss of life

Safety and the Nervous System

Every mental process and physical action of the body is associated with the structures of the central and peripheral nervous systems. Therefore, any injury to the brain or the spinal cord can be serious. A severe blow to the head can bruise the brain and cause temporary or permanent loss of mental and physical abilities. For example, the back of the brain controls vision. An injury in this region could result in the loss of vision.

Although the spinal cord is surrounded by the vertebrae of your spine, spinal cord injuries do occur. They can be just as dangerous as a brain injury. Injury to the spine can bring about damage to nerve pathways and result in paralysis (puh RA luh suhs), which is the loss of muscle movement. As shown in **Figure 8,** a neck injury that damages certain nerves could prevent a person from breathing. Major causes of head and spinal injuries include automobile, motorcycle, and bicycle accidents, as well as sports injuries. Just like wearing safety belts in automobiles, it is important to wear the appropriate safety gear while playing sports and riding on bicycles and skateboards.

Figure 8 Head and spinal cord damage can result in paralysis, depending on where the injury occurs.
Explain *why it is important to wear safety equipment and safety belts.*

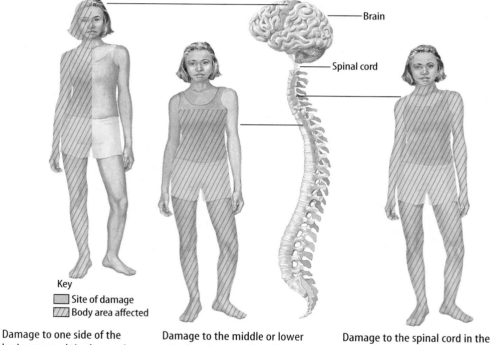

Brain

Spinal cord

Key
- Site of damage
- Body area affected

Damage to one side of the brain can result in the paralysis of the opposite side of the body.

Damage to the middle or lower spinal cord can result in the legs and possibly part of the torso being paralyzed.

Damage to the spinal cord in the lower neck area can cause the body to be paralyzed from the neck down.

600 CHAPTER 21 Control and Coordination

Science Journal

Recovering from Injury Christopher Reeve, the actor who portrayed Superman in the movies, suffered severe injuries while horseback riding. Ask students to describe in their Science Journals his progress in adapting to and dealing with his paralysis. L2 LS **Linguistic**

Teacher FYI

Head Injuries A closed head injury does not involve any breaks in the skull. Loss of consciousness and diminished brain function may result. In an open head injury, the skull bones are penetrated. There is then the added risk of infection. Immediate surgery is necessary to clean and repair the wound.

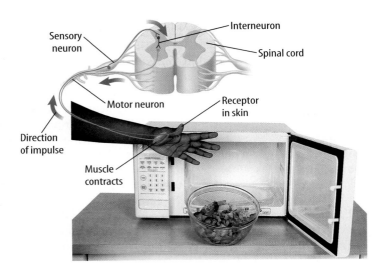

Sensory neuron
Interneuron
Spinal cord
Motor neuron
Receptor in skin
Direction of impulse
Muscle contracts

Figure 9 Your response in a reflex is controlled in your spinal cord, not your brain.

Reflexes You experience a reflex if you accidentally touch something sharp, something extremely hot or cold, or when you cough or vomit. A **reflex** is an involuntary, automatic response to a stimulus. You can't control reflexes because they occur before you know what has happened. A reflex involves a simple nerve pathway called a reflex arc, as illustrated in **Figure 9.**

Imagine that while walking on a sandy beach, a pain suddenly shoots through your foot as you step on the sharp edge of a broken shell. Sensory receptors in your foot respond to this sharp object, and an impulse is sent to the spinal cord. As you just learned, the impulse passes to an interneuron in the spinal cord that immediately relays the impulse to motor neurons. Motor neurons transmit the impulse to muscles in your leg. Instantly, without thinking, you lift up your leg in response to the sharp-edged shell. This is a withdrawal reflex.

A reflex allows the body to respond without having to think about what action to take. Reflex responses are controlled in your spinal cord, not in your brain. Your brain acts after the reflex to help you figure out what to do to make the pain stop.

Reading Check *Why are reflexes important?*

Do you remember reading at the beginning of this chapter about being frightened after a lamp was broken? What would have happened if your breathing and heart rate didn't calm down within a few minutes? Your body systems can't be kept in a state of continual excitement. The organs of your nervous system control and coordinate body responses. This helps maintain homeostasis within your body.

Science Online

Topic: Reflexes and Paralysis
Visit life.msscience.com for Web links to information about reflexes and paralysis.

Activity Make a small poster that illustrates what you learn.

Teacher FYI

Dying Brain Alzheimer's disease is the result of brain neurons slowly dying. This results in less production of the chemical needed for neurons to communicate with each other.

Reading Check

Answer They allow quick reactions to dangerous situations without having to think about what to do.

Text Question Answer
If your breathing and heart rate hadn't calmed down, you might have lost consciousness; your body systems would not have been able to keep up with your high rate of respiration and heartbeat.

Figure 10 Caffeine, a substance found in colas, coffee, chocolate, and some teas, can cause excitability and sleeplessness.

Drugs and the Nervous System

Many drugs, such as alcohol and caffeine, directly affect your nervous system. When swallowed, alcohol passes directly through the walls of the stomach and small intestine into the circulatory system. After it is inside the circulatory system, it can travel throughout your body. Upon reaching neurons, alcohol moves through their cell membranes and disrupts their normal cell functions. As a result, this drug slows the activities of the central nervous system and is classified as a depressant. Muscle control, judgment, reasoning, memory, and concentration also are impaired. Heavy alcohol use destroys brain and liver cells.

A stimulant is a drug that speeds up the activity of the central nervous system. Caffeine is a stimulant found in coffee, tea, cocoa, and many soft drinks, as shown in **Figure 10.** Too much caffeine can increase heart rate and aggravates restlessness, tremors, and insomnia in some people. It also can stimulate the kidneys to produce more urine.

Think again about a scare from a loud noise. The organs of your nervous system control and coordinate responses to maintain homeostasis within your body. This task might be more difficult when your body must cope with the effects of drugs.

section ① review

Summary

How the Nervous System Works
- The nervous system responds to stimuli to maintain homeostasis.
- To move from one neuron to another, an impulse crosses a synapse.

The Central Nervous System
- The brain controls all body activities.
- Spinal neurons carry impulses from all parts of the body to the brain.

The Peripheral Nervous System
- The somatic system controls voluntary actions and the autonomic system controls involuntary actions.

Safety and the Nervous System
- The spinal cord controls reflex responses.

Drugs and the Nervous System
- Many drugs affect your nervous system.

Self Check

1. **Draw and label** the parts of a neuron.
2. **Compare and contrast** the central and peripheral nervous systems.
3. **Explain** why you have trouble falling asleep after drinking several cups of hot cocoa.
4. **Explain** the advantage of having reflexes controlled by the spinal cord.
5. **Think Critically** Explain why many medications caution the consumer not to operate heavy machinery.

Applying Skills

6. **Concept Map** Prepare an events-chain concept map of the different kinds of neurons that pass an impulse from a stimulus to a response.
7. **Use a Word Processor** Create a flowchart showing the reflex pathway of a nerve impulse when you step on a sharp object. Label the body parts involved in each step.

602 CHAPTER 21 Control and Coordination

  Science Online life.msscience.com/self_check_quiz

section ① review

IMPROVING REACTION TIME

Your reflexes allow you to react quickly without thinking. Sometimes you can improve how quickly you react. Complete this lab to see if you can decrease your reaction time.

● Real-World Question

How can reaction time be improved?

Goals
- **Observe** reflexes.
- **Identify** stimuli and responses.

Materials
metric ruler

● Procedure

1. Make a data table in your Science Journal to record where the ruler is caught during this lab. Possible column heads are *Trial, Right Hand,* and *Left Hand.*

2. Have a partner hold the ruler as shown.

3. Hold the thumb and index finger of your right hand apart at the bottom of the ruler. Do not touch the ruler.

4. Your partner must let go of the ruler without warning you.

5. Catch the ruler between your thumb and finger by quickly bringing them together.

Communicating Your Data

Compare your conclusions with those of other students in your class. **For more help, refer to the** Science Skill Handbook.

6. Repeat this lab several times and record in a data table where the ruler was caught.

7. Repeat this lab with your left hand.

● Conclude and Apply

1. **Identify** the stimulus, response, and variable in this lab.

2. Use the table on the right to determine your reaction time.

3. **Calculate** the average reaction times for both your right and left hand.

4. **Compare** the response of your writing hand and your other hand for this lab.

Reaction Time	
Where Caught (cm)	**Reaction Time(s)**
5	0.10
10	0.14
15	0.17
20	0.20
25	0.23
30	0.25

5. Draw a conclusion about how practice relates to stimulus-response time.

603

Communicating Your Data

Students should discuss why their reaction times were or were not the same.

● Real-World Question

Purpose Students observe reaction time. L2 COOP LEARN LS **Kinesthetic**

Process Skills observe, communicate, use numbers, recognize and use spatial relationships, measure in SI, interpret data

Time Required 30 minutes

Teaching Strategy Students should keep their eyes on the ruler as their partners release it.

Answers to Questions

1. stimulus: the ruler falling; response: catching the ruler; variable: which hand is used
2. Answers will vary.
3. To find the average, students should add all reaction times for each hand separately and divide by the number of trials.
4. Answers will vary. Generally, the writing hand reacts faster.
5. With practice, stimulus-response time usually improves.

☑ Assessment

Performance To further assess students' abilities to measure and improve reaction time, have them repeat the experiment with slight variations. Have students blindfolded, and instruct their partners to tell them when they drop the ruler. See how quickly they can react to verbal stimuli. Use **Performance Assessment in the Science Classroom,** p. 97.

The Senses

Bellringer

Section Focus Transparencies also are available on the Interactive Chalkboard CD-ROM.

 L2 ELL

Tie to Prior Knowledge

Telephone System Have students compare the sensory system of information processing with that of a telephone system. Have them brainstorm similarities and differences. L2

as you read

What **You'll Learn**

- **List** the sensory receptors in each sense organ.
- **Explain** what type of stimulus each sense organ responds to and how.
- **Explain** why healthy senses are needed.

Why **It's Important**

Your senses make you aware of your environment, enable you to enjoy your world, and help keep you safe.

Review Vocabulary
sense organ: specialized organ that, when stimulated, initiates a process of sensory perception

New Vocabulary
- retina
- olfactory cell
- cochlea
- taste bud

The Body's Alert System

"Danger . . . danger . . . code-red alert! An unidentified vessel has entered the spaceship's energy force field. All crew members are to be on alert!" Like spaceships in science fiction movies, your body has an alert system, too—your sense organs. You might see a bird, hear a dog bark, or smell popcorn. You can enjoy the taste of salt on a pretzel, the touch of a fuzzy peach, or feel heat from a warm, cozy fire. Light rays, sound waves, heat, chemicals, or pressure that comes into your personal territory will stimulate your sense organs. Sense organs are adapted for intercepting these different stimuli. They are then converted into impulses by the nervous system.

Vision

Think about the different kinds of objects you might look at every day. It's amazing that with one glance you might see the words on this page, the color illustrations, and your classmate sitting next to you. The eye, shown in **Figure 11,** is the vision sense organ. Your eyes have unique adaptations that usually enable you to see shapes of objects, shadows, and color.

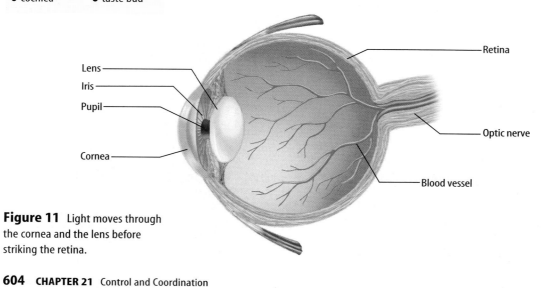

Lens
Iris
Pupil
Cornea
Retina
Optic nerve
Blood vessel

Figure 11 Light moves through the cornea and the lens before striking the retina.

Section 2 Resource Manager

Chapter *FAST FILE* Resources
Transparency Activity, p. 43
Directed Reading for Content Mastery, pp. 21, 22
Enrichment, p. 30
Reinforcement, p. 28
MiniLAB, pp. 3, 4
Lab Activity, pp. 13–16

Lab Worksheet, pp. 7–8
Earth Science Critical Thinking/Problem Solving, p. 22
Cultural Diversity, pp. 15, 61
Home and Community Involvement, p. 28
Lab Management and Safety, p. 65

How do you see? Light travels in a straight line unless something causes it to refract or change direction. Your eyes are equipped with structures that refract light. Two of these structures are the cornea and the lens. As light enters the eye, it passes through the cornea—the transparent section at the front of the eye—and is refracted. Then light passes through a lens and is refracted again. The lens directs the light onto the retina (RET nuh). The **retina** is a tissue at the back of the eye that is sensitive to light energy. Two types of cells called rods and cones are found in the retina. Cones respond to bright light and color. Rods respond to dim light. They are used to help you detect shape and movement. Light energy stimulates impulses in these cells.

The impulses pass to the optic nerve. This nerve carries the impulses to the vision area of the cortex, located on your brain's cerebrum. The image transmitted from the retina to the brain is upside down and reversed. The brain interprets the image correctly, and you see what you are looking at. The brain also interprets the images received by both eyes. It blends them into one image that gives you a sense of distance. This allows you to tell how close or how far away something is.

 **Reading Check** *What difficulties would a person who had vision only in one eye encounter?*

Lenses

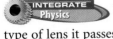 Light is refracted when it passes through a lens. The way it refracts depends on the type of lens it passes through. A lens that is thicker in the middle and thinner on the edges is called a convex lens. As shown in **Figure 12,** the lens in your eye refracts light so that it passes through a point, called a focal point. Convex lenses can be used to magnify objects. The light passes through a convex lens and enters the eye in such a way that your brain interprets the image as enlarged.

A lens that is thicker at its edges than in its middle is called a concave lens. Follow the light rays in **Figure 12** as they pass through a concave lens. You'll see that this kind of lens causes the parallel light to spread out.

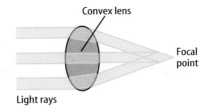 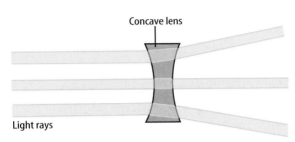

Figure 12 Light passing through a convex lens is refracted toward the center and passes through a focal point. Light that passes through a concave lens is refracted outward.
Name *the type of lens found in a microscope.*

2 Teach

Quick Demo
Light Rays
Materials double convex lens
Estimated Time 10 minutes
Procedure Use a double convex lens to illustrate the refraction and focusing of light rays similar to that which occurs in the eye. L2

IDENTIFYING Misconceptions

Seeing Eyes Students may think that human eyes "see" by sending rays toward an object. Refer to page 592F for teaching strategies that address this misconception.

✓ Reading Check

Answer It would be difficult to perceive depth.

Caption Answer
Figure 12 convex lens

Use an Analogy
Cameras and Eyes Have students open up a camera to view the internal components and compare them to the human eye. What part of the eye is like the diaphragm of the camera? the iris What part of the camera is like the retina? the film L2

Differentiated Instruction

Challenge Have students research the phenomenon of afterimage, where an image is still perceived after its external cause is gone. Afterimage may be positive, corresponding in color or brightness to the original image, or negative, being less bright or of colors complementary to the original. A common afterimage is the spot of light seen after a camera flash has been fired. L3

Curriculum Connection

History Have students find out how Helen Keller was able to communicate even though she was deprived of sight and hearing at an early age. Her teacher, Anne Sullivan, taught Helen to feel objects and associate them with words spelled out by finger signals on her palm, to read sentences by feeling raised words on cardboard, and to make her own sentences by arranging words in a frame. L2

Activity

Eyeglass Shape Have students who wear corrective eyeglasses examine the lenses to determine whether they are concave or convex. L1

Quick Demo

Magnifying Lens

Materials 5-cm × 5-cm sheet of clear plastic wrap, newspaper, and water

Estimated Time 10 minutes

Procedure Place the plastic wrap over the newspaper and place one drop of water on the plastic wrap. Have students note how the curved surface of the water drop acts as a lens and magnifies the print. L2

Telescopes A third lens is needed to make the inverted image right-side up for normal viewing.

Use Science Words

Word Origin Cataracts are a disorder of the eye in which the lens becomes cloudy and vision is not clear. The word *cataract* can also mean "a great waterfall" or "a downpour of water." How are these meanings related? With cataracts on the lens of the eye, vision is like looking through a wall of water.

Telescopes Refracting telescopes have two convex lenses for viewing objects in space. The larger lens collects light and forms an inverted, or upside-down, image of the object. The second lens magnifies the inverted image. In your Science Journal, hypothesize why telescopes used to view things on Earth have three lenses, not two.

Figure 13 Glasses and contact lenses sharpen your vision.

A nearsighted person cannot see distant objects because the image is focused in front of the retina.

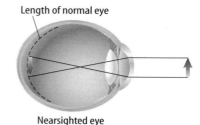

Nearsighted eye

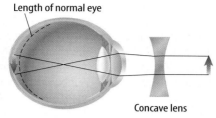

Concave lens

A concave lens corrects nearsightedness.

A farsighted person cannot see close objects because the image is focused behind the retina.

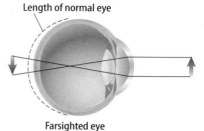

Farsighted eye

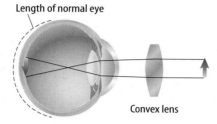

Convex lens

A convex lens corrects farsightedness.

Correcting Vision Problems Do you wear contact lenses or eyeglasses to correct your vision? Are you nearsighted or farsighted? In an eye with normal vision, light rays are focused onto the retina by the coordinated actions of the eye muscles, the cornea, and the lens. The image formed on the retina is interpreted by the brain as being sharp and clear. However, if the eyeball is too long from front to back, as illustrated in **Figure 13,** light from objects is focused in front of the retina. This happens because the shape of the eyeball and lens cannot be changed enough by the eye muscles to focus a sharp image onto the retina. The image that reaches the retina is blurred. This condition is called nearsightedness—near objects are seen more clearly than distant objects. To correct nearsightedness, concave lenses are used to help focus images sharply on the retina.

Similarly, vision correction is needed when the eyeball is too short from front to back. In this case, light from objects is focused behind the retina despite the coordinated actions of the eye muscles, cornea, and lens. This condition is called farsightedness, also as illustrated in **Figure 13,** because distant objects are clearer than near objects. Convex lenses correct farsightedness.

 LAB DEMONSTRATION

Purpose to find the area of insensitivity to light on the retina, called the blind spot

Materials 3-in × 5-in card, black pen

Preparation Draw a black dot 0.5 cm in diameter near the left edge of the horizontally-held card. Draw an X 5 cm to the right of the dot.

Procedure Hold the card at arm's length. Close the right eye and look only at the X. Slowly move the card toward the face. Measure the distance of the card from the face when the dot is no longer visible.

Expected Outcome Students observe that the

dot disappears when the card is 15 to 20 cm from the face.

Assessment

Why do you not have a blind spot whenever you are looking at things? The brain interprets the images from your eyes as a complete picture.

Hearing

Whether it's the roar of a rocket launch, the cheers at a football game, or the distant song of a robin in a tree, sound waves are necessary for hearing sound. Sound energy is to hearing as light energy is to vision. When an object vibrates, sound waves are produced. These waves can travel through solids, liquids, and gases as illustrated in **Figure 14.** When the waves reach your ear, they usually stimulate nerve cells deep within your ear. Impulses are sent to the brain. When the sound impulse reaches the hearing area of the cortex, it responds and you hear a sound.

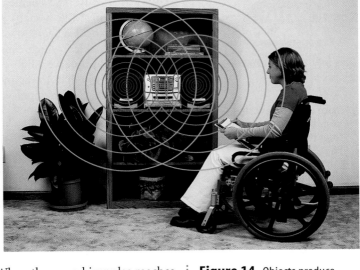

Figure 14 Objects produce sound waves that can be heard by your ears.

The Outer Ear and Middle Ear **Figure 15** shows that your ear is divided into three sections—the outer ear, middle ear, and inner ear. Your outer ear intercepts sound waves and funnels them down the ear canal to the middle ear. The sound waves cause the eardrum to vibrate much like the membrane on a musical drum vibrates when you tap it. These vibrations then move through three tiny bones called the hammer, anvil, and stirrup. The stirrup bone rests against a second membrane on an opening to the inner ear.

Figure 15 Your ear responds to sound waves and to changes in the position of your head.

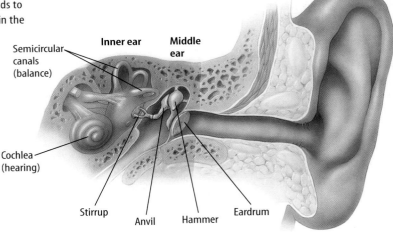

Outer ear

Inner ear

Middle ear

Semicircular canals (balance)

Cochlea (hearing)

Stirrup

Anvil

Hammer

Eardrum

SECTION 2 The Senses **607**

Purpose to observe and make inferences concerning the factors that affect students' ability to maintain balance L2 ELL

Materials two narrow strips of paper, masking tape

Teaching Strategies

• Partners should take turns standing and observing.

• Record whether the person standing tends to lean more to one side or the other.

Safety Precautions Some people may become disoriented. Alert students to be prepared to help someone who looks as if he or she might fall.

Analysis

1. When the eyes were closed; when the eyes are open, a person can focus on a point to help the body remain balanced.

2. Answers could include such conditions as an inner ear infection or loud, continuous noise.

Assessment

Performance To further assess students' understanding of balance, have them repeat the lab with feet apart or arms extended sideways. Use **Performance Assessment in the Science Classroom,** p. 97. L2

Caption Answer

Figure 16 Spinning makes the fluids in the inner ear send impulses to the brain that conflict with the actual position of the head. Dizziness results.

Observing Balance Control

Procedure

1. Place **two narrow strips of paper** on the wall to form two parallel vertical lines 20–25 cm apart. Have a person stand between them for 3 min, without leaning on the wall.

2. Observe how well balance is maintained.

3. Have the person close his or her eyes, then stand within the lines for 3 min.

Analysis

1. When was balance more difficult to maintain? Why?

2. What other factors might cause a person to lose his or her sense of balance?

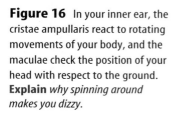

Figure 16 In your inner ear, the cristae ampullaris react to rotating movements of your body, and the maculae check the position of your head with respect to the ground. **Explain** *why spinning around makes you dizzy.*

The Inner Ear The **cochlea** (KOH klee uh) is a fluid-filled structure shaped like a snail's shell. When the stirrup vibrates, fluids in the cochlea begin to vibrate. These vibrations bend hair cells in the cochlea, which causes electrical impulses to be sent to the brain by a nerve. High-pitched sounds make the endings move differently than lower sounds do. Depending on how the nerve endings are stimulated, you hear a different type of sound.

Balance Structures in your inner ear also control your body's balance. Structures called the cristae ampullaris (KRIHS tee • am pyew LEER ihs) and the maculae (MA kyah lee), illustrated in **Figure 16,** sense different types of body movement.

Both structures contain tiny hair cells. As your body moves, gel-like fluid surrounding the hair cells moves and stimulates the nerve cells at the base of the hair cells. This produces nerve impulses that are sent to the brain, which interprets the body movements. The brain, in turn, sends impulses to skeletal muscles, resulting in other body movements that maintain balance.

The cristae ampullaris react to rotating body movements. Fluid in the semicircular canals swirls when the body rotates. This causes the gel-like fluid around the hair cells to move and a stimulus is sent to the brain. In a similar way, when the head tips, the gel-like fluid surrounding the hair cells in the maculae is pulled down by gravity. The hair cells are then stimulated and the brain interprets that the head has tilted.

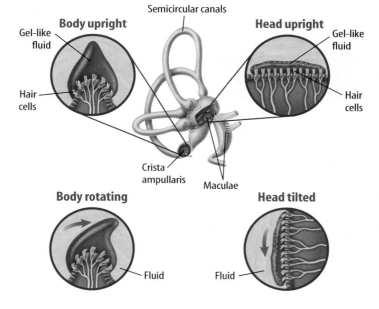

608 CHAPTER 21 Control and Coordination

Cultural Diversity

Drums Drums are used by cultures worldwide. Drums made in various shapes and sizes and from various materials have different pitches. Have students research how drums are made in different areas of the world and infer what all drums have in common. If possible, have them compare the sounds of different drums. L2

Differentiated Instruction

Visually Impaired and Hearing Impaired Ask students to clip advertisements from the "help wanted" section of a newspaper about jobs that require keenness of certain senses. They should put these ads in their Science Journals, along with brief descriptions of how and why specific senses such as hearing, vision, balance and coordination, or smell would be involved. L2

Smell

Some sharks can sense as few as ten drops of tuna liquid in an average-sized swimming pool. Even though your ability to detect odors is not as good as a shark's, your sense of smell is still important. Smell can determine which foods you eat. Strong memories or feelings also can be responses to something you smell.

You smell food because it gives off molecules into the air. These molecules stimulate sensitive nerve cells, called **olfactory** (ohl FAK tree) **cells,** in your nasal passages. Olfactory cells are kept moist by mucus. When molecules in the air dissolve in this moisture, the cells become stimulated. If enough molecules are present, an impulse starts in these cells, then travels to the brain where the stimulus is interpreted. If the stimulus is recognized from a previous experience, you can identify the odor. If you don't recognize a particular odor, it is remembered and may be identified the next time you encounter it.

Science Online

Topic: Sense of Smell
Visit life.msscience.com for Web links to information about the sense of smell in humans compared to that of other mammals.

Activity In your Science Journal, summarize your research.

Applying Math   **Solve a One-Step Equation**

SPEED OF SOUND You see the flash of fireworks and then four seconds later, you hear the boom because light waves travel faster than sound waves. Light travels so fast that you see it almost instantaneously. Sound, on the other hand, travels at 340 m/s. How far away are you from the source of the fireworks?

Solution

1 *This is what you know:*   • time: $t = 4$ s; speed of sound: $v = 340$ m/s

2 *This is what you need to find out:*   How far are you away from the fireworks?

3 *This is the procedure you need to use:*
   • Use the equation: $d = vt$
   • Substitute known values and solve:
     $d = (340 \text{ m/s})(4 \text{ s})$
     $d = 1360$ m

4 *Check your answer:*   Divide your answer by time. You should get speed.

Practice Problems

1. A hiker standing at one end of a lake hears his echo 2.5 s after he shouts. It was reflected by a cliff at the end of the lake. How long is the lake?

2. If you see a flash of lightning during a thunderstorm and it takes 5 s to hear the thunder, how far away is the lightning?

 For more practice, visit
life.msscience.com/ math_practice

SECTION 2 The Senses **609**

Teacher FYI

Desensitized Smell The sense of smell can become desensitized to a specific odor if it is exposed to it for a period of time. If you walk into a movie theater, you are instantly aware of the odor of popcorn. After a while, however, the odor is hardly noticeable because your chemoreceptors have become desensitized.

Purpose Students observe the difference in the sense of smell between males and females.
L2 IS **Kinesthetic**

Materials small samples of food, colognes, or household products; cotton balls; blindfold

Teaching Strategy Place a small amount of the odorous substance on a cotton ball for each sniff test. Do not use a cotton ball for more than one person.

Safety Precautions Students should not use any substances with strong, noxious odors (e.g., ammonia). Survey students before class to determine whether any of them have allergies or asthma that might be affected by the odors.

Analysis
1. Answers may vary, but more females should correctly identify specific odors.
2. Generally, females are more acutely aware of odors than are males.

Assessment

Performance Have students conduct a test of identifying odors while blindfolded. Use **Performance Assessment in the Science Classroom,** p. 97.

Reading Check

Answer It has to be dissolved in water.

Comparing Sense of Smell

Procedure
1. To test your classmates' abilities to recognize different odors, blindfold them one at a time, then pass near their noses small **samples of different foods, colognes, or household products.** WARNING: *Do not eat or drink anything in the lab. Do not use any products that give off noxious fumes.*
2. Ask each student to identify the different samples.
3. Record each student's response in a data table according to his or her gender.

Analysis
1. Compare the numbers of correctly identified odors for males and females.
2. What can you conclude about the differences between males and females in their abilities to recognize odors?

Figure 17 Taste buds are made up of a group of sensory cells with tiny taste hairs projecting from them. When food is taken into the mouth, it is dissolved in saliva. This mixture then stimulates receptor sites on the taste hairs, and an impulse is sent to the brain.

Taste

Sometimes you taste a new food with the tip of your tongue and find that it tastes sweet. Then when you chew it, you are surprised to find that it tastes bitter. **Taste buds** on your tongue, like the one in **Figure 17,** are the major sensory receptors for taste. About 10,000 taste buds are found all over your tongue, enabling you to tell one taste from another.

Tasting Food Taste buds respond to chemical stimuli. Most taste buds respond to several taste sensations. However, certain areas of the tongue are more receptive to one taste than another. The five taste sensations on the tongue are sweet, salty, sour, bitter, and the taste of MSG (monosodium glutamate). When you think of hot french fries, your mouth begins to water. This response is helpful because in order to taste something, it has to be dissolved in water. Saliva begins this process. This solution of saliva and food washes over the taste buds, and impulses are sent to your brain. The brain interprets the impulses, and you identify the tastes.

Reading Check *What needs to happen to food before you are able to taste it?*

Smell and Taste Smell and taste are related. The sense of smell is needed to identify some foods such as chocolate. When saliva in your mouth mixes with the chocolate, odors travel up the nasal passage in the back of your throat. The olfactory cells are stimulated, and the taste and smell of chocolate are sensed. So when you have a stuffy nose and some foods seem tasteless, it may be because the food's molecules are blocked from contacting the olfactory cells in your nasal passages.

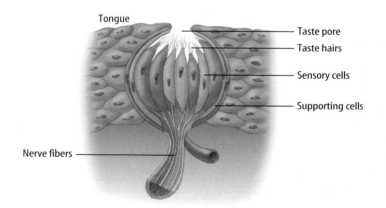

Tongue — Taste pore — Taste hairs — Sensory cells — Supporting cells — Nerve fibers

Cultural Diversity

Flavor Enhancement In many cultures, certain herbs and spices are used to enhance the flavors of foods. Asian foods often contain such spices as coriander, cumin, curry, fenugreek, ginger, star anise, turmeric, or Szechuan pepper. Have students find and share with the class a recipe that uses one of these spices. L1

Other Sensory Receptors in the Body

As you are reading at school, you suddenly experience a bad pain in your lower right abdomen. The pain is not going away and you yell for help. Several hours later, you are resting in a hospital bed. The doctor has removed the source of your problem—your appendix. If not removed, a burst appendix can spread poison throughout your body.

Your internal organs have several kinds of sensory receptors. These receptors respond to touch, pressure, pain, and temperature. They pick up changes in touch, pressure, and temperature and transmit impulses to the brain or spinal cord. In turn, your body responds to this new information.

Sensory receptors also are located throughout your skin. As shown in **Figure 18,** your fingertips have many different types of receptors for touch. As a result, you can tell whether an object is rough or smooth, hot or cold, and hard or soft. Your lips are sensitive to heat and prevent you from drinking something so hot that it would burn you. Pressure-sensitive skin cells warn you of danger and enable you to move to avoid injury.

The body responds to protect itself from harm. All of your body's senses work together to maintain homeostasis. Your senses help you enjoy or avoid things around you. You constantly react to your environment because of information received by your senses.

Figure 18 Many of the sensations picked up by receptors in the skin are stimulated by mechanical energy. Pressure, motion, and touch are examples.

section 2 review

Summary

Vision
- Light causes impulses that pass to the optic nerve. Your brain interprets the image.

Lenses
- Convex lenses and concave lenses are used to correct vision.

Hearing
- Sound waves stimulate nerve cells in the inner ear.
- Structures in the inner ear sense body movements.

Smell
- Molecules in the air stimulate nasal nerve cells, which allow you to smell.

Taste
- Taste buds are sensory receptors.

Self Check

1. **List** the types of stimuli your ears respond to.
2. **Describe** the sensory receptors for the eyes and nose.
3. **Explain** why it is important to have sensory receptors for pain and pressure in your internal organs.
4. **Outline** the role of saliva in tasting.
5. **Think Critically** Unlike many other organs, the brain is insensitive to pain. What is the advantage of this?

Applying Skills

6. **Make and Use Tables** Organize the information on senses in a table that names the sense organs and which stimuli they respond to.
7. **Communicate** Write a paragraph in your Science Journal that describes what each of the following objects would feel like: ice cube, snake, silk blouse, sandpaper, jelly, and smooth rock.

 Science Online life.msscience.com/self_check_quiz

SECTION 2 The Senses **611**

section 2 review

1. sound waves
2. eyes: rods and cones; nose: olfactory cells
3. Internal sensory receptors alert the brain when something is wrong. This allows the body to respond and protect itself and to maintain homeostasis.
4. Saliva dissolves food, enabling the food to wash over the taste buds.
5. The brain can continue to function when injured, allowing the body to carry out activities for survival.
6. eyes—light; tongue—taste; ears—sound; skin and other organs—touch, pressure, pain, temperature; nose—odors
7. Possible answers: ice cube—cold, smooth, hard; snake—rough; silk blouse—soft, smooth; sandpaper—rough, scratchy; jelly—sticky, squishy; smooth rock—hard, smooth

---

3 Assess

DAILY INTERVENTION

Check for Understanding

Visual-Spatial What design elements would be necessary for a robot to handle an egg? The robot would have to sense that the egg is a fragile object and then be able to manipulate it without applying too much pressure.

Reteach

Sensory Concept Map Have students make concept maps of the sensory organs described in this section. L2 [IS] **Visual-Spatial** [P]

✓ Assessment

Process Provide students with illustrations of people engaged in various activities and have them describe the sense organs involved and the different types of energy that stimulate the sensory receptors. Use **Performance Assessment in the Science Classroom,** p. 89. L2

BENCH TESTED

⊳ Real-World Question

Purpose Students design and carry out an experiment to determine skin sensitivity on various parts of the body by testing for the location of receptors in the skin. L2 ELL COOP LEARN LS **Kinesthetic**

Process Skills observe, form a hypothesis, design an experiment, interpret data, make and use tables, compare

Time Required two class periods

Materials Obtain materials for cooperative groups. Prepare the test cards the day before the lab to allow the glue to dry.

Safety Precautions Caution students not to apply heavy pressure when using any contact-point device.

⊳ Form a Hypothesis

Possible Hypothesis The fingertips are the most sensitive areas of the skin.

⊳ Test Your Hypothesis

Possible Procedures

- Predict which skin areas are most sensitive to touch. Rank the areas from most (5) to least (1) sensitive in a data table.
- Glue toothpicks onto a card so that one side has a pair 1 mm apart, and another side has a pair 3 mm apart. Another card should have pairs 5 mm and 10 mm apart.

Design Your Own

Skin Sensitivity

⊳ Real-World Question

Your body responds to touch, pressure, temperature, and other stimuli. Not all parts of your body are equally sensitive to stimuli. Some areas are more sensitive than others are. For example, your lips are sensitive to heat. This protects you from burning your mouth and tongue. Now think about touch. How sensitive is the skin on various parts of your body to touch? Which areas can distinguish the smallest amount of distance between stimuli? What areas of the body are most sensitive to touch?

Goals
- **Observe** the sensitivity to touch on specific areas of the body.
- **Design** an experiment that tests the effects of a variable, such as how close the contact points are, to determine which body areas can distinguish which stimuli are closest to one another.

Possible Materials
3-in × 5-in index card
toothpicks
tape
*glue
metric ruler
*Alternate materials

Safety Precautions
🔥 🥽 ✋

WARNING: *Do not apply heavy pressure when touching the toothpicks to the skin of your classmates.*

⊳ Form a Hypothesis

Based on your experiences, state a hypothesis about which of the following five areas of the body—fingertip, forearm, back of the neck, palm, and back of the hand—you believe to be most sensitive. Rank the areas from 5 (most sensitive) to 1 (least sensitive).

Alternative Inquiry Lab

Extend the Lab Make this Lab an Inquiry Lab by building on the experience. Encourage students to use what they have learned about touch to brainstorm questions about the ability of your fingertips to distinguish between different textures. Have each student group choose one question to explore. Eliminate unsafe or impractical questions. Ask them to list the materials they need to explore their questions. Students should have their plans for additional experiments approved before continuing. Gather all of the necessary materials and then conduct the experiments.

Using Scientific Methods

◉ Test Your Hypothesis

Make a Plan

1. As a group, agree upon and write the hypothesis statement.

2. As a group, list the steps you need to test your hypothesis. Describe exactly what you will do at each step. Consider the following as you list the steps. How will you know that sight is not a factor? How will you use the card shown on the right to determine sensitivity to touch? How will you determine that one or both points are sensed?

3. **Design** a data table in your Science Journal to record your observations.

4. Reread your entire experiment to make sure that all steps are in the correct order.

5. **Identify** constants, variables, and controls of the experiment.

Follow Your Plan

1. Make sure your teacher approves your plan before you start.

2. Carry out the experiment as planned.

3. While the experiment is going on, write down any observations that you make and complete the data table in your Science Journal.

◉ Analyze Your Data

1. **Identify** which part of the body is least sensitive and which part is most sensitive.

2. **Identify** which part of the body tested can distinguish between the closest stimuli.

3. **Compare** your results with those of other groups.

4. Rank body parts tested from most to least sensitive. Did your results from this investigation support your hypothesis? Explain.

◉ Conclude and Apply

1. Based on the results of your investigation, what can you infer about the distribution of touch receptors on the skin?

2. What other parts of your body would you predict to be less sensitive? Explain your predictions.

Your Data

Write a report to share with your class about body parts of animals that are sensitive to touch. **For more help, refer to the** Science Skill Handbook.

LAB **613**

Student Data Table

Felt two points (mm)					
Body Part Tested	Predictions	1	3	5	10
Fingertip	5	−	+	+	+
Palm	4	−	−	+	+
Back of hand	3	−	−	−	+
Forearm	1	−	−	−	−
Back of neck	2	−	−	−	−

Your Data

Students can use the Internet or texts from the school library to gather data on animals with special sense organs on their legs, ears, noses, and mouth parts.

- With partner's eyes closed, carefully touch the skin with the pair 1 mm apart. If partner feels two points, record a plus (+). If partner feels one point, record a minus (−). Repeat using the other pairs.

Teaching Strategy Have students vary the order of toothpick pairs they use.

Expected Outcome The more sensitive areas are the fingertips, palms, and cheeks. Less sensitive are the backs of the hands, forearms, and back of the neck.

◉ Analyze Your Data

Answers to Questions

1. least: backs of the hands, forearms, back of neck; most: fingertips, palms, cheeks
2. fingertips and usually the palms
3. Results should be consistent.
4. Answers will vary.

Error Analysis Have students compare their results and their hypotheses and explain any differences that occurred.

◉ Conclude and Apply

1. Fingertip touch receptors are closer together than those of the backs of the hands and forearms. Receptors in the palms and back of the neck vary.
2. Answers may include the back and the legs because they rarely are used to sense an object.

Performance To further assess students' understanding of skin sensitivity, have them repeat this lab on the lower part of the leg and on the foot. Use **PASC**, p. 97. L2

Science and Language Arts

Understanding Literature

Diction and Tone Other examples of diction conveying a pleasant tone in the passage are *excitement of newly installed light, bright with iced drinks,* and *easy sun-washed days and purple dusks.*

Respond to the Reading

1. Nel seems happy about the return of Sula.

2. The phrases that describe Nel doing "a little dance" and being "moved to smile" help the reader understand Nel's feelings.

3. **Linking Science and Writing** Students should convey their character's dislike through the description of his or her nervous system's response to stimuli from the January environment.

 Neurological Process Nel's dance is a complex neurological process. However, it is a response to other sensory systems that are also neurological processes, such as the process of seeing. The eye's retina contains receptors that respond to light. The retina is the back part of the eye that contains cells called photoreceptors. Photoreceptors respond to light by generating electrical impulses that travel out of the eye through the optic nerve. Nel is able to see the sheen and glimmer of May because of this neurological process.

Sula
by Toni Morrison

In the following passage from Sula, *a novel by Toni Morrison, the author describes Nel's response to the arrival of her old friend Sula.*

Nel alone noticed the peculiar quality of the May that followed the leaving of the birds. It had a sheen, a glimmering as of green, rain-soaked Saturday nights (lit by the excitement of newly installed street lights); of lemon-yellow afternoons bright with iced drinks and splashes of daffodils. It showed in the damp faces of her children and the river-smoothness of their voices. Even her own body was not immune to the magic. She would sit on the floor to sew as she had done as a girl, fold her legs up under her or do a little dance that fitted some tune in her head. There were easy sun-washed days and purple dusks . . . .

Although it was she alone who saw this magic, she did not wonder at it. She knew it was all due to Sula's return to the Bottom.

Understanding Literature

Diction and Tone An author's choice of words, or diction, can help convey a certain tone in the writing. In the passage, Toni Morrison's word choices help the reader understand that the character Nel is enjoying the month of May. Find two more examples in which diction conveys a pleasant tone.

Respond to the Reading

1. Describe, in your own words, how Nel feels about the return of her friend Sula.
2. What parts of the passage help you determine Nel's feelings?
3. **Linking Science and Writing** Write a paragraph describing the month of January that clearly shows a person's dislike for the month.

 In the passage, Nel has a physical reaction to her environment. She is moved to "do a little dance" in response to the sights and sounds of May. This action is an example of a voluntary response to stimuli from outside the body. Movement of the body is a coordinated effort of the skeletal, muscular, and nervous system. Nel can dance because motor neurons conduct impulses from the brain to her muscles.

614 CHAPTER 21 Control and Coordination

Resources for Teachers and Students

"A Symphony in the Brain: The Evolution of the New Brain Wave Biofeedback", by Jim Robbins, *Atlantic Monthly Press,* May 2000

The Bluest Eye, Penguin USA, 2000

"Beloved", *Plume,* reprint edition, September 1998

The Man Who Mistook His Wife for a Hat, by Oliver Sacks, Touchstone Books, April 1998

Reviewing Main Ideas

Section 1 The Nervous System

1. Your body constantly is receiving a variety of stimuli from inside and outside the body. The nervous system responds to these stimuli to maintain homeostasis.

2. A neuron is the basic unit of structure and function of the nervous system.

3. A stimulus is detected by sensory neurons. Electrical impulses are carried to the interneurons and transmitted to the motor neurons. The result is the movement of a body part.

4. A response that is made automatically is a reflex.

5. The central nervous system contains the brain and spinal cord. The peripheral nervous system is made up of cranial and spinal nerves.

6. Many drugs, such as alcohol and caffeine, have a direct effect on your nervous system.

Section 2 The Senses

1. Your senses respond to stimuli. The eyes respond to light energy, and the ears respond to sound waves.

2. Olfactory cells of the nose and taste buds of the tongue are stimulated by chemicals.

3. Sensory receptors in your internal organs and skin respond to touch, pressure, pain, and temperature.

4. Your senses enable you to enjoy or avoid things around you. You are able to react to the changing conditions of your environment.

Visualizing Main Ideas

Copy and complete the following concept map about the nervous system.

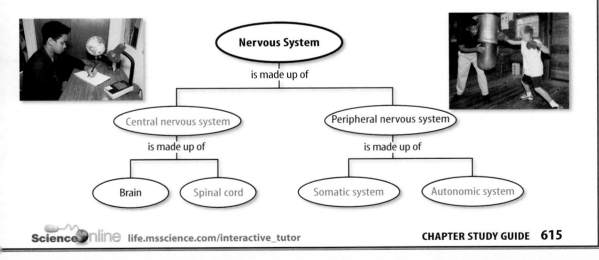

Nervous System

is made up of

Central nervous system — Peripheral nervous system

is made up of

Brain — Spinal cord

is made up of

Somatic system — Autonomic system

Science Online life.msscience.com/interactive_tutor

CHAPTER STUDY GUIDE 615

Identifying Misconceptions

Assess

Use this assessment as follow-up to the F page at the beginning of this chapter.

Procedure Draw on the board the correct model of how light reflects off an object and toward the eye to cause vision. Draw several other models, such as the misconception that light comes from the eye to cause vision. Have students individually assess the models and decide what is correct and incorrect about each diagram. Ask students to identify which diagram is most correct.

Expected Outcome After completing the Sight Box activity, students should be able to recognize a model which shows light from a light source reflecting off of an object and toward the eye as the most correct model.

Reviewing Main Ideas

Summary statements can be used by students to review the major concepts of the chapter.

Visualizing Main Ideas

See student page.

Visit life.msscience.com
/self_check_quiz
/interactive_tutor
/vocabulary_puzzlemaker
/chapter_review
/standardized_test

Assessment Transparency

For additional assessment questions, use the *Assessment Transparency* located in the transparency book.

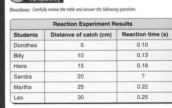

Assessment

Assessment Transparency **Control and Coordination**

Directions: *Carefully review the table and answer the following questions.*

Reaction Experiment Results

Students	Distance of catch (cm)	Reaction time (s)
Dorothea	5	0.10
Billy	10	0.13
Hans	15	0.16
Sandra	20	?
Martha	25	0.22
Leo	30	0.25

1. According to the information in the table, the student with the lowest reaction time is ___.
   A Leo   C Hans
   B Billy   D Dorothea

2. Based on the relationship between catch distance and reaction time, which is most likely Sandra's reaction time?
   F 0.10 s   H 0.19 s
   G 0.18 s   J 0.21 s

3. Eleanor, another student, is asked to participate in the experiment. Her reaction time was determined to be 0.23 seconds. Based on the information in the table, Eleanor's catch distance would be ___.
   A 31.15 cm   C 24.25 cm
   B 26.67 cm   D 21.67 cm

Control and Coordination

Using Vocabulary

1. Axons carry messages away from the cell body. Dendrites receive and carry messages to the cell body.

2. central nervous system—brain and spinal cord; peripheral nervous system—all the nerves outside the central nervous system

3. The cerebellum coordinates voluntary muscle movement. The cerebrum is where impulses are interpreted, memory is stored, and movements are controlled.

4. A reflex is an involuntary, automatic response to a stimulus. A synapse is the small space between an axon and a dendrite.

5. The brain stem is part of the brain. A neuron is a nerve cell.

6. An olfactory cell detects odors; a taste bud detects tastes.

7. A dendrite is part of a neuron. A synapse is the small space between an axon and a dendrite.

8. The cerebrum is a part of the brain. The central nervous system consists of the brain and the spinal cord.

9. The retina is a tissue of the eye. The cochlea is a structure in the inner ear.

10. A synapse is a small space between an axon and a dendrite. A neuron is a nerve cell.

Checking Concepts

11. D	16. C
12. B	17. A
13. C	18. B
14. D	19. C
15. A	20. C

Thinking Critically

21. Possible responses: so messages do not get mixed; so that responses can be coordinated

---

Using Vocabulary

axon p. 595
brain stem p. 598
central nervous system
  p. 597
cerebellum p. 598
cerebrum p. 598
cochlea p. 608
dendrite p. 595
homeostasis p. 595

neuron p. 595
olfactory cell p. 609
peripheral nervous system
  p. 597
reflex p. 601
retina p. 605
synapse p. 597
taste bud p. 610

Explain the difference between the vocabulary words in each of the following sets.

1. axon—dendrite

2. central nervous system—peripheral nervous system

3. cerebellum—cerebrum

4. reflex—synapse

5. brain stem—neuron

6. olfactory cell—taste bud

7. dendrite—synapse

8. cerebrum—central nervous system

9. retina—cochlea

10. synapse—neuron

Checking Concepts

Choose the word or phrase that best answers the question.

11. How do impulses cross synapses between neurons?
    A) by osmosis
    B) through interneurons
    C) through a cell body
    D) by a chemical

12. Which of the following is in the inner ear?
    A) anvil   C) eardrum
    B) hammer   D) cochlea

---

13. What are neurons called that detect stimuli in the skin and eyes?
    A) interneurons   C) motor neurons
    B) synapses   D) sensory neurons

14. Which of the following does the skin not sense?
    A) pain   C) temperature
    B) pressure   D) taste

15. What part of the brain controls voluntary muscles?
    A) cerebellum   C) cerebrum
    B) brain stem   D) pons

16. What part of the brain has an outer layer called the cortex?
    A) pons   C) cerebrum
    B) brain stem   D) spinal cord

17. What does the somatic system of the PNS control?
    A) skeletal muscles   C) glands
    B) heart   D) salivary glands

18. What part of the eye is light finally focused on?
    A) lens   C) pupil
    B) retina   D) cornea

19. What is the largest part of the brain?
    A) cerebellum   C) cerebrum
    B) brain stem   D) pons

Use the illustration below to answer question 20.

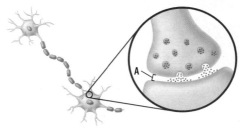

20. What is the name given to A?
    A) axon   C) synapse
    B) dendrite   D) nucleus

Science Online   life.msscience.com/vocabulary_puzzlemaker

Use the ExamView® Pro Testmaker CD-ROM to:
- create multiple versions of tests
- create modified tests with one mouse click for inclusion students
- edit existing questions and add your own questions
- build tests aligned with state standards using built-in State Curriculum Tags
- change English tests to Spanish with one mouse click and vice versa

Thinking Critically

21. Describe why it is helpful to have impulses move only in one direction in a neuron.

22. Describe how smell and taste are related.

23. Form a Hypothesis If a fly were to land on your face and another one on your back, which might you feel first? How could you test your choice?

24. Concept Map Copy and complete this events-chain concept map to show the correct sequence of the structures through which light passes in the eye.

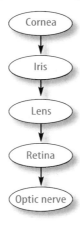

25. Classify Group the types of neurons as to their location and direction of impulse.

26. Compare and contrast the structures and functions of the cerebrum, cerebellum, and brain stem. Include in your discussion the following functions: balance, involuntary muscle movements, muscle tone, memory, voluntary muscles, thinking, and senses.

27. Draw Conclusions If an impulse traveled down one neuron but failed to move on to the next neuron, what might you conclude about the first neuron?

 Science Online life.msscience.com/chapter_review

Performance Activities

28. Illustrate In an emergency room, the doctor notices that a patient has uncoordinated body movements and has difficulty maintaining his balance. Draw and label the part of the brain that may have been injured.

Applying Math

29. Sound Waves How deep is a cave if you shout into the cave and it takes 1.5 seconds to hear your echo? Remember that the speed of sound is 340 m/s.

Use the paragraph and table below to answer question 30.

A police officer brought the following table into a school to educate students about the dangers of drinking and driving.

Approximate Blood Alcohol Percentage for Men

Drinks	Body Weight in Kilograms							
	45.4	54.4	63.5	72.6	81.6	90.7	99.8	108.9
1	0.04	0.03	0.03	0.02	0.02	0.02	0.02	0.02
2	0.08	0.06	0.05	0.05	0.04	0.04	0.03	0.03
3	0.11	0.09	0.08	0.07	0.06	0.06	0.05	0.05
4	0.15	0.12	0.11	0.09	0.08	0.08	0.07	0.06
5	0.19	0.16	0.13	0.12	0.11	0.09	0.09	0.08

Subtract 0.01% for each 40 minutes of drinking. One drink is 40 mL of 80-proof liquor, 355 mL of beer, or 148 mL of table wine.

30. Blood Alcohol A 72-kg man has been tested for blood alcohol content. His blood alcohol percentage is 0.07. Based upon the information in the table above, about how much has he had to drink?

A) 628 mL of 80-proof liquor

B) 1,064 mL of beer

C) 295 mL of table wine

D) four drinks

Thinking Critically

22. When food is put into the mouth and made moist, both the taste buds and olfactory cells are stimulated, and the food item is sensed by both.

23. The sense of touch is more pronounced on the face than on the back. One could check this by using something lightweight, such as a feather or small paintbrush, to test the sensitivity of the face and back.

24. See student page.

25. Sensory neurons are located in the sense organs and spinal cord; they carry impulses to the brain. Interneurons are located in the central nervous system; they carry impulses from the central nervous system to motor neurons. Motor neurons are in muscles and glands; they carry impulses from the brain to muscles and glands.

26. cerebrum—voluntary muscles, memory, senses, thinking; cerebellum—balance, muscle tone; brain stem—coordinates involuntary muscle movements, controls heartbeat, breathing, and blood pressure

27. It may be lacking the nerve-transmitting chemical released by axons.

Performance Activities

28. Drawings should indicate that the cerebellum is injured. Use **PASC**, p. 127.

Applying Math

National Math Standards

1, 5, 9

29. 510 m

30. B

☑ **Assessment** **Resources**

Reproducible Masters

Chapter *Fast File* Resources
Chapter Review, pp. 35–36
Chapter Tests, pp. 37–40
Assessment Transparency Activity, p. 47

Glencoe Science Web site
Chapter Review Test
Standardized Test Practice

Glencoe Technology
Assessment Transparency
Exam*View*® Pro Testmaker
MindJogger Videoquiz
Interactive Chalkboard

Answer Sheet A practice answer sheet can be found at life.msscience.com/answer_sheet.

S A M P L E

Part 1 | Multiple Choice

1. B
2. B
3. B
4. C
5. C
6. D
7. A
8. D
9. B

Part 1 | Multiple Choice

Record your answers on the answer sheet provided by your teacher or on a sheet of paper.

1. An internal or external change that brings about a response is called a
   A. reflex.   **C.** receptor.
   B. stimulus.   **D.** heartbeat.

Use the illustration below to answer questions 2–4.

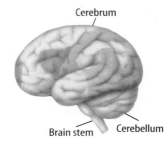

Cerebrum

Brain stem   Cerebellum

2. Which part of the brain helps in maintaining balance?
   A. cerebrum   **C.** brain stem
   B. cerebellum   **D.** no brain region

3. Which part of the brain controls involuntary actions?
   A. cerebrum   **C.** brain stem
   B. cerebellum   **D.** no brain region

4. In which part of the brain is memory stored?
   A. cerebrum   **C.** brain stem
   B. cerebellum   **D.** no brain region

5. Which of the following structures helps control the body's balance?
   A. retina   **C.** cochlea
   B. eardrum   **D.** cristae ampullaris

Test-Taking Tip

Focus On Your Test During the test, keep your eyes on your own paper. If you need to rest them, close them or look up at the ceiling.

Use the table below to answer questions 6 and 7.

Approximate Blood Alcohol Percentage for Men								
	Body Weight in Kilograms							
Drinks	45.4	54.4	63.5	72.6	81.6	90.7	99.8	108.9
1	0.04	0.03	0.03	0.02	0.02	0.02	0.02	0.02
2	0.08	0.06	0.05	0.05	0.04	0.04	0.03	0.03
3	0.11	0.09	0.08	0.07	0.06	0.06	0.05	0.05
4	0.15	0.12	0.11	0.09	0.08	0.08	0.07	0.06
5	0.19	0.16	0.13	0.12	0.11	0.09	0.09	0.08

Subtract 0.01% for each 40 minutes of drinking. One drink is 40 mL of 80-proof liquor, 355 mL of beer, or 148 mL of table wine.

6. In Michigan, it is illegal for drivers under 21 years of age to drink alcohol. Underage drivers can be arrested for drinking and driving if their blood alcohol percentage is more than 0.02 percent. According to this information, how many drinks would it take a 72-kg man to exceed this limit?
   A. three   **C.** one
   B. two   **D.** zero

7. In some states, the legal blood alcohol percentage limit for driving while under the influence of alcohol is 0.08 percent. According to this information, how many drinks would a 54-kg man have to consume to exceed this limit?
   A. four   **C.** two
   B. three   **D.** one

8. What neurons conduct impulses from the brain to glands?
   A. dendrites   **C.** sensory neurons
   B. interneurons   **D.** motor neurons

9. What carries impulses from the eye to the vision area of the brain?
   A. visual cortex   **C.** sensory neurons
   B. optic nerve   **D.** dendrites

Part 2 | Short Response/Grid In

10. Because the brain and spinal cord are surrounded by bone, the space where the fluid is cannot expand. If the amount of fluid increases, the pressure that the fluid exerts will be increased because there is nowhere for the fluid to go. Thus, more pressure will be put on the brain.

11. 658 + 99 = 757; 757 10% = 75.7. Approximately 76 people.

12. 605 + 76 = 681 deaths; 76/681 = .11 = 11%

13. 1997

14. Jeremy used a convex lens. Convex lenses can be used to magnify objects. A convex lens is thicker in the middle.

15. Alcohol is classified as a depressant because it slows the activities of the central nervous system.

Part 2 | Short Response/Grid In

Record your answers on the answer sheet provided by your teacher or on a sheet of paper.

10. Meningitis is an infection of the fluid that surrounds the spinal cord and the brain. Meningitis can be caused by bacteria or viruses. In bacterial meningitis, the amount of fluid in the brain and spinal cord may increase. What do you think might happen if the amount of fluid increases?

Use the table below to answer questions 11–13.

Number of Bicycle Deaths per Year		
Year	Male	Female
1996	654	107
1997	712	99
1998	658	99
1999	656	94
2000	605	76

Data from Insurance Institute for Highway Safety

11. Head injuries are the most serious injuries that are found in people who died in bicycle accidents. Ninety percent of the deaths were in people who were not wearing bicycle helmets. Using the data in the table, approximately how many of the people (male and female) who died in bicycle accidents in 1998 were wearing bicycle helmets?

12. In 2000, what percentage of the people who died were women?

13. Which of the years from 1996 to 2000 had the greatest total number of bicycle deaths?

14. Jeremy used a magnifying lens to study an earthworm. What kind of lens did he use? What part of this type of lens is the thickest?

15. Explain why alcohol is classified as a depressant.

Part 3 | Open Ended

Record your answers on a sheet of paper.

16. Compare and contrast the somatic and autonomic systems.

Use the illustration below to answer question 17.

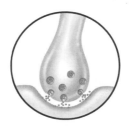

17. Identify the structure in the illustration. Explain what might happen if chemical was not released here.

18. Inez and Maria went to the ice cream parlor. They both ordered strawberry sundaes. Marie thought that the sundae was made with fresh strawberries, because it tasted so great. Inez thought that her sundae did not have much flavor. What could be the reason that Inez's sundae was tasteless? Explain why.

Use the illustration below to answer question 19.

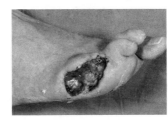

19. The person with this foot sore has diabetes. People with diabetes often lose sensation in their feet. Explain why a sore like the one in the photograph might develop if skin sensory receptors were not working properly.

nose prevents the food molecules from reaching the olfactory cells in the nasal passages and the strawberry sundae seems tasteless.

19. In a person without diabetes, the skin normally has pain receptors. Pain receptors would warn the person that there is an infection. Because the skin receptors for pain are not working, the person with diabetes will not feel the pain that would tell the person that there is an infection.

Rubrics

For more help evaluating open-ended assessment questions, see the rubric on p. 10T.

Part 3 | Open Ended

16. The somatic system controls voluntary actions. It is made up of the cranial and spinal nerves that go from the central nervous system to the skeletal muscles. The autonomic nervous system controls involuntary actions such as heart rate, breathing, digestion, and glandular functions.

17. The structure is a synapse. Neurons do not touch each other. Impulses travel from one axon to the next because of an impulse-transmitting chemical at the synapse. If the axon did not release the chemical, then the impulse will not be transmitted to the next axon. The impulse will stop there.

18. Inez may have a stuffy nose. Smell and taste are related. The sense of smell is needed to identify some foods. When saliva mixes in the mouth, the odors travel up the nasal passage in the back of the throat. The olfactory cells are stimulated, and the taste and smell of the strawberries is sensed. A stuffy

Section/Objectives	Standards		Labs/Features
Chapter Opener	**National**	**State/Local**	**Launch Lab:** Model a Chemical Message, p. 621 **Foldables,** p. 621
	See p. 16–17T for a Key to Standards.		
Section 1 The Endocrine System ⏱ 2 sessions 📦 1 block 1. **Define** how hormones function. 2. **Identify** different endocrine glands and the effects of the hormones they produce. 3. **Describe** how a feedback system works in your body.	National Content Standards: UCP.1–UCP.3, UCP.5, A.1, A.2, C.1–C.3		**Applying Math:** Glucose Levels, p. 623 **Visualizing the Endocrine System,** p. 624
Section 2 The Reproductive System ⏱ 2 sessions 📦 1 block 4. **Identify** the function of the reproductive system. 5. **Compare and contrast** the major structures of the male and female reproductive systems. 6. **Sequence** the stages of the menstrual cycle.	National Content Standards: UCP.1–UCP.3, UCP.5, A.1, A.2, C.1–C.3		**Science Online,** p. 629 **MiniLAB:** Graphing Hormone Levels, p. 630 **Lab:** Interpreting Diagrams, p. 632
Section 3 Human Life Stages ⏱ 3 sessions 📦 1.5 blocks 7. **Describe** the fertilization of a human egg. 8. **List** the major events in the development of an embryo and fetus. 9. **Describe** the developmental stages of infancy, childhood, adolescence, and adulthood.	National Content Standards: UCP.1–UCP.3, UCP.5, A.1, A.2, B.2, C.1, C.3, C5		**Integrate Career,** p. 634 **MiniLAB:** Interpreting Fetal Development, p. 636 **Science Online,** p. 637 **Integrate Physics,** p. 640 **Lab:** Changing Body Proportions, p. 642 **Science Stats:** Facts About Infants, p. 644

Lab Materials	Reproducible Resources	Section Assessment	Technology
Launch Lab: filter paper; metric ruler; plastic, ceramic, or glass plate; baking soda; salt; dropper; vinegar	**Chapter FAST FILE Resources** Foldables Worksheet, p. 15 Directed Reading Overview, p. 17 Note-taking Worksheets, pp. 31–33	GLENCOE'S ASSESSMENT ADVANTAGE	Teacher**Works** includes: • Interactive Teacher Edition • Lesson Planner with calendar • Access to all program blacklines • Correlations to standards • Web links ▭ Video Lab
Need materials? Contact Science Kit at 1-800-828-7777 or www.sciencekit.com on the Internet.	**Chapter FAST FILE Resources** Transparency Activity, p. 42 Enrichment, p. 28 Reinforcement, p. 25 Directed Reading, p. 18 Lab Activity, pp. 9–11 Transparency Activity, pp. 45–46	Portfolio Visual Learning, p. 625 **Performance** Applying Math, p. 623 Applying Skills, p. 626 **Content** Section Review, p. 626	Section Focus Transparency Teaching Transparency Virtual Labs CD-ROM Guided Reading Audio Program Interactive Chalkboard CD-ROM
MiniLAB: graph paper **Lab:** paper, pencil	**Chapter FAST FILE Resources** Transparency Activity, p. 43 MiniLAB, p. 3 Enrichment, p. 29 Reinforcement, p. 26 Directed Reading, p. 18 Lab Worksheet, pp. 5–6	Portfolio Science Journal, p. 629 **Performance** MiniLAB, p. 630 Applying Math, p. 631 **Content** Section Review, p. 631	Section Focus Transparency Virtual Labs CD-ROM Guided Reading Audio Program Interactive Chalkboard CD-ROM
MiniLAB: graph paper **Lab:** tape measure, erasable pencil, graph paper	**Chapter FAST FILE Resources** Transparency Activity, p. 44 MiniLAB, p. 4 Enrichment, p. 30 Reinforcement, p. 27 Directed Reading, pp. 19, 20 Lab Worksheet, pp. 7–8 Lab Activity, pp. 13–14 **Lab Management and Safety,** p. 70	Portfolio Make a Model, p. 634 **Performance** MiniLAB, p. 636 Applying Skills, p. 641 **Content** Section Review, p. 641	Section Focus Transparency Virtual Labs CD-ROM Guided Reading Audio Program Interactive Chalkboard CD-ROM

End of Chapter Assessment

GLENCOE'S ASSESSMENT ADVANTAGE

Blackline Masters	Technology	Professional Series
Chapter FAST FILE Resources Chapter Review, pp. 35–36 Chapter Tests, pp. 37–40 **Standardized Test Practice,** pp. 91–94	▭ MindJogger Videoquiz ● Virtual Labs CD-ROM ● ExamView® Pro Testmaker ● TeacherWorks CD-ROM ● Interactive Chalkboard CD-ROM	**Performance Assessment in the Science Classroom (PASC)**

chapter Regulation and Reproduction

Transparencies

Section Focus

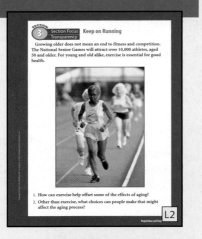

This is a representation of key blackline masters available in the Teacher Classroom Resources. See Resource Manager boxes within the chapter for additional information.

Key to Teaching Strategies

The following designations will help you decide which activities are appropriate for your students.

L1 Level 1 activities should be appropriate for students with learning difficulties.

L2 Level 2 activities should be within the ability range of all students.

L3 Level 3 activities are designed for above-average students.

ELL ELL activities should be within the ability range of English-Language Learners.

COOP LEARN Cooperative Learning activities are designed for small group work.

LS Multiple Learning Styles logos, as described on page 12T, are used throughout to indicate strategies that address different learning styles.

P These strategies represent student products that can be placed into a best-work portfolio.

PBL Problem-Based Learning activities apply real-world situations to learning.

Assessment

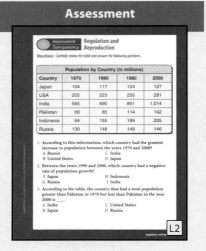

Teaching

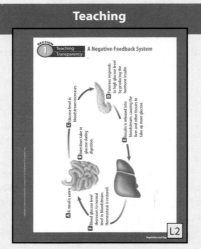

Hands-on Activities

Student Text Lab Worksheet

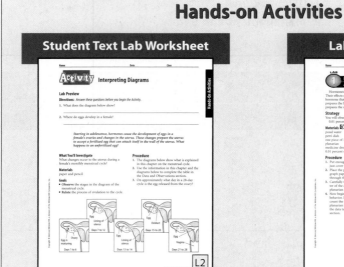

Laboratory Activities

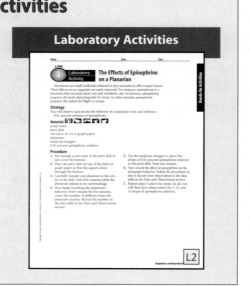

Meeting Different Ability Levels

Content Outline

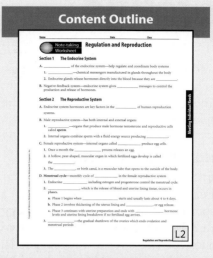

L2

Reinforcement

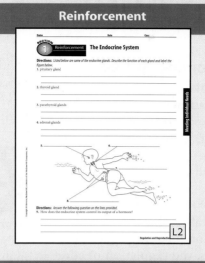

L2

Enrichment

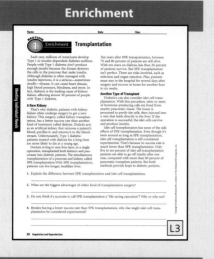

L3

Directed Reading (English/Spanish)

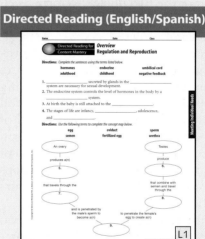

L1

Study Guide

L2

Reading Essentials

L1

Assessment

Test Practice Workbook

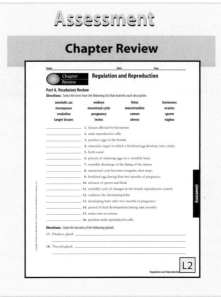

L2

Chapter Review

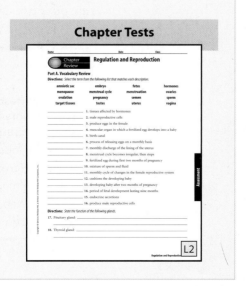

L2

Chapter Tests

L2

Science Content Background

section 1

The Endocrine System
Regulation

The endocrine system uses hormones to control body functions such as defense, hunger, growth and reproduction. All organs of the endocrine system are glands that produce and empty hormones into the circulatory system.

The anterior lobe of the pituitary gland produces hormones that cause the stimulation of growth, the production of milk, the regulation of thyroid gland secretions, the regulation of adrenal cortex secretions, the stimulation of egg and sperm production, and egg release.

The posterior lobe of the pituitary gland aids in the regulation of water secretion by the kidneys, muscle contractions during labor, and the contraction of milk-producing glands.

The pituitary's intermediate lobe controls melanin production, which determines skin color.

section 2

The Reproductive System
Hormones

Hormones produced by the endocrine system control sexual development, maturation, and functioning of the reproductive system. Hormones stimulate the production and release of sperm and semen in the male reproductive system. In the female reproductive system, hormones stimulate the production and release of ova, or eggs. Hormones also play a role during labor and birth. In later years, menopause is brought on when the body stops producing certain hormones.

section 3

Human Life Stages
Embryonic Development

Fertilization is the union of a sperm cell from a male with an egg from a female. Fertilization results in two events: (1) fusion of the sperm and egg cells, including fusion of the two nuclei, to form a cell called a zygote, and (2) activation of the new cell to begin division and growth.

Once a sperm fertilizes an egg, the egg produces an outer protective layer. Next, the zygote divides into thousands of smaller cells that cling together like a ball of soap bubbles. After several days and until about two weeks later, the ball of cells begins to differentiate into three parts: an outer layer of cells that attaches to the uterus of the mother, an inner mass of cells that develops into the embryo, and a fluid-filled sac that surrounds the embryo.

The next phase, which occurs between two and eight weeks after fertilization, involves specialization of cells into primary organ systems. This set of events marks the end of the embryo stage and the beginning of the fetal stage.

chapter content resources

Internet Resources
For additional content background, visit
life.msscience.com to:
- access your book online
- find references to related articles in popular science magazines
- access Web links with related content background
- access current events with science journal topics

Print Resources
How the Endocrine System Works, by J. Matthew Neal, Blackwell Publishers, 2001
Endocrine and Reproductive Systems, by Susan Dudley Gold and Melissa Kim, Enslow Publishers, Inc., 2003

IDENTIFYING ▷ Misconceptions

Find Out What Students Think

Students may think that . . .

Fertilization and embryonic development are mysterious processes that are not understandable.

Many students may find the concepts of fertilization and embryonic development very abstract. Using concrete demonstrations and activities will help these students understand the processes and sequences of events that occur.

Demonstration

- Using two different colors of clay, form a large ball from one color, representing an egg cell, and many smaller balls from the second color, representing sperm cells. Fertilization can be modeled by molding the "egg" and "sperm" into one ball. Explain that this fertilized cell is called a zygote. No other sperm cells can fuse with the egg cell at this point because the zygote produces a protective barrier blocking other sperm cells. Emphasize that the molding together of the sperm and egg cells is a simulation of the combining of genetic material from both.

- Next, model the phase of rapid cell division by dividing the ball into many smaller, connected balls. Explain that these cells cling together like a ball of soap bubbles. Continue by drawing the "soap bubble" stage on the board and labeling it as time from fertilization to a few days.

- Next, draw the three-part stage and the specialization. Label these drawings as "a few days to 2 weeks" and "2 weeks to 8 weeks," respectively.

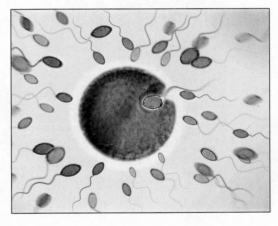

VCG/FPG International

Promote Understanding

Activity

After discussion, have students draw diagrams of the events that occur from fertilization through the stages of early development to the early fetal stage. Have students work in small groups to explain to one another their diagrams and the events that take place during each stage.

Assess

After completing the chapter, see *Identifying Misconceptions* in the Study Guide at the end of the chapter.

Chapter Vocabulary

Science Journal Student responses will vary, but may include dispatchers answering an incoming emergency call, dispatching emergency crews to the scene, and monitoring the situation to see if additional help is needed.

INTERACTIVE CHALKBOARD
with Image Bank

PowerPoint® Presentations

This CD-ROM is an editable Microsoft® PowerPoint® presentation that includes:
- a pre-made presentation for every chapter
- interactive graphics
- animations
- audio clips
- image bank
- all new section and chapter questions
- Standardized Test Practice
- transparencies
- pre-lab questions for all labs
- Foldables directions
- links to life.mssscience.com

Regulation and Reproduction

chapter preview

sections

1 The Endocrine System

2 The Reproductive System
Lab Interpreting Diagrams

3 Human Life Stages
Lab Changing Body Proportions

Virtual Lab What are the stages of development before birth?

Where's the emergency?

The fire station control room blinks with panels of buttons and monitors. Dispatchers can access and relay emergency information quickly using this complex monitoring system. In a similar way, your body's endocrine system monitors and controls the actions of many of your body's functions.

Science Journal Write a paragraph describing how an emergency call might be handled at a fire station.

620

Theme Connection

Stability, Change, and Energy The endocrine system maintains stable body functions and responds to changes. The unique functioning of the reproductive system is dependent on energy for cell division and differentiation of cells.

About the Photo

Fighting Fires Fire department dispatchers must maintain a vigilant watch over the communications equipment in the control room. Emergency calls are received and monitored and information is passed along to the personnel responding to the scene of an emergency. The dispatchers also may be in contact with other emergency companies in order to receive or provide additional help.

Start-Up Activities

Launch LAB

Model a Chemical Message

Your body has systems that work together to coordinate your body's activities. One of these systems sends chemical messages through your blood to certain tissues, which, in turn, respond. Do the lab below to see how a chemical signal can be sent.

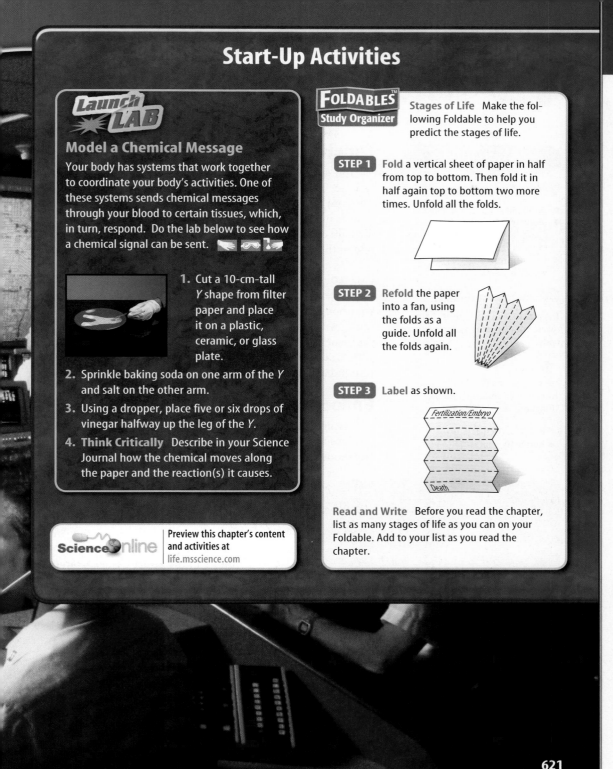

1. Cut a 10-cm-tall *Y* shape from filter paper and place it on a plastic, ceramic, or glass plate.

2. Sprinkle baking soda on one arm of the *Y* and salt on the other arm.

3. Using a dropper, place five or six drops of vinegar halfway up the leg of the *Y*.

4. **Think Critically** Describe in your Science Journal how the chemical moves along the paper and the reaction(s) it causes.

Science Online Preview this chapter's content and activities at life.msscience.com

FOLDABLES Study Organizer

Stages of Life Make the following Foldable to help you predict the stages of life.

STEP 1 Fold a vertical sheet of paper in half from top to bottom. Then fold it in half again top to bottom two more times. Unfold all the folds.

STEP 2 Refold the paper into a fan, using the folds as a guide. Unfold all the folds again.

STEP 3 Label as shown.

Fertilization/Embryo

Death

Read and Write Before you read the chapter, list as many stages of life as you can on your Foldable. Add to your list as you read the chapter.

Launch LAB

Purpose Use the Launch Lab to introduce students to the endocrine system. [L2] [LS] **Visual-Spatial**

Preparation Cut Y-shaped pieces of filter paper before class.

Materials filter paper or coffee filters; baking soda; salt; vinegar; plastic, ceramic, or glass plate; dropper

Teaching Strategy Have students observe the bubbles that form when the vinegar and baking soda react.

Think Critically

Students should observe the vinegar moving along the leg of the Y and then into the arms of the Y. The vinegar reacts with the baking soda and bubbles are produced.

Assessment

Performance Have students repeat this lab using baking powder in place of baking soda and water instead of vinegar and observe the reaction. Use **Performance Assessment in the Science Classroom,** p. 97.

FOLDABLES Study Organizer Dinah Zike Study Fold

Student preparation materials for this Foldable are available in the **Chapter *FAST FILE* Resources.**

The Endocrine System

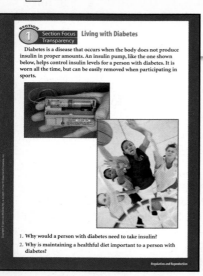

Tie to Prior Knowledge

Stimuli Have students recall how their bodies react to stimuli such as the touching of a hot object or how they respond to a loud noise.

✔ Reading Check

Answer to speed up and slow down certain cellular activities

---

as you read

What You'll Learn
- **Define** how hormones function.
- **Identify** different endocrine glands and the effects of the hormones they produce.
- **Describe** how a feedback system works in your body.

Why It's Important
The endocrine system uses chemicals to control many systems in your body.

🔎 **Review Vocabulary**
tissue: groups of cells that work together to perform a specific function

New Vocabulary
● hormone

Functions of the Endocrine System

You go through the dark hallways of a haunted house. You can't see a thing. Your heart is pounding. Suddenly, a monster steps out in front of you. You scream and jump backwards. Your body is prepared to defend itself or get away. Preparing the body for fight or flight in times of emergency, as shown in **Figure 1,** is one of the functions of the body's control systems.

Control Systems All of your body's systems work together, but the endocrine (EN duh krun) and the nervous systems are your body's control systems. The endocrine system sends chemical messages in your blood that affect specific tissues called target tissues. The nervous system sends rapid impulses to and from your brain, then throughout your body. Your body does not respond as quickly to chemical messages as it does to impulses.

Endocrine Glands

Tissues found throughout your body called endocrine glands produce the chemical messages called **hormones** (HOR mohnz). Hormones can speed up or slow down certain cellular processes. Some glands in your body release their products through small tubes called ducts. Endocrine glands are ductless and each endocrine gland releases its hormone directly into the blood. Then, the blood transports the hormone to the target tissue. A target tissue usually is located in the body far from the location of the endocrine gland that produced the hormone to which it responds.

✔ **Reading Check** *What is the function of hormones?*

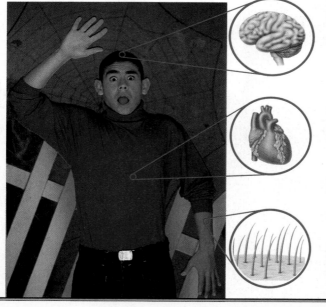

Figure 1 Your endocrine system enables many parts of your body to respond immediately in a fearful situation.

Section 1 Resource Manager

Chapter *FAST FILE* Resources
Transparency Activity, pp. 42, 45–46
Directed Reading for Content Mastery, pp. 17, 18
Note-taking Worksheets, pp. 31–33
Enrichment, p. 28

Lab Activity, pp. 9–11
Reinforcement, p. 25

Gland Functions Endocrine glands have many functions in the body. The functions include the regulation of its internal environment, adaptation to stressful situations, promotion of growth and development, and the coordination of circulation, digestion, and the absorption of food. **Figure 2** on the next two pages shows some of the body's endocrine glands.

Applying Math   Use Percentages

GLUCOSE LEVELS Calculate how much higher the blood sugar (glucose) level of a diabetic is before breakfast when compared to a nondiabetic before breakfast. Express this number as a percentage of the nondiabetic sugar level before breakfast.

Solution

1 *This is what you know:*
- nondiabetic blood sugar at 0 h = 0.85 g sugar/L blood
- diabetic blood sugar at 0 h = 1.8 g sugar/L blood

2 *This is what you need to find out:*
How much higher is the glucose level of a diabetic person than that of a nondiabetic person before breakfast?

3 *This is the procedure you need to use:*
- Find the difference in glucose levels:
  1.8 g/L − 0.85 g/L = 0.95 g/L
- Use this equation:

$$\frac{\text{difference between values}}{\text{nondiabetic value}} \times 100\% = \text{percent difference}$$

- Substitute in the known values:

$$\frac{0.95}{0.85} \times 100\% = 112\%$$

- Before breakfast, a diabetic's blood sugar is about 112 percent higher than that of a nondiabetic.

4 *Check your answer:*
Change 112% to a decimal then multiply it by 0.85. You should get 0.95.

Practice Problems

1. Express as a percentage how much higher the blood sugar value is for a diabetic person compared to a nondiabetic person 1 h after breakfast.

2. Express as a percentage how much higher the blood sugar value is for a diabetic person compared to a nondiabetic person 3 h and 6 h after breakfast.

 For more practice, visit life.msscience.com/math_practice

SECTION 1   The Endocrine System   **623**

Applying Math

National Math Standards
Correlation to Mathematics Objectives
1, 9

Answers to Practice Problems

1. Hour one = 130 / 110 × 100 = 118 %

2. Hour three = 95 / 85 × 100 = 111 %

   Hour six = 110 / 70 × 100 = 157%

Note: student answers may vary slightly due to the values read from the graph. Accept answers that are reasonably close.

Teacher FYI

Hormone Production In addition to hormones produced by endocrine glands, other organs also produce hormones. Endocrine cells in the stomach produce a hormone that regulates the release of its digestive enzymes. The kidneys release a hormone that controls the rate of production of red blood cells. The heart makes a hormone that regulates blood pressure and volume.

Differentiated Instruction

English-Language Learners Have students make flashcards with the name of a gland on one side and the hormone it produces on the other. Student pairs can quiz each other using the flashcards. [L2]

Visualizing the Endocrine System

Have students examine the pictures and read the captions. Then ask the following questions.

How do hormones from the thyroid gland and the parathyroid gland work together? Possible answers: Both glands release hormones that work together to regulate the levels of calcium in the blood.

What could be the result if a person's thymus gland was not functioning properly? Possible answer: The thymus gland produces hormones that stimulate the production of cells involved in immune reactions. Without these cells the body has difficulty fighting infection.

Activity

Negative Feedback Have students write and act out a skit that demonstrates the negative feedback cycle of hormone regulation. Students can break into groups of 6 or 7 and produce the skits. The instructor would need to provide a different sequence of events for each student group. Each student can play the role of the brain, a hormone or an endocrine gland, and one student can be the messenger between the body and the brain. L2

Figure 2

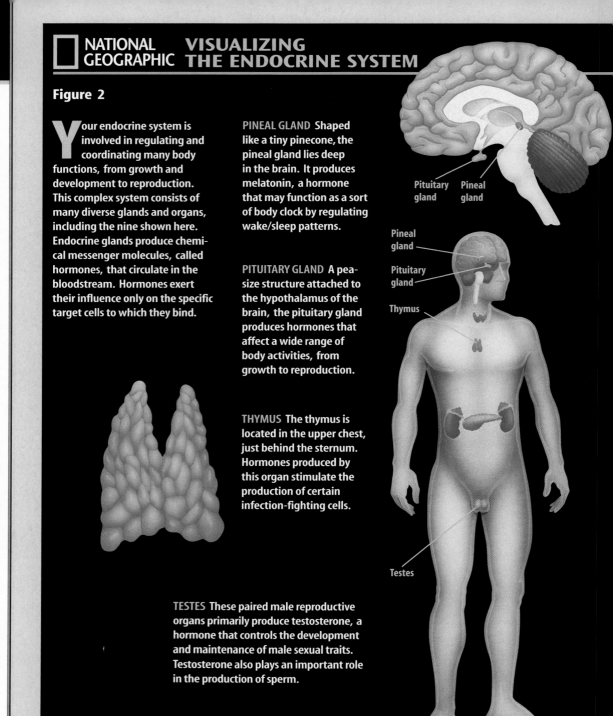

Your endocrine system is involved in regulating and coordinating many body functions, from growth and development to reproduction. This complex system consists of many diverse glands and organs, including the nine shown here. Endocrine glands produce chemical messenger molecules, called hormones, that circulate in the bloodstream. Hormones exert their influence only on the specific target cells to which they bind.

PINEAL GLAND Shaped like a tiny pinecone, the pineal gland lies deep in the brain. It produces melatonin, a hormone that may function as a sort of body clock by regulating wake/sleep patterns.

PITUITARY GLAND A pea-size structure attached to the hypothalamus of the brain, the pituitary gland produces hormones that affect a wide range of body activities, from growth to reproduction.

THYMUS The thymus is located in the upper chest, just behind the sternum. Hormones produced by this organ stimulate the production of certain infection-fighting cells.

TESTES These paired male reproductive organs primarily produce testosterone, a hormone that controls the development and maintenance of male sexual traits. Testosterone also plays an important role in the production of sperm.

Pituitary gland
Pineal gland
Pineal gland
Pituitary gland
Thymus
Testes

624 CHAPTER 22 Regulation and Reproduction

Differentiated Instruction

Challenge Have students research disorders of the endocrine system such as Graves' disease, Cushing's Syndrome, Addison's disease, diabetes, gigantism and acromegaly. Ask students to make a list of questions they would use to interview a person with one of these disorders. L3

Teacher FYI

SAD An overproduction of melatonin is hypothesized by scientists to be one cause of Seasonal Affective Disorder (SAD). SAD is a type of depression that some people suffer when there are fewer hours of daylight during winter months. The treatment of SAD includes exposing sufferers to artificial bright light for several hours at a time.

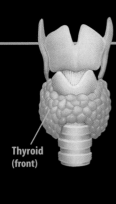

Thyroid (front)

THYROID GLAND Located below the larynx, the bi-lobed thyroid gland is richly supplied with blood vessels. It produces hormones that regulate metabolic rate, control the uptake of calcium by bones, and promote normal nervous system development.

PARATHYROID GLANDS Attached to the back surface of the thyroid are tiny parathyroids, which help regulate calcium levels in the body. Calcium is important for bone growth and maintenance, as well as for muscle contraction and nerve impulse transmission.

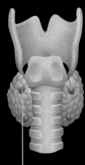

Parathyroid (back)

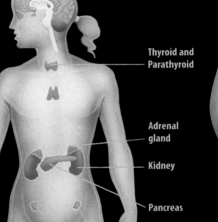

Thyroid and Parathyroid

Adrenal gland

Kidney

Pancreas

Ovaries

ADRENAL GLANDS On top of each of your kidneys is an adrenal gland. This complex endocrine gland produces a variety of hormones. Some play a critical role in helping your body adapt to physical and emotional stress. Others help stabilize blood sugar levels.

PANCREAS Scattered throughout the pancreas are millions of tiny clusters of endocrine tissue called the islets of Langerhans. Cells that make up the islets produce hormones that help control sugar levels in the bloodstream.

OVARIES Found deep in the pelvic cavity, ovaries produce female sex hormones known as estrogen and progesterone. These hormones regulate the female reproductive cycle and are responsible for producing and maintaining female sex characteristics.

SECTION 1 The Endocrine System **625**

Curriculum Connection

Language Arts The word *adrenal* is derived from two Latin words: *ad-* meaning "to," and *renalis*, meaning "kidneys." How is this word related to the location of the adrenal glands? The adrenal glands are located on top of the kidneys.

Fun Fact

The pituitary gland produces TSH, a hormone that promotes the production of thyroxin by the thyroid gland. Thyroxin helps regulate growth and development in immature animals. It also speeds up metabolism in all animals.

Excessive Growth Hormones Infer the probable results of too much growth hormone in the blood of a young person. The person would grow at an accelerated rate and become abnormally tall. What if there were too little of the hormone produced? Shortness might result.

3 Assess

DAILY INTERVENTION

Check for Understanding
Visual-Spatial On simple diagrams of the human body, have students draw and label the glands of the endocrine system. [L2]

Reteach
Hormone Pathways Using a chart of the circulatory system, have students trace the pathway of a hormone to its target tissue. [L2]
LS Kinesthetic

✔ Assessment

Content Make a table describing the characteristics and components of the endocrine system. Use **Performance Assessment in the Science Classroom,** p. 109.

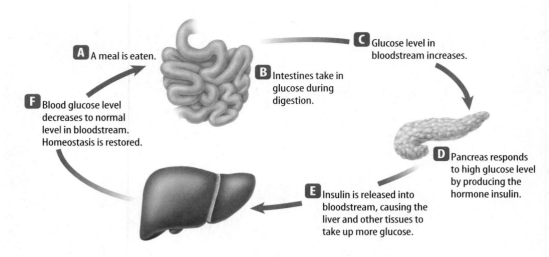

A A meal is eaten.

B Intestines take in glucose during digestion.

C Glucose level in bloodstream increases.

D Pancreas responds to high glucose level by producing the hormone insulin.

E Insulin is released into bloodstream, causing the liver and other tissues to take up more glucose.

F Blood glucose level decreases to normal level in bloodstream. Homeostasis is restored.

Figure 3 Many internal body conditions, such as hormone level, blood sugar level, and body temperature, are controlled by negative-feedback systems.

A Negative-Feedback System

To control the amount of hormones that are in your body, the endocrine system sends chemical messages back and forth within itself. This is called a negative-feedback system. It works much the way a thermostat works. When the temperature in a room drops below a set level, the thermostat signals the furnace to turn on. Once the furnace has raised the temperature in the room to the set level, the thermostat signals the furnace to shut off. It will continue to stay off until the thermostat signals that the temperature has dropped again. **Figure 3** shows how a negative-feedback system controls the level of glucose in your bloodstream.

---

section ① review

Summary

Functions of the Endocrine System
- The nervous system and the endocrine system are the control systems of your body.
- The endocrine system uses hormones to deliver messages to the body.

Endocrine Glands
- Endocrine glands release hormones directly into the bloodstream.

A Negative-Feedback System
- The endocrine system uses a negative-feedback system to control the amount of hormones in your body.

Self Check

1. **Explain** the function of hormones.
2. **Choose** one endocrine gland. How does it work?
3. **Describe** a negative-feedback system.
4. **Think Critically** Glucose is required for cellular respiration, the process that releases energy within cells. How would a lack of insulin affect this process?

Applying Skills

5. **Predict** why the circulatory system is a good mechanism for delivering hormones throughout the body.
6. **Research** recent treatments for growth disorders involving the pituitary gland. Write a brief paragraph of your results in your Science Journal.

 Science Online life.msscience.com/self_check_quiz

---

section ① review

1. Hormones regulate certain cellular activities.
2. Pancreas—secretes insulin to regulate glucose levels; refer to **Figure 2** for other possible answers.
3. a system that uses blood hormone levels to signal when a gland should and should not secrete the hormone
4. Insulin causes tissues to take up more glucose, without which cells can't carry on respiration.
5. The circulatory system reaches every cell of the body.
6. Answers will vary. Possible topic: the use of hormone therapy to stimulate growth in young children.

The Reproductive System

Reproduction and the Endocrine System

Reproduction is the process that continues life on Earth. Most human body systems, such as the digestive system and the nervous system, are the same in males and females, but this is not true for the reproductive system. Males and females each have structures specialized for their roles in reproduction. Although structurally different, both the male and female reproductive systems are adapted to allow for a series of events that can lead to the birth of a baby.

Hormones are the key to how the human reproductive system functions, as shown in **Figure 4.** Sex hormones are necessary for the development of sexual characteristics, such as breast development in females and facial hair growth in males. Hormones from the pituitary gland also begin the production of eggs in females and sperm in males. Eggs and sperm transfer hereditary information from one generation to the next.

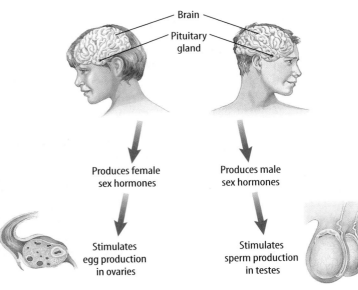

Produces female sex hormones → Stimulates egg production in ovaries

Produces male sex hormones → Stimulates sperm production in testes

Brain
Pituitary gland

Figure 4 The pituitary gland produces hormones that control the male and female reproductive systems.

as you read

What You'll Learn
- **Identify** the function of the reproductive system.
- **Compare and contrast** the major structures of the male and female reproductive systems.
- **Sequence** the stages of the menstrual cycle.

Why It's Important
Human reproductive systems help ensure that human life continues on Earth.

Review Vocabulary
cilia: short, hairlike structures that extend from a cell

New Vocabulary
- testes
- sperm
- semen
- ovary
- ovulation
- uterus
- vagina
- menstrual cycle
- menstruation

SECTION 2 The Reproductive System **627**

Section 2 Resource Manager

Chapter *FAST FILE* Resources

Transparency Activity, p. 43

Directed Reading for Content Mastery, p. 18

Enrichment, p. 29

Reinforcement, p. 26

MiniLAB, p. 3

Lab Worksheet, pp. 5–6

Fun Fact

Sperm production is a continuous process from puberty throughout the life of a male. Egg production in females begins before birth. There is no production after birth. Each ovary may have nearly a million primary oocytes—cells from which eggs form.

Activity

Sperm Shapes Have students draw a diagram of a sperm, like the one in **Figure 5**. Then ask them to draw a sperm with a very large, round head and a curly tail. Ask students to compare the two sperm and determine which one would be more likely to fertilize an egg. The sperm, like the one in **Figure 5,** would be more likely to fertilize an egg. The streamlined head reduces friction as it moves through liquids. The straight tail propels the sperm in a direction that can be against gravity. L2

Use an Analogy

Flagellate Protozoans The movement of sperm is not unlike the movement of flagellate protozoans. Wavelike movements of the tail propel the organism forward. ⓘⓢ **Visual-Spatial**

Discussion

Functions of Semen What other functions does semen have in addition to carrying the sperm? Chemical substances in semen provide energy for sperm movement. Explain that because semen is slightly alkaline, it protects sperm from acidic conditions, such as those found in the female reproductive system.

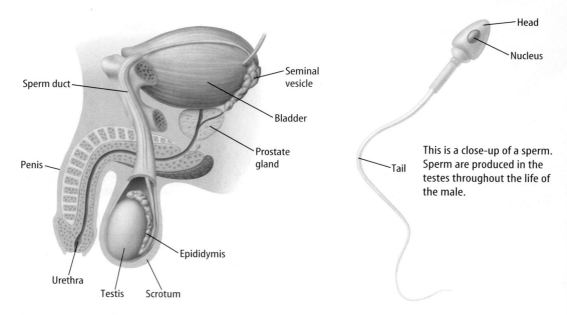

Figure 5 The structures of the male reproductive system are shown from the side of the body.

This is a close-up of a sperm. Sperm are produced in the testes throughout the life of the male.

The Male Reproductive System

The male reproductive system is made up of external and internal organs. The external organs of the male reproductive system are the penis and scrotum, shown in **Figure 5.** The scrotum contains two organs called testes (TES teez). As males mature sexually, the **testes** begin to produce testosterone, the male hormone, and **sperm,** which are male reproductive cells.

Sperm Each sperm cell has a head and tail. The head contains hereditary information, and the tail moves the sperm. Because the scrotum is located outside the body cavity, the testes, where sperm are produced, are kept at a lower temperature than the rest of the body. Sperm are produced in greater numbers at lower temperatures.

Many organs help in the production, transportation, and storage of sperm. After sperm are produced, they travel from the testes through sperm ducts that circle the bladder. Behind the bladder, a gland called the seminal vesicle provides sperm with a fluid. This fluid supplies the sperm with an energy source and helps them move. This mixture of sperm and fluid is called **semen** (SEE mun). Semen leaves the body through the urethra, which is the same tube that carries urine from the body. However, semen and urine never mix. A muscle at the back of the bladder contracts to prevent urine from entering the urethra as sperm leave the body.

Curriculum Connection

Language Arts Have students look up the words *sperm* and *ovary* and find out why the Latin roots are appropriate to their meanings. The Late Latin term *sperma* means seed; the Latin term *ovum* means egg. L1 ⓘⓢ **Linguistic**

Differentiated Instruction

Learning Disabled Have students use tracing paper to trace the structures of the male and female reproductive systems shown in **Figures 5** and **6.** Ask them to label each structure and include the diagrams in their journals to use as study tools. L1

The Female Reproductive System

Unlike male reproductive organs, most of the reproductive organs of the female are inside the body. The **ovaries**—the female sex organs—are located in the lower part of the body cavity. Each of the two ovaries is about the size and shape of an almond. **Figure 6** shows the different organs of the female reproductive system.

The Egg When a female is born, she already has all of the cells in her ovaries that eventually will develop into eggs—the female reproductive cells. At puberty, eggs start to develop in her ovaries because of specific sex hormones.

About once a month, an egg is released from an ovary in a hormone-controlled process called **ovulation** (ahv yuh LAY shun). The two ovaries release eggs on alternating months. One month, an egg is released from an ovary. The next month, the other ovary releases an egg, and so on. After the egg is released, it enters the oviduct. If a sperm fertilizes the egg, it usually happens in an oviduct. Short, hairlike structures called cilia help sweep the egg through the oviduct toward the uterus (YEW tuh rus).

✔ **Reading Check** *When are eggs released by the ovaries?*

The **uterus** is a hollow, pear-shaped, muscular organ with thick walls in which a fertilized egg develops. The lower end of the uterus, the cervix, narrows and is connected to the outside of the body by a muscular tube called the **vagina** (vuh JI nuh). The vagina also is called the birth canal because during birth, a baby travels through this tube from the uterus to the outside of the mother's body.

Science Online

Topic: Ovarian Cysts
Visit life.mssciencе.com for Web links to information about ovarian cysts.

Activity Make a small pamphlet explaining what cysts are and how they can be treated.

Figure 6 The structures of the female reproductive system are internal.
Name *where eggs develop in the female reproductive system.*

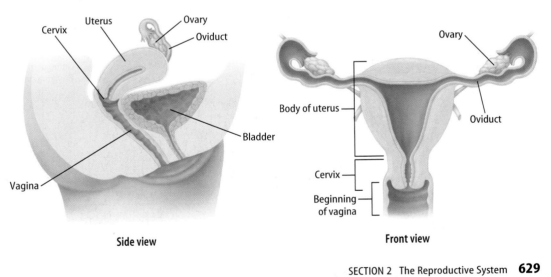

Side view

Front view

- Cervix
- Uterus
- Ovary
- Oviduct
- Bladder
- Vagina

- Body of uterus
- Ovary
- Oviduct
- Cervix
- Beginning of vagina

SECTION 2 The Reproductive System **629**

Graphing Hormone Levels

Procedure
Make a line graph of this table.

Hormone Changes	
Day	**Level of Hormone**
1	12
5	14
9	15
13	70
17	13
21	12
25	8

Analysis
1. On what day is the highest level of hormone present?
2. What event takes place around the time of the highest hormone level?

The Menstrual Cycle

How is the female body prepared for having a baby? The **menstrual cycle** is the monthly cycle of changes in the female reproductive system. Before and after an egg is released from an ovary, the uterus undergoes changes. The menstrual cycle of a human female averages 28 days. However, the cycle can vary in some individuals from 20 to 40 days. Changes include the maturing of an egg, the production of female sex hormones, the preparation of the uterus to receive a fertilized egg, and menstrual flow.

✔ **Reading Check** *What is the menstrual cycle?*

Endocrine Control Hormones control the entire menstrual cycle. The pituitary gland responds to chemical messages from the hypothalamus by releasing several hormones. These hormones start the development of eggs in the ovary. They also start the production of other hormones in the ovary, including estrogen (ES truh jun) and progesterone (proh JES tuh rohn). The interaction of all these hormones results in the physical processes of the menstrual cycle.

Phase One As shown in **Figure 7,** the first day of phase 1 starts when menstrual flow begins. Menstrual flow consists of blood and tissue cells released from the thickened lining of the uterus. This flow usually continues for four to six days and is called **menstruation** (men STRAY shun).

Figure 7 The three phases of the menstrual cycle make up the monthly changes in the female reproductive system.
Explain *why the uterine lining thickens.*

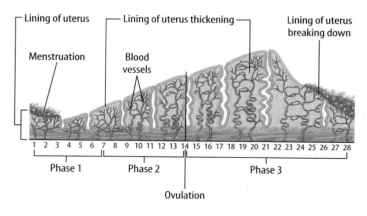

Differentiated Instruction

Challenge Some women going through menopause experience some of the same symptoms as women beginning their menstrual cycles. Have students research to find out why this happens. Both are experiencing changing levels of hormones. [L3]

Teacher FYI

Premenstrual Syndrome During the week before menstruation, a woman may experience premenstrual syndrome (PMS). Symptoms include depression, fatigue, headache, irritability, nervousness, and lack of concentration. Diet, exercise, and aspirin or other medicines are used to lessen the discomfort.

Phase Two Hormones cause the lining of the uterus to thicken in phase 2. Hormones also control the development of an egg in the ovary. Ovulation occurs about 14 days before menstruation begins. Once the egg is released, it must be fertilized within 24 h or it usually begins to break down. Because sperm can survive in a female's body for up to three days, fertilization can occur soon after ovulation.

Phase Three Hormones produced by the ovaries continue to cause an increase in the thickness of the uterine lining during phase 3. If a fertilized egg does arrive, the uterus is ready to support and nourish the developing embryo. If the egg is not fertilized, the lining of the uterus breaks down as the hormone levels decrease. Menstruation begins and the cycle repeats itself.

Menopause For most females, the first menstrual period happens between ages nine years and 13 years and continues until 45 years of age to 60 years of age. Then, a gradual reduction of menstruation takes place as hormone production by the ovaries begins to shut down. Menopause occurs when both ovulation and menstrual periods end. It can take several years for the completion of menopause. As **Figure 8** indicates, menopause does not inhibit a woman's ability to enjoy an active life.

Figure 8 This older woman enjoys exercising with her granddaughter.

section 2 review

Summary

Reproduction and the Endocrine System
- Reproduction is the process that continues life.
- The human reproductive system needs hormones to function.

The Male Reproductive System
- Sperm are produced in the testes and leave the male through the penis.

The Female Reproductive System
- Eggs are produced in the ovaries and, if fertilized, can develop in the uterus.

The Menstrual Cycle
- A female's menstrual cycle occurs approximately every 28 days.
- If an egg is not fertilized, the lining of the uterus breaks down and is shed in a process called menstruation.

Self Check

1. **Identify** the major function of male and female reproductive systems in humans.
2. **Explain** the movement of sperm through the male reproductive system.
3. **Compare and contrast** the major organs and structures of the male and female reproductive systems.
4. **Sequence** the stages of the menstrual cycle in a human female using diagrams and captions.
5. **Think Critically** Adolescent females often require additional amounts of iron in their diet. Explain.

Applying Math

6. **Order of Operations** Usually, one egg is released each month during a female's reproductive years. If menstruation begins at 12 years of age and ends at 50 years of age, calculate the number of eggs her body can release during her reproductive years.

 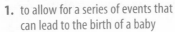 life.msscience.com/self_check_quiz

section 2 review

1. to allow for a series of events that can lead to the birth of a baby
2. testes→tubes that encircle the bladder→seminal vesical→urethra
3. Sex cell production: female—ovaries within the body; male—testes in scrotum outside of body; movement of sex cells: female—eggs released from ovary and swept into oviduct and uterus; male—sperm swim from testes through sperm duct and into the urethra.
4. Phase one: menstrual flow begins; phase two: wall of uterus thickens, ovulation occurs; phase three: wall of uterus continues to thicken; if a fertilized egg arrives, it implants into the wall; if a fertilized egg does not arrive, the lining deteriorates.
5. The body may have a temporary iron deficiency resulting from loss of blood during menstruation.
6. 50 years − 12 years = 38 years; 38 years × 1 egg/month × 12 month/year = 456 eggs

Real-World Question

Purpose Students examine and interpret diagrams of the menstrual cycle. L2 LS **Visual-Spatial**

Process Skills observe, interpret data

Time Required 40 minutes

Procedure

Teaching Strategy Stress to students the importance of examining labels and captions when interpreting diagrams.

Conclude and Apply

1. 28 days
2. days 7 to 28
3. If fertilization does not occur, menstruation takes place, another egg is released, and the process is repeated.
4. about 14

Interpreting Diagrams

Starting in adolescence, hormones cause the development of eggs in the ovary and changes in the uterus. These changes prepare the uterus to accept a fertilized egg that can attach itself in the wall of the uterus. What happens to an unfertilized egg?

Menstruation Cycle

Days	Condition of Uterus	What Happens
1–6	breakdown of lining	menstruation
7–12	lining begins to thicken	egg matures in ovary
13–14	lining is thicker	ovulation
15–18	lining thickens	egg moves to uterus

Real-World Question

What changes occur to the uterus during a female's monthly menstrual cycle?

Goals
- **Observe** the stages of the menstrual cycle in the diagram.
- **Relate** the process of ovulation to the cycle.

Materials
paper   pencil

Procedure

1. The diagrams below illustrate the menstrual cycle.
2. Copy and complete the data table using information in this chapter and diagrams below.
3. On approximately what day in a 28-day cycle is the egg released from the ovary?

Conclude and Apply

1. **Infer** how many days the average menstrual cycle lasts.
2. **State** on what days the lining of the uterus builds up.
3. **Infer** why this process is called a cycle.
4. **Calculate** how many days before menstruation ovulation usually occurs.

Communicating Your Data

Compare your data table with those of other students in your class. **For more help, refer to the** Science Skill Handbook.

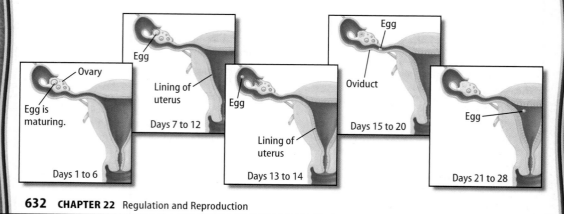

Egg
Ovary
Egg is maturing.
Days 1 to 6

Lining of uterus
Egg
Days 7 to 12

Egg
Lining of uterus
Days 13 to 14

Egg
Oviduct
Days 15 to 20

Egg
Days 21 to 28

632 CHAPTER 22 Regulation and Reproduction

Content Have students use the diagrams to write a summary of the process of menstruation. The lining of the uterus is shed and then builds up. The egg matures, is released, and travels to the uterus. If it is fertilized, pregnancy results. If it is not, the cycle repeats. Use **Performance Assessment in the Science Classroom,** p. 159.

Communicating Your Data

Students should discuss why their interpretations of the diagram did or did not agree. They can cite references to support their arguments.

section 3

Human Life Stages

The Function of the Reproductive System

Before the invention of powerful microscopes, some people imagined an egg or a sperm to be a tiny person that grew inside a female. In the latter part of the 1700s, experiments using amphibians showed that contact between an egg and sperm is necessary for the development of life. With the development of the cell theory in the 1800s, scientists recognized that a human develops from an egg that has been fertilized by a sperm. The uniting of a sperm and an egg is known as fertilization. Fertilization, as shown in **Figure 9,** usually takes place in the oviduct.

Fertilization

INTEGRATE Chemistry

Although 200 million to 300 million sperm can be deposited in the vagina, only several thousand reach an egg in the oviduct. As they enter the female, the sperm come into contact with chemical secretions in the vagina. It appears that this contact causes a change in the membrane of the sperm. The sperm then become capable of fertilizing the egg. The one sperm that makes successful contact with the egg releases an enzyme from the saclike structure on its head. Enzymes help speed up chemical reactions that have a direct effect on the protective membranes on the egg's surface. The structure of the egg's membrane is disrupted, and the sperm head can enter the egg.

Zygote Formation Once a sperm has entered the egg, changes in the electric charge of the egg's membrane prevent other sperm from entering the egg. At this point, the nucleus of the successful sperm joins with the nucleus of the egg. This joining of nuclei creates a fertilized cell called the zygote. It begins to undergo many cell divisions.

Figure 9 After the sperm releases enzymes that disrupt the egg's membrane, it penetrates the egg.

Color-enhanced SEM Magnification: 340×

as you read

What **You'll Learn**
- **Describe** the fertilization of a human egg.
- **List** the major events in the development of an embryo and fetus.
- **Describe** the developmental stages of infancy, childhood, adolescence, and adulthood.

Why **It's Important**
Fertilization begins the entire process of human growth and development.

Review Vocabulary
nutrient: substance in food that provides energy and materials for cell development, growth, and repair

New Vocabulary
- pregnancy
- embryo
- amniotic sac
- fetus
- fetal stress

1 Motivate

INTERACTIVE CHALKBOARD PowerPoint® Presentations

Bellringer

Section Focus Transparencies also are available on the Interactive Chalkboard CD-ROM.
L2 ELL

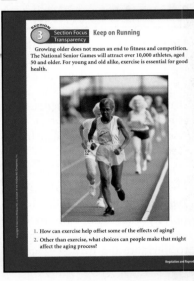

Tie to Prior Knowledge

Life Stages Display photographs of people in different life stages, e.g., an infant, a small child, an adolescent, a young adult, and an older adult. Explain that these represent life stages and ask how many students can identify. Ask what stage they are in.

Section 3 Resource Manager

Chapter *FAST FILE* Resources
Transparency Activity, p. 44
Directed Reading for Content Mastery, pp. 19, 20
MiniLAB, p. 4
Enrichment, p. 30
Reinforcement, p. 27

Lab Activity, pp. 13–14
Lab Worksheet, pp. 7–8
Home and Community Involvement, p. 43
Life Science Critical Thinking/Problem Solving, p. 19
Reading and Writing Skill Activities, p. 39
Lab Management and Safety, p. 70

Word Usage Have students compare the biological use of the word *fertilization* to the agronomic use of the word. Biologists use fertilization to refer to the process by which two sex cells join to produce offspring. Agronomists use fertilization to refer to the application of manure or chemicals to make soil more fertile. L2 **LS** Linguistic

Visual Learning

Figure 10 What are the differences between the development of fraternal and identical twins? Fraternal twins develop from two separate eggs that have been fertilized by two different sperm. Identical twins result when one egg is fertilized by one sperm and the resulting zygote splits.

Make a Model

Zygote Growth Have students use polystyrene foam balls to construct four- and eight-cell models to illustrate the earliest stages of zygote growth. L2 **LS** Kinesthetic P

Midwives education: nursing degree or a science or health background; skills: monitor the baby and mother during pregnancy and labor, guide the birthing process, examine and care for newborns, maintain health records and write reports

Research the requirements needed to become a midwife in your state.

Figure 10 The development of fraternal and identical twins is different.

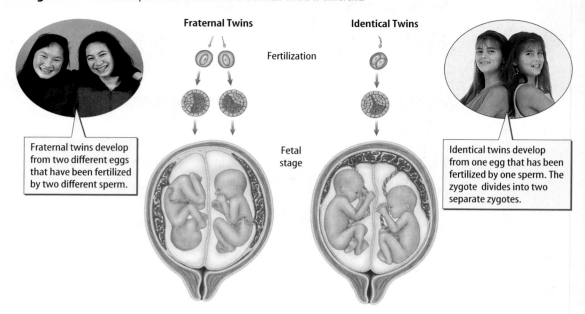

Fraternal Twins

Identical Twins

Fertilization

Fetal stage

Fraternal twins develop from two different eggs that have been fertilized by two different sperm.

Identical twins develop from one egg that has been fertilized by one sperm. The zygote divides into two separate zygotes.

INTEGRATE Career

Midwives Some women choose to deliver their babies at home rather than at a hospital. An at-home birth can be attended by a certified nurse-midwife. Research to find the educational and skill requirements of a nurse-midwife.

Multiple Births

Sometimes two eggs leave the ovary at the same time. If both eggs are fertilized and both develop, fraternal twins are born. Fraternal twins, as shown in **Figure 10,** can be two girls, two boys, or a boy and a girl. Because fraternal twins come from two eggs, they only resemble each other.

Because identical twin zygotes develop from the same egg and sperm, as explained in **Figure 10,** they have the same hereditary information. These identical zygotes develop into identical twins, which are either two girls or two boys. Multiple births also can occur when three or more eggs are produced at one time or when the zygote separates into three or more parts.

Development Before Birth

After fertilization, the zygote moves along the oviduct to the uterus. During this time, the zygote is dividing and forming into a ball of cells. After about seven days, the zygote attaches to the wall of the uterus, which has been thickening in preparation to receive a zygote, as shown in **Figure 11.** If attached to the wall of the uterus, the zygote will develop into a baby in about nine months. This period of development from fertilized egg to birth is known as **pregnancy.**

Curriculum Connection

Health Have students research ectopic pregnancies. How frequently do they occur? 1 in every 250–300 pregnancies How does the female know there is a problem? She experiences pain and bleeding. What is the treatment? Ectopic pregnancies often end in a miscarriage; if not miscarried, surgical removal of the fetus is sometimes necessary; abdominal pregnancies can be carried to term and the baby delivered by C-section. L2

Active Reading

Speculation About Effects/Prediction Journal This strategy allows students to examine events and speculate about their possible long-term effects. Have students divide their papers in half. On the left side record "What happened." On the right side, write "What might/should happen as a result of this." Have students use this strategy to write about an aspect of human life stages.

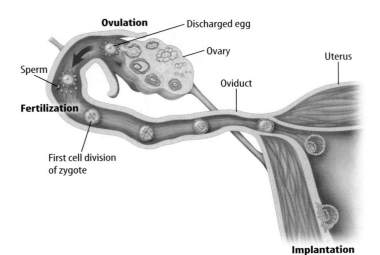

Ovulation — Discharged egg

— Ovary

Sperm

Uterus

Oviduct

Fertilization

First cell division
of zygote

Implantation

Figure 11 After a few days of rapid cell division, the zygote, now a ball of cells, reaches the lining of the uterus, where it attaches itself to the lining for development.

The Embryo After the zygote attaches to the wall of the uterus, it is known as an **embryo,** illustrated in **Figure 12.** It receives nutrients from fluids in the uterus until the placenta (plu SEN tuh) develops from tissues of the uterus and the embryo. An umbilical cord develops that connects the embryo to the placenta. In the placenta, materials diffuse between the mother's blood and the embryo's blood, but their bloods do not mix. Blood vessels in the umbilical cord carry nutrients and oxygen from the mother's blood through the placenta to the embryo. Other substances in the mother's blood can move into the embryo, including drugs, toxins, and disease organisms. Wastes from the embryo are carried in other blood vessels in the umbilical cord through the placenta to the mother's blood.

✔ **Reading Check** *Why must a pregnant woman avoid alcohol, tobacco, and harmful drugs?*

Pregnancy in humans lasts about 38 to 39 weeks. During the third week, a thin membrane called the **amniotic** (am nee AH tihk) **sac** begins to form around the embryo. The amniotic sac is filled with a clear liquid called amniotic fluid, which acts as a cushion for the embryo and stores nutrients and wastes.

During the first two months of development, the embryo's major organs form and the heart structure begins to beat. At five weeks, the embryo has a head with eyes, nose, and mouth features. During the sixth and seventh weeks, fingers and toes develop.

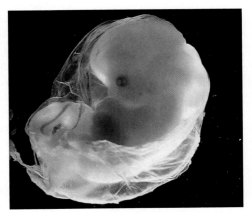

Figure 12 By two months, the developing embryo is about 2.5 cm long and is beginning to develop recognizable features.

SECTION 3 Human Life Stages **635**

✔ **Reading Check**

Answer Any substances taken in by the mother and carried in her blood can pass to the embryo through the umbilical cord and cause the embryo damage.

Inquiry Lab

Fetal Development

Purpose to familiarize students with the stages of development during pregnancy

Possible Materials library or Internet sources

Estimated Time 50 minutes

Teaching Strategies
• Divide students into three groups and have each group study a trimester of pregnancy.
• Students can describe body features and organs that have formed, length and weight of the baby, and which senses have developed.
• Students could also describe developmental milestones reached during the trimester. L2 PBL
• Students could also research the effects of alcohol, drugs, and smoking on the fetus. Have them make posters to share with the health class about these dangers.

For additional inquiry activities, see *Science Inquiry Labs.*

Differentiated Instruction

Challenge Have students research the unusual breeding processes of such animals as the sea horse and midwife toad. In both, the fertilized eggs are carried by the male until the young are ready to be born. L3

Figure 13 A fetus at about 16 weeks is approximately 15 cm long and weighs 140 g. **Describe** *the changes that take place in a fetus by the end of the seventh month.*

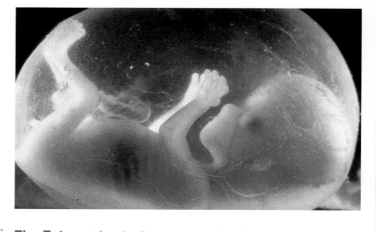

The Fetus After the first two months of pregnancy, the developing embryo is called a **fetus,** shown in **Figure 13.** At this time, body organs are present. Around the third month, the fetus is 8 cm to 9 cm long. The mother may feel the fetus move. The fetus can even suck its thumb. By the fourth month, an ultrasound test can determine the sex of the fetus. The fetus is 30 cm to 38 cm in length by the end of the seventh month of pregnancy. Fatty tissue builds up under the skin, and the fetus looks less wrinkled. By the ninth month, the fetus usually has shifted to a head-down position within the uterus, a position beneficial for delivery. The head usually is in contact with the opening of the uterus to the vagina. The fetus is about 50 cm in length and weighs from 2.5 kg to 3.5 kg.

The Birthing Process

The process of childbirth, as shown in **Figure 14,** begins with labor, the muscular contractions of the uterus. As the contractions increase in strength and number, the amniotic sac usually breaks and releases its fluid. Over a period of hours, the contractions cause the opening of the uterus to widen. More powerful and more frequent contractions push the baby out through the vagina into its new environment.

Delivery Often a mother is given assistance by a doctor during the delivery of the baby. As the baby emerges from the birth canal, a check is made to determine if the umbilical cord is wrapped around the baby's neck or any body part. When the head is free, any fluid in the baby's nose and mouth is removed by suction. After the head and shoulders appear, contractions force the baby out completely. Up to an hour after delivery, contractions occur that push the placenta out of the mother's body.

636   CHAPTER 22 Regulation and Reproduction

Cesarean Section Sometimes a baby must be delivered before labor begins or before it is completed. At other times, a baby cannot be delivered through the birth canal because the mother's pelvis might be too small or the baby might be in the wrong birthing position. In cases like these, surgery called a cesarean (suh SEER ee uhn) section is performed. An incision is made through the mother's abdominal wall, then through the wall of the uterus. The baby is delivered through this opening.

✔ **Reading Check** *What is a cesarean section?*

After Birth When the baby is born, it is attached to the umbilical cord. The person assisting with the birth clamps the cord in two places and cuts it between the clamps. The baby does not feel any pain from this procedure. The baby might cry, which is the result of air being forced into its lungs. The scar that forms where the cord was attached is called the navel.

Science Online

Topic: Cesarean Sections
Visit life.mscience.com for Web links to information about cesarean section delivery.

Activity Make a chart listing the advantages and disadvantages of a cesarean section delivery.

Figure 14 Childbirth begins with labor. The opening to the uterus widens, and the baby passes through.

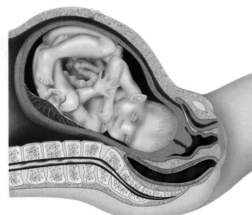
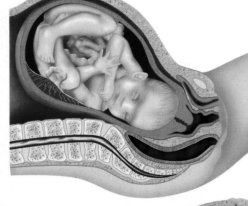

The fetus moves into the opening of the birth canal, and the uterus begins to widen.

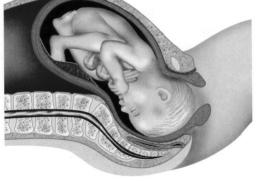

The base of the uterus is completely dilated.

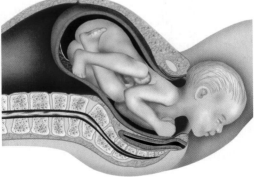

The fetus is pushed out through the birth canal.

SECTION 3 Human Life Stages **637**

Word Origin *Neonatal* means "newborn," and refers to a child younger than one month. *Neo-* is from the Greek and means "new" or "recent." Ask students to find words with this root and explain their meanings. Neophyte is a beginner, neolithic is the new stone age, neogenic refers to newly formed rocks and minerals. L2 **Linguistic**

Discussion

Newborn Reaction How might a newborn react to loud sounds or bright lights? Possible answer: he or she might be startled by loud sounds and bright lights.

Teacher FYI

Post-birth Care Certain animals are ready to care for themselves immediately after birth. Precocial birds such as ducks are able to immediately move around and take care of themselves. Other self-sufficient animals are deer, hares, bison, and many types of insects, fish, amphibians, and reptiles. However, many of these animals, though mobile, still depend upon their mothers for food.

Fun Fact

The major constituents of human milk are water, proteins, fats, and lactose, a carbohydrate. In addition, there are small amounts of vitamins and electrolytes.

Stages After Birth

Defined stages of development occur after birth, based on the major developments that take place during those specific years. Infancy lasts from birth to around 18 months of age. Childhood extends from the end of infancy to sexual maturity, or puberty. The years of adolescence vary, but they usually are considered to be the teen years. Adulthood covers the years of age from the early 20s until life ends, with older adulthood considered to be over 60. The age spans of these different stages are not set, and scientists differ in their opinions regarding them.

Infancy What type of environment must the infant adjust to after birth? The experiences the fetus goes through during birth cause **fetal stress.** The fetus has emerged from an environment that was dark, watery, a constant temperature, and nearly soundless. In addition, the fetus might have been forced through the constricted birth canal. However, in a short period of time, the infant's body becomes adapted to its new world.

The first four weeks after birth are known as the neonatal (nee oh NAY tul) period. The term *neonatal* means "newborn." During this time, the baby's body begins to function normally. Unlike the newborn of some other animals, human babies, such as the one shown in **Figure 15,** depend on other humans for their survival. In contrast, many other animals, such as the young horse also shown in **Figure 15,** begin walking a few hours after they are born.

Figure 15 Human babies are more dependent upon their caregivers than many other mammals are.

Infants and toddlers are completely dependent upon caregivers for all their needs.

Other young mammals are more self-sufficient. This colt is able to stand within an hour after birth.

638 CHAPTER 22 Regulation and Reproduction

Differentiated Instruction

Behaviorally Disordered Have students bring photos of themselves at various stages and describe favorite activities they remember from these stages. L1

Science Journal

Immunizations Babies and young children need certain vaccines to prevent disease. Have students find out what vaccinations are recommended between birth and age 6. Between birth and 6 yrs. old, the following vaccines are recommended: Polio; Hepatitis B; Diphtheria, Tetanus, Pertussis; Varicella or Chicken Pox; Haemophilus Influenza B; Measles, Mumps, Rubella; Pneumococcal. L2

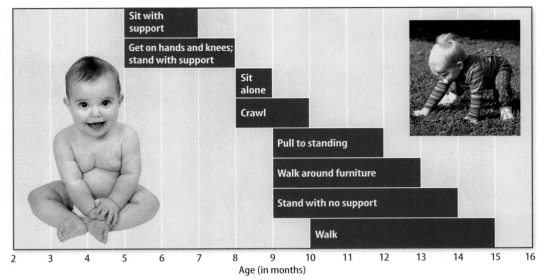

Sit with support
Get on hands and knees; stand with support
Sit alone
Crawl
Pull to standing
Walk around furniture
Stand with no support
Walk

Age (in months)
2 3 4 5 6 7 8 9 10 11 12 13 14 15 16

During these first 18 months, infants show increased physical coordination, mental development, and rapid growth. Many infants will triple their weight in the first year. **Figure 16** shows the extremely rapid development of the nervous and muscular systems during this stage, which enables infants to start interacting with the world around them.

Childhood   After infancy is childhood, which lasts until about puberty, or sexual maturity. Sexual maturity occurs around 12 years of age. Overall, growth during early childhood is rather rapid, although the physical growth rate for height and weight is not as rapid as it is in infancy. Between two and three years of age, the child learns to control his or her bladder and bowels. At age two to three, most children can speak in simple sentences. Around age four, the child is able to get dressed and undressed with some help. By age five, many children can read a limited number of words. By age six, children usually have lost their chubby baby appearance, as seen in **Figure 17.** However, muscular coordination and mental abilities continue to develop. Throughout this stage, children develop their abilities to speak, read, write, and reason. These ages of development are only guidelines because each child develops at a different rate.

Figure 16   Infants show rapid development in their nervous and muscular systems through 18 months of age.

Figure 17   Children, like these kindergartners, grow and develop at different rates.

SECTION 3 Human Life Stages   **639**

Activity

Parent Survey Have students conduct a survey of parents with young children. Have them ask questions such as: What changes did you notice at different ages? What stage seemed to have the most changes? L2
IS **Interpersonal**

Make a Model

Time line Have students make a time line of the stages from infancy to adulthood using long pieces of paper. Identify various milestones such as the start of walking, puberty, and menopause. L2 **IS** **Kinesthetic**

Discussion

Speech Have students think about how they learned to talk. How might hearing problems in young children cause speech problems? Children learn speech by listening to others. If they have a hearing problem, they cannot properly hear the sounds of speech. They are unable to reproduce sounds that other people can understand.

Quick Demo

Life Stages

Materials diagrams or photos of animals and humans in different life stages
Estimated Time 15 minutes
Procedure Show students the diagrams or photos of animals and humans. Ask students to point out the similarities and differences between the animals and the humans during similar life stages. L2

Differentiated Instruction

Challenge Have students observe a lower elementary or preschool classroom. What adaptations would they have to make to teach this chapter to the class they observed? Have them make a sample presentation to your class, pretending they are preschoolers. Have a class discussion on how they modified the chapter and why. L3

SECTION 3 Human Life Stages   **639**

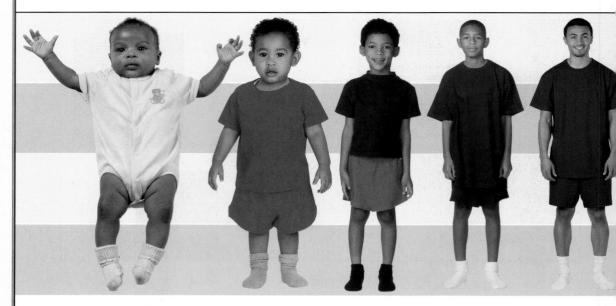

Figure 18 The proportions of body parts change over time as the body develops.
Describe *how the head changes proportion.*

Adolescent Growth During adolescence, body parts do not all grow at the same rate. Legs grow longer before the upper body lengthens. This changes the body's center of gravity, the point at which the body maintains its balance. This is one cause of teenager clumsiness. In your Science Journal, write a paragraph about how this might affect playing sports.

Adolescence Adolescence usually begins around age 12 or 13. A part of adolescence is puberty—the time of development when a person becomes physically able to reproduce. For girls, puberty occurs between ages nine and 13. For boys, puberty occurs between ages 13 and 16. During puberty, hormones produced by the pituitary gland cause changes in the body. These hormones produce reproductive cells and sex hormones. Secondary sex characteristics also develop. In females, the breasts develop, pubic and underarm hair appears, and fatty tissue is added to the buttocks and thighs. In males, the hormones cause a deepened voice, an increase in muscle size, and the growth of facial, pubic, and underarm hair.

Adolescence usually is when the final growth spurt occurs. Because the time when hormones begin working varies among individuals and between males and females, growth rates differ. Girls often begin their final growth phase at about age 11 and end around age 16. Boys usually start their growth spurt at age 13 and end around 18 years of age.

Adulthood The final stage of development, adulthood, begins with the end of adolescence and continues through old age. This is when the growth of the muscular and skeletal system stops. **Figure 18** shows how body proportions change as you age.

People from age 45 to age 60 are sometimes considered middle-aged adults. During these years, physical strength begins to decline. Blood circulation and respiration become less efficient. Bones become more brittle, and the skin becomes wrinkled.

Older Adulthood People over the age of 60 may experience an overall decline in their physical body systems. The cells that make up these systems no longer function as well as they did at a younger age. Connective tissues lose their elasticity, causing muscles and joints to be less flexible. Bones become thinner and more brittle. Hearing and vision are less sensitive. The lungs and heart work less efficiently. However, exercise and eating well over a lifetime can help extend the health of one's body systems. Many healthy older adults enjoy full lives and embrace challenges, as shown in **Figure 19.**

Figure 19 Astronaut and Senator John Glenn traveled into space twice. In 1962, at age 40, he was the first U.S. citizen to orbit Earth. He was part of the space shuttle crew in 1998 at age 77. Senator Glenn has helped change people's views of what many older adults are capable of doing.

 **Reading Check** *What physical changes occur during late adulthood?*

Human Life Spans Seventy-seven years is the average life span—from birth to death—of humans in the United States, although an increasing number of people live much longer. However, body systems break down with age, resulting in eventual death. Death can occur earlier than old age for many reasons, including diseases, accidents, and bad health choices.

section 3 review

Summary

Fertilization
- Fertilization is the uniting of a sperm and an egg.

Development Before Birth
- Pregnancy begins when an egg is fertilized and lasts until birth.

The Birthing Process
- Birth begins with labor. Contractions force the baby out of the mother's body.

Stages After Birth
- Infancy (birth to 18 months) and childhood (until age 12) are periods of physical and mental growth.
- A person becomes physically able to reproduce during adolescence. Adulthood is the final stage of development.

Self Check

1. **Describe** what happens when an egg is fertilized in a female.
2. **Explain** what happens to an embryo during the first two months of pregnancy.
3. **Describe** the major events that occur during childbirth.
4. **Name** the stage of development that you are in. What physical changes have occurred or will occur during this stage of human development?
5. **Think Critically** Why is it hard to compare the growth and development of different adolescents?

Applying Skills

6. **Use a Spreadsheet** Using your text and other resources, make a spreadsheet for the stages of human development from a zygote to a fetus. Title one column *Zygote,* another *Embryo*, and a third *Fetus*. Complete the spreadsheet.

Reading Check

Answer Connective tissue loses elasticity, bones become brittle, hearing and vision are less sensitive, and the lungs and heart work less efficiently.

3 Assess

DAILY INTERVENTION

Check for Understanding

Logical-Mathematical Have students graph the length of time a developing human is termed a *zygote*, an *embryo*, and a *fetus*.

Reteach

Life Stages Divide the class into groups and have each group write descriptions of a particular life stage—one per index card. Mix up the cards, divide the class into teams, and read the descriptions. Students take turns stating the life stage. The team with the greatest number of correct answers wins. L2 ELL
Visual-Spatial

Assessment

Performance To further assess students' understanding of neonatal development, have them construct a time line to correspond with the stages of neonatal development. Use **Performance Assessment in the Science Classroom,** p. 163.

section 3 review

1. sperm and egg nuclei combine, producing a zygote; egg membrane changes; cell division begins
2. Amniotic sac and placenta develop, major organs form, and the heart structure begins to beat.
3. Events include contraction, rupture of the amniotic sac, and widening

of the uterus's opening to allow the baby to pass through the cervix and the birth canal.
4. Adolescence; sex hormones are produced, secondary sex characteristics develop, last growth spurt occurs.
5. Each person has his or her own rate of development.

6. Zygote undergoes cell divisions, forms a ball of cells, and attaches to the uterine wall; see information in "Development Before Birth".

⊙ Real-World Question

Purpose Students measure the body proportions of adolescents and infer how body proportions differ between males and females.
L2 IN **Logical-Mathematical**

Process Skills calculate, compare, graph, infer

Time Required 40 minutes

⊙ Procedure

Alternate Materials Students may use metersticks instead of a tape measure. Masking tape can be used to mark heights on the wall instead of pencil marks.

Teaching Strategy Encourage students to measure each dimension twice to improve accuracy.

Goals
- ■ **Measure** specific body proportions of adolescents.
- ■ **Infer** how body proportions differ between adolescent males and females.

Materials
tape measure
erasable pencil
graph paper

Changing Body Proportions

⊙ Real-World Question

The ancient Greeks believed that the perfect body was completely balanced. Arms and legs should not be too long or short. A person's head should not be too large or small. The extra-large muscles of a body builder would have been ugly to the Greeks. How do you think they viewed the bodies of infants and children? Infants and young children have much different body proportions than adults, and teenagers often go through growth spurts that quickly change their body proportions. How do the body proportions differ between adolescent males and females?

⊙ Procedure

1. Copy the data table in your Science Journal and record the gender of each person that you measure.

2. Measure each person's head circumference by starting in the middle of the forehead and wrapping the tape measure once around the head. Record these measurements.

Alternative Inquiry Lab

Measuring Body Changes Students can observe many people of different ages to decide which body parts they will choose to measure. Encourage them to observe a broad age range of people from infants to the elderly. From their observations, students can design an experiment to test how different body proportions change over the life spans of humans.

Students can create a data table for their measurements, graphing their data using line graphs or bar graphs. Encourage students to generate charts and graphs electronically. Encourage students to explore and test other body changes such as weight.

3. Measure each person's arm length from the top of the shoulder to the tip of the middle finger while the arm is held straight out to the side of the body. Record these measurements.

4. Ask each person to remove his or her shoes and stand next to a wall. Mark their height with an erasable pencil and measure their height from the floor to the mark. Record these measurements in the data table.

5. **Combine** your data with that of your classmates. Find the averages of head circumference, arm length, and height. Then, find these averages for males and females.

6. Make a bar graph of your calculations in step 5. Plot the measurements on the *y*-axis and plot all of the averages along the *x*-axis.

7. **Calculate** the proportion of average head circumference to average height for everyone in your class by dividing the average head circumference by the average height. Repeat this calculation for males and females.

8. **Calculate** the proportion of average arm length to average height for everyone in your class by dividing the average arm length by the average height. Repeat this calculation for males and females.

Age and Body Measurements			
Gender of Person	Head Circumference (cm)	Arm Length (cm)	Height (cm)
	Answers will vary.		

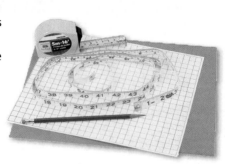

Analyze Your Data
Analyze whether adolescent males or females have larger head circumferences or longer arms. Which group has the larger proportion of head circumference or arm length to height?

Conclude and Apply
Explain if this lab supports the information in this chapter about the differences between growth rates of adolescent males and females.

*C*ommunicating **Your Data**

Construct data tables on poster board showing your results and those of your classmates. Discuss with your classmates why these results might be different.

Analyze Your Data

Expected Outcome Because adolescent girls generally undergo growth sooner than adolescent males, their body parts will be in different proportions than those of adolescent males.

Answers to Questions Answers will vary depending on students' measurements.

Error Analysis Form students into groups of four or five and have each student compare his or her data with that of other group members. If data disagree, have each group list reasons for discrepancies.

Conclude and Apply

Answers will vary but data should support chapter information about differences in growth rates between adolescent males and females.

✓ Assessment

Portfolio Ask students to draw what they envision as the Greek ideal of a perfectly proportioned body.

LAB 643

*C*ommunicating **Your Data**

Encourage students to use a spreadsheet program to construct their data tables.

Content Background

Mammals can be divided into three groups based on their development. Humans are placentals: a mammal whose young develop in the female parent's uterus. The offspring of placental mammals are usually comparatively well developed. Marsupials, like the kangaroo shown in this feature, give birth to less-developed young, which usually develop in a pouch, or attached to the mother's body. Monotremes are mammals that lay eggs.

Discussion

Kangaroo Babies Why might a baby kangaroo need to spend such a long period of time in its mother's pouch after it is born? Possible answer: Kangaroo babies are not developed enough to survive outside of the pouch when they are born, they need a period of protected growth and development.

Activity

Animal Independence Assign small groups of students an animal to research. Have the students find the age at which the young become independent from their parents. Have the students compare their findings on a bar graph.

Applying Math

elephant, about 5%

Find Out About It

Students can use reference material to explore the life spans of different animals. Explain that the life span of humans varies greatly between countries, so the statistic that different students use for this number may vary.

SCIENCE Stats

Facts About Infants

Did you know...

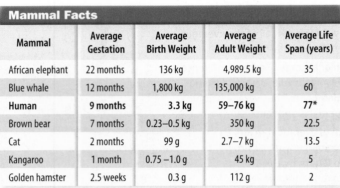

...**Humans and chimpanzees share** about 99 percent of their genes. Although humans look different than chimps, reproduction is similar and gestation is the same—about nine months. Youngsters of both species lose their baby teeth at about six years of age.

Mammal	Average Gestation	Average Birth Weight	Average Adult Weight	Average Life Span (years)
African elephant	22 months	136 kg	4,989.5 kg	35
Blue whale	12 months	1,800 kg	135,000 kg	60
Human	9 months	3.3 kg	59–76 kg	77*
Brown bear	7 months	0.23–0.5 kg	350 kg	22.5
Cat	2 months	99 g	2.7–7 kg	13.5
Kangaroo	1 month	0.75 –1.0 g	45 kg	5
Golden hamster	2.5 weeks	0.3 g	112 g	2

*In the United States

Applying Math Assume that a female of each mammal listed in the table above is pregnant once during her life. Which mammal is pregnant for the greatest proportion of her life?

...**Of about 4,000 species of mammals,** only three lay eggs: the platypus, the short-beaked echidna (ih KIHD nuh), and the long-beaked echidna.

Echidna

Find Out About It

Visit life.msscience.com/science_stats to research which species of vertebrate animals has the longest life span and which has the shortest. Present your findings in a table that also shows the life span of humans.

644 CHAPTER 22 Regulation and Reproduction

Visual Learning

Mammal Facts Ask students to compare the birth weights of humans and whales as a percent of adult weight. They will find that whales are born at about 1.5% of the weight they will be as adults, while humans are born at 4.5% to 5.5% of their adult weight. Proportionately, newborn humans are larger than newborn whales. Have students determine which animals listed in the chart are born at the smallest (brown bear) and the largest (human) proportion of their adult weight.

Reviewing Main Ideas

Section 1 | The Endocrine System

1. Endocrine glands secrete hormones directly into the bloodstream. They affect specific tissues in the body.

2. A change in the body causes an endocrine gland to function. Hormone production slows or stops when homeostasis is reached.

Section 2 | The Reproductive System

1. Reproductive systems allow new organisms to be formed.

2. The testes produce sperm, which leave the male body through the penis.

3. The female ovaries produce eggs. If fertilized, an egg develops into a fetus within the uterus.

4. An unfertilized egg and the built-up lining of the uterus are shed in menstruation.

Section 3 | Human Life Stages

1. After fertilization, the zygote becomes an embryo, then a fetus. Twins occur when two eggs are fertilized or when a zygote divides after fertilization.

2. Birth begins with labor. The amniotic sac breaks. Then, usually after several hours, contractions force the baby out of the mother's body.

3. Infancy, from birth to 18 months of age, is a period of rapid growth of mental and physical skills. Childhood lasts until age 12 and involves further physical and mental development.

4. Adolescence is when a person becomes physically able to reproduce. In adulthood, physical development is complete and body systems become less efficient. Death occurs at the end of life.

Visualizing Main Ideas

Copy and complete the following table on life stages.

Human Development		
Stages of Life	**Age Range**	**Physical Development**
Infant	birth–18 months	sits, stands, words spoken
Childhood	18 months–12 years	walks, speaks, writes, reads
Adolescent	12–18 years	physically able to reproduce, sexual characteristics develop, final growth spurt
Adulthood	18 years–death	end of muscular and skeletal growth

Science Online life.msscience.com/interactive_tutor

CHAPTER STUDY GUIDE 645

Reviewing Main Ideas

Summary statements can be used by students to review the major concepts of the chapter.

Visualizing Main Ideas

See student page.

Visit life.msscience.com
/self_check_quiz
/interactive_tutor
/vocabulary_puzzlemaker
/chapter_review
/standardized_test

Assessment Transparency

For additional assessment questions, use the *Assessment Transparency* located in the transparency book.

Assessment

Assessment Transparency | Regulation and Reproduction

Directions: *Carefully review the table and answer the following questions.*

Population by Country (in millions)				
Country	**1970**	**1980**	**1990**	**2000**
Japan	104	117	124	127
USA	205	223	250	281
India	555	690	851	1,014
Pakistan	66	85	114	142
Indonesia	94	155	189	225
Russia	130	148	148	146

1. According to this information, which country had the greatest increase in population between the years 1970 and 2000?
   A Russia   C India
   B United States D Japan

2. Between the years 1990 and 2000, which country had a negative rate of population growth?
   F Japan   H Indonesia
   G Russia   J India

3. According to the table, the country that had a total population greater than Pakistan in 1970 but less than Pakistan in the year 2000 is ___.
   A India   C United States
   B Japan   D Russia

Regulation and Reproduction

Identifying Misconceptions

Assess

Use this assessment as follow-up to page F at the beginning of this chapter.

Activity Ask students to describe the events that take place during fertilization and what the new cell is called. Give students a handout or write on the board the stages of development (0 to a few days, a few days to 2 weeks, and 2 weeks to 8 weeks). Have students fill in the stages with diagrams and/or verbal descriptions.

Expected Outcome Students should know that during fertilization sperm and egg cells fuse, their nuclei fuse, and the new cell is called a zygote. Only one sperm can fuse with an egg cell. They should draw or describe the "soap bubble" stage, the three-part state, and the differentiation stage.

Using Vocabulary

1. Semen
2. pregnancy
3. an embryo
4. uterus
5. amniotic sac
6. ovary

Checking Concepts

7. A	12. B
8. C	13. A
9. D	14. B
10. C	15. C
11. A	16. B

Using Vocabulary

amniotic sac p.635
embryo p.635
fetal stress p.638
fetus p.636
hormone p.622
menstrual cycle p.630
menstruation p.630
ovary p.629

ovulation p.629
pregnancy p.634
semen p.628
sperm p.628
testes p.628
uterus p.629
vagina p.629

Fill in the blank with the correct vocabulary word or words.

1. _____ is a mixture of sperm and fluid.

2. The time of the development until the birth of a baby is known as _____.

3. During the first two months of pregnancy, the unborn child is known as a(n) _____.

4. The _____ is a hollow, pear-shaped muscular organ.

5. The _____ is the membrane that protects the unborn child.

6. The _____ is the organ that produces eggs.

Checking Concepts

Choose the word or phrase that best answers the question.

7. Where is the egg usually fertilized?
   A) oviduct   **C)** vagina
   B) uterus   **D)** ovary

8. What are the chemicals produced by the endocrine system?
   A) enzymes   **C)** hormones
   B) target tissues **D)** saliva

9. Which gland produces melatonin?
   A) adrenal   **C)** pancreas
   B) thyroid   **D)** pineal

10. Where does the embryo develop?
    A) oviduct   **C)** uterus
    B) ovary   **D)** vagina

Use the figure below to answer question 11.

Prevalence of Diabetes per 100 Adults, United States, 2001

KEY: ☐ <4%   ☐ 4−4.9%   ▨ 5−5.9%   ▩ 6+%

11. Using the figure above, which state has the lowest incidence of diabetes?
    A) Wyoming   **C)** Michigan
    B) Florida   **D)** Washington

12. What is the monthly process that releases an egg called?
    A) fertilization **C)** menstruation
    B) ovulation   **D)** puberty

13. What is the union of an egg and a sperm?
    A) fertilization **C)** menstruation
    B) ovulation   **D)** puberty

14. During what stage of development does the amniotic sac form?
    A) zygote   **C)** fetus
    B) embryo   **D)** newborn

15. When does puberty occur?
    A) childhood **C)** adolescence
    B) adulthood **D)** infancy

16. During which period does growth stop?
    A) childhood **C)** adolescence
    B) adulthood **D)** infancy

 Science Online life.msscience.com/vocabulary_puzzlemaker

Use the Exam*View*® Pro Testmaker CD-ROM to:
- create multiple versions of tests
- create modified tests with one mouse click for inclusion students
- edit existing questions and add your own questions
- build tests aligned with state standards using built-in State Curriculum Tags
- change English tests to Spanish with one mouse click and vice versa

Thinking Critically

17. List the effects that adrenal gland hormones can have on your body as you prepare to run a race.

18. Explain the similar functions of the ovaries and testes.

Use the diagram below to answer question 19.

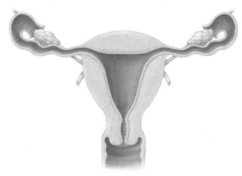

19. Identify the structure in the above diagram in which each process occurs: ovulation, fertilization, and implantation.

20. Compare and contrast your endocrine system with the thermostat in your home.

21. Explain if quadruplets—four babies born at one birth—are always identical or always fraternal, or if they can be either.

22. Predict During the ninth month of pregnancy, the fetus develops a white, greasy coating. Predict what the function of this coating might be.

23. Form a hypothesis about the effect of raising identical twins apart from each other.

24. Classify each of the following structures as female or male and internal or external: ovary, penis, scrotum, testes, uterus, and vagina.

Science Online life.msscience.com/chapter_review

Performance Activities

25. Letter Find newspaper or magazine articles on the effects of smoking on the health of the developing embryo and newborn. Write a letter to the editor about why a mother's smoking is damaging to her unborn baby's health.

Applying Math

26. Blood Sugar Levels Carol is diabetic and has a fasting blood sugar level of 180 mg/dL. Luisa does not have diabetes and has a fasting blood sugar level of 90 mg/dL. Express as a percentage how much higher the fasting blood sugar level is for Carol as compared to that for Luisa.

Use the graph below to answer questions 27 and 28.

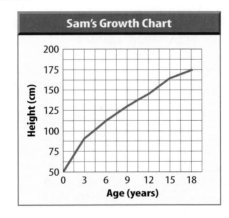

Sam's Growth Chart

27. Early Childhood Growth The graph above charts Sam's growth from birth to 18 years of age. According to the graph, how much taller was Sam at 12 years of age than he was at 3 years of age?

28. Adolescent Growth According to the graph, how much did Sam grow between 12 and 18 years of age?

Thinking Critically

17. Adrenal hormones cause your heart to beat faster, increasing blood flow to major organs and giving a sense of increased strength.

18. Both are paired organs that produce sex cells.

19. ovulation—ovary; fertilization—oviduct; implantation—uterus

20. According to the level of hormone in the blood, the target tissue sends a chemical message back to the gland to stop or start hormone secretion. Likewise, the thermostat in a house signals the heating or air conditioning unit to start or stop according to the temperature in the house. Both are negative-feedback systems.

21. Either; zygote splits into four parts—identical quadruplets; four eggs fertilized by four different sperm—fraternal quadruplets.

22. This coating aids in the movement of the baby through the birth canal.

23. Students might hypothesize that they will be the same because of their genes or that the environment will have an effect, making them different.

24. female internal: ovary, uterus, vagina; male external: penis, scrotum, testes

Performance Activities

25. Information in the letter might include how smoking reduces the oxygen supply to the fetus, increases the heart rate and blood pressure, and interferes with body chemistry. Use **Performance Assessment in the Science Classroom,** p. 139.

Applying Math

National Math Standards

1, 5, 9

26. $\frac{180-90}{90} \times 100 = 100\%$

27. $145-90 = 55$ cm

28. $175-145 = 30$ cm

Assessment Resources

Reproducible Masters

Chapter _Fast File_ Resources
   Chapter Review, pp. 35–36
   Chapter Tests, pp. 37–40
   Assessment Transparency Activity, p. 47

Glencoe Science Web site
   Chapter Review Test
   Standardized Test Practice

Glencoe Technology

   Assessment Transparency
   Exam_View_® Pro Testmaker
   MindJogger Videoquiz
   Interactive Chalkboard

FAST FILE

Answer Sheet A practice answer sheet can be found at life.msscience.com/answer_sheet.

SAMPLE

Part 1 Multiple Choice

1. B	4. C	7. A
2. A	5. A	8. B
3. D	6. C	

Part 1 Multiple Choice

Record your answers on the answer sheet provided by your teacher or on a sheet of paper.

1. When do eggs start to develop in the ovaries?
   A. before birth   **C.** during childhood
   B. at puberty   **D.** during infancy

Use the graph below to answers questions 2 and 3.

United States Syphilis Rates (1970–1997)

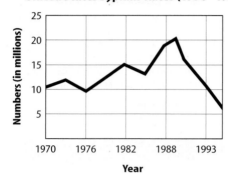

2. According to the information in the graph, in which year was the syphilis rate the lowest?
   A. 1976   **C.** 1988
   B. 1982   **D.** 1993

3. According to the information in the graph, during which years was there a decrease in the syphilis rate?
   A. 1970–1972   **C.** 1988–1990
   B. 1976–1982   **D.** 1990–1993

4. Which of the following glands is found in the neck?
   A. pineal   **C.** thyroid
   B. adrenal   **D.** pancreas

Test-Taking Tip

Bar Graphs On a bar graph, line up each bar with its corresponding value by laying your pencil between the two points.

---

5. What is the mixture of sperm and fluid called?
   A. semen   **C.** seminal vesicle
   B. testes   **D.** epididymis

Use the table below to answer questions 6–8.

Results of Folic Acid on Development of Neural Tube Defect		
Group	**Babies with Neural Tube Defect**	**Babies without Neural Tube Defect**
Group I—Folic Acid	6	497
Group II—No Folic Acid	21	581

(From CDC)

6. Researchers have found that the B-vitamin folic acid can prevent neural tube defects. In a study done in Europe in 1991, one group of pregnant women was given extra folic acid, and the other group did not receive extra folic acid. What percentage of babies were born with a neural tube defect in Group II?
   A. 1.0%   **C.** 3.0%
   B. 2.5%   **D.** 4.0%

7. What percentage of babies were born with a neural tube defect in Group I?
   A. 1.0%   **C.** 3.0%
   B. 2.5%   **D.** 4.0%

8. Which of the following statements is true regarding the data in this table?
   A. Folic acid had no effect on the percentage of babies with a neural tube defect.
   B. Extra folic acid decreased the percentage of babies with a neural tube defect.
   C. Extra folic acid increased the percentage of babies with a neural tube defect.
   D. Group I and Group II had the same percentage of babies born with a neural tube defect.

648 STANDARDIZED TEST PRACTICE

Part 2 Short Response/Grid In

9. Endocrine glands are ductless. Hormones from endocrine glands pour directly into the blood. Saliva from salivary glands goes through tubes called ducts.

10. Parathyroid hormone helps regulate calcium levels in the body.

11. The cilia help sweep the egg through the oviduct toward the uterus.

12. 14/28 = 1/2 = 50%

13. 7/28 = 1/4 = 25%

14. day 14

15. Amniotic fluid is made during the embryo stage. Amniotic fluid acts as a cushion for the embryo and stores nutrients and wastes.

16. during infancy

17. During the first two months of development, because this is when the embryo's major organs form.

Part 2 | Short Response/Grid In

Record your answers on the answer sheet provided by your teacher or on a sheet of paper.

9. How are endocrine glands different from salivary glands?

10. What does parathyroid hormone do for the body?

11. What is the function of the cilia in the oviduct?

Use the illustration below to answer questions 12 and 13.

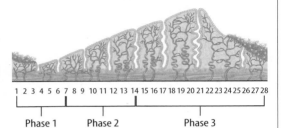

1 2 3 4 5 6 7 8 9 10 11 12 13 14 15 16 17 18 19 20 21 22 23 24 25 26 27 28

Phase 1   Phase 2   Phase 3

12. According to the illustration, what percentage of the menstrual cycle is phase 3?

13. According to the illustration, what percentage of the menstrual cycle is phase 2?

14. According to the illustration, on which day does ovulation occur?

15. During which stage of development before birth does amniotic fluid develop? What is the purpose of amniotic fluid?

16. During which stage of development after birth is physical growth and development the most rapid?

17. Rubella, also know as German measles, is caused by a virus. If a pregnant woman is infected with rubella, the virus can affect the formation of major organs, such as the heart, in the fetus. During which stage of development before birth would a rubella infection be most dangerous?

Part 3 | Open Ended

Record your answers on a sheet of paper.

18. Predict how each of the following factors may affect sperm production: hot environment, illness with fever, testes located inside the body cavity, and injury to the testes. Explain your answer.

19. Sexually transmitted diseases can cause infection of the female reproductive organs, including the oviduct. Infection of the oviduct can result in scarring. What might happen to an egg that enters a scarred oviduct?

Use the table below to answer question 20.

Pre-eclampsia Risk in Pregnancy	
Risk Factors	**Risk Ratio**
First pregnancy	3:1
Over 40 years of age	3:1
Family history	5:1
Chronic hypertension	10:1
Chronic renal disease	20:1
Antiphospholipid syndrome	10:1
Diabetes mellitus	2:1
Twin birth	4:1
Angiotensinogen gene T235	
Homozygous	20:1
Heterozygous	4:1

20. Pre-eclampsia is a condition that can develop in a woman after 20 weeks of pregnancy. It involves the development of hypertension or high blood pressure, an abnormal amount of protein in urine, and swelling. Infer why a woman with chronic hypertension has a higher risk of developing pre-eclampsia than a woman without hypertension.

Part 3 | Open Ended

18. All these will result in a decrease in sperm production. Sperm are produced in greater numbers at lower temperatures.

19. Because of the scarring, the egg will not travel normally through the oviduct. It may become stuck in the oviduct.

20. A woman with chronic hypertension is ten times more likely to develop pre-eclampsia during pregnancy than a woman without hypertension. Pre-eclampsia could make her hypertension worse.

Rubrics

The following rubrics are sample scoring devices for short response and open-ended questions.

Short Response

Points	Description
2	The student demonstrates a thorough understanding of the science of the task. The response may contain minor flaws that do not detract from the demonstration of a thorough understanding.
1	The student has provided a response that is only partially correct.
0	The student has provided a completely incorrect solution or no response at all.

Open Ended

Points	Description
4	The student demonstrates a thorough understanding of the science of the task. The response may contain minor flaws that do not detract from the demonstration of a thorough understanding.
3	The student demonstrates an understanding of the science of the task. The response is essentially correct and demonstrates an essential but less than thorough understanding of the science.
2	The student demonstrates only a partial understanding of the science of the task. Although the student may have used the correct approach to a solution or may have provided a correct solution, the work lacks an essential understanding of the underlying science concepts.
1	The student demonstrates a very limited understanding of the science of the task. The response is incomplete and exhibits many flaws.
0	The student provides a completely incorrect solution or no response at all.

chapter 23 Organizer

Section/Objectives	Standards		Labs/Features
	National	**State/Local**	
Chapter Opener	See pp.16T–17T for a Key to Standards.		**Launch Lab:** How do diseases spread?, p. 651 **Foldables,** p. 651
Section 1 The Immune System ⏱ 2 sessions 🧊 1 block 1. **Describe** the natural defenses your body has against disease. 2. **Explain** the difference between an antigen and an antibody. 3. **Compare and contrast** active and passive immunity.	National Content Standards: UCP.2, UCP.5, A.1, A.2, C.1–C.3, C.5, F.1, G.2		**Science Online,** p. 654 **MiniLAB:** Determining Reproduction Rates, p. 655
Section 2 Infectious Diseases ⏱ 2 sessions 🧊 1 block 4. **Describe** the work of Pasteur, Koch, and Lister in the discovery and prevention of disease. 5. **Identify** diseases caused by viruses and bacteria. 6. **List** sexually transmitted diseases, their causes, and treatments. 7. **Explain** how HIV affects the immune system.	National Content Standards: UCP.2, UCP.5, A.1, C.1–C.3, C.5, E.1, F.1, F.4, F.5		**Integrate Social Studies,** p. 658 **Visualizing Koch's Rules,** p. 659 **MiniLAB:** Observing Antiseptic Action, p. 660 **Applying Science:** Has the annual percentage of deaths from major diseases changed?, p. 661 **Science Online,** p. 663 **Lab:** Microorganisms and Disease, p. 665
Section 3 Noninfectious Diseases ⏱ 3 sessions 🧊 1.5 blocks 8. **Define** noninfectious diseases and list causes of them. 9. **Describe** the basic characteristics of cancer. 10. **Explain** what happens during an allergic reaction.	National Content Standards: UCP.2, UCP.5, A.1, A.2, C.1–C.3, C.5, F.1, F.3–F.5, G.1, G.2		**Integrate Environment,** p. 669 **Lab:** Defensive Saliva, p. 672 **Science Stats:** Battling Bacteria, p. 674

Glencoe Exclusive!
Teacher Works™
All-In-One Planner and Resource Center

Lab Materials	Reproducible Resources	Section Assessment	Technology
Launch Lab: cotton ball, peppermint food flavoring	**Chapter *FAST FILE* Resources** Foldables Worksheet, p. 15 Directed Reading Overview, p. 17 Note-taking Worksheets, pp. 31–33	GLENCOE'S ASSESSMENT ADVANTAGE	**TeacherWorks** includes: • Interactive Teacher Edition • Lesson Planner with calendar • Access to all program blacklines • Correlations to standards • Web links
MiniLAB: 31 pennies, calculator *Need materials?* Contact Science Kit at 1-800-828-7777 or www.sciencekit.com on the Internet.	**Chapter *FAST FILE* Resources** Transparency Activity, p. 42 MiniLAB, p. 3 Lab Activity, pp. 9–12 Enrichment, p. 28 Reinforcement, p. 25 Directed Reading, p. 18 Transparency Activity, pp. 45–46	Portfolio Differentiated Instruction, p. 653 Performance MiniLAB, p. 655 Applying Skills, p. 666 Content Section Review, p. 666	Section Focus Transparency Teaching Transparency Virtual Labs CD-ROM Guided Reading Audio Program Interactive Chalkboard CD-ROM
MiniLAB: glass plate, dried yeast, hydrogen peroxide, dropper **Lab:** 6 fresh apples, rotting apple, rubbing alcohol, 6 self-sealing plastic bags, labels, gloves, paper towels, sandpaper, cotton ball, soap and water, newspaper	**Chapter *FAST FILE* Resources** Transparency Activity, p. 43 MiniLAB, p. 4 Enrichment, p. 29 Reinforcement, p. 26 Directed Reading, p. 19 Lab Worksheet, pp. 5–6 **Cultural Diversity,** p. 17 **Mathematics Skill Activities,** p. 1 **Reading and Writing Skill Activities,** pp. 25, 31	Portfolio Science Journal, p. 660 Performance MiniLAB, p. 660 Applying Science, p. 661 Applying Skills, p. 664 Content Section Review, p. 664	Section Focus Transparency Virtual Labs CD-ROM Guided Reading Audio Program Interactive Chalkboard CD-ROM Video Lab
Lab: head of red cabbage, cooking pot, coffee filter, drinking glasses, clear ammonia, baking soda, water, spoon, white vinegar, lemon juice, orange juice	**Chapter *FAST FILE* Resources** Transparency Activity, p. 44 Lab Activity, pp. 13–14 Enrichment, p. 30 Reinforcement, p. 27 Directed Reading, pp. 19, 20 Lab Worksheet, pp. 7–8 **Lab Management and Safety,** p. 70	Performance Applying Skills, p. 671 Content Section Review, p. 671	Section Focus Transparency Virtual Labs CD-ROM Guided Reading Audio Program Interactive Chalkboard CD-ROM

End of Chapter Assessment

GLENCOE'S ASSESSMENT ADVANTAGE

Blackline Masters	Technology	Professional Series
Chapter *FAST FILE* Resources Chapter Review, pp. 35–36 Chapter Tests, pp. 37–40 **Standardized Test Practice,** pp. 95–98	MindJogger Videoquiz Virtual Labs CD-ROM Exam*View*® Pro Testmaker TeacherWorks CD-ROM Interactive Chalkboard CD-ROM	**Performance Assessment in the Science Classroom (PASC)**

Transparencies

Section Focus

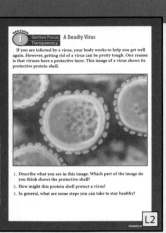

Section Focus Transparency 1 A Deadly Virus

If you are infected by a virus, your body works to help you get well again. However, getting rid of a virus can be pretty tough. One reason is that viruses have a protective layer. This image of a virus shows its protective protein shell.

1. Describe what you see in this image. Which part of the image do you think shows the protective shell?
2. How might this protein shell protect a virus?
3. In general, what are some steps you can take to stay healthy?

L2

Section Focus Transparency 2 The Invisible World

The first person to see many microorganisms, including bacteria, was Antonie van Leeuwenhoek (1632–1723). Leeuwenhoek wasn't a scientist by training, and he didn't invent the microscope. But he did learn to grind lenses very skillfully, and his small but powerful microscopes allowed him to see what no one else ever had.

1. What advantages do microscopes give researchers?
2. How would a more powerful microscope help Leeuwenhoek see what other people could not?
3. One of Leeuwenhoek's microscopes is shown on the right. Where do you think he placed the sample he wished to magnify?

L2

Section Focus Transparency 3 Ah-Chooo! (Gesundheit)

Organisms are not the only things that can make you sick. Matter present in the environment, such as toxic chemicals, particles, and certain types of fibers, also can cause disease. The spiny spheres you see below are responsible for a certain type of allergic reaction that afflicts many people. Can you guess what they are?

1. How do allergies affect people?
2. What kind of help is there for allergy sufferers?
3. If people work around materials such as asbestos, burning tar, or smoke, what kinds of safety equipment should they use?

L2

This is a representation of key blackline masters available in the Teacher Classroom Resources. See Resource Manager boxes within the chapter for additional information.

Key to Teaching Strategies

The following designations will help you decide which activities are appropriate for your students.

L1 Level 1 activities should be appropriate for students with learning difficulties.

L2 Level 2 activities should be within the ability range of all students.

L3 Level 3 activities are designed for above-average students.

ELL ELL activities should be within the ability range of English-Language Learners.

COOP LEARN Cooperative Learning activities are designed for small group work.

LS Multiple Learning Styles logos, as described on page 12T, are used throughout to indicate strategies that address different learning styles.

P These strategies represent student products that can be placed into a best-work portfolio.

PBL Problem-Based Learning activities apply real-world situations to learning.

Assessment

Assessment Transparency Immunity and Disease

Directions: Carefully review the table and answer the following questions.

Estimated HIV/AIDS in Western Europe, 1999			
Country	Adult Population Living with HIV/AIDS	Transmission	
		IV Drug Use	Contaminated Blood
France	0.43%	24%	5%
Germany	0.10%	15%	5%
Greece	0.16%	5%	9%
Portugal	0.74%	49%	3%
Spain	0.58%	66%	2%

1. According to the table, which country has the highest percentage of people with HIV/AIDS?
   A France
   B Germany
   C Portugal
   D Spain
2. According to the table, which country has the highest percentage of infection by blood transfusions?
   F France
   G Germany
   H Greece
   J Portugal
3. According to the table, which country has the highest percentage of people infected by drug use?
   A France
   B Germany
   C Spain
   D Greece

L2

Teaching

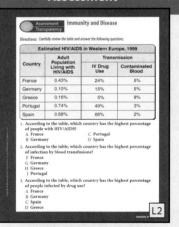

Teaching Transparency 1 Response of the Immune System

L2

Hands-on Activities

Student Text Lab Worksheet

Activity Microorganisms and Disease

Lab Preview
Directions: Answer these questions before you begin the Activity.
1. Which safety symbols are associated with this activity?

2. What is the source of microorganisms in this activity?

Microorganisms are everywhere. Washing your hands and disinfecting items you use helps remove some of these organisms.

What You'll Investigate
How do microorganisms cause infection?

Materials
fresh apples (8)   self-sealing plastic bags (8)   paper towels   soap and water
rotting apple   labels and pencil   sandpaper   newspaper
rubbing alcohol (5 mL)   latex gloves   cotton ball

Goals
• **Observe** the transmission of microorganisms.
• **Relate** microorganisms to infections.

Safety Precautions
CAUTION: *Do not eat the apples. Do not remove goggles until the activity and cleanup are completed. When you complete the experiment, give all bags to your teacher for disposal, then wash your hands.*

Procedure
1. Label the plastic bags 1 through 8. Put on gloves. Place a fresh apple in bag 1.
2. Rub the rotting apple over the other five apples. This is your source of microorganisms. CAUTION: *Don't touch your face.*
3. Put one apple in bag 2.
4. Hold one apple 1.5 m above the floor and drop it on a newspaper. Put it in bag 3.
5. Rub one apple with sandpaper. Place this apple in bag 4.
6. Wash one apple with soap and water. Dry it well. Put this apple in bag 5.
7. Use a cotton ball to spread alcohol over the last apple. Let it air dry. Place it in bag 6.
8. Seal all bags and put them in a dark place.
9. On day 3 and day 7, compare all of the apples without removing them from the bags. Record your observations in Table 1.

L2

Laboratory Activities

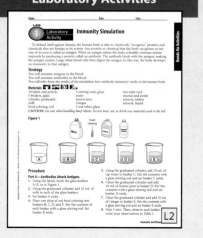

Laboratory Activity 1 Immunity Simulation

To defend itself against disease, the human body is able to chemically "recognize" proteins and chemicals that are foreign to its system. Any protein or chemical that the body recognizes as not one of its own is called an antigen. When an antigen enters the body, a healthy immune system responds by producing a protein called an antibody. The antibody binds with the antigen, making the antigen useless. Large white blood cells then digest the antigen. In this way, the body develops an immunity to that antigen.

Strategy
You will simulate antigens in the blood.
You will simulate antibodies in the blood.
You will infer from the results of the simulation how antibody immunity works in the human body.

Materials
10 labels and pencils   5 stirring rods, glass   test-tube rack
5 beakers, glass   water   mortar and pestle
cylinder, graduated   lemon juice   antacid, tablets
milk   vinegar   antacid, liquid
food coloring, red   5 test tubes, glass
CAUTION: *Use care when handling sharp objects. Do not taste, eat, or drink any materials used in the lab.*

Figure 1

Procedure
Part A—Antibodies Attack Antigens
1. Using the labels, mark the glass beakers A–E, as in Figure 1.
2. Using the graduated cylinder, add 25 mL of milk to each of the glass beakers.
3. Set beaker A aside.
4. Place one drop of red food coloring into beakers B, C, D, and E. Stir the contents of each beaker with a glass stirring rod. Set beaker B aside.
5. Using the graduated cylinder, add 10 mL of tap water to beaker C. Stir the contents with a glass stirring rod and set beaker C aside.
6. Clean the graduated cylinder and add 10 mL of lemon juice to beaker D. Stir the contents with a glass stirring rod and set beaker D aside.
7. Clean the graduated cylinder and add 10 mL of vinegar to beaker E. Stir the contents with a glass stirring rod and set beaker E aside.
8. Wait 3 min. Then, observe each beaker and write your observations in Table 1.

L2

Meeting Different Ability Levels

Content Outline

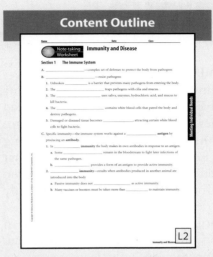

Note-taking Worksheet — Immunity and Disease

L2

Reinforcement

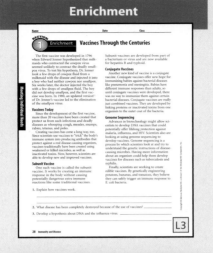

Reinforcement — The Immune System

L2

Enrichment

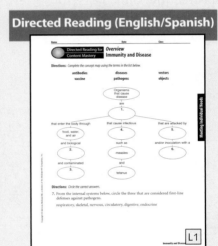

Enrichment — Vaccines Through the Centuries

L3

Directed Reading (English/Spanish)

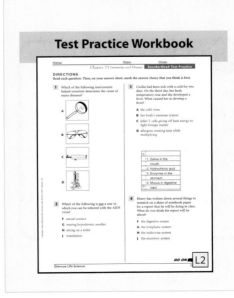

Directed Reading for Content Mastery — Overview — Immunity and Disease

L1

Study Guide

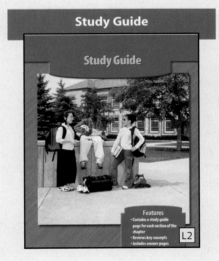

Study Guide

Features
- Contains a study guide page for each section of the chapter
- Reviews key concepts
- Includes answer pages

L2

Reading Essentials

Reading Essentials for Glencoe Science
An Interactive Student Workbook

Features
- Condensed core content
- Actively involves students in reading
- Reinforces key vocabulary

L1

Assessment

Test Practice Workbook

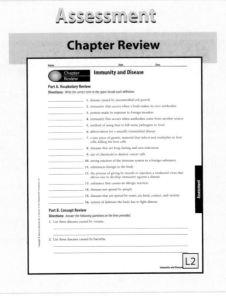

Chapter 23 Immunity and Disease — Standardized Test Practice

L2

Chapter Review

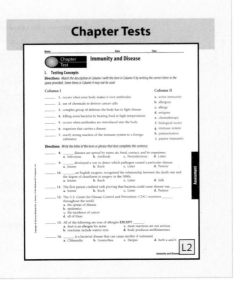

Chapter Review — Immunity and Disease

L2

Chapter Tests

Chapter Test — Immunity and Disease

L2

Science Content Background

section 1

The Immune System

Immunity

The lymphatic system produces various white blood cells, each of which fights a specific type of antigen. This type of defense is called specific immunity.

Active Immunity

Active immunity can be natural or induced. A natural active immunity develops after a person contracts and recovers from diseases such as measles or mumps. Defensive proteins, called antibodies, produced in the body counteract the invading microorganism's proteins called antigens. The interaction between antigens and antibodies stimulates the release of histamine and complement compounds.

Artificial active immunity is an induced immunity. A person is given an injection or an oral dose of a noninfectious disease antigen. The body forms antibodies against the antigen, providing immunity. The noninfectious antigens come from three sources:

1) microorganism secretions that have been detoxified,
2) dead microorganisms, and
3) living microorganisms.

Booster shots may be required to keep the artificial immunity active.

Passive Immunity

Passive immunity can be either natural or induced. Passive artificial immunity is acquired when antibodies produced in another animal are injected into the body. The serum containing the antibodies is often obtained from horses that were inoculated with disease antigens and then produced antibodies within their own body systems.

Passive natural immunity is that which an infant receives from its mother via the placenta. Because this protection only lasts for a few months, the child must be given inoculations to establish his or her own immunity to diseases.

Aaron Haupt/Photo Researchers, Inc.

chapter content resources

Internet Resources
For additional content background, visit
life.msscience.com to:
- access your book online
- find references to related articles in popular science magazines
- access Web links with related content background
- access current events with science journal topics

Print Resources
How the Immune System Works, by Lauren Sompayrac, Blackwell Publishers, 2002
Immune System, by Pam Walker and Elaine Wood, Gale Group, 2002
The Human Body for Every Kid, by Janice VanCleave, Wiley, John & Sons, Incorporated, 1995

section 2
Infectious Diseases
Germ Theory

In early history, the causes of diseases were associated with the anger of the gods, sorcerers, evil vapors, or imbalances of body fluids. By the early and mid 1800s, researchers, such as French chemist Louis Pasteur, developed a germ theory that indicated microorganisms might be responsible for disease. It is now known that pathogenic organisms such as viruses, bacteria, yeasts, protozoans, flatworms, roundworms, and hookworms cause disease by secreting toxins, by destroying red blood cells, or by ingesting tissues. Infectious, or communicable diseases, can be transmitted from one organism to another by food, through the air, by insects, by parasites, or by sexual contact or exchange of body fluids. Bacteria and viruses cause sexually transmitted diseases.

Preventing Food Spoilage

Before the causes of diseases were discovered, various methods were used to prevent foods from spoiling. Foods were dried, smoked, pickled, or salted to prevent the growth of microorganisms. Establishment of the germ theory led to the use of chemicals and Pasteur's idea of the use of heat to destroy pathogens. Additional modern methods of safeguarding food include the use of extreme cold, steam, and radiation.

Germs in the Body

Some organisms are able to gain entrance to the body through the thin membranes of the eyes, nose, and mouth. Good hygiene habits such as washing with soap and water, remove many potentially troublesome organisms from the surface of the skin. After germs enter the body, some are unable to function because body temperature is either too warm or too cool, the pH of body fluids is unsuitable, or the available nutrients are inappropriate for their metabolism.

section 3
Noninfectious Diseases
Causes and Cures

Some diseases and disorders are noninfectious. Although they are not contracted from other people or from objects, these conditions are usually unavoidable. Some noninfectious diseases are the result of poor nutrition. People who do not have access to a proper diet or people who do not choose a balanced diet are prone to such diseases. Other noninfectious diseases and disorders are the result of inheriting certain genes. Such genetic disorders include cystic fibrosis, hemophilia, Huntington's chorea, muscular dystrophy, sickle-cell anemia, and Tay-Sachs disease.

Toxins, or chemicals, introduced into the body through breathing, touching, drinking, or eating, can cause noninfectious diseases such as allergies, emphysema, and cancer. Prevention is the first line of defense for these diseases. Early detection of some diseases, such as cancer, paired with appropriate drug treatment and/or surgery, is a second line of defense.

Teacher to Teacher

Jeff Remington
Palmyra Middle School
Palmyra, Pennsylvania

"I obtain a non-toxic 100% synthetic organic colorant whose plastic particles are 5 microns and smaller (available at hospital supply stores in orange or blue) to simulate germs. Sprinkle a small amount of the powder on the hands of a few students and/or on classroom surfaces. After your students shake hands or touch the surfaces, use an ultra-violet lamp (black light) to demonstrate the transfer of 'germs' to one another."

Jeff Remington

Chapter Vocabulary

immune system, p. 652
antigen, p. 654
antibody, p. 654
active immunity, p. 655
passive immunity, p. 655
vaccination, p. 655
pasteurization, p. 658
virus, p. 658
infectious disease, p. 661
biological vector, p. 661
sexually transmitted disease (STD), p. 662
noninfectious diseases, p. 666
allergy, p. 666
allergen, p. 667
chemotherapy, p. 670

Science Journal Student responses should include a foreign substance invading the blood and being attacked by white blood cells.

INTERACTIVE CHALKBOARD with Image Bank

PowerPoint® Presentations

This CD-ROM is an editable Microsoft® PowerPoint® presentation that includes:

- a pre-made presentation for every chapter
- interactive graphics
- animations
- audio clips
- image bank
- all new section and chapter questions
- Standardized Test Practice
- transparencies
- pre-lab questions for all labs
- Foldables directions
- links to life.msscience.com

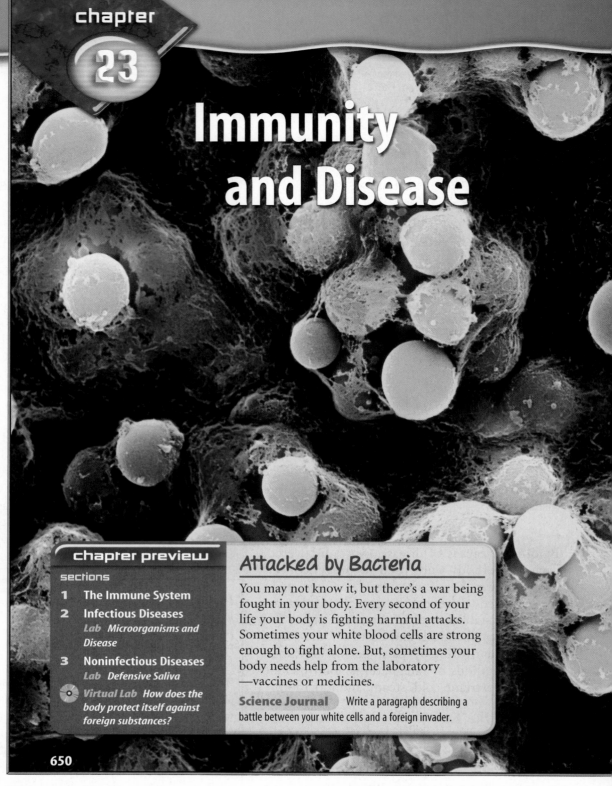

Immunity and Disease

chapter preview

sections

1 The Immune System

2 Infectious Diseases
Lab Microorganisms and Disease

3 Noninfectious Diseases
Lab Defensive Saliva

Virtual Lab How does the body protect itself against foreign substances?

Attacked by Bacteria

You may not know it, but there's a war being fought in your body. Every second of your life your body is fighting harmful attacks. Sometimes your white blood cells are strong enough to fight alone. But, sometimes your body needs help from the laboratory —vaccines or medicines.

Science Journal Write a paragraph describing a battle between your white cells and a foreign invader.

650

Theme Connection

Systems and Interactions One major theme of science is interaction among systems. This chapter focuses on interactions within the body. Natural defenses in the body aid in preventing disease. Vaccines also provide active immunity to body systems.

About the Photo

Fighting Infection The yellow spheres in this scanning electron micrograph are *Streptococcus pyrogens* bacteria. These bacteria grow like a string of beads and are among the most common disease-causing bacteria in humans. *S. pyrogens* can cause a sore throat and is associated with strep throat and scarlet fever. The bacteria can spread from person to person when bacteria-containing droplets are coughed or exhaled into the air.

Start-Up Activities

How do diseases spread?

Knowing how diseases are spread will help you understand how your body fights disease. You can discover one way diseases are spread by doing the following lab.

1. Wash your hands before and after this lab. Don't touch your face until the lab is completed and your hands are washed.

2. Work with a partner. Place a drop of peppermint food flavoring on a cotton ball. Pretend that the flavoring is a mass of cold viruses.

3. Use the cotton ball to rub an X over the palm of your right hand. Let it dry.

4. Shake hands with your partner.

5. Have your partner shake hands with another student. Then each student should smell their hands.

6. **Think Critically** In your Science Journal, note how many persons your "virus" infected. Write a paragraph describing some ways the spread of diseases could be stopped.

Classifying Diseases Make the following Foldable to classify human diseases as either infectious or noninfectious.

STEP 1 Fold a sheet of paper in half lengthwise.

STEP 2 Fold paper down 2.5 cm from the top. (Hint: From the tip of your index finger to your middle knuckle is about 2.5 cm.)

STEP 3 Open and draw lines along the 2.5-cm fold. Label as shown.

Read and Write As you read the chapter, classify human diseases as infectious or noninfectious by listing them on the proper fold.

Preview this chapter's content and activities at life.msscience.com

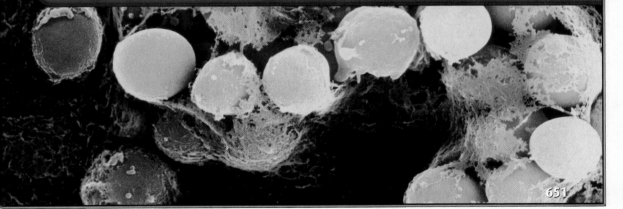

651

Purpose Use this Launch Lab to introduce students to how disease can spread. L1 ELL

LS Kinesthetic

Preparation Before beginning this activity, obtain food flavoring and cotton balls.

Materials peppermint food flavoring, one cotton ball for each pair

Alternate Materials Other flavors, such as orange, almond, or banana, can be used.

Teaching Strategies

• Have students discuss how the mass of cold virus could have gotten on the hands in the first place.
• Have students infer whether the infection could be passed around on drinking glasses and handkerchiefs.

Safety Precautions Following the activity, have students wash their hands thoroughly.

Think Critically

Possible answer: Many diseases are spread through physical contact. The spread of some diseases can be stopped by carefully washing eating utensils and hands with warm water and soap.

Assessment

Oral Have students determine whether any flavoring remains on their hands after washing them. Discuss how washing hands affects the spread of disease. Use **Performance Assessment in the Science Classroom,** p. 89.

 Dinah Zike Study Fold

Student preparation materials for this Foldable are available in the Chapter *FAST FILE* Resources.

The Immune System

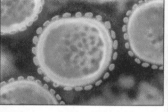
as you read

What You'll Learn

- **Describe** the natural defenses your body has against disease.
- **Explain** the difference between an antigen and an antibody.
- **Compare and contrast** active and passive immunity.

Why It's Important

Your body's defenses fight the pathogens that you are exposed to every day.

🔍 Review Vocabulary

enzyme: a type of protein that speeds up chemical reactions in the body

New Vocabulary

- immune system
- antigen
- antibody
- active immunity
- passive immunity
- vaccination

Lines of Defense

The Sun has just begun to peek over the horizon, casting an orange glow on the land. A skunk ambles down a dirt path. Behind the skunk, you and your dog come over a hill for your morning exercise. Suddenly, the skunk stops and raises its tail high in the air. Your dog creeps forward. "No!" you shout. The dog ignores your command. Without further warning, the skunk sprays your dog. Yelping pitifully and carrying an awful stench, your dog takes off. The skunk used its scent to protect itself. Its first-line defense was to warn your dog with its posture. Its second-line defense was its spray. Just as the skunk protects itself from predators, your body also protects itself from harm.

Your body has many ways to defend itself. Its first-line defenses work against harmful substances and all types of disease-causing organisms, called pathogens (PA thuh junz). Your second-line defenses are specific and work against specific pathogens. This complex group of defenses is called your **immune system.** Tonsils, shown in **Figure 1,** are one of the immune system organs that protect your body.

✔ Reading Check *What types of defenses does your body have?*

First-Line Defenses Your skin and respiratory, digestive, and circulatory systems are first-line defenses against pathogens. As shown in **Figure 2,** the skin is a barrier that prevents many pathogens from entering your body. Although most pathogens can't get through unbroken skin, they can get into your body easily through a cut or through your mouth and the membranes in your nose and eyes. The conditions on the skin can affect pathogens. Perspiration contains substances that can slow the growth of some pathogens. At times, secretions from the skin's oil glands and perspiration are acidic. Some pathogens cannot grow in this acidic environment.

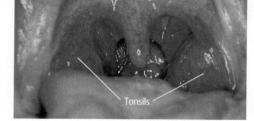

Tonsils

Figure 1 Tonsils help prevent infection in your respiratory and digestive tract.

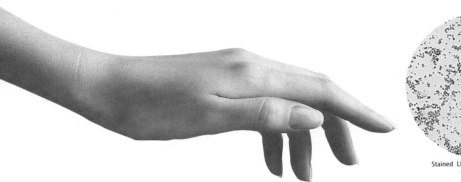

Stained LM Magnification: 1000×

Internal First-Line Defenses Your respiratory system traps pathogens with hairlike structures, called cilia (SIH lee uh), and mucus. Mucus contains an enzyme that weakens the cell walls of some pathogens. When you cough or sneeze, you get rid of some of these trapped pathogens.

Your digestive system has several defenses against pathogens—saliva, enzymes, hydrochloric acid, and mucus. Saliva in your mouth contains substances that kill bacteria. Also, enzymes (EN zimez) in your stomach, pancreas, and liver help destroy pathogens. Hydrochloric acid in your stomach helps digest your food. It also kills some bacteria and stops the activity of some viruses that enter your body on the food that you eat. The mucus found on the walls of your digestive tract contains a chemical that coats bacteria and prevents them from binding to the inner lining of your digestive organs.

Your circulatory system contains white blood cells, like the one in **Figure 3,** that surround and digest foreign organisms and chemicals. These white blood cells constantly patrol your body, sweeping up and digesting bacteria that invade. They slip between cells of tiny blood vessels called capillaries. If the white blood cells cannot destroy the bacteria fast enough, you might develop a fever. Many pathogens are sensitive to temperature. A slight increase in body temperature slows their growth and activity but speeds up your body's defenses.

Inflammation When tissue is damaged by injury or infected by pathogens, it becomes inflamed. Signs of inflammation include redness, temperature increase, swelling, and pain. Chemical substances released by damaged cells cause capillary walls to expand, allowing more blood to flow into the area. Other chemicals released by damaged tissue attract certain white blood cells that surround and take in pathogenic bacteria. If pathogens get past these first-line defenses, your body uses another line of defense called specific immunity.

Figure 2 Most pathogens, like the staphylococci bacteria shown above, cannot pass through unbroken skin.
Infer *what happens if staphylococci bacteria enter your body through your skin.*

Figure 3 A white blood cell leaves a capillary. It will search out and destroy harmful microorganisms in your body tissues.

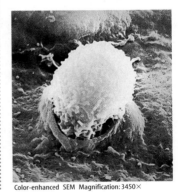

Color-enhanced SEM Magnification: 3450×

SECTION 1 The Immune System **653**

2 Teach

Caption Answer
Figure 2 The pathogen could infect the wound and could enter the bloodstream to infect the rest of the body.

Activity
Sweat Acidity Have students test the acidity of their sweat using pH indicator paper. Sweat may range from pH 3.0 to slightly alkaline. L2 **Kinesthetic**

Fun Fact

The saliva of cats and dogs contains various substances that can kill bacteria. The licking of wounds aids in the healing process.

Discussion
Fevers Why should a fever not be ignored? Fevers are an indication of infection, a sign that the body is fighting a pathogen. Temperatures over 104°F are potentially dangerous and medical help should be sought immediately.

IDENTIFYING Misconceptions

Fever Cures There is an old adage that "sweating out a fever" will rid the body of it. Extra blankets and keeping a room extra warm will only cause the patient's temperature to rise. Drinking lots of fluids and taking medicines recommended by a physician are better remedies.

Differentiated Instruction

Challenge Have students research the discovery of chemicals that destroy or inhibit the functions of viruses. Have them write two or three paragraphs on what they find. L3 **ELL** **Linguistic** P

Visual Learning

Figure 2 Have students discuss how the surface of the skin may be broken. Possible answers: Falls and accidents may cause cuts, punctures, and scrapes of the skin that can allow the entrance of bacteria.

Figure 4 The response of your immune system to disease-causing organisms can be divided into four steps—recognition, mobilization, disposal, and immunity.
Explain the function of B cells.

Specific Immunity When your body fights disease, it is battling complex molecules that don't belong there. Molecules that are foreign to your body are called **antigens** (AN tih junz). Antigens can be separate molecules or they can be found on the surface of a pathogen. For example, the protein in the cell membrane of a bacterium can be an antigen. When your immune system recognizes molecules as being foreign to your body, as in **Figure 4,** special lymphocytes called T cells respond. Lymphocytes are a type of white blood cell. One type of T cells, called killer T cells, releases enzymes that help destroy invading foreign matter. Another type of T cells, called helper T cells, turns on the immune system. They stimulate other lymphocytes, known as B cells, to form antibodies.

An **antibody** is a protein made in response to a specific antigen. The antibody attaches to the antigen and makes it useless. This can happen in several ways. The pathogen might not be able to stay attached to a cell. It might be changed in such a way that a killer T cell can capture it more easily or the pathogen can be destroyed.

✓ Reading Check **What is an antibody?**

Another type of lymphocyte, called memory B cells, also has antibodies for the specific pathogen. Memory B cells remain in the blood ready to defend against an invasion by that same pathogen another time.

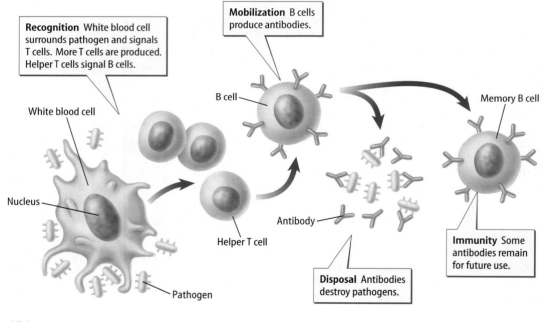

654 CHAPTER 23 Immunity and Disease

Active Immunity Antibodies help your body build defenses in two ways—actively and passively. In **active immunity** your body makes its own antibodies in response to an antigen. **Passive immunity** results when antibodies that have been produced in another animal are introduced into your body.

When a pathogen invades your body and quickly multiplies, you get sick. Your body immediately starts to make antibodies to attack the pathogen. After enough antibodies form, you usually get better. Some antibodies stay on duty in your blood, and more are produced rapidly if the pathogen enters your body again. Because of this defense system you usually get certain diseases such as chicken pox only once. Why can you catch a cold over and over? There are many different cold viruses that give you similar symptoms. As you grow older and are exposed to many more types of pathogens, you will build immunity to each one.

Vaccination A vaccine is a form of an antigen that gives you immunity against a disease. A vaccine only can prevent a disease, not cure it. The process of giving a vaccine by injection or by mouth is called **vaccination.** If a specific vaccine is injected into your body, your body forms antibodies against that pathogen. If you later encounter the same pathogen, your bloodstream already has antibodies that are needed to fight and destroy it. Vaccines have helped reduce cases of childhood diseases, as shown in **Table 1.**

Mini LAB

Determining Reproduction Rates

Procedure

1. Place **one penny** on a table. Imagine that the penny is a bacterium that can divide every 10 min.
2. Place **two pennies** below the first penny to form a triangle. These represent the two new bacteria after the first bacterium divides.
3. Repeat three more divisions, placing two pennies under each penny as described above.
4. Calculate how many bacteria you would have after 5 h of reproduction. Graph your data.

Analysis

1. How many bacteria are present after 5 h?
2. Why is it important to take antibiotics promptly if you have an infection?

Try at Home

Mini LAB

Purpose to model bacterial reproduction

Materials pennies, paper, pencil, calculator

Teaching Strategies

• Make sure students understand that bacteria reproduce exponentially, allowing their populations to grow very quickly.
• Students should label the vertical axis of the graph *Bacteria* (thousands) and the horizontal axis *Time* (hours).

Analysis

1. At the five-hour point, there will be 1,073,741,824 bacteria.
2. Taking antibiotics promptly will inhibit the reproduction of bacteria. It is also important to take all of the antibiotic prescribed. Failing to do so will leave a few bacteria that can reinfect the body.

Assessment

Performance To further assess students' understanding of bacterial infections, have them research a variety of bacteria that cause common infections. Possible topics: staphylococci, streptococci, *Mycobacterium tuberculosis, Treponema pallidum* Use **Performance Assessment in the Science Classroom,** p. 97.

Try at Home

Table 1 Annual Cases of Disease Before and After Vaccine Availability in the U.S.		
Disease	**Before**	**After**
Measles	503,282	89
Diptheria	175,885	1
Tetanus	1,314	34
Mumps	152,209	606
Rubella	47,745	345
Pertussis (whooping cough)	147,271	6,279

Data from the National Immunization Program, CDC

Differentiated Instruction

Visually Impaired Photocopy and enlarge Figure 4. Use a felt-tip pen to outline the edges of the cells and the arrows in the illustration for use by visually impaired students. L2

Curriculum Connection

History In 1796, Edward Jenner pioneered the use of vaccines by inoculating a young boy with cowpox material to keep him from contracting the deadly disease smallpox. Editorial cartoons in the newspaper ridiculed the treatment and showed illustrations of people growing cow parts on their bodies as a result of being vaccinated. Have students find out more about Jenner's work. L2

3 Assess

DAILY INTERVENTION

Check for Understanding

Visual-Spatial Have students make a flowchart detailing the four steps of an immune system response. [L2]

Reteach

Body Defenses Use an anatomy chart or model to illustrate the various body systems involved in defense against microbes. [L2] [LS]
Visual-Spatial

☑ Assessment

Portfolio To assess students' understanding of active and passive immunity, have them draw a concept map comparing and contrasting the two. Use **Performance Assessment in the Science Classroom,** p. 161.

Virtual Labs

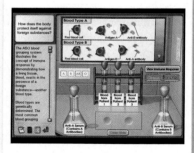

Foreign Invaders *How does the body protect itself against foreign substances?*

Figure 5 The Td vaccine, which protects against tetanus and diphtheria, usually is injected into the arm.

Passive Immunity Passive immunity does not last as long as active immunity does. For example, you were born with all the antibodies that your mother had in her blood. However, these antibodies stayed with you for only a few months. Because newborn babies lose their passive immunity in a few months, they need to be vaccinated to develop their own immunity.

Tetanus Tetanus is a disease caused by a common soil bacterium. The bacterium produces a chemical that paralyzes muscles. Puncture wounds, deep cuts, and other wounds can be infected by this bacterium. Several times in early childhood you received active vaccines, as shown in **Figure 5,** that stimulated antibody production to tetanus toxin. You should continue to get vaccines or boosters every ten years to maintain protection. Booster shots for diphtheria, which is a dangerous infectious respiratory disease, are given in the same vaccine with tetanus.

---

section 1 review

Summary

Lines of Defense

- Your body's immune system protects you from harmful substances called pathogens.
- First-line defenses work against harmful substances and all types of pathogens.
- Second-line defenses work against specific pathogens.
- Antibodies help protect your body against specific foreign molecules called antigens.
- Your body gets antibodies through active immunity and passive immunity.
- Vaccines help you develop active immunity against a disease.
- You need to receive booster shots for some vaccines to maintain protection.

Self Check

1. **Describe** how harmful bacteria cause infections in your body.
2. **List** the natural defenses your body has against disease.
3. **Explain** how your immune system reacts when it detects an antigen.
4. **Compare and contrast** active and passive immunity.
5. **Think Critically** Several diseases have symptoms similar to those of measles. Why doesn't the measles vaccine protect you from all of these diseases?

Applying Skills

6. **Make Models** Create models of the different types of T cells, antigens, and B cells from clay, construction paper, or other art materials. Use them to explain how T cells function in the immune system.

Science Online life.msscience.com/self_check_quiz

---

section 1 review

1. Harmful bacteria enter your body and rapidly reproduce, causing you to get sick.
2. white blood cells, cilia, mucus, coughing, enzymes in the digestive system, hydrochloric acid solution, active immunity, sneezing, saliva, skin, perspiration, fever
3. The body starts to make antibodies against the antigen to destroy it. After the antigen is destroyed, some antibodies remain in the bloodstream to combat the return of the antigen.
4. Both confer immunity; active immunity—the body makes its own antibodies, long-term immunity; passive immunity—antibodies are introduced, short-term immunity.
5. Antibodies formed to fight a specific antigen will protect only against that antigen.
6. Models should show the role of T cells in the response of the immune system to antigens.

section 2

Infectious Diseases

Disease in History

For centuries, people have feared outbreaks of disease. The plague, smallpox, and influenza have killed millions of people worldwide. Today, the causes of these diseases are known, and treatments can prevent or cure them. But even today, there are diseases such as the Ebola virus in Africa that cannot be cured. Outbreaks of new diseases, such as severe acute respiratory syndrome (SARS), shown in **Table 2,** also occur.

Microorganisms With the invention of the microscope in the latter part of the seventeenth century, bacteria, yeast, and mold spores were seen for the first time. However, it took almost 200 years more to discover the relationship between some of them and disease. Scientists gradually learned that microorganisms were responsible for fermentation and decay. If decay-causing microorganisms could cause changes in other organisms, it was hypothesized that microorganisms could cause diseases and carry them from one person to another. Scientists did not make a connection between viruses and disease transmission until the late 1800s and early 1900s.

as you read

What You'll Learn

- **Describe** the work of Pasteur, Koch, and Lister in the discovery and prevention of disease.
- **Identify** diseases caused by viruses and bacteria.
- **List** sexually transmitted diseases, their causes, and treatments.
- **Explain** how HIV affects the immune system.

Why It's Important

You can help prevent certain illnesses if you know what causes disease and how disease spreads.

Review Vocabulary

protist: a one- or many-celled organism that lives in moist or wet surroundings

New Vocabulary

- pasteurization
- virus
- infectious disease
- biological vector
- sexually transmitted disease (STD)

Table 2 Probable Cases of SARS (November 1, 2002 to July 7, 2003)		
Country	**Number of Cases**	**Number of Deaths**
Canada	251	38
China	7,756	730
Singapore	206	32
United States	73	0
Vietnam	63	5
Other countries	90	7

Data from the World Health Organization

---

1 Motivate

Bellringer

Section Focus Transparencies also are available on the Interactive Chalkboard CD-ROM.

L2 ELL

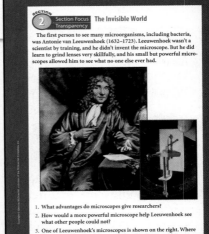

Tie to Prior Knowledge

SARS Have students compare the student population figure of their school with the 812 people who died of SARS worldwide. This is a graphic way of illustrating the effect disease has on history.

Section 2 Resource Manager

Chapter _FAST FILE_ Resources

Transparency Activity, p. 43

MiniLAB, p. 4

Reinforcement, p. 26

Enrichment, p. 29

Directed Reading for Content Mastery, p. 19

Lab Worksheet, pp. 5–6

Cultural Diversity, p. 17

Mathematics Skill Activities, p. 1

Reading and Writing Skill Activities, pp. 25, 31

Quick Demo

Bacteria

Materials microscope, prepared microscope slides of various stained bacteria (different sizes and shapes)

Estimated Time 10 minutes

Procedure Using a microscope, show students prepared slides of various bacteria. Ask students to compare the sizes and shapes of the different bacteria.

Reading Check

Answer The virus invades the host cell and multiples within it; the host cell dies when the viruses break out of it.

INTEGRATE History

Jenner realized that dairy workers were resistant to catching smallpox if they had acquired cowpox, a similar, but milder disease. To test his theory, he infected a young boy with cowpox, then later with smallpox. The boy became ill, then made a full recovery.

Make a Model

Display Koch's Rules Have students prepare a display of Koch's rules. Use agar or gelatin petri dishes. Place several bright-colored cake decorations (nonpareils) on the surface of the medium. The color will diffuse onto the surface to give the appearance of bacterial colonies. L2 LS **Kinesthetic and Visual-Spatial**

INTEGRATE History

Disease Immunity Edward Jenner demonstrated that a vaccine could be produced to prevent smallpox. However, it wasn't until Louis Pasteur applied his germ theory to the process that the mechanism of vaccinations was understood. Pasteur demonstrated that germs cause diseases and that vaccines, which contained small amounts of disease organisms, could cause the body to build immunity to that disease without causing it. Research Jenner and write a summary in your Science Journal about his discovery of the smallpox vaccine.

Disease Organisms The French chemist Louis Pasteur learned that microorganisms cause disease in humans. Many scientists of his time did not believe that microorganisms could harm larger organisms, such as humans. However, Pasteur discovered that microorganisms could spoil wine and milk. He then realized that microorganisms could attack the human body in the same way. Pasteur invented **pasteurization** (pas chuh ruh ZAY shun), which is the process of heating a liquid to a specific temperature that kills most bacteria.

Today, it is known that many diseases are caused by bacteria, certain viruses, protists (PROH tihsts), or fungi. Bacteria cause tetanus, tuberculosis, strep throat, and bacterial pneumonia. Malaria and sleeping sickness are caused by protists. Fungi are the pathogens for athlete's foot and ringworm. Viruses are the cause of many common diseases—colds, influenza, AIDS, measles, mumps, smallpox, and SARS.

Many harmful bacteria that infect your body can reproduce rapidly. The conditions in your body, such as temperature and available nutrients, help the bacteria grow and multiply. Bacteria can slow down the normal growth and metabolic activities of body cells and tissues. Some bacteria even produce toxins that kill cells on contact.

A **virus** is a minute piece of genetic material surrounded by a protein coating that infects and multiplies in host cells. The host cells die when the viruses break out of them. These new viruses infect other cells, leading to the destruction of tissues or the interruption of vital body activities.

Reading Check *What is the relationship between a virus and a host cell?*

Pathogenic protists, such as the organisms that cause malaria, can destroy tissues and blood cells or interfere with normal body functions. In a similar manner, fungus infections can cause athlete's foot, nonhealing wounds, chronic lung disease, or inflammation of the membranes of the brain.

Koch's Rules Many diseases caused by pathogens can be treated with medicines. In many cases, these organisms need to be identified before specific treatment can begin. Today, a method developed in the nineteenth century still is used to identify organisms.

Pasteur may have shown that bacteria cause disease, but he didn't know how to tell which specific organism causes which disease. It was a young German doctor, Robert Koch, who first developed a way to isolate and grow one type of bacterium at a time, as shown in **Figure 6.**

658 **CHAPTER 23** Immunity and Disease

 LAB DEMONSTRATION

Purpose to observe microorganism growth

Materials sterile agar or gelatin plates, masking tape

Preparation Make or obtain prepared sterile agar petri plates. Have students wash their hands.

Procedure Have students lightly press their fingertips onto the surface of a sterile agar plate. Tape plates shut and place them in a dark place. Observe daily for several days. Do not open plates. Properly dispose of plates. Wash hands thoroughly.

Expected Outcome Small bacterial colonies and mold growth should be observed.

Assessment

Why was there microbial growth even after hands were washed? Not all microorganisms were washed off the hands; some may have been in the air. How could more microorganisms have been removed from the hands? by washing them with antiseptic

Figure 6

In the 1880s, German doctor Robert Koch developed a series of methods for identifying which organism was the cause of a particular disease. Koch's Rules are still in use today. Developed mainly for determining the cause of particular diseases in humans and other animals, these rules have been used for identifying diseases in plants as well.

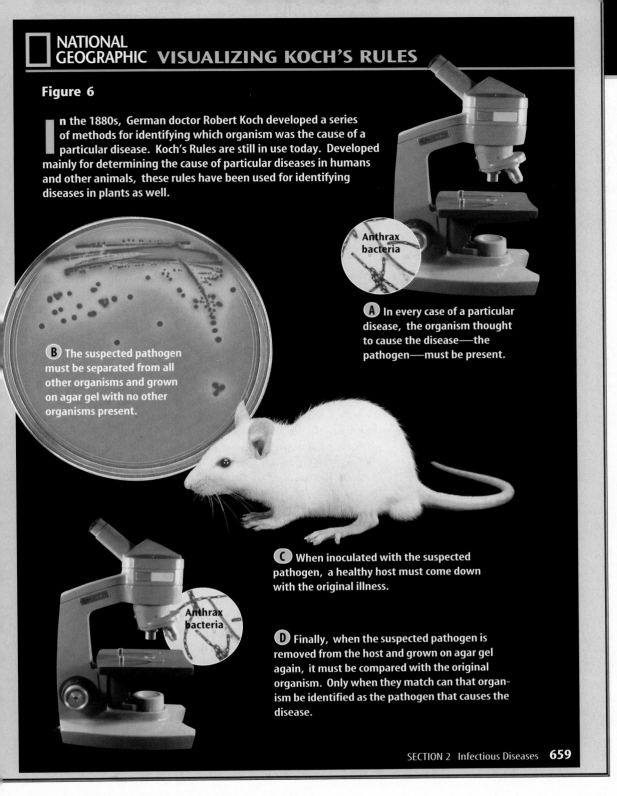

Anthrax bacteria

A In every case of a particular disease, the organism thought to cause the disease—the pathogen—must be present.

B The suspected pathogen must be separated from all other organisms and grown on agar gel with no other organisms present.

C When inoculated with the suspected pathogen, a healthy host must come down with the original illness.

Anthrax bacteria

D Finally, when the suspected pathogen is removed from the host and grown on agar gel again, it must be compared with the original organism. Only when they match can that organism be identified as the pathogen that causes the disease.

SECTION 2 Infectious Diseases **659**

Visualizing Koch's Rules

Have students examine the pictures and read the captions. Then ask the following questions.

Why does the suspected pathogen need to be grown on agar with no other organisms present? A suspected organism needs to be isolated (grown in a pure culture) to make sure that the suspected pathogen and only the suspected pathogen is inoculated into the healthy host. If not, there would be no way to know which organism caused the disease.

Why is it important to prove that a particular pathogen causes a particular disease? Possible answer: Knowing which pathogen causes a disease can help scientists develop treatments and preventative measures.

Activity

Skit Have students write and perform a skit demonstrating Koch's rules. Possible characters include Robert Koch, and a person or animal with a disease. Props: mouse, microscope, and petri dishes. L2 IS **Interpersonal**

Differentiated Instruction

English-Language Learners Have students prepare a chart of the contributions made by Pasteur, Koch, and Lister to the discovery and prevention of disease. Use the charts to check their understanding of these concepts. L2

Challenge Have students find out more about anthrax, a disease that Koch studied. Possible topics to investigate include which animals are affected, symptoms of the disease, how the disease is detected, and treatment. Have students make posters to explain what they learned. L3

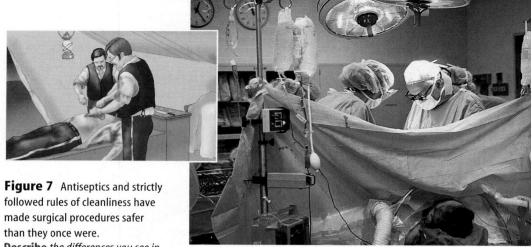

Figure 7 Antiseptics and strictly followed rules of cleanliness have made surgical procedures safer than they once were.
Describe *the differences you see in the two operating scenes shown.*

Mini LAB

Observing Antiseptic Action

Procedure
1. Place a few grains of **dried yeast** onto a **glass plate** or a saucer.
2. Add two drops of **hydrogen peroxide** to the yeast. Observe.
3. Clean up and wash hands before removing goggles.

Analysis
1. How does the action of hydrogen peroxide mechanically clean a wound?
2. Explain why hydrogen peroxide is classified as an antiseptic.

Keeping Clean Washing your hands before or after certain activities should be part of your daily routine. Restaurant employees are required to wash their hands immediately after using the rest room. Medical professionals wash their hands before examining each patient. However, hand washing was not always a routine, even for doctors. Into the late 1800s, doctors such as those in **Figure 7** regularly operated in their street clothes and with bare, unwashed hands. A bloody apron and well-used tools were considered signs of prestige for a surgeon. More patients died from the infections that they contracted during or after the surgery than from the surgery itself.

Joseph Lister, an English surgeon, recognized the relationship between the infection rate and cleanliness. Lister dramatically reduced the number of deaths among his patients by washing their skin and his hands with carbolic (kar BAH lihk) acid, which is a liquid that kills pathogens. Lister also used carbolic acid to clean his instruments and soak bandages, and he even sprayed the air with it. The odor was strong and it irritated the skin, but more and more people began to survive surgical procedures.

Modern Operating Procedures Today antiseptics and antiseptic soaps are used to kill pathogens on skin. Every person on the surgical team washes his or her hands thoroughly and wears sterile gloves and a covering gown. The patient's skin is cleaned around the area of the body to be operated on and then covered with sterile cloths. Tools that are used to operate on the patient and all operating room equipment also are sterilized. Even the air is filtered.

✔ Reading Check
What are three ways that pathogens are reduced in today's operating room?

660 CHAPTER 23 Immunity and Disease

How Diseases Are Spread

You walk into your kitchen before school. Your younger sister sits at the table eating a bowl of cereal. She has a fever, a runny nose, and a cough. She coughs loudly. "Hey, cover your mouth! I don't want to catch your cold," you tell her. A disease that is caused by a virus, bacterium, protist, or fungus and is spread from an infected organism or the environment to another organism is called an **infectious disease.** Infectious diseases are spread by direct contact with the infected organism, through water and air, on food, by contact with contaminated objects, and by disease-carrying organisms called **biological vectors.** Examples of vectors that have been sources of disease are rats, birds, cats, dogs, mosquitoes, fleas, and flies, as shown in **Figure 8.**

People also can be carriers of disease. When you have influenza and sneeze, you expel thousands of virus particles into the air. Colds and many other diseases are spread through contact. Each time you turn a doorknob, press the button on a water fountain, or use a telephone, your skin comes in contact with bacteria and viruses, which is why regular handwashing is recommended. The Centers for Disease Control and Prevention (CDC) in Atlanta, Georgia, monitors the spread of diseases throughout the United States. The CDC also tracks worldwide epidemics and watches for diseases brought into the United States.

Figure 8 When flies land on food, they can transport pathogens from one location to another.

Applying Science

Has the annual percentage of deaths from major diseases changed?

Each year, many people die from diseases. Medical science has found numerous ways to treat and cure disease. Have new medicines, improved surgery techniques, and healthier lifestyles helped decrease the number of deaths from disease? By using your ability to interpret data tables, you can find out.

Identifying the Problem
The table to the right shows the percentage of total deaths due to six major diseases for a 50-year period. Study the data. Can you see any trends in the percentage of deaths?

Solving the Problem
1. Has the percentage increased for any disease that is listed?
2. What factors could have contributed to this increase?

Percentage of Deaths Due to Major Disease				
Disease	Year			
	1950	1980	1990	2000
Heart	37.1	38.3	33.5	29.6
Cancer	14.6	20.9	23.5	23.0
Stroke	10.8	8.6	6.7	7.0
Diabetes	1.7	1.8	2.2	2.9
Pneumonia and flu	3.3	2.7	3.7	2.7

Fun Fact

Joseph Lister's ideas led to another advancement in medical history. Robert Johnson heard Lister speak on antiseptic techniques in 1876. Ten years later, Johnson and his brothers founded Johnson & Johnson to produce sterile surgical dressings. An employee attached small pieces of the sterile gauze to surgical tape, producing the first adhesive bandage.

IDENTIFYING Misconceptions

STD Transmission There is a belief that sexually transmitted diseases can be contracted through casual contact, such as touching a person who has the disease or handling an object touched by such a person. STDs are not transmitted through casual contact. There must be direct contact with bodily fluids such as blood, semen, or vaginal secretions.

Teacher FYI

Hidden Syphilis In the development of untreated syphilis, there is a period when victims may believe they have healed. Lesions heal and outward symptoms disappear. However, the bacteria have already migrated to many parts of the body such as the spleen, liver, and various sites in the circulatory and nervous systems. After a few months the bacteria again manifest themselves through skin and mouth rashes and the loss of hair and teeth. These outward symptoms also may disappear and once again give false hope of healing. If untreated for long enough, syphilis can attack the brain and cause mental illness.

Sexually Transmitted Diseases

Infectious diseases that are passed from person to person during sexual contact are called **sexually transmitted diseases (STDs)**. STDs are caused by bacteria or viruses.

Bacterial STDs Gonorrhea (gah nuh REE uh), chlamydia (kluh MIH dee uh), and syphilis (SIH fuh lus) are STDs caused by bacteria. The bacteria that cause gonorrhea and syphilis are shown in **Figure 9.** A person may have gonorrhea or chlamydia for some time before symptoms appear. When symptoms do appear, they can include painful urination, genital discharge, and genital sores. Antibiotics are used to treat these diseases. Some of the bacteria that cause gonorrhea may be resistant to the antibiotics usually used to treat the infection. However, the disease usually can be treated with other antibiotics. If they are untreated, gonorrhea and chlamydia can leave a person sterile because the reproductive organs can be damaged permanently.

Syphilis has three stages. In stage 1, a sore that lasts 10 to 14 days appears on the mouth or genitals. Stage 2 may involve a rash, fever, and swollen lymph glands. Within weeks to a year, these symptoms usually disappear. The person with syphilis often believes that the disease has gone away, but it hasn't. If he or she does not seek treatment, the disease advances to stage 3, when syphilis may infect the cardiovascular and nervous systems. In all stages, syphilis is treatable with antibiotics. However, the damage to body organs in stage 3 cannot be reversed and death can result.

Viral STDs Genital herpes, a lifelong viral disease, causes painful blisters on the sex organs. This type of herpes can be transmitted during sexual contact or from an infected mother to her child during birth. The herpes virus hides in the body for long periods of time and then reappears suddenly. Herpes has no cure, and no vaccine can prevent it. However, the symptoms of herpes can be treated with antiviral medicines.

Figure 9 Bacteria that cause gonorrhea and syphilis can be destroyed with antibiotics.
Explain why a person might not get treatment for a syphilis infection.

Gonorrhea bacteria

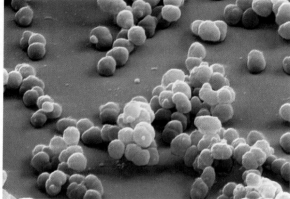

Color-enhanced TEM Magnification: 12000×

Syphilis bacteria

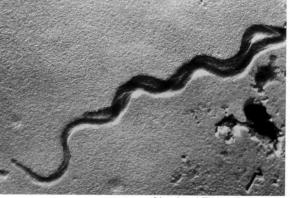

Color-enhanced SEM Magnification: 45000×

662 CHAPTER 23 Immunity and Disease

Curriculum Connection

Health The previous indiscriminate use of antibiotics in the treatment of STDs has resulted in the development of drug-resistant strains of bacteria. Modern methods of treatment use more potent forms of antibiotics and combinations of drugs. Ask students to write a paragraph about the problems that drug-resistant bacteria pose for individuals and society. L2 **ELL** IS **Linguistic**

HIV and Your Immune System

Human immunodeficiency virus (HIV) can exist in blood and body fluids. This virus can hide in body cells, sometimes for years. You can become infected with HIV by having sex with an HIV-infected person or by reusing an HIV-contaminated hypodermic needle for an injection. However, a freshly unwrapped sterile needle cannot transmit infection. The risk of getting HIV through blood transfusion is small because all donated blood is tested for the presence of HIV. A pregnant female with HIV can infect her child when the virus passes through the placenta. The child also may become infected from contacts with blood during the birth process or when nursing after birth.

Reading Check *What are ways that a person can become infected with HIV?*

HIV cannot multiply outside the body, and it does not survive long in the environment. The virus cannot be transmitted by touching an infected person, by handling objects used by the person unless they are contaminated with body fluids, or from contact with a toilet seat.

AIDS An HIV infection can lead to Acquired Immune Deficiency Syndrome (AIDS), which is a disease that attacks the body's immune system. HIV, as shown in **Figure 10,** is different from other viruses. It attacks the helper T cells in the immune system. The virus enters the T cell and multiplies. When the infected cell bursts open, it releases more HIV. These infect other T cells. Soon, so many T cells are destroyed that not enough B cells are stimulated to produce antibodies. The body no longer has an effective way to fight invading antigens. The immune system then is unable to fight HIV or any other pathogen. For this reason, when people with AIDS die it is from other diseases such as tuberculosis (too bur kyuh LOH sus), pneumonia, or cancer.

From 1981 to 2001, more than 816,000 cases of AIDS were documented in the United States. At this time the disease has no known cure. However, several medications help treat AIDS in some patients. One group of medicines interferes with the way that the virus multiplies in the host cell and is effective if it is used in the early stages of the disease. Another group of medicines that is being tested blocks the entrance of HIV into the host cell. These medicines prevent the pathogen from binding to the cell's surface.

Science Online

Topic: AIDS
Visit life.msscience.com for Web links to information about the number of AIDS cases worldwide.

Activity Make a graph showing the number of AIDS cases in seven countries.

Figure 10 A person can be infected with HIV and not show any symptoms of the infection for several years.
Infer *why this characteristic makes the spread of AIDS more likely.*

Color-enhanced TEM Magnification: 40000×

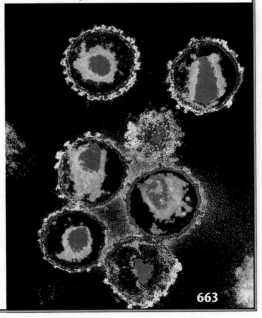

Teacher FYI

AIDS Beginnings The first case of AIDS was reported in the United States in 1981. It was not until 1984 that research teams in France and the United States identified the virus responsible for the disease. There is evidence that the disease was originally transmitted from African green monkeys to humans, possibly from the bite of a monkey.

Discussion

Detecting HIV How can a person determine if he or she is infected with HIV? A blood sample is taken and analyzed for the antibodies against the virus. The presence of the antibodies confirms the person has HIV.

Caption Answer

Figure 10 A person may not take the necessary health precautions to avoid spreading the virus if he or she is unaware that the disease was contracted.

Cultural Diversity

Native American Herbs Explorers and pioneers in the Americas learned a great deal from Native Americans about the healing power of certain herbs. Have students find out about the use of herbs by Native Americans in the treatment of disease symptoms. Possible topics: ipecac, cinchona, witch hazel, and cascara sagrada L2 IS **Linguistic**

Discussion

Good Health Habits What are other good health habits that can help the body fight disease? Possible answer: Getting sufficient sleep allows the body to repair itself and restore energy resources. Drinking lots of water each day helps maintain body fluids necessary for bodily functions.

3 Assess

DAILY INTERVENTION

Check for Understanding

Linguistic Have students write a paragraph explaining why it is difficult to stop the spread of HIV. L2

Reteach

Microorganisms Review the concept of microorganisms as causes of infections and the need for cleanliness. L1

✔ Assessment

Portfolio Assess students' abilities to recognize cause and effect by having them describe in writing the effect of sneezing on the spread of microorganisms. Use **Performance Assessment in the Science Classroom,** p. 159.

Figure 11 Proper hand washing includes using warm water and soap. The soapy lather must be rubbed over the hands, wrists, fingers, and thumbs for 15–20 s. Thoroughly rinse and dry with a clean towel.

Fighting Disease

Washing a small wound with soap and water is the first step in preventing an infection. Cleaning the wound with an antiseptic and covering it with a bandage are other steps. Is it necessary to wash your body to help prevent diseases? Yes! In addition to reducing body odor, washing your body removes and destroys some surface microorganisms. In medical facilities, hand washing, shown in **Figure 11,** is important to reduce the spread of pathogens. It is also important for everyone to wash his or her hands to reduce the spread of disease.

In your mouth, microorganisms are responsible for mouth odor and tooth decay. Using dental floss and routine tooth brushing keep these organisms under control.

Exercise and good nutrition help the circulatory and respiratory systems work more effectively. Good health habits, including getting enough rest and eating well-balanced meals, can make you less susceptible to the actions of disease organisms such as those that cause colds and flu. Keeping up with recommended immunizations and having annual health checkups also can help you stay healthy.

section 2 review

Summary

Disease in History
- Pasteur, Koch, and Lister played key roles in disease discovery and prevention.

How Diseases Are Spread
- Diseases are spread by air, water, food, animals, and through contact with pathogens.

Sexually Transmitted Diseases
- STDs, such as gonorrhea and herpes, are caused by either bacteria or viruses.

HIV and Your Immune System
- HIV can lead to AIDS, a disease of the immune system.

Fighting Disease
- Cleanliness, exercise, and good health habits can help prevent disease.

Self Check

1. **Explain** how the discoveries of Pasteur, Koch, and Lister help in the battle against the spread of disease.
2. **Identify** three infectious diseases caused by a virus and three caused by a bacterium.
3. **Define** sexually transmitted diseases. How are they contracted and treated?
4. **Describe** the way HIV affects the immune system and how it is different from other viruses.
5. **Think Critically** In what ways does Koch's procedure demonstrate the use of scientific methods?

Applying Skills

6. **Recognize Cause and Effect** How is poor cleanliness related to the spread of disease? Write your answer in your Science Journal.

 Science Online life.msscience.com/self_check_quiz

section 2 review

1. Pasteur: discovered bacteria could cause disease; Koch: developed methods to isolate bacteria; Lister: related infection to lack of cleanliness.
2. Possible answer: virus—colds, AIDS, measles; bacterium—tetanus, strep throat, tuberculosis
3. contracted through sexual activity with an infected person; bacterial STDs are treated with antibiotics; symptoms of viral STDs often can be alleviated with antiviral medicines
4. HIV destroys T cells so not enough B cells are stimulated to produce antibodies. Unlike other viruses, HIV attacks the helper T cells.
5. Possible answer: Koch used strict isolation techniques and retested suspected pathogens.
6. Poor cleanliness can allow disease organisms on the body to be transmitted to other people through physical contact or contact with a common object.

MICROORGANISMS AND DISEASE

Microorganisms are everywhere. Washing your hands and disinfecting items you use helps remove some of these organisms.

Real-World Question

How do microorganisms cause infection?

Goals
- **Observe** the transmission of microorganisms.
- **Relate** microorganisms to infections.

Materials

fresh apples (6)   paper towels
rotting apple   sandpaper
rubbing alcohol (5 mL)   cotton ball
self-sealing plastic bags (6)   soap and water
labels and pencil   newspaper
gloves

Safety Precautions

WARNING: *Do not eat the apples.* When you complete the experiment, give all bags to your teacher for disposal.

Procedure

1. **Label** the plastic bags *1* through *6*. Put on gloves. Place a fresh apple in bag *1*.

2. **Rub** the rotting apple over the other five apples. This is your source of microorganisms. **WARNING:** *Do not touch your face.*

3. Put one apple in bag *2*.

4. Hold one apple 1.5 m above a newspaper on the floor and drop it. Put it in bag *3*.

5. Rub one apple with sandpaper. Place this apple in bag *4*.

6. Wash one apple with soap and water. Dry well and put it in bag *5*.

7. Use a cotton ball to spread alcohol over the last apple. Let it air dry. Place it in bag *6*.

8. Seal all bags and put them in a dark place.

9. Copy the data table below. On days 3 and 7, compare all apples without removing them from the bags. **Record** your observations.

Apple Observations

Condition	Day 3	Day 7
1. Fresh	no change	no change
2. Untreated	no change	some decay
3. Dropped	brown spots	some decay
4. Rubbed with sandpaper	some brown at soft areas	decay at soft areas
5. Washed with soap and water	no change	little or no change
6. Covered with alcohol	no change	no change

Conclude and Apply

1. **Infer** how this experiment relates to infections on your skin.

2. **Explain** why it is important to clean a wound.

Communicating Your Data

Prepare a poster illustrating the advantages of washing hands to avoid the spread of disease. Get permission to put the poster near a school rest room.

Communicating Your Data

Students may want to include other good health habits that will help them fight disease. Posters dealing with good nutrition might be posted near the school cafeteria.

Real-World Question

Purpose to predict and explain how microbes spread L2 LS **Visual-Spatial**

Process Skills observe and infer, predict, interpret data, compare and contrast, recognize cause and effect, separate and control variables

Time Required 30 minutes for initial setup; 15 minutes of observation time on days 3 and 7

Procedure

Safety Precautions Have students wash their hands after handling microorganisms. Provide for safe disposal of the rotting apples.

Teaching Strategy Point out that bruises may be caused by bacteria.

Conclude and Apply

1. Pathogens can cause infections by entering damaged or cut surfaces on an organism's skin.
2. Cleaning a wound removes pathogens and prevents infection.

✓ Assessment

Performance To further assess students' understanding of microorganisms and disease, repeat the activity using 3% hydrogen peroxide to clean an infected apple. Determine whether it stops bacterial growth. Use **Performance Assessment in the Science Classroom,** p. 97.

666 **CHAPTER 23** Immunity and Disease

Bellringer

Section Focus Transparencies also are available on the Interactive Chalkboard CD-ROM.

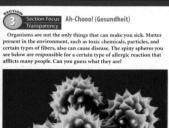

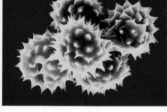

Section Focus Transparency Ah-Chooo! (Gesundheit)

Organisms are not the only things that can make you sick. Matter present in the environment, such as toxic chemicals, particles, and certain types of fibers, also can cause disease. The spiny spheres you see below are responsible for a certain type of allergic reaction that afflicts many people. Can you guess what they are?

1. How do allergies affect people?
2. What kind of help is there for allergy sufferers?
3. If people work around materials such as asbestos, burning tar, or smoke, what kinds of safety equipment should they use?

Immunity and Disease

Tie to Prior Knowledge

Can't Catch It Have students recall that some diseases are not "catching." This means they are not transmitted by pathogens. Have students list as many of these diseases as they can. Possible answers: cancer, heart disease, leukemia, diabetes

---

section
3 Noninfectious Diseases

as you read

What **You'll Learn**
- **Define** noninfectious diseases and list causes of them.
- **Describe** the basic characteristics of cancer.
- **Explain** what happens during an allergic reaction.
- **Explain** how chemicals in the environment can be harmful to humans.

Why **It's Important**

Knowing the causes of noninfectious diseases can help you understand their prevention and treatment.

Review Vocabulary
gene: a section of DNA on a chromosome that carries instructions for making a specific protein

New Vocabulary
- noninfectious disease
- allergy
- allergen
- chemotherapy

Figure 12 Allergic reactions are caused by many things.

Hives are one kind of allergic reaction.

Some common substances stimulate allergic responses in people.

Chronic Disease

It's a beautiful, late-summer day. Flowers are blooming everywhere. You and your cousin hurry to get to the ballpark before the first pitch of the game. "Achoo!" Your cousin sneezes. Her eyes are watery and red. "Oh no! I sure don't want to catch that cold," you mutter. "I don't have a cold," she responds, "it's my allergies." Not all diseases are caused by pathogens. Diseases and disorders such as diabetes, allergies, asthma, cancer, and heart disease are **noninfectious diseases.** They are not spread from one person to another. Many are chronic (KRAH nihk). This means that they can last for a long time. Although some chronic diseases can be cured, others cannot.

Some infectious diseases can be chronic too. For example, deer ticks carry a bacterium that causes Lyme disease. This bacterium can affect the nervous system, heart, and joints for weeks to years. It can become chronic if not treated. Antibiotics will kill the bacteria, but some damage cannot be reversed.

Allergies

If you've had an itchy rash after eating a certain food, you probably have an allergy to that food. An **allergy** is an overly strong reaction of the immune system to a foreign substance. Many people have allergic reactions, such as the one shown in **Figure 12,** to cosmetics, shellfish, strawberries, peanuts, and insect stings. Most allergic reactions are minor. However, severe allergic reactions can occur, causing shock and even death if they aren't treated promptly.

666 **CHAPTER 23** Immunity and Disease

Section 3 Resource Manager

Chapter *FAST FILE* Resources
Transparency Activity, pp. 44
Lab Activity, pp. 13–14
Enrichment, p. 30
Reinforcement, p. 27
Directed Reading for Content Mastery, pp. 19, 20
Lab Worksheet, pp. 7–8

Lab Management and Safety, p. 70
Home and Community Involvement, p. 45
Life Science Critical Thinking/Problem Solving, pp. 4, 17
Performance Assessment in the Science Classroom, p. 48

Allergens Substances that cause an allergic response are called **allergens.** Some chemicals, certain foods, pollen, molds, some antibiotics, and dust are allergens for some people. Some foods cause hives or stomach cramps and diarrhea. Pollen can cause a stuffy nose, breathing difficulties, watery eyes, and a tired feeling in some people. Dust can contain cat and dog dander and dust mites, as shown in **Figure 13.** Asthma (AZ muh) is a lung disorder that is associated with reactions to allergens. A person with asthma can have shortness of breath, wheezing, and coughing when he or she comes into contact with something they are allergic to.

When you come in contact with an allergen, your immune system usually forms antibodies. Your body reacts by releasing chemicals called histamines (HIHS tuh meenz) that promote red, swollen tissues. Antihistamines are medications that can be used to treat allergic reactions and asthma. Some severe allergies are treated with repeated injections of small doses of the allergen. This allows your body to become less sensitive to the allergen.

 **Reading Check** *What does your body release in response to an allergen?*

Diabetes

A chronic disease associated with the levels of insulin produced by the pancreas is diabetes. Insulin is a hormone that enables glucose to pass from the bloodstream into your cells. Doctors recognize two types of diabetes—Type 1 and Type 2. Type 1 diabetes is the result of too little or no insulin production. In Type 2 diabetes, your body cannot properly process the insulin. Symptoms of diabetes include fatigue, excessive thirst, frequent urination, and tingling sensations in the hands and feet.

If glucose levels in the blood remain high for a long time, health problems can develop. These problems can include blurred vision, kidney failure, heart attack, stroke, loss of feeling in the feet, and the loss of consciousness (diabetic coma). Patients with Type 1 diabetes, as shown in **Figure 14,** must monitor their intake of sugars and usually require daily injections of insulin to control their glucose levels. Careful monitoring of diet and weight usually are enough to control Type 2 diabetes. Since 1980, there has been an increase in the number of people with diabetes. Although the cause of diabetes is unknown, scientists have discovered that Type 2 diabetes is more common in people who are overweight and that it might be inherited.

Color-enhanced SEM Magnification: 245×

Figure 13 Dust mites are smaller than a period at the end of a sentence. They can live in pillows, mattresses, carpets, furniture, and other places.

Figure 14 Type 1 diabetes requires daily monitoring by either checking the amount of glucose in blood or the amount excreted in urine.

Teacher FYI

Anaphylactic Shock Sometimes the body may experience an intense reaction to an allergen, causing blood vessels to dilate and bronchiole tubes to constrict. This condition is known as anaphylactic shock and can lead to death if not treated. A single beesting to a hypersensitive person can trigger anaphylactic shock.

✓ **Reading Check**

Answer histamines

Fun Fact

Dander—human or animal skin flakes—is a favorite food of dust mites. Humans shed about six grams of dead skin each week, so dust mites rarely go hungry.

Use an Analogy

Antihistamine Action The neutralizing action of antihistamines to the histamines produced in allergic reactions can be compared to acids neutralizing bases in chemical reactions.

Teacher FYI

Diabetes Numbers An estimated 17 million people in the United States have diabetes, but only two-thirds of them are aware of it. Only about 10 percent of people with diabetes have Type 1; about 90 percent have Type 2.

Differentiated Instruction

Challenge Have a team of students prepare a joint report and a poster on first-aid procedures for individuals who are experiencing a severe allergic reaction. Have them present their material to the class. L3 ELL COOP LEARN IS **Interpersonal**

Teacher FYI

Pollutants and Disease Many people are exposed to chemicals and other pollutants that adversely affect the environment. Chemicals released into the air can damage the ozone layer and produce smog and acid precipitation. Agricultural chemicals build up in our waterways. Research to understand the cause-and-effect relationship between pollutants and some chronic diseases is underway.

Activity

Bottled Water Have students compare the chemicals in bottled spring water with those found in their tap water at home. L2
ELL **Ⓝ Visual-Spatial**

Quick Demo

Water Contamination

Materials sponge, metal or plastic pan, food coloring, dropper, paper cup with holes punched in the bottom, water

Estimated Time 15 minutes

Procedure Raise one end of the pan, using a book to prop it up. Pour a small amount of water into the pan. Put the sponge at the elevated end of the pan. Dispense 3–4 drops of food coloring onto the sponge. Using water and the paper cup with holes, make it "rain" over the sponge. Have students observe the path of the food coloring. If the food coloring represents a chemical spill, what happens to the chemical when it rains?

Chemicals and Disease

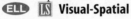

Chemicals are everywhere—in your body, the foods you eat, cosmetics, cleaning products, pesticides, fertilizers, and building materials. Of the thousands of chemical substances used by consumers, less than two percent are harmful. Those chemicals that are harmful to living things are called toxins, as shown in **Figure 15.** Toxins can cause birth defects, cell mutations, cancers, tissue damage, chronic diseases, and death.

The Effects The amount of a chemical that is taken into your body and how long your body is in contact with it determine how it affects you. For example, low levels of a toxin might cause cardiac or respiratory problems. However, higher levels of the same toxin might cause death. Some chemicals, such as the asbestos shown in **Figure 15,** can be inhaled over a long period of time. Eventually, the asbestos can cause chronic diseases of the lungs. Lead-based paints, if ingested, can accumulate in your body and eventually cause damage to the central nervous system. Another toxin, ethyl (EH thul) alcohol, is found in beer, wine, and liquor. It can cause birth defects in the children of mothers who drink alcohol during pregnancy.

Manufacturing, mining, transportation, and farming produce chemical wastes. These chemical substances interfere with the ability of soil, water, and air to support life. Pollution, caused by harmful chemicals, sometimes produces chronic diseases in humans. For example, long-term exposure to carbon monoxide, sulfur oxides, and nitrogen oxides in the air might cause a number of diseases, including bronchitis, emphysema (em fuh ZEE muh), and lung cancer.

Figure 15 Toxins can be in the environment.

Chemical spills can be dangerous and might end up in groundwater.

These scientists are testing the contents of barrels found in a dump.

Asbestos, if inhaled into the lungs over a long period of time, can cause chronic diseases of the lungs. Protective clothing must be worn when removing asbestos.

668

Curriculum Connection

Health Have an employee of the Environmental Protection Agency explain how various pollutants are monitored in the local community and discuss any health problems associated with the pollutants. Ask students to have questions prepared. L2 **Ⓝ Linguistic**

Visual Learning

Figure 15 These figures show harmful chemicals that have been found and are being properly disposed of. What are some examples of chemicals that may be improperly disposed of and will not be found? Possible answer: Homeowners may dispose of hazardous chemicals such as batteries, paints, and pesticides with their regular trash.

Table 3 Characteristics of Cancer Cells
Cell growth is uncontrolled.
These cells do not function as part of your body.
The cells take up space and interfere with normal bodily functions.
The cells travel throughout your body.
The cells produce tumors and abnormal growths anywhere in your body.

Cancer

Cancer has been a disease of humans since ancient times. Egyptian mummies show evidence of bone cancer. Ancient Greek scientists described several different kinds of cancers. Even medieval manuscripts report details about the disease.

Cancer is the name given to a group of closely related diseases that result from uncontrolled cell growth. It is a complicated disease, and no one fully understands how cancers form. Characteristics of cancer cells are shown in **Table 3.** Certain regulatory molecules in the body control the beginning and ending of cell division. If this control is lost, a mass of cells called a tumor (TEW mur) results from this abnormal growth. Tumors can occur anywhere in your body. Cancerous cells can leave a tumor, spread throughout the body via blood and lymph vessels, and then invade other tissues.

Reading Check *How do cancers spread?*

Types of Cancers Cancers can develop in any body tissue or organ. Leukemia (lew KEE mee uh) is a cancer of white blood cells. The cancerous white blood cells are immature and are no longer effective in fighting disease. The cancer cells multiply in the bone marrow and crowd out red blood cells, normal white blood cells, and platelets. Cancer of the lungs often starts in the bronchi and then spreads into the lungs. The surface area for air exchange in the lungs is reduced and breathing becomes difficult. Colorectal cancer, or cancer of the large intestine, is one of the leading causes of death among men and women. Changes in bowel movements and blood in the feces may be indications of the disease. In breast cancer, tumors grow in the breast. The second most common cancer in males is cancer of the prostate gland, which is an organ that surrounds the urethra.

Dioxin Danger Dioxin is a dangerous chemical found in small amounts in certain herbicides. It can cause miscarriages, cancers, and liver disorders. Research to find out about the dioxin contamination in Times Beach, Missouri. Write a brief report in your Science Journal.

Figure 16 Tobacco products have been linked directly to lung cancer. Some chemicals around the home are carcinogenic. **Explain** *why labels should not be removed from cleaning products.*

Causes In the latter part of the eighteenth century, a British physician recognized the association of soot to cancer in chimney sweeps. Since that time, scientists have learned more about causes of cancer. Research done in the 1940s and 1950s related genes to cancer.

Although not all the causes of cancer are known, many causes have been identified. Smoking has been linked to lung cancer. Lung cancer is the leading cause of cancer deaths for males in the United States. Exposure to certain chemicals also can increase your chances of developing cancer. These substances, called carcinogens (kar SIH nuh junz), include asbestos, various solvents, heavy metals, alcohol, and home and garden chemicals, as shown in **Figure 16.**

Exposure to X rays, nuclear radiation, and ultraviolet radiation of the Sun also increases your risk of getting cancer. Exposure to ultraviolet radiation might lead to skin cancer. Certain foods that are cured, or smoked, including barbecued meats, can give rise to cancers. Some food additives and certain viruses are suspected of causing cancers. Some people have a genetic predisposition for cancer, meaning that they have genes that make them more susceptible to the disease. This does not mean that they definitely will have cancer, but if it is triggered by certain factors they have a greater chance of developing cancer.

Treatment Surgery to remove cancerous tissue, radiation with X rays to kill cancer cells, and chemotherapy are some treatments for cancer. **Chemotherapy** (kee moh THER uh pee) is the use of chemicals to destroy cancer cells. However, early detection of cancer is the key to any successful treatment.

Research in the science of immune processes, called immunology, has led to some new approaches for treating cancer. For example, specialized antibodies produced in the laboratory are being tested as anticancer agents. These antibodies are used as carriers to deliver medicines and radioactive substances directly to cancer cells. In another test, killer T cells are removed from a cancer patient and treated with chemicals that stimulate T cell production. The treated cells are then reinjected into the patient. Trial tests have shown some success in destroying certain types of cancer cells with this technique.

670 CHAPTER 23 Immunity and Disease

Curriculum Connection

Health People who smoke pipes or cigars generally do not inhale. This reduces their chances for developing lung cancer and emphysema. However, since the burning tobacco is in close contact with the mouth and these products have a higher content of nicotine and tars than cigarettes, the smoker has a high risk of developing cancers of the lips and mouth. Have students make a poster to illustrate these facts. L2 **Kinesthetic**

Prevention Knowing some causes of cancer might help you prevent it. The first step is to know the early warning signs, shown in **Table 4.** Medical attention and treatments such as chemotherapy or surgery in the early stages of some cancers can cure or keep them inactive.

A second step in cancer prevention concerns lifestyle choices. Choosing not to use tobacco and alcohol products can help prevent mouth and lung cancers and the other associated respiratory and circulatory system diseases. Selecting a healthy diet without many foods that are high in fats, salt, and sugar also might reduce your chances of developing cancer. Using sunscreen lotions and limiting the amount of time that you expose your skin to direct sunlight are good preventive measures against skin cancer. Before using harmful home or garden chemicals, carefully read the entire label and precisely follow precautions and directions for use.

Inhaling certain air pollutants such as carbon monoxide, sulfur dioxide, and asbestos fibers is dangerous to your health. To keep the air cleaner, the U.S. Government has regulations such as the Clean Air Act. These laws are intended to reduce the amount of these substances that are released into the air.

Table 4 Early Warning Signs of Cancer
Changes in bowel or bladder habits
A sore that does not heal
Unusual bleeding or discharge
Thickening or lump in the breast or elsewhere
Indigestion or difficulty swallowing
Obvious change in a wart or mole
Nagging cough or hoarseness

Provided by the National Cancer Institute

section 3 review

Summary

Chronic Disease
- Chronic diseases last for a long time.
- Allergies are strong reactions to foreign substances.
- Diabetes is a chronic disease associated with your body's insulin levels.

Chemicals and Disease
- Harmful chemicals can cause birth defects, cancers, chronic diseases, and death.

Cancer
- Cancer results from uncontrolled cell growth.
- Early detection and healthy lifestyle choices can help in the treatment or prevention of some cancers.

Self Check

1. **Infer** why diabetes is classified as a noninfectious disease.
2. **Describe** how toxins in the environment can be harmful to your body.
3. **Explain** how cancer cells affect body organ functions.
4. **Identify** some ways your body can respond to allergens.
5. **Think Critically** Joel has an ear infection. The doctor prescribes an antibiotic. After taking the antibiotic, Joel breaks out in a rash. What is happening to him?

Applying Math

6. **Make and Use Tables** Make a table that relates several causes of cancer and their effects on your body.

section 3 review

1. Diabetes is not caused by a pathogen.
2. Exposure to environmental toxins can increase your chances of developing cancer.
3. crowd out blood cells in bone marrow; reduce surface area for gas exchange in lungs
4. Your immune system forms antibodies; your body reacts by releasing chemicals called histamines.
5. Joel's immune system formed antibodies and he seems to be having an allergic reaction to the antibiotic.
6. cause: smoking, effect: impaired lung functioning; cause: ultraviolet light, effect: abnormal skin growths; cause: asbestos, effect: impaired lung functioning

Real-World Question

Purpose Students determine how bicarbonates in saliva protect their mouths from bacteria and chemical substances. [L2]

COOP LEARN [IS] **Kinesthetic**

Process Skills prepare a data table, observe, compare, identify and manipulate controls and variables, explain, predict

Time Required two 45-minute periods

Possible Materials

- The red cabbage juice should be prepared by chopping the cabbage into small pieces and boiling the pieces for 20 to 30 minutes. The juice must be filtered before it is used as an indicator.
- Dilute HCl can be used in place of vinegar or lemon juice. Prepare dilute acid by dissolving 80 mL of concentrated Wheal in 1 L of water.

Safety Precautions Students should wear safety goggles. Caution students not to eat or drink anything in science class.

Form a Hypothesis

Possible Hypothesis Many students will hypothesize that bicarbonates will neutralize acids to some degree.

LAB Design Your Own

Defensive Saliva

Goals
- **Design** an experiment to test the reaction of a bicarbonate to acids and bases.
- **Test** the reaction of a bicarbonate to acids and bases.

Possible Materials
head of red cabbage
cooking pot
coffee filter
drinking glasses
clear household ammonia
baking soda
water
spoon
white vinegar
lemon juice
orange juice

Safety Precautions

WARNING: *Never eat or drink anything used in an investigation.*

Real-World Question

What happens when you think about a juicy cheeseburger or smell freshly baked bread? Your mouth starts making saliva. Saliva is the first line of defense for fighting harmful bacteria, acids, and bases entering your body. Saliva contains salts, including bicarbonates. An example of a bicarbonate found in your kitchen is baking soda. Bicarbonates help to maintain normal pH levels in your mouth. When surfaces in your mouth have normal pH levels, the growth of bacteria is slowed and the effects of acids and bases are reduced. In this activity, you will design your own experiment to show the importance of saliva bicarbonates. How do the bicarbonates in saliva work to protect your mouth from harmful bacteria, acids, and bases?

Form a Hypothesis

Based on your reading in the text, form a hypothesis to explain how the bicarbonates in saliva react to acids and bases.

Alternative Inquiry Lab

The Effect of Bicarbonates As an alternate lab, have students design an experiment to test the effect of bicarbonates on acids and bases using red and blue litmus paper instead of cabbage juice. Acids will turn blue litmus paper red; bases will turn red litmus paper blue.

Students can extend the lab by testing bicarbonates used in over-the-counter medicines to neutralize acids and bases. Common bicarbonates include: magnesium carbonate ($MgCO_3$), calcium carbonate ($CaCO_3$), and sodium bicarbonate (NaHCO).

⊙ Test Your Hypothesis

Make a Plan

1. **List** the materials you will need for your experiment. Red cabbage juice can be used as an indicator to test for acids and bases. Vinegar and citrus juices are acids, ammonia is a base, and baking soda (bicarbonate of soda) is a bicarbonate.

2. **Describe** how you will prepare the red cabbage juice and how you will use it to test for the presence of acids and bases.

3. **Describe** how you will test the effect of bicarbonate on acids and bases.

4. **List** the steps you will take to set up and complete your experiment. Describe exactly what you will do in each step.

5. Prepare a data table in your Science Journal to record your observations.

6. Examine the steps of your experiment to make certain they are in logical order.

Follow Your Plan

1. Ask your teacher to examine the steps of your experiment and data table before you start.

2. Conduct your experiment according to the approved plan.

3. **Record** your observations in your data table.

⊙ Analyze Your Data

1. **Compare** the color change of the acids and bases in the cabbage juice.

2. **Describe** how well the bicarbonate neutralized the acids and bases.

3. **Identify** any problems you had while setting up and conducting your experiment.

⊙ Conclude and Apply

1. **Conclude** whether or not your results support your hypothesis.

2. **Explain** why your saliva contains a bicarbonate based on your experiment.

3. **Predict** how quickly bacteria would grow in your glass containing acid compared to another glass containing acid and the bicarbonate.

4. **Describe** how saliva protects your mouth from bacteria.

5. **Predict** what would happen if your saliva were made of only water.

ommunicating Your Data

Using what you learned in this experiment, create a poster about the importance of good dental hygiene. Invite a dental hygienist to speak to your class.

LAB 673

✔ Assessment

Oral Have students explain how the strength of acids, bases, and neutral substances are compared. pH values of 1 to 6 indicate acids with 1 being the strongest. pH values of 8 to 14 are bases with 14 being the strongest base. Neutral substances have a value of 7.

ommunicating Your Data

Encourage students to illustrate their posters with drawings. They may wish to make the poster a cartoon in which the main character is a tooth that explains the steps in good oral hygiene.

⊙ Test Your Hypothesis

Possible Procedure Add four parts acid or base to one part red cabbage juice indicator. Add a spoonful of bicarbonate a little at a time until a color change is observed. Proportions of the ingredients may have to be adjusted depending on their strength.

Teaching Strategies Most students will be familiar with the terms *acid* and *base* and understand that a base is the opposite of an acid.

Expected Outcomes The bicarbonate should neutralize both acids and bases as indicated by the appropriate color change.

⊙ Analyze Your Data

Answers to Questions

1. Acids turn pink; bases turn green.
2. All the solutions will turn blue, signifying both acids and bases are neutralized.
3. Common problems include the preparation of cabbage juice and determining the proportions of the substances.

Error Analysis Have students compare the color changes that occurred during their experiments and explain why differences were observed.

⊙ Conclude and Apply

1. Answers will vary.
2. Bicarbonates in saliva neutralize harmful acids and bases.
3. Bacteria would grow more rapidly in acid without bicarbonate added.
4. Bicarbonates maintain neutral pH levels to slow bacterial growth.
5. Acids and bases from foods would easily damage tooth enamel.

SCIENCE Stats

Content Background

The development of antibiotics has significantly changed medicine. Injuries and illnesses that were once fatal are now easily treated. How do antibiotics kill bacteria without harming the cells of the person being treated? The key is the differences between bacterial cells and animal cells. For example, some antibiotics work by inhibiting cell wall formation. Because human cells do not have a cell wall, the drug does not affect them. Other antibiotics are less specific to bacterial characteristics, and therefore more toxic to humans.

Discussion

New Developments Why is there always a need for newly developed or discovered antibiotics? Bacteria develop resistance to antibiotics over time. A newly developed or discovered antibiotic may allow treatment of bacteria that have developed resistance to other drugs.

Activity

Interview Have student pairs interview their grandparents or older family friends. Have students ask about treatments for disease and infection that were used in the past. If interview subjects are not available, have students use reference materials to find their information. Students should present their findings to the class. IS **Interpersonal**

Applying Math

Answer about 7.2 million

Find Out About It

Have interested students research ethnobotany, the scientific study of plants used by particular cultural groups. Researchers in this field have explored many substances used as medicine in different areas of the world. Students should report their findings to the class. L2 IS **Linguistic**

SCIENCE Stats

Battling Bacteria

Did you know...

... The term *antibiotic* was first coined by an American microbiologist. The scientist received a Nobel prize in 1952 for the discovery of streptomycin (strep toh MY suhn), an antibiotic used against tuberculosis.

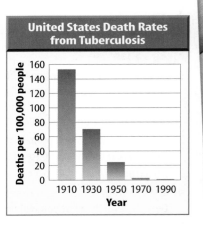

United States Death Rates from Tuberculosis

...In recent decades many bacteria have become resistant to antibiotics. For example, one group of bacteria that cause illnesses of the stomach and intestines—*Shigella* (shih GEL uh)—became harder to control. In 1985, less than one third of *Shigella* were resistant to the antibiotic ampicillin (am puh SI luhn). By 1991, however, more than two thirds of *Shigella* were resistant to the drug.

Applying Math It is believed that 30 percent of the antibiotics prescribed for ear infections are unnecessary. Using the graph, calculate the number of unnecessary prescriptions.

Antibiotics Prescribed Each Year in the United States

Type of infection: Sinus infections, Sore throat, Bronchitis, Common cold, Ear infections

Number of prescriptions (in millions): 0, 5, 10, 15, 20, 25

...People have long used natural remedies to treat infections. These remedies include garlic, *Echinacea* (purple coneflower), and an antibiotic called squalamine, found in sharks' stomachs.

Find Out About It

Visit life.msscience.com/science_stats to research the production of four antibiotics. Create a graph comparing the number of kilograms of each antibiotic produced in one year.

674 CHAPTER 23 Immunity and Disease

Visual Learning

The Term *Antibiotic* Have students use the data in the graph to determine the effectiveness of antibiotics on decreasing the number of deaths due to tuberculosis. Deaths decreased from 25 per 100,000 in 1950 (before antibiotics) to 3 per 100,000 in 1970 (after antibiotics).

Reviewing Main Ideas

Section 1 | The Immune System

1. Your body is protected against most pathogens by the immune system.

2. Active immunity is long lasting, but passive immunity is not.

3. Antigens are foreign molecules in your body. Your body makes an antibody that attaches to an antigen, making it harmless.

Section 2 | Infectious Diseases

1. Pasteur and Koch discovered that microorganisms cause diseases. Lister learned that cleanliness helps control microorganisms.

2. Pathogens can be spread by air, water, food, and animal contact. Bacteria, viruses, fungi, and protists can cause infectious diseases.

3. Sexually transmitted diseases can be passed between persons during sexual contact.

4. HIV damages your body's immune system.

Section 3 | Noninfectious Diseases

1. Causes of noninfectious diseases, such as diabetes and cancer, include genetics, chemicals, poor diet, and uncontrolled cell growth.

2. An allergy is a reaction of the immune system to a foreign substance.

3. Cancer results from uncontrolled cell growth, causing cells to multiply, spread through the body, and invade normal tissue.

4. Cancer is treated with surgery, chemotherapy, and radiation. Early detection can help cure or slow some cancers.

Visualizing Main Ideas

Copy and complete the following concept map on infectious diseases.

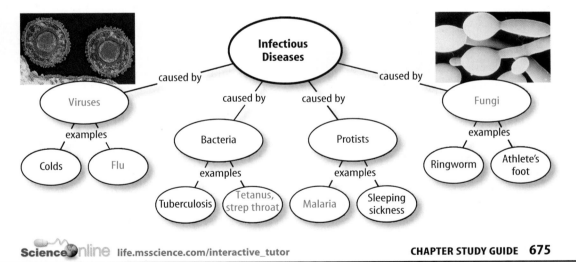

 life.msscience.com/interactive_tutor

CHAPTER STUDY GUIDE 675

Reviewing Main Ideas

Summary statements can be used by students to review the major concepts of the chapter.

Visualizing Main Ideas

See student page.

Visit **life.msscience.com**
 /self_check_quiz
 /interactive_tutor
 /vocabulary_puzzlemaker
 /chapter_review
 /standardized_test
 /field_guide

Assessment Transparency

For additional assessment questions, use the *Assessment Transparency* located in the transparency book.

Assessment

Assessment Transparency — Immunity and Disease

Directions: Carefully review the table and answer the following questions.

Estimated HIV/AIDS in Western Europe, 1999			
Country	Adult Population Living with HIV/AIDS	Transmission	
		IV Drug Use	Contaminated Blood
France	0.43%	24%	5%
Germany	0.10%	15%	5%
Greece	0.16%	5%	9%
Portugal	0.74%	49%	3%
Spain	0.58%	66%	2%

1. According to the table, which country has the highest percentage of people with HIV/AIDS?
   A France   C Portugal
   B Germany   D Spain
2. According to the table, which country has the highest percentage of infection by blood transfusions?
   F France
   G Germany
   H Greece
   J Portugal
3. According to the table, which country has the highest percentage of people infected by drug use?
   A France
   B Germany
   C Spain
   D Greece

Immunity and Disease

Using Vocabulary

1. antigen
2. biological vector
3. infectious disease
4. vaccination
5. Active immunity
6. allergen
7. pasteurization
8. noninfectious disease

Checking Concepts

9. A
10. D
11. A
12. D
13. A
14. C
15. A
16. C
17. A
18. A

chapter **23** Review

Using Vocabulary

active immunity p. 655	infectious disease p. 661
allergen p. 667	noninfectious disease p. 666
allergy p. 666	passive immunity p. 655
antibody p. 654	pasteurization p. 658
antigen p. 654	sexually transmitted
biological vector p. 661	disease (STD) p. 662
chemotherapy p. 670	vaccination p. 655
immune system p. 652	virus p. 658

Fill in the blanks with the correct vocabulary words.

1. A(n) _____ can cause infectious diseases.
2. A disease-carrying organism is called a(n) _____.
3. Measles is an example of _____.
4. Injection of weakened viruses is called _____.
5. _____ occurs when your body makes its own antibodies.
6. A(n) _____ stimulates histamine release.
7. Heating a liquid to kill harmful bacteria is called _____.
8. Diabetes is an example of a(n) _____ disease.

Checking Concepts

Choose the word or phrase that best answers the question.

9. Which of the following has not been found to be a biological vector?

A)   **B)**   **C)**   **D)**

10. How can infectious diseases be caused?
    A) heredity   **C)** chemicals
    B) allergies   **D)** organisms

11. How do scientists know that a pathogen causes a specific disease?
    A) It is present in all cases of the disease.
    B) It does not infect other animals.
    C) It causes other diseases.
    D) It is treated with heat.

12. What is formed in the blood to fight invading antigens?
    A) hormones   **C)** pathogens
    B) allergens   **D)** antibodies

13. Which of the following is one of your body's general defenses against some pathogens?
    A) stomach enzymes
    B) HIV
    C) some vaccines
    D) hormones

14. Which of the following is known as an infectious disease?
    A) allergies   **C)** syphilis
    B) asthma   **D)** diabetes

15. Which disease is caused by a virus that attacks white blood cells?
    A) AIDS   **C)** flu
    B) measles   **D)** polio

16. Which of the following is a characteristic of cancer cells?
    A) controlled cell growth
    B) help your body stay healthy
    C) interfere with normal body functions
    D) do not multiply or spread

17. Which of the following is caused by a virus?
    A) AIDS   **C)** ringworm
    B) gonorrhea   **D)** syphilis

18. How can cancer cells be destroyed?
    A) chemotherapy   **C)** vaccines
    B) antigens   **D)** viruses

Science Online life.msscience.com/vocabulary_puzzlemaker

Use the ExamView® Pro Testmaker CD-ROM to:
- create multiple versions of tests
- create modified tests with one mouse click for inclusion students
- edit existing questions and add your own questions
- build tests aligned with state standards using built-in State Curriculum Tags
- change English tests to Spanish with one mouse click and vice versa

Thinking Critically

19. **Explain** if it is better to vaccinate people or to wait until they build up their own immunity.

20. **Infer** what advantage a breast-fed baby might have compared to a formula-fed baby.

21. **Describe** how your body protects itself from antigens.

22. **Explain** how helper T cells and B cells work to eliminate antigens.

23. **Compare and contrast** antibodies, antigens, and antibiotics.

Use the graph below to answer question 24.

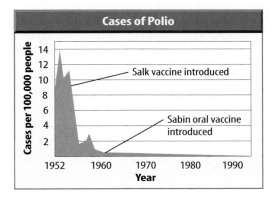

Cases of Polio

24. **Interpret Data** Using the graph above, explain the rate of polio cases between 1952 and 1965. What conclusions can you draw about the effectiveness of the polio vaccines?

25. **Concept Map** Make a network-tree concept map that compares the various defenses your body has against diseases. Compare general defenses, active immunity, and passive immunity.

 Science Online life.msscience.com/chapter_review

Performance Activities

26. **Poster** Design and construct a poster to illustrate how a person with the flu could spread the disease to family members, classmates, and others.

Applying Math

27. **Antibiotic Tablets** You have an earache and your doctor prescribes an antibiotic to treat the infection. The antibiotic can be taken as a tablet at dosages of 400 mg or 1,000 mg. How many 400 mg tablets are needed to equal one 1,000 mg tablet?

Use the graph below to answer questions 28 and 29.

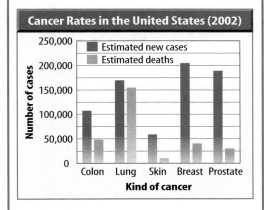

Cancer Rates in the United States (2002)

28. **Cancer Cases** The graph above shows the estimated number of new cases and estimated number of deaths for various cancers in the year 2002. Which cancer occurs most frequently? Most infrequently? Estimate the difference between new cases of colon cancer and new cases of skin cancer.

29. **Cancer Deaths** Estimate the difference between deaths from lung cancer and deaths from prostate cancer.

Thinking Critically

19. In many cases, it is better to vaccinate, as the antigens introduced by vaccinations are usually weakened or killed, and will therefore not cause the person to get the disease.

20. Breast-fed babies receive passive immunity from antibodies in their mother's milk.

21. Your skin prevents pathogens from entering the body, white blood cells destroy pathogens, cilia and mucus trap pathogens, and digestive juices kill pathogens that enter the stomach.

22. Helper T cells activate the immune system. B cells form antibodies and remain in the blood to defend against future attacks by the same antigen.

23. Antigens—foreign proteins and chemicals that invade your body; antibodies—formed by your immune system to destroy antigens; antibiotics—medicines that destroy or neutralize pathogens in the body

24. rate dropped after the vaccine was introduced; the dramatic decline was a result of the vaccine

25. General—fever, white blood cells; active immunity—production of antibodies, long-term; passive immunity—antibodies given to body, short-term

Performance Activities

26. Poster could show a person sneezing without covering the mouth and nose, coughing over food, and handling objects without washing hands. Use **Performance Assessment in the Science Classroom,** p. 145.

Applying Math

National Math Standards

1, 5, 6

27. $1,000 \div 400 = 2.5$ tablets

28. breast; skin; $107,000 - 58,000 = 49,000$

29. $155,000 - 30,000 = 125,000$

✓ Assessment — Resources

Reproducible Masters

Chapter *Fast File* Resources
  Chapter Review, pp. 35–36
  Chapter Tests, pp. 37–40
  Assessment Transparency Activity, p. 42

Glencoe Science Web site
  Chapter Review Test
  Standardized Test Practice

Glencoe Technology

  Assessment Transparency
  Exam*View*® Pro Testmaker
  MindJogger Videoquiz
  Interactive Chalkboard

Answer Sheet A practice answer sheet can be found at life.msscience.com/answer_sheet.

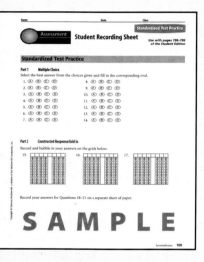

S A M P L E

Part 1 | Multiple Choice

1. D
2. B
3. C
4. A
5. C
6. D

Part 2 | Short Response

7. washing small wounds with soap and water; washing the body, especially the hands; brushing teeth and using dental floss

8. in the respiratory system, weakens the cell walls of some pathogens; in the digestive tract, coats bacteria and prevents them from binding to the digestive organs

9. Second-line defenses work against only specific pathogens.

10. "Chewing tobacco and snuff cause cancer"

11. "It's safe to smoke for only a year or two," and "Smoking can help you when you're bored"; second pair: "Seeing someone smoke turns me off," and "I strongly dislike being around smokers."

12. overall negative opinions about smoking

Part 1 | Multiple Choice

Record your answers on the answer sheet provided by your teacher or on a sheet of paper.

Use the graph below to answer questions 1 and 2.

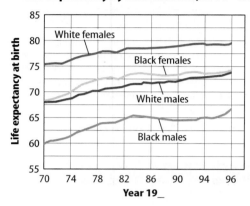

Life Expectancy by Race and Sex, 1970–1997

1. According to the information in the graph, which group had the lowest life expectancy in both 1975 and 1994?
   A. white males
   B. black females
   C. white females
   D. black males

2. A reasonable hypothesis based on the information in the graph is that life expectancy
   A. decreased for black males between 1970 and 1984.
   B. is longer for females than for males.
   C. decreased for white males between 1970 and 1980.
   D. is longer for males than for females.

3. Which of the following is NOT a sign of inflammation?
   A. redness
   C. bleeding
   B. pain
   D. swelling

Use the table below to answer questions 4–6.

Causes of Disease Before and After Vaccine Availability in the U.S.		
Disease	**Average Number of Cases per Year Before Vaccine Available**	**Cases in 1998 After Vaccine Available**
Measles	503,282	89
Diphtheria	175,885	1
Tetanus	1,314	34
Mumps	152,209	606
Rubella	47,745	345
Pertussis (whooping cough)	147,271	6,279

Data from the National Immunization Program, CDC

4. Which of the following diseases had the highest number of cases before vaccine?
   A. diphtheria
   C. rubella
   B. mumps
   D. pertussis

5. Which of the following diseases had the highest number of cases after vaccine?
   A. measles
   C. mumps
   B. tetanus
   D. rubella

6. Which of the diseases in the table are caused by bacteria?
   A. measles, rubella, mumps
   B. measles, tetanus, mumps
   C. mumps, pertussis, rubella
   D. tetanus, pertussis, diphtheria

Test-Taking Tip

Missing Information Questions will often ask about missing information. Notice what is missing as well as what is given.

Question 6 Base your answer on choices that can be found in the text, such as *measles* and *tetanus*.

Part 3 | Open Ended

13. Active immunity is longer lasting because the body makes its own antibodies in response to an antigen. Some antibodies stay on duty in the blood, and more are rapidly produced if the pathogen enters the body again.

14. Dr. Cavazos can use Koch's Rules: identify the bacteria in every case of the disease, grow the organism with no other organisms present, inoculate the organism into a healthy host which then gets the disease, and remove the organism from the host then grow an organism identical to the original one.

15. Infectious diseases are caused by a pathogen, are spread from an infected organism to other organisms, and may be chronic. Noninfectious diseases are not spread from one person to another, are not caused by a pathogen, and many are chronic.

16. No, the person already has active immunity against measles because the person already had the disease

Part 2 | Short Response/Grid In

Record your answers on the answer sheet provided by your teacher or on a sheet of paper.

7. What are some health practices that can help fight infectious disease?

8. How does mucus help defend your body?

9. Why are the body's second-line defenses called specific immunity?

Use the table below to answer questions 10–12.

Teen Opinions on Smoking			
All numbers are percentages	Agree	Disagree	No opinion or don't know
Seeing someone smoke turns me off	67	22	10
I'd rather date people who don't smoke	86	8	6
It's safe to smoke for only a year or two	7	92	1
Smoking can help you when you're bored	7	92	1
Smoking helps reduce stress	21	78	3
Smoking helps keep your weight down	18	80	2
Chewing tobacco and snuff cause cancer	95	2	3
I strongly dislike being around smokers	65	22	13

Data from CDC

10. According to the table, which statement had the highest percentage of teen agreement?

11. According to the table, which pairs of statements had the same percentages of teen disagreement?

12. According to the information in the table, do teens generally have positive or negative opinions about smoking? Explain.

 life.msscience.com/standardized_test

Part 3 | Open Ended

Record your answers on a sheet of paper.

13. Which is longer lasting—active immunity or passive immunity? Why?

14. Dr. Cavazos has isolated a bacterium that she thinks causes a recently discovered disease. How can she prove it? What steps should she follow?

15. Compare and contrast infectious and noninfectious diseases.

16. Would a vaccination against measles be helpful if a person already had the disease a year ago? Explain.

17. Compare and contrast Type 1 and Type 2 diabetes.

Use the illustration below to answer questions 18 and 19.

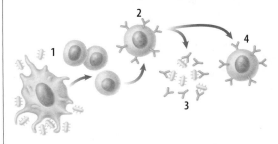

18. Explain the four steps of the immune system response.

19. Sometimes a person is born without the cells labeled *2* in the illustration above. If this person was given a vaccination for tetanus, what results would be expected? Explain.

STANDARDIZED TEST PRACTICE   679

Rubrics

The following rubrics are sample scoring devices for short response and open-ended questions.

Short Response

Points	Description
2	The student demonstrates a thorough understanding of the science of the task. The response may contain minor flaws that do not detract from the demonstration of a thorough understanding.
1	The student has provided a response that is only partially correct.
0	The student has provided a completely incorrect solution or no response at all.

Open Ended

Points	Description
4	The student demonstrates a thorough understanding of the science of the task. The response may contain minor flaws that do not detract from the demonstration of a thorough understanding.
3	The student demonstrates an understanding of the science of the task. The response is essentially correct and demonstrates an essential but less than thorough understanding of the science.
2	The student demonstrates only a partial understanding of the science of the task. Although the student may have used the correct approach to a solution or may have provided a correct solution, the work lacks an essential understanding of the underlying science concepts.
1	The student demonstrates a very limited understanding of the science of the task. The response is incomplete and exhibits many flaws.
0	The student provides a completely incorrect solution or no response at all.

and produced antibodies against it.

17. Both types result in high glucose levels in the blood. Type 1 diabetes is the result of too little or no insulin production. In type 2 diabetes, the body cannot properly process the insulin.

18. Four stages: 1. Recognition; white blood cells surround pathogens

and signal T cells. More T cells are produced. Helper T cells signal B cells. 2. Mobilization: B cells produce antibodies. 3. Disposal: Antibodies destroy pathogens. 4. Immunity: Some antibodies remain for future use.

19. The cell is a B cell which makes antibodies. If these cells are

absent, no antibodies could be made. If the person were given a vaccination against tetanus, no antibodies against tetanus would be made and the person could get tetanus.

unit 5

Unit Contents

Web Quest *Barrier Islands: To Build or Not To Build?* is a student-driven Web research activity designed to inform citizens of the controversy surrounding the development and use of barrier islands. Students will investigate the geological and physical nature of these specialized ecosystems and how they change over time. Students then use their new knowledge to form their own opinion about development and use of barrier islands. In a letter to the editor of an environmental magazine, each student will try to convince readers that his or her conclusions are correct and motivate readers to take appropriate action.

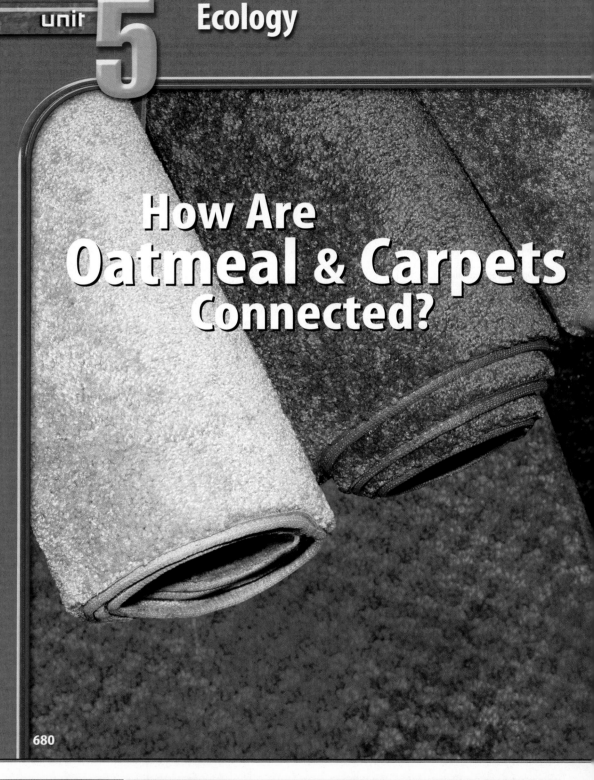

unit 5 Ecology

How Are Oatmeal & Carpets Connected?

680

PROJECT CRISS℠

Study Skills

Organize Information Main idea and detail notes help students to organize important information. Have the students make two columns on their paper. In the left column, have them list 3–4 dwindling natural resources about which they are most concerned. In the right column, have them list possible solutions.

Main Idea (Resource)	Detail (Action needed)
Rain forests	Write letters to businesses to encourage responsible use of rain forest resources.

NATIONAL GEOGRAPHIC

In the 1850s, the first oatmeal mill began operation in the United States. Over the next few decades, hot, creamy oatmeal became a popular breakfast cereal across the country. By the early 1900s, oatmeal was getting some stiff competition from newly invented cold breakfast cereals such as cornflakes. Hot or cold, cereal had become a breakfast staple. But the processing of oats and corn for cereal leaves behind waste products—oat hulls and corncobs. In 1922, a cereal company discovered it could do something useful with these waste products. The company used oat hulls to make a substance called furfural. Today, furfural also is made from corncobs and other cereal waste products. Manufacturers use furfural in the production of synthetic rubber, plastic, and nylon—including the nylon that goes into carpets.

unit ⚡ projects

Visit life.msscience.com/unit_project to find project ideas and resources. Projects include:

- **Career** You are an environmental scientist as you design your own ecosystem-interaction web to demonstrate relationships from birth to death of your specific organism.
- **Technology** Chart your research results on the manufacturing of different materials. Compare cost, energy use, resources, and environmental concerns.
- **Model** Design your own two-week personal conservation project. Decide how you can make a difference as you reduce, reuse, and recycle.
- **WebQuest** Investigate the *Barrier Islands* ecosystem, then form an opinion as to whether developers should build on these environmentally fragile islands.

unit ⚡ projects

Career As a class, brainstorm a list of plants and animals that live in your local ecosystem. Assign each student a specific organism. Ask students to think like an environmentalist as they research 10 interactions for their particular organism. Remind them to include all possible interactions in the ecosystem, such as food chains, symbiosis, and predator and prey, from reproductive conception to death. Have students design a large web to demonstrate their organism's ecosystem.

Technology Have students conduct research to learn what happens when plastics, metals, glass, paper, and polystyrene are manufactured. Have students design a chart to compare the materials used in production. Categories might include natural resources, equipment and materials, energy use, cost, safety concerns, location, and environmental concerns. Ask students to reflect on each component and how recycled materials affect the different categories.

Model Have students design a personal conservation project. This two-week commitment to reduce, reuse, and recycle can culminate in a class presentation of their original plan, how they implemented their system of conservation, and the results.

Additional Resources For more information, resources, and assessment rubrics, visit life.msscience.com/unit_project

---

NATIONAL GEOGRAPHIC   How Are Oatmeal & Carpets Connected?

Furfural can be produced by treating carbohydrates, which are long chains of simple sugars. Commercially, furfural often is used as an industrial solvent. It also is used in the production of certain resins. When furfural is reduced chemically, it produces furfural alcohol. This alcohol then is polymerized to produce resins that are heat- and alkali-resistant.

Section/Objectives	Standards		Labs/Features
Chapter Opener	**National**	**State/Local**	**Launch Lab:** How do lawn organisms survive? p. 683 **Foldables,** p. 683
	See pp. 16T–17T for a Key to Standards.		
Section 1 Living Earth 🕐 2 sessions 📦 1 block 1. **Identify** places where life is found on Earth. 2. **Define** ecology. 3. **Observe** how the environment influences life.	National Content Standards: UCP.1, UCP.2, UCP.3, A.1, A.2, C.2		**Science Online,** p. 686
Section 2 Populations 🕐 2 sessions 📦 1 block 4. **Identify** methods for estimating population sizes. 5. **Explain** how competition limits population growth. 6. **List** factors that influence changes in population size.	National Content Standards: UCP.1– UCP.5, A.1, A.2, C.1–C.5, F.2		**MiniLAB:** Observe Seedling Competition, p. 689 **Applying Science:** Do you have too many crickets?, p. 691 **Science Online,** p. 692 **MiniLAB:** Comparing Biotic Potential, p. 693 **Visualizing Population Growth,** p. 694
Section 3 Interactions Within Communities 🕐 3 sessions 📦 1.5 blocks 7. **Describe** how organisms obtain energy for life. 8. **Explain** how organisms interact. 9. **Recognize** that every organism occupies a niche.	National Content Standards: UCP.1–UCP.5, A.1, A.2, C.1, C.2, C.4, C.5, F.2		**Integrate Chemistry,** p. 697 **Integrate History,** p. 699 **Lab:** Feeding Habits of Planaria, p. 701 **Lab:** Population Growth in Fruit Flies, p. 702 **Science and History:** The Census measures a human population, p. 704

Lab Materials	Reproducible Resources	Section Assessment	Technology
Launch Lab: a section of sod, magnifying lens	**Chapter *FAST FILE* Resources** Foldables Worksheet, p. 17 Directed Reading Overview, p. 19 Note-taking Worksheets, pp. 33–35	GLENCOE'S **ASSESSMENT** ADVANTAGE	Teacher**Works** includes: • Interactive Teacher Edition • Lesson Planner with calendar • Access to all program blacklines • Correlations to standards • Web links
Need materials? Contact Science Kit at 1-800-828-7777 or www.sciencekit.com on the Internet.	**Chapter *FAST FILE* Resources** Transparency Activity, p. 44 Enrichment, p. 30 Reinforcement, p. 27 Directed Reading, p. 20	Portfolio Activity, p. 686 Performance Applying Skills, p. 687 Content Challenge, p. 686 Section Review, p. 687	Section Focus Transparency Virtual Labs CD-ROM Guided Reading Audio Program Interactive Chalkboard CD-ROM
MiniLAB: 2 pots of plants, moist potting soil, radish seeds, watering can, basin, metric ruler **MiniLAB:** whole fruit, plastic knife, paper towels	**Chapter *FAST FILE* Resources** Transparency Activity, p. 45 MiniLAB, pp. 3, 4 Enrichment, p. 31 Reinforcement, p. 28 Directed Reading, p. 20 Transparency Activity, pp. 47–48 **Mathematics Skill Activities,** p. 5	Portfolio Differentiated Instruction, p. 691 Performance MiniLAB, p. 689 Applying Science, p. 691 MiniLAB, p. 693 Applying Skills, p. 695 Content Challenge, p. 691 Section Review, p. 695	Section Focus Transparency Teaching Transparency Virtual Labs CD-ROM Guided Reading Audio Program Interactive Chalkboard CD-ROM Video Lab
Lab: small bowl, several planarians, lettuce leaf, raw liver or meat, several guppies, pond or stream water, magnifying lens **Lab:** fruit flies; fruit fly culture kit; food items (banana, orange peel, or other fruit); water; culture containers; cloth, plastic, or other tops for containers; magnifying lens; heating or cooling source	**Chapter *FAST FILE* Resources** Transparency Activity, p. 46 Lab Worksheets, pp. 5–6, 7–8 Enrichment, p. 32 Reinforcement, p. 29 Directed Reading, pp. 21, 22 Lab Activities, pp. 9–11, 13–16 **Home and Community Involvement,** p. 47 **Lab Management and Safety,** p. 71	Portfolio Science Journal, p. 699 Performance Applying Skills, p. 700 Content Challenge, p. 698 Section Review, p. 700	Section Focus Transparency Virtual Labs CD-ROM Guided Reading Audio Program Interactive Chalkboard CD-ROM

End of Chapter Assessment

GLENCOE'S **ASSESSMENT** ADVANTAGE

Blackline Masters	Technology	Professional Series
Chapter *FAST FILE* Resources Chapter Review, pp. 37–38 Chapter Tests, pp. 39–42 **Standardized Test Practice,** pp. 99–102	MindJogger Videoquiz Virtual Labs CD-ROM Exam*View*® Pro Testmaker TeacherWorks CD-ROM Interactive Chalkboard CD-ROM	**Performance Assessment in the Science Classroom (PASC)**

Transparencies

Section Focus

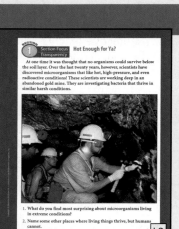

This is a representation of key blackline masters available in the Teacher Classroom Resources. See Resource Manager boxes within the chapter for additional information.

Key to Teaching Strategies

The following designations will help you decide which activities are appropriate for your students.

L1 Level 1 activities should be appropriate for students with learning difficulties.

L2 Level 2 activities should be within the ability range of all students.

L3 Level 3 activities are designed for above-average students.

ELL ELL activities should be within the ability range of English-Language Learners.

COOP LEARN Cooperative Learning activities are designed for small group work.

LS Multiple Learning Styles logos, as described on page 12T, are used throughout to indicate strategies that address different learning styles.

P These strategies represent student products that can be placed into a best-work portfolio.

PBL Problem-Based Learning activities apply real-world situations to learning.

Assessment

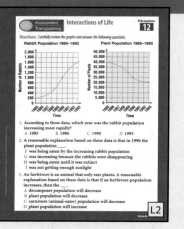

Teaching

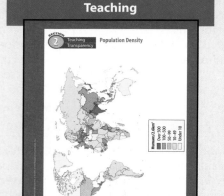

Hands-on Activities

Student Text Lab Worksheet

Laboratory Activities

Meeting Different Ability Levels

Content Outline

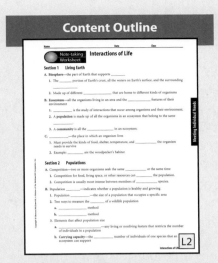

Reinforcement

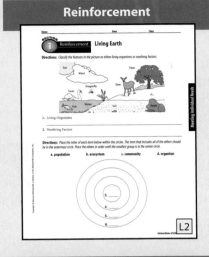

Enrichment

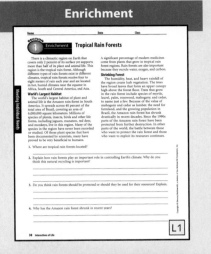

Directed Reading (English/Spanish)

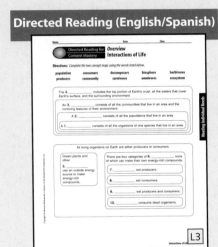

Study Guide

Reading Essentials

Assessment

Test Practice Workbook

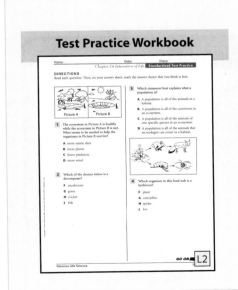

Chapter Review

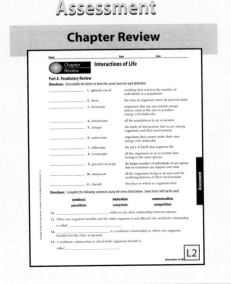

Chapter Tests

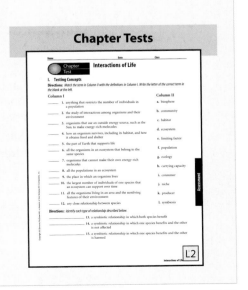

Science Content Background

section 1 — Living Earth
Understanding Ecosystems

The biosphere is the total part of Earth where life can exist and includes a great variety of conditions. An ecosystem is a smaller area consisting of the organisms and nonliving features that interact in the system. Sir Arthur George Tansley, a British plant ecologist, coined the word *ecosystem* in 1935.

section 2 — Populations
Population Size

Population size is an important characteristic, but it can be difficult to measure. Animal population size is influenced by the amount of food and space available. Natural populations cannot increase forever. Population density measures how crowded a population is. It is always expressed as the number of individuals per unit area or volume.

Carrying Capacity

When a population's size is no longer increasing, it has reached the carrying capacity of its ecosystem. The carrying capacity is the greatest number of individuals that a given environment is capable of supporting under a given set of conditions. If a population is at carrying capacity, the number of organisms born in a given period of time is balanced by the number of organisms that die during that same time.

section 3 — Interactions Within Communities
Types of Interactions

Organisms within a community interact in many ways. Plants and other photosynthetic organisms produce sugars that they use as food. Animals, fungi, and other non-photosynthetic organisms must consume other organisms for food. In addition to predator/prey or producer/consumer relationships, organisms may participate in symbiotic relationships, such as mutualism, commensalism, and parasitism, or they may compete with other species with similar needs for resources. A single species interacts directly or indirectly with nearly all the other species in its community. For example, a squirrel in a forest interacts not only with the plants it eats or with the predators that eat it but also with the plants it uses for cover or shelter, with insects that share its nest, with other animals that use its abandoned nest for shelter, with the bacteria that live on its skin, and so on.

chapter content resources

Internet Resources
For additional content background, visit
life.msscience.com to:
- access your book online
- find references to related articles in popular science magazines
- access Web links with related content background
- access current events with science journal topics

Print Resources
Ecology, A Pocket Guide, by Ernest Callenbach, University of California Press, 1998
Basics of Environmental Science, by Michael Allaby, Routledge, 2000
The Ages of Gaia, by James Lovelock, W.W. Norton, 1988

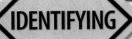

IDENTIFYING ▷ Misconceptions

Find Out What Students Think

Students may think that . . .

Plants do not depend on other organisms.

Organisms do not depend on one another.

Interdependence is primarily predator/prey relationships.

While most students can draw a picture of a natural community that includes producers, herbivores, and predators, few can explain their selections in terms of ecological relationships. Many students understand that the organisms they have depicted belong in the environment, but they don't understand how the organisms interact with one another and with the nonliving environment. While students may be able to identify predator/prey relationships, or plant/ herbivore relationships, they seldom understand other types of relationships, nor do they see how interconnected one organism may be with many other organisms in its environment.

Activity

Have students draw a terrestrial community, using the local environment as a model. Their drawings should include several different types of organisms. Ask students to indicate as many interactions between organisms as they can. Then have them describe, aloud or in essay form, how each organism in the picture interacts with other organisms. Note the types and complexity of interactions that students describe.

Promote Understanding

Activity

After students read Section 3, organize the class into teams of three or four students. Assign each team a color. Have each team make 10 or so flags from paper corresponding to their team's color and toothpicks.

- Take the class outside to a grassy or weedy area of the school grounds.

- Have teams hunt for examples of organisms interacting in various ways, including consumption, competition, and symbiosis, and mark with a flag each area where an interaction is occurring. On each flag, team members should identify the type of interaction and write a short description in their Science Journals of what they found. Encourage students to include drawings along with their verbal descriptions.

- Give students time to examine the findings of other teams before gathering up the flags and returning to the classroom.

- Have representatives from each team report their findings to the class. Encourage teams to include their drawings of the interactions they observed.

When all teams have reported, discuss the relationships discovered by the class. Focus the discussion on a few organisms identified by most teams. Challenge students to brainstorm a list of ways in which those organisms interact with other organisms. L2

Assess

After completing the chapter, see *Identifying Misconceptions* in the Study Guide at the end of the chapter.

Chapter Vocabulary

biosphere, p. 684
ecosystem, p. 685
ecology, p. 685
population, p. 686
community, p. 686
habitat, p. 687
limiting factor, p. 690
carrying capacity, p. 691
producer, p. 696
consumer, p. 697
symbiosis, p. 698
mutualism, p. 698
commensalism, p. 698
parasitism, p. 698
niche, p. 699

Science Journal Student responses will vary, but may include feeding relationships, such as birds eating fruit or nuts from trees, or other relationships, such as trees providing nesting sites for birds or insects.

INTERACTIVE CHALKBOARD with Image Bank

PowerPoint® Presentations

This CD-ROM is an editable Microsoft® PowerPoint® presentation that includes:
* a pre-made presentation for every chapter
* interactive graphics
* animations
* audio clips
* image bank
* all new section and chapter questions
* Standardized Test Practice
* transparencies
* pre-lab questions for all labs
* Foldables directions
* links to life.msscience.com

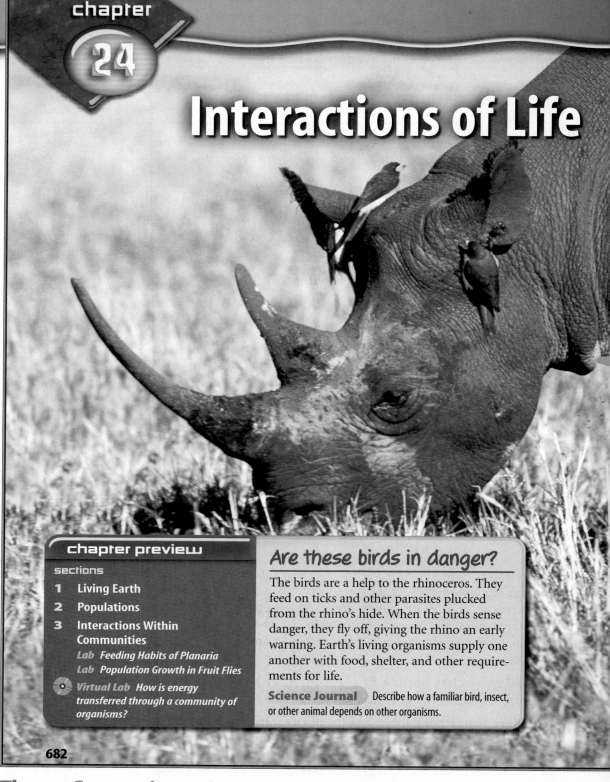

Interactions of Life

chapter preview

sections

1 **Living Earth**

2 **Populations**

3 **Interactions Within Communities**
   Lab Feeding Habits of Planaria
   Lab Population Growth in Fruit Flies
   Virtual Lab How is energy transferred through a community of organisms?

Are these birds in danger?

The birds are a help to the rhinoceros. They feed on ticks and other parasites plucked from the rhino's hide. When the birds sense danger, they fly off, giving the rhino an early warning. Earth's living organisms supply one another with food, shelter, and other requirements for life.

Science Journal Describe how a familiar bird, insect, or other animal depends on other organisms.

682

Theme Connection

Systems and Interactions A discussion of ecosystems, habitats, and communities shows how organisms interact. These interactions within the system affect population sizes and organisms' abilities to survive in their environments.

About the Photo

Mutualism The tick bird, or oxpecker, has a mutualistic relationship with the rhinoceros and with other mammals. The bird helps keep mammals free from ticks and other external parasites. The legs and sharp claws of the oxpecker are well adapted for clinging to fur or hide. Each bird obtains almost all of its food from the mammal host and can consume thousands of tick larvae or close to 100 adult ticks daily.

Start-Up Activities

How do lawn organisms survive?

You probably have taken thousands of footsteps on grassy lawns or playing fields. If you look closely at the grass, you'll see that each blade is attached to roots in the soil. How do grass plants obtain everything they need to live and grow? What other kinds of organisms live in the grass? The following lab will give you a chance to take a closer look at the life in a lawn.

1. Examine a section of sod from a lawn.
2. How do the roots of the grass plants hold the soil?
3. Do you see signs of other living things besides grass?
4. **Think Critically** In your Science Journal, answer the above questions and describe any organisms that are present in your section of sod. Explain how these organisms might affect the growth of grass plants. Draw a picture of your section of sod.

Preview this chapter's content and activities at life.msscience.com

---

FOLDABLES™ Study Organizer

Ecology Make the following Foldable to help organize information about one of your favorite wild animals and its role in an ecosystem.

STEP 1 Fold a vertical sheet of paper from side to side. Make the front edge 1.25 cm shorter than the back edge.

STEP 2 Turn lengthwise and **fold** into thirds.

STEP 3 Unfold and cut only the top layer along both folds to make three tabs. **Label** each tab.

Identify Questions Before you read the chapter, write what you already know about your favorite animal under the left tab of your Foldable. As you read the chapter, write how the animal is part of a population and a community under the appropriate tabs.

683

1 Motivate

Tie to Prior Knowledge

Habitats Ask students to identify several habitats—the places where plants and animals live. Have them describe living and non-living things in those habitats. L2

Answer the top portion of the crust, surface water, and Earth's atmosphere

as you read

What You'll Learn
- **Identify** places where life is found on Earth.
- **Define** ecology.
- **Observe** how the environment influences life.

Why It's Important
All living things on Earth depend on each other for survival.

Review Vocabulary
adaptation: any variation that makes an organism better suited to its environment

New Vocabulary
- biosphere
- population
- ecosystem
- community
- ecology
- habitat

The Biosphere

What makes Earth different from other planets in the solar system? One difference is Earth's abundance of living organisms. The part of Earth that supports life is the **biosphere** (BI uh sfihr). The biosphere includes the top portion of Earth's crust, all the waters that cover Earth's surface, and the atmosphere that surrounds Earth.

Reading Check   *What three things make up the biosphere?*

As **Figure 1** shows, the biosphere is made up of different environments that are home to different kinds of organisms. For example, desert environments receive little rain. Cactus plants, coyotes, and lizards are included in the life of the desert. Tropical rain forest environments receive plenty of rain and warm weather. Parrots, monkeys, and tens of thousands of other organisms live in the rain forest. Coral reefs form in warm, shallow ocean waters. Arctic regions near the north pole are covered with ice and snow. Polar bears, seals, and walruses live in the arctic.

Arctic

Desert

Coral reef

Figure 1 Earth's biosphere consists of many environments, including ocean waters, polar regions, and deserts.

684   CHAPTER 24 Interactions of Life

Section 1 Resource Manager

Chapter *FAST FILE* Resources
Transparency Activity, p. 44

Reinforcement, p. 27

Directed Reading for Content Mastery, pp. 19, 20

Enrichment, p. 30

Note-taking Worksheets, pp. 33–35

Life on Earth In our solar system, Earth is the third planet from the Sun. The amount of energy that reaches Earth from the Sun helps make the temperature just right for life. Mercury, the planet closest to the Sun, is too hot during the day and too cold at night to make life possible there. Venus, the second planet from the Sun, has a thick, carbon dioxide atmosphere and high temperatures. It is unlikely that life could survive there. Mars, the fourth planet, is much colder than Earth because it is farther from the Sun and has a thinner atmosphere. It might support microscopic life, but none has been found. The planets beyond Mars probably do not receive enough heat and light from the Sun to have the right conditions for life.

Ecosystems

On a visit to Yellowstone National Park in Wyoming, you might see a prairie scene like the one shown in **Figure 2.** Bison graze on prairie grass. Cowbirds follow the bison, catching grasshoppers that jump away from the bisons' hooves. This scene is part of an ecosystem. An **ecosystem** consists of all the organisms living in an area, as well as the nonliving parts of that environment. Bison, grass, birds, and insects are living organisms of this prairie ecosystem. Water, temperature, sunlight, soil, and air are nonliving features of this prairie ecosystem. **Ecology** is the study of interactions that occur among organisms and their environments. Ecologists are scientists who study these interactions.

Reading Check *What is an ecosystem?*

Figure 2 Ecosystems are made up of living organisms and the nonliving factors of their environment. In this prairie ecosystem, cowbirds eat insects and bison graze on grass.
List *other kinds of organisms that might live in this ecosystem.*

SECTION 1 Living Earth **685**

Cultural Diversity

Varieties of Ecosystems Have students who are originally from different cities, states, or countries describe to the class ecosystems from where they used to live. Encourage these students to explain why the ecosystem is important to the people in that area. Show the locations of these areas on a map after students describe them. L2

Caption Answer

Figure 2 Possible answers: rabbits, prairie dogs, antelope, small shrubs, hawks

Reading Check

Answer all living organisms and nonliving features of an area

Fun Fact

Both penguins and polar bears live in ice-covered regions, so why is it impossible to see a penguin and a polar bear in the wild at the same time? Polar bears live only in the Arctic, near the North Pole. Penguins live only in the southern hemisphere and in the Antarctic, near the South Pole.

Quick Demo
Locating Ecosystems
Materials globe or large world map
Estimated Time 10 minutes
Procedure Use the globe to show students the location of Earth's tropical regions (area between the Tropic of Cancer and the Tropic of Capricorn). Point out that tropical rain forests and coral reefs are two ecosystems that occur only in tropical areas. Also show students the Arctic region, (area above the Arctic circle) and point out that this icy region is where polar bears, walruses, harp seals, and other cold-tolerant organisms live.

Activity

Communities Ask students to observe a natural setting and draw or photograph a community that contains visible plant and animal life. Have students place their drawings or photographs, along with a list of the populations observed, in their Science Journals. L2 ELL LS
Naturalist P

Visual Learning

Figure 3 What communities are present in the ecosystem shown in this figure? deer, birds, rabbits, grasses, trees

Science Online

Topic: Human Population Data

Visit life.msscience.com for Web links to information about the estimated human population size for the world today.

Activity Create a graph that shows how the human population has changed between the year 2000 and this year.

Figure 3 The living world is arranged in several levels of organization.

Populations

Suppose you meet an ecologist who studies how a herd of bison moves from place to place and how the female bison in the herd care for their young. This ecologist is studying the members of a population. A **population** is made up of all organisms of the same species that live in an area at the same time. For example, all the bison in a prairie ecosystem are one population. All the cowbirds in this ecosystem make up a different population. The grasshoppers make up yet another population.

Ecologists often study how populations interact. For example, an ecologist might try to answer questions about several prairie species. How does grazing by bison affect the growth of prairie grass? How does grazing influence the insects that live in the grass and the birds that eat those insects? This ecologist is studying a community. A **community** is all the populations of all species living in an ecosystem. The prairie community is made of populations of bison, grasshoppers, cowbirds, and all other species in the prairie ecosystem. An arctic community might include populations of fish, seals that eat fish, and polar bears that hunt and eat seals. **Figure 3** shows how organisms, populations, communities, and ecosystems are related.

Differentiated Instruction

Learning Disabled Give student pairs a one-inch column of newspaper text. Ask them to find, circle, and count different populations. For example, have them find the population of the letter *P* by circling each *P* and counting to determine population size. Explain that one letter is an organism, each type of letter is a population, and all the types of letters are a community. L1

Challenge Have students research the natural habitat of an organism and then tell the class five interesting things about this habitat. L3 LS
Naturalist

Habitats

Each organism in an ecosystem needs a place to live. The place in which an organism lives is called its **habitat.** The animals shown in **Figure 4** live in a forest ecosystem. Trees are the woodpecker's habitat. These birds use their strong beaks to pry insects from tree bark or break open acorns and nuts. Woodpeckers usually nest in holes in dead trees. The salamander's habitat is the forest floor, beneath fallen leaves and twigs. Salamanders avoid sunlight and seek damp, dark places. This animal eats small worms, insects, and slugs. An organism's habitat provides the kinds of food and shelter, the temperature, and the amount of moisture the organism needs to survive.

Figure 4 The trees of the forest provide a habitat for woodpeckers and other birds. This salamander's habitat is the moist forest floor.

 section 1 review

Summary

The Biosphere
- The biosphere is the portion of Earth that supports life.

Ecosystems
- An ecosystem is made up of the living organisms and nonliving parts of an area.

Populations
- A population is made up of all members of a species that live in the same ecosystem.
- A community consists of all the populations in an ecosystem.

Habitats
- A habitat is where an organism lives.

Self Check

1. **List** three parts of the Earth included in the biosphere.
2. **Define** the term *ecology*.
3. **Compare and contrast** the terms *habitat* and *biosphere*.
4. **Identify** the major difference between a community and a population, and give one example of each.
5. **Think Critically** Does the amount of rain that falls in an area determine which kinds of organisms can live there? Why or why not?

Applying Skills

6. **Form a hypothesis** about how a population of dandelion plants might be affected by a population of rabbits.

Science Online life.msscience.com/self_check_quiz

SECTION 1 Living Earth **687**

section 1 review

1. Earth's crust, surface waters, atmosphere
2. the study of the interactions between organisms and between organisms and their environment
3. Habitat—place where organisms live; the biosphere includes all Earth's habitats.
4. A population is a single species living in an area. Example: all the maple trees of the Catskill Mountains. A community is all the populations that live in an area. Example: all the species of the Catskill Mountains.
5. Yes; organisms that need a lot of water cannot exist in areas with little rainfall.
6. Answers will vary. If students are aware that rabbits eat dandelions, their hypotheses should indicate that a rabbit population would limit the size of a dandelion population in the same community.

SECTION 1 Living Earth **687**

1 Motivate

Bellringer

Section Focus Transparencies also are available on the Interactive Chalkboard CD-ROM. L2 ELL

Tie to Prior Knowledge

Requirements for Life Have students recall the needs of living things. food, water, oxygen, shelter, living space Knowing what living things need to grow and reproduce will be helpful in understanding limiting factors. L1

---

section 2 Populations

as you read

What You'll Learn
- **Identify** methods for estimating population sizes.
- **Explain** how competition limits population growth.
- **List** factors that influence changes in population size.

Why It's Important
Competition caused by population growth reduces the amount of food, living space, and other resources available to organisms, including humans.

Review Vocabulary
natural selection: hypothesis that states organisms with traits best suited to their environment are more likely to survive and reproduce

New Vocabulary
- limiting factor
- carrying capacity

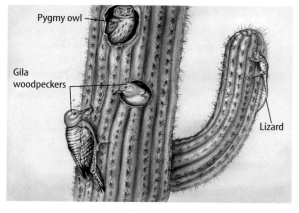

Pygmy owl

Gila woodpeckers

Lizard

Competition

Wild crickets feed on plant material at night. They hide under leaves or in dark damp places during the day. In some pet shops, crickets are raised in cages and fed to pet reptiles. Crickets require plenty of food, water, and hiding places. As a population of caged crickets grows, extra food and more hiding places are needed. To avoid crowding, some crickets might have to be moved to other cages.

Food and Space Organisms living in the wild do not always have enough food or living space. The Gila woodpecker, shown in **Figure 5,** lives in the Sonoran Desert of Arizona and Mexico. This woodpecker makes its nest by drilling a hole in a saguaro (suh GWAR oh) cactus. Woodpeckers must compete with each other for nesting spots. Competition occurs when two or more organisms seek the same resource at the same time.

Growth Limits Competition limits population size. If available nesting spaces are limited, some woodpeckers will not be able to raise young. Gila woodpeckers eat cactus fruit, berries, and insects. If food becomes scarce, some woodpeckers might not survive to reproduce. Competition for food, living space, or other resources can limit population growth.

In nature, the most intense competition is usually among individuals of the same species, because they need the same kinds of food and shelter. Competition also takes place among different species. For example, after a Gila woodpecker has abandoned its nest, owls, flycatchers, snakes, and lizards might compete for the shelter of the empty hole.

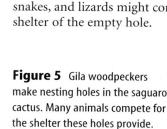

Figure 5 Gila woodpeckers make nesting holes in the saguaro cactus. Many animals compete for the shelter these holes provide.

Section 2 Resource Manager

Chapter *FAST FILE* Resources
Transparency Activity, pp. 45, 47–48
Directed Reading for Content Mastery, p. 20
MiniLAB, pp. 3, 4
Enrichment, p. 31
Reinforcement, p. 28

Reading and Writing Skill Activities, p. 1
Mathematics Skill Activities, p. 5
Life Science Critical Thinking/Problem Solving, pp. 12, 13

Population Size

Ecologists often need to measure the size of a population. This information can indicate whether or not a population is healthy and growing. Population counts can help identify populations that could be in danger of disappearing.

Some populations are easy to measure. If you were raising crickets, you could measure the size of your cricket population simply by counting all the crickets in the container. What if you wanted to compare the cricket populations in two different containers? You would calculate the number of crickets per square meter (m^2) of your container. The number of individuals of one species per a specific area is called population density. **Figure 6** shows Earth's human population density.

✔ Reading Check *What is population density?*

Measuring Populations Counting crickets can be tricky. They look alike, move a lot, and hide. The same cricket could be counted more than once, and others could be completely missed. Ecologists have similar problems when measuring wildlife populations. One of the methods they use is called trap-mark-release. Suppose you want to count wild rabbits. Rabbits live underground and come out at dawn and dusk to eat. Ecologists set traps that capture rabbits without injuring them. Each captured rabbit is marked and released. Later, another sample of rabbits is captured. Some of these rabbits will have marks, but many will not. By comparing the number of marked and unmarked rabbits in the second sample, ecologists can estimate the population size.

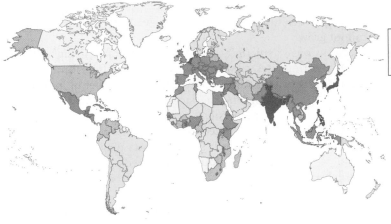

Humans/2.6km²	
■ Over 500	☐ 10–49
■ 100–500	☐ Under 10
	☐ 50–99

Figure 6 This map shows human population density.
Interpret Illustrations *Which countries have the highest population density?*

SECTION 2 Populations **689**

Mini LAB

Observing Seedling Competition
Procedure 🌊 🧤
1. Fill **two plant pots** with **moist potting soil.**
2. Plant **radish seeds** in one pot, following the spacing instructions on the seed packet. Label this pot *Recommended Spacing*.
3. Plant **radish seeds** in the second pot, spaced half the recommended distance apart. Label this pot *Densely Populated*. Wash your hands.
4. Keep the soil moist. When the seeds sprout, move them to a well-lit area.
5. Measure and record in your **Science Journal** the height of the seedlings every two days for two weeks.

Analysis
1. Which plants grew faster?
2. Which plants looked healthiest after two weeks?
3. How did competition influence the plants?

Try at Home

SECTION 2 Populations **689**

Discussion

Population Size Why would people want to know the population size of organisms such as deer? Ecologists may want the data for research. Game and fish departments may want the information to decide how many hunting permits to issue.

Caption Answer

Figure 7 Answers will vary. Students may suggest that they can count the number of wildebeests in the enlarged square, and then multiply by 20, the number of squares in the entire photograph.

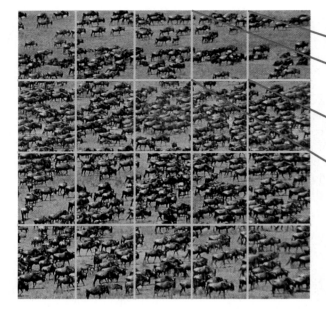

Figure 7 Ecologists can estimate population size by making a sample count. Wildebeests graze on the grassy plains of Africa.
Draw Conclusions *How could you use the enlarged square to estimate the number of wildebeests in the entire photograph?*

Sample Counts What if you wanted to count rabbits over a large area? Ecologists use sample counts to estimate the sizes of large populations. To estimate the number of rabbits in an area of 100 acres, for example, you could count the rabbits in one acre and multiply by 100 to estimate the population size. **Figure 7** shows another approach to sample counting.

Limiting Factors One grass plant can produce hundreds of seeds. Imagine those seeds drifting onto a vacant field. Many of the seeds sprout and grow into grass plants that produce hundreds more seeds. Soon the field is covered with grass. Can this grass population keep growing forever? Suppose the seeds of wildflowers or trees drift onto the field. If those seeds sprout, trees and flowers would compete with grasses for sunlight, soil, and water. Even if the grasses did not have to compete with other plants, they might eventually use up all the space in the field. When no more living space is available, the population cannot grow.

In any ecosystem, the availability of food, water, living space, mates, nesting sites, and other resources is often limited. A **limiting factor** is anything that restricts the number of individuals in a population. Limiting factors include living and nonliving features of the ecosystem.

A limiting factor can affect more than one population in a community. Suppose a lack of rain limits plant growth in a meadow. Fewer plants produce fewer seeds. For seed-eating mice, this reduction in the food supply could become a limiting factor. A smaller mouse population could, in turn, become a limiting factor for the hawks and owls that feed on mice.

690 CHAPTER 24 Interactions of Life

Carrying Capacity A population of robins lives in a grove of trees in a park. Over several years, the number of robins increases and nesting space becomes scarce. Nesting space is a limiting factor that prevents the robin population from getting any larger. This ecosystem has reached its carrying capacity for robins. **Carrying capacity** is the largest number of individuals of one species that an ecosystem can support over time. If a population begins to exceed the environment's carrying capacity, some individuals will not have enough resources. They could die or be forced to move elsewhere, like the deer shown in **Figure 8.**

Figure 8 These deer might have moved into a residential area because a nearby forest's carrying capacity for deer has been reached.

 **Reading Check** *How are limiting factors related to carrying capacity?*

Applying Science

Do you have too many crickets?

You've decided to raise crickets to sell to pet stores. A friend says you should not allow the cricket population density to go over 210 crickets/m^2. Use what you've learned in this section to measure the population density in your cricket tanks.

Identifying the Problem

The table on the right lists the areas and populations of your three cricket tanks. How can you determine if too many crickets are in one tank? If a tank contains too many crickets, what could you do? Explain why too many crickets in a tank might be a problem.

Solving the Problem

1. Do any of the tanks contain too many crickets? Could you make the population density of the three tanks equal by moving crickets from one tank to another? If so, which tank would you move crickets into?

Cricket Population

Tank	Area (m^2)	Number of Crickets
1	0.80	200
2	0.80	150
3	1.5	315

2. Wild crickets living in a field have a population density of 2.4 crickets/m^2. If the field's area is 250 m^2, what is the approximate size of the cricket population? Why would the population density of crickets in a field be lower than the population density of crickets in a tank?

Differentiated Instruction

Table 1 Which country has the fastest population growth? *Zimbabwe* Which country has the slowest growth? *Germany* What does a negative growth rate mean? *Death rate is greater than birthrate.*

Quick Demo

Observing Seed Distribution

Materials seeds that travel, such as dandelion, maple, and foxtails or burr clover

Estimated Time 10 minutes

Safety Precautions Be sure students wear appropriate outdoor clothing and use insect protection, if necessary.

Procedure Blow on the dandelion seeds to show how easily they move through the air. Drop a maple seed to show how its "wings" make the seed move. Demonstrate how foxtails and burr clover cling to fur or clothing. Discuss with students the advantages of a seed being able to move away from the parent plant. *reduces competition for space and nutrients between offspring and parent*

Fun Fact

Why are the ants that sometimes invade people's kitchens so hard to get rid of? One reason could be population size. A typical colony of Argentine ants numbers about 1 million individuals. Scientists have discovered a "supercolony" of Argentine ants that extends from Italy to Spain and contains billions of individuals.

Science Online

Topic: Birthrates and Death Rates
Visit life.msscience.com for Web links to information about birthrates and death rates for the human population.

Activity Find out whether the human population worldwide is increasing because of rising birthrates or declining death rates.

Table 1 Population Growth

	Birthrate*	Death Rate*	Population Increase (percent)
Rapid-Growth Countries			
Jordan	38.8	5.5	3.3
Uganda	50.8	21.8	2.9
Zimbabwe	34.3	9.4	5.2
Slow-Growth Countries			
Germany	9.4	10.8	−1.5
Sweden	10.8	10.6	0.1
United States	14.8	8.8	0.6

*Number per 1,000 people

Biotic Potential What would happen if no limiting factors restricted the growth of a population? Think about a population that has an unlimited supply of food, water, and living space. The climate is favorable. Population growth is not limited by diseases, predators, or competition with other species. Under ideal conditions like these, the population would continue to grow.

The highest rate of reproduction under ideal conditions is a population's biotic potential. The larger the number of offspring that are produced by parent organisms, the higher the biotic potential of the species will be. Compare an avocado tree to a tangerine tree. Assume that each tree produces the same number of fruits. Each avocado fruit contains one large seed. Each tangerine fruit contains a dozen seeds or more. Because the tangerine tree produces more seeds per fruit, it has a higher biotic potential than the avocado tree.

Changes in Populations

Birthrates and death rates also influence the size of a population and its rate of growth. A population gets larger when the number of individuals born is greater than the number of individuals that die. When the number of deaths is greater than the number of births, populations get smaller. Take the squirrels living in New York City's Central Park as an example. In one year, if 900 squirrels are born and 800 die, the population increases by 100. If 400 squirrels are born and 500 die, the population decreases by 100.

The same is true for human populations. **Table 1** shows birthrates, death rates, and population changes for several countries around the world. In countries with faster population growth, birthrates are much higher than death rates. In countries with slower population growth, birthrates are only slightly higher than death rates. In Germany, where the population is getting smaller, the birthrate is lower than the death rate.

Differentiated Instruction

Hearing Impaired Have students use index cards to make flipbooks showing variations in population growth. On the first cards, have them show a few organisms followed by exponential growth. Next, have them show how competition for resources affects the population. Finally, have them show a constant population size. Suggest they include a line graph that indicates change in population size in each scene. L2

Teacher FYI

Offspring Some organisms produce few offspring and some produce many. Fewer offspring benefit because they can be supplied with more of the parents' resources. Having many offspring increases the odds that one or more will survive to reproduce.

Figure 9 Mangrove seeds sprout while they are still attached to the parent tree. Some sprouted seeds drop into the mud below the parent tree and continue to grow. Others drop into the water and can be carried away by tides and ocean currents. When they wash ashore, they might start a new population of mangroves or add to an existing mangrove population.

Moving Around Most animals can move easily from place to place, and these movements can affect population size. For example, a male mountain sheep might wander many miles in search of a mate. After he finds a mate, their offspring might establish a completely new population of mountain sheep far from the male's original population.

Many bird species move from one place to another during their annual migrations. During the summer, populations of Baltimore orioles are found throughout eastern North America. During the winter, these populations disappear because the birds migrate to Central America. They spend the winter there, where the climate is mild and food supplies are plentiful. When summer approaches, the orioles migrate back to North America.

Even plants and microscopic organisms can move from place to place, carried by wind, water, or animals. The tiny spores of mushrooms, mosses, and ferns float through the air. The seeds of dandelions, maple trees, and other plants have feathery or winglike growths that allow them to be carried by wind. Spine-covered seeds hitch rides by clinging to animal fur or people's clothing. Many kinds of seeds can be transported by river and ocean currents. Mangrove trees growing along Florida's Gulf Coast, shown in **Figure 9,** provide an example of how water moves seeds.

Mini LAB

Comparing Biotic Potential

Procedure
1. Remove all the seeds from a **whole fruit.** Do not put fruit or seeds in your mouth.
2. Count the total number of seeds in the fruit. Wash your hands, then record these data in your **Science Journal.**
3. Compare your seed totals with those of classmates who examined other types of fruit.

Analysis
1. Which type of fruit had the most seeds? Which had the fewest seeds?
2. What is an advantage of producing many seeds? Can you think of a possible disadvantage?
3. To estimate the total number of seeds produced by a tomato plant, what would you need to know?

Mini LAB

Purpose Students observe and compare the number of seeds in different types of fruit. L2 ELL
LS **Logical-Mathematical**
Materials plastic knives, paper towels, assorted fruits

Teaching Strategies
• Ask students to bring in fruits from home.
• Explain that many of our vegetables are actually fruits, including tomatoes, eggplants, and squashes.

Safety Precautions Instruct students on the proper way to handle and use the plastic knives.

Analysis
1. Tomatoes and strawberries have many seeds; avocados and peaches have one seed.
2. Advantage: There is a greater chance that a seed will find an optimal place to grow. Disadvantage: The seeds are small and carry few nutrients.
3. how many tomatoes the plant produces and about how many seeds are produced by each tomato

Assessment

Oral Based on the number of seeds contained in each fruit, which has a greater biotic potential—a nectarine or a watermelon? Explain. A watermelon—it contains many seeds, while a nectarine contains only one. Use **Performance Assessment in the Science Classroom,** p. 89.

Active Reading

Four-Corner Discussion This strategy encourages debate. Make four signs: Strongly Agree, Agree, Disagree, Strongly Disagree. Place one sign in each corner of the room. Write on the board a statement that will elicit reactions from students. Have students respond on paper. After several minutes, direct them to move to the corner with the sign that most closely reflects their opinions. In the corners, students share responses. Each group selects a spokesperson to report the group's opinions. After all reports, open the floor for debate. Allow students who change their opinions to change corners. Use this strategy to discuss the causes of change in populations. L2

Visualizing Population Growth

Have students examine the pictures and read the captions. Then ask the following question.

What happens when a population exceeds carrying capacity? Possible answer: There may not be enough resources to support all members of the population. It is likely that members will begin to die from lack of resources such as food and water.

Activity

Data Table Have students graph the following data on predator-prey cycles between lynx and snowshoe hares.

Years	# of lynx	# of hares
1845	30,000	18,000
1850	10,000	40,000
1855	30,000	78,000
1860	8,000	21,000
1865	67,000	71,000
1870	7,000	12,000
1875	40,000	99,000
1880	12,000	9,000

What is the pattern between the population numbers of the lynx and the hares? As the number of hares increases, the number of lynx increases. As the larger lynx population feeds on hares, the number of hares decreases, followed by a decrease in the number of lynx. L2

NATIONAL GEOGRAPHIC VISUALIZING POPULATION GROWTH

Figure 10

When a species enters an ecosystem that has abundant food, water, and other resources, its population can flourish. Beginning with a few organisms, the population increases until the number of organisms and available resources are in balance. At that point, population growth slows or stops. A graph of these changes over time produces an S-curve, as shown here for coyotes.

CARRYING CAPACITY

EXPONENTIAL GROWTH

BEGINNING GROWTH

Population

Time

BEGINNING GROWTH During the first few years, population growth is slow, because there are few adults to produce young. As the population grows, so does the number of breeding adults.

EXPONENTIAL GROWTH As the number of adults in the population grows, so does the number of births. The coyote population undergoes exponential growth, quickly increasing in size.

CARRYING CAPACITY As resources become less plentiful, the birthrate declines and the death rate may rise. Population growth slows. The coyote population has reached the environmental carrying capacity—the maximum number of coyotes that the environment can sustain.

694 CHAPTER 24 Interactions of Life

Curriculum Connection

Math The bacterium *E. coli* can double in population size every 20 minutes under suitable conditions. Starting with a single bacterium, have students calculate the length of time it would take for the population to reach 1 million. The population would reach 1 million in only 6 hours and 40 minutes. L2

Logical-Mathematical

Exponential Growth When a species moves into a new area with plenty of food, living space, and other resources, the population grows quickly, in a pattern called exponential growth. Exponential growth means that the larger a population gets, the faster it grows. Over time, the population will reach the ecosystem's carrying capacity for that species. **Figure 10** shows each stage in this pattern of population growth.

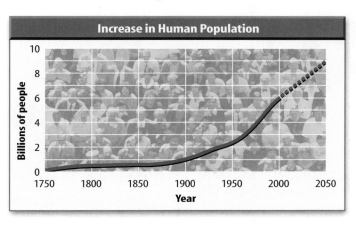

Increase in Human Population

(graph: Billions of people vs. Year, 1750–2050)

As a population approaches its ecosystem's carrying capacity, competition for living space and other resources increases. As you can see in **Figure 11,** Earth's human population shows exponential growth. By the year 2050, the population could reach 9 billion. You probably have read about or experienced some of the competition associated with human population growth, such as freeway traffic jams, crowded subways and buses, or housing shortages. As population density increases, people are forced to live closer to one another. Infectious diseases can spread easily when people are crowded together.

Figure 11 The size of the human population is increasing by about 1.6 percent per year.
Identify *the factors that affect human population growth.*

3 Assess

DAILY INTERVENTION

Check for Understanding
Coop Learn Ask students to work in groups to (a) guess the size of your school's seventh-grade population, (b) devise a way to more accurately estimate that population size, and (c) give reasons for seventh-grade immigration and emigration. L1

Reteach
Ecosystem Interactions Display photographs of organisms common to an ecosystem, such as a coniferous forest or a desert. Work with students to create a list of species present in the ecosystem. Discuss interactions that take place among the species, and how those interactions relate to competition, limiting factors, and carrying capacity. L1

✔ Assessment

Performance Have students research the population trends of an endangered species. Ask students to graph the data, showing numbers of individuals on the vertical axis and year on the horizontal axis. Have students describe the growth curve. Use **Performance Assessment in the Science Classroom,** p. 111. L2

---

section 2 review

Summary

Competition
- When more than one organism needs the same resource, competition occurs.
- Competition limits population size.

Population Size
- Population density is the number of individuals per unit area.
- Limiting factors are resources that restrict population size.
- An ecosystem's carrying capacity is the largest population it can support.
- Biotic potential is the highest possible rate of growth for a population.

Changes in Populations
- Birthrates, death rates, and movement from place to place affect population size.

Self Check

1. **Describe** three ways in which ecologists can estimate the size of a population.
2. **Explain** how birthrates and death rates influence the size of a population.
3. **Explain** how carrying capacity influences the number of organisms in an ecosystem.
4. **Think Critically** Why are food and water the limiting factors that usually have the greatest effect on population size?

Applying Skills

5. **Make and use a table** on changes in the size of a deer population in Arizona. Use the following data. In 1910 there were 6 deer; in 1915, 36 deer; in 1920, 143 deer; in 1925, 86 deer; and in 1935, 26 deer. Explain what might have caused these changes.

---

section 2 review

1. Count all individuals. Trap-mark-release: trap and mark two samples of the population, then compare the number of marked and unmarked individuals in the second sample. Sample counts: count the number of individuals in one part of an area, then multiply by the number of portions making up the entire area.
2. population increase, birthrate > death rate; population decrease, death rate > birthrate; population unchanged, birthrate = death rate
3. places a limit on the number of organisms that can survive
4. All living things require food and water, so their supply can affect population size.
5. Possible answer: The population grew when predators were eliminated. When the deer exceeded carrying capacity, their numbers were again reduced.

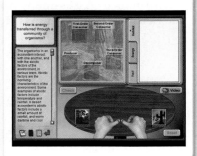
Interactions Within Communities

as you read

What You'll Learn
- **Describe** how organisms obtain energy for life.
- **Explain** how organisms interact.
- **Recognize** that every organism occupies a niche.

Why It's Important
Obtaining food, shelter, and other needs is crucial to the survival of all living organisms, including you.

🔍 Review Vocabulary
social behavior: interactions among members of the same species

New Vocabulary
- producer
- consumer
- symbiosis
- mutualism
- commensalism
- parasitism
- niche

Obtaining Energy

Just as a car engine needs a constant supply of gasoline, living organisms need a constant supply of energy. The energy that fuels most life on Earth comes from the Sun. Some organisms use the Sun's energy to create energy-rich molecules through the process of photosynthesis. The energy-rich molecules, usually sugars, serve as food. They are made up of different combinations of carbon, hydrogen, and oxygen atoms. Energy is stored in the chemical bonds that hold the atoms of these molecules together. When the molecules break apart—for example, during digestion—the energy in the chemical bonds is released to fuel life processes.

Producers Organisms that use an outside energy source like the Sun to make energy-rich molecules are called **producers.** Most producers contain chlorophyll (KLOR uh fihl), a chemical that is required for photosynthesis. As shown in **Figure 12,** green plants are producers. Some producers do not contain chlorophyll and do not use energy from the Sun. Instead, they make energy-rich molecules through a process called chemosynthesis (kee moh SIHN thuh sus). These organisms can be found near volcanic vents on the ocean floor. Inorganic molecules in the water provide the energy source for chemosynthesis.

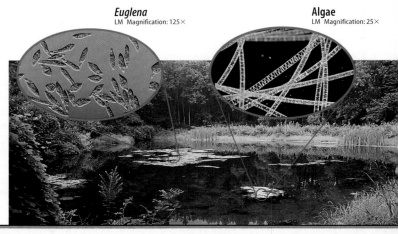

Euglena
LM Magnification: 125×

Algae
LM Magnification: 25×

Figure 12 Green plants, including the grasses that surround this pond, are producers. The pond water also contains producers, including microscopic organisms like *Euglena* and algae.

696

Section 3 Resource Manager

Chapter *FAST FILE* Resources
Transparency Activity, p. 46
Enrichment, p. 32
Directed Reading for Content Mastery, pp. 21, 22
Reinforcement, p. 29

Lab Worksheets, pp. 5–6, 7–8
Lab Activities, pp. 9–11, 13–16
Reading and Writing Skill Activities, p. 49
Cultural Diversity, p. 13
Home and Community Involvement, p. 47
Lab Management and Safety, p. 71

Figure 13 Four categories of consumers are shown.
Identify *the consumer category that would apply to a bear. What about a mushroom?*

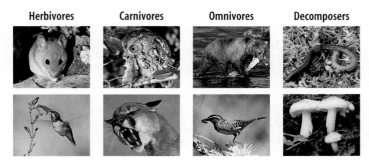

Herbivores   Carnivores   Omnivores   Decomposers

Consumers Organisms that cannot make their own energy-rich molecules are called **consumers.** Consumers obtain energy by eating other organisms. **Figure 13** shows the four general categories of consumers. Herbivores are the vegetarians of the world. They include rabbits, deer, and other plant eaters. Carnivores are animals that eat other animals. Frogs and spiders are carnivores that eat insects. Omnivores, including pigs and humans, eat mostly plants and animals. Decomposers, including fungi, bacteria, and earthworms, consume wastes and dead organisms. Decomposers help recycle once-living matter by breaking it down into simple, energy-rich substances. These substances might serve as food for decomposers, be absorbed by plant roots, or be consumed by other organisms.

✓ Reading Check *How are producers different from consumers?*

Food Chains Ecology includes the study of how organisms depend on each other for food. A food chain is a simple model of the feeding relationships in an ecosystem. For example, shrubs are food for deer, and deer are food for mountain lions, as illustrated in **Figure 14.** What food chain would include you?

INTEGRATE Chemistry

Glucose The nutrient molecule produced during photosynthesis is glucose. Look up the chemical structure of glucose and draw it in your Science Journal.

Figure 14 Food chains illustrate how consumers obtain energy from other organisms in an ecosystem.

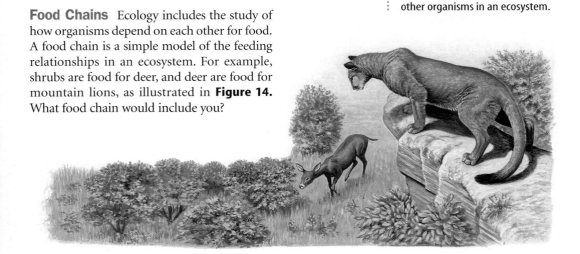

SECTION 3 Interactions Within Communities **697**

Text Question Answer

Accept any answer that shows a human eating food derived from a plant or animal. For example, in Figure 14, humans might replace the mountain lion, because humans eat venison.

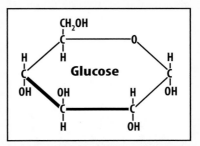
Text Question Answer

Accept any answer that shows a human eating food derived from a plant or animal. For example, in Figure 14, humans might replace the mountain lion, because humans eat venison.

Figure 15 Many examples of symbiotic relationships exist in nature.

Lichens are a result of mutualism.

Clown fish and sea anemones have a commensal relationship.

LM Magnification: 128×

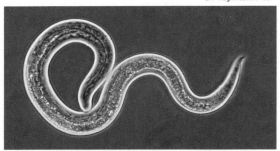

Some roundworms are parasites that rob nutrients from their hosts.

Symbiotic Relationships

Not all relationships among organisms involve food. Many organisms live together and share resources in other ways. Any close relationship between species is called **symbiosis.**

Mutualism You may have noticed crusty lichens growing on fences, trees, or rocks. Lichens, like those shown in **Figure 15,** are made up of an alga or a cyanobacterium that lives within the tissues of a fungus. Through photosynthesis, the cyanobacterium or alga supplies energy to itself and the fungus. The fungus provides a protected space in which the cyanobacterium or alga can live. Both organisms benefit from this association. A symbiotic relationship in which both species benefit is called **mutualism** (MYEW chuh wuh lih zum).

Commensalism If you've ever visited a marine aquarium, you might have seen the ocean organisms shown in **Figure 15.** The creature with gently waving, tubelike tentacles is a sea anemone. The tentacles contain a mild poison. Anemones use their tentacles to capture shrimp, fish, and other small animals to eat. The striped clown fish can swim among the tentacles without being harmed. The anemone's tentacles protect the clown fish from predators. In this relationship, the clown fish benefits but the sea anemone is not helped or hurt. A symbiotic relationship in which one organism benefits and the other is not affected is called **commensalism** (kuh MEN suh lih zum).

Parasitism Pet cats or dogs sometimes have to be treated for worms. Roundworms, like the one shown in **Figure 15,** are common in puppies. This roundworm attaches itself to the inside of the puppy's intestine and feeds on nutrients in the puppy's blood. The puppy may have abdominal pain, bloating, and diarrhea. If the infection is severe, the puppy might die. A symbiotic relationship in which one organism benefits but the other is harmed is called **parasitism** (PER uh suh tih zum).

698 CHAPTER 24 Interactions of Life

Niches

One habitat might contain hundreds or even thousands of species. Look at the rotting log habitat shown in **Figure 16.** A rotting log in a forest can be home to many species of insects, including termites that eat decaying wood and ants that feed on the termites. Other species that live on or under the rotting log include millipedes, centipedes, spiders, and worms. You might think that competition for resources would make it impossible for so many species to live in the same habitat. However, each species has different requirements for its survival. As a result, each species has its own niche (NICH). An organism's **niche** is its role in its environment—how it obtains food and shelter, finds a mate, cares for its young, and avoids danger.

☑ Reading Check   *Why does each species have its own niche?*

Special adaptations that improve survival are often part of an organism's niche. Milkweed plants contain a poison that prevents many insects from feeding on them. Monarch butterfly caterpillars have an adaptation that allows them to eat milkweed. Monarchs can take advantage of a food resource that other species cannot use. Milkweed poison also helps protect monarchs from predators. When the caterpillars eat milkweed, they become slightly poisonous. Birds avoid eating monarchs because they learn that the caterpillars and adult butterflies have an awful taste and can make them sick.

Plant Poisons The poison in milkweed is similar to the drug digitalis. Small amounts of digitalis are used to treat heart ailments in humans, but it is poisonous in large doses. Research the history of digitalis as a medicine. In your Science Journal, list diseases for which it was used but is no longer used.

Figure 16 Different adaptations enable each species living in this rotting log to have its own niche. Termites eat wood. They make tunnels inside the log. Millipedes feed on plant matter and find shelter beneath the log. Wolf spiders capture insects living in and around the log.

Termites

Millipede

Wolf spider

SECTION 3   Interactions Within Communities   **699**

Figure 17 The alligator is a predator. The turtle is its prey.

Predator and Prey When you think of survival in the wild, you might imagine an antelope running away from a lion. An organism's niche includes how it avoids being eaten and how it finds or captures its food. Predators, like the one shown in **Figure 17,** are consumers that capture and eat other consumers. The prey is the organism that is captured by the predator. The presence of predators usually increases the number of different species that can live in an ecosystem. Predators limit the size of prey populations. As a result, food and other resources are less likely to become scarce, and competition between species is reduced.

Cooperation Individual organisms often cooperate in ways that improve survival. For example, a white-tailed deer that detects the presence of wolves or coyotes will alert the other deer in the herd. Many insects, such as ants and honeybees, live in social groups. Different individuals perform different tasks required for the survival of the entire nest. Soldier ants protect workers that go out of the nest to gather food. Worker ants feed and care for ant larvae that hatch from eggs laid by the queen. These cooperative actions improve survival and are a part of the specie's niche.

---

section 3 review

Summary

Obtaining Energy

● All life requires a constant supply of energy.

● Most producers make food by photosynthesis using light energy.

● Consumers cannot make food. They obtain energy by eating producers or other consumers.

● A food chain models the feeding relationships between species.

Symbiotic Relationships

● Symbiosis is any close relationship between species.

● Mutualism, commensalism, and parasitism are types of symbiosis.

● An organism's niche describes the ways in which the organism obtains food, avoids danger, and finds shelter.

Self Check

1. **Explain** why all consumers depend on producers for food.

2. **Describe** a mutualistic relationship between two imaginary organisms. Name the organisms and explain how each benefits.

3. **Compare and contrast** the terms *habitat* and *niche*.

4. **Think Critically** A parasite can obtain food only from a host organism. Explain why most parasites weaken, but do not kill, their hosts.

Applying Skills

5. **Design an experiment** to classify the symbiotic relationship that exists between two hypothetical organisms. Animal A definitely benefits from its relationship with Plant B, but it is not clear whether Plant B benefits, is harmed, or is unaffected.

---

section 3 review

1. Producers can make their own carbohydrates from nonliving materials; other types of organisms cannot do this and must feed on producers, either directly or indirectly.

2. Answers will vary but both organisms should benefit from the relationship.

3. The place an organism lives is its habitat. How an organism survives is its niche.

4. If a parasite kills its host, the parasite also will die.

5. Answers will vary but should include a sample of Animal A grown with Plant B. This will be compared to a sample of Plant B grown alone.

Feeding Habits of Planaria

You probably have watched minnows darting about in a stream. It is not as easy to observe organisms that live at the bottom of a stream, beneath rocks, logs, and dead leaves. Countless stream organisms, including insect larvae, worms, and microscopic organisms, live out of your view. One such organism is a type of flatworm called a planarian. In this lab, you will find out about the eating habits of planarians.

◉ Real-World Question

What food items do planarians prefer to eat?

Goals
- **Observe** the food preference of planarians.
- **Infer** what planarians eat in the wild.

Materials
small bowl
planarians (several)
lettuce leaf
raw liver or meat

guppies (several)
pond or stream water
magnifying lens

Safety Precautions

Magnification: Unknown

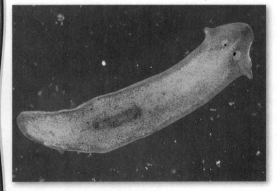

◉ Procedure

1. Fill the bowl with stream water.
2. Place a lettuce leaf, piece of raw liver, and several guppies in the bowl. Add the planarians. Wash your hands.
3. **Observe** what happens inside the bowl for at least 20 minutes. Do not disturb the bowl or its contents. Use a magnifying lens to look at the planarians.
4. **Record** all of your observations in your Science Journal.

◉ Conclude and Apply

1. **Name** the food the planarians preferred.
2. **Infer** what planarians might eat when in their natural environment.
3. **Describe,** based on your observations during this lab, a planarian's niche in a stream ecosystem.
4. **Predict** where in a stream you might find planarians. Use references to find out whether your prediction is correct.

𝒞ommunicating
Your Data

Share your results with other students in your class. Plan an adult-supervised trip with several classmates to a local stream to search for planarians in their native habitat. **For more help, refer to the** Science Skill Handbook.

LAB 701

𝒞ommunicating
Your Data

Have students write a paragraph describing their results. They can exchange papers with a classmate to see their results. L2

☑ Assessment

Performance Ask students to infer how their results might have differed had they used tap water instead of stream water. Tap water contains chemicals toxic to soft bodied animals and could kill the planarians. Use **Performance Assessment in the Science Classroom,** p. 89. L2

◉ Real-World Question

Purpose Students observe the eating habits of planarians and infer what wild planarians eat.
L2 IN Visual-Spatial

Process Skills observe, predict, infer

Time Required 30 minutes

◉ Procedure

Safety Precautions Instruct students to handle planarians with care and to wash their hands after the lab.

Teaching Strategy To house the planarians for an extended period of time, change the water of their bowls every other day and keep a small piece of liver in the bowl.

Troubleshooting
- Set up a bowl of planarians to serve as a reference.
- The piece of liver should be about the size of a quarter.
- Tell students to cover their dishes for a few minutes; planaria do not like light.

◉ Conclude and Apply

1. liver
2. Most planaria are carnivorous night feeders. They eat protozoans, tiny snails, worms, and dead animals.
3. Although planarians prey on slow-moving animals, they primarily scavenge dead organisms from the bottom of streams.
4. Planarians live in slow-moving or still portions of a stream where dead organisms settle to the stream bottom. They are found beneath rotting leaves or rocks.

Real-World Question

Purpose Students will test the effect of a change in one environmental factor on the rate of growth of a fruit fly population. L2

Process Skills identify a question, form hypotheses, test a hypothesis, identify and manipulate variables, collect data, make and use tables, record data, record observations, analyze results, form operational definitions, evaluate other's data and conclusions, communicate, make and use graphs

Time Required two 45-minute periods and once weekly observations for one to two months

Possible Materials Standard fruit fly culture kits are available from biological supply houses. Possible culture containers include mayonnaise jars or other empty, sanitized food jars.

Safety Precautions

• Students should take care not to release their fruit flies within the school building.

• Used fruit fly culture containers can contain bacteria and mold, and should not be reused for other purposes.

Design Your Own

Goals
■ **Identify** the environmental factors needed by a population of fruit flies.
■ **Design** an experiment to investigate how a change in one environmental factor affects in any way the size of a fruit fly population.
■ **Observe** and **measure** changes in population size.

Possible Materials
fruit flies
standard fruit fly
   culture kit
food items (banana,
   orange peel, or other
   fruit)
water
heating or cooling source
culture containers
cloth, plastic, or other tops
   for culture containers
magnifying lens

Safety Precautions

POPULATION GROWTH IN FRUIT FLIES

Real-World Question

Populations can grow at an exponential rate only if the environment provides the right amount of food, shelter, air, moisture, heat, living space, and other factors. You probably have seen fruit flies hovering near ripe bananas or other fruit. Fruit flies are fast-growing organisms often raised in science laboratories. The flies are kept in culture tubes and fed a diet of specially prepared food flakes. Can you improve on this standard growing method to achieve faster population growth? Will a change in one environmental factor affect the growth of a fruit fly population?

Form a Hypothesis

Based on your reading about fruit flies, state a hypothesis about how changing one environmental factor will affect the rate of growth of a fruit fly population.

Test Your Hypothesis

Make a Plan

1. As a group, decide on one environmental factor to investigate. Agree on a hypothesis about how a change in this factor will affect population growth. Decide how you will test your hypothesis, and identify the experimental results that would support your hypothesis.

2. **List** the steps you will need to take to test your hypothesis. Describe exactly what you will do. List your materials.

3. **Determine** the method you will use to measure changes in the size of your fruit fly populations.

702 CHAPTER 24 Interactions of Life

Data Table:

Fruit Fly Population			
Culture number	**Number of Flies**		
	Date	Date	Date	Date
1				
2				
3				

Form a Hypothesis

Possible Hypothesis Students' hypotheses should reflect a change in one environmental factor, such as type of food, amount of water, or size of container, and its possible effect on the rate of growth of the fruit fly population. For example: A larger living space will result in a faster-growing fruit fly population.

4. Prepare a data table in your Science Journal to record weekly measurements of your fruit fly populations.

5. Read the entire experiment and make sure all of the steps are in a logical order.

6. **Research** the standard method used to raise fruit flies in the laboratory. Use this method as the control in your experiment.

7. **Identify** all constants, variables, and controls in your experiment.

Follow Your Plan

1. Make sure your teacher approves your plan before you start.

2. Carry out your experiment.

3. **Measure** the growth of your fruit fly populations weekly and record the data in your data table.

● Analyze Your Data

1. **Identify** the constants and the variables in your experiment.

2. **Compare** changes in the size of your control population with changes in your experimental population. Which population grew faster?

3. **Make and Use Graphs** Using the information in your data table, make a line graph that shows how the sizes of your two fruit fly populations changed over time. Use a different colored pencil for each population's line on the graph.

● Conclude and Apply

1. **Explain** whether or not the results support your hypothesis.

2. **Compare** the growth of your control and experimental populations. Did either population reach exponential growth? How do you know?

Communicating Your Data

Compare the results of your experiment with those of other students in your class. **For more help, refer to the** Science Skill Handbook.

● Test Your Hypothesis

Possible Procedures Provide two equal-sized populations of fruit flies with the same food, moisture, and temperature, but two different-sized containers to test the effect of living area on fruit fly population growth. Make observations over the next one to two months. The fruit fly's life cycle is about two weeks, so students should see rapid changes in population size.

Teaching Strategy Most students are familiar with fruit flies "appearing" near ripe fruit. Have students consider the source of these flies. Sometimes eggs were already present; other times flies have used their strong sense of smell to locate the ripe fruit.

Expected Outcome Most results will show that any extreme change from the standard method of maintaining fruit flies will result in a decreased rate of population growth.

● Analyze Your Data

Answers to Questions

1. Answers will vary.
2. Answers will vary.
3. Student graphs will vary. Check students' work.

Error Analysis Have students compare their results and their hypotheses and explain why differences occurred. [L2]

● Conclude and Apply

1. Answers will be determined by student's hypotheses.
2. A population shows exponential growth if it increases at a fixed percentage per time period. Student answers will depend on results.

Communicating Your Data

Students can make an electronic spreadsheet that allows comparison of data about different environmental factors that affect the rate of growth of the fruit fly population. [L3]

✔ Assessment

Oral Have students explain the relationship between environmental conditions and population growth in fruit flies. Flies achieve the fastest rate of growth when all the conditions in their environment are at optimal levels. Any change in these conditions will result in a decrease in population growth rates. Use **Performance Assessment in the Science Classroom,** p. 89. [L1]

TIME SCIENCE AND HISTORY

SCIENCE CAN CHANGE THE COURSE OF HISTORY!

The Census measures a human population

Content Background

The U.S. Congress and the Electoral College are made up of representatives from each state. The number of representatives and electors from each state is determined by the state's population and updated by the census every 10 years. To make sure each Congress member represents an equal number of people, congressional districts are reapportioned according to the census.

Discussion

Age Why do you think it is important for the census to include information about the ages of U.S residents? *Possible answers: Knowing the ages of children indicates the number of schools needed in the near future. The number of middle-aged adults indicates how many seniors might enter government programs such as Social Security and Medicare in coming years.*

Activity

2000 Census Results Have students research results of the 2000 Census for their state, their region of the country, and the U.S. as a whole. Ask them to write a paragraph in their Science Journal comparing changes in the population of their state or region with changes that took place nation-wide. *Nationwide, the population rose by 32.7 million, or 13.2 percent, between 1990 and 2000. The western region grew faster than other regions of the country.* L2

Counting people is important to the United States and to many other countries around the world. It helps governments determine the distribution of people in the various regions of a nation. To obtain this information, the government takes a census—a count of how many people are living in their country on a particular day at a particular time, and in a particular place. A census is a snapshot of a country's population.

Counting on the Count

When the United States government was formed, its founders set up the House of Representatives based on population. Areas with more people had more government representatives, and areas with fewer people had fewer representatives. In 1787, the requirement for a census became part of the U.S. Constitution. A census must be taken every ten years so the proper number of representatives for each state can be calculated.

The Short Form

Before 1970, United States census data was collected by field workers. They went door to door to count the number of people living in each household. Since then, the census has been done mostly by mail. Census data are important in deciding how to distribute government services and funding.

The 2000 Snapshot

One of the findings of the 2000 Census is that the U.S. population is becoming more equally spread out across age groups. Census officials estimate that by 2020 the population of children, middle-aged people, and senior citizens will be about equal. It's predicted also that there will be more people who are over 100 years old than ever before. Federal, state, and local governments will be using the results of the 2000 Census for years to come as they plan our future.

Census Develop a school census. What questions will you ask? (Don't ask questions that are too personal.) Who will ask them? How will you make sure you counted everyone? Using the results, can you make any predictions about your school's future or its current students?

Science Online

For more information, visit life.msscience.com/time

Census Today, the entire census is taken using a mail-in form. Have students develop a short mail-in form to take a school census. Have groups write questions to include on the forms. Challenge students to design the form so that it is understand-able. After the census is taken, have students discuss challenges they encountered. L2

Resources for Teachers and Students

Who Counts? The Politics of Census-Taking in Contemporary America, by Margo J. Anderson and Stephen E. Fienberg, Russell Sage Foundation, New York. 1999

Census Brief 2000: Population Change and Distribution 1990–2000, by Marc J. Perry and Paul J. Mackun, U.S. Census Bureau, U.S. Department of Commerce, 2001

Reviewing Main Ideas

Section 1 Living Earth

1. Ecology is the study of interactions that take place in the biosphere.

2. A population is made up of all organisms of one species living in an area at the same time.

3. A community is made up of all the populations living in one ecosystem.

4. Living and nonliving factors affect an organism's ability to survive in its habitat.

Section 2 Populations

1. Population size can be estimated by counting a sample of a total population.

2. Competition for limiting factors can restrict the size of a population.

3. Population growth is affected by birthrate, death rate, and the movement of individuals into or out of a community.

4. Exponential population growth can occur in environments that provide a species with plenty of food, shelter, and other resources.

Section 3 Interactions Within Communities

1. All life requires energy.

2. Most producers use light to make food in the form of energy-rich molecules. Consumers obtain energy by eating other organisms.

3. Mutualism, commensalism, and parasitism are the three kinds of symbiosis.

4. Every species has its own niche, which includes adaptations for survival.

Reviewing Main Ideas

Summary statements can be used by students to review the major concepts of the chapter.

Visualizing Main Ideas

See student page.

Visit life.msscience.com
  /self_check_quiz
  /interactive_tutor
  /vocabulary_puzzlemaker
  /chapter_review
  /standardized_test
  /field_guide

Assessment Transparency

For additional assessment questions, use the *Assessment Transparency* located in the transparency book.

Visualizing Main Ideas

Copy and complete the following concept map on communities.

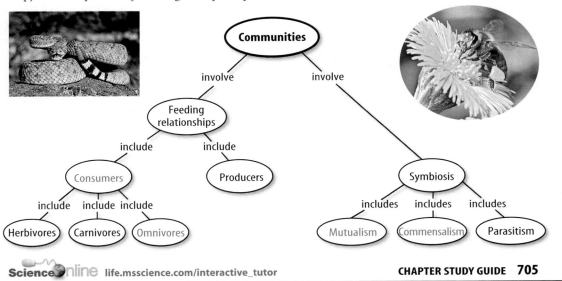

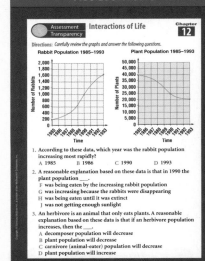

◆ Identifying Misconceptions   Assess

Use the assessment as follow-up to page F at the beginning of the chapter.
Activity After completing the activity in which students find and label interactions outdoors, have students again draw a picture of a natural community. Have students describe the interactions in the picture. L1

Expected Outcome In this second drawing, students should be able to identify more relationships among organisms. The interactions they depict should include not only predation, but also various types of symbiosis. L3

chapter Review 24

Using Vocabulary

1. Habitat is the place an organism lives. Niche refers to adaptations that help an organism survive.

2. Both describe symbiotic relationships. In mutualism both organisms benefit. In commensalism, one organism benefits, and the other neither benefits nor is harmed.

3. Carrying capacity is the largest number of individuals of one species that an ecosystem can support. Limiting factors restrict carrying capacity.

4. An ecosystem is all the living and nonliving components of an area. The biosphere is the part of Earth that supports life. It is made up of many ecosystems.

5. Producers make their own food. Consumers eat producers or other consumers for food.

6. An ecosystem is all the living and nonliving components of an area. A population is all the individuals of one species living in an area.

7. A community is all the different species in an area. A population refers to one species in an area.

8. Symbiosis describes a close relationship between species. Parasitism is a type of symbiosis in which one species benefits and the other species is harmed.

9. An ecosystem is all the living and nonliving components of an area. Ecology is the study of interactions between these components.

10. Both are types of symbiosis. In parasitism, one species benefits, and the other is harmed. In commensalism, one organism benefits, and the other neither benefits nor is harmed.

Checking Concepts

11. A	14. D	17. C
12. C	15. B	18. C
13. D	16. A	19. A

Using Vocabulary

biosphere p. 684	limiting factor p. 690
carrying capacity p. 691	mutualism p. 698
commensalism p. 698	niche p. 699
community p. 686	parasitism p. 698
consumer p. 697	population p. 686
ecology p. 685	producer p. 696
ecosystem p. 685	symbiosis p. 698
habitat p. 687	

Explain the difference between the vocabulary words in each of the following sets.

1. niche—habitat

2. mutualism—commensalism

3. limiting factor—carrying capacity

4. biosphere—ecosystem

5. producer—consumer

6. population—ecosystem

7. community—population

8. parasitism—symbiosis

9. ecosystem—ecology

10. parasitism—commensalism

Checking Concepts

Choose the word or phrase that best answers the question.

11. Which of the following is a living factor in the environment?
   A) animals
   B) air
   C) sunlight
   D) soil

12. What is made up of all the populations in an area?
   A) niches
   B) habitats
   C) community
   D) ecosystem

13. What does the number of individuals in a population that occupies an area of a specific size describe?
   A) clumping
   B) size
   C) spacing
   D) density

14. Which of the following animals is an example of an herbivore?
   A) wolf
   B) moss
   C) tree
   D) rabbit

15. What term best describes a symbiotic relationship in which one species is helped and the other is harmed?
   A) mutualism
   B) parasitism
   C) commensalism
   D) consumerism

16. Which of the following conditions tends to increase the size of a population?
   A) births exceed deaths
   B) population size exceeds the carrying capacity
   C) movements out of an area exceed movements into the area
   D) severe drought

17. Which of the following is most likely to be a limiting factor in a population of fish living in the shallow water of a large lake?
   A) sunlight
   B) water
   C) food
   D) soil

18. In which of the following categories does the pictured organism belong?
   A) herbivore
   B) carnivore
   C) producer
   D) consumer

19. Which pair of words is incorrect?
   A) black bear—carnivore
   B) grasshopper—herbivore
   C) pig—omnivore
   D) lion—carnivore

Science Online life.msscience.com/vocabulary_puzzlemaker

Use the ExamView® Pro Testmaker CD-ROM to:
- create multiple versions of tests
- create modified tests with one mouse click for inclusion students
- edit existing questions and add your own questions
- build tests aligned with state standards using built-in State Curriculum Tags
- change English tests to Spanish with one mouse click and vice versa

Thinking Critically

20. Infer why a parasite has a harmful effect on the organism it infects.

21. Explain what factors affect carrying capacity.

22. Describe your own habitat and niche.

23. Make and Use Tables Copy and complete the following table.

Types of Symbiosis		
Organism A	**Organism B**	**Relationship**
Gains	Doesn't gain or lose	Commensalism
Gains	Gains	Mutualism
Gains	Loses	Parasitism

24. Explain how several different niches can exist in the same habitat.

25. Make a model of a food chain using the following organisms: grass, snake, mouse, and hawk.

26. Predict Dandelion seeds can float great distances on the wind with the help of white, featherlike attachments. Predict how a dandelion seed's ability to be carried on the wind helps reduce competition among dandelion plants.

27. Classify the following relationships as parasitism, commensalism, or mutualism: a shark and a remora fish that cleans and eats parasites from the shark's gills; head lice and a human; a spiny sea urchin and a tiny fish that hides from predators by floating among the sea urchin's spines.

28. Compare and contrast the diets of omnivores and herbivores. Give examples of each.

29. List three ways exponential growth in the human population affects people's lives.

Science Online life.msscience.com/chapter_review

Performance Activities

30. Poster Use photographs from old magazines to create a poster that shows at least three different food chains. Illustrate energy pathways from organism to organism and from organisms to the environment. Display your poster for your classmates.

Applying Math

31. Measuring Populations An ecologist wants to know the size of a population of wild daisy plants growing in a meadow that measures 1,000 m². The ecologist counts 30 daisy plants in a sample area of 100 m². What is the estimated population of daisies in the entire meadow?

Use the table below to answer question 32.

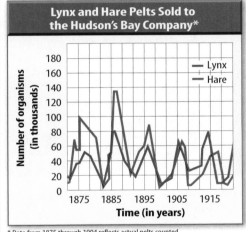

Lynx and Hare Pelts Sold to the Hudson's Bay Company*

* Data from 1875 through 1904 reflects actual pelts counted.
Data from 1905 through 1915 is based on answers to questionnaire.

32. Changes in Populations The graph above shows changes over time in the sizes of lynx and rabbit populations in an ecosystem. What does the graph tell you about the relationship between these two species? Explain how they influence each other's population size.

Thinking Critically

20. It may absorb nutrients from the organism, as does a tapeworm living inside a human's intestine, or spread disease from one organism to another, as mosquitos spread malaria.

21. Possible answers: food, water, shelter, space, birthrates and death rates, immigration, emigration

22. Description of habitat should include where the student lives. Description of niche should include adaptations and behaviors that enhance the student's survival.

23. See student page.

24. Organisms are adapted to feed on different foods, hunt at different times, and nest in different places. Therefore many niches can exist in the same habitat.

25. grass, mouse, snake, hawk

26. Individual seeds are able to move far from the parent plant, which helps reduce population density.

27. mutualism; parasitism; commensalism

28. Both eat plants. Omnivores, such as pigs and humans, eat both plants and animals. Herbivores, such as goats, eat only plants.

29. traffic, lack of housing, more rapid spread of disease, food shortages

Performance Activities

30. Food chains should move from producers to consumers. Use **PASC**, p. 145.

Applying Math

National Math Standards

1, 6, 7

31. 300

32. Shows a predator-prey relationship: lynxes eat hares. As the hare population rises, the lynx population also rises, because more food is available. As the hare population decreases, there is less food for lynxes, so the lynx population declines.

✓ **Assessment** **Resources**

Reproducible Masters
Chapter *Fast File* Resources
Chapter Review, pp. 37–38
Chapter Tests, pp. 39–42
Assessment Transparency Activity, p. 49
Glencoe Science Web site
Chapter Review Test
Standardized Test Practice

Glencoe Technology
Assessment Transparency
Exam*View*® Pro Testmaker
MindJogger Videoquiz
Interactive Chalkboard

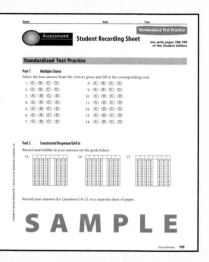

Part 1 | Multiple Choice

1. C
2. C
3. B
4. D
5. A
6. A
7. A
8. B
9. D
10. C

Part 1 | Multiple Choice

Record your answers on the answer sheet provided by your teacher or on a sheet of paper.

1. Which of the following terms is defined in part by nonliving factors?
   - **A.** population
   - **B.** community
   - **C.** ecosystem
   - **D.** niche

2. Which of the follow terms would include all places where organisms live on Earth?
   - **A.** ecosystem
   - **B.** habitat
   - **C.** biosphere
   - **D.** community

3. Which of the following is not a method of measuring populations?
   - **A.** total count
   - **B.** trap-release
   - **C.** sample count
   - **D.** trap-mark-release

Use the photo below to answer questions 4 and 5.

4. Dead plants at the bottom of this pond are consumed by
   - **A.** omnivores.
   - **B.** herbivores.
   - **C.** carnivores.
   - **D.** decomposers.

5. If the pond shrinks in size, what effect will this have on the population density of the pond's minnow species?
   - **A.** It will increase.
   - **B.** It will decrease.
   - **C.** It will stay the same.
   - **D.** No effect; it is not a limiting factor.

6. Which of the following includes organisms that can directly convert energy from the Sun into food?
   - **A.** producers
   - **B.** decomposers
   - **C.** omnivores
   - **D.** consumers

7. You have a symbiotic relationship with bacteria in your digestive system. These bacteria break down food you ingest, and you get vital nutrients from them. Which type of symbiosis is this?
   - **A.** mutualism
   - **B.** barbarism
   - **C.** commensalism
   - **D.** parasitism

Use the photo below to answer questions 8 and 9.

8. An eastern screech owl might compete with which organism most intensely for resources?
   - **A.** mouse
   - **B.** hawk
   - **C.** mountain lion
   - **D.** wren

9. Which of the following organisms might compete with the mouse for seeds?
   - **A.** hawk
   - **B.** lion
   - **C.** fox
   - **D.** sparrow

10. Which of the following is an example of a community?
    - **A.** all the white-tailed deer in a forest
    - **B.** all the trees, soil, and water in a forest
    - **C.** all the plants and animals in a wetland
    - **D.** all the cattails in a wetland

708 STANDARDIZED TEST PRACTICE

Part 2 | Short Response/Grid In

11. Hawks are a limiting factor for population A but not population B. Limiting factors for population B could be another predator, food, water, habitat space, or another competitive species for these resources.

12. Diagram should depict energy flow arrows going from the Sun (and possibly inorganic chemicals) to producers, from producers to consumers, from producers and consumers to decomposers.

Part 2 | Short Response/Grid In

Record your answers on the answer sheet provided by your teacher or on a sheet of paper.

Use the graph below to answer question 11.

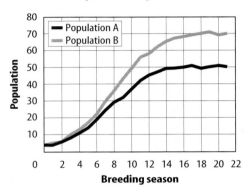

Mouse Population Exposed to Predators

11. The graph depicts the growth of two white-footed mice populations, one exposed to hawks (population A) and one without hawks (population B). Are hawks a limiting factor for either mouse population? If not, then what other factor could be a limiting factor for that population?

12. Diagram the flow of energy through an ecosystem. Include the sources of energy, producers, consumers, and decomposers in the ecosystem.

Test-Taking Tip

Understand the Question Be sure you understand the question before you read the answer choices. Make special note of words like NOT or EXCEPT. Read and consider choices before you mark your answer sheet.

Question 11 Make sure you understand which mouse population is subject to predation by hawks and which mouse population do hawks not affect.

Part 3 | Open Ended

Record your answers on a sheet of paper.

13. The colors and patterns of the viceroy butterfly are similar to the monarch butterfly, however, the viceroy caterpillars don't feed on milkweed. How does the viceroy butterfly benefit from this adaptation of its appearance? Under what circumstance would this adaptation not benefit the viceroy? Why?

Use the illustration below to answer question 14.

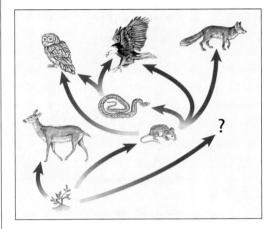

14. The illustration depicts a food web for a particular ecosystem. If the "?" is another mouse species population that is introduced into the ecosystem, explain what impact this would have on the species populations in the ecosystem.

15. Identify and explain possible limiting factors that would control the size of an ant colony.

16. How would you measure the size of a population of gray squirrels in a woodland? Explain which method you would choose and why.

for food resources. The diagram should be modified to include energy flow arrows from the introduced mouse population to the four predator populations.

15. Possible limiting factors: temperature, water, food, space, predators. Answer should include a reasonable explanation as to why the factor is limiting.

16. Trap-mark-release would ensure individuals were not counted more than once. A nest count would give an estimate of the number of breeding pairs in the woodland. A complete population count would be difficult, since squirrels in the wild can be wary of humans and a means of identifying each individual would be needed.

Rubrics

For more help evaluating open-ended assessment questions, see the rubric on p. 10T.

Part 3 | Open Ended

13. The viceroy butterfly benefits because predators avoid eating them due to their similar appearance to the monarch butterfly. This adaptation would not be beneficial if viceroys moved into an area where there are no monarchs. In this case, predators would not have learned to avoid monarch butterflies and would eat the viceroy butterflies.

14. The existing mouse population would have the most intense competition for resources with the introduced mouse population. This might lead to a reduction in the size of the original mouse population. However, the new mouse population can also serve as a prey species for the predators, owls, eagles, foxes and snakes, which may reduce predation pressure on the original mouse population. If the introduced mouse population eats the same vegetation as the deer population, then the deer population may have to compete

Section/Objectives	Standards		Labs/Features
Chapter Opener	National	State/Local	**Launch Lab:** Earth Has Many Ecosystems, p. 711 **Foldables,** p. 711
	See pp. 16T–17T for a Key to Standards.		
Section 1 Abiotic Factors ⏱ 2 sessions 📦 1 block 1. **Identify** common abiotic factors in most ecosystems. 2. **List** the components of air that are needed for life. 3. **Explain** how climate influences life in an ecosystem.	National Content Standards: UCP.1–UCP.4 A.1, A.2, B.3, C.4, D.1		**MiniLAB:** Determining Soil Makeup, p. 714 **Applying Math:** Temperature Changes, p. 716 **Integrate Career,** p. 717 **Science Online,** p. 717 **Lab:** Humus Farm, p. 719
Section 2 Cycles in Nature ⏱ 2 sessions 📦 1 block 4. **Explain** the importance of Earth's water cycle. 5. **Diagram** the carbon cycle. 6. **Recognize** the role of nitrogen in life on Earth.	National Content Standards: UCP.1–UCP.3, UCP.5, A.1, A.2, B.3, C.1, C.3–C.5, D.1		**MiniLAB:** Comparing Fertilizers, p. 723 **Visualizing the Carbon Cycle,** p. 724 **Science Online,** p. 725
Section 3 Energy Flow ⏱ 3 sessions 📦 1.5 blocks 7. **Explain** how organisms produce energy-rich compounds. 8. **Describe** how energy flows through ecosystems. 9. **Recognize** how much energy is available at different levels in a food chain.	National Content Standards: B.3, C.1, C.5, D.1		**Integrate Earth Science,** p. 727 **Lab:** Where does the mass of a plant come from?, pp. 730–731 **Science Stats:** Extreme Climates, p. 732

Lab Materials	Reproducible Resources	Section Assessment	Technology
Launch Lab: globe or world map, weather references	**Chapter FAST FILE Resources** Foldables Worksheet, p. 17 Directed Reading Overview, p.19 Note-taking Worksheets, pp. 33–34	GLENCOE'S ASSESSMENT ADVANTAGE	TeacherWorks includes: • Interactive Teacher Edition • Lesson Planner with calendar • Access to all program blacklines • Correlations to standards • Web links
MiniLAB: soil (2 cups), quart jar with lid, water, dishwashing liquid (1 teaspoon), watch or clock, metric ruler **Lab:** widemouthed jar, soil, grass clippings or green leaves, water, marker, metric ruler, graduated cylinder	**Chapter FAST FILE Resources** Transparency Activity, p. 44 MiniLAB, p. 3 Enrichment, p. 30 Reinforcement, p. 27 Directed Reading, p. 20 Lab Activity, pp. 9–12 Lab Worksheet, pp. 5–6 **Cultural Diversity,** p. 33 **Reading and Writing Skill Activities,** p. 3	**Portfolio** Assessment, p. 718 **Performance** MiniLAB, p. 714 Applying Math, p. 716 Applying Math, p. 718 **Content** Section Review, p. 718	Section Focus Transparency Virtual Labs CD-ROM Guided Reading Audio Program Interactive Chalkboard CD-ROM Video Lab
MiniLAB: labels (and prices) of 3 brands of houseplant fertilizer	**Chapter FAST FILE Resources** Transparency Activity, p. 45 MiniLAB, p. 4 Enrichment, p. 31 Reinforcement, p. 28 Directed Reading, p. 21 Lab Activity, pp. 13–16	**Portfolio** Activity, p. 724 **Performance** MiniLAB, p. 723 Applying Skills, p. 725 **Content** Section Review, p. 725	Section Focus Transparency Virtual Labs CD-ROM Guided Reading Audio Program Interactive Chalkboard CD-ROM
Lab: 8 oz. plastic or paper cup, potting soil to fill cup, scale or balance, radish seeds (4), water, paper towels *Need materials?* Contact Science Kit at 1-800-828-7777 or www.sciencekit.com on the Internet.	**Chapter FAST FILE Resources** Transparency Activity, p. 46 Enrichment, p. 32 Reinforcement, p. 29 Directed Reading, pp. 21, 22 Transparency Activity, pp. 47–48 Lab Worksheet, pp. 7–8 **Lab Management and Safety,** p. 38	**Portfolio** Activity, p. 727 Visual Learning, p. 728 **Performance** Applying Math, p. 729 **Content** Section Review, p. 729	Section Focus Transparency Teaching Transparency Virtual Labs CD-ROM Guided Reading Audio Program Interactive Chalkboard CD-ROM

End of Chapter Assessment

GLENCOE'S ASSESSMENT ADVANTAGE

Blackline Masters	Technology	Professional Series
Chapter FAST FILE Resources Chapter Review, pp. 37–38 Chapter Tests, pp. 39–42 **Standardized Test Practice,** pp. 103–106	MindJogger Videoquiz Virtual Labs CD-ROM ExamView® Pro Testmaker TeacherWorks CD-ROM Interactive Chalkboard CD-ROM	**Performance Assessment in the Science Classroom (PASC)**

Transparencies

Section Focus

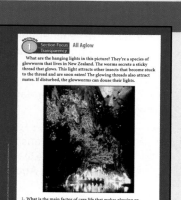

Section Focus Transparency 1 All Aglow

What are the hanging lights in this picture? They're a species of glowworm that lives in New Zealand. The worms secrete a sticky thread that glows. This light attracts other insects that become stuck to the thread and are soon eaten! The glowing threads also attract mates. If disturbed, the glowworms can douse their lights.

1. What is the main factor of cave life that makes glowing an advantage for the glowworm?
2. When might glowing not be an advantage?
3. What environmental factors might a glowworm need in order to stay alive?

L2

Section Focus Transparency 2 A Vital Job

All living things generate waste products. Luckily, some living things decompose and recycle that waste. Fungi, a group of plants that includes mushrooms, are great decomposers. The decomposing actions of fungi release nutrients back into the environment.

1. What are these mushrooms living on?
2. If there were no decomposers, what might happen?
3. Describe the role of fungi in recycling nutrients.

L2

Section Focus Transparency 3 What's for dinner?

Living things need energy to survive. Plants can get the energy they need directly from the Sun. Other organisms feed on plants or animals in order to get energy. This family is having a nutritious dinner. How many different kinds of food can you see in this picture?

1. How do living things use energy?
2. How do apple trees get energy? How do fish get energy?
3. Some organisms are said to be at the top of the food chain. What does this expression mean? Does a food chain ever end? Explain.

L2

This is a representation of key blackline masters available in the Teacher Classroom Resources. See Resource Manager boxes within the chapter for additional information.

Key to Teaching Strategies

The following designations will help you decide which activities are appropriate for your students.

L1 Level 1 activities should be appropriate for students with learning difficulties.

L2 Level 2 activities should be within the ability range of all students.

L3 Level 3 activities are designed for above-average students.

ELL ELL activities should be within the ability range of English-Language Learners.

COOP LEARN Cooperative Learning activities are designed for small group work.

LS Multiple Learning Styles logos, as described on page 12T, are used throughout to indicate strategies that address different learning styles.

P These strategies represent student products that can be placed into a best-work portfolio.

PBL Problem-Based Learning activities apply real-world situations to learning.

Assessment

Assessment Transparency The Nonliving Environment

Directions: Carefully review the graph and answer the following questions.

Temperature Ranges

■ Normal Temperature Range
X Lowest Temperature Recorded

1. At which altitude was the lowest possible temperature recorded?
A 1000 m   C 2000 m
B 1500 m   D 2500 m
2. Which altitude could have a measured temperature of 20°C?
F 500 m   H 2000 m
G 1000 m   J 2500 m
3. At which altitude is the normal range of temperatures the widest?
A 500 m   C 2000 m
B 1000 m   D 2500 m

L2

Teaching

Teaching Transparency 3 Food Web

L2

Hands-on Activities

Student Text Lab Worksheet

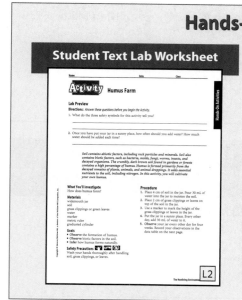

Activity Humus Farm

Lab Preview

Directions: Answer these questions before you begin the Activity.

1. What do the three safety symbols for this activity tell you?

2. Once you have put your jar in a sunny place, how often should you add water? How much water should be added each time?

Soil contains abiotic factors, including rock particles and minerals. Soil also contains biotic organisms. The crumbly, dark brown soil found in gardens or forests contains a high percentage of humus. Humus is formed primarily from the decayed remains of plants, animals, and animal droppings. It adds essential nutrients to the soil, including nitrogen. In this activity, you will cultivate your own humus.

What You'll Investigate
How does humus form?

Materials
widemouth jar
soil
grass clippings or green leaves
water
marker
metric ruler
graduated cylinder

Goals
• Observe the formation of humus.
• Observe biotic factors in the soil.
• Infer how humus forms naturally.

Safety Precautions
Wash your hands thoroughly after handling soil, grass clippings, or leaves.

Procedure
1. Place 4 cm of soil in the jar. Pour 30 mL of water into the jar to moisten the soil.
2. Place 2 cm of grass clippings or leaves on top of the soil in the jar.
3. Use a marker to mark the height of the grass clippings or leaves in the jar.
4. Put the jar in a sunny place. Every other day, add 30 mL of water to it.
5. Observe your jar every other day for four weeks. Record your observations in the data table on the next page.

L2

Laboratory Activities

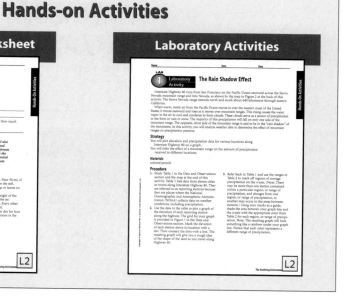

Laboratory Activity 1 The Rain Shadow Effect

Interstate Highway 80 runs from San Francisco on the Pacific Ocean eastward across the Sierra Nevada mountain range and into Nevada, as shown by the map in Figure 2 at the back of this activity. The Sierra Nevada range extends north and south about 640 kilometers through eastern California.

When warm, moist air from the Pacific Ocean moves in over the western coast of the United States, it moves eastward and rises as it moves over mountain ranges. This rising causes the water vapor in the air to cool and condense to form clouds. These clouds serve as a source of precipitation in the form or rain or snow. The majority of this precipitation will fall on only one side of the mountain range. The opposite, dryer side of the mountain range is said to be in the "rain shadow" of the mountains. In this activity, you will analyze weather data to determine the effect of mountain ranges on precipitation patterns.

Strategy
You will plot elevation and precipitation data for various locations along Interstate Highway 80 on a graph.
You will infer the effect of a mountain range on the amount of precipitation received in different locations.

Materials
colored pencils

Procedure
1. Study Table 1 in the Data and Observations section and the map at the end of this activity. Table 1 lists data from eleven cities or towns along Interstate Highway 80. They are referred to as reporting stations because they are places where the National Oceanographic and Atmospheric Administration (NOAA) collects data on weather conditions, including precipitation.
2. Use the data in the table to plot a graph of the elevation of each reporting station along the highway. The grid for your graph is provided in Figure 1 in the Data and Observations section. Mark the elevation of each station above its location with a dot. Then connect the dots with a line. The resulting graph will give you a rough idea of the shape of the land as you travel along Highway 80.
3. Refer back to Table 1 and use the ranges in Table 2 to mark off regions of average precipitation on the x-axis. (Note: There may be more than one station contained within a particular region, or range of precipitation, and changes from one region, or range of precipitation, to another may occur in the area between stations.) Using your marks as a guide, shade the area between your graph line and the x-axis with the appropriate color from Table 2 for each region, or range of precipitation. Note: The resulting graph will look something like a rainbow under your graph line. Notice that each color represents a different range of precipitation.

L2

Resource Manager

Meeting Different Ability Levels

Content Outline

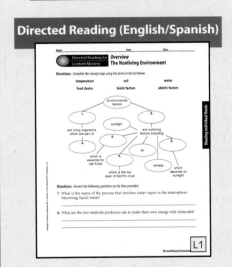

L2

Reinforcement

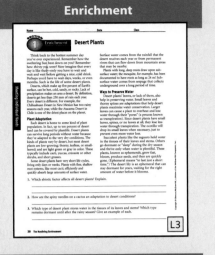

L2

Enrichment

L3

Directed Reading (English/Spanish)

L1

Study Guide

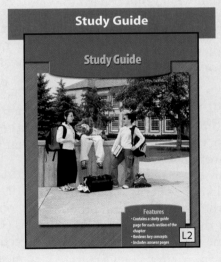

L2

Reading Essentials

L1

Assessment

Test Practice Workbook

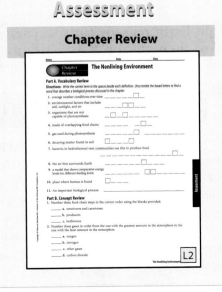

L2

Chapter Review

L2

Chapter Tests

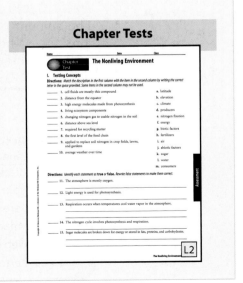

L2

Science Content Background

section 1 Abiotic Factors

Importance to Life

Important abiotic factors include air, water, soil, sunlight, temperature, and climate. These factors are interrelated and can vary from environment to environment and over time. Consider temperature, which changes from hour to hour, day to day, season to season, and year to year. Abiotic and biotic factors are not independent. Lack of rainfall can cause a drought in a grassland. The animals that depend on plants for food would find it hard to survive. Many of the factors are predictable and cyclic, but may have extreme variations. Some can be influenced by other factors such as pollution in air, water, and soil.

section 2 Cycles in Nature

Natural Recycling

Matter, in the form of nutrients, moves through the organisms at each trophic level in an ecosystem. But matter cannot be replenished like the energy from sunlight. The atoms of carbon, nitrogen, and other elements that make up the bodies of organisms alive today are the same atoms that have been on Earth since life began. Matter is constantly being recycled.

Water Cycle

The amount of water on Earth remains fairly constant. While some of the water on Earth cycles, much of it is held in oceans or as ice and does not enter the cycle. At a given time, the atmosphere holds about 12,000 cubic kilometers of water, while all the freshwater rivers and lakes hold 120,000 cubic kilometers. Every day about 1,200 cubic kilometers of water evaporates from the ground or transpires from plants and about the same amount falls back to the surface as rain.

Nitrogen Cycle

Nitrogen gas makes up about 79 percent of the atmosphere, but cannot be utilized by plants in this form. In addition to fixation in the soil by bacteria, the high energy of lightning and cosmic radiation combines nitrogen with oxygen into usable nitrates that are carried to Earth with precipitation. The nitrogen in fertilizers is artificially fixed in processing plants. Nitrogen, which is taken up directly by plants and incorporated into plant tissue, enters the food web when plants are consumed.

Carbon Cycle

In 1994, it was reported that the total amount of carbon available on Earth was about 47,000 gigatons (1 gigaton = 1 billion metric tons). About 83 percent of the available carbon was in the oceans, 22 percent in fossil fuels, and four percent in dead organic matter, living organisism, and soils. Only two percent was in the atmosphere. Many scientist believe that the accelerated greenhouse effect is caused by an increased amount of carbon dioxide in the atmosphere, due largely to the burning of fossil fuels.

chapter content resources

Internet Resources
For additional content background, visit
life.msscience.com to:
- access your book online
- find references to related articles in popular science magazines
- access Web links with related content background
- access current events with science journal topics

Print Resources
The Weather Book (2nd edition), by Jack Williams, Vintage Books, 1997
The Water Cycle, by Theresa Greenaway, Raintree/ Steck Vaughn, 2000
Food Webs, by Stuart L. Pimm, University of Chicago Press, 2002

Energy Flow

Food Chains

The law of conservation of energy states that energy cannot be created or destroyed, but can change from one form to another. The energy in an ecosystem is passed from one organism to another through a series of interactions called a food chain. Food chains, food webs and ecological pyramids show how energy moves in only one direction through the trophic levels of an ecosystem and how energy is lost at each transition, from one trophic level to the next. The energy is lost to the environment in the form of heat generated by the body processes of organisms. Although the heat is ultimately lost to the environment, it also serves the purpose of maintaining the body temperature of the organism. Sunlight is the source of most energy, so energy is constantly being replaced.

Food Webs

Some food webs are terrestrial, some are aquatic, and some are combinations. Two types of food webs are grazing and detrital. Detritivores are organisms such as crabs and earthworms that consume dead or decomposing organic matter. The largest amount of energy passes through detrital food webs.

Fritz Polking/Peter Arnold, Inc.

The Nonliving Environment

Chapter Vocabulary

Science Journal Answers may include water, sand, rocks, and sunlight. Order of importance and explanations will vary.

INTERACTIVE CHALKBOARD with Image Bank

PowerPoint® Presentations

This CD-ROM is an editable Microsoft® PowerPoint® presentation that includes:

- a pre-made presentation for every chapter
- interactive graphics
- animations
- audio clips
- image bank
- all new section and chapter questions
- Standardized Test Practice
- transparencies
- pre-lab questions for all labs
- Foldables directions
- links to life.msscience.com

chapter preview

sections

1 Abiotic Factors
Lab Humus Farm

2 Cycles in Nature

3 Energy Flow
Lab Where does the mass of a plant come from?

Virtual Lab How do organisms react to changes in abiotic factors?

710

Sun, Surf, and Sand

Living things on this coast directly or indirectly depend on nonliving things, such as sunlight, water, and rocks, for energy and raw materials needed for their life processes. In this chapter, you will read how these and other nonliving things affect life on Earth.

Science Journal List all the nonliving things that you can see in this picture in order of importance. Explain your reasoning for the order you chose.

Theme Connection

Systems and Interactions The ingredients for life are a part of the nonliving environment. Organisms can't exist without interaction with nonliving systems.

About the Photo

Nonliving Factors Everywhere on Earth nonliving factors can be observed, including along the coast of Oregon, as shown in this picture. These nonliving factors provide every living organism with the essential elements of life.

Start-Up Activities

Earth Has Many Ecosystems

Do you live in a dry, sandy region covered with cactus plants or desert scrub? Is your home in the mountains? Does snow fall during the winter? In this chapter, you'll learn why the nonliving factors in each ecosystem are different. The following lab will get you started.

1. Locate your city or town on a globe or world map. Find your latitude. Latitude shows your distance from the equator and is expressed in degrees, minutes, and seconds.

2. Locate another city with the same latitude as your city but on a different continent.

3. Locate a third city with latitude close to the equator.

4. Using references, compare average annual precipitation and average high and low temperatures for all three cities.

5. **Think Critically** Hypothesize how latitude affects average temperatures and rainfall.

Preview this chapter's content and activities at
life.mnscience.com

Nonliving Factors Make the following Foldable to help you understand the cause and effect relationships within the nonliving environment.

STEP 1 **Fold** two vertical sheets of paper in half from top to bottom. **Cut** the papers in half along the folds.

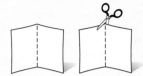

STEP 2 Discard one piece and **fold** the three vertical pieces in half from top to bottom.

STEP 3 **Turn** the papers horizontally. **Tape** the short ends of the pieces together (overlapping the edges slightly).

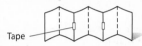
Tape

STEP 4 On one side, **label** the folds: *Nonliving, Water, Soil, Wind, Temperature,* and *Elevation.* **Draw** a picture of a familiar ecosystem on the other side.

Sequence As you read the chapter, write on the folds how each nonliving factor affects the environment that you draw.

711

1 Motivate

Bellringer

Section Focus Transparencies
also are available on the
Interactive Chalkboard CD-ROM.

Section Focus Transparency All Aglow

What are the hanging lights in this picture? They're a species of glowworm that lives in New Zealand. The worms secrete a sticky thread that glows. This light attracts other insects that become stuck to the thread and are soon eaten! The glowing threads also attract mates. If disturbed, the glowworms can douse their lights.

1. What is the main factor of cave life that makes glowing an advantage for the glowworm?
2. When might glowing not be an advantage?
3. What environmental factors might a glowworm need in order to stay alive?

The Nonliving Environment

Tie to Prior Knowledge

Survival of Living Things Have students examine a fish tank or a scene from nature. Ask them to identify nonliving things that are important for living things to survive. L2

section 1

Abiotic Factors

as you read

What You'll Learn

- **Identify** common abiotic factors in most ecosystems.
- **List** the components of air that are needed for life.
- **Explain** how climate influences life in an ecosystem.

Why It's Important

Knowing how organisms depend on the nonliving world can help humans maintain a healthy environment.

Review Vocabulary
environment: everything, such as climate, soil, and living things, that surrounds and affects an organism

New Vocabulary
- biotic
- soil
- abiotic
- climate
- atmosphere

Environmental Factors

Living organisms depend on one another for food and shelter. The leaves of plants provide food and a home for grasshoppers, caterpillars, and other insects. Many birds depend on insects for food. Dead plants and animals decay and become part of the soil. The features of the environment that are alive, or were once alive, are called **biotic** (bi AH tihk) factors. The term *biotic* means "living."

Biotic factors are not the only things in an environment that are important to life. Most plants cannot grow without sunlight, air, water, and soil. Animals cannot survive without air, water, or the warmth that sunlight provides. The nonliving, physical features of the environment are called **abiotic** (ay bi AH tihk) factors. The prefix *a* means "not." The term *abiotic* means "not living." Abiotic factors include air, water, soil, sunlight, temperature, and climate. The abiotic factors in an environment often determine which kinds of organisms can live there. For example, water is an important abiotic factor in the environment, as shown in **Figure 1.**

Figure 1 Abiotic factors—air, water, soil, sunlight, temperature, and climate—influence all life on Earth.

712 CHAPTER 25

Section 1 Resource Manager

Chapter FAST FILE Resources
Transparency Activity, p. 44
Directed Reading for Content Mastery, pp. 19, 20
Note-taking Worksheets, pp. 33–34
MiniLAB, p. 3
Lab, pp. 9–12
Enrichment, p. 30

Reinforcement, p. 27
Lab Worksheet, pp. 5–6
Cultural Diversity, p. 33
Reading and Writing Skill Activities, p. 3
Performance Assessment in the Science Classroom, p. 48

Air

Air is invisible and plentiful, so it is easily overlooked as an abiotic factor of the environment. The air that surrounds Earth is called the **atmosphere.** Air contains 78 percent nitrogen, 21 percent oxygen, 0.94 percent argon, 0.03 percent carbon dioxide, and trace amounts of other gases. Some of these gases provide substances that support life.

Carbon dioxide (CO_2) is required for photosynthesis. Photosynthesis—a series of chemical reactions—uses CO_2, water, and energy from sunlight to produce sugar molecules. Organisms, like plants, that can use photosynthesis are called producers because they produce their own food. During photosynthesis, oxygen is released into the atmosphere.

When a candle burns, oxygen from the air chemically combines with the molecules of candle wax. Chemical energy stored in the wax is converted and released as heat and light energy. In a similar way, cells use oxygen to release the chemical energy stored in sugar molecules. This process is called respiration. Through respiration, cells obtain the energy needed for all life processes. Air-breathing animals aren't the only organisms that need oxygen. Plants, some bacteria, algae, fish, and other organisms need oxygen for respiration.

Water

Water is essential to life on Earth. It is a major ingredient of the fluid inside the cells of all organisms. In fact, most organisms are 50 percent to 95 percent water. Respiration, digestion, photosynthesis, and many other important life processes can take place only in the presence of water. As **Figure 2** shows, environments that have plenty of water usually support a greater diversity of and a larger number of organisms than environments that have little water.

Figure 2 Water is an important abiotic factor in deserts and rain forests.

Life in deserts is limited to species that can survive for long periods without water.

Thousands of species can live in lush rain forests where rain falls almost every day.

SECTION 1 Abiotic Factors **713**

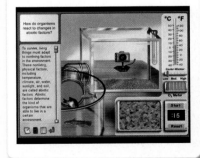

Fun Fact

One gram of soil may contain hundreds of millions of organisms.

Mini LAB

Purpose Students investigate the components that make up soil. L2 [IS] **Kinesthetic**

Materials two cups soil, large jar with lid, water, alum or dishwashing liquid, spoon, metric ruler

Teaching Strategy Review the components of soil before students carry out the activity.

Analysis

1. Clay is likely suspended in the water.
2. Answers will vary. It is likely that silt will form the greatest component.

Assessment

Oral Why did you examine the sample at different times? Different-sized particles settle at different rates. Use **Performance Assessment in the Science Classroom,** p. 89. L2

Caption Answer

Figure 3 These fish often depend on biotic materials that fall from above.

Mini LAB

Determining Soil Makeup

Procedure 🔬🧤👕

1. Collect 2 cups of **soil.** Remove large pieces of debris and break up clods.
2. Put the soil in a **quart jar** or **similar container that has a lid.**
3. Fill the container with **water** and add 1 teaspoon of **dishwashing liquid.**
4. Put the lid on tightly and shake the container.
5. After 1 min, measure and record the depth of sand that settled on the bottom.
6. After 2 h, measure and record the depth of silt that settles on top of the sand.
7. After 24 h, measure and record the depth of the layer between the silt and the floating organic matter.

Analysis

1. Clay particles are so small that they can remain suspended in water. Where is the clay in your sample?
2. Is sand, silt, or clay the greatest part of your soil sample?

Try at Home

Soil

Soil is a mixture of mineral and rock particles, the remains of dead organisms, water, and air. It is the topmost layer of Earth's crust, and it supports plant growth. Soil is formed, in part, of rock that has been broken down into tiny particles.

Soil is considered an abiotic factor because most of it is made up of nonliving rock and mineral particles. However, soil also contains living organisms and the decaying remains of dead organisms. Soil life includes bacteria, fungi, insects, and worms. The decaying matter found in soil is called humus. Soils contain different combinations of sand, clay, and humus. The type of soil present in a region has an important influence on the kinds of plant life that grow there.

Sunlight

All life requires energy, and sunlight is the energy source for almost all life on Earth. During photosynthesis, producers convert light energy into chemical energy that is stored in sugar molecules. Consumers are organisms that cannot make their own food. Energy is passed to consumers when they eat producers or other consumers. As shown in **Figure 3,** photosynthesis cannot take place if light is never available.

Shady forest

Bottom of deep ocean

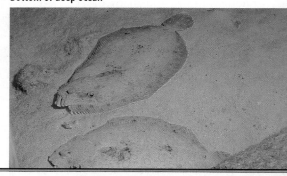

Figure 3 Photosynthesis requires light. Little sunlight reaches the shady forest floor, so plant growth beneath trees is limited. Sunlight does not reach into deep lake or ocean waters. Photosynthesis can take place only in shallow water or near the water's surface.
Infer how fish that live at the bottom of the deep ocean obtain energy.

LAB DEMONSTRATION

Purpose to determine the amount of humus in soil

Materials Bunsen burner, crucible, topsoil rich in humus, goggles, scale

Preparation Obtain and dry topsoil before class. Explain to students that humus can burn, but the rest of soil cannot.

Procedure Weigh a crucible, fill it with soil, and then weigh the soil-filled crucible. Heat it on high for 10 min. Allow it to cool and reweigh it. Determine the mass of humus and its percentage of original soil mass.

Expected Outcome Topsoils are 2–15% humus.

Assessment

Give students the following measurements and have them calculate the mass and percentage of humus in soil.

initial mass = 10 grams; final mass = 9 grams

mass of humus = 1 gram; 10% of original soil L2

Figure 4 Temperature is an abiotic factor that can affect an organism's survival.

The penguin has a thick layer of fat to hold in heat and keep the bird from freezing. These emperor penguins huddle together for added warmth.

The Arabian camel stores fat only in its hump. This way, the camel loses heat from other parts of its body, which helps it stay cool in the hot desert.

Temperature

Sunlight supplies life on Earth with light energy for photosynthesis and heat energy for warmth. Most organisms can survive only if their body temperatures stay within the range of 0°C to 50°C. Water freezes at 0°C. The penguins in **Figure 4** are adapted for survival in the freezing Antarctic. Camels can survive the hot temperatures of the Arabian Desert because their bodies are adapted for staying cool. The temperature of a region depends in part on the amount of sunlight it receives. The amount of sunlight depends on the land's latitude and elevation.

✓ **Reading Check** *What does sunlight provide for life on Earth?*

Latitude In this chapter's Launch Lab, you discovered that temperature is affected by latitude. You found that cities located at latitudes farther from the equator tend to have colder temperatures than cities at latitudes nearer to the equator. As **Figure 5** shows, polar regions receive less of the Sun's energy than equatorial regions. Near the equator, sunlight strikes Earth directly. Near the poles, sunlight strikes Earth at an angle, which spreads the energy over a larger area.

Figure 5 Because Earth is curved, latitudes farther from the equator are colder than latitudes near the equator.

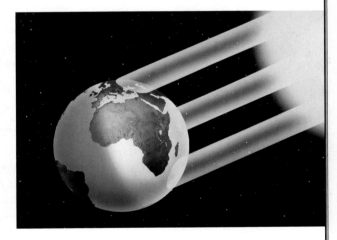

Visual Learning

Figure 4 Have students identify other adaptations camels have to their native desert environment. Possible answers: Their feet are widespread to enable them to walk easily on sand; to protect them from blowing sand, they have a double row of eyelashes, haired ear openings, and the ability to close their nostrils; they also have keen senses of sight and smell. L2

✓ **Reading Check**

Answer Sunlight provides light and heat. Students may also say that, through the process of photosynthesis, sunlight provides energy for life processes.

Inquiry Lab

Water Cycle
Purpose to explore the water cycle
Possible Materials plastic bag, clear sealed container
Estimated Time four weeks
Teaching Strategies
• Students could gather topsoil and add water, or collect mud from a pond and seal it in a clear container.
• Students could predict and observe how water moves throughout the sealed environment condensing on the inner surface and evaporating.
• Students can predict and observe what influence the plants have on the cycle.
• Allow students to explore other questions that arise.

For additional inquiry activities, see
Science Inquiry Labs.

Differentiated Instruction

Challenge Have students research the high and low temperatures at the north pole and the equator. Have students compare the findings with the area where they live and graph the results. L3

Curriculum Connection

Health Sunlight prevents rickets because it enables the skin to produce vitamin D. Ingesting vitamin D in food will also prevent rickets. Have students research which foods are good sources of vitamin D. Foods rich in vitamin D include milk, eggs, fortified breakfast cereals, sardines, salmon, beef, and margarine. L2

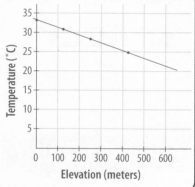

Figure 6 The stunted growth of these trees is a result of abiotic factors.

Elevation If you have climbed or driven up a mountain, you probably noticed that the temperature got cooler as you went higher. A region's elevation, or distance above sea level, affects its temperature. Earth's atmosphere acts as insulation that traps the Sun's heat. At higher elevations, the atmosphere is thinner than it is at lower elevations. Air becomes warmer when sunlight heats molecules in the air. Because there are fewer molecules at higher elevations, air temperatures there tend to be cooler.

At higher elevations, trees are shorter and the ground is rocky, as shown in **Figure 6.** Above the timberline—the elevation beyond which trees do not grow—plant life is limited to low-growing plants. The tops of some mountains are so cold that no plants can survive. Some mountain peaks are covered with snow year-round.

Applying Math   Solve for an Unknown

TEMPERATURE CHANGES You climb a mountain and record the temperature every 1,000 m of elevation. The temperature is 30°C at 304.8 m, 25°C at 609.6 m, 20°C at 914.4 m, 15°C at 1,219.2 m, and 5°C at 1,828.8 m. Make a graph of the data. Use your graph to predict the temperature at an altitude of 2,133.6 m.

Solution

1 *This is what you know:*   The data can be written as ordered pairs (elevation, temperature). The ordered pairs for these data are (304.8, 30), (609.6, 25), (914.4, 20), (1,219.2, 15), (1,828.8, 5).

2 *This is what you want to find:*   Predict the temperature at an elevation of 2,133.6 m.

3 *This is what you need to do:*   Graph the data by plotting elevation on the x-axis and temperature on the y-axis.

4 *Predict the temperature at 2,133.6 m:*   Extend the graph line to predict the temperature at 2,133.6 m.

Practice Problems

1. Temperatures on another mountain are 33°C at sea level, 31°C at 125 m, 29°C at 250 m, and 26°C at 425 m. Graph the data and predict the temperature at 550 m.

2. Predict what the temperature would be at 375 m.

Science Online   For more practice, visit life.msscience.com/math_practice

Cultural Diversity

Kenyan Runners Many great long-distance runners are from the Kalenjin tribe in a high-altitude area of Kenya. Why might great runners come from this area? Possible answers: Because of lower oxygen levels at high altitudes, these Kenyans may have adaptations for increased cardiovascular efficiency; their high-altitude training may help them produce more red blood cells; there may also be social reasons. L2

Climate

In Fairbanks, Alaska, winter temperatures may be as low as −52°C, and more than a meter of snow might fall in one month. In Key West, Florida, snow never falls and winter temperatures rarely dip below 5°C. These two cities have different climates. **Climate** refers to an area's average weather conditions over time, including temperature, rainfall or other precipitation, and wind.

For the majority of living things, temperature and precipitation are the two most important components of climate. The average temperature and rainfall in an area influence the type of life found there. Suppose a region has an average temperature of 25°C and receives an average of less than 25 cm of rain every year. It is likely to be the home of cactus plants and other desert life. A region with similar temperatures that receives more than 300 cm of rain every year is probably a tropical rain forest.

Wind Heat energy from the Sun not only determines temperature, but also is responsible for the wind. The air is made up of molecules of gas. As the temperature increases, the molecules spread farther apart. As a result, warm air is lighter than cold air. Colder air sinks below warmer air and pushes it upward, as shown in **Figure 7**. These motions create air currents that are called wind.

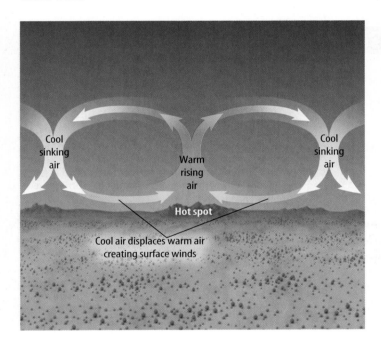

Cool sinking air

Warm rising air

Cool sinking air

Hot spot

Cool air displaces warm air creating surface winds

INTEGRATE Career

Farmer Changes in weather have a strong influence in crop production. Farmers sometimes adapt by changing planting and harvesting dates, selecting a different crop, or changing water use. In your Science Journal, describe another profession affected by climate.

Science Online

Topic: Weather Data
Visit life.msscience.com for Web links to information about recent weather data for your area.

Activity In your Science Journal, describe how these weather conditions affect plants or animals that live in your area.

Figure 7 Winds are created when sunlight heats some portions of Earth's surface more than others. In areas that receive more heat, the air becomes warmer. Cold air sinks beneath the warm air, forcing the warm air upward.

Discussion

Weather and Climate Weather refers to the day-to-day atmospheric conditions in an area. Climate takes a long-term view and describes the general weather conditions associated with an area. Discuss with students the weather and climate differences for their environment.

INTEGRATE Career

Farmer Answers will vary but should describe how climate affects the profession. An example is a fisherman who can find it difficult to navigate in adverse weather. Fish movements and populations also can be influenced by weather.

Research Have students investigate historical methods of predicting weather conditions. For example, how did farmers know when to plant crops?

Quick Demo

Rain Shadow Effect
Materials sponge
Estimated Time one minute
Procedure Show the rain shadow effect by moving a damp sponge over an imaginary mountain. As air rises, explain that it cools and water vapor condenses into rain. Squeeze the sponge to show rain. As air descends on the other side of the mountain, it warms. Any remaining water in the air changes back to water vapor. L2 ELL
IS **Visual-Spatial**

Differentiated Instruction

Learning Disabled Show students a globe and explain that since areas near the equator receive more direct sunshine, they are much warmer than areas toward the poles. As hot air is pushed aloft near the equator, cooler air rushes in to take its place. This causes wind, which is responsible for precipitation patterns. L1 IS **Visual-Spatial**

Teacher FYI

Cascade Mountains The Cascade Mountains, part of the Pacific mountain system, extend from California to Canada. The tallest peak in this range is Mt. Ranier, which reaches 4,392 m (14,410 ft). Most of the peaks are extinct volcanoes, although some have erupted in the recent past. Mount St. Helens is one of these, with eruptions in 1980 and 1981.

3 Assess

DAILY INTERVENTION

Check for Understanding

Challenge Have students investigate how professional greenhouses increase the levels of carbon dioxide and the temperature to achieve an optimal plant growing environment. L3

Reteach

Abiotic Factors Have students explain how water, air, and temperature can affect life. L1 LS **Naturalist**

✓ Assessment

Portfolio Have students cut out pictures from magazines that illustrate abiotic factors in an ecosystem and use the pictures to make posters. Direct students to label each abiotic factor. Use **Performance Assessment in the Science Classroom**, p. 145. L2 P

Figure 8 In Washington State, the western side of the Cascade Mountains receives an average of 101 cm of rain each year. The eastern side of the Cascades is in a rain shadow that receives only about 25 cm of rain per year.

INTEGRATE Earth Science

The Rain Shadow Effect The presence of mountains can affect rainfall patterns. As **Figure 8** shows, wind blowing toward one side of a mountain is forced upward by the mountain's shape. As the air nears the top of the mountain, it cools. When air cools, the moisture it contains falls as rain or snow. By the time the cool air crosses over the top of the mountain, it has lost most of its moisture. The other side of the mountain range receives much less precipitation. It is not uncommon to find lush forests on one side of a mountain range and desert on the other side.

section 1 review

Summary

Environmental Factors
- Organisms depend on one another as well as sunlight, air, water, and soil.

Air, Water, and Soil
- Some of the gases in air provide substances to support life.
- Water is a major component of the cells in all organisms.
- Soil supports plant growth.

Sunlight, Temperature, and Climate
- Light energy supports almost all life on Earth.
- Most organisms require temperature between 0°C and 50°C to survive.
- For most organisms, temperature and precipitation are the two most important components of climate.

Self Check

1. **Compare and contrast** biotic factors and abiotic factors in ecosystems.

2. **Explain** why soil is considered an abiotic factor and a biotic factor.

3. **Think Critically** On day 1, you hike in shade under tall trees. On day 2, the trees are shorter and farther apart. On day 3, you see small plants but no trees. On day 4, you see snow. What abiotic factors might contribute to these changes?

Applying Math

4. **Use an Electronic Spreadsheet** Obtain two months of temperature and precipitation data for two cities in your state. Enter the data in a spreadsheet and calculate average daily temperature and precipitation. Use your calculations to compare the two climates.

718 CHAPTER 25 The Nonliving Environment

Science nline life.msscience.com/self_check_quiz

section 1 review

1. Biotic factors are, or once were, living. Abiotic factors are nonliving.
2. While it is mostly nonliving material, there are many things living in soil, as well as decaying organic matter called humus.
3. Changes in elevation, which influence temperature, are probably responsible. This could occur on a mountain, as you reach and surpass the timberline.
4. Spreadsheets should result in average temperature and rainfall for two different cities.

Humus Farm

Besides abiotic factors, such as rock particles and minerals, soil also contains biotic factors, including bacteria, molds, fungi, worms, insects, and decayed organisms. Crumbly, dark brown soil contains a high percentage of humus that is formed primarily from the decayed remains of plants, animals, and animal droppings. In this lab, you will cultivate your own humus.

Real-World Question

How does humus form?

Goals
- **Observe** the formation of humus.
- **Observe** biotic factors in the soil.
- **Infer** how humus forms naturally.

Materials
widemouthed jar	water
soil	marker
grass clippings	metric ruler
or green leaves	graduated cylinder

Safety Precautions

Wash your hands thoroughly after handling soil, grass clippings, or leaves.

Procedure

1. Copy the data table below into your Science Journal.
2. Place 4 cm of soil in the jar. Pour 30 mL of water into the jar to moisten the soil.
3. Place 2 cm of grass clippings or green leaves on top of the soil in the jar.
4. Use a marker to mark the height of the grass clippings or green leaves in the jar.
5. Put the jar in a sunny place. Every other day, add 30 mL of water to it. In your Science Journal, write a prediction of what you think will happen in your jar.
6. **Observe** your jar every other day for four weeks. Record your observations in your data table.

Conclude and Apply

1. **Describe** what happened during your investigation.
2. **Infer** how molds and bacteria help the process of humus formation.
3. **Infer** how humus forms on forest floors or in grasslands.

Humus Formation

Date	Observations
	Answers will vary.

Communicating Your Data

Compare your humus farm with those of your classmates. With several classmates, write a recipe for creating the richest humus. Ask your teacher to post your recipe in the classroom. **For more help, refer to the** Science Skill Handbook.

LAB   719

Communicating Your Data

Students may want to consult cookbooks to see how the ingredients for recipes are written and arranged.

☑ Assessment

Process Ask students to discuss how forest ecosystems would be affected if leaf litter did not become humus. Use **Performance Assessment in the Science Classroom**, p. 93. L2

Real-World Question

Purpose Students observe humus formation over several weeks. L2 IS **Visual-Spatial**

Process Skills observe, describe, infer

Time Required 25 minutes for setup; 5-minute observation periods every other day for four weeks

Alternate Materials If green leaves are used instead of grass clippings, the leaves must be chopped in order for the activity to work.

Safety Precautions Instruct students to wash their hands when finished.

Procedure

Teaching Strategy Encourage students to bring in leaf litter to be used in the activity.

Troubleshooting To be certain the humus farms get enough water, assign a person from each group to water the jars every other day. Keep grass clippings moist but not waterlogged. Do not seal jars.

Conclude and Apply

1. Students first observe the growth of mold. As the mold and decomposing bacteria break down the clippings or litter, large particles of organic matter will form. These particles are the beginning of humus.
2. Molds and bacteria decompose materials into organic particles.
3. Organic materials fall to the ground and are decomposed into organic particles.

as you read

What You'll Learn

- **Explain** the importance of Earth's water cycle.
- **Diagram** the carbon cycle.
- **Recognize** the role of nitrogen in life on Earth.

Why It's Important

The recycling of matter on Earth demonstrates natural processes.

🔍 Review Vocabulary

biosphere: the part of the world in which life can exist

New Vocabulary

- evaporation
- condensation
- water cycle
- nitrogen fixation
- nitrogen cycle
- carbon cycle

The Cycles of Matter

Imagine an aquarium containing water, fish, snails, plants, algae, and bacteria. The tank is sealed so that only light can enter. Food, water, and air cannot be added. Will the organisms in this environment survive? Through photosynthesis, plants and algae produce their own food. They also supply oxygen to the tank. Fish and snails take in oxygen and eat plants and algae. Wastes from fish and snails fertilize plants and algae. Organisms that die are decomposed by the bacteria. The organisms in this closed environment can survive because the materials are recycled. A constant supply of light energy is the only requirement. Earth's biosphere also contains a fixed amount of water, carbon, nitrogen, oxygen, and other materials required for life. These materials cycle through the environment and are reused by different organisms.

The Water Cycle

If you leave a glass of water on a sunny windowsill, the water will evaporate. **Evaporation** takes place when liquid water changes into water vapor, which is a gas, and enters the atmosphere, shown in **Figure 9.** Water evaporates from the surfaces of lakes, streams, puddles, and oceans. Water vapor enters the atmosphere from plant leaves in a process known as transpiration (trans puh RAY shun). Animals release water vapor into the air when they exhale. Water also returns to the environment from animal wastes.

Figure 9 Water vapor is a gas that is present in the atmosphere.

Transpiration

Precipitation

Condensation

Evaporation

Groundwater

Movement of Water Vapor Students may think that the same water falls in a given area again and again. Emphasize that water vapor moves great distances in the air all over Earth; that water in lakes, rivers, and streams is always moving; that currents in the ocean are constantly moving; and that groundwater may move great distances.

Condensation Water vapor that has been released into the atmosphere eventually comes into contact with colder air. The temperature of the water vapor drops. Over time, the water vapor cools enough to change back into liquid water. The process of changing from a gas to a liquid is called **condensation.** Water vapor condenses on particles of dust in the air, forming tiny droplets. At first, the droplets clump together to form clouds. When they become large and heavy enough, they fall to the ground as rain or other precipitation. As the diagram in **Figure 10** shows, the **water cycle** is a model that describes how water moves from the surface of Earth to the atmosphere and back to the surface again.

Water Use Data about the amount of water people take from reservoirs, rivers, and lakes for use in households, businesses, agriculture, and power production is shown in **Table 1.** These actions can reduce the amount of water that evaporates into the atmosphere. They also can influence how much water returns to the atmosphere by limiting the amount of water available to plants and animals.

Figure 10 The water cycle involves evaporation, condensation, and precipitation. Water molecules can follow several pathways through the water cycle.
Identify *as many water cycle pathways as you can from this diagram.*

Table 1   U.S. Estimated Water Use in 1995

Water Use	Millions of Gallons per Day	Percent of Total
Homes and Businesses	41,600	12.2
Industry and Mining	28,000	8.2
Farms and Ranches	139,200	40.9
Electricity Production	131,800	38.7

SECTION 2 Cycles in Nature   **721**

Caption Answer
Figure 10 Pathways include precipitation, evaporation, transpiration, seeping into groundwater, and runoff from the ground into other bodies of water.

Visual Learning

Table 1 Which type of water use consumes the most water? farms and ranches Suggest a reason why. Possible answers: irrigation of crops or grasses, watering of livestock

Quick Demo
Condensation
Materials glass cup, ice
Estimated Time five minutes
Procedure Place some water and ice in a glass cup and place it on a table. Wait briefly and examine the outside of the glass. Explain that when warm air that contains water vapor contacts a cool surface, the water vapor condenses into liquid water.

Teacher FYI

Balancing Systems Although it is possible to achieve a closed aquarium system, it is not easy. The system must be perfectly balanced between producer and consumer, and this balance must remain constant over time.

Science Journal

Water Stories Have students imagine they are molecules of water. They should each make up a story about how they travel and what they encounter as they go through one complete cycle of the water cycle. L2 LS **Linguistic**

The Nitrogen Cycle

The element nitrogen is important to all living things. Nitrogen is a necessary ingredient of proteins. Proteins are required for the life processes that take place in the cells of all organisms. Nitrogen is also an essential part of the DNA of all organisms. Although nitrogen is the most plentiful gas in the atmosphere, most organisms cannot use nitrogen directly from the air. Plants need nitrogen that has been combined with other elements to form nitrogen compounds. Through a process called **nitrogen fixation,** some types of soil bacteria can form the nitrogen compounds that plants need. Plants absorb these nitrogen compounds through their roots. Animals obtain the nitrogen they need by eating plants or other animals. When dead organisms decay, the nitrogen in their bodies returns to the soil or to the atmosphere. This transfer of nitrogen from the atmosphere to the soil, to living organisms, and back to the atmosphere is called the **nitrogen cycle,** shown in **Figure 11.**

✔ **Reading Check** *What is nitrogen fixation?*

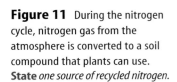

Figure 11 During the nitrogen cycle, nitrogen gas from the atmosphere is converted to a soil compound that plants can use. **State** *one source of recycled nitrogen.*

Nitrogen gas is changed into usable compounds by lightning or by nitrogen-fixing bacteria that live on the roots of certain plants.

Plants use nitrogen compounds to build cells.

Animals eat plants. Animal wastes return some nitrogen compounds to the soil.

Animals and plants die and decompose, releasing nitrogen compounds back into the soil.

Figure 12 The swollen nodules on the roots of soybean plants contain colonies of nitrogen-fixing bacteria that help restore nitrogen to the soil. The bacteria depend on the plant for food, while the plant depends on the bacteria to form the nitrogen compounds the plant needs.

Soybeans

Nodules on roots

Nitrogen-fixing bacteria

Stained LM Magnification: 1000×

Soil Nitrogen Human activities can affect the part of the nitrogen cycle that takes place in the soil. If a farmer grows a crop, such as corn or wheat, most of the plant material is taken away when the crop is harvested. The plants are not left in the field to decay and return their nitrogen compounds to the soil. If these nitrogen compounds are not replaced, the soil could become infertile. You might have noticed that adding fertilizer to soil can make plants grow greener, bushier, or taller. Most fertilizers contain the kinds of nitrogen compounds that plants need for growth. Fertilizers can be used to replace soil nitrogen in crop fields, lawns, and gardens. Compost and animal manure also contain nitrogen compounds that plants can use. They also can be added to soil to improve fertility.

Another method farmers use to replace soil nitrogen is to grow nitrogen-fixing crops. Most nitrogen-fixing bacteria live on or in the roots of certain plants. Some plants, such as peas, clover, and beans, including the soybeans shown in **Figure 12,** have roots with swollen nodules that contain nitrogen-fixing bacteria. These bacteria supply nitrogen compounds to the soybean plants and add nitrogen compounds to the soil.

Comparing Fertilizers

Procedure

1. Examine the three numbers (e.g., 5-10-5) on the **labels of three brands of houseplant fertilizer.** The numbers indicate the percentages of nitrogen, phosphorus, and potassium, respectively, that the product contains.
2. Compare the prices of the three brands of fertilizer.
3. Compare the amount of each brand needed to fertilize a typical houseplant.

Analysis

1. **Identify** the brand with the highest percentage of nitrogen.
2. **Calculate** which brand is the most expensive source of nitrogen. The least expensive.

Visualizing the Carbon Cycle

Have students examine the pictures and read the captions. Then ask the following questions.

What activities release carbon dioxide into the atmosphere? The burning of fossil fuels, the decomposition of carbon-containing molecules by decomposers, and the breakdown of sugar molecules in plants and by other organisms releases carbon dioxide into the atmosphere.

Why is this process called a cycle? Possible answer: Plants use carbon dioxide from the atmosphere to make sugars. The plants then are consumed by other organisms and the carbon dioxide is released back into the atmosphere as a waste product.

Activity

Carbon Cycle Have students make their own diagram of the carbon cycle, without looking at this page, and label each part. L2 IS
Visual-Spatial P

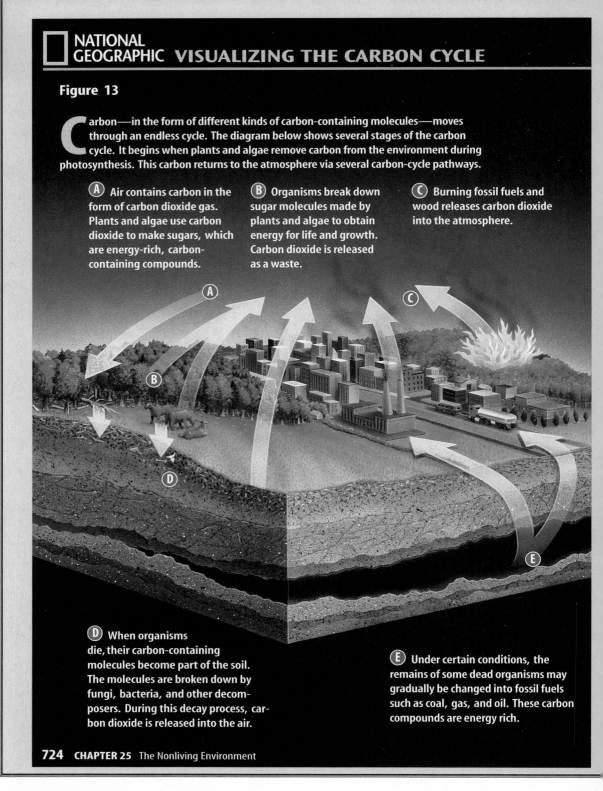

NATIONAL GEOGRAPHIC VISUALIZING THE CARBON CYCLE

Figure 13

Carbon—in the form of different kinds of carbon-containing molecules—moves through an endless cycle. The diagram below shows several stages of the carbon cycle. It begins when plants and algae remove carbon from the environment during photosynthesis. This carbon returns to the atmosphere via several carbon-cycle pathways.

A Air contains carbon in the form of carbon dioxide gas. Plants and algae use carbon dioxide to make sugars, which are energy-rich, carbon-containing compounds.

B Organisms break down sugar molecules made by plants and algae to obtain energy for life and growth. Carbon dioxide is released as a waste.

C Burning fossil fuels and wood releases carbon dioxide into the atmosphere.

D When organisms die, their carbon-containing molecules become part of the soil. The molecules are broken down by fungi, bacteria, and other decomposers. During this decay process, carbon dioxide is released into the air.

E Under certain conditions, the remains of some dead organisms may gradually be changed into fossil fuels such as coal, gas, and oil. These carbon compounds are energy rich.

Differentiated Instruction

English-Language Learners Have students work in groups to prepare a concept map that describes the carbon cycle. Have them include terms such as *consumers*, *photosynthesis*, *respiration*, and *producers*.
 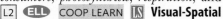 L2 ELL COOP LEARN IS **Visual-Spatial**

The Carbon Cycle

Carbon atoms are found in the molecules that make up living organisms. Carbon is an important part of soil humus, which is formed when dead organisms decay, and it is found in the atmosphere as carbon dioxide gas (CO_2). The **carbon cycle** describes how carbon molecules move between the living and nonliving world, as shown in **Figure 13.**

The carbon cycle begins when producers remove CO_2 from the air during photosynthesis. They use CO_2, water, and sunlight to produce energy-rich sugar molecules. Energy is released from these molecules during respiration—the chemical process that provides energy for cells. Respiration uses oxygen and releases CO_2. Photosynthesis uses CO_2 and releases oxygen. These two processes help recycle carbon on Earth.

✅ **Reading Check** *How does carbon dioxide enter the atmosphere?*

Human activities also release CO_2 into the atmosphere. Fossil fuels such as gasoline, coal, and heating oil are the remains of organisms that lived millions of years ago. These fuels are made of energy-rich, carbon-based molecules. When people burn these fuels, CO_2 is released into the atmosphere as a waste product. People also use wood for construction and for fuel. Trees that are harvested for these purposes no longer remove CO_2 from the atmosphere during photosynthesis. The amount of CO_2 in the atmosphere is increasing. Extra CO_2 could trap more heat from the Sun and cause average temperatures on Earth to rise.

Science Online

Topic: Life Processes
Visit life.msscience.com for Web links to information about chemical equations that describe photosynthesis and respiration.

Activity Use these equations to explain how respiration is the reverse of photosynthesis.

✅ **Reading Check**

Answer as a by-product of cellular respiration

3 Assess

DAILY INTERVENTION

Check for Understanding

Challenge Suppose you covered all the bodies of water on Earth with oil. How would this affect the water cycle? Possible answers: water could not evaporate; the water cycle would be disrupted; a drought may result. L3

Reteach

Cycles of Matter Ask students to explain the different paths water vapor, carbon, and nitrogen in the air would follow before they could enter a plant. L2 LS **Naturalist**

✅ Assessment

Portfolio Have students draw a diagram of the nitrogen cycle. Use **Performance Assessment in the Science Classroom,** p. 127. L2

---

section 2 review

Summary

The Cycles of Matter
- Earth's biosphere contains a fixed amount of water, carbon, nitrogen, oxygen, and other materials that cycle through the environment.

The Water Cycle
- Water cycles through the environment using several pathways.

The Nitrogen Cycle
- Some types of bacteria can form nitrogen compounds that plants and animals can use.

The Carbon Cycle
- Producers remove CO_2 from the air during photosynthesis and produce O_2.
- Consumers remove O_2 and produce CO_2.

Self Check

1. **Describe** the water cycle.
2. **Infer** how burning fossil fuels might affect the makeup of gases in the atmosphere.
3. **Explain** why plants, animals, and other organisms need nitrogen.
4. **Think Critically** Most chemical fertilizers contain nitrogen, phosphorous, and potassium. If they do not contain carbon, how do plants obtain carbon?

Applying Skills

5. **Identify and Manipulate Variables and Controls** Describe an experiment that would determine whether extra carbon dioxide enhances the growth of tomato plants.

---

section 2 review

1. Cycles should include evaporation, condensation, and precipitation.
2. It could result in an increase in the concentration of carbon dioxide.
3. to make amino acids for proteins and nucleic acids
4. Plants can get carbon from the atmosphere.
5. Answers will vary, but should include one group with normal CO_2 and one with extra CO_2. An operational definition of the growth of the tomato plants should be given, along with plans for taking measurements.

Converting Energy

All living things are made of matter, and all living things need energy. Matter and energy move through the natural world in different ways. Matter can be recycled over and over again. The recycling of matter requires energy. Energy is not recycled, but it is converted from one form to another. The conversion of energy is important to all life on Earth.

Photosynthesis During photosynthesis, producers convert light energy into the chemical energy in sugar molecules. Some of these sugar molecules are broken down as energy. Others are used to build complex carbohydrate molecules that become part of the producer's body. Fats and proteins also contain stored energy.

Chemosynthesis Not all producers rely on light for energy. During the 1970s, scientists exploring the ocean floor were amazed to find communities teeming with life. These communities were at a depth of almost 3.2 km and living in total darkness. They were found near powerful hydrothermal vents like the one shown in **Figure 14.**

Figure 14 Chemicals in the water that flows from hydrothermal vents provide bacteria with a source of energy. The bacterial producers use this energy to make nutrients through the process of chemosynthesis. Consumers, such as tubeworms, feed on the bacteria.

726 CHAPTER 25

Hydrothermal Vents A hydrothermal vent is a deep crack in the ocean floor through which the heat of molten magma can escape. The water from hydrothermal vents is extremely hot from contact with molten rock that lies deep in Earth's crust.

Because no sunlight reaches these deep ocean regions, plants or algae cannot grow there. How do the organisms living in this community obtain energy? Scientists learned that the hot water contains nutrients such as sulfur molecules that bacteria use to produce their own food. The production of energy-rich nutrient molecules from chemicals is called **chemosynthesis** (kee moh SIHN thuh sus). Consumers living in the hydrothermal vent communities rely on chemosynthetic bacteria for nutrients and energy. Chemosynthesis and photosynthesis allow producers to make their own energy-rich molecules.

✔ **Reading Check** *What is chemosynthesis?*

Energy Transfer

Energy can be converted from one form to another. It also can be transferred from one organism to another. Consumers cannot make their own food. Instead, they obtain energy by eating producers or other consumers. The energy stored in the molecules of one organism is transferred to another organism. That organism can oxidize food to release energy that it can use for maintenance and growth or is transformed into heat. At the same time, the matter that makes up those molecules is transferred from one organism to another.

Food Chains A food chain is a way of showing how matter and energy pass from one organism to another. Producers—plants, algae, and other organisms that are capable of photosynthesis or chemosynthesis—are always the first step in a food chain. Animals that consume producers such as herbivores are the second step. Carnivores and omnivores—animals that eat other consumers—are the third and higher steps of food chains. One example of a food chain is shown in **Figure 15.**

Hydrothermal Vents The first hydrothermal vent community discovered was found along the Galápagos rift zone. A rift zone forms where two plates of Earth's crust are spreading apart. In your Science Journal, describe the energy source that heats the water in the hydrothermal vents of the Galápagos rift zone.

Figure 15 In this food chain, grasses are producers, marmots are herbivores that eat the grasses, and grizzly bears are consumers that eat marmots. The arrows show the direction in which matter and energy flow. **Infer** *what might happen if grizzly bears disappeared from this ecosystem.*

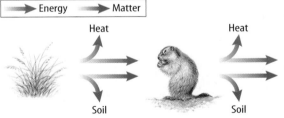

SECTION 3 Energy Flow **727**

Food Webs A forest community includes many feeding relationships. These relationships can be too complex to show with a food chain. For example, grizzly bears eat many different organisms, including berries, insects, chipmunks, and fish. Berries are eaten by bears, birds, insects, and other animals. A bear carcass might be eaten by wolves, birds, or insects. A **food web** is a model that shows all the possible feeding relationships among the organisms in a community. A food web is made up of many different food chains, as shown in **Figure 16.**

Energy Pyramids

Food chains usually have at least three links, but rarely more than five. This limit exists because the amount of available energy is reduced as you move from one level to the next in a food chain. Imagine a grass plant that absorbs energy from the Sun. The plant uses some of this energy to grow and produce seeds. Some of the energy is stored in the seeds.

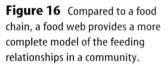

Figure 16 Compared to a food chain, a food web provides a more complete model of the feeding relationships in a community.

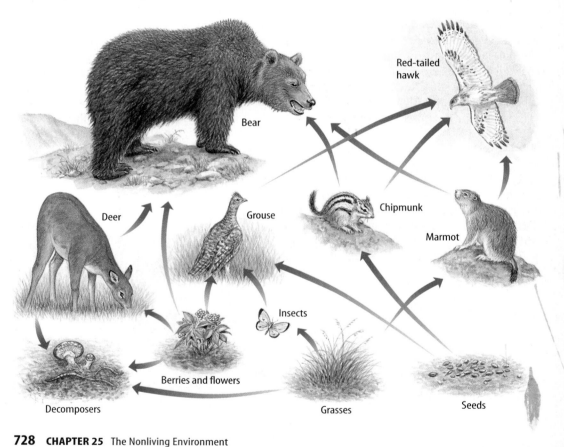

Red-tailed hawk

Bear

Deer

Grouse

Chipmunk

Marmot

Insects

Berries and flowers

Decomposers

Grasses

Seeds

Available Energy When a mouse eats grass seeds, energy stored in the seeds is transferred to the mouse. However, most of the energy the plant absorbed from the Sun was used for the plant's growth. The mouse uses energy from the seed for its own life processes, including respiration, digestion, and growth. Some of this energy was given off as heat. A hawk that eats the mouse obtains even less energy. The amount of available energy is reduced from one feeding level of a food chain to another.

An **energy pyramid,** like the one in **Figure 17,** shows the amount of energy available at each feeding level in an ecosystem. The bottom of the pyramid, which represents all of the producers, is the first feeding level. It is the largest level because it contains the most energy and the largest number of organisms. As you move up the pyramid, the transfer of energy is less efficient and each level becomes smaller. Only about ten percent of the energy available at each feeding level of an energy pyramid is transferred to the next higher level.

Carnivores

Herbivores

Producers

Figure 17 An energy pyramid shows that each feeding level has less energy than the one below it. **Describe** what would happen if the hawks and snakes outnumbered the rabbits and mice in this ecosystem.

 **Reading Check** *Why does the first feeding level of an energy pyramid contain the most energy?*

---

section **3** review

Summary

Converting Energy
- Most producers convert light energy into chemical energy.
- Some producers can produce their own food using energy in chemicals such as sulfur.

Energy Transfer
- Producers convert energy into forms that other organisms can use.
- Food chains show how matter and energy pass from one organism to another.

Energy Pyramids
- Energy pyramids show the amount of energy available at each feeding level.
- The amount of available energy decreases from the base to the top of the energy pyramid.

Self Check

1. **Compare and contrast** a food web and an energy pyramid.
2. **Explain** why there is a limit to the number of links in a food chain.
3. **Think Critically** Use your knowledge of food chains and the energy pyramid to explain why the number of mice in a grassland ecosystem is greater than the number of hawks.

Applying Math

4. **Solve One-Step Equations** A forest has 24,055,000 kilocalories (kcals) of producers, 2,515,000 kcals of herbivores, and 235,000 kcals of carnivores. How much energy is lost between producers and herbivores? Between herbivores and carnivores?

Science⊗nline life.msscience.com/self_check_quiz

SECTION 3 Energy Flow **729**

---

section **3** review

1. A food web shows the path of energy and matter in an ecosystem. An energy pyramid shows the amount of energy available at each level.
2. because a significant amount of energy is lost at each level
3. Hawks eat mice. For the mice to support the hawk population, there must be far more energy at the mouse level than at the hawk level. Since mice are smaller than hawks, this means that there must be many more mice than hawks.
4. producers and herbivores: 21,540,000 kcal; herbivores and carnivores: 2,280,000 kcal

---

SECTION 3 Energy Flow **729**

▶ Real-World Question

Purpose Students perform a variation of Johannes Baptista Van Helmont's famous experiment to determine if plants get their mass from the soil. L2 LS **Logical-Mathematical**

Process Skills observe, measure, predict, interpret data, use numbers

Time Required 45 minutes to set up; three weeks for the plants to grow; 1 hour for the final measurements, calculations, and cleanup

▶ Procedure

Safety Precautions Caution students to wash their hands after handling plants and soil.

Teaching Strategy This experiment helps uncover and correct the misconception that the material for a mass increase in a plant comes from the soil. Prior to getting results, ask students if most of the mass gained by the radish plants will come from the soil. If they don't think it will come from the soil, ask where they think it will come from.

Goals
- **Measure** the mass of soil before and after radish plants have been grown in it.
- **Measure** the mass of radish plants grown in the soil.
- **Analyze** the data to determine whether the mass gained by the plants equals the mass lost by the soil.

Materials
8-oz plastic or paper cup
potting soil to fill cup
scale or balance
radish seeds (4)
water
paper towels

Safety Precautions

Where does the mass of a plant come from?

▶ Real-World Question

An enormous oak tree starts out as a tiny acorn. The acorn sprouts in dark, moist soil. Roots grow down through the soil. Its stem and leaves grow up toward the light and air. Year after year, the tree grows taller, its trunk grows thicker, and its roots grow deeper. It becomes a towering oak that produces thousands of acorns of its own. An oak tree has much more mass than an acorn. Where does this mass come from? The soil? The air? In this activity, you'll find out by conducting an experiment with radish plants. Does all of the matter in a radish plant come from the soil?

Differentiated Instruction

Learning Disabled Help students understand the purpose of the investigation. Hand students a piece of two-by-four lumber so they can feel how heavy it is. Ask them where the weight of the tree came from. The weight came from the food the tree produced and utilized to build its body. L1

Alternative Inquiry Lab

Plant Growth What factors influence the mass of a plant? Partner with a local farmer or your soil conservation district to plan an investigation of the compounds used to increase plant mass and farm profits. Students should research all of the issues surrounding these compounds, conduct the research, and present their findings. PBL

Procedure

1. Copy the data table into your Science Journal.
2. Fill the cup with dry soil.
3. Find the mass of the cup of soil and record this value in your data table.
4. Moisten the soil in the cup. Plant four radish seeds 2 cm deep in the soil. Space the seeds an equal distance apart. Wash your hands.
5. Add water to keep the soil barely moist as the seeds sprout and grow.
6. When the plants have developed four to six true leaves, usually after two to three weeks, carefully remove the plants from the soil. Gently brush the soil off the roots. Make sure all the soil remains in the cup.
7. Spread the plants out on a paper towel. Place the plants and the cup of soil in a warm area to dry out.
8. When the plants are dry, measure their mass and record this value in your data table. Write this number with a plus sign in the Gain or Loss column.
9. When the soil is dry, find the mass of the cup of soil. Record this value in your data table. Subtract the End mass from the Start mass and record this number with a minus sign in the Gain or Loss column.

Mass of Soil and Radish Plants

	Start	End	Gain (+) or Loss (−)
Mass of dry soil and cup	75.8 g	75.7 g	0.1 g −
Mass of dried radish plants	0 g	2.1 g	2.1 g +

Analyze Your Data

1. **Calculate** how much mass was gained or lost by the soil. By the radish plants.
2. Did the mass of the plants come completely from the soil? How do you know?

Conclude and Apply

1. In the early 1600s, a Belgian scientist named J. B. van Helmont conducted this experiment with a willow tree. What is the advantage of using radishes instead of a tree?
2. **Predict** where all of the mass gained by the plants came from.

Communicating Your Data

Compare your conclusions with those of other students in your class. **For more help, refer to the** Science Skill Handbook.

Analyze Your Data

Expected Outcome The radish plants' mass gain will be more than the soil's mass loss.

Answers to Questions

1. Answers will vary, but the soil will have a very small mass loss and the plants will have a much larger mass gain.
2. No, because the mass loss of the soil is smaller than the mass gain of the plants.

Error Analysis Some errors may occur because the plants and soil are not completely dry. However, this usually does not affect the conclusion.

Conclude and Apply

1. Radishes grow faster and use less space. You can get a quantitative amount of mass gained and lost.
2. Answers will vary, but should include carbon dioxide from the air and water from the soil.

✔ Assessment

Content Pretend that you grew a willow tree for five years like Van Helmont. Write down how much mass the tree might have gained and how much mass the soil might have lost. Use **Performance Assessment in the Science Classroom,** p. 89. L2

Communicating Your Data

Have students post their data tables on a bulletin board for other students to see.

Content Background

The term *climate* refers to the average weather of a region over a period of time. Earth has many climates. The main influences on the climate of a region include:

- wind, which distributes moisture and heat
- distance from the equator, which influences solar radiation
- large bodies of water, which decreases temperature variation
- altitude, which affects temperature
- presence of mountains, which influence precipitation

Discussion

Temperature How would the annual temperature variation on an ocean island compare to the mainland at the same latitude? Students should infer that the large body of water would decrease annual temperature variation on the island.

Activity

Daily Record Have students work as a class to record and graph daily high and low temperatures each day for a month. L2

Applying Math

241.3 cm per month

Graph It

Have students graph the average monthly rainfall in your area. Compare the precipitation received in your location to that received in a tropical rain forest. Ask students to predict how the local environment would change if the amount of precipitation increased. L2

SCIENCE Stats

Extreme Climates

Did you know...

... The greatest snowfall in one year occurred at Mount Baker in Washington State. Approximately 2,896 cm of snow fell during the 1998–99, 12-month snowfall season. That's enough snow to bury an eight-story building.

2,896 cm

Applying Math What was the average monthly snowfall at Mount Baker during the 1998–99 snowfall season?

... The hottest climate in the United States is found in Death Valley, California. In July 1913, Death Valley reached approximately 57°C. As a comparison, a comfortable room temperature is about 20°C.

... The record low temperature of a frigid −89°C was set in Antarctica in 1983. As a comparison, the temperature of a home freezer is about −15°C.

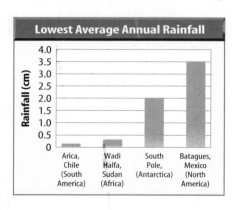

Lowest Average Annual Rainfall

Rainfall (cm): 4.0, 3.5, 3.0, 2.5, 2.0, 1.5, 1.0, 0.5, 0

Arica, Chile (South America); Wadi Halfa, Sudan (Africa); South Pole, (Antarctica); Batagues, Mexico (North America)

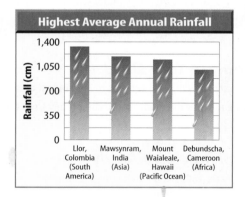

Highest Average Annual Rainfall

Rainfall (cm): 1,400, 1,050, 700, 350, 0

Llor, Colombia (South America); Mawsynram, India (Asia); Mount Waialeale, Hawaii (Pacific Ocean); Debundscha, Cameroon (Africa)

Graph It

Visit life.msscience.com/science_stats to find the average monthly rainfall in a tropical rain forest. Make a line graph to show how the amount of precipitation changes during the 12 months of the year.

Visual Learning

Lowest Average Annual Rainfall, Highest Average Annual Rainfall Have each student choose one location represented on each graph and use the annual rainfall number to calculate an average monthly rainfall number for each location. Then, have students cut a strip of paper the same height as the average amount of monthly rainfall in each of the locations they have chosen. Use the paper strips for comparison. L2 LS **Visual-Spatial**

Reviewing Main Ideas

Section 1 **Abiotic Factors**

1. Abiotic factors include air, water, soil, sunlight, temperature, and climate.

2. The availability of water and light influences where life exists on Earth.

3. Soil and climate have an important influence on the types of organisms that can survive in different environments.

4. High latitudes and elevations generally have lower average temperatures.

Section 2 **Cycles in Nature**

1. Matter is limited on Earth and is recycled through the environment.

2. The water cycle involves evaporation, condensation, and precipitation.

3. The carbon cycle involves photosynthesis and respiration.

4. Nitrogen in the form of soil compounds enters plants, which then are consumed by other organisms.

Section 3 **Energy Flow**

1. Producers make energy-rich molecules through photosynthesis or chemosynthesis.

2. When organisms feed on other organisms, they obtain matter and energy.

3. Matter can be recycled, but energy cannot.

4. Food webs are models of the complex feeding relationships in communities.

5. Available energy decreases as you go to higher feeding levels in an energy pyramid.

Visualizing Main Ideas

This diagram represents photosynthesis in a leaf. Match each letter with one of the following terms: light, carbon dioxide, *or* oxygen.

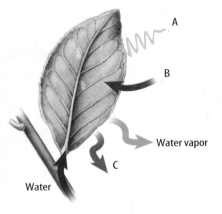

A

B

Water vapor

C

Water

Science Online life.msscience.com/interactive_tutor

CHAPTER STUDY GUIDE **733**

Reviewing Main Ideas

Summary statements can be used by students to review the major concepts of the chapter.

Visualizing Main Ideas

A—light; B—carbon dioxide; C—oxygen

Science Online

Visit life.msscience.com
  /self_check_quiz
  /interactive_tutor
  /vocabulary_puzzlemaker
  /chapter_review
  /standardized_test

Assessment Transparency

For additional assessment questions, use the *Assessment Transparency* located in the transparency book.

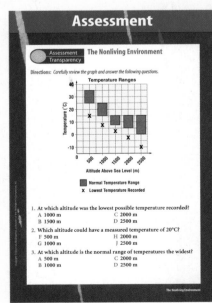

Using Vocabulary

1. evaporation
2. nitrogen fixation
3. nitrogen cycle
4. chemosynthesis
5. carbon cycle
6. condensation
7. water cycle
8. carbon cycle

Checking Concepts

9. B
10. B
11. D
12. A
13. A
14. B
15. A
16. C
17. B

Using Vocabulary

abiotic p. 712	energy pyramid p. 729
atmosphere p. 713	evaporation p. 720
biotic p. 712	food web p. 728
carbon cycle p. 725	nitrogen cycle p. 722
chemosynthesis p. 727	nitrogen fixation p. 722
climate p. 717	soil p. 714
condensation p. 721	water cycle p. 721

Which vocabulary word best corresponds to each of the following events?

1. A liquid changes to a gas.

2. Some types of bacteria form nitrogen compounds in the soil.

3. Decaying plants add nitrogen to the soil.

4. Chemical energy is used to make energy-rich molecules.

5. Decaying plants add carbon to the soil.

6. A gas changes to a liquid.

7. Water flows downhill into a stream. The stream flows into a lake, and water evaporates from the lake.

8. Burning coal and exhaust from automobiles release carbon into the air.

Checking Concepts

Choose the word or phrase that best answers the question.

9. Which of the following is an abiotic factor?
   A) penguins   **C)** soil bacteria
   B) rain   **D)** redwood trees

Use the equation below to answer question 10.

$$CO_2 + H_2O \xrightarrow[\text{energy}]{\text{light}} \text{sugar} + O_2$$

10. Which of the following processes is shown in the equation above?
    A) condensation   **C)** burning
    B) photosynthesis **D)** respiration

11. Which of the following applies to latitudes farther from the equator?
    A) higher elevations
    B) higher temperatures
    C) higher precipitation levels
    D) lower temperatures

12. Water vapor forming droplets that form clouds directly involves which process?
    A) condensation   **C)** evaporation
    B) respiration   **D)** transpiration

13. Which one of the following components of air is least necessary for life on Earth?
    A) argon   **C)** carbon dioxide
    B) nitrogen   **D)** oxygen

14. Which group makes up the largest level of an energy pyramid?
    A) herbivores   **C)** decomposers
    B) producers   **D)** carnivores

15. Earth receives a constant supply of which of the following items?
    A) light energy   **C)** nitrogen
    B) carbon   **D)** water

16. Which of these is an energy source for chemosynthesis?
    A) sunlight   **C)** sulfur molecules
    B) moonlight   **D)** carnivores

Use the illustration below to answer question 17.

17. What is the illustration above an example of?
    A) food chain   **C)** energy pyramid
    B) food web   **D)** carbon cycle

Science Online life.msscience.com/vocabulary_puzzlemaker

Use the ExamView® Pro Testmaker CD-ROM to:

- create multiple versions of tests
- create modified tests with one mouse click for inclusion students
- edit existing questions and add your own questions
- build tests aligned with state standards using built-in State Curriculum Tags
- change English tests to Spanish with one mouse click and vice versa

Thinking Critically

18. **Draw a Conclusion** A country has many starving people. Should they grow vegetables and corn to eat, or should they grow corn to feed cattle so they can eat beef? Explain.

19. **Explain** why a food web is a better model of energy flow than a food chain.

20. **Infer** Do bacteria need nitrogen? Why or why not?

21. **Describe** why it is often easier to walk through an old, mature forest of tall trees than through a young forest of small trees.

22. **Explain** why giant sequoia trees grow on the west side of California's Inyo Mountains and Death Valley, a desert, is on the east side of the mountains.

23. **Concept Map** Copy and complete this food web using the following information: *caterpillars and rabbits eat grasses, raccoons eat rabbits and mice, mice eat grass seeds,* and *birds eat caterpillars.*

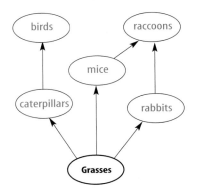

24. **Form a Hypothesis** For each hectare of land, ecologists found 10,000 kcals of producers, 10,000 kcals of herbivores, and 2,000 kcals of carnivores. Suggest a reason why producer and herbivore levels are equal.

Science Online life.msscience.com/chapter_review

25. **Recognize Cause and Effect** A lake in Kenya has been taken over by a floating weed. How could you determine if nitrogen fertilizer runoff from farms is causing the problem?

Performance Activities

26. **Poster** Use magazine photographs to make a visual representation of the water cycle.

Applying Math

27. **Energy Budget** Raymond Lindeman, from the University of Minnesota, was the first person to calculate the total energy budget of an entire community at Cedar Bog Lake in MN. He found the total amount of energy produced by producers was 1,114 kilocalories per meter squared per year. About 20% of the 1,114 kilocalories were used up during respiration. How many kilocalories were used during respiration?

28. **Kilocalorie Use** Of the 600 kilocalories of producers available to a caterpillar, the caterpillar consumes about 150 kilocalories. About 25% of the 150 kilocalories is used to maintain its life processes and is lost as heat, while 16% cannot be digested. How many kilocalories are lost as heat? What percentage of the 600 kilocalories is available to the next feeding level?

Use the table below to answer question 29.

Mighty Migrators	
Species	**Distance (km)**
Desert locust	4,800
Caribou	800
Green turtle	1,900
Arctic tern	35,000
Gray whale	19,000

29. **Make and Use Graphs** Climate can cause populations to move from place to place. Make a bar graph of migration distances shown above.

Thinking Critically

18. The country should grow corn and other vegetables for the people to eat. If they grow corn to feed cattle, most of the energy of the corn will be lost.

19. Webs show complex interactions rather than the simple interactions of a chain.

20. Yes; nitrogen is an important component of DNA and proteins.

21. In the mature forest, the tall trees block most of the sunlight from reaching the floor. There is therefore little plant growth, making it easy to walk.

22. As the air blows over the mountains from the ocean on the west side, it cools and loses moisture. Thus there is a forest on one side, but a desert on the other.

23. See student page.

24. Reasons may include a poor growth year for plants or a very good year for herbivore reproduction.

25. Possible answer: Ask farmers to restrict their use of nitrogen fertilizer and see if this clears up the lake.

Performance Activities

26. Posters will vary, but should show how the cycle continues. Use **Performance Assessment in the Science Classroom,** p. 145.

Applying Math

National Math Standards

1, 5, 6, 9

27. 222.8 kilocalories

28. 37.5 kilocalories were lost as heat, and 14.75% of the 600 kilocalories are available to the next feeding level.

29. From highest bar to lowest: Arctic tern, gray whale, desert locust, green turtle, caribou

✓ Assessment Resources

Reproducible Masters

Chapter *Fast File* Resources
Chapter Review, pp. 39–40
Chapter Tests, pp. 41–44
Assessment Transparency Activity, p. 51

Glencoe Science Web site
Chapter Review Test
Standardized Test Practice

Glencoe Technology
- Assessment Transparency
- Exam*View*® Pro Testmaker
- MindJogger Videoquiz
- Interactive Chalkboard

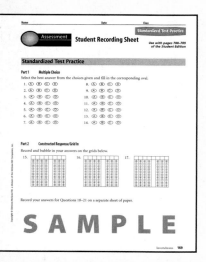

Answer Sheet A practice answer sheet can be found at life.msscience.com/answer_sheet.

Part 1 | Multiple Choice

1. B
2. B
3. B
4. C
5. A
6. D
7. C
8. D
9. C
10. B

Part 1 | Multiple Choice

Record your answers on the answer sheet provided by your teacher or on a sheet of paper.

1. The abiotic factor that provides energy for nearly all life on Earth is
   A. air.   C. water.
   B. sunlight.   D. soil.

2. Which of the following is characteristic of places at high elevations?
   A. fertile soil
   B. fewer molecules in the air
   C. tall trees
   D. warm temperatures

Use the diagram below to answer questions 3 and 4.

3. The air at point C is
   A. dry and warm.
   B. dry and cool.
   C. moist and warm.
   D. moist and cool.

4. The air at point A is
   A. dry and warm.
   B. dry and cool.
   C. moist and warm.
   D. moist and cool.

5. What process do plants use to return water vapor to the atmosphere?
   A. transpiration   C. respiration
   B. evaporation   D. condensation

6. Clouds form as a result of what process?
   A. evaporation   C. respiration
   B. transpiration   D. condensation

Use the illustration of the nitrogen cycle below to answer questions 7 and 8.

7. Which of the following items shown in the diagram contribute to the nitrogen cycle by releasing AND absorbing nitrogen?
   A. the decaying organism only
   B. the trees only
   C. the trees and the grazing cows
   D. the lightning and the decaying organism

8. Which of the following items shown in the diagram contribute to the nitrogen cycle by ONLY releasing nitrogen?
   A. the decaying organism only
   B. the trees only
   C. the trees and the grazing cows
   D. the lightning and the decaying organism

9. Where is most of the energy found in an energy pyramid?
   A. at the top level
   B. in the middle levels
   C. at the bottom level
   D. all levels are the same

10. What organisms remove carbon dioxide gas from the air during photosynthesis?
    A. consumers   C. herbivores
    B. producers   D. omnivores

Part 2 | Short Response/Grid In

11. Possible answers: water—essential part of all cells, required for many life processes; soil—provides nutrients for plants to grow, includes important bacteria, fungi, insets, and worms

12. farms and ranches

13. about 51%

14. on or in the roots of certain plants such as peas, clover, beans and soybeans

15. Possible answers: burning fossil fuels, during the decaying process of organisms, during respiration

16. They use sulfur molecules and other nutrients as an energy source to make their own food.

17. grasses → rabbit → weasel → coyote

Part 2 | Short Response/Grid In

*Record your answers on the answer sheet
provided by your teacher or on a sheet of paper.*

11. Give two examples of abiotic factors and
describe how each one is important to
biotic factors.

Use the table below to answer questions 12 and 13.

U.S. Estimated Water Use in 1995		
Water Use	**Millions of Gallons per Day**	**Percent of Total**
Homes and Businesses	41,600	12.2
Industry and Mining	28,000	8.2
Farms and Ranches	139,200	40.9
Electricity Production	131,800	38.7

12. According to the table above, what
accounted for the highest water use in the
U.S. in 1995?

13. What percentage of the total amount of
water use results from electricity production and homes and business combined?

14. Where are nitrogen-fixing bacteria found?

15. Describe two ways that carbon is released
into the atmosphere.

16. How are organisms near hydrothermal
vents deep in the ocean able to survive?

17. Use a diagram to represent the transfer of
energy among these organisms: a weasel, a
rabbit, grasses, and a coyote.

Test-Taking Tip

Answer All Questions Never leave any answer blank.

Part 3 | Open Ended

Record your answers on a sheet of paper.

18. Explain how a decrease in the amount of
sunlight would affect producers that use
photosynthesis, and producers that use
chemosynthesis.

19. Describe how wind and wind currents are
produced.

20. Use the water cycle to explain why beads
of water form on the outside of a glass of
iced water on a hot day.

21. Draw a flowchart that shows how soy
beans, deer, and nitrogen-fixing bacteria
help cycle nitrogen from the atmosphere,
to the soil, to living organisms, and back
to the atmosphere.

Use the diagram below to answer questions 22 and 23.

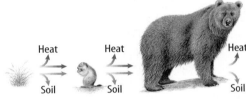

Heat   Heat   Heat
Soil   Soil   Soil

22. What term is used for the diagram above?
Explain how the diagram represents
energy transfer.

23. Explain how the grass and bear populations would be affected if the marmot
population suddenly declined.

24. Compare and contrast an energy pyramid
and a food web.

25. What happens to the energy in organisms
at the top of an energy pyramid when
they die?

22. food chain The grass is eaten by the
marmot and the marmot is eaten by
the bear. Energy from the grass is
transferred to the marmot, and
then to the bear.

23. With fewer marmots, the grass population would increase. The bear
population would find a different
source of food or its population
would decline.

24. An energy pyramid shows the
amount of energy available at each
level of an ecosystem. A food web
shows the feeding relationships
among organisms in a community.

25. When an organism dies, the energy
in it is used by decomposers.

Rubrics

For more help evaluating open-
ended assessment questions, see
the rubric on p. 10T.

Part 3 | Open Ended

18. Producers that use photosynthesis
would not be able to produce as
much food so they would decline.
Producers that use chemosynthesis
would not be affected since they
do not require sunlight to make
their food.

19. Wind occurs when sunlight unevenly
heats Earth. As air is warmed, it rises

and the colder air sinks beneath it.
The movement of cold and warm air
creates wind currents.

20. When the cold liquid in the glass
comes into contact with the
warmer air outside of it, the water
vapor that it evaporating condenses on the outside of the glass
and forms beads of water.

21. Nitrogen-fixing bacteria turn
nitrogen from the air into useful
compounds → soy beans use
these nitrogen compounds to grow
→ deer consume nitrogen when
they eat the soy beans → deer die
and their decaying bodies return
the nitrogen compounds to the soil

Section/Objectives	Standards		Labs/Features
Chapter Opener	**National**	**State/Local**	**Launch Lab:** What environment do houseplants need?, p. 739 **Foldables,** p. 739
	See pp. 16T–17T for a Key to Standards.		
Section 1 How Ecosystems Change 🕐 2 sessions 📦 1 block 1. **Explain** how ecosystems change over time. 2. **Describe** how new communities begin in areas without life. 3. **Compare** pioneer communities and climax communities.	National Content Standards: UCP.1–UCP.5, A.1, A.2, C.1, C.3, C.4		**Science Online,** p. 741 **Visualizing Secondary Succession,** p. 742
Section 2 Biomes 🕐 2 sessions 📦 1 block 4. **Explain** how climate influences land environments. 5. **Identify** seven biomes of Earth. 6. **Describe** the adaptations of organisms found in each biome.	National Content Standards: UCP.1, UCP.2, UCP.3, UCP.5, A.1, A.2, C.1, C.3, C.4		**MiniLAB:** Modeling Rain Forest Leaves, p. 748 **Integrate Earth Science,** p. 750 **Lab:** Studying a Land Ecosystem, p. 752
Section 3 Aquatic Ecosystems 🕐 3 sessions 📦 1.5 blocks 7. **Compare** flowing freshwater and standing freshwater ecosystems. 8. **Identify** and describe important saltwater ecosystems. 9. **Identify** problems that affect aquatic ecosystems.	National Content Standards: UCP.1, UCP.2, UCP.3, UCP.5, A.1, A.2, C.1, C.3–C.5, F.2		**MiniLAB:** Modeling Freshwater Environments, p. 754 **Integrate Career,** p. 755 **Applying Math:** Convert Units, p. 756 **Science Online,** p. 757 **Lab:** Exploring Wetlands, p. 760 **Science and Society:** Creating Wetlands to Purify Wastewater, p. 762

Glencoe Exclusive!
TeacherWorks™
All-In-One Planner and Resource Center

Lab Materials	Reproducible Resources	Section Assessment	Technology
Launch Lab: houseplant	**Chapter FAST FILE Resources** Foldables Worksheet, p. 15 Directed Reading Overview, p. 17 Note-taking Worksheets, pp. 31–33	GLENCOE'S ASSESSMENT ADVANTAGE	Teacher**Works** includes: • Interactive Teacher Edition • Lesson Planner with calendar • Access to all program blacklines • Correlations to standards • Web links
Need materials? Contact Science Kit at 1-800-828-7777 or www.sciencekit.com on the Internet.	**Chapter FAST FILE Resources** Transparency Activity, p. 42 Enrichment, p. 28 Reinforcement, p. 25 Directed Reading, p. 18 Lab Activity, pp. 9–10	Portfolio Visual Learning, p. 742 Performance Applying Math, p. 743 Content Section Review, p. 743	Section Focus Transparency Virtual Labs CD-ROM Guided Reading Audio Program Interactive Chalkboard CD-ROM
MiniLAB: poster board, metric ruler, scissors, sink, water, spray bottle **Lab:** graph paper, thermometer, magnifying lens, notebook, binoculars, pencil, field guides, compass, tape measure	**Chapter FAST FILE Resources** MiniLAB, p. 3 Transparency Activity, p. 43 Enrichment, p. 29 Reinforcement, p. 26 Directed Reading, p. 19 Lab Worksheet, pp. 5–6 **Reading and Writing Skill Activities,** p. 1	Portfolio Assessment, p. 751 Performance MiniLAB, p. 748 Applying Skills, p. 751 Content Section Review, p. 751	Section Focus Transparency Virtual Labs CD-ROM Guided Reading Audio Program Interactive Chalkboard CD-ROM Video Lab
MiniLAB: pond sediment or debris; pond plants, pond water, and organisms; clear-plastic container with lid; net; magnifying lens **Lab:** Internet sites or reference sources on wetlands	**Chapter FAST FILE Resources** MiniLAB, p. 4 Transparency Activity, p. 44 Enrichment, p. 30 Reinforcement, p. 27 Directed Reading, pp. 19, 20 Lab Worksheet, pp. 7–8 Lab Activity, pp. 11–14 Transparency Activity, pp. 45–46 **Lab Management and Safety,** p. 37	Portfolio Science Journal, p. 756 Performance MiniLAB, p. 754 Applying Math, p. 756 Applying Skills, p. 759 Content Section Review, p. 759	Section Focus Transparency Teaching Transparency Virtual Labs CD-ROM Guided Reading Audio Program Interactive Chalkboard CD-ROM

End of Chapter Assessment

GLENCOE'S ASSESSMENT ADVANTAGE

Blackline Masters	Technology	Professional Series
Chapter FAST FILE Resources Chapter Review, pp. 35–36 Chapter Tests, pp. 37–40 **Standardized Test Practice,** pp. 107–110	MindJogger Videoquiz Virtual Labs CD-ROM ExamView® Pro Testmaker TeacherWorks CD-ROM Interactive Chalkboard CD-ROM	**Performance Assessment in the Science Classroom (PASC)**

Transparencies

Section Focus

Section 1 Section Focus Transparency New Land, New Life

Both photographs below are of Surtsey, an island near Iceland. Surtsey was created in 1963 by a volcanic eruption. Surtsey provides a wonderful opportunity for scientists to study how life starts in a new area.

1. Describe what you see in the first picture. Would you expect plants or animals to be able to live there?

2. What evidence of life do you see in the second picture?

3. How has Surtsey changed? How might it continue to change?

L2

Section 2 Section Focus Transparency Sentinel

This unusual tree is a type of quiver tree. This rare species is found in parts of South Africa and Namibia. This particular type of quiver tree is critically endangered; estimates show fewer than 200 full-grown trees left.

1. Describe the characteristics of the quiver tree from the photo.
2. What kind of environment does this tree lives in?
3. Hypothesize what factors might threaten the quiver tree?

L2

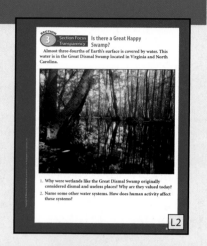

Section 3 Section Focus Transparency Is there a Great Happy Swamp?

Almost three-fourths of Earth's surface is covered by water. This water is in the Great Dismal Swamp located in Virginia and North Carolina.

1. Why were wetlands like the Great Dismal Swamp originally considered dismal and useless places? Why are they valued today?
2. Name some other water systems. How does human activity affect these systems?

L2

This is a representation of key blackline masters available in the Teacher Classroom Resources. See Resource Manager boxes within the chapter for additional information.

Assessment

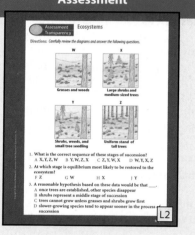

Assessment Transparency Ecosystems

Directions: Carefully review the diagrams and answer the following questions.

W	X
Grasses and weeds	Large shrubs and medium-sized trees

Y	Z
Shrubs, weeds, and small tree seedling	Uniform stand of tall trees

1. What is the correct sequence of these stages of succession?
   A X, Y, Z, W   B Y, W, Z, X   C Z, Y, W, X   D W, Y, X, Z
2. At which stage is equilibrium most likely to be restored to the ecosystem?
   F Z   G W   H X   J Y
3. A reasonable hypothesis based on these data would be that ___.
   A once trees are established, other species disappear
   B shrubs represent a middle stage of succession
   C trees cannot grow unless grasses and shrubs grow first
   D slower-growing species tend to appear sooner in the process of succession

L2

Teaching

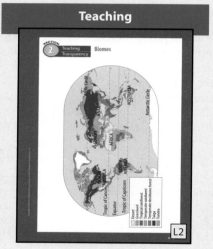

Section 2 Teaching Transparency Biomes

L2

Key to Teaching Strategies

The following designations will help you decide which activities are appropriate for your students.

L1 Level 1 activities should be appropriate for students with learning difficulties.

L2 Level 2 activities should be within the ability range of all students.

L3 Level 3 activities are designed for above-average students.

ELL ELL activities should be within the ability range of English-Language Learners.

COOP LEARN Cooperative Learning activities are designed for small group work.

LS Multiple Learning Styles logos, as described on page 12T, are used throughout to indicate strategies that address different learning styles.

P These strategies represent student products that can be placed into a best-work portfolio.

PBL Problem-Based Learning activities apply real-world situations to learning.

Hands-on Activities

Student Text Lab Worksheet

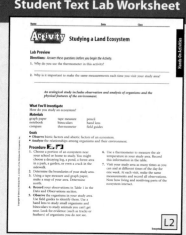

Activity Studying a Land Ecosystem

Lab Preview
Directions: Answer these questions before you begin the Activity.

1. Why do you use the thermometer in this activity?

2. Why is it important to make the same measurements each time you visit your study area?

An ecological study includes observation and analysis of organisms and the physical features of the environment.

What You'll Investigate
How do you study an ecosystem?

Materials
graph paper   tape measure   pencil
notebook   binoculars   hand lens
compass   thermometer   field guides

Goals
• Observe biotic factors and abiotic factors of an ecosystem.
• Analyze the relationships among organisms and their environment.

Procedure

1. Choose a portion of an ecosystem near your school or home to study. You might choose a decaying log, a pond, a forest area in a park, a garden, or even a crack in the sidewalk.
2. Determine the boundaries of your study area.
3. Using a tape measure and graph paper, make a map of your area. Determine north.
4. Record your observations in Table 1 in the Data and Observations section.
5. Observe the organisms in your study area. Use field guides to identify them. Use a hand lens to study small organisms and binoculars to study any animals you can't get near. Look for evidence (such as tracks or feathers) of organisms you do not see.
6. Use a thermometer to measure the air temperature in your study area. Record this information in the table.
7. Visit your study area as many times as you can and at different times of the day for one week. At each visit, make the same measurements and record all observations. Note how living and nonliving parts of the ecosystem interact.

L2

Laboratory Activities

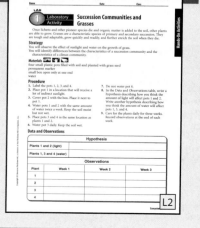

Laboratory Activity 1 Succession Communities and Grasses

Once lichens and other pioneer species die and organic matter is added to the soil, other plants are able to grow. Grasses are a characteristic species of primary and secondary succession. They are tough and adaptable, grow quickly and readily, and further enrich the soil when they die.

Strategy
You will observe the effect of sunlight and water on the growth of grass. You will identify differences between the characteristics of a succession community and the characteristics of a climax community.

Materials
four small plastic pots filled with soil and planted with grass seed
permanent marker
small box open only at one end
water

Procedure

1. Label the pots 1, 2, 3, and 4.
2. Place pot 1 in a location that will receive a lot of indirect sunlight.
3. Cover pot 2 with the box. Place it next to pot 1.
4. Water pots 1 and 2 with the same amount of water twice a week. Keep the soil moist but not wet.
5. Place pots 3 and 4 in the same location as plants 1 and 2.
6. Water pot 3 daily. Keep the soil wet.
7. Do not water pot 4.
8. In the Data and Observations table, write a hypothesis describing how you think the amount of light will affect pots 1 and 2. Write another hypothesis describing how you think the amount of water will affect pots 1, 3, and 4.
9. Care for the plants daily for three weeks. Record observations at the end of each week.

Data and Observations

Hypothesis		
Plants 1 and 2 (light)		
Plants 1, 3 and 4 (water)		

Observations			
Plant	Week 1	Week 2	Week 3
1			
2			
3			
4			

L2

Meeting Different Ability Levels

Content Outline

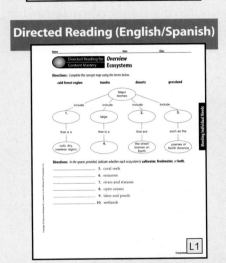

Reinforcement

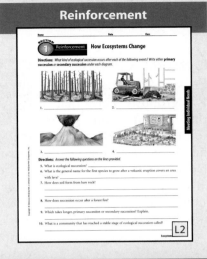

Enrichment

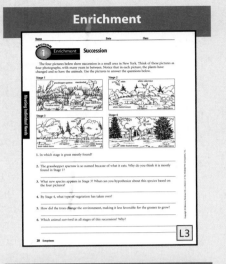

Directed Reading (English/Spanish)

Study Guide

Reading Essentials

Assessment

Test Practice Workbook

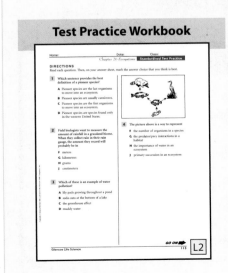

Chapter Review

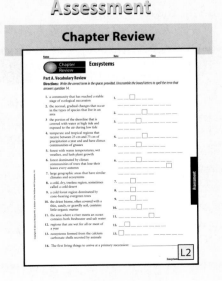

Chapter Tests

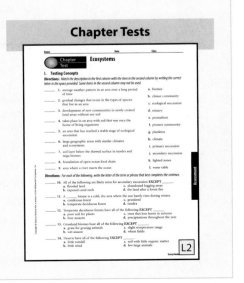

Science Content Background

section 1 — How Ecosystems Change

Defining Ecosystems

A system is a group of parts that work together to form a functioning whole. Some common examples of systems include cars, watches, and digestive systems. An ecosystem is groups of organisms interacting with each other and their environment through a flow of energy and cycling of matter. It is the interdependence of all the parts that makes the whole a system.

section 2 — Biomes

Tundra

The arctic tundra receives less energy from the Sun than does any other biome. The Sun's energy is dispersed over a greater area at higher latitudes. The Sun's rays lose much of their energy because they must travel diagonally through the atmosphere.

Desert

Desert covers less than 5% of North America. The North American deserts are the Mojave, Sonoran, Great Basin, and Chihuahuan. Temperatures in the desert undergo drastic changes over a 24-hour period. Daytime temperatures can be 30°C higher than nighttime readings. These fluctuations occur because of the lack of heat-retaining moisture in the desert air.

section 3 — Aquatic Ecosystems

Nutrients in Aquatic Ecosystems

In aquatic ecosystems, nutrients tend to sink below the light zone where many organisms cannot use them. In the ocean, the process that moves the bottom water with its valuable nutrients up to the surface is called an upwelling. In an upwelling, winds and currents work together near the continental shelf. The winds carry water away from land. Bottom water with its nutrients is pulled up into the photic zone to replace water that has moved out to sea. Upwellings occur in only a few places. One such place is along the coast of Peru.

Kevin & Cat Sweeney/DRK Photo

---

chapter content resources

Internet Resources

For additional content background, visit **life.msscience.com** to:

- access your book online
- find references to related articles in popular science magazines
- access Web links with related content background
- access current events with science journal topics

Print Resources

Blue Planet, by Andrew Byatt et. al., DK Publishing, 2001

Wetlands, by William Mitsch and James G. Gosselink, John Wiley & Sons, 2000

What is a Biome? (Science of Living Things), by Bobbie Kalman, Crabtree Publishing Co., 1999

Ecology of Desert Systems, by Walter Whitford, Academic Press, 2002

Misconceptions

Find Out What Students Think

Students may think that . . .

Systems only exist as parts of an organism or process.

Ecosystems consist of only a few interactions among living things in an area.

Students often do not understand the nature of systems in general, and they understand even less about the specific aspects of an ecosystem. Students may have learned that some things are called systems or ecosystems, but they may not be aware that ecosystems consist of parts, subsystems, and many interactions between biotic and abiotic factors.

Discussion

Show a photo of a bicycle, or bring in a bicycle for students to examine. Have students describe what they see. It is likely that students will respond that they see a bike. Point out that although there is one bicycle functioning as a whole unit, the bicycle consists of many components such as wheels, seat, chain, pedals, and so on. If any one of these components is removed, the bicycle will not function properly. The individual parts work together to do what a bicycle is supposed to do. In addition, in order for the bike to function, it needs an input of energy from a rider. Like a bicycle, an ecosystem is made up of many components, both abiotic (nonliving) and biotic (living), and it receives energy in the form of light and heat from the Sun.

Promote Understanding

Activity

Have students make a terrarium or display a completed terrarium.

- Discuss the biotic (living) and abiotic (nonliving) factors included in the terrarium, such as plants, insects, light, water, soil, and air.

- Have students diagram connections between the components. Then relate these connections to the flow of energy and cycling of materials. What do you think would happen if one of the components of the terrarium were removed? Explain that if a component such as light were removed, the plants would not be able to photosynthesize. Have students discuss the long-term effects of this event.

The plants would die, the insects that eat the plants would not have food, and so on.

- Emphasize that the removal of light would cause the ecosystem to function improperly. Underscore this idea, using a diagram of the flow of energy and cycling of materials in the terrarium.

As an extension, have students choose another component of the terrarium and discuss how its removal would affect all other components of the terrarium.

Assess

After completing the chapter, see *Identifying Misconceptions* in the Study Guide at the end of the chapter.

Chapter Vocabulary

Science Journal Traits of trees would include thick bark and high branches. Shrub traits would include rhizomes and root systems that sprout after they've been burned back.

INTERACTIVE CHALKBOARD
with Image Bank

PowerPoint® Presentations

This CD-ROM is an editable Microsoft® PowerPoint® presentation that includes:
- a pre-made presentation for every chapter
- interactive graphics
- animations
- audio clips
- image bank
- all new section and chapter questions
- Standardized Test Practice
- transparencies
- pre-lab questions for all labs
- Foldables directions
- links to life.msscience.com

Ecosystems

chapter preview

sections

1 **How Ecosystems Change**

2 **Biomes**
   Lab *Studying a Land Ecosystem*

3 **Aquatic Ecosystems**
   Lab *Exploring Wetlands*

   Virtual Lab *What are the different types of land environments?*

738

The Benefits of Wildfires

Ecosystems are places where organisms, including humans, interact with each other and with their physical environment. In some ecosystems, wildfires are an essential part of the physical environment. Organisms in these ecosystems are well adapted to the changes that fire brings, and can benefit from wildfires.

Science Journal What traits might plants on this burning Montana hillside have that enable them to survive?

Theme Connection

Stability and Change Ecosystems change in ways that can be predicted. In the process of succession, each community affects the environment, often producing conditions that result in the community's replacement.

About the Photo

Wildfire The 2000 fire season was long, difficult, and expensive. Over 120,000 fires burned more than 8 million acres in the United States, costing more than a billion dollars. The largest fire burned for over two months and blackened almost 300,000 acres in western Montana. Many ecosystems rely on fire in order to regenerate themselves, so fire is beneficial and necessary for many ecosystems.

Start-Up Activities

What environment do houseplants need?

The plants growing in your classroom or home may not look like the same types of plants that you find growing outside. Many indoor plants don't grow well outside in most North American climates. Do the lab below to determine what type of environment most houseplants thrive in.

1. Examine a healthy houseplant in your classroom or home.

2. Describe the environmental conditions found in your classroom or home. For example, is the air humid or dry? Is the room warm or cool? Does the temperature stay about the same, or change during the day?

3. Using observations from step 1 and descriptions from step 2, hypothesize about the natural environment of the plants in your classroom or home.

4. **Think Critically** In your Science Journal, record the observations that led to your hypothesis. How would you design an experiment to test your hypothesis?

Primary and Secondary Succession Make the following Foldable to help you illustrate the main ideas about succession.

STEP 1 Fold a vertical sheet of paper in half from top to bottom.

STEP 2 Fold in half from side to side with the fold at the top.

STEP 3 Unfold the paper once. Cut only the fold of the top flap to make two tabs.

STEP 4 Turn the paper vertically and label on the front tabs as shown.

Illustrate and Label As you read the chapter, define terms and collect information under the appropriate tabs.

Science Online Preview this chapter's content and activities at life.msscience.com

Launch LAB

Purpose Students observe common houseplants and make hypotheses about the climate of the area they originally inhabited. L2 IS **Naturalist**

Preparation Establish successfully growing houseplants in your classroom several weeks before the start of this chapter.

Materials houseplants; optional thermometers and humidity meter

Teaching Strategies
- Help students describe the amount of light, heat, and moisture the plants receive.
- Have students compare their observations and hypotheses with other students. Discuss differences and similarities.

Think Critically
Houseplants generally grow best when they have moist soil, moderate temperatures, and medium to low light. These plants are typically found in the understories of tropical rain forests. Students might suggest placing different specimens of the same type of plant in bright and low light, or giving them varying amounts of water.

Assessment
Oral Have students explain how the local climate may affect houseplants if they were planted outside the school for one year. Use **Performance Assessment in the Science Classroom**, p. 89.

 Dinah Zike Study Fold

Student preparation materials for this Foldable are available in the Chapter *FAST FILE* Resources.

How Ecosystems Change

1 Motivate

Bellringer

Section Focus Transparencies also are available on the Interactive Chalkboard CD-ROM.

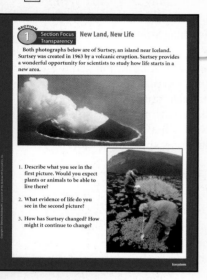

SECTION
1 Section Focus Transparency — New Land, New Life

Both photographs below are of Surtsey, an island near Iceland. Surtsey was created in 1963 by a volcanic eruption. Surtsey provides a wonderful opportunity for scientists to study how life starts in a new area.

1. Describe what you see in the first picture. Would you expect plants or animals to be able to live there?

2. What evidence of life do you see in the second picture?

3. How has Surtsey changed? How might it continue to change?

Ecosystem

Tie to Prior Knowledge

Local Succession Relate the idea of succession to examples found in the local environment. For example, there may be abandoned lots or farm fields showing succession. Many communities are allowing roadside grass areas to revert back to their natural states.

as you read

What You'll Learn
- **Explain** how ecosystems change over time.
- **Describe** how new communities begin in areas without life.
- **Compare** pioneer species and climax communities.

Why It's Important
Understanding ecosystems and your role in them can help you manage your impact on them and predict the changes that may happen in the future.

Review Vocabulary
ecosystem: community of living organisms interacting with each other and their physical environment

New Vocabulary
- succession
- pioneer species
- climax community

Ecological Succession

What would happen if the lawn at your home were never cut? The grass would get longer, as in **Figure 1,** and soon it would look like a meadow. Later, larger plants would grow from seeds brought to the area by animals or wind. Then, trees might sprout. In fact, in 20 years or less you wouldn't be able to tell that the land was once a mowed lawn. An ecologist can tell you what type of ecosystem your lawn would become. If it would become a forest, they can tell you how long it would take and predict the type of trees that would grow there. **Succession** refers to the normal, gradual changes that occur in the types of species that live in an area. Succession occurs differently in different places around the world.

Primary Succession As lava flows from the mouth of a volcano, it is so hot that it destroys everything in its path. When it cools, lava forms new land composed of rock. It is hard to imagine that this land eventually could become a forest or grassland someday.

The process of succession that begins in a place previously without plants is called primary succession. It starts with the arrival of living things such as lichens (LI kunz). These living things, called **pioneer species,** are the first to inhabit an area. They survive drought, extreme heat and cold, and other harsh conditions and often start the soil-building process.

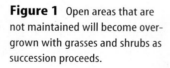

Figure 1 Open areas that are not maintained will become overgrown with grasses and shrubs as succession proceeds.

Section 1 Resource Manager

Chapter *FAST FILE* Resources

Transparency Activity, p. 42

Directed Reading for Content Mastery, pp. 17, 18

Note-taking Worksheets, pp. 31–33

Enrichment, p. 28

Reinforcement, p. 25

Lab Activity, pp. 9–10

Figure 2 Lichens, like these in Colorado, are fragile and take many years to grow. They often cling to bare rock where many other organisms can't survive. **Describe** *how lichens form soil.*

New Soil During primary succession, shown in **Figure 2,** soil begins to form as lichens and the forces of weather and erosion help break down rocks into smaller pieces. When lichens die, they decay, adding small amounts of organic matter to the rock. Plants such as mosses and ferns can grow in this new soil. Eventually, these plants die, adding more organic material. The soil layer thickens, and grasses, wildflowers, and other plants begin to take over. When these plants die, they add more nutrients to the soil. This buildup is enough to support the growth of shrubs and trees. All the while, insects, small birds, and mammals have begun to move in. What was once bare rock now supports a variety of life.

Secondary Succession What happens when a fire, such as the one in **Figure 3,** disturbs a forest or when a building is torn down in a city? After a forest fire, not much seems to be left except dead trees and ash-covered soil. After the rubble of a building is removed, all that remains is bare soil. However, these places do not remain lifeless for long. The soil already contains the seeds of weeds, grasses, and trees. More seeds are carried to the area by wind and birds. Other wildlife may move in. Succession that begins in a place that already has soil and was once the home of living organisms is called secondary succession. Because soil already is present, secondary succession occurs faster and has different pioneer species than primary succession does.

Topic: Eutrophication
Visit life.msscience.com for Web links to information about eutrophication (yoo truh fih KAY shun)—secondary succession in an aquatic ecosystem.

Activity Using the information that you find, illustrate or describe in your Science Journal this process for a small freshwater lake.

✅ **Reading Check** *Which type of succession usually starts without soil?*

Caption Answer
Figure 2 Lichens help to break down rocks into smaller pieces. When lichens die, they decay, adding small amounts of organic material to the soil.

Discussion
Wildfires Throughout much of the 20th century, fire suppression was thought to be good stewardship of the land. However, by the 1940s, many ecologists realized that fire was an important element of change for ecosystems. By the 1970s, Yellowstone and other national parks had instituted a "natural fire management plan" which ensured that naturally ignited wildfires would burn freely as an ecosystem process. The televised images of Yellowstone burning in 1988 brought emotional responses from the public. Many offered to donate seedlings to plant, including species that are more "fire-resistant". Explain why well-intentioned offers would damage Yellowstone Park's ecosystem in the long run. Possible answers: Introducing new tree species would change the system completely. Many organisms are dependent on those tree species that are not fire-resistant. Fire returns nutrients to the soil and encourages succession.

✅ **Reading Check**

Answer primary succession

Quick Demo
Lichens
Materials rocks with a variety of lichens growing on them
Estimated Time 10 minutes
Procedure Show rocks and point out the different lichens. You may choose to pass the rocks around, but stress that lichens are fragile and remind students not to rub the lichens off. These are the organisms that help to form soil.

Teacher FYI

Secondary Pioneers The small size of lichens and mosses makes them successful in the harsh environments typical of primary succession. Fast reproduction is a characteristic of secondary pioneers. These plants, which often pop up in gardens, are usually called weeds.

Curriculum Connection

History As the eastern United States was settled by Europeans, large tracts of forest were converted into farmland. With increasing industrialization, many of the farms were abandoned and the land reverted back into forests. Ask students to determine the past extent of the eastern forests and draw a map of this region.

Visualizing Secondary Succession

Have students examine the pictures and read the captions. Then ask the following questions.

What characteristics would make a seed likely to survive a fire? A seed that is surrounded by a thick seed coat is more likely to survive a fire than one with a thin seed coat.

As succession proceeds, what changes will occur in the population of plants found on the forest floor? At first, plants that need lots of sunlight can live on the forest floor, because there are no tall trees to block the sunlight. As trees grow and mature there will be less sunlight penetrating to the forest floor, so species that require less light will be found.

Activity

Song Lyrics Have the students work in teams to write song lyrics that describe secondary succession. Students can write lyrics that fit any melody they know and enjoy. The steps of secondary succession should be clearly and accurately described in the lyrics.

NATIONAL GEOGRAPHIC VISUALIZING SECONDARY SUCCESSION

Figure 3

In the summer of 1988, wind-driven flames like those shown in the background photo swept through Yellowstone National Park, scorching nearly a million acres. The Yellowstone fire was one of the largest forest fires in United States history. The images on this page show secondary succession—the process of ecological regeneration—triggered by the fire.

▶ After the fire, burned timber and blackened soil seemed to be all that remained. However, the fire didn't destroy the seeds that were protected under the soil.

◀ Within weeks, grasses and other plants were beginning to grow in the burned areas. Ecological succession was underway.

▶ Many burned areas in the park opened new plots for stands of trees. This picture shows young lodgepole pines in August 1999. The forest habitat of America's oldest national park is being restored gradually through secondary succession.

742 CHAPTER 26 Ecosystems

Visual Learning

Figure 3 Have students make an outline of the stages in secondary succession that are shown. Then, have them go back and fill in any stages that aren't shown. P

Differentiated Instruction

Challenge In some areas, under certain circumstances, natural fires are not put out. In many areas, resource managers do controlled burns. Have students research to find out why this is done. Students can take on the role of education officers and inform the rest of the class about the importance of fire in certain ecosystems. L3

742 CHAPTER 26 Ecosystems

Figure 4 This beech-maple forest is an example of a climax community.

Climax Communities A community of plants that is relatively stable and undisturbed and has reached an end stage of succession is called a **climax community.** The beech-maple forest shown in **Figure 4** is an example of a community that has reached the end of succession. New trees grow when larger, older trees die. The individual trees change, but the species remain stable. There are fewer changes of species in a climax community over time, as long as the community isn't disturbed by wildfire, avalanche, or human activities.

Primary succession begins in areas with no previous vegetation. It can take hundreds or even thousands of years to develop into a climax community. Secondary succession is usually a shorter process, but it still can take a century or more.

Summary

Ecological Succession

- Succession is the natural, gradual changes over time of species in a community.
- Primary succession occurs in areas that previously were without soil or plants.
- Secondary succession occurs in areas where soil has been disturbed.
- Climax communities have reached an end stage of succession and are stable.
- Climax communities have less diversity than communities in mid-succession.

Self Check

1. **Compare** primary and secondary succession.
2. **Describe** adaptations of pioneer species.
3. **Infer** the kind of succession that will take place on an abandoned, unpaved country road.
4. **Think Critically** Show the sequence of events in primary succession. Include the term *climax community.*

Applying Math

5. **Solve One-Step Equations** A tombstone etched with 1802 as the date of death has a lichen on it that is 6 cm in diameter. If the lichen began growing in 1802, calculate its average yearly rate of growth.

1. Primary succession occurs in areas without soil and usually previously without plants. Secondary succession occurs in areas with soil and plants previously.
2. Pioneer species are adapted to survive drought, extreme heat and cold, and other harsh conditions.
3. secondary succession
4. More sunlight and water reach the forest floor, enabling more species of plants to survive. As trees grow into a climax forest, the environmental conditions are more limiting and fewer species are adapted to live in those conditions.
5. Growth per year = 6 cm / (current year − 1802). For example, if the year is 2002 then 6 cm / (2002 − 1802) = 0.03 cm per yr.

IDENTIFYING Misconceptions

Ecosystems Students may think that ecosystems consist of only a few interactions among living things in an area. Refer to page F at the beginning of this chapter for teaching strategies that address this misconception.

3 Assess

DAILY INTERVENTION

Check for Understanding

Visual-Spatial Have students diagram succession of a pond ecosystem to a forest in their area. [L2]

Reteach

Forest Succession Arrange the stages of succession for a forest community out of sequence in a diagram. Photocopy the diagram and have students use numbers to put the pictures in the proper sequence. [L2]
LS Logical-Mathematical

Assessment

Content Have students write a paragraph identifying how each of the following is undergoing succession: a cornfield after a flood, the area around a volcanic eruption, and a newly formed sandbar in a river. Use **Performance Assessment in the Science Classroom,** p. 159.

1 Motivate

Bellringer

Section Focus Transparencies also are available on the Interactive Chalkboard CD-ROM.

L2 ELL

SECTION 2 Section Focus Transparency — Sentinel

This unusual tree is a type of quiver tree. This rare species is found in parts of South Africa and Namibia. This particular type of quiver tree is critically endangered; estimates show fewer than 200 full-grown trees left.

1. Describe the characteristics of the quiver tree from the photo.
2. What kind of environment does this tree lives in?
3. Hypothesize what factors might threaten the quiver tree?

Ecosystems

Tie to Prior Knowledge

Biome Organisms Choose a biome that students are likely to have some knowledge about, but don't live in, such as a desert or a tropical rain forest. Have students make a list of organisms that live in that biome and the biome in which they live. Then have students hypothesize why different plants and animals live in these different biomes.

---

section 2 Biomes

as you read

What You'll Learn

- **Explain** how climate influences land environments.
- **Identify** seven biomes of Earth.
- **Describe** the adaptations of organisms found in each biome.

Why It's Important

Resources that you need to survive are found in a variety of biomes.

◉ Review Vocabulary

climate: the average weather conditions of an area over many years

New Vocabulary

- ● biome
- ● tundra
- ● taiga
- ● temperate deciduous forest
- ● temperate rain forest
- ● tropical rain forest
- ● desert
- ● grassland

Factors That Affect Biomes

Does a desert in Arizona have anything in common with a desert in Africa? Both have heat, little rain, poor soil, water-conserving plants with thorns, and lizards. Even widely separated regions of the world can have similar biomes because they have similar climates. Climate is the average weather pattern in an area over a long period of time. The two most important climatic factors that affect life in an area are temperature and precipitation.

Major Biomes

Large geographic areas that have similar climates and ecosystems are called **biomes** (BI ohmz). Seven common types of land biomes are mapped in **Figure 5.** Areas with similar climates produce similar climax communities. Tropical rain forests are climax communities found near the equator, where temperatures are warm and rainfall is plentiful. Coniferous forests grow where winter temperatures are cold and rainfall is moderate.

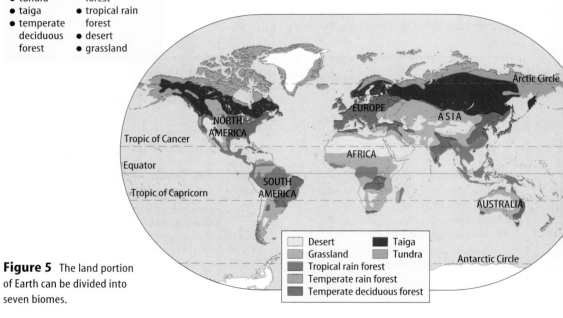

Desert	Taiga
Grassland	Tundra
Tropical rain forest	
Temperate rain forest	
Temperate deciduous forest	

Figure 5 The land portion of Earth can be divided into seven biomes.

744 CHAPTER 26 Ecosystems

Section 2 Resource Manager

Chapter *FAST FILE* Resources
Transparency Activity, p. 43
Enrichment, p. 29
Directed Reading for Content Mastery, p. 19
MiniLAB, p. 3
Reinforcement, p. 26
Lab Worksheet, pp. 5–6

Reading and Writing Skill Activities, p. 1
Earth Science Critical Thinking/Problem Solving, p. 6
Life Science Critical Thinking/Problem Solving, p. 5

Tundra At latitudes just south of the north pole or at high elevations, a biome can be found that receives little precipitation but is covered with ice most of the year. The **tundra** is a cold, dry, treeless region, sometimes called a cold desert. Precipitation averages less than 25 cm per year. Winters in the Arctic can be six to nine months long. For some of these months, the Sun never appears above the horizon and it is dark 24 hours a day. The average daily temperature is about –12°C. For a few days during the short, cold summer, the Sun is always visible. Only the top portion of soil thaws in the summer. Below the thawed surface is a layer of permanently frozen soil called permafrost, shown in **Figure 6.** Alpine tundra, found above the treeline on high mountains, have similar climates. Tundra soil has few nutrients because the cold temperatures slow the process of decomposition.

Tundra Life Tundra plants are adapted to drought and cold. They include mosses, grasses, and small shrubs, as seen in **Figure 7.** Many lichens grow on the tundra. During the summer, mosquitoes, blackflies, and other biting insects fill the air. Migratory birds such as ducks, geese, shorebirds, and songbirds nest on the Arctic tundra during the summer. Other inhabitants include hawks, snowy owls, and willow grouse. Mice, voles, lemmings, arctic hares, caribou, reindeer, and musk oxen also are found there.

People are concerned about overgrazing by animals on the tundra. Fences, roads, and pipelines have disrupted the migratory routes of some animals and forced them to stay in a limited area. Because the growing season is so short, plants and other vegetation can take decades to recover from damage.

Figure 6 This permafrost in Alaska is covered by soil that freezes in the winter and thaws in the summer.
Infer *what types of problems this might cause for people living in this area.*

Figure 7 Lichens, mosses, grasses, and small shrubs thrive on the tundra. Ptarmigan also live on the tundra. In winter, their feathers turn white. Extra feathers on their feet keep them warm and prevent them from sinking into the snow.

Tundra

Ptarmigan

2 Teach

Quick Demo
Arctic Tundra Light
Materials globe, flashlight
Estimated Time 10 minutes
Procedure Use the flashlight to model the rays of the Sun shining on Earth. The globe should be at a 23.5% angle (to model Earth's tilt). Students should be able to observe why some winter days in the Arctic tundra have 24 hours of darkness and some summer days have 24 hours of light.

Caption Answer
Figure 6 Permafrost makes it impossible to farm the land.

Discussion
Environment Choice Would you prefer to live in a house with ten acres of land in the tundra or in a small apartment in New York City? Have students defend their responses.

Fun Fact

The nose botfly has unique adaptations for surviving the cold winter. It lays its eggs in the nose of a caribou. The maggots emerge and travel to the caribou's throat where they are kept warm. In the spring, caribou cough the maggots up. The maggots pupate and then become flies.

Teacher FYI

Lichens Limited light and heat, and a short growing season are factors that limit producer growth in the tundra. Lichen species here grow extremely slowly—only 1/6 cm per year. It can take 40 years for lichens to recover from damage caused by a passing herd of caribou.

Cultural Diversity

Inuit Life Have students research the Inuit, who live in the Arctic tundra, and report on how they have adapted to the harsh climate. L2
LS **Linguistic**

Word Origin "Taiga" comes from the Russian word *taiga*, which means "swampy forest." Ask students why this is a good description of the taiga biome. The taiga is a cold forest region that is warmer and wetter than the tundra.

Caption Answer

Figure 8 Wide feet enable the lynx to run across the top of snow.

IDENTIFYING
Misconceptions

Climate and Biomes Students may think that the location of a particular biome on Earth is permanent. They may not realize that changes in climate have affected the locations of biomes and probably will continue to do so in the future.

Quick Demo

Biome Precipitation

Materials strips of paper cut to appropriate length to represent the amount of precipitation in centimeters for each biome, tape

Estimated Time 5 minutes

Procedure Tape the strips of paper to the board as you discuss the biomes. Start with a strip of paper that represents the amount of rainfall in your area.

Figure 8 The taiga is dominated by cone-bearing trees. The lynx, a mammal adapted to life in the taiga, has broad, heavily furred feet that act like snowshoes to prevent it from sinking in the snow.
Infer *why "snowshoe feet" are important for a lynx.*

Taiga South of the tundra—between latitudes 50°N and 60°N and stretching across North America, northern Europe, and Asia—is the world's largest biome. The **taiga** (TI guh), shown in **Figure 8,** is a cold, forest region dominated by cone-bearing evergreen trees. Although the winter is long and cold, the taiga is warmer and wetter than the tundra. Precipitation is mostly snow and averages 35 cm to 100 cm each year.

Most soils of the taiga thaw completely during the summer, making it possible for trees to grow. However, permafrost is present in the extreme northern regions of the taiga. The forests of the taiga might be so dense that little sunlight penetrates the trees to reach the forest floor. However, some lichens and mosses do grow on the forest floor. Moose, lynx, shrews, bears, and foxes are some of the animals that live in the taiga.

Temperate Deciduous Forest Temperate regions usually have four distinct seasons each year. Annual precipitation ranges from about 75 cm to 150 cm and is distributed throughout the year. Temperatures range from below freezing during the winter to 30°C or more during the warmest days of summer.

Figure 9 White-tailed deer are one of many species that you can find in a deciduous forest. In autumn, the leaves on deciduous trees change color and fall to the ground.

746 CHAPTER 26 Ecosystems

Science Journal

Metric Measurements Students should become familiar with metric measurements, such as those used in this section for temperature. Have them convert the following Celsius temperatures to Fahrenheit:

10°C (50˚F); 0°C (32˚F); 20°C (68˚F); 30°C (86˚F)

Differentiated Instruction

Learning Disabled A concept map of "The Forests of the World" may help students visualize the relationship between taiga, temperate deciduous forest, temperate rain forest, and tropical rain forest. L1 IS **Visual-Spatial**

Temperate Forest Life Many evergreen trees grow in the temperate regions of the world. However, most of the temperate forests in Europe and North America are dominated by climax communities of deciduous trees, which lose their leaves every autumn. These forests, like the one in **Figure 9,** are called **temperate deciduous forests.** In the United States, most of them are located east of the Mississippi River.

When European settlers first came to America, they cut trees to create farmland and to supply wood. As forests were cut, organisms lost their habitats. When agriculture shifted from the eastern to the midwestern and western states, secondary succession began, and trees eventually returned to some areas. Now, nearly as many trees grow in the New England states as did before the American Revolutionary War. Many trees are located in smaller patches. Yet, the recovery of large forests such as those in the Adirondack Mountains in New York State shows the result of secondary succession.

Temperate Rain Forest New Zealand, southern Chile, and the Pacific Northwest of the United States are some of the places where **temperate rain forests,** shown in **Figure 10,** are found. The average temperature of a temperate rain forest ranges from 9°C to 12°C. Precipitation ranges from 200 cm to 400 cm per year.

Trees with needlelike leaves dominate these forests, including the Douglas fir, western red cedar, and spruce. Many grow to great heights. Animals of the temperate rain forest include the black bear, cougar, bobcat, northern spotted owl, and marbled murrelet. Many species of amphibians also inhabit the temperate rain forest, including salamanders.

The logging industry in the Northwest provides jobs for many people. However, it also removes large parts of the temperate rain forest and destroys the habitat of many organisms. Many logging companies now are required to replant trees to replace the ones they cut down. Also, some rain forest areas are protected as national parks and forests.

Figure 10 In the Olympic rain forest in Washington State, mosses and lichens blanket the ground and hang from the trees. Wet areas are perfect habitats for amphibians like the Pacific giant salamander above.

Make a Model

Land Use Have students:

(a) use long wooden dowels representing trees to show how the land in the Northeastern United States looked before European settlers,

(b) remove the dowels and put up short dowel fences and black paper roads to represent how the land looked when it was made into farms,

(c) return many of the long dowels but keep the fences and roads to show the return of trees. Make the point that although trees are present, many animals are restricted in their movement.

Virtual Labs

Environment *What are the different types of land environments?*

Differentiated Instruction

Challenge Six common land biomes are presented in this chapter. Students may be assigned other biomes to research, such as tidal wetlands, extreme deserts, bogs, chapparal, continental slope, temperate oceans, tropic savannahs, or coastal arctic tundra. Have them present their findings to the class as posters or other visuals.
L3 IS **Visual-Spatial**

Teacher FYI

Spotted Owls The spotted owl is an endangered species that lives in old-growth temperate forests. These forests are over 100 years old. Clear-cutting the forest and planting new trees destroys the necessary habitat of these birds.

Purpose Students observe rain forest leaves, analyze their structures, and relate leaf structure to leaf function. [L2]

LS Kinesthetic

Materials poster board, pencil, scissors, sink, water, spray bottle

Teaching Strategy Show students philodendron or ficus leaves so they can see real drip tips.

Analysis

1. the leaf with the drip tip
2. Removing water from the leaf's surface prohibits growth of mosses, fungi, or other moisture-loving organisms that could compete with the plant.

Assessment

Process Ask students how they could perform a similar experiment but obtain quantitative results. Answers should involve the measurement of the amount of water falling off the leaves using a graduated cylinder. Use **Performance Assessment in the Science Classroom,** p. 105.

Try at Home

✔ Reading Check

Answer forest floor, understory, canopy, emergents

Figure 11 Tropical rain forests are lush environments that contain such a large variety of species that many have not been discovered.

Modeling Rain Forest Leaves

Procedure

1. Draw an oval leaf about 10 cm long on a piece of **poster board.** Cut it out.
2. Draw a second leaf the same size but make one end pointed. This is called a drip tip. Cut this leaf out.
3. Hold your hands palm-side up over a **sink** and have someone lay a leaf on each one. Point the drip tip away from you. Tilt your hands down but do not allow the leaves to fall off.
4. Have someone gently spray water on the leaves and observe what happens.

Analysis

1. From which leaf does water drain faster?
2. Infer why it is an advantage for a leaf to get rid of water quickly in a rain forest.

Try at Home

Tropical Rain Forest Warm temperatures, wet weather, and lush plant growth are found in **tropical rain forests.** These forests are warm because they are near the equator. The average temperature, about 25°C, doesn't vary much between night and day. Most tropical rain forests receive at least 200 cm of rain annually. Some receive as much as 600 cm of rain each year.

Tropical rain forests, like the one in **Figure 11,** are home to an astonishing variety of organisms. They are one of the most biologically diverse places in the world. For example, one tree in a South American rain forest might contain more species of ants than exist in all of the British Isles.

Tropical Rain Forest Life Different animals and plants live in different parts of the rain forest. Scientists divide the rain forest into zones based on the types of plants and animals that live there, just as a library separates books about different topics onto separate shelves. The zones include: forest floor, understory, canopy, and emergents, as shown in **Figure 12.** These zones often blend together, but their existence provide different habitats for many diverse organisms to live in the tropical rain forest.

✔ Reading Check *What are the four zones of a tropical rain forest?*

Although tropical rain forests support a huge variety of organisms, the soil of the rain forest contains few nutrients. Over the years, nutrients have been washed out of the soil by rain. On the forest floor, decomposers immediately break down organic matter, making nutrients available to the plants again.

LAB DEMONSTRATION

Purpose to show the stabilizing effect of buttress roots on rain forest trees

Materials 3 paper towel tubes, scissors, tape, trough with thin layer of sand

Preparation Cut out four buttresses (which resemble rocket fins) from a paper towel tube, and tape them to one tube.

Procedure Rain forest tree roots don't grow very deep. Push the paper towel tubes (one with butresses, one without) 1 cm into the sand. Blow on the tubes to see which falls first.

Expected Outcome The tube without buttresses will fall first.

Assessment

Why do buttresses make trees more stable? They give a tree a wider base. Why would a rain forest tree have buttresses but not a temperate forest tree? Rain forest tree roots do not penetrate the soil as deeply.

Human Impact Farmers that live in tropical areas clear the land to farm and to sell the valuable wood. After a few years, the crops use up the nutrients in the soil, and the farmers must clear more land. As a result, tropical rain forest habitats are being destroyed. Through education, people are realizing the value and potential value of preserving the species of the rain forest. In some areas, logging is prohibited. In other areas, farmers are taught new methods of farming so they do not have to clear rain forest lands continually.

Figure 12 Tropical rain forests contain abundant and diverse organisms.

Use an Analogy

Rain Forest v. Library The layers of a rain forest are comparable to the shelves of a library. Just as the shelves provide more space for books, the layers of the rain forest provide more niches for supporting life. This is one of the reasons rain forests are biologically diverse.

Activity

Rain Forest Zones Have students make charts of the main features of the four major zones of the tropical rain forest: the emergents, canopy, understory, and forest floor. L2 IS **Naturalist**

Emergents These giant trees are much higher than the average canopy tree. Birds, such as the macaw, and insects are found here.

Canopy The canopy includes the upper parts of the trees. It's full of life—insects, birds, reptiles, and mammals.

Understory This dark, cool environment is under the canopy leaves but above the ground. Many insects, reptiles, and amphibians live in the understory.

Forest Floor The forest floor is home to many insects and the largest mammals in the rain forest generally live here.

Visual Learning

Figure 12 Ask students to explain how conditions above the canopy differ from conditions below the canopy. much more sunlight and wind above the canopy, darker and more humid below the canopy

Desertification Areas with heavy agriculture in the Southwest are the most likely to be affected by desertification in the United States. Changes in climate and human activities also contribute to desertification, which is the loss of productivity of land in arid or semi-arid areas.

Research Have students research the expansion of the Sahara in Africa. Create a map that shows the change in its boundaries over the last 50 years.

Cold Deserts A common idea about deserts is that they are hot, dry places. While this is true of the majority of deserts, there are some cold deserts such as Patagonia in Argentina. Cold deserts are usually caused by their remoteness from the coast, or by mountains that block moist coastal winds. The largest cold desert is in central Asia.

Fun Fact

At one time, the grassland biome covered nearly half of the land on Earth. Today, most of the grassland is used by humans for growing crops, raising animals, and housing.

Desertification When vegetation is removed from soil in areas that receive little rain, the dry, unprotected surface can be blown away. If the soil remains bare, a desert might form. This process is called desertification. Look on a biome map and hypothesize about which areas of the United States are most likely to become deserts.

Figure 13 Desert plants, like these in the Sonoran Desert, are adapted for survival in the extreme conditions of the desert biome. The giant hairy scorpion found in some deserts has a venomous sting.

Desert The driest biome on Earth is the **desert.** Deserts receive less than 25 cm of rain each year and support little plant life. Some desert areas receive no rain for years. When rain does come, it quickly drains away. Any water that remains on the ground evaporates rapidly.

Most deserts, like the one in **Figure 13,** are covered with a thin, sandy, or gravelly soil that contains little organic matter. Due to the lack of water, desert plants are spaced far apart and much of the ground is bare. Barren, windblown sand dunes are characteristics of the driest deserts.

☑ **Reading Check** *Why is much of a desert bare ground?*

Desert Life Desert plants are adapted for survival in the extreme dryness and hot and cold temperatures of this biome. Most desert plants are able to store water. Cactus plants are probably the most familiar desert plants of the western hemisphere. Desert animals also have adaptations that help them survive the extreme conditions. Some, like the kangaroo rat, never need to drink water. They get all the moisture they need from the breakdown of food during digestion. Most animals are active only during the night, late afternoon, or early morning when temperatures are less extreme. Few large animals are found in the desert.

In order to provide water for desert cities, rivers and streams have been diverted. When this happens, wildlife tends to move closer to cities in their search for food and water. Education about desert environments has led to an awareness of the impact of human activities. As a result, large areas of desert have been set aside as national parks and wilderness areas to protect desert habitats.

Cultural Diversity

Biomes and Dress Discuss how the dress of people in different areas is influenced by the biome in which they live. For example, Arabic people may wear long robes to shield themselves from the desert heat. Inuits may dress in animal skins to insulate themselves from the cold. Encourage interested students to present a show of "Biome Fashions Around the World." COOP LEARN

Grasslands Temperate and tropical regions that receive between 25 cm and 75 cm of precipitation each year and are dominated by climax communities of grasses are called **grasslands.** Most grasslands have a dry season, when little or no rain falls. This lack of moisture prevents the development of forests. Grasslands are found in many places around the world, and they have a variety of names. The prairies and plains of North America, the steppes of Asia, the savannas of Africa shown in **Figure 14,** and the pampas of South America are types of grasslands.

Figure 14 Animals such as zebras and wildebeests are adapted to life on the savannas in Africa.

Grasslands Life The most noticeable animals in grassland biomes are usually mammals that graze on the stems, leaves, and seeds of grass plants. Kangaroos graze in the grasslands of Australia. In Africa, communities of animals such as wildebeests, impalas, and zebras thrive in the savannas.

Grasslands are perfect for growing many crops such as wheat, rye, oats, barley, and corn. Grasslands also are used to raise cattle and sheep. However, overgrazing can result in the death of grasses and the loss of valuable topsoil from erosion. Most farmers and ranchers take precautions to prevent the loss of valuable habitats and soil.

section 2 review

Summary

Major Biomes

- Tundra, sometimes called a cold desert, can be divided into two types: arctic and alpine.

- Taiga is the world's largest biome. It is a cold forest region with long winters.

- Temperate regions have either a deciduous forest biome or a rain forest biome.

- Tropical rain forests are one of the most biologically diverse biomes.

- Humans have a huge impact on tropical rain forests.

- The driest biome is the desert. Desert organisms are adapted for extreme dryness and temperatures.

- Grasslands provide food for wildlife, livestock, and humans.

Self Check

1. **Determine** which two biomes are the driest.

2. **Compare and contrast** tundra organisms and desert organisms.

3. **Identify** the biggest climatic difference between a temperate rain forest and a tropical rain forest.

4. **Explain** why the soil of tropical rain forests make poor farmland.

5. **Think Critically** If you climb a mountain in Arizona, you might reach an area where the trees resemble the taiga trees in northern Canada. Why would a taiga forest exist in Arizona?

Applying Skills

6. **Record Observations** Animals have adaptations that help them survive in their environments. Make a list of animals that live in your area, and record the physical or behavioral adaptations that help them survive.

Science Online life.msscience.com/self_check_quiz

SECTION 2 Biomes **751**

section 2 review

1. desert and tundra
2. Tundra organisms are adapted to survive cold and drought. Desert organisms are adapted to survive extreme dryness, and large temperature fluctuations.
3. Tropical rain forests are warmer (have a higher average tempera-

ture) than temperate rain forests, and tend to have more precipitation.
4. The rain forest has very nutrient-poor soil that is easily eroded.
5. Temperatures cool with increased elevation, so places with higher altitude in warm areas can resemble the taiga.

6. Answers will vary but should include adaptations to survive conditions including cold or heat, humidity or dryness, and land or aquatic environments.

BENCH TESTED

▶ Real-World Question

Purpose Students conduct a study of an ecosystem and determine how the living things interact with each other and the environment. L2

IS Intrapersonal

Process Skills observe, classify, communicate, define operationally, recognize cause and effect, predict

Time Required 50 minutes for setup, four weeks to make observations

▶ Procedure

Teaching Strategies

• Arrange for students to check out binoculars, field guides, and other useful materials from the science classroom and library.

• Approve the ecosystems chosen by the students before they begin their observations.

• Offer students a set time each day to discuss any problems they may have concerning their method of study.

▶ Conclude and Apply

1. Populations would be affected by changes in temperature, water, or other abiotic factors. The entire ecosystem could be disrupted.
2. Other populations could be affected.
3. Possible hypotheses: competition for available resources could make one population extinct or forced away; students may hypothesize about results from favorable or unfavorable interactions among the populations in response to the introduction of a new population.

Studying a Land Ecosystem

An ecological study includes observation and analysis of organisms and the physical features of the environment.

▶ Real-World Question

How do you study an ecosystem?

Goals
■ **Observe** biotic factors and abiotic factors of an ecosystem.
■ **Analyze** the relationships among organisms and their environments.

Materials

graph paper	field guides
binoculars	notebook
thermometer	compass
pencil	tape measure
magnifying lens	

Safety Precautions 🔥 ✋ 🥽 🧤

▶ Procedure

1. Choose a portion of an ecosystem to study. You might choose a decaying log, a pond, a garden, or even a crack in the sidewalk.
2. Determine the boundaries of your study area.
3. Using a tape measure and graph paper, make a map of your area. Determine north.
4. **Record** your observations in a table similar to the one shown on this page.
5. **Observe** the organisms in your study area. Use field guides to identify them. Use a magnifying lens to study small organisms and binoculars to study animals you can't get near. Look for evidence (such as tracks or feathers) of organisms you do not see.

6. Measure and record the air temperature in your study area.
7. Visit your study area many times and at different times of day for one week. At each visit, make the same measurements and record all observations. Note how the living and nonliving parts of the ecosystem interact.

Environmental Observations		
Date		
Time of day		
Temperature	Answers will vary.	
Organisms observed		
Comments		

▶ Conclude and Apply

1. **Predict** what might happen if one or more abiotic factors were changed suddenly.
2. **Infer** what might happen if one or more populations of plants or animals were removed from the area.
3. **Form a hypothesis** to explain how a new population of organisms might affect your ecosystem.

Communicating Your Data

Make a classroom display of all data recorded. **For more help, refer to the** Science Skill Handbook.

✔ Assessment

Performance Have students alter the ecosystem in a way that is not harmful. Have them observe how foreign materials affect the behavior of living things in the ecosystem. Use **Performance Assessment in the Science Classroom,** p. 97.

Communicating Your Data

You may choose to display the best student posters along one wall. Allow volunteers to present their poster and data to the class in a short presentation.

Aquatic Ecosystems

Freshwater Ecosystems

In a land environment, temperature and precipitation are the most important factors that determine which species can survive. In aquatic environments, water temperature, the amount of sunlight present, and the amounts of dissolved oxygen and salt in the water are important. Earth's freshwater ecosystems include flowing water such as rivers and streams and standing water such as lakes, ponds, and wetlands.

Rivers and Streams Flowing freshwater environments vary from small, gurgling brooks to large, slow-moving rivers. Currents can quickly wash loose particles downstream, leaving a rocky or gravelly bottom. As the water tumbles and splashes, as shown in **Figure 15,** air from the atmosphere mixes in. Naturally fast-flowing streams usually have clearer water and higher oxygen content than slow-flowing streams.

Most nutrients that support life in flowing-water ecosystems are washed into the water from land. In areas where the water movement slows, such as in the pools of streams or in large rivers, debris settles to the bottom. These environments tend to have higher nutrient levels and more plant growth. They contain organisms that are not as well adapted to swiftly flowing water, such as freshwater mussels, minnows, and leeches.

as you read

What **You'll Learn**
- **Compare** flowing freshwater and standing freshwater ecosystems.
- **Identify** and describe important saltwater ecosystems.
- **Identify** problems that affect aquatic ecosystems.

Why **It's Important**
All of the life processes in your body depend on water.

Review Vocabulary
aquatic: growing or living in water

New Vocabulary
- wetland
- intertidal zone
- coral reef
- estuary

Figure 15 Streams like this one are high in oxygen because of the swift, tumbling water.
Determine *where most nutrients in streams come from.*

Section 3 Resource Manager

Chapter *FAST FILE* Resources
Transparency Activity, pp. 44, 45–46
Directed Reading for Content Mastery, pp. 19, 20
Enrichment, p. 30
MiniLAB, p. 4
Reinforcement, p. 27
Lab Worksheet, pp. 7–8

Mathematics Skill Activities, p. 9
Home and Community Involvement, p. 45
Cultural Diversity, p. 7
Earth Science Critical Thinking/Problem Solving, p. 1
Lab Management and Safety, p. 37

Mini LAB

Purpose Students observe a freshwater ecosystem. L2

IS **Naturalist**

Materials clear plastic container, material from the bottom of a pond, pond organisms, net, pond water, magnifying lens

Teaching Strategy Make sure students don't disturb the container excessively while observing, as sediment stirred up will make observations difficult.

Safety Precaution Make sure to get permission from the land owner or appropriate authorities before collecting samples from the pond.

Analysis

Students' paragraphs will vary depending on organisms obtained.

Assessment

Oral Have students use their observations from the MiniLAB to identify adaptations of the organisms. Use **Performance Assessment in the Science Classroom,** p. 89.

Mini LAB

Modeling Freshwater Environments

Procedure

1. Obtain a sample of **pond sediment or debris, plants, water, and organisms** from your teacher.
2. Cover the bottom of a **clear-plastic container** with about 2 cm of the debris.
3. Add one or two plants to the container.
4. Carefully pour pond water into the container until it is about two-thirds full.
5. Use a **net** to add several organisms to the water. Seal the container.
6. Using a **magnifying lens,** observe as many organisms as possible. Record your observations. Return your sample to its original habitat.

Analysis
Write a short paragraph describing the organisms in your sample. How did the organisms interact with each other?

Human Impact People use rivers and streams for many activities. Once regarded as a free place to dump sewage and other pollutants, many people now recognize the damage this causes. Treating sewage and restricting pollutants have led to an improvement in the water quality in some rivers.

Lakes and Ponds When a low place in the land fills with rainwater, snowmelt, or water from an overflowing stream, a lake or pond might form. Pond or lake water hardly moves. It contains more plants than flowing-water environments contain.

Lakes, such as the one shown in **Figure 16,** are larger and deeper than ponds. They have more open water because most plant growth is limited to shallow areas along the shoreline. In fact, organisms found in the warm, sunlit waters of the shorelines often are similar to those found in ponds. If you were to dive to the bottom, you would discover few, if any, plants or algae growing. Colder temperatures and lower light levels limit the types of organisms that can live in deep lake waters. Floating in the warm, sunlit waters near the surface of freshwater lakes and ponds are microscopic algae, plants, and other organisms known as plankton.

A pond is a small, shallow body of water. Because ponds are shallow, they are filled with animal and plant life. Sunlight usually penetrates to the bottom. The warm, sunlit water promotes the growth of plants and algae. In fact, many ponds are filled almost completely with plant material, so the only clear, open water is at the center. Because of the lush growth in pond environments, they tend to be high in nutrients.

Figure 16 Ponds contain more vegetation than lakes contain. The population of organisms in the shallow water of lakes is high. Fewer types of organisms live in the deeper water.

Differentiated Instruction

Physically Challenged If students have difficulty with manual dexterity in the MiniLAB, mount the magnifying glass on a ring stand. Have them look through the magnifying glass and slowly move the plastic container.

Visually Impaired Have a small shallow container represent a pond and a larger container represent a lake. Form a "V" with a plastic sheet. Incline the V at a steep angle, and pour water down it to represent a stream. Hold the V at a slighter angle, and pour a greater volume of water down it. This represents a river. Have students put their hands into the four conditions to feel the differences.

Water Pollution Human activities can harm freshwater environments. Fertilizer-filled runoff from farms and lawns, as well as sewage dumped into the water, can lead to excessive growth of algae and plants in lakes and ponds. The growth and decay of these organisms reduces the oxygen level in the water, which makes it difficult for some organisms to survive. To prevent problems, sewage is treated before it is released. People also are being educated about problems associated with polluting lakes and ponds. Fines and penalties are issued to people caught polluting waterways. These controls have led to the recovery of many freshwater ecosystems.

Wetlands As the name suggests, **wetlands,** shown in **Figure 17,** are regions that are wet for all or most of a year. They are found in regions that lie between landmasses and water. Other names for wetlands include swamps, bogs, and fens. Some people refer to wetlands as biological supermarkets. They are fertile ecosystems, but only plants that are adapted to water-logged soil survive there. Wetland animals include beavers, muskrats, alligators, and the endangered bog turtle. Many migratory bird populations use wetlands as breeding grounds.

Reading Check *Where are wetlands found?*

Wetlands once were considered to be useless, disease-ridden places. Many were drained and destroyed to make roads, farmland, shopping centers, and housing developments. Only recently have people begun to understand the importance of wetlands. Products that come from wetlands, including fish, shellfish, cranberries, and plants, are valuable resources. Now many developers are restoring wetlands, and in most states access to land through wetlands is prohibited.

Figure 17 Life in the Florida Everglades was threatened due to pollution, drought, and draining of the water. Conservation efforts are being made in an attempt to preserve this ecosystem.

Environmental Author Rachel Carson (1907–1964) was a scientist that turned her knowledge and love of the environment into articles and books. After 15 years as an editor for the U.S. Fish and Wildlife Service, she resigned and devoted her time to writing. She probably is known best for her book *Silent Spring,* in which she warned about the long-term effects of the misuse of pesticides. In your Science Journal, compile a list of other authors who write about environmental issues.

Curriculum Connection

History Have students research the Seminole people of Florida and how they survived attacks by the United States Army by hiding in the Everglades. L2

Quick Demo

Saltwater v. Freshwater

Materials two identical natural corks, two containers, freshwater, salt water

Estimated Time 5 minutes

Procedure Float one cork in freshwater and the other in salt water. Students should observe that the cork in salt water floats higher than the one in freshwater. Explain that this occurs because salt water is more dense than freshwater.

Make a Model

Estuaries Ask students to use clay, colored water, or other materials to show the mixing of freshwater and salt water when a river and ocean combine to form an estuary.

Activity

Dissolved Oxygen From a science supply company, purchase kits that measure the dissolved oxygen in water. Compare different bodies of water such as lakes, streams, and oceans. L3

LS **Naturalist**

Saltwater Ecosystems

About 95 percent of the water on the surface of Earth contains high concentrations of various salts. The amount of dissolved salts in water is called salinity. The average ocean salinity is about 35 g of salts per 1,000 g of water. Saltwater ecosystems include oceans, seas, a few inland lakes such as the Great Salt Lake in Utah, coastal inlets, and estuaries.

Applying Math   Convert Units

TEMPERATURE Organisms that live around hydrothermal vents in the ocean deal with temperatures that range from 1.7°C to 371°C. You have probably seen temperatures measured in degrees Celsius (°C) and degrees Fahrenheit (°F). Which one are you familiar with? If you know the temperature in one system, you can convert it to the other.

You have a Fahrenheit thermometer and measure the water temperature of a pond at 59°F. What is that temperature in degrees Celsius?

Solution

1 *This is what you know:* water temperature in degrees Fahrenheit = 59°F

2 *This is what you need to find out:* The water temperature in degrees Celsius.

3 *This is the procedure you need to use:*
- Solve the equation for degrees Celsius:
  $(°C × 1.8) + 32 = °F$
  $°C = (°F − 32)/1.8$
- Substitute the known value:
  $°C = (59°F − 32)/1.8 = 15°C$
- Water temperature that is 59°F is 15°C.

4 *Check your answer:* Substitute the Celsius temperature back into the original equation. You should get 59.

Practice Problems

1. The thermometer outside your classroom reads 78°F. What is the temperature in degrees Celsius?

2. If lake water was 12°C in October and 23°C in May, what is the difference in degrees Fahrenheit?

For more practice, visit life.msscience.com/math_practice

Science Journal

Marine Biomes Have students compare estuaries and oceans. As part of this comparison, ask students to focus on living and nonliving factors associated with each ecosystem. Have them write a paragraph about each biome in their Science Journals. P

Fun Fact

The largest tides occur when Earth, the Sun, and the Moon are in line. This is when the combined gravities of the Sun and Moon have their greatest effect on Earth's waters.

Open Oceans Life abounds in the open ocean. Scientists divide the ocean into different life zones, based on the depth to which sunlight penetrates the water. The lighted zone of the ocean is the upper 200 m or so. It is the home of the plankton that make up the foundation of the food chain in the open ocean. Below about 200 m is the dark zone of the ocean. Animals living in this region feed on material that floats down from the lighted zone, or they feed on each other. A few organisms are able to produce their own food.

Coral Reefs One of the most diverse ecosystems in the world is the coral reef. **Coral reefs** are formed over long periods of time from the calcium carbonate skeletons secreted by animals called corals. When corals die, their skeletons remain. Over time, the skeletal deposits form reefs such as the Great Barrier Reef off the coast of Australia, shown in **Figure 18.**

Reefs do not adapt well to long-term stress. Runoff from fields, sewage, and increased sedimentation from cleared land harm reef ecosystems. Organizations like the Environmental Protection Agency have developed management plans to protect the diversity of coral reefs. These plans treat a coral reef as a system that includes all the areas that surround the reef. Keeping the areas around reefs healthy will result in a healthy environment for the coral reef ecosystem.

Science Online

Topic: Coral Reefs
Visit life.msscience.com for Web links to information about coral reef ecosystems.

Activity Construct a diorama of a coral reef. Include as many different kinds of organisms as you can for a coral reef ecosystem.

Figure 18 The lighter areas around this island are part of the Great Barrier Reef. It comprises about 3,000 reefs and about 900 islands. Reefs contain colorful fish and a large variety of other organisms.

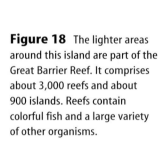

IDENTIFYING Misconceptions

Anemones and Corals Students may think that sea anemones and the coral in coral reefs are plants rather than animals. Help them realize that they are animals that feed on small organisms in the water.

Quick Demo
Calcium Carbonate Skeleton
Materials piece or pieces of coral such as those found in saltwater aquariums
Estimated Time 5 minutes
Procedure Hold up or pass around the piece or pieces of coral. Explain that this is the calcium carbonate skeleton left behind by the once-living coral.

Discussion
Osmosis Because freshwater fish have saltier blood than the surrounding water, water tends to move into the fish by osmosis. Freshwater fish are covered with scales and a mucous secretion that slows the movement of water into their tissues. The kidneys are adapted to filter out excess water, and they excrete large amounts of dilute urine. Saltwater fish have less salt in their blood than the surrounding water. What direction would water tend to diffuse? outward What adaptations would you expect saltwater fish to have to prevent water loss from their body? Marine fish drink sea water and excrete the excess salts.

Active Reading

Jigsaw In this collaborative learning technique, individuals become experts on a portion of a text and share their expertise with a small group, called their home group. Everyone shares responsibility for learning the assigned reading. Assign each person in each home group an expert number (1 through 5, for example). Have students gather into the expert groups that correspond to the number they were assigned. Have them read, discuss, and master chapter concepts, and determine how best to teach them to their home groups. Have students return to their home groups and share the content they learned in their expert groups. Have students use the Jigsaw strategy with the text on aquatic ecosystems.

Figure 19 Explain that sea stars have special adaptions that enable them to inhabit the intertidal zone. One of these adaptations is the presence of numerous small tube feet under each arm, which enable the sea star to resist being swept away by the tide.

Caption Answer

Figure 20 crabs, clams, oysters

Reading Check

Answer freshwater carries tons of nutrients from inland soils to estuaries

Inquiry Lab

Biome Investigation

Purpose to observe what affects organisms within biomes, by studying a student-made ecosystem

Possible Materials large jars, soda bottles, or aquaria; variety of living organisms; water; soil

Estimated Time 1 or 2 class sessions for research and set-up

Teaching Strategies

• Have student groups choose a biome to study. If space is an issue, have the class vote on 1 or 2 biomes to study.

• Students can construct a mini-ecosystem that would be part of the chosen biome. They should research to ensure their environment is accurate.

• Encourage students to make comparisons to the real world, contrasting their ecosystem to the biome in which you live.

• Allow them to explore questions that arise as they observe the system.

For additional inquiry activities, see *Science Inquiry Labs.*

Figure 19 As the tide recedes, small pools of seawater are left behind. These pools contain a variety of organisms such as sea stars and periwinkles.

Sea star

Periwinkles

INTEGRATE Earth Science

Seashores All of Earth's landmasses are bordered by ocean water. The shallow waters along the world's coastlines contain a variety of saltwater ecosystems, all of which are influenced by the tides and by the action of waves. The gravitational pull of the Moon, and to a lesser extent, the Sun, on Earth causes the tides to rise and fall each day. The height of the tides varies according to the phases of the Moon, the season, and the slope of the shoreline. The **intertidal zone** is the portion of the shoreline that is covered with water at high tide and exposed to the air during low tide. Organisms that live in the intertidal zone, such as those in **Figure 19,** must be adapted to dramatic changes in temperature, moisture, and salinity and must be able to withstand the force of wave action.

Estuaries Almost every river on Earth eventually flows into an ocean. The area where a river meets an ocean and contains a mixture of freshwater and salt water is called an **estuary** (ES chuh wer ee). Other names for estuaries include bays, lagoons, harbors, inlets, and sounds. They are located near coastlines and border the land. Salinity in estuaries changes with the amount of freshwater brought in by rivers and streams, and with the amount of salt water pushed inland by the ocean tides.

Estuaries, shown in **Figure 20,** are extremely fertile, productive environments because freshwater streams bring in tons of nutrients washed from inland soils. Therefore, nutrient levels in estuaries are higher than in freshwater ecosystems or other saltwater ecosystems.

758 CHAPTER 26 Ecosystems

Curriculum Connection

Geography Have students locate Australia on a globe and then identify the location of the Great Barrier Reef. L1 IN **Visual-Spatial**

Differentiated Instruction

Challenge Ask students to make up a story about a molecule of water in a cloud falling to Earth as a raindrop. Direct students to have it pass through three aquatic ecosystems before it evaporates and begins the process again. Have students share their stories with the class. L3

Figure 20 The Chesapeake Bay is an estuary rich in resources. Fish and shrimp are harvested by commercial fishing boats.

Describe *what other resources can be found in estuaries.*

Estuary Life Organisms found in estuaries include many species of algae, salt-tolerant grasses, shrimp, crabs, clams, oysters, snails, worms, and fish. Estuaries also serve as important nurseries for many species of ocean fish. Estuaries provide much of the seafood consumed by humans.

 **Reading Check** *Why are estuaries more fertile than other aquatic ecosystems?*

section 3 review

Summary

Freshwater Ecosystems

- Temperature, light, salt, and dissolved oxygen are important factors.
- Rivers, streams, lakes, ponds, and wetlands are freshwater ecosystems.
- Human activities, such as too much lawn fertilizer, can pollute aquatic ecosystems.

Saltwater Ecosystems

- About 95 percent of Earth's water contains dissolved salts.
- Saltwater ecosystems include open oceans, coral reefs, seashores, and estuaries.
- Organisms that live on seashores have adaptations that enable them to survive dramatic changes in temperature, moisture, and salinity.
- Estuaries serve as nursery areas for many species of ocean fish.

Self Check

1. **Identify** the similarities and differences between a lake and a stream.
2. **Compare and contrast** the dark zone of the ocean with the forest floor of a tropical rain forest. What living or nonliving factors affect these areas?
3. **Explain** why fewer plants are at the bottom of deep lakes.
4. **Infer** what adaptations are necessary for organisms that live in the intertidal zone.
5. **Think Critically** Would you expect a fast moving mountain stream or the Mississippi River to have more dissolved oxygen? Explain.

Applying Skills

6. **Communicate** Wetlands trap and slowly release rain, snow, and groundwater. Describe in your Science Journal what might happen to a town located on a floodplain if nearby wetlands are destroyed.

section 3 review

1. Both contain freshwater. A lake has standing water, low oxygen levels, and rich plant growth in shallow water. A stream has swift-moving water, high oxygen levels, and a rocky bottom with little plant life.
2. Both contain scavengers and decomposers; both are affected by temperature and lack of light. The dark zone is a cold environment, and the rain forest is warm.
3. Cold temperatures and low light levels limit the types of organisms that can grow there.
4. Such organisms must be able to adapt to drastic changes in temperature, moisture, and salinity; they must be able to withstand wave motion.
5. fast moving stream; more oxygen is mixed into the water
6. The town would flood much more often.

---

3 Assess

DAILY INTERVENTION

Check for Understanding

Kinesthetic Provide each student with a note card on which the name or picture of a wetland element has been placed. Examples might include: algae, perch, dragonfly nymph, rock, osprey, frog, or snake. Have students stand in a circle. Have one student hold onto the end of a skein of yarn. That student selects another student in the circle, and while still holding onto the yarn, passes the skein to that student and states how the two elements may interact. For example, a student with a dragonfly nymph card would pass the yarn to the student with the rock card and say the dragonfly perches on the rock. Have students continue passing the yarn and making connections until a web forms. Emphasize that everyone in the circle is connected either directly or indirectly, just like the elements in an ecosystem.

Reteach

Ocean Ecosystems Write on the chalkboard or on an overhead transparency a description of the three major ocean ecosystems. Have students identify each one.

L2 **IS** **Naturalist**

 Assessment

Process Assess students' understanding by having them compare and contrast the salinity of rivers, estuaries, and the open ocean in their Science Journals. Rivers have lower salinity than oceans. The amount of salt in an estuary varies, but they contain more salt than rivers, and less than oceans. Use **PASC,** p. 175.

BENCH TESTED

▶ Real-World Question

Purpose

Internet Students use Internet sites that can be accessed through life.msscience.com/internet_lab.
L2

Non-Internet Sources Collect pamphlets from a variety of wetlands conservancy groups.

Time Required three to five days

▶ Make a Plan

Preparation

Internet To run through the steps that the students will follow, visit

life.msscience.com/internet_lab.

Non-Internet Organize printed materials by wetlands regions.

▶ Follow Your Plan

Teaching Strategy Remind students to investigate how the amount of wetlands areas has changed over the last 25 years, and how that has made an impact on native plants and animals.

Exploring Wetlands

▶ Real-World Question

Wetlands, such as the one shown below, are an important part of the environment. These fertile ecosystems support unique plants and animals that can survive only in wetland conditions. The more you understand the importance of wetlands, the more you can do to preserve and protect them. Why are wetlands an important part of the ecosystem?

Goals
■ **Identify** wetland regions in the United States.
■ **Describe** the significance of the wetland ecosystem.
■ **Identify** plant and animal species native to a wetland region.
■ **Identify** strategies for supporting the preservation of wetlands.

Data Source
Science Online
Visit life.msscience.com/internet_lab for more information about wetland environments and for data collected by other students.

Alternative Inquiry Lab

Real-World Connection Have groups take on different roles associated with a problem about wetlands. For example, one group can be engineers asked to provide an environmental impact study on a proposed construction site in the wetlands area. Another group can be legislators determining whether to grant the construction permits while another group acts as business executives assessing the cost and benefits of building in this location. Students should conduct this research and present their final recommendations. PBL

Make a Plan

1. **Determine** where some major wetlands are located in the United States.
2. **Identify** one wetland area to study in depth. Where is it located? Is it classified as a marsh, bog, or something else?
3. **Explain** the role this ecosystem plays in the overall ecology of the area.
4. **Research information** about the plants and animals that live in the wetland environment you are researching.
5. **Investigate** what laws protect the wetland you are studying.

Follow Your Plan

1. Make sure your teacher approves your plan before you start.
2. Perform the investigation.
3. Post your data at the link shown below.

Analyze Your Data

1. **Describe** the wetland area you have researched. What region of the United States is it located in? What other ecological factors are found in that region?
2. **Outline** the laws protecting the wetland you are investigating. How long have the laws been in place?
3. **List** the plants and animals native to the wetland area you are researching. Are those plants and animals found in other parts of the region or the United States? What adaptations do the plants and animals have that help them survive in a wetland environment?

Conclude and Apply

1. **Infer** Are all wetlands the same?
2. **Determine** what the ecological significance of the wetland area that you studied for that region of the country is.
3. **Draw Conclusions** Why should wetland environments be protected?
4. **Summarize** what people can do to support the continued preservation of wetland environments in the United States.

Communicating Your Data

Find this lab using the link below. **Post** your data in the table provided. **Review** other students' data to learn about other wetland environments in the United States.

Science Online

life.msscience.com/internet_lab

Analyze Your Data

1. Answers will be based on the students' individual research.
2. Most laws protecting wetlands are federal and may include: The Clean Water Act (1972), Federal Highway Act of 1968, Estuary Protection Act (1972), National Wildlife Refuge Acts (numerous), and North American Wetlands Conservation Act (1980). In addition, more than half of the states have wetland laws.
3. Answers will vary based on the students' individual research. Some wetland plants have structures to keep their photosynthetic cells near the surface of the water and in the sunlight. Wetland trees, such as the cypress, have structures like tent stakes that provide support. Some wetland birds have more hemoglobin in their blood for extra oxygen, enabling them to stay underwater. Amphibian eggs develop quickly through the tadpole stage in case the wetland dries out.

Conclude and Apply

1. Wetlands regions are not all the same. Depending on where they are located, one area may have different species of plants than another.
2. Answers will vary. Remind students to think about the plants and animals that live in that wetlands region and if those species are found elsewhere.
3. Answers will vary. Students should investigate the amount of open space in that region.
4. Answers will vary. Have students find out about conservancy groups and their work to preserve wetlands regions.

✔ Assessment

Portfolio Have students make a wetlands field guide for the area they investigated. Include maps and pictures. Have them describe how to support wetlands preservation. Use **Performance Assessment in the Science Classroom,** p. 129.

Communicating Your Data

Have students organize their field guides with section names. Suggest Native Animals and Maps to help them arrange their information.

Content Background

The idea of using wetlands to process municipal wastewater was first conceived in the 1970s.

Many wetlands are being restored or constructed. A constructed wetland mimics the action of a natural marsh. A substructure prevents polluted inflow from leaching into the soil before the wetland has processed it. Troughs are filled with sand and soil and then planted with appropriate wetland vegetation. Inflow volume, local climate, and degree of pre-processing of the wastewater determine the size and nature of a constructed wetland.

In some areas, the aim of wetlands water treatment is to enable the direct reuse of the outflow. Most constructed wetlands in the U.S. are in the South and West where the warm climate ensures year-round plant growth, but there are experimental wetland projects in the northern U.S. and southern Canada.

Discussion

Wastewater Treatment Have students research municipal wastewater treatment and individual septic systems. Under what circumstances might wetlands be a better option? Possible answer: In arid regions where groundwater is depleted by well drilling and irrigation and low-lying areas where high water tables compromise standard leach fields. Are there any instances of natural wetlands being used for wastewater treatment? Possible answer: Arcata, California

Investigate the Issue

Sludge Students can research methods of dealing with "sludge." Have them present the findings in a graph format and discuss the implications of their data.

TIME 〉 SCIENCE AND *Society*
SCIENCE ISSUES THAT AFFECT YOU!

Creating Wetlands to Purify Wastewater

Pebbles were added to the Corrales wetlands to help with drainage.

Water irises thrived in the wetlands, less than a year after planting.

Students enjoy pure water from the Corrales wetlands after it is filtered.

When you wash your hands or flush the toilet, do you think about where the wastewater goes? In most places, it eventually ends up being processed in a traditional sewage-treatment facility. But some places are experimenting with a new method that processes wastewater by creating wetlands. Wetlands are home to filtering plants, such as cattails, and sewage-eating bacteria.

In 1996, school officials at the Corrales Elementary School in Albuquerque, New Mexico, faced a big problem. The old wastewater-treatment system had failed. Replacing it was going to cost a lot of money. Instead of constructing a new sewage-treatment plant, school officials decided to create a natural wetlands system. The wetlands system could do the job less expensively, while protecting the environment.

Today, this wetlands efficiently converts polluted water into cleaner water that's good for the environment. U.S. government officials are monitoring this alternative sewage-treatment system to see if it is successful. So far, so good!

Wetlands filter water through the actions of the plants and microorganisms that live there. When plants absorb water into their roots, some also take up pollutants. The plants convert the pollutants to forms that are not dangerous. At the same time, bacteria and other microorganisms are filtering water as they feed. Water moves slowly through wetlands, so the organisms have plenty of time to do their work. Wetlands built by people to filter small amounts of pollutants are called "constructed wetlands". In many places, constructed wetlands are better at cleaning wastewater than sewers or septic systems.

Visit and Observe Visit a wetlands and create a field journal of your observations. Draw the plants and animals you see. Use a field guide to help identify the wildlife. If you don't live near a wetlands, use resources to research wetlands environments.

Science online

For more information, visit life.msscience.com/time

Visit and Observe Lead a discussion on how a constructed wetland benefits wildlife. In coastal areas, the discussion may include the importance of marshes to the ocean food chain. Near river systems, the effect on wildlife can be discussed in light of the flood control function of wetlands. Discuss how the decline in total wetland acreage can affect the food chain in general.

Resources for Teachers and Students

Constructed Wetlands in the Sustainable Landscape by Craig S. Campbell and Michael H. Ogden. New York, NY: John Wiley & Sons, 1999

U.S. Department of Agriculture National Agricultural Library Water Quality Information Center 10301 Baltimore Avenue, Beltsville, MD 20705

Reviewing Main Ideas

Section 1 How Ecosystems Change

1. Ecological succession is the gradual change from one plant community to another.

2. Primary succession begins in a place where no plants were before.

3. Secondary succession begins in a place that has soil and was once the home of living organisms.

4. A climax community has reached a stable stage of ecological succession.

Section 2 Biomes

1. Temperature and precipitation help determine the climate of a region.

2. Large geographic areas with similar climax communities are called biomes.

3. Earth's land biomes include tundra, taiga, temperate deciduous forest, temperate rain forest, tropical rain forest, grassland, and desert.

Section 3 Aquatic Ecosystems

1. Freshwater ecosystems include streams, rivers, lakes, ponds, and wetlands.

2. Wetlands are areas that are covered with water most of the year. They are found in regions that lie between land-masses and water.

3. Saltwater ecosystems include estuaries, seashores, coral reefs, a few inland lakes, and the deep ocean.

4. Estuaries are fertile transitional zones between freshwater and saltwater environments.

Visualizing Main Ideas

Copy and complete this concept map about land biomes.

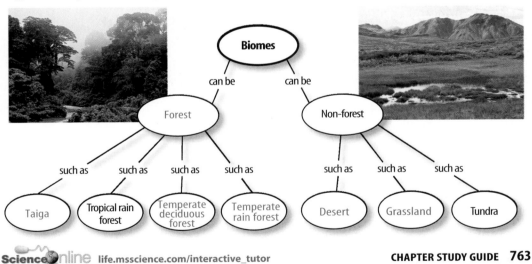

Biomes

can be — Forest — such as — Taiga, Tropical rain forest, Temperate deciduous forest, Temperate rain forest

can be — Non-forest — such as — Desert, Grassland, Tundra

 life.msscience.com/interactive_tutor

CHAPTER STUDY GUIDE 763

Reviewing Main Ideas

Summary statements can be used by students to review the major concepts of the chapter.

Visualizing Main Ideas

See student page.

Visit life.msscience.com
/self_check_quiz
/interactive_tutor
/vocabulary_puzzlemaker
/chapter_review
/standardized_test
/field_guide

Assessment Transparency

For additional assessment questions, use the *Assessment Transparency* located in the transparency book.

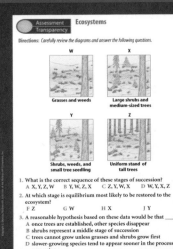

Identifying Misconceptions

Use the assessment as follow-up to page F at the beginning of this chapter.

Discussion Ask students to think of components that go into a particular ecosystem, such as a marine or forest ecosystem. Have them draw connections between the components. Have the students pick a few components to remove.

Ask students to explain what happens to the flow of energy and/or cycling of materials if these components are removed. While removing some components may not cause the system to collapse, it may not be able to function optimally without them.

Using Vocabulary

1. succession
2. climax community
3. temperate deciduous forest
4. temperate rain forest
5. tropical rain forests
6. estuary

Checking Concepts

7. B
8. A
9. B
10. C
11. B
12. A
13. B
14. D

Using Vocabulary

biome p. 744	succession p. 740
climax community p. 743	taiga p. 746
coral reef p. 757	temperate deciduous
desert p. 750	forest p. 747
estuary p. 758	temperate rain forest p. 747
grassland p. 751	tropical rain forest p. 748
intertidal zone p. 758	tundra p. 745
pioneer species p. 740	wetland p. 755

Fill in the blanks with the correct vocabulary word or words.

1. _____ refers to the normal changes in the types of species that live in communities.

2. A(n) _____ is a group of organisms found in a stable stage of succession.

3. Deciduous trees are dominant in the _____.

4. The average temperature in _____ is between 9°C and 12°C.

5. _____ are the most biologically diverse biomes in the world.

6. A(n) _____ is an area where freshwater meets the ocean.

Checking Concepts

Choose the word or phrase that best answers the question.

7. What are tundra and desert examples of?
   A) ecosystems
   C) habitats
   B) biomes
   D) communities

8. What is a hot, dry biome called?
   A) desert
   C) coral reef
   B) tundra
   D) grassland

9. Where would organisms that are adapted to live in slightly salty water be found?
   A) lake
   C) open ocean
   B) estuary
   D) intertidal zone

10. Which biome contains mostly frozen soil called permafrost?
    A) taiga
    B) temperate rain forest
    C) tundra
    D) temperate deciduous forest

11. A new island is formed from a volcanic eruption. Which species probably would be the first to grow and survive?
    A) palm trees
    C) grasses
    B) lichens
    D) ferns

12. What would the changes in communities that take place on a recently formed volcanic island best be described as?
    A) primary succession
    B) secondary succession
    C) tertiary succession
    D) magma

13. What is the stable end stage of succession?
    A) pioneer species
    B) climax community
    C) limiting factor
    D) permafrost

Use the illustration below to answer question 14.

Observed Fire Danger Class—June, 2003

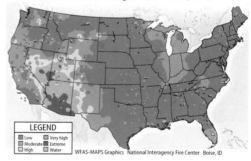

LEGEND
Low Very high
Moderate Extreme
High Water
WFAS-MAPS Graphics National Interagency Fire Center Boise, ID

14. Which area of the U.S. had the highest observed fire danger on June 20, 2003?
    A) northeast
    C) northwest
    B) southeast
    D) southwest

Science Online life.msscience.com/vocabulary_puzzlemaker

Use the ExamView® Pro Testmaker CD-ROM to:
- create multiple versions of tests
- create modified tests with one mouse click for inclusion students
- edit existing questions and add your own questions
- build tests aligned with state standards using built-in State Curriculum Tags
- change English tests to Spanish with one mouse click and vice versa

Thinking Critically

15. Explain In most cases, would a soil sample from a temperate deciduous forest be more or less nutrient-rich than a soil sample from a tropical rain forest?

16. Explain why some plant seeds need fire in order to germinate. How does this give these plants an advantage in secondary succession?

17. Determine A grassy meadow borders a beech-maple forest. Is one of these ecosystems undergoing succession? Why?

18. Infer why tundra plants are usually small.

19. Make and Use a Table Copy and complete the following table about aquatic ecosystems. Include these terms: *intertidal zone, lake, pond, coral reef, open ocean, river, estuary,* and *stream.*

Aquatic Ecosystems

Saltwater	Freshwater
intertidal zone	lake
coral reef	pond
open ocean	river
estuary	stream

20. Recognize Cause and Effect Wildfires like the one in Yellowstone National Park in 1988, cause many changes to the land. Determine the effect of a fire on an area that has reached its climax community.

Performance Activities

21. Oral Presentation Research a biome not in this chapter. Find out about its climate and location, and which organisms live there. Present this information to your class.

 Science Online life.msscience.com/chapter_review

Applying Math

Use the table below to answer question 22.

Rainfall Amounts

Biome	Average Precipitation/Year (cm)
Taiga	50
Temperate rain forest	200
Tropical rain forest	400
Desert	25
Temperate deciduous forest	150
Tundra	25

22. Biome Precipitation How many times more precipitation does the tropical rain forest biome receive than the taiga or desert?

Use the graph below to answer question 23.

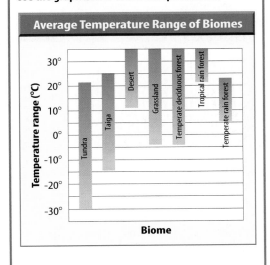

Average Temperature Range of Biomes

23. Biome Temperatures According to the graph, which biome has the greatest and which biome has the least variation in temperature throughout the year? Estimate the difference between the two.

Thinking Critically

15. Temperate deciduous forest would have more nutrient-rich soil than the rain forest. Nutrients are cycled much faster in the rain forest.

16. Some seeds have thick seed coats that require scarring by fire, or are in cones that open and release the seeds only as a result of fire. When fire destroys other plants, these seeds sprout first and growth is rapid because there is less competition for resources.

17. The grassy meadow is undergoing succession towards becoming a forest.

18. Less than 25 cm of precipitation falls; sunlight is limited, and temperatures are too cold for plant growth most of the year.

19. See student page.

20. Fire will cause the climax community to undergo secondary succession and different plants can grow. Ecosystems not in climax communities are more diverse.

Performance Activities

21. Answers will vary.

Applying Math

National Math Standards

5

22. 8 times more than taiga, 16 times more than desert

23. tundra has the greatest variation, tropical rain forest has the least variation; about 34 cm/yr difference

---

✔ Assessment Resources

📁 **Reproducible Masters**

Chapter *Fast File* Resources
  Chapter Review, pp. 35–36
  Chapter Tests, pp. 37–40
  Assessment Transparency Activity, p. 47

Glencoe Science Web site
  Chapter Review Test
  Standardized Test Practice

Glencoe Technology

🔘 Assessment Transparency
🔘 Exam*View*® Pro Testmaker
🔘 MindJogger Videoquiz
🔘 Interactive Chalkboard

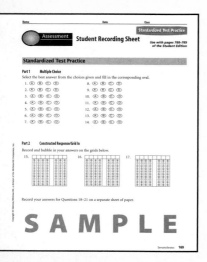

Answer Sheet A practice answer sheet can be found at life.msscience.com/answer_sheet.

SAMPLE

Part 1 Multiple Choice

1. B
2. B
3. A
4. D
5. C
6. C
7. B

Part 1 Multiple Choice

Record your answers on the answer sheet provided by your teacher or on a sheet of paper.

1. What two factors are most responsible for limiting life in a particular area?
   A. sunlight and temperature
   B. precipitation and temperature
   C. precipitation and sunlight
   D. soil conditions and precipitation

2. Which of the following forms during primary succession?
   A. trees   C. wildlife
   B. soil   D. grasses

Use the illustrations below to answer questions 3 and 4.

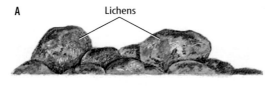

A   Lichens

B

3. Which of the following statements best describes what is represented by A?
   A. Primary succession is occurring.
   B. Secondary succession is occurring.
   C. A forest fire has probably occurred.
   D. The climax stage has been reached.

4. Which of the following statements best describes what is represented by B?
   A. The climax stage has been reached.
   B. Pioneer species are forming soil.
   C. Bare rock covers most of the area.
   D. Secondary succession is occurring.

Use the map below to answer questions 5 and 6.

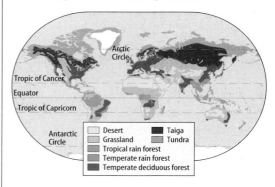

Arctic Circle
Tropic of Cancer
Equator
Tropic of Capricorn
Antarctic Circle

Desert
Grassland
Tropical rain forest
Temperate rain forest
Temperate deciduous forest
Taiga
Tundra

5. What biome is located in the latitudes just south of the north pole?
   A. taiga
   B. temperate deciduous rain forest
   C. tundra
   D. temperate rain forest

6. The tropical rainforest biome is found primarily near the
   A. Arctic Circle.
   B. Tropic of Cancer.
   C. equator.
   D. Tropic of Capricorn.

7. Which of the following is composed of a mix of salt water and freshwater?
   A. an intertidal zone
   B. an estuary
   C. a seashore
   D. a coral reef

Test-Taking Tip

Come Prepared Bring at least two sharpened No. 2 pencils and a good eraser to the test. Check to make sure that your eraser completely removes all pencil marks.

Part 2 Short Response/Grid In

8. cranberries, fish, shellfish

9. Primary succession takes longer because soil must be formed first before plants and other organisms can survive in the area.

10. taiga; The lynx's coat protects it from the cold temperatures, and its broad feet help it move through the snow.

11. desert; the scorpion does not require a lot of water and it is active at night, when temperatures are cooler.

12. most rainfall—tropical rain forest; least rainfall—desert and tundra

13. Grasslands do not receive enough precipitation for most forests to develop.

14. swamp, bog, marsh; fish, beavers, alligators, migratory birds

15. plankton; They are the foundation of the ocean food chain.

Part 2 | Short Response/Grid In

Record your answers on the answer sheet provided by your teacher or on a sheet of paper.

8. Name two products that come from wetlands.

9. Which takes longer, primary succession or secondary succession? Why?

Use the photos below to answer questions 10 and 11.

10. In what biome would you most likely find A? How is this animal adapted to survive in its biome?

11. In what biome would you most likely find B? How is this animal adapted to survive in its biome?

12. Which biome receives the most rainfall per year? Which receives the least rainfall?

13. Why are forests unlikely to develop in grasslands?

14. What are two kinds of wetlands? What kinds of animals are found in wetlands?

15. What organisms inhabit the upper zone of the open ocean and why are they so important?

Part 3 | Open Ended

Record your answers on a sheet of paper.

16. Explain how lichens contribute to the process of soil formation.

17. Compare and contrast a freshwater lake ecosystem with a freshwater pond ecosystem.

18. What special adaptations must all of the organisms that live in the intertidal zone have?

19. What are the differences between the temperate rain forest biome and the tropical rain forest biome?

Use the illustration below to answer questions 20 and 21.

Zone A
Zone B
Zone C
Zone D

20. Identify and describe zone C in the diagram. What kinds of wildlife are found there?

21. Identify zone D and zone A. Describe the environment in each zone. Why might an organism that lives in zone A not be able to survive in zone D?

22. Discuss the effects of human impact on freshwater environments like lakes and ponds.

21. Zone A is the emergent zone. Organisms that live there require a lot of sunlight and space. Zone D, the forest floor, would be too dark for organisms that require a lot of sunlight to survive.

22. Runoff from fertilized lawns and farmland, along with sewage and other pollutants, eventually reaches lakes and ponds where algae and plants grow excessively. This reduces the oxygen level in the water, which makes it difficult for other organisms to live.

Rubrics

For more help evaluating open-ended assessment questions, see the rubric on p. 10T.

Part 3 | Open Ended

16. They break down rocks. When the lichens die, they decay, adding organic matter to the rock. This is the beginning of new soil.

17. Both are aquatic ecosystems. Lakes are deeper and larger than ponds. Deep parts of the lake are colder than the shallow parts so different organisms live in each part of the lake. Ponds can be completely filled with plant material, with open water located at the center.

18. They must be able to withstand significant changes in temperature, moisture, and salinity, as well as the force of wave action.

19. The temperate rain forest receives less rainfall than the tropical rain forest and the temperature is not as high. There is greater biological diversity in the tropical rain forest.

20. Understory. It is dark and cool and provides a habitat for insects, reptiles, amphibians, and some mammals.

Section/Objectives	Standards		Labs/Features
Chapter Opener	**National**	**State/Local**	**Launch Lab:** What happens when topsoil is left unprotected?, p. 769 **Foldables,** p. 769
	See pp. 16T–17T for a Key to Standards.		
Section 1 Resources 🕐 2 sessions 📦 1 block 1. **Compare** renewable and nonrenewable resources. 2. **List** uses of fossil fuels. 3. **Identify** alternatives to fossil fuel use.	National Content Standards: UCP.2, UCP.3, A.1, A.2, F.2		**MiniLAB:** Observing Mineral Mining Effects, p. 772 **Integrate Social Studies,** p. 773 **Visualizing Solar Energy,** p. 777
Section 2 Pollution 🕐 2 sessions 📦 1 block 4. **Describe** types of air pollution. 5. **Identify** causes of water pollution. 6. **Explain** methods that can be used to prevent erosion.	National Content Standards: UCP.2, UCP.3, A.1, A.2, F.2		**MiniLAB:** Measuring Acid Rain, p. 779 **Science Online,** p. 780 **Integrate Health,** p. 782 **Lab:** The Greenhouse Effect, p. 787
Section 3 The Three Rs of Conservation 🕐 3 sessions 📦 1.5 blocks 7. **Recognize** ways you can reduce your use of natural resources. 8. **Explain** how you can reuse resources to promote conservation. 9. **Describe** how many materials can be recycled.	National Content Standards: UCP.2, UCP.3, A.1, A.2, F.2		**Science Online,** p. 790 **Applying Science:** What items are you recycling at home?, p. 790 **Lab:** Solar Cooking, p. 792 **Science and Language Arts:** Beauty Plagiarized, p. 794

Lab Materials	Reproducible Resources	Section Assessment	Technology
Launch Lab: moist sand, potting soil, plastic basin or aluminum-foil baking pan, moss, water, spray bottle, beaker	**Chapter *FAST FILE* Resources** Foldables Worksheet, p. 17 Directed Reading Overview, p. 19 Note-taking Worksheets, pp. 33–35	**GLENCOE'S ASSESSMENT ADVANTAGE**	**Teacher Works** includes: • Interactive Teacher Edition • Lesson Planner with calendar • Access to all program blacklines • Correlations to standards • Web links
MiniLAB: chocolate-chip cookie, paper plate, toothpick *Need materials?* Contact Science Kit at 1-800-828-7777 or www.sciencekit.com on the Internet.	**Chapter *FAST FILE* Resources** Transparency Activity, p. 44 MiniLAB, p. 3 Enrichment, p. 30 Reinforcement, p. 27 Directed Reading, p. 20 **Cultural Diversity,** p. 41 **Mathematics Skill Activities,** p. 9	Portfolio Activity, p. 777 Performance MiniLAB, p. 772 Applying Math, p. 776 Content Section Review, p. 776	🔈 Section Focus Transparency 💿 Virtual Labs CD-ROM 🎧 Guided Reading Audio Program 💿 Interactive Chalkboard CD-ROM
MiniLAB: cup, rainwater, pH indicator paper, tap water, distilled water **Lab:** 1-L clear plastic soft-drink bottle with top cut off and label removed (2), 2 thermometers, potting soil, masking tape, plastic wrap, rubber band, lamp with 100-W lightbulb, watch or clock with second hand	**Chapter *FAST FILE* Resources** Transparency Activity, p. 45 MiniLAB, p. 4 Enrichment, p. 31 Reinforcement, p. 28 Directed Reading, p. 21 Lab Worksheet, pp. 5–6 Lab Activity, pp. 9–12 Transparency Activity, pp. 47–48	Portfolio Assessment, p. 786 Performance MiniLAB, p. 779 Applying Math, p. 782 Content Section Review, p. 782	🔈 Section Focus Transparency 🔈 Teaching Transparency 💿 Virtual Labs CD-ROM 🎧 Guided Reading Audio Program 💿 Interactive Chalkboard CD-ROM 📼 Video Lab
Lab: poster board, cardboard boxes, aluminum foil, string, wire coat hangers, clear plastic sheets, black cookware, thermometer, stopwatch, glue, tape, scissors	**Chapter *FAST FILE* Resources** Transparency Activity, p. 46 Enrichment, p. 32 Reinforcement, p. 29 Directed Reading, pp. 21, 22 Lab Worksheet, pp. 7–8 Lab Activity, pp. 13–16 **Lab Management and Safety,** p. 37	Portfolio Challenge, p. 790 Performance Applying Science, p. 790 Applying Skills, p. 791 Content Section Review, p. 791	🔈 Section Focus Transparency 💿 Virtual Labs CD-ROM 🎧 Guided Reading Audio Program 💿 Interactive Chalkboard CD-ROM

End of Chapter Assessment

GLENCOE'S ASSESSMENT ADVANTAGE

Blackline Masters	Technology	Professional Series
Chapter *FAST FILE* Resources Chapter Review, pp. 37–38 Chapter Tests, pp. 39–42 **Standardized Test Practice,** pp. 111–114	📼 MindJogger Videoquiz 💿 Virtual Labs CD-ROM 💿 Exam*View*® Pro Testmaker 💿 TeacherWorks CD-ROM 💿 Interactive Chalkboard CD-ROM	**Performance Assessment in the Science Classroom (PASC)**

Transparencies

Section Focus

1 Section Focus Transparency — The Material World

Many of the items you use in your daily life are made from materials that come from nature. On the other hand, some items you use are made from manufactured materials.

1. What kinds of materials can you identify in the scene above?
2. Where do you think the materials you identified come from?
3. Can the materials you named be replaced or will they eventually disappear?

L2

2 Section Focus Transparency — Ocean-Sized Ice Cubes

One of the concerns with rising worldwide temperatures is the melting of ice at Earth's poles. Ice floating in water, as found in the Arctic Ocean, won't raise sea levels if it melts. But ice-sheets on land, as found in Greenland and Antarctica, do contain enough water to raise sea levels if they melt.

1. What is happening in the picture above?
2. What might cause ice sheets to melt?
3. Do you think human activity could affect the amount of ice that melts in Antarctica? Why or why not?

L2

3 Section Focus Transparency — The Art of Recycling

Many artists work with paints or other specific materials, but sometimes artists work with whatever happens to be lying around. This goat was made from objects that many people throw away without a second thought.

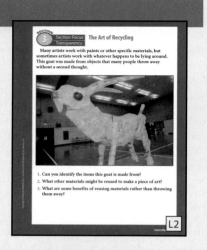

1. Can you identify the items this goat is made from?
2. What other materials might be reused to make a piece of art?
3. What are some benefits of reusing materials rather than throwing them away?

L2

This is a representation of key blackline masters available in the Teacher Classroom Resources. See Resource Manager boxes within the chapter for additional information.

Key to Teaching Strategies

The following designations will help you decide which activities are appropriate for your students.

L1 Level 1 activities should be appropriate for students with learning difficulties.

L2 Level 2 activities should be within the ability range of all students.

L3 Level 3 activities are designed for above-average students.

ELL ELL activities should be within the ability range of English Language Learners.

COOP LEARN Cooperative Learning activities are designed for small group work.

LS Multiple Learning Styles logos, as described on page 12T, are used throughout to indicate strategies that address different learning styles.

P These strategies represent student products that can be placed into a best-work portfolio.

PBL Problem-Based Learning activities apply real-world situations to learning.

Assessment

Assessment Transparency — Conserving Resources

Directions: Carefully review the table and answer the following questions.

Alternatives to Fossil Fuels

Type	How it works	Environmental impacts
Hydroelectric power	Energy of moving water is converted into electrical energy.	Habitats destroyed by dams
Wind power	Energy of moving air is converted into electrical energy.	No significant problem
Nuclear power	Energy of nuclear fission heats water, which is used to generate electricity.	Produces hazardous waste and has risk of accidents
Solar power	Energy from the Sun is absorbed and converted into heat and electrical energy.	No significant problem

1. According to the table, a windmill would be an example of ___.
   A hydroelectric power   C nuclear power
   B wind power   D solar power
2. Which of these could be added to the table?
   F Coal power   H Gasoline power
   G Oil power   I Geothermal power
3. According to the table, which fuel is most likely to affect human health?
   A Hydroelectric power   C Nuclear power
   B Wind power   D Solar power

L2

Teaching

2 Teaching Transparency — Groundwater

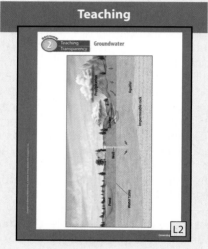

L2

Hands-on Activities

Student Text Lab Worksheet

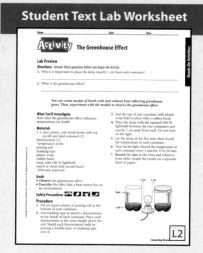

Activity — The Greenhouse Effect

Lab Preview
Directions: Answer these questions before you begin the Activity.
1. Why is it important to place the lamp exactly 1 cm from each container?

2. What is the greenhouse effect?

You can create models of Earth with and without heat-reflecting greenhouse gases. Then, experiment with the models to observe the greenhouse effect.

What You'll Investigate
How does the greenhouse effect influence temperatures on Earth?

Materials
1-L clear, plastic, soft drink bottle with top cut off and label removed (2)
thermometer (2)
*temperature probe
potting soil
masking tape
plastic wrap
rubber band
lamp with 100-W lightbulb
watch or clock with second hand
*Alternate materials

Goals
• Observe the greenhouse effect.
• Describe the effect that a heat source has on an environment.

Safety Precautions

Procedure
1. Put an equal volume of potting soil in the bottom of each container.
2. Use masking tape to attach a thermometer to the inside of each container. Place each thermometer at the same height above the soil. Shield each thermometer bulb by putting a double layer of masking tape over it.

3. Seal the top of one container with plastic wrap held in place with a rubber band.
4. Place the lamp with the exposed 100-W lightbulb between the two containers and exactly 1 cm away from each. Do not turn on the light.
5. Let the setup sit for five min, then record the temperature in each container.
6. Turn on the light. Record the temperature in each container every 2 min for 15 to 20 min.
7. Record the data in the Data and Observations table. Graph the results on a separate sheet of paper.

L2

Laboratory Activities

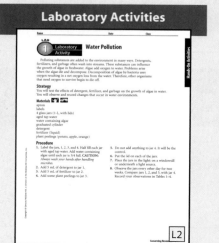

1 Laboratory Activity — Water Pollution

Polluting substances are added to the environment in many ways. Detergents, fertilizers, and garbage often wash into streams. These substances can influence the growth of algae in freshwater. Algae add oxygen to water. Problems arise when the algae die and decompose. Decomposition of algae by bacteria uses oxygen resulting in a net oxygen loss from the water. Therefore, other organisms that need oxygen to survive begin to die off.

Strategy
You will test the effects of detergent, fertilizer, and garbage on the growth of algae in water. You will observe and record changes that occur in water environments.

Materials
apron
labels
4 glass jars (1-L, with lids)
aged tap water
water containing algae
graduated cylinder
detergent
fertilizer (liquid)
plant peelings (potato, apple, orange)

Procedure
1. Label the jars, 1, 2, 3, and 4. Half fill each jar with aged tap water. Add water containing algae until each jar is 3/4 full. CAUTION: Always wash your hands after handling microbes.
2. Add 5 mL of detergent to jar 1.
3. Add 5 mL of fertilizer to jar 2.
4. Add some plant peelings to jar 3.

5. Do not add anything to jar 4. It will be the control.
6. Put the lid on each of the jars.
7. Place the jars in the light on a windowsill or underneath a light source.
8. Observe the jars every other day for two weeks. Compare jars 1, 2, and 3, with jar 4. Record your observations in Tables 1–4.

L2

Meeting Different Ability Levels

Content Outline

Note-taking Worksheet — Conserving Resources

Section 1 Resources

A. _____ resources—parts of the environment that are useful or necessary for living organisms to survive.
  1. A natural resource that is constantly recycled or replaced by nature is a _____ resource.
  2. Natural resources that are used up more quickly than they can be replaced are called _____ resources; for example, **petroleum** takes hundreds of millions of years to form.

B. _____ such as coal, oil, and natural gas are nonrenewable energy resources that form in Earth's crust over very long periods of time.

C. _____ energy sources can be used to help conserve fossil fuels.
  1. _____ power—energy from falling water used to generate electricity
  2. _____—wind turns the blades of a turbine, which powers an electric generator.
  3. Nuclear power—the fusion of _____ atoms generates **nuclear energy** that is used to produce electricity.
  4. Geothermal power plants use **geothermal energy** from the _____ in Earth's crust to generate electricity.
  5. _____ energy can be captured in photovoltaic cells, which turn sunlight into electric current, or in materials that retain heat.

Section 2 Pollution

A. A _____ is a substance that contaminates the air, land, or water.

B. _____ pollution sources include soot, smoke, ash, and gases such as carbon dioxide, carbon monoxide, nitrogen oxides, and sulfur oxides.

C. _____ is created when sunlight reacts with pollutants.

L2

Reinforcement

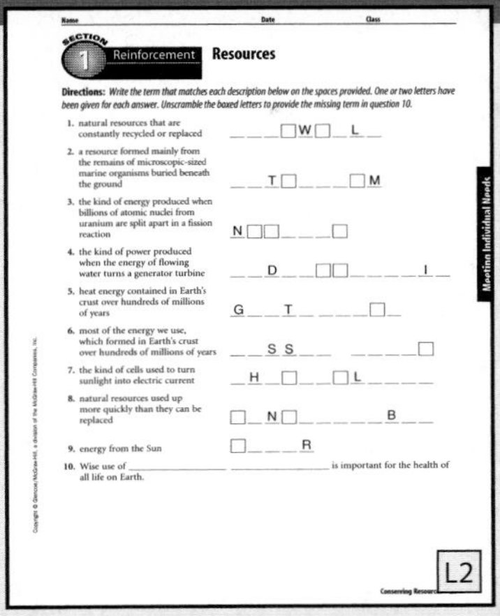

Reinforcement — Resources

Directions: Write the term that matches each description below on the spaces provided. One or two letters have been given for each answer. Unscramble the boxed letters to provide the missing term in question 10.

1. natural resources that are constantly recycled or replaced ___ W ___ L ___
2. a resource formed mainly from the remains of microscopic-sized marine organisms buried beneath the ground ___ T ___ M
3. the kind of energy produced when billions of atomic nuclei from uranium are split apart in a fission reaction N ___ ___
4. the kind of power produced when the energy of flowing water turns a generator turbine D ___ ___ I
5. heat energy contained in Earth's crust over hundreds of millions of years G ___ T ___
6. most of the energy we use, which formed in Earth's crust over hundreds of millions of years S S ___
7. the kind of cells used to turn sunlight into electric current H ___ ___ L
8. natural resources used up more quickly than they can be replaced ___ N ___ ___ B
9. energy from the Sun R ___
10. Wise use of _____ is important for the health of all life on Earth.

L2

Enrichment

Enrichment — Really Hot Stuff

Thousands of people living on the eastern side of the Sierra Nevada mountain range in California are directly affected by a major volcanic eruption that occurred over 760,000 years ago. At that time the Long Valley Caldera was formed. A caldera is any broad crater-like basin that results from the collapse of a volcano.

Today the Long Valley Caldera is about 15 km wide and 30 km long. It has been constantly monitored since an earthquake in 1980 indicated increased activity beneath the areas near Mammoth Lakes and much of Inyo and Mono counties.

The current series of eruptions has been going on for the past 5,000 years. They are caused by underground explosions that blast molten rock (magma), rock fragments, and ash rising from 150 m to as high as 10 km or more. It is the ash deposits that can cause the most damage to the landscape for hundreds of kilometers.

Hot Springs and Fumaroles
One of the byproducts of this ongoing sub-surface "cooking" is a remarkable series of hot springs, fumaroles (steam vents), and resulting mineral deposits called a hydrothermal system. The system's springs are found mostly in the eastern portion of the caldera.

The altitude there is lower. The fumaroles are found in the higher western half. This underground hot water system is receiving close attention from the U.S. Geological Department as well as scientists from all the counties affected by the frequent minor eruptions. The effects of the movements on plant life, trees, above-ground waterways, as well as the possibilities of future eruptions are being monitored.

A Handy Energy Source
One of the benefits of these springs is that the residents of the Mammoth Mountain area can use geothermal heat to make energy. This energy is converted into electricity by turbines in a local hydrothermal power plant. However, as volcanic activity continues the future of the Mammoth hydrothermal power station is uncertain.

Fortunately there have been no volcanic eruptions in the area for about 200 years, but the earthquakes are still numerous. The most obvious signs of activity beneath the surface are found in the springs located in Little Hot Creek and Hot Creek Gorge. As little as 30 years ago, it was possible to sit or swim in these waters. But today they are fenced off and tourists stand in awe as the waters boil and spout scalding water high into the air.

1. What is the name for an area created by a collapsed volcano?
2. Approximately how long ago did the eastern Sierra suffer a major catastrophic eruption?
3. What byproduct of an eruption causes the greatest threat to the landscape?
4. In what fairly recent year did the earthquake occur that brought so much attention to the Mammoth Lakes area?

L3

Directed Reading (English/Spanish)

Directed Reading for Content Mastery — Overview, Conserving Resources

Directions: Use the clues below to complete the crossword puzzle.

recycle erosion acid pollutant hydro
nuclear power natural conservation smog

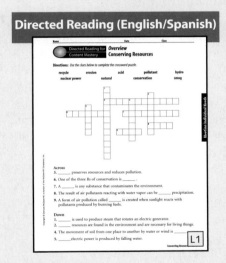

Across
3. _____ preserves resources and reduces pollution.
6. One of the three Rs of conservation is _____.
7. A _____ is any substance that contaminates the environment.
8. The result of air pollutants reacting with water vapor can be _____ precipitation.
9. A form of air pollution called _____ is created when sunlight reacts with pollutants produced by burning fuels.

Down
1. _____ is used to produce steam that rotates an electric generator.
2. _____ resources are found in the environment and are necessary for living things.
4. The movement of soil from one place to another by water or wind is _____.
5. _____ electric power is produced by falling water.

L1

Study Guide

Study Guide

Features
• Contains a study guide page for each section of the chapter
• Reviews key concepts
• Includes answer pages

L2

Reading Essentials

Reading Essentials for Glencoe Science
An Interactive Student Workbook

Features
• Condensed core content
• Actively involves students in reading
• Reinforces key vocabulary

L1

Assessment

Test Practice Workbook

Chapter 27 Conserving Resources — **Standardized Test Practice**

DIRECTIONS
Read each question. Then, on your answer sheet, mark the answer choice that you think is best.

1 Which of the following is considered a renewable resource?
  A coal
  B water
  C soda can
  D petroleum

2 Factory wastewater can be an environmental problem when it
  F is released into the air around the factory
  G is released into rivers and contaminates them
  H is recycled into new materials
  J is sent into the ozone layer

3 The evening news reports that modern technology is going to help reduce the problems of smog and the greenhouse effect. Which of these is the news report talking about?
  A finding replacements for CFCs
  B composting more garbage
  C using alternatives to fossil fuels
  D building containers for nuclear waste

Directions: This chart shows information from a pond collected over several months as its pH was changed by acid rain. Use the information in the chart to answer Numbers 4–5 below.

Month	pH level	Number of fish	Number of lily pads	Visibility	Temp (°C)
May	5.9	50	200	very cloudy	62
June	5.5	30	185	a little cloudy	64
July	4.9	20	100	clear	63
Aug.	4.2	5	30	clear	64

4 Which measurement did not seem to be affected by the pH of the pond?
  F number of fish
  G number of lily pads
  H visibility
  J temperature

5 A neighboring pond that is a similar size is somewhat cloudy and has 31 fish, 150 lily pads, and a temperature of 62°C. What is the most likely pH of this pond?
  A 5.9
  B 5.5
  C 4.9
  D 4.2

GO ON

Glencoe Life Science

L2

Chapter Review

Chapter Review — Conserving Resources

Part A. Vocabulary Review
Directions: Select the term from the following list that matches each description.

acid precipitation   renewable resources   nonrenewable resources
erosion   global warming   greenhouse effect   natural resources
recycling   smog   geothermal energy   hazardous wastes
nuclear energy   ozone depletion   pollutant

1. parts of the environment that are useful or necessary for the survival of living organisms
2. produced when billions of uranium nuclei are split apart in a nuclear fission reaction
3. reuse of a resource that requires changing or reprocessing the resource
4. resources that are constantly recycled or replaced by nature
5. movement of soil by water or wind
6. resources that are constantly recycled or replaced by nature
7. waste materials that are very harmful to human health or poisonous to living organisms
8. mist, rain, snow, sleet, or hail with a pH below 5.6
9. heat-trapping feature of the atmosphere
10. form of air pollution created when sunlight reacts with pollutants produced by burning fuels
11. potential warming of Earth
12. natural resources that are used up more quickly than they can be replaced
13. heat energy contained in Earth's crust
14. movement of soil by wind and water
15. thinning of Earth's protective ozone layer
16. substance that contaminates the environment

L2

Chapter Tests

Chapter Test — Conserving Resources

I. Testing Concepts
Directions: Match the terms in Column I with the definitions in Column II by writing the correct letter in the space provided.

Column I
1. natural materials in the environment used by organisms for survival
2. natural resources that are continually recycled or replaced by nature
3. natural resources that are limited and that are replaced by nature only over hundreds of millions of years
4. trapping of heat by atmospheric gases
5. movement of soil by water or wind
6. kind of pollution formed when sunlight reacts with pollutants from burning fuels
7. devices used by satellites and calculators to turn sunlight into electricity
8. pollutant gases that react chemically with ozone, causing ozone depletion
9. kind of pollution formed when air pollutants from the burning of fossil fuels react with water in the atmosphere
10. waste materials that are harmful to human health or poisonous to living organisms

Column II
a. CFCs
b. erosion
c. greenhouse effect
d. hazardous waste
e. natural resources
f. nonrenewable resources
g. acid precipitation
h. renewable resources
i. photovoltaic cells
j. smog

Directions: For each of the following, write the letter of the term or phrase that best completes the sentence.

11. All of the following are fossil fuels EXCEPT _____.
  a. natural gas   b. coal   c. petroleum   d. wood
12. Natural resources that are used up more quickly than they can be replaced are _____.
  a. pollutants   c. renewable resources
  b. nonrenewable resources   d. toxic wastes
13. Ways of reducing smog include all the following EXCEPT _____.
  a. taking trains   c. driving cars that burn gasoline
  b. using buses   d. driving electric cars

L2

Science Content Background

Resources

Renewable Resources

Renewable resources include trees in forests; fish in lakes, rivers, and oceans; fertile agricultural soil; and freshwater in lakes and rivers. Nature replaces these resources, and they can be used forever as long as they are not overexploited in the short term. Some resources, like agricultural soil, can be considered renewable or nonrenewable. Soil is constantly replaced but at a very slow rate.

Nonrenewable Resources

Nonrenewable resources, which include minerals and fossil fuels, are present in limited supplies and are depleted by use. They are not replenished by natural processes within a reasonable amount of time. Fossil fuels, for example, take millions of years to form. Recycling nonrenewable resources can help sustain the supply of certain substances. In the future, most products will contain some recycled material.

Nuclear Power

In 1942, Enrico Fermi established the first successful controlled nuclear chain reaction. Nuclear fission reactions release a great deal of energy, several million times the energy of a typical chemical reaction. Nuclear reactors use uranium-235 for the production of power. Once started, the reactions are self-sustaining: the neutrons released by each splitting in turn split other atoms, causing a chain reaction. There is no danger of nuclear chain reactions starting in nature since uranium-235 makes up only 0.71% of the naturally occurring uranium. Most of the remainder is uranium-238, which is not fissible.

Pollution

Acid Precipitation

Acid precipitation is a worldwide problem. Reports of highly acidic precipitation have come from Canada, England, Germany, France, Scandinavia, and the United States. Precipitation is normally slightly acidic, with a pH between 5.6 and 5.7 that is caused by atmospheric carbonic acid. But acid precipitation sometimes has a concentration of acid 1,000 times higher than normal. The average precipitation in much of the northeastern part of the United States and adjoining parts of Ontario has a pH between 4.0 and 4.5.

Greenhouse Effect

Carbon dioxide is one of the most abundant of the greenhouse gases. It occurs as a natural consequence of respiration. However, carbon dioxide is emitted into the atmosphere as a waste product of energy production. Coal, oil, natural gas, and biomass are burned to provide heat and electricity for industrial processes, home heating, and cooking. These sources are increasing the amount of carbon dioxide in the atmosphere. Some evidence suggests that increased levels of carbon dioxide in the atmosphere may cause Earth's average temperature to increase.

Ozone Depletion

Ozone, a molecule made up of three oxygen atoms, traps excess ultraviolet radiation and prevents it from reaching Earth. In 1985, it was

---

Teacher to Teacher
Steve Federman
Loveland Middle School
Loveland, Ohio

"To emphasize the effect of coal mining on our land, I give each student a soft cookie with raisins or chocolate chips and a toothpick. Their objective is to use a toothpick carefully to mine all the chocolate chips (raisins) out of the cookie while leaving the cookie intact."

Steve Federman

discovered that a significant thinning of the ozone layer over the Antarctic occurred during the southern hemisphere's spring. Some regions of the ozone layer showed 95 percent depletion. Ozone depletion is also occurring farther north. Measurements in arctic regions suggest a thinning of the ozone layer there. These findings have caused countries to stop producing ozone-destroying chemicals.

Soil Loss

Erosion is a natural process that has occurred since Earth was formed. Humans have little control over the erosion caused by glaciers, rivers, and oceans. A number of human activities, mainly farming and logging, have increased erosion. Scientists estimate that between 2 and 3 billion metric tons of soil are lost from farmlands in the United States each year.

Soil Pollution—Solid Wastes

About 90 percent of our solid wastes are disposed of on land, mostly in landfills. Several methods of producing energy from solid waste are used on a small scale and further research is being done in this area. One example is a combustion chamber lined with water lines in which selected wastes are burned and the heat is used to produce steam to power a generator.

Telegraph Colour Library/FPG International

section 3 — The Three Rs of Conservation

Recycle

In 1999, the overall recycling rate in the U.S. was 28 percent, with the composting of yard waste accounting for 2/5 of this. The overall recycling rate of plastic soft-drink containers was only 34.9 percent, 26.3 percent for glass containers, and 57.2 percent for steel cans. Paper and paper products are the most voluminous waste products, and they make up about 42 percent of the solid waste produced in the United States.

chapter content resources

Internet Resources
For additional content background, visit life.msscience.com to:
- access your book online
- find references to related articles in popular science magazines
- access Web links with related content background
- access current events with science journal topics

Print Resources
Understanding Garbage and Our Environment, by Andrea Nolan, McGraw-Hill Trade, 1998

Air Pollution (True Books), by Rhonda Lucas Donald, Children's Press, 2001

Global Warming: The Threat of the Earth's Changing Climate, by Laurence Pringle, SeaStar Books, 2003

Chapter Vocabulary

natural resource, p. 770
renewable resource, p. 770
nonrenewable resource, p. 771
petroleum, p. 771
fossil fuel, p. 772
hydroelectric power, p. 773
nuclear energy, p. 774
geothermal energy, p. 775
pollutant, p. 778
acid precipitation, p. 779
greenhouse effect, p. 780
ozone depletion, p. 781
erosion, p. 785
hazardous waste, p. 786
recycling, p. 789

Science Journal Woods, food crops, and soil are examples. Wood can provide shelter and home furnishings, food crops are needed for our own consumption and by other animals, and soil is needed by farmers to produce crops and it filters water.

INTERACTIVE CHALKBOARD with Image Bank

PowerPoint® Presentations

This CD-ROM is an editable Microsoft® PowerPoint® presentation that includes:

- a pre-made presentation for every chapter
- interactive graphics
- animations
- audio clips
- image bank
- all new section and chapter questions
- Standardized Test Practice
- transparencies
- pre-lab questions for all labs
- Foldables directions
- links to life.msscience.com

Conserving Resources

chapter preview

sections

1 Resources

2 Pollution
   Lab The Greenhouse Effect

3 The Three Rs of Conservation
   Lab Solar Cooking

   Virtual Lab When is water safe to drink?

Resources Fuel Our Lives

Resources, such as clean water and air, are commonly taken for granted. We depend on water and air to survive. Fossil fuels are another type of resource, and we depend on them for energy. However, fossil fuels can pollute our air and water.

Science Journal List some other resources that we depend on and describe how we use them.

Theme Connection

Energy Even though the total amount of energy on Earth remains constant, the sources of usable energy are limited. Energy is often transformed from one form to another, such as fossil fuel energy into electricity and then into light energy.

About the Photo

Pollution Three major sources of pollution are municipal, industrial, and agricultural wastes. It is estimated that 1.5 billion people worldwide lack safe drinking water and at least 5 million people die from waterborne diseases each year.

Start-Up Activities

What happens when topsoil is left unprotected?

Plants grow in the top, nutrient-rich layer, called topsoil. Plants help keep topsoil in place by protecting it from wind and rain. Try the following experiment to find out what happens when topsoil is left unprotected.

1. Use a mixture of moist sand and potting soil to create a miniature landscape in a plastic basin or aluminum-foil baking pan. Form hills and valleys in your landscape.

2. Use clumps of moss to cover areas of your landscape. Leave some sloping portions without plant cover.

3. Simulate a rainstorm over your landscape by spraying water on it from a spray bottle or by pouring a slow stream of water on it from a beaker.

4. **Think Critically** In your Science Journal, record your observations and describe what happened to the land that was not protected by plant cover.

Science Online Preview this chapter's content and activities at
life.msscience.com

Study Organizer

Resources Make the following Foldable to help you organize information and diagram ideas about renewable and nonrenewable resources.

STEP 1 Fold a sheet of paper in half lengthwise. Make the back edge about 5 cm longer than the front edge.

STEP 2 Turn the paper so the fold is on the bottom. Then **fold** in half.

STEP 3 Unfold and cut only the top layer along the fold to make two tabs. Label the Foldable as shown.

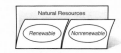

Make a Concept Map Before you read the chapter, list examples of each type of natural resource you already know on the back of the appropriate tabs. As you read the chapter, add to your lists.

Purpose Use the Launch Lab to show students how plant cover protects topsoil. L2 ELL IS **Kinesthetic**

Preparation Mix one part sand and two parts topsoil.

Materials sand and topsoil mixture, containers, clumps of moss or grass, spray bottles, beaker

Teaching Strategies
• Have students vary the strength of the spray to simulate both light and heavy rainfall and compare the results.
• Point out that water flowing downhill is called "runoff." Have students note the formation of small streams and observe what happens to the land under and around these streams. Students should infer that this is how streams and rivers are formed.

Think Critically
Water washes the uncovered soil down slopes, forming gullies.

✓ Assessment

Performance Have students reuse the materials to demonstrate the effects of terracing. Remove the plants and form two hills, one with a steady incline and one with a series of ridges (terraces) cut into the incline. Observe what happens as rain falls. Soil does not wash away on the incline with ridges. Use **Performance Assessment in the Science Classroom,** p. 89.

Study Organizer Dinah Zike **Study Fold**

Student preparation materials for this Foldable are available in the Chapter *Fast File* Resources.

1 Motivate

Bellringer

Section Focus Transparencies
also are available on the
Interactive Chalkboard CD-ROM.

L2 **ELL**

Section Focus
Transparency

The Material World

Many of the items you use in your daily life are made from materials that come from nature. On the other hand, some items you use are made from manufactured materials.

1. What kinds of materials can you identify in the scene above?
2. Where do you think the materials you identified come from?
3. Can the materials you named be replaced or will they eventually disappear?

Conserving Resources

Tie to Prior Knowledge

Oil Hold up a bottle of corn oil and a quart of motor oil. Ask students to explain how they are similar and different? Both are oil and come from living things. Corn is a renewable resource that grew in one summer. The motor oil is a nonrenewable resource that took millions of years to form from the remains of organisms.

---

section 1

Resources

as you read

What You'll Learn

- **Compare** renewable and nonrenewable resources.
- **List** uses of fossil fuels.
- **Identify** alternatives to fossil fuel use.

Why It's Important

Wise use of natural resources is important for the health of all life on Earth.

◉ Review Vocabulary

geyser: a spring that emits intermittent jets of heated water and steam

New Vocabulary

- natural resource
- renewable resource
- nonrenewable resource
- petroleum
- fossil fuel
- hydroelectric power
- nuclear energy
- geothermal energy

Figure 1 Cotton and wood are renewable resources. Cotton cloth is used for rugs, curtains, and clothing. A new crop of cotton can be grown every year. Wood is used for furniture, building materials, and paper. It will take 20 years for these young trees to grow large enough to harvest.

Natural Resources

An earthworm burrowing in moist soil eats decaying plant material. A robin catches the worm and flies to a tree. The leaves of the tree use sunlight during photosynthesis. Leaves fall to the ground, decay, and perhaps become an earthworm's meal. What do these living things have in common? They rely on Earth's **natural resources**—the parts of the environment that are useful or necessary for the survival of living organisms.

What kinds of natural resources do you use? Like other organisms, you need food, air, and water. You also use resources that are needed to make everything from clothes to cars. Natural resources supply energy for automobiles and power plants. Although some natural resources are plentiful, others are not.

Renewable Resources The Sun, an inexhaustible resource, provides a constant supply of heat and light. Rain fills lakes and streams with water. When plants carry out photosynthesis, they add oxygen to the air. Sunlight, water, air, and the crops shown in **Figure 1** are examples of renewable resources. A **renewable resource** is any natural resource that is recycled or replaced constantly by nature.

Cotton plants

Tree farm

Supply and Demand Even though renewable resources are recycled or replaced, they are sometimes in short supply. Rain and melted snow replace the water in streams, lakes, and reservoirs. Sometimes, there may not be enough rain or snowmelt to meet all the needs of people, plants, and animals. In some parts of the world, especially desert regions, water and other resources usually are scarce. Other resources can be used instead, as shown in **Figure 2.**

Nonrenewable Resources Natural resources that are used up more quickly than they can be replaced by natural processes are **nonrenewable resources.** Earth's supply of nonrenewable resources is limited. You use nonrenewable resources when you take home groceries in a plastic bag, paint a wall, or travel by car. Plastics, paints, and gasoline are made from an important nonrenewable resource called petroleum, or oil. **Petroleum** is formed mostly from the remains of microscopic marine organisms buried in Earth's crust. It is nonrenewable because it takes hundreds of millions of years for it to form.

✔ Reading Check *What are nonrenewable resources?*

Minerals and metals found in Earth's crust are nonrenewable resources. Petroleum is a mineral. So are diamonds and the graphite in pencil lead. The aluminum used to make soft-drink cans is a metal. Iron, copper, tin, gold, silver, tungsten, and uranium also are metals. Many manufactured items, like the car shown in **Figure 3,** are made from nonrenewable resources.

Figure 2 In parts of Africa, firewood has become scarce. People in this village now use solar energy instead of wood for cooking.

Figure 3 Iron, a nonrenewable resource, is the main ingredient in steel. Steel is used to make cars, trucks, appliances, buildings, bridges, and even tires.
Infer *what other nonrenewable resources are used to build a car.*

SECTION 1 Resources **771**

SECTION 1 Resources **771**

Purpose to "mine" a model mineral deposit and attempt to restore the site to its original condition L1 ⟦IS⟧ **Kinesthetic**

Materials chocolate-chip, oat-meal-raisin cookie, or nut filled brownie; paper plate; toothpick

Teaching Strategy Suggest students use drops of water to soften the surface if they have trouble removing the "minerals."

Analysis

1. Students will experience difficulty in the restoration process.
2. The minerals closer to the surface are easier to remove than those found deeper within Earth's crust.
3. An ecosystem could be permanently damaged by mining.

Assessment

Oral Which do you think is more expensive: mining at the surface or deep within Earth's crust? Explain. In general, surface mining is less expensive. It doesn't require as much machinery or time.

Use **Performance Assessment in the Science Classroom,** p. 89.

Try at Home

Caption Answer

Figure 4 Coal, oil, and natural gas are fossil fuels that provided 84 percent of the energy used in the U.S. in 1999.

Observing Mineral Mining Effects

Procedure 🞖 🖾 🖾

1. Place a **chocolate-chip cookie** on a **paper plate**. Pretend the chips are mineral deposits and the rest of the cookie is Earth's crust.
2. Use a **toothpick** to locate and dig up the mineral deposits. Try to disturb the land as little as possible.
3. When mining is completed, try to restore the land to its original condition.

Analysis

1. How well were you able to restore the land?
2. Compare the difficulty of digging for mineral deposits found close to the surface with digging for those found deep in Earth's crust.
3. Describe environmental changes that might result from a mining operation.

Try at Home

Figure 4 Coal is a fossil fuel. It often is obtained by strip mining, which removes all the soil above the coal deposit. The soil is replaced, but it takes many years for the ecosystem to recover.
Identify *the resource that provided 84 percent of the energy used in the United States in 1999.*

Fossil Fuels

Coal, oil, and natural gas are nonrenewable resources that supply energy. Most of the energy you use comes from these fossil fuels, as the graph in **Figure 4** shows. **Fossil fuels** are fuels formed in Earth's crust over hundreds of millions of years. Cars, buses, trains, and airplanes are powered by gasoline, diesel fuel, and jet fuel, which are made from oil. Coal is used in many power plants to produce electricity. Natural gas is used in manufacturing, for heating and cooking, and sometimes as a vehicle fuel.

Fossil Fuel Conservation Billions of people all over the world use fossil fuels every day. Because fossil fuels are nonrenewable, Earth's supply of them is limited. In the future, they may become more expensive and difficult to obtain. Also, the use of fossil fuels can lead to environmental problems. For example, mining coal can require stripping away thick layers of soil and rock, as shown in **Figure 4,** which destroys ecosystems. Another problem is that fossil fuels must be burned to release the energy stored in them. The burning of fossil fuels produces waste gases that cause air pollution, including smog and acid rain. For these reasons, many people suggest reducing the use of fossil fuels and finding other sources of energy.

You can use simple conservation measures to help reduce fossil fuel use. Switch off the light when you leave a room and turn off the television when you're not watching it. These actions reduce your use of electricity, which often is produced in power plants that burn fossil fuels. Hundreds of millions of automobiles are in use in the United States. Riding in a car pool or taking public transportation uses fewer liters of gasoline than driving alone in a car. Walking or riding a bicycle uses even less fossil fuel. Reducing fossil fuel use has an added benefit—the less you use, the more money you save.

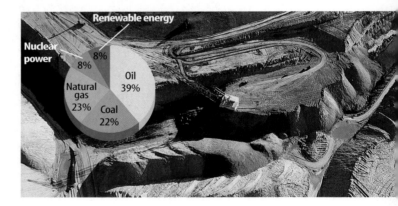

Renewable energy
Nuclear power 8%
8%
Natural gas 23%
Oil 39%
Coal 22%

Curriculum Connection

Social Studies Have students investigate ways petroleum was used in ancient cultures. Egyptians used petroleum to help preserve mummies. The Chinese used petroleum to heat and light their homes and to cook. Tar pits supplied crude oil that was used for fuel, cooking, and lighting in Latin America. At the same time, petroleum was used in Europe for lubricating wagon wheels and to make ointments.
L3 ⟦IS⟧ **Naturalist**

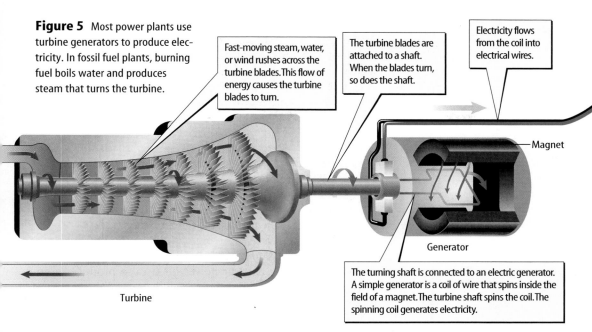

Figure 5 Most power plants use turbine generators to produce electricity. In fossil fuel plants, burning fuel boils water and produces steam that turns the turbine.

Fast-moving steam, water, or wind rushes across the turbine blades. This flow of energy causes the turbine blades to turn.

The turbine blades are attached to a shaft. When the blades turn, so does the shaft.

Electricity flows from the coil into electrical wires.

Magnet

Generator

The turning shaft is connected to an electric generator. A simple generator is a coil of wire that spins inside the field of a magnet. The turbine shaft spins the coil. The spinning coil generates electricity.

Turbine

Alternatives to Fossil Fuels

Another approach to reducing fossil fuel use is to develop other sources of energy. Much of the electricity used today comes from power plants that burn fossil fuels. As **Figure 5** shows, electricity is generated when a rotating turbine turns a coil of wires in the magnetic field of an electric generator. Fossil-fuel power plants boil water to produce steam that turns the turbine. Alternative energy sources, including water, wind, and atomic energy can be used instead of fossil fuels to turn turbines. Also, solar cells can produce electricity using only sunlight, with no turbines at all. Some of these alternative energy sources—particularly wind and solar energy—are so plentiful they could be considered inexhaustible resources.

Water Power Water is a renewable energy source that can be used to generate electricity. **Hydroelectric power** is electricity that is produced when the energy of falling water is used to turn the turbines of an electric generator. Hydroelectric power does not contribute to air pollution because no fuel is burned. However, it does present environmental concerns. Building a hydroelectric plant usually involves constructing a dam across a river. The dam raises the water level high enough to produce the energy required for electricity generation. Many acres behind the dam are flooded, destroying land habitats and changing part of the river into a lake.

Energy Oil and natural gas are used to produce over 60 percent of the energy supply in the United States. Over half of the oil used is imported from other countries. Many scientists suggest that emissions from the burning of fossil fuels are principally responsible for global warming. In your Science Journal, write what you might do to persuade utility companies to increase their use of water, wind, and solar power.

Differentiated Instruction

Visually Impaired Natural waterfalls are not numerous enough or high enough, so dams are often built to raise the water level. Height is an important determinant of the amount of hydroelectric power produced. Have students feel the effects of water dropped from a cup held one, two, and four feet above their hands. L1 LS **Kinesthetic**

Fun Fact

The movement of coils of wire within a magnetic field is how electricity is produced. This electricity is called alternating current (AC) as opposed to electricity from batteries or photovoltaic cells, which is called direct current (DC).

Figure 5 Have students trace the process of producing electricity using a turbine generator. Then have students identify at which point of the process different energy sources can be used to generate the energy. at the first stage of the process, where the turbine blades are turned L2

Teacher **FYI**

Niagara Falls Students may wonder why they don't see the water actually turning turbines at waterfalls such as Niagara Falls. The reason is that water diverted before it actually gets to the falls is what goes through the turbines. During the night at Niagara Falls, more water is diverted than in the day in order to keep the daytime visitors happy.

Discussion

Hydroelectricity Hydroelectricity is a clean way to produce electricity, but should dams that flood thousands of acres be built? Have students discuss the advantages and disadvantages of this type of electricity production. Advantages: clean, doesn't use nonrenewable resources, provides inexpensive electricity; disadvantages: loss of natural habitats or human communities

Energy Letters could be written to legislators asking them to propose or support bills that would reduce the use of fossil fuels and generate funds to support and improve the use of alternative energy.

Research Have students investigate new advances in technology that could promote the use of alternate energy sources such as wind and solar energy.

Make a Model

Turbines Use a pinwheel and a fan to show how wind can be used to turn a turbine. Give some pinwheels to students and ask them to find the spot on the school grounds that would be best for generating electricity using the wind. L1 ELL IS
Naturalist

Discussion

Windmills Ask students to compare modern windmills with old-style windmills found in Holland, Spain, or the United States. They both have blades that are turned by the force of the wind. Modern windmills are more streamlined and generate electricity. Older ones were used to grind grain or pump water from underground.

Caption Answer

Figure 6 A fast-moving neutron from the nucleus of a uranium atom collides with another atom. The collision splits the atom, releasing more neutrons and producing heat.

Wind Power Wind power is another renewable energy source that can be used for electricity production. Wind turns the blades of a turbine, which powers an electric generator. When winds blow at least 32 km/h, energy is produced. Wind power does not cause air pollution, but electricity can be produced only when the wind is blowing. So far, wind power accounts for only a small percentage of the electricity used worldwide.

Nuclear Power Another alternative to fossil fuels makes use of the huge amounts of energy in the nuclei of atoms, as shown in **Figure 6. Nuclear energy** is released when billions of atomic nuclei from uranium, a radioactive element, are split apart in a nuclear fission reaction. This energy is used to produce steam that rotates the turbine blades of an electric generator.

Nuclear power does not contribute to air pollution. However, uranium is a nonrenewable resource, and mining it can disrupt ecosystems. Nuclear power plants also produce radioactive wastes that can seriously harm living organisms. Some of these wastes remain radioactive for thousands of years, and their safe disposal is a problem that has not yet been solved. Accidents also are a danger.

Figure 6 Nuclear power plants are designed to withstand the high energy produced by nuclear reactions.
Describe how heat is produced in a nuclear reactor.

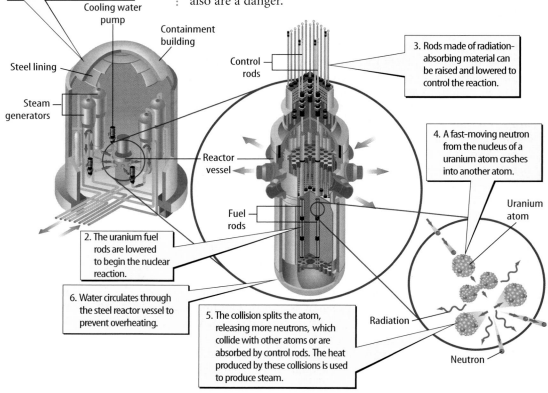

1. The containment building is made of concrete lined with steel. The reactor vessel and steam generators are housed inside.

Cooling water pump

Containment building

Steel lining

Steam generators

Control rods

Reactor vessel

Fuel rods

3. Rods made of radiation-absorbing material can be raised and lowered to control the reaction.

4. A fast-moving neutron from the nucleus of a uranium atom crashes into another atom.

Uranium atom

2. The uranium fuel rods are lowered to begin the nuclear reaction.

6. Water circulates through the steel reactor vessel to prevent overheating.

5. The collision splits the atom, releasing more neutrons, which collide with other atoms or are absorbed by control rods. The heat produced by these collisions is used to produce steam.

Radiation

Neutron

774 CHAPTER 27 Conserving Resources

Science Journal

Nuclear Power Plant Sometimes people think something is a good idea but they don't want it in their own backyards. Have students describe in their journals how they might feel and what they might do if they learned of plans to build a nuclear power plant near their neighborhood.
L2 IS **Intrapersonal**

Teacher FYI

Yucca Mountain The Yucca Mountain nuclear waste disposal site in Nevada has been under consideration since the late 1980s. To date, it is not operational and some people still are not convinced of the site's safety.

Geothermal Energy The hot, molten rock that lies deep beneath Earth's surface is also a source of energy. You see the effects of this energy when lava and hot gases escape from an erupting volcano or when hot water spews from a geyser. The heat energy contained in Earth's crust is called **geothermal energy.** Most geothermal power plants use this energy to produce steam to generate electricity.

Geothermal energy for power plants is available only where natural geysers or volcanoes are found. A geothermal power plant in California uses steam produced by geysers. The island nation of Iceland was formed by volcanoes, and geothermal energy is plentiful there. Geothermal power plants supply heat and electricity to about 90 percent of the homes in Iceland. Outdoor swimming areas also are heated with geothermal energy, as shown in **Figure 7.**

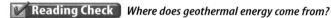

Reading Check *Where does geothermal energy come from?*

Solar Energy The most inexhaustible source of energy for all life on Earth is the Sun. Solar energy is an alternative to fossil fuels. One use of solar energy is in solar-heated buildings. During winter in the northern hemisphere, the parts of a building that face south receive the most sunlight. Large windows placed on the south side of a building help heat it by allowing warm sunshine into the building during the day. Floors and walls of most solar-heated buildings are made of materials that absorb heat during the day. During the night, the stored heat is released slowly, keeping the building warm. **Figure 8** shows how solar energy can be used.

Figure 7 In Iceland, a geothermal power plant pumps hot water out of the ground to heat buildings and generate electricity. Leftover hot water goes into this lake, making it warm enough for swimming even when the ground is covered with snow.

Figure 8 The Zion National Park Visitor Center in Utah is a solar-heated building designed to save energy. The roof holds solar panels that are used to generate electricity. High windows can be opened to circulate air and help cool the building on hot days. The overhanging roof shades the windows during summer.

SECTION 1 Resources **775**

Use Science Words
Word Meaning Have students think about the parts of the word *geothermal. Geo* refers to Earth, and *thermal* refers to heat. Have students list other words that have either of these word parts in them. Possible answers: geology, geography, geomagnetic; thermometer, thermostat, homeotherm L2

Reading Check

Geothermal energy comes from the heat energy contained in Earth's crust.

Quick Demo
Energy
Materials radiometer
Estimated Time two minutes
Procedure Place the radiometer in an area where light will shine on the vanes. Have students speculate what causes the vanes to turn. Block the light, and have them observe the vanes slowing and eventually stopping. Explain the radiant energy is reflected from the polished sides of the vanes and is absorbed by the dark sides of the vanes. This raises the temperature of the dark surfaces. The air near the dark surfaces also is heated and exerts pressure on the dark surfaces, causing the rotor to turn.

Teacher FYI
Solar Cooking Nongovernmental organizations in the United States are promoting solar cooking in regions where firewood has become scarce. In African refugee villages and in many other areas, women and men are trained to make and use simple solar cookers in exchange for training others. Cooker designs are modified to make use of materials that are inexpensive and easy to obtain locally.

Differentiated Instruction

Challenge Have interested students research tidal energy, nuclear fusion, or biomass fuels as alternative energy sources and present their findings in a poster. After students have examined all the posters, have them discuss which energy source they think has the most potential. L3

English-Language Learners Have students sort the following terms into renewable and nonrenewable resources: sisal, palladium, paprika, topaz, papaya, vinegar, diamond. Suggest they use a dictionary or the Internet to look up unfamiliar words. renewable: sisal, paprika, papaya, vinegar; nonrenewable: topaz, palladium, diamond L2

Check for Understanding

Logical-Mathematical Using the board, brainstorm with students about the methods we use to obtain energy. Have them determine whether each source of energy is renewable or not and how the energy is obtained. L2

Reteach

Using Resources Have students list reasons why renewable resources should be used wisely and nonrenewable resources should be conserved. L1

☑ Assessment

Oral Have students explain which energy alternative to fossil fuels they think has the most promise to decrease fossil fuel use. Have them justify their answers. Use **Performance Assessment in the Science Classroom,** p. 89. L2

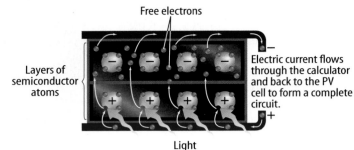

Free electrons

Layers of semiconductor atoms

Electric current flows through the calculator and back to the PV cell to form a complete circuit.

Light

Figure 9 Light energy from the Sun travels in tiny packets of energy called photons. Photons crash into the atoms of PV cells, knocking electrons loose. These electrons create an electric current.

Solar Cells Do you know how a solar-powered calculator works? How do spacecraft use sunlight to generate electricity? These devices use photovoltaic (foh toh vohl TAY ihk) cells to turn sunlight into electric current, as shown in **Figure 9.** Photovoltaic (PV) cells are small and easy to use. However, they produce electricity only in sunlight, so batteries are needed to store electricity for use at night or on cloudy days. Also, PV cells presently are too expensive to use for generating large amounts of electricity. Improvements in this technology continue to be made, and prices probably will go down in the future. As **Figure 10** shows, solar buildings and PV cells are just two of the many ways solar energy can be used to replace fossil fuels.

---

section 1 review

Summary

Natural Resources

- All living things depend on natural resources to survive.
- Some resources are renewable, while other resources, such as petroleum, are nonrenewable.

Fossil Fuels

- Most of the energy that humans use comes from fossil fuels.
- Fossil fuels must be burned to release the energy stored in them, which causes air pollution.

Alternatives to Fossil Fuels

- Alternatives to fossil fuels include water power, wind power, nuclear power, geothermal energy, and solar energy.
- The Sun provides the most inexhaustible supply of energy for all life on Earth.

Self Check

1. **Summarize** What are natural resources?
2. **Compare and contrast** renewable and nonrenewable resources. Give five examples of each.
3. **Describe** the advantages and disadvantages of using nuclear power.
4. **Describe** two ways solar energy can be used to reduce fossil fuel use.
5. **Think Critically** Explain why the water that is used to cool the reactor vessel of a nuclear power plant is kept separate from the water that is heated to produce steam for the turbine generators.

Applying Math

6. **Solve One-Step Equations** Most cars in the U.S. are driven about 10,000 miles each year. If a car can travel 30 miles on one gallon of gasoline, how many gallons will it use in a year?

Science nline life.msscience.com/self_check_quiz

---

section 1 review

1. the raw materials that organisms use for survival or to enhance life
2. renewable: can be replaced quickly by nature, include water, plants, animals, sunlight, air; nonrenewable: cannot be replaced quickly by nature, include petroleum, diamonds, metals, phosphorous, topsoil.
3. advantage—produces huge amounts of energy, does not contribute to air pollution; disadvantage—nonrenewable, produces radioactive wastes that are difficult to dispose of
4. passively, to heat homes (and water) and thus reduce use of fuels
   for this purpose; directly, to make electricity directly so that fossil fuels don't have to be burned
5. to prevent possible radioactive contamination
6. $10,000/30 = 333.33$ gallons per year

Figure 10

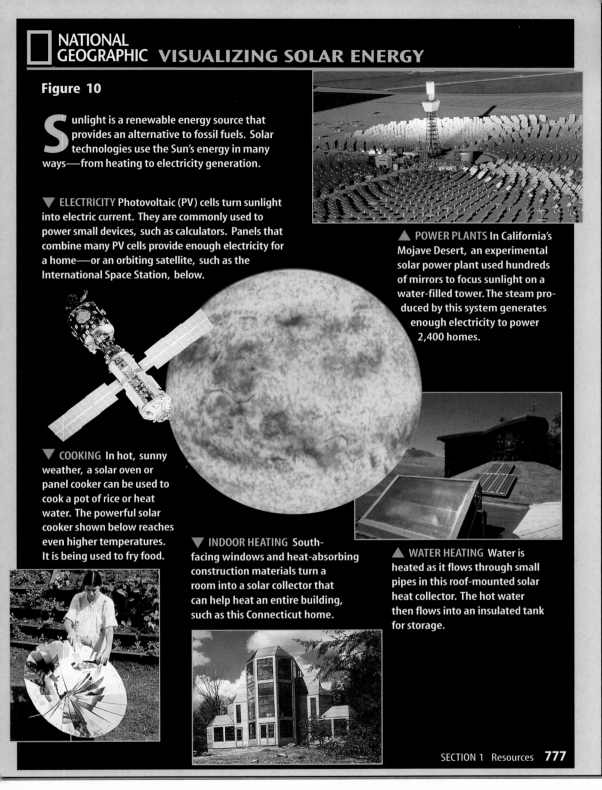

Sunlight is a renewable energy source that provides an alternative to fossil fuels. Solar technologies use the Sun's energy in many ways—from heating to electricity generation.

▼ **ELECTRICITY** Photovoltaic (PV) cells turn sunlight into electric current. They are commonly used to power small devices, such as calculators. Panels that combine many PV cells provide enough electricity for a home—or an orbiting satellite, such as the International Space Station, below.

▲ **POWER PLANTS** In California's Mojave Desert, an experimental solar power plant used hundreds of mirrors to focus sunlight on a water-filled tower. The steam produced by this system generates enough electricity to power 2,400 homes.

▼ **COOKING** In hot, sunny weather, a solar oven or panel cooker can be used to cook a pot of rice or heat water. The powerful solar cooker shown below reaches even higher temperatures. It is being used to fry food.

▼ **INDOOR HEATING** South-facing windows and heat-absorbing construction materials turn a room into a solar collector that can help heat an entire building, such as this Connecticut home.

▲ **WATER HEATING** Water is heated as it flows through small pipes in this roof-mounted solar heat collector. The hot water then flows into an insulated tank for storage.

SECTION 1 Resources **777**

NATIONAL GEOGRAPHIC

Visualizing Solar Energy

Have students examine the pictures and read the captions. Then ask the following questions.

How are photovoltic cells similar to chloroplasts? How are they different? Possible answer: Both chloroplasts and photovoltic cells capture sunlight and turn it into another form of energy. Chloroplasts convert solar energy to chemical energy, and photovoltic cells convert solar energy into electric energy.

What are some potential disadvantages of using solar energy as the only source of energy for your home? How could you overcome these disadvantages? Possible answer: Solar energy might not be consistent or reliable; a cloudy day could result in no heat or electricity. However, a method of storing solar energy for future use would overcome this problem.

Activity

Capture the Sun's Energy Have students work in pairs to make posters that diagram an innovative way to capture or use the Sun's energy. Encourage creative and different thinking. Have students explain their diagrams to the class. L3 P

Differentiated Instruction

Challenge Have students research the percentage of energy used in the United States that was supplied by solar energy in the past year. Have the students compare this percentage to the percentage in 1950. L3

as you read

What You'll Learn

- **Describe** types of air pollution.
- **Identify** causes of water pollution.
- **Explain** methods that can be used to prevent erosion.

Why It's Important

By understanding the causes of pollution, you can help solve pollution problems.

Review Vocabulary

atmosphere: the whole mass of air surrounding Earth

New Vocabulary

- pollutant
- acid precipitation
- greenhouse effect
- ozone depletion
- erosion
- hazardous waste

Keeping the Environment Healthy

More than six billion people live on Earth. This large human population puts a strain on the environment, but each person can make a difference. You can help safeguard the environment by paying attention to how your use of natural resources affects air, land, and water.

Air Pollution

On a still, sunny day in almost any large city, you might see a dark haze in the air, like that in **Figure 11.** The haze comes from pollutants that form when wood or fuels are burned. A **pollutant** is a substance that contaminates the environment. Air pollutants include soot, smoke, ash, and gases such as carbon dioxide, carbon monoxide, nitrogen oxides, and sulfur oxides. Wherever cars, trucks, airplanes, factories, homes, or power plants are found, air pollution is likely. Air pollution also can be caused by volcanic eruptions, wind-blown dust and sand, forest fires, and the evaporation of paints and other chemicals.

Smog is a form of air pollution created when sunlight reacts with pollutants produced by burning fuels. It can irritate the eyes and make breathing difficult for people with asthma or other lung diseases. Smog can be reduced if people take buses or trains instead of driving or if they use vehicles, such as electric cars, that produce fewer pollutants than gasoline-powered vehicles.

Figure 11 The term *smog* was used for the first time in the early 1900s to describe the mixture of smoke and fog that often covers large cities in the industrial world. **Infer** *how smog can be reduced in large cities.*

Section 2 Resource Manager

Chapter *FAST FILE* Resources
Transparency Activity, pp. 45, 47–48
Directed Reading for Content Mastery, p. 21
MiniLAB, p. 4
Enrichment, p. 31
Lab Activity, pp. 9–12

Reinforcement, p. 28
Lab Worksheet, pp. 5–6
Reading and Writing Skill Activities, pp. 19, 29
Performance Assessment in the Science Classroom, p. 48

Figure 12 Compare these two photographs of the same statue. The photo on the left was taken before acid rain became a problem. The photo on the right shows acid rain damage. The pH scale, shown below, indicates whether a solution is acidic or basic.

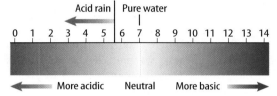

Acid Precipitation

Water vapor condenses on dust particles in the air to form droplets that combine to create clouds. Eventually, the droplets become large enough to fall to the ground as precipitation—mist, rain, snow, sleet, or hail. Air pollutants from the burning of fossil fuels can react with water in the atmosphere to form strong acids. Acidity is measured by a value called pH, as shown in **Figure 12. Acid precipitation** has a pH below 5.6.

Effects of Acid Rain Acid precipitation washes nutrients from the soil, which can lead to the death of trees and other plants. Runoff from acid rain that flows into a lake or pond can lower the pH of the water. If algae and microscopic organisms cannot survive in the acidic water, fish and other organisms that depend on them for food also die.

Preventing Acid Rain Sulfur from burning coal and nitrogen oxides from vehicle exhaust are the pollutants primarily responsible for acid rain. Using low-sulfur fuels, such as natural gas or low-sulfur coal, can help reduce acid precipitation. However, these fuels are less plentiful and more expensive than high-sulfur coal. Smokestacks that remove sulfur dioxide before it enters the atmosphere also help. Reducing automobile use and keeping car engines properly tuned can reduce acid rain caused by nitrogen oxide pollution. The use of electric cars, or hybrid-fuel cars that can run on electricity as well as gasoline, also could help.

Mini LAB

Measuring Acid Rain

Procedure
1. Collect **rainwater** by placing a clean **cup** outdoors. Do not collect rainwater that has been in contact with any object or organism.
2. Dip a piece of **pH indicator paper** into the sample.
3. Compare the color of the paper to the pH chart provided. Record the pH of the rainwater.
4. Use separate pieces of pH paper to test the pH of **tap water** and **distilled water**. Record these results.

Analysis
1. Is the rainwater acidic, basic, or neutral?
2. How does the pH of the rainwater compare with the pH of tap water? With the pH of distilled water?

Curriculum Connection

Social Studies Vinegar is a mild acid that has been used for hundreds of years to preserve foods. Pickles and sauerkraut are examples of foods that were developed to take advantage of vinegar's acidic properties, which kill many microorganisms. Have students research other foods that are prepared in pickling solution. Fish, fruits and vegetables, and pig's feet are pickled, to name a few. L2

Discussion

Automobile Usage Guide students to predict the effects of increased automobile usage on renewable resources such as trees and crops. Have them draw conclusions about the effects of other human activities on Earth's renewable resources.

Mini LAB

Purpose Students collect samples and determine the pH of rainwater. L2 COOP LEARN LS **Kinesthetic**

Materials cups, pH paper, rain gauge (optional), rainwater, tap water, distilled water

Teaching Strategies
• If your school has a rain gauge, this is a convenient place to obtain rainwater. Otherwise, cups can be placed outside to catch rain.
• Have students test the pH of rain on different days throughout the school year to detect variations.

Analysis
1. The pH of most rainwater is acidic and averages 5.6. Student results may range from a pH of 4 to 7.
2. Tap water pH varies, but in most of the U.S. it is about 6; distilled water always has a pH of 7.

Assessment

Performance Set up several liquids of unknown pH. Have students use pH paper to test each and determine whether it is an acid or base. Then have them make a chart showing the pH of each unknown liquid and comparing the liquids with substances of known pH. Use **Performance Assessment in the Science Classroom,** p. 109.

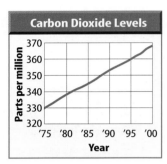

Carbon Dioxide Levels

Figure 13 The moment you step inside a greenhouse, you feel the results of the greenhouse effect. Heat trapped by the glass walls warms the air inside. In a similar way, atmospheric greenhouse gases trap heat close to Earth's surface.

Greenhouse Effect

Sunlight travels through the atmosphere to Earth's surface. Some of this sunlight normally is reflected back into space. The rest is trapped by certain atmospheric gases, as shown in **Figure 13.** This heat-trapping feature of the atmosphere is the **greenhouse effect.** Without it, temperatures on Earth probably would be too cold to support life.

Atmospheric gases that trap heat are called greenhouse gases. One of the most important greenhouse gases is carbon dioxide (CO_2). CO_2 is a normal part of the atmosphere. It is also a waste product that forms when fossil fuels are burned. Over the past century, more fossil fuels have been burned than ever before, which is increasing the percentage of CO_2 in the atmosphere. The atmosphere might be trapping more of the Sun's heat, making Earth warmer. A rise in Earth's average temperature, possibly caused by an increase in greenhouse gases, is known as global warming.

Global Warming Temperature data collected from 1895 through 1995 indicate that Earth's average temperature increased about 1°C during that 100-year period. No one is certain whether this rise was caused by human activities or is a natural part of Earth's weather cycle. What kinds of changes might be caused by global warming? Changing rainfall patterns could alter ecosystems and affect the kinds of crops that can be grown in different parts of the world. The number of storms and hurricanes might increase. The polar ice caps might begin to melt, raising sea levels and flooding coastal areas. Warmer weather might allow tropical diseases, such as malaria, to become more widespread. Many people feel that the possibility of global warming is a good reason to reduce fossil fuel use.

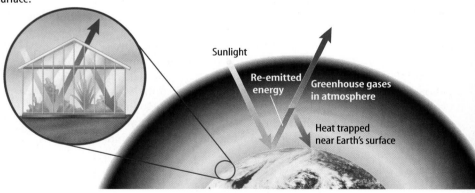

Sunlight

Re-emitted energy

Greenhouse gases in atmosphere

Heat trapped near Earth's surface

780 CHAPTER 27 Conserving Resources

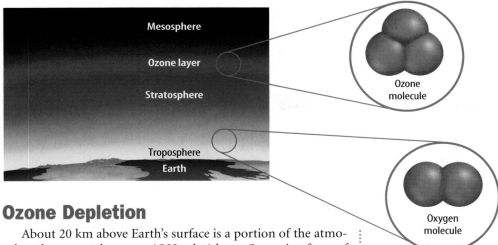

Ozone Depletion

About 20 km above Earth's surface is a portion of the atmosphere known as the ozone (OH zohn) layer. Ozone is a form of oxygen, as shown in **Figure 14.** The ozone layer absorbs some of the Sun's harmful ultraviolet (UV) radiation. UV radiation can damage living cells.

Every year, the ozone layer temporarily becomes thinner over each polar region during its spring season. The thinning of the ozone layer is called **ozone depletion.** This problem is caused by certain pollutant gases, especially chlorofluorocarbons (klor oh FLOR oh kar bunz) (CFCs). CFCs are used in the cooling systems of refrigerators, freezers, and air conditioners. When CFCs leak into the air, they slowly rise into the atmosphere until they arrive at the ozone layer. CFCs react chemically with ozone, breaking apart the ozone molecules.

UV Radiation Because of ozone depletion, the amount of UV radiation that reaches Earth's surface could be increasing. UV radiation could be causing a rise in the number of skin cancer cases in humans. It also might be harming other organisms. The ozone layer is so important to the survival of life on Earth that world governments and industries have agreed to stop making and using CFCs.

Ozone that is high in the upper atmosphere protects life on Earth. Near Earth's surface though, it can be harmful. Ozone is produced when fossil fuels are burned. This ozone stays in the lower atmosphere, where it pollutes the air. Ozone damages the lungs and other sensitive tissues of animals and plants. For example, it can cause the needles of a Ponderosa pine to drop, harming growth.

✔ **Reading Check** *What is the difference between ozone in the upper atmosphere and ozone in the lower atmosphere?*

Figure 14 The atmosphere's ozone layer absorbs large amounts of UV radiation, preventing it from reaching Earth's surface. Ozone molecules are made of three oxygen atoms. They are formed in a chemical reaction between sunlight and oxygen. The oxygen you breathe has two oxygen atoms in each molecule.
Infer *what will happen if the ozone layer continues to thin.*

Teacher FYI

CFCs Although the production of CFC has halted, there is a reserve supply available for air conditioning and refrigeration units. In many cases, HFCs are being used as coolants to replace CFCs, as they do not lead to ozone depletion.

Quick Demo
Chemical Bonds
Materials none
Estimated Time one minute
Procedure Have two students join hands to represent the normal state of oxygen (O_2) and three students join hands to represent ozone (O_3). L1

✔ **Reading Check**

Answer Ozone in the upper atmosphere is helpful to life; ozone in the lower atmosphere can be harmful to life as it pollutes the air.

IDENTIFYING Misconceptions

Cause and Effect Students sometimes confuse common environmental problems. For example, they may think that not littering will help with the problem of acid rain. Make sure that for each problem, students understand the related causes and effects and what can be done to reduce the problem.

Caption Answer

Figure 14 The amount of UV radiation that reaches Earth could increase. This could cause an increase in the number of skin cancer cases in humans and might cause harm to other organisms.

Differentiated Instruction

Challenge Have students research monthly and annual changes in the ozone layer. Have students present graphs showing their results and discuss what environmental factors might explain the changes in the ozone layer. L3

Cultural Diversity

Sun Exposure Australia leads the world in skin cancer because of the many fair-skinned people, the ozone hole over the country, and changes in culture. In the past, wealthy Australians avoided the Sun. After WWI, Australians embraced a tanned look. As a result, skin cancer rates rapidly increased. It has now become a culturally accepted practice to have children wear hats when they go outside.

Figure 15 The map shows the potential for radon exposure in different parts of the United States. **Identify** *the area of the country with soils that produce the most radon gas.*

Indoor Air Pollution

Air pollution can occur indoors. Today's buildings are better insulated to conserve energy. However, better insulation reduces the flow of air into and out of a building, so air pollutants can build up indoors. For example, burning cigarettes release hazardous particles and gases into the air. Even nonsmokers can suffer ill effects from secondhand cigarette smoke. As a result, smoking no longer is allowed in many public and private buildings. Paints, carpets, glues and adhesives, printers, and photocopy machines also give off dangerous gases, including formaldehyde. Like cigarette smoke, formaldehyde is a carcinogen, which means it can cause cancer.

Carbon Monoxide Carbon monoxide (CO) is a poisonous gas that is produced whenever charcoal, natural gas, kerosene, or other fuels are burned. CO poisoning can cause serious illness or death. Fuel-burning stoves and heaters must be designed to prevent CO from building up indoors. CO is colorless and odorless, so it is difficult to detect. Alarms that provide warning of a dangerous buildup of CO are being used in more and more homes.

Radon Radon is a naturally occurring, radioactive gas that is given off by some types of rock and soil, as shown in **Figure 15.** Radon has no color or odor. It can seep into basements and the lower floors of buildings. Radon exposure is the second leading cause of lung cancer in this country. A radon detector sounds an alarm when levels of the gas in indoor air become too high. If radon is present, increasing a building's ventilation can eliminate any damaging effects.

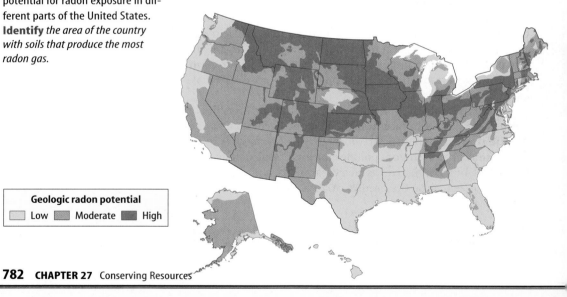

Geologic radon potential
☐ Low ▨ Moderate ■ High

When rain falls on roads and parking lots, it can wash oil and grease onto the soil and into nearby streams.

Rain can wash agricultural pesticides and fertilizers into lakes, streams, or oceans.

Industrial wastes are sometimes released directly into surface waters.

Figure 16 Pollution of surface waters can occur in several ways, as shown above.

Water Pollution

Pollutants enter water, too. Air pollutants can drift into water or be washed out of the sky by rain. Rain can wash land pollutants into waterways, as shown in **Figure 16.** Wastewater from factories and sewage-treatment plants often is released into waterways. In the United States and many other countries, laws require that wastewater be treated to remove pollutants before it is released. But, in many parts of the world, wastewater treatment is not always possible. Pollution also enters water when people dump litter or waste materials into rivers, lakes, and oceans.

Surface Water Some water pollutants poison fish and other wildlife, and can be harmful to people who swim in or drink the water. For example, chemical pesticides sprayed on farmland can wash into lakes and streams. These chemicals can harm the insects that fish, turtles, or frogs rely on for food. Shortages of food can lead to deaths among water-dwelling animals. Some pollutants, especially those containing mercury and other metals, can build up in the tissues of fish. Eating contaminated fish and shellfish can transfer these metals to people, birds, and other animals. In some areas, people are advised not to eat fish or shellfish taken from polluted waterways.

Algal blooms are another water pollution problem. Raw sewage and excess fertilizer contain large amounts of nitrogen. If they are washed into a lake or pond, they can cause the rapid growth of algae. When the algae die, they are decomposed by huge numbers of bacteria that use up much of the oxygen in the water. Fish and other organisms can die from a lack of oxygen in the water.

SECTION 2 Pollution **783**

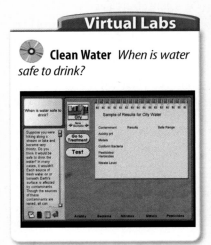
Cultural Diversity

Significance of Water Water is so important for civilization that it has become part of human culture. Water and waterscapes have been described in words, drawings, songs, and other art forms by all cultures on Earth. Water also plays an important part in religion. From Japanese Shintoism to Christianity, water symbolizes cleansing in spiritual ceremonies.

Figure 18 Have students study the illustration. Emphasize that groundwater is an important source of water for many people. Then prepare a beaker with sand or soil on top and gravel on the bottom. Pour a little water on the soil's surface and show students how the water percolates through the layers to the bottom of the beaker. Have students relate this to the movement of groundwater shown in the illustration. L2 IS **Visual-Spatial**

Inquiry Lab

Oil Cleanup

Purpose to explore the process and cleanup of oil spills and discuss waste disposal of materials

Possible Materials cooking oil, clear-plastic bin, cotton balls, aquarium net, sand, liquid detergent, string, plastic spoons, paper towels, garbage bag

Estimated Time 1 class period

Teaching Strategies

• You can have students work in groups and assign each group a bin of water.

• Students can predict and observe what will happen to the oil when it is poured into the water.

• Students can write a procedure using the materials available to clean up the oil spill and then follow their procedure.

• After collecting their data, students can write suggestions for doing the experiment better. PBL

• Have students contact the nearest Hazmat agency and inquire about spills that have occured locally and how they were handled. Have them compare their methods with Hazmat's to consider better ideas.

For additional inquiry activities, see *Science Inquiry Labs*.

Figure 17 In 1996, the oil tanker *Sea Empress* spilled more than 72 million kg of oil into the sea along the coast of Wales. More than $40 million was spent on the cleanup effort, but thousands of ocean organisms were destroyed, including birds, fish, and shellfish.

Ocean Water Rivers and streams eventually flow into oceans, bringing their pollutants along. Also, polluted water can enter the ocean in coastal areas where factories, sewage-treatment plants, or shipping activities are located. Oil spills are a well-known ocean pollution problem. About 4 billion kg of oil are spilled into ocean waters every year. Much of that oil comes from ships that use ocean water to wash out their fuel tanks. Oil also can come from oil tanker wrecks, as shown in **Figure 17.**

Groundwater Pollution can affect water that seeps underground, as shown in **Figure 18.** Groundwater is water that collects between particles of soil and rock. It comes from precipitation and runoff that soaks into the soil. This water can flow slowly through permeable layers of rock called aquifers. If this water comes into contact with pollutants as it moves through the soil and into an aquifer, the aquifer could become polluted. Polluted groundwater is difficult—and sometimes impossible—to clean. In some parts of the country, chemicals leaking from underground storage tanks have created groundwater pollution problems.

Figure 18 Water from rainfall slowly filters through sand or soil until it is trapped in underground aquifers. Pollutants picked up by the water as it filters through the soil can contaminate water wells.

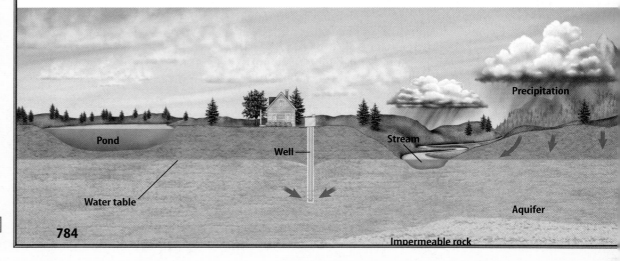

Pond | Well | Stream | Precipitation | Water table | Aquifer | Impermeable rock

784

Science Journal

Well Water Have students imagine that they depend on a well as their source of water. They find out that pesticides that can injure their health have seeped into the groundwater the well draws from. Have students write in their Science Journals the changes they will make in their use of the well's water. L2 IS **Intrapersonal**

Differentiated Instruction

Hearing Impaired Fill a funnel with soil and place it in a beaker. Add a teaspoon of food coloring to the top of the soil. Slowly pour water through the funnel. At first, water flowing out of the funnel is probably clear, but eventually colored water exits. Explain that soil may act as a filter for a time, but eventually pollutants will work their way through the soil. L1 ELL

Contour plowing reduces the downhill flow of water.

Figure 19 The farming methods shown here help prevent soil erosion.
Infer *why soil erosion is a concern for farmers.*

On steep hillsides, flat areas called terraces reduce downhill flow.

In strip cropping, cover crops are planted between rows to reduce wind erosion.

In no-till farming, soil is never left bare.

Soil Loss

Fertile topsoil is important to plant growth. New topsoil takes hundreds or thousands of years to form. The Launch Lab at the beginning of this chapter shows that rain washes away loose topsoil. Wind also blows it away. The movement of soil from one place to another is called **erosion** (ih ROH zhun). Eroded soil that washes into a river or stream can block sunlight and slow photosynthesis. It also can harm fish, clams, and other organisms. Erosion is a natural process, but human activities increase it. When a farmer plows a field or a forest is cut down, soil is left bare. Bare soil is more easily carried away by rain and wind. **Figure 19** shows some methods farmers use to reduce soil erosion.

Soil Pollution

Soil can become polluted when air pollutants drift to the ground or when water leaves pollutants behind as it flows through the soil. Soil also can be polluted when people toss litter on the ground or dispose of trash in landfills.

Solid Wastes What happens to the trash you throw out every week? What do people do with old refrigerators, TVs, and toys? Most of this solid waste is dumped in landfills. Most landfills are designed to seal out air and water. This helps prevent pollutants from seeping into surrounding soil, but it slows normal decay processes. Even food scraps and paper, which usually break down quickly, can last for decades in a landfill. In populated areas, landfills fill up quickly. Reducing the amount of trash people generate can reduce the need for new landfills.

Caption Answer

Figure 19 Erosion carries away nutrient-rich topsoil that farmers need to grow crops.

Quick Demo

Biodegradable Waste

Materials container of trash including a glass bottle, aluminum can, plastic wrappers, a coffee filter with grounds, vegetable peelings, eggshells, and other household items

Estimated Time three minutes

Procedure Using rubber gloves, remove items from the container of trash. Have students discuss whether the item is biodegradable. Explain that the biodegradable wastes may decay, but the nonbiodegradable wastes will not.

Activity

Cleaning Products Many household cleaners contain toxic chemicals. Numerous new products are available that are just as effective, but do not contain harmful chemicals. Have students obtain an adult's permission to investigate cleaning products in their homes to see what kinds of ingredients they contain. Caution students to take care when handling cleaning products or other chemicals. L2

Fun Fact

Americans represent approximately 5% of the world's population and generate 30% of the world's garbage.

Differentiated Instruction

Challenge Have students calculate the following: If your family produces an average of 1.8 kg of solid waste per person per day, how much waste will your entire family generate in the month of October? Answers will vary depending on the number of family members (f). Students should use the following equation to solve this problem: $(f \times 1.8) \times 31 =$ amount of waste produced by the family. L3

Teacher FYI

Erosion Pollution refers to the degradation of the environment. Erosion fits into this definition because as valuable topsoil is lost, land becomes less fertile. The erosion of land in arid areas may make these places resemble deserts, a process called desertification.

SECTION 2 Pollution 785

3 Assess

DAILY INTERVENTION

Check for Understanding

Visual-Spatial Present pictures displaying various types of pollution and have students explain the cause and effect of the pollution.

Reteach

Pollution Have students make a chart summarizing the causes and effects of air pollution, soil pollution, and water pollution. L2

✔ **Assessment**

Content Have student pairs work together to write a song or poem about the dangers of environmental pollution. Use **Performance Assessment in the Science Classroom,** p. 151. L2 P

Figure 20 Leftover paints, batteries, pesticides, drain cleaners, and medicines are hazardous wastes that should not be discarded in the trash. They should never be poured down a drain, onto the ground, or into a storm sewer. Most communities have collection facilities where people can dispose of hazardous materials like these.

Hazardous Wastes Waste materials that are harmful to human health or poisonous to living organisms are **hazardous wastes.** They include dangerous chemicals, such as pesticides, oil, and petroleum-based solvents used in industry. They also include radioactive wastes from nuclear power plants, from hospitals that use radioactive materials to treat disease, and from nuclear weapons production. Many household items also are considered hazardous, such as those shown in **Figure 20.** If these materials are dumped into landfills, they could seep into the soil, surface water, or groundwater over time. Hazardous wastes usually are handled separately from trash. They are treated in ways that prevent environmental pollution.

✔ **Reading Check** *What are hazardous wastes?*

---

section ② review

Summary

Air Pollution and Acid Precipitation
- Vehicles, volcanoes, forest fires, and even wind-blown dust and sand can cause air pollution.
- Acid rain washes nutrients from the soil, which can harm plants.

Greenhouse Effect and Ozone Depletion
- CO_2 is a greenhouse gas that helps warm Earth.
- The ozone layer protects life on Earth.

Indoor Air Pollution, Water Pollution, Soil Loss, and Soil Pollution
- Pollutants can build up inside of buildings.
- There are many sources of water pollutants.
- Wind and rain can erode bare soil.
- Pollutants in soil decay more slowly than in air.

Self Check

1. **List** four ways that air pollution affects the environment.
2. **Explain** how an algal bloom can affect other pond organisms.
3. **Describe** possible causes and effects of ozone depletion.
4. **Think Critically** How could hazardous wastes in landfills eventually affect groundwater?

Applying Math

5. **Solve a One-Step Equation** A solution of pH 4 is 10 times more acidic than one of pH 5, and it is 10 times more acidic than a solution of pH 6. How many times more acidic is the solution of pH 4 than the one of pH 6?

786 CHAPTER 27 Conserving Resources

 Science Online life.msscience.com/self_check_quiz

---

section ② review

1. smog, acid rain, enhanced greenhouse effect, ozone depletion
2. Algal blooms grow and eventually die. Their decay uses up oxygen, making it difficult for other organisms to survive.

3. CFCs that escape into the air can cause ozone depletion; as ozone is depleted, more UV radiation reached Earth, resulting in more cases of skin cancer.

4. They can leach into the soil and be picked up by groundwater, making the water hazardous for people to drink.
5. A solution with a pH of 4 is 100 times more acidic than a solution with a pH of 6.

The Greenhouse Effect

You can create models of Earth with and without heat-reflecting green-house gases. Then, experiment with the models to observe the greenhouse effect.

▶ Real-World Question

How does the greenhouse effect influence temperatures on Earth?

Goals

- **Observe** the greenhouse effect.
- **Describe** the effect that a heat source has on an environment.

Materials

1-L clear-plastic, soft-drink bottles with tops cut off and labels removed (2)
thermometers (2)
*temperature probe
potting soil
masking tape
plastic wrap
rubber band
lamp with 100-W lightbulb
watch or clock with second hand
*Alternate materials

Safety Precautions

▶ Procedure

1. Copy the data table and use it to record your temperature measurements.
2. Put an equal volume of potting soil in the bottom of each container.
3. Use masking tape to attach a thermometer to the inside of each container. Place each thermometer at the same height above the soil. Shield each thermometer bulb by putting a double layer of masking tape over it.

Changes in Temperature

Time (min)	Open Container Temperature (°C)	Closed Container Temperature (°C)
0		
2		
4		
6		

4. Seal the top of one container with plastic wrap held in place with a rubber band.
5. Place the lamp with the exposed 100-W lightbulb between the two containers and exactly 1 cm away from each. Do not turn on the light.
6. Let the setup sit for 5 min, then record the temperature in each container.
7. Turn on the light. Record the temperature in each container every 2 min for 15 min to 20 min. Graph the results.

▶ Conclude and Apply

1. **Compare and contrast** temperatures in each container at the end of the experiment.
2. **Infer** What does the lightbulb represent in this experimental model? What does the plastic wrap represent?

Communicating Your Data

Average the data obtained in the experiments conducted by all the groups in your class. Prepare a line graph of these data. **For more help, refer to the** Science Skill Handbook.

LAB **787**

✓ Assessment

Oral Have students summarize the information in their graphs in writing. Make sure summaries are clear and concise. Use **Performance Assessment in the Science Classroom,** p. 113.

Communicating Your Data

Have students write the final temperatures for the two conditions on the board. Students should compare data and see if the results were the same for everyone. Discuss how differences may have occurred.

▶ Real-World Question

Purpose Students make models of the atmosphere and determine what happens when light shines on the model. L2
COOP LEARN IS **Interpersonal**

Process Skills model, observe and infer, interpret data, communicate, compare and contrast, recognize cause and effect, measure in SI, make and use tables, make and use graphs

Time Required 50 minutes

Safety Precautions Caution students to use care in working with thermometers and 100-W lightbulbs. Use only alcohol thermometers.

Teaching Strategies

- Drafts can affect results.
- Make sure the thermometers face outward to make it easier for students to read them.

Troubleshooting If the two thermometers did not read the same temperature when the experiment began, adjust readings so both data sets can be plotted on the same graph.

▶ Conclude and Apply

1. The temperatures of both containers has increased. The container covered with plastic wrap had a greater increase.
2. The light bulb represents the Sun; the plastic wrap represents carbon dioxide in the atmosphere.

LAB **787**

section 3

The Three Rs of Conservation

as you read

What You'll Learn
- **Recognize** ways you can reduce your use of natural resources.
- **Explain** how you can reuse resources to promote conservation.
- **Describe** how many materials can be recycled.

Why It's Important
Conservation preserves resources and reduces pollution.

Review Vocabulary
reprocessing: to subject to a special process or treatment in preparation for reuse

New Vocabulary
- recycling

Figure 21 Worn-out automobile tires can have other useful purposes.

Conservation

A teacher travels to school in a car pool. In the school cafeteria, students place glass bottles and cans in separate containers from the rest of the garbage. Conservation efforts like these can help prevent shortages of natural resources, slow growth of landfills, reduce pollution levels, and save people money. Every time a new landfill is created, an ecosystem is disturbed. Reducing the need for landfills is a major benefit of conservation. The three Rs of conservation are reduce, reuse, and recycle.

Reduce

You contribute to conservation whenever you reduce your use of natural resources. You use less fossil fuel when you walk or ride a bicycle instead of taking the bus or riding in a car. If you buy a carton of milk, reduce your use of petroleum by telling the clerk you don't need a plastic bag to carry it in.

You also can avoid buying things you don't need. For example, most of the paper, plastic, and cardboard used to package items for display on store shelves is thrown away as soon as the product is brought home. You can look for products with less packaging or with packaging made from recycled materials. What are some other ways you can reduce your use of natural resources?

Reuse

Another way to help conserve natural resources is to use items more than once. Reusing an item means using it again without changing it or reprocessing it, as shown in **Figure 21.** Bring reusable canvas bags to the grocery store to carry home your purchases. Donate clothes you've outgrown to charity so that others can reuse them. Take reusable plates and utensils on picnics instead of disposable paper items.

Recycle

If you can't avoid using an item, and if you can't reuse it, the next best thing is to recycle it. **Recycling** is a form of reuse that requires changing or reprocessing an item or natural resource. If your city or town has a curbside recycling program, you already separate recyclables from the rest of your garbage. Materials that can be recycled include glass, metals, paper, plastics, and yard and kitchen waste.

✓ Reading Check *How is recycling different from reusing?*

Plastics Plastic is more difficult to recycle than other materials, mainly because several types of plastic are in use. A recycle code marked on every plastic container indicates the type of plastic it is made of. Plastic soft-drink bottles, like the one shown in **Figure 22,** are made of type 1 plastic and are the easiest to recycle. Most plastic bags are made of type 2 or type 4 plastic; they can be reused as well as recycled. Types 6 and 7 can't be recycled at all because they are made of a mixture of different plastics. Each type of plastic must be separated carefully before it is recycled because a single piece of a different type of plastic can ruin an entire batch.

Figure 22 Many soft-drink bottles are made of PETE, which is the most common type of recyclable plastic. It can be melted down and spun into fibers to make carpets, paintbrushes, rope, and clothing. **Identify** *other products made out of recycled materials.*

SECTION 3   The Three Rs of Conservation   **789**

Differentiated Instruction

Challenge Have students find as many products as they can that are recycled and what material they are made up of. Then have them research the types of material that are commonly recycled and present a report of their findings. L3

Visual Learning

Figure 22 The objects in these photographs are made from the same type 1 plastic (PET). Ask students to bring in materials with this symbol on them. When the objects are collected, discuss why recycling is a good idea. Possible answer: It reduces the amount of nonbiodegradable materials going into landfills. L2

Text Question Answer
Possible answer: Turn off lights in vacant rooms.

Discussion

Over-Packaging Bring in a product that is clearly over-packaged. Have students suggest ways to reduce the amount of material used in the packaging of this item.

Activity

Brainstorm Find an item that is commonly thrown out, such as a plastic soft-drink bottle. Have students brainstorm a list of possible ways to reuse the bottle. L2 ELL IS **Interpersonal**

✓ Reading Check

Answer Reusing does not require reprocessing; recycling does.

Caption Answer

Figure 22 Packaging, paper, glass bottles, furniture, auto parts, and construction and landscaping products are some examples of materials made from recycled material.

Quick Demo

Recycling

Materials cans, cereal boxes, other products with recycling symbol or made from recycled material

Estimated Time one minute

Procedure Lay products out on a table and have students note whether the packaging has a recycle symbol or if the package states that it is made of recycled material. Explain that many products can be recycled and made from recycled materials.

IDENTIFYING Misconceptions

Recycled Paper Many people think that recycled paper is paper that has been used by consumers. Most of it, however, comes from wood or paper scrap in logging or paper manufacturing. Some companies indicate how much recycled paper comes directly from consumers by labeling the percent that is post-consumer content.

Applying Science

Answer

Students' lists should include some of each type of item. Possible exceptions would be yard wastes, depending on the season, and newspapers. The percentages will depend on student data. Tin cans are steel cans coated with tin. They should be included.

Science Online

Topic: Recycling
Visit life.msscience.com for Web links to information about recycling bottles and cans.

Activity Write one argument in support of a money deposit for bottles and cans and one argument against it. Provide data to support one of your arguments.

Metals The manufacturing industry has been recycling all kinds of metals, especially steel, for decades. At least 25 percent of the steel in cans, appliances, and automobiles is recycled steel. Up to 100 percent of the steel in plates and beams used to build skyscrapers is made from reprocessed steel. About one metric ton of recycled steel saves about 1.1 metric tons of iron ore and 0.5 metric ton of coal. Using recycled steel to make new steel products reduces energy use by 75 percent. Other metals, including iron, copper, aluminum, and lead also can be recycled.

You can conserve metals by recycling food cans, which are mostly steel, and aluminum cans. It takes less energy to make a can from recycled aluminum than from raw materials. Also, remember that recycled cans do not take up space in landfills.

Glass When sterilized, glass bottles and jars can be reused. They also can be melted and re-formed into new bottles, especially those made of clear glass. Most glass bottles already contain at least 25 percent recycled glass. Glass can be recycled again and again. It never needs to be thrown away. Recycling about one metric ton of glass saves more than one metric ton of mineral resources and reduces the energy used to make new glass by 25 percent or more.

Applying Science

What items are you recycling at home?

Many communities have recycling programs. Recyclable items may be picked up at the curbside, taken to a collection site, or the resident may hire a licensed recycling handler to pick them up. What do you recycle in your home?

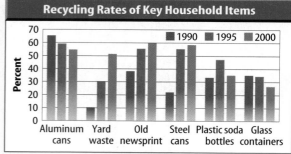

Source: U.S. EPA, 2003

Identifying the Problem

This bar graph shows the recycling rates in the U. S. of six types of household items for the years 1990, 1995, and 2000. What are you and your classmates' recycling rates?

Solving the Problem

For one week, list each glass, plastic, and aluminum item you use. Note which items you throw away and which ones you recycle. Calculate the percentage of glass, plastic, and aluminum you recycled. How do your percentages compare with those on the graph?

Teacher FYI

Compost Composting is considered recycling because the form of the materials is changed (through decay) so they can be used again.

Differentiated Instruction

Challenge Have students investigate the trash generated by your school's cafeteria. Challenge them to devise a plan to reduce the amount of trash that is thrown away. Have them write a report on their investigation and plan. L3 P

Paper Used paper is recycled into paper towels, insulation, newsprint, cardboard, and stationery. Ranchers and dairy farmers sometimes use shredded paper instead of straw for bedding in barns and stables. Used paper can be made into compost. Recycling about one metric ton of paper saves 17 trees, more than 26,000 L of water, close to 1,900 L of oil, and more than 4,000 kW of electric energy. You can do your part by recycling newspapers, notebook and printer paper, cardboard, and junk mail.

 **Reading Check** *What nonrenewable resource(s) do you conserve by recycling paper?*

Compost Grass clippings, leaves, and fruit and vegetable scraps that are discarded in a landfill can remain there for decades without breaking down. The same items can be turned into soil-enriching compost in just a few weeks, as shown in **Figure 23.** Many communities distribute compost bins to encourage residents to recycle fruit and vegetable scraps and yard waste.

Buy Recycled People have become so good at recycling that recyclable materials are piling up, just waiting to be put to use. You can help by reading labels when you shop and choosing products that contain recycled materials. What other ways of recycling natural resources can you think of?

Figure 23 Composting is a way of turning plant material you would otherwise throw away into rich garden soil. Dry leaves and weeds, grass clippings, vegetable trimmings, and nonmeat food scraps can be composted.

---

section 3 review

Summary

Conservation
- The three Rs of conservation are reduce, reuse, and recycle.

Reduce
- You can contribute to conservation by reducing your use of natural resources.

Reuse
- Some items can be used more than once, such as reusable canvas bags for groceries.

Recycle
- Some items can be recycled, including some plastics, metal, glass, and paper.
- Grass clippings, leaves, and fruit and vegetable scraps can be composted into rich garden soil.

Self Check

1. **Describe** at least three actions you could take to reduce your use of natural resources.
2. **Describe** how you could reuse three items people usually throw away.
3. **Think Critically** Why is reusing something better than recycling it?

Applying Skills

4. **Make and Use Tables** Make a table of data of the number of aluminum cans thrown away in the United States: 2.7 billion in 1970; 11.1 billion in 1974; 21.3 billion in 1978; 22.7 billion in 1982; 35.0 billion in 1986; 33.8 billion in 1990; 38.5 billion in 1994; 45.5 billion in 1998; 50.7 billion in 2001.

---

3 Assess

DAILY INTERVENTION

Check for Understanding
Visual-Spatial Place students in small groups and show them various items such as bottles, tin cans, paper, plastic bags, and fruit. Have them decide whether they could reduce their use of the product, reuse it, or recycle it. L2

Reteach
Glass Bottles Ask students to give their opinions about whether a soft-drink company should reuse glass bottles by washing them out or recycle the bottles by melting them and making new ones. L1 **Linguistic**

Assessment

Content Hold up a newspaper and ask students to write specific examples of how a community can reduce its use of newspapers, reuse newspapers, and recycle newspapers.

---

section 3 review

1. Possible answers: turn off lights in vacant rooms, buy materials with less packaging, carpool, buy items made from recycled materials
2. Possible answers: store water in plastic soft-drink bottles, use plastic grocery bags as trash can liners, use margarine tubs to store left-over food.
3. There is less energy used in reusing than in recycling.
4. Check tables for accuracy.

BENCH TESTED

Real-World Question

Purpose Students will design and build a solar cooker.

Process Skills design and make a model, research, compare

Time Required one class period

Discussion Discuss with students the problems some people in the world face just trying to cook a meal. Explain to students that in some places where fuel is scarce, people use solar cookers to prepare food. Why do people cook most food? *Possible answers: to improve taste, to kill harmful bacteria* Why does cooking food require energy? *Energy is needed to raise the temperature of the food.*

Alternate Materials Oven bags are available at most supermarkets. Kitchen timers are available at most hardware stores.

Safety Precautions Remind students to use insulated gloves or tongs when handling hot objects.

LAB Model and Invent

S☼lar Cooking

Goals
- **Research** designs for solar panel cookers or box cookers.
- **Design** a solar cooker that can be used to cook food.
- **Plan** an experiment to measure the effectiveness of your solar cooker.

Possible Materials
poster board
cardboard boxes
aluminum foil
string
wire coat hangers
clear plastic sheets
*oven bags
black cookware
thermometer
stopwatch
*timer
glue
tape
scissors
*Alternate materials

Safety Precautions

WARNING: *Be careful when cutting materials. Your solar cooker will get hot. Use insulated gloves or tongs to handle hot objects.*

Real-World Question

The disappearance of forests in some places on Earth has made firewood extremely difficult and expensive to obtain. People living in these regions often have to travel long distances or sell some of their food to get firewood. This can be a serious problem for people who may not have much food to begin with. Is there a way they could cook food without using firewood? How would you design and build a cooking device that uses the Sun's energy?

Make the Model

1. **Design** a solar cooker. In your Science Journal, explain why you chose this design and draw a picture of it.
2. **Write** a summary explaining how you will measure the effectiveness of your solar cooker. What will you measure? How will you collect and organize your data? How will you present your results?

Fun Fact

The Sun converts approximately 4 million tons of hydrogen gas into energy every second.

Differentiated Instruction

Learning Disabled Assign these students the task of gathering the materials their group decides they want to use. L1

Using Scientific Methods

3. **Compare** your solar cooker design to those of other students.

4. Share your experimental plan with students in your class. Discuss the reasoning behind your plan. Be specific about what you intend to test and how you are going to test it.

5. Make sure your teacher approves your plan before you start working on your model.

6. Using all of the information you have gathered, construct a solar cooker that follows your design.

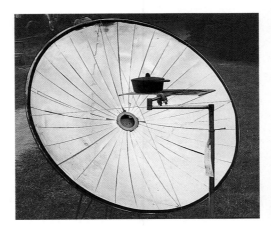

Test the Model

1. **Test** your design to determine how well it works. Try out a classmate's design. How do the two compare?

Analyze Your Data

1. Combine the results for your entire class and decide which type of solar cooker was most effective. How could you design a more effective solar cooker, based on what you learned from this activity?

2. **Infer** Do you think your results might have been different if you tested your solar cooker on a different day? Explain. Why might a solar cooker be more useful in some regions of the world than in others?

Conclude and Apply

1. **Infer** Based on what you've read and the results obtained by you and your classmates, do you think that your solar cooker could boil water? Explain.

2. **Compare** the amount of time needed to cook food with a solar cooker and with more traditional cooking methods. Assuming plenty of sunlight is available, would you prefer to use a solar cooker or a traditional oven? Explain.

Communicating Your Data

Prepare a demonstration showing how to use a solar cooker. Present your demonstration to another class of students or to a group of friends or relatives. **For more help, refer to the** Science Skill Handbook.

LAB   793

Assessment

Process Have students use a foam cup of water with a thermometer in it to test whether their solar ovens can boil water. Be sure that each group uses the same amount of water for the test and that students record the time it takes to boil the water. Based on the results, have students rank the solar cooker designs from best to worst. Use **Performance Assessment in the Science Classroom,** p. 97.

Communicating Your Data

Students should prepare a poster that shows the construction of their solar cooker and an explanation of how it works.

Make a Model

Teaching Strategies

- Comparisons of solar cookers will be difficult if students do not use the same method of testing them.

- You might want to have a cook-off with the two best solar ovens to see which one could cook a small red potato in the shortest time. Be sure both potatoes are the same size.

- Students can move the cookers during the testing to keep them in the sunlight.

Test Your Model

Expected Outcome Solar cookers should be able to raise the temperature of a cup of water to at least 75°C. A well-designed cooker might reach temperatures approaching 150°C.

Analyze Your Data

1. Answers will depend on the designs of the solar cookers that are compared.

2. Results would vary in different weather conditions. Solar cookers function best on clear, sunny days. Solar cookers are more useful in areas that have many clear, sunny days.

Conclude and Apply

1. Answers will depend on the success of the design. Some well-designed cookers could boil water.

2. Solar cookers generally take two to three times as long to cook a meal as a traditional oven. However, the energy for a solar cooker is free and the energy for a traditional oven is not.

LAB   793

Understanding Literature

Cause and Effect Answers will vary but might include that bottle caps litter the picnic area and that exhaust fumes from cars make the snow banks dark and gray.

Respond to the Reading

1. The four verses correspond to the four seasons.
2. Human activity (civilization) has plagiarized beauty.
3. **Linking Science and Writing** Students could review chapter and list conservation methods to include in their poem.

 **Renewing Resources**

Even renewable resources can be rendered nonrenewable. This happens when renewable resources are removed at a rate that prevents their renewal, or if the environment that supports them deteriorates faster than renewal can take place. For example, although forests are considered a renewable resource, if they are not carefully managed they can disappear as a result of excessive logging or clear-cutting. Also, although Earth's supply of air is inexhaustible, the quality of Earth's air can be affected by human activity, and air quality directly affects other renewable resources.

Beauty Plagiarized
by Amitabha Mukerjee

I wandered lonely as a cloud –
Except for a motorboat,
Nary a soul in sight.
Beside the lake beneath the trees,
Next to the barbed wire fence,
There was a picnic table
And beer bottle caps from many years.
A boat ramp to the left,
And the chimney from a power station on the
    other side,
A summer haze hung in the air,
And the lazy drone of traffic far away.

Crimson autumn of mists and mellow fruitfulness
Blue plastic covers the swimming pools
The leaves fall so I can see
Dark glass reflections in the building
That came up
where the pine cones crunched underfoot . . .

And then it is snow
White lining on trees and rooftops . . .
And through my windshield wipers
The snow is piled dark and grey . . .
Next to my driveway where I check my mail
Little footprints on fresh snow —
A visiting rabbit.

I knew a bank where the wild thyme blew
Over-canopied with luscious woodbine
It is now a landfill —
Fermentation of civilization
Flowers on TV
Hyacinth rose tulip chrysanthemum
Acres of colour
Wind up wrapped in decorous plastic,
In this landfill where oxlips grew. . .

Understanding Literature

Cause and Effect Recognizing cause-and-effect relationships can help you make sense out of what you read. One event causes another event. The second event is the effect of the first event. In the poem, the author describes the causes and effects of pollution and waste. What effects do pollution and the use of nonrenewable resources have on nature in the poem?

Respond to the Reading

1. To plagiarize is to copy without giving credit to the source. In this poem, who or what has plagiarized beauty?
2. What do the four verses in the poem correspond to?
3. **Linking Science and Writing** Write a poem that shows how conservation methods could restore the beauty in nature.

 The poet makes a connection between the four seasons of the year and the pollution and waste products created by human activity, or civilization. For example, in the spring, a landfill for dumping garbage replaces a field of wildflowers. Describing four seasons instead of one reinforces the poet's message that the beauty of nature has been stolen, or plagiarized.

Resources for Teachers and Students

A Walk in the Woods: Rediscovering America on the Appalachian Trail, by Bill Bryson, Broadway Books, 1999

The Best American Science & Nature Writing 2000, ed. Burkhard Bilger, Houghton Mifflin Co., 2000

Lost Woods: The Discovered Writing of Rachel Carson, by Rachel Carson, ed. Linda Lear, Beacon Press, 1999

Reviewing Main Ideas

Section 1 Resources

1. Natural resources are the parts of the environment that supply materials needed for the survival of living organisms.

2. Renewable resources are being replaced continually by natural processes.

3. Nonrenewable resources cannot be replaced or are replaced very slowly.

4. Energy sources include fossil fuels, wind, solar energy, geothermal energy, hydroelectric power, and nuclear power.

Section 2 Pollution

1. Most air pollution is made up of waste products from the burning of fossil fuels.

2. The greenhouse effect is the warming of Earth by a blanket of heat-reflecting gases in the atmosphere.

3. Water can be polluted by acid rain and by the spilling of oil or other wastes into waterways.

4. Solid wastes and hazardous wastes dumped on land or disposed of in landfills can pollute the soil. Erosion can cause the loss of fertile topsoil.

Section 3 The Three Rs of Conservation

1. You can reduce your use of natural resources in many ways.

2. Reusing items is an excellent way to practice conservation.

3. In recycling, materials are changed in some way so that they can be used again.

4. Materials that can be recycled include paper, metals, glass, plastics, yard waste, and nonmeat kitchen scraps.

Visualizing Main Ideas

Copy and complete the following concept map using the terms smog, acid precipitation, *and* ozone depletion.

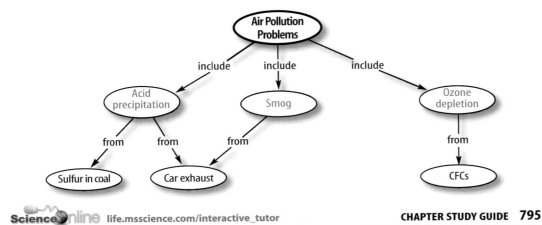

Reviewing Main Ideas

Summary statements can be used by students to review the major concepts of the chapter.

Visualizing Main Ideas

See student page.

Visit life.msscience.com
/self_check_quiz
/interactive_tutor
/vocabulary_puzzlemaker
/chapter_review
/standardized_test

Assessment Transparency

For additional assessment questions, use the *Assessment Transparency* located in the transparency book.

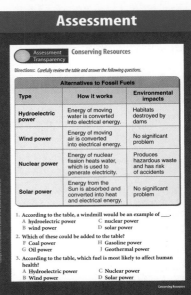

Using Vocabulary

1. Petroleum is a type of fossil fuel.

2. Erosion produces pollutants and degrades the environment.

3. These are both types of air pollution, but one does not cause the other.

4. The burning of fossil fuels and the release of excess carbon dioxide may enhance the greenhouse effect.

5. The use of nuclear energy generates radioactive materials, which are hazardous wastes.

6. The use of hydroelectric power can decrease the use of fossil fuels.

7. Coal is a fossil fuel. The burning of coal that contains sulfur causes acid precipitation.

8. The pollutant called CFC causes ozone depletion.

9. Recycling is a good way of conserving nonrenewable resources.

10. The use of geothermal energy can decrease the use of fossil fuels.

Checking Concepts

11. B	14. B	17. B
12. C	15. C	18. A
13. C	16. C	

Thinking Critically

19. Most geothermal energy is used to produce steam that rotates turbine blades of an electric generator.

20. Fossil fuels were formed from plants and animals. Wood is from a plant.

21. Desert region; sunshine is more constant there than at the poles.

22. to prevent erosion of topsoil

23. Yes; it is constantly replaced and has many uses.

24. Solar, wind, geothermal, and water energy are renewable resources. Nuclear energy is not a renewable resource, but no severe shortages are expected.

25. Reusing the bag would save energy because it wouldn't need to be changed back into its raw form and then a new bag made.

Using Vocabulary

acid precipitation p. 779
erosion p. 785
fossil fuel p. 772
geothermal energy p. 775
greenhouse effect p. 780
hazardous waste p. 786
hydroelectric power p. 773
natural resource p. 770

nonrenewable
 resource p. 771
nuclear energy p. 774
ozone depletion p. 781
petroleum p. 771
pollutant p. 778
recycling p. 789
renewable resource p. 770

Explain the differences in the vocabulary words given below. Then explain how the words are related. Use complete sentences in your answers.

1. fossil fuel—petroleum

2. erosion—pollutant

3. ozone depletion—acid precipitation

4. greenhouse effect—fossil fuels

5. hazardous wastes—nuclear energy

6. hydroelectric power—fossil fuels

7. acid precipitation—fossil fuels

8. ozone depletion—pollutant

9. recycle—nonrenewable resources

10. geothermal energy—fossil fuels

Checking Concepts

Choose the word or phrase that best answers the question.

11. An architect wants to design a solar house in the northern hemisphere. For maximum warmth, which side of the house should have the most windows?
 A) north   C) east
 B) south   D) west

12. Of the following, which is considered a renewable resource?
 A) coal   C) sunlight
 B) oil   D) aluminum

Science Online life.msscience.com/vocabulary_puzzlemaker

Use the photo below to answer question 13.

13. Which energy resource is shown in the photo?
 A) solar energy
 B) geothermal energy
 C) hydroelectric energy
 D) photovoltaic energy

14. Which of the following is a fossil fuel?
 A) wood   C) nuclear power
 B) oil   D) photovoltaic cell

15. Which of the following contributes to ozone depletion?
 A) carbon dioxide   C) CFCs
 B) radon   D) carbon monoxide

16. What is a substance that contaminates the environment called?
 A) acid rain   C) pollutant
 B) pollution   D) ozone

17. If there were no greenhouse effect in Earth's atmosphere, which of the following statements would be true?
 A) Earth would be much hotter.
 B) Earth would be much colder.
 C) The temperature of Earth would be the same.
 D) The polar ice caps would melt.

18. Which of the following can change solar energy into electricity?
 A) photovoltaic cells
 B) smog
 C) nuclear power plants
 D) geothermal power plants

Use the Exam*View*® Pro Testmaker CD-ROM to:
- create multiple versions of tests
- create modified tests with one mouse click for inclusion students
- edit existing questions and add your own questions
- build tests aligned with state standards using built-in State Curriculum Tags
- change English tests to Spanish with one mouse click and vice versa

Thinking Critically

19. Explain how geothermal energy is used to produce electricity.

20. Infer why burning wood and burning fossil fuels produce similar pollutants.

Use the photos below to answer question 21.

21. Draw a Conclusion Which would make a better location for a solar power plant—a polar region (left) or a desert region (right)? Why?

22. Explain why it is beneficial to grow a different crop on soil after the major crop has been harvested.

23. Infer Is garbage a renewable resource? Why or why not?

24. Summarize Solar, nuclear, wind, water, and geothermal energy are alternatives to fossil fuels. Are they all renewable? Why or why not?

25. Draw Conclusions Would you save more energy by recycling or reusing a plastic bag?

26. Recognize Cause and Effect Forests use large amounts of carbon dioxide during photosynthesis. How might cutting down a large percentage of Earth's forests affect the greenhouse effect?

27. Form a hypothesis about why Americans throw away more aluminum cans each year.

28. Compare and contrast contour farming, terracing, strip cropping, and no-till farming.

 ScienceOnline life.msscience.com/chapter_review

Performance Activities

29. Poster Create a poster to illustrate and describe three things students at your school can do to conserve natural resources.

Applying Math

Use the table below to answer questions 30 and 31.

Estimated Recycling Rates	
Item	**Percent Recycled**
Aluminum cans	60
Glass beverage bottles	31
Plastic soft-drink containers	37
Newsprint	56
Magazines	23

30. Recycling Rates Make a bar graph of the data above.

31. Bottle Recycling For every 1,000 glass beverage bottles that are produced, how many are recycled?

32. Nonrenewable Resources 45.8 billion (45,800,000,000) cans were thrown away in 2000. If it takes 33.79 cans to equal one pound and the average scrap value is $0.58/lb, then what was the total dollar value of the discarded cans?

33. Ozone Depletion The thin ozone layer called the "ozone hole" over Antarctica reached nearly 27,000,000 km^2 in 1998. To conceptualize this, the United States has a geographical area of 9,363,130 km^2. How much larger is the "ozone hole" in comparison to the United States?

34. Increased CO_2 Levels To determine the effects of increased CO_2 levels in the atmosphere, scientists increased the CO_2 concentration by 70 percent in an enclosed rain forest environment. If the initial CO_2 concentration was 430 parts per million, what was it after the increase?

CHAPTER REVIEW 797

26. Cutting large forests could result in more carbon dioxide in the atmosphere, possibly resulting in an enhanced greenhouse effect and accelerated global warming.

27. Answers will vary. Students should support their answers.

28. Contour farming and terracing are similar in that they are farming methods for hillsides that reduce soil erosion. Strip cropping compares to no-till farming in that they are both methods of reducing soil erosion by leaving soil covered by vegetation. The first two methods contrast to the last two in that they are used on hillsides, while the last two are used on level ground.

Performance Activities

29. Posters should involve reducing, reusing, or recycling. Use **Performance Assessment in the Science Classroom,** p. 145.

Applying Math

National Math Standards
1, 2, 5, 9

30. bars (highest to lowest): aluminum cans, newsprint, plastic soft-drink containers, glass beverage bottles, magazines

31. 310 are recycled

32. $786, 149, 748

33. 2.88 times larger

34. $430 + (430 \times 0.7) = 731$ ppm

 Assessment Resources

Reproducible Masters

Chapter *Fast File* Resources
 Chapter Review, pp. 37–38
 Chapter Tests, pp. 39–42
 Assessment Transparency Activity, p. 49

Glencoe Science Web site
 Chapter Review Test
 Standardized Test Practice

Glencoe Technology
 Assessment Transparency
 Exam*View*® Pro Testmaker
 MindJogger Videoquiz
 Interactive Chalkboard

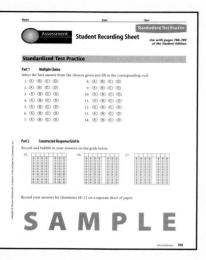

FAST FILE

Answer Sheet A practice answer sheet can be found at life.msscience.com/answer_sheet.

S A M P L E

Part 1 | Multiple Choice

1. B	**4.** C	**7.** C
2. A	**5.** B	**8.** B
3. A	**6.** D	**9.** A

Part 2 | Short Response

10. Possible answers: renewable source—water, sunlight, wind; nonrenewable source—coal, oil, natural gas

11. solar energy or solar power

12. Benefit—it is renewable, it does not pollute; drawback—you need sunlight to make it work, not as convenient as using fossil fuels.

13. Possible answers: use public transportation, use electric cars, use hand mowers

14. Acid rain has a pH of 5.6 or below. The rain collected by the students is almost neutral on the pH scale. It is not acid rain.

15. Without the greenhouse effect, the heat from Earth would escape into space and the temperatures on Earth would be too cold for us to survive.

16. raw sewage or fertilizers

Part 1 | Multiple Choice

Record your answers on the answer sheet provided by your teacher or on a sheet of paper.

1. From what natural resource are plastics, paints, and gasoline made?
- **A.** coal
- **B.** petroleum
- **C.** iron ore
- **D.** natural gas

Use the illustration below to answer questions 2–4.

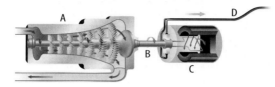

2. What is produced by the mechanism shown in the illustration?
- **A.** electricity
- **B.** coal
- **C.** petroleum
- **D.** plastic

3. In which section are the turbine blades found?
- **A.** A
- **B.** B
- **C.** C
- **D.** D

4. Which section represents the generator?
- **A.** A
- **B.** B
- **C.** C
- **D.** D

5. Which of the following is necessary for the production of hydroelectric power?
- **A.** wind
- **B.** access to a river
- **C.** exposure to sunlight
- **D.** heat from below Earth's crust

6. With which type of alternative energy are photovoltaic cells used?
- **A.** hydroelectric power
- **B.** geothermal energy
- **C.** nuclear energy
- **D.** solar energy

7. Which of the following is a type of air pollution that results when sunlight reacts with pollutants produced by burning fuels?
- **A.** ozones
- **B.** acid rain
- **C.** smog
- **D.** UV radiation

Use the photograph below to answer questions 8 and 9.

8. What is the name of the method of farming illustrated above?
- **A.** contour plowing
- **B.** strip cropping
- **C.** terracing
- **D.** no-till farming

9. What is the purpose of the method shown in the illustration?
- **A.** to decrease soil erosion from wind
- **B.** to decrease soil erosion from water flow
- **C.** to decrease acid rain production
- **D.** to increase the return of nutrients to the soil

Test-Taking Tip

Qualifying Terms Look for qualifiers in a question. Such questions are not looking for absolute answers. Qualifiers could be words such as most likely, most common, or least common.

Question 18 The qualifier in this question is *possible*. This indicates that there is uncertainty about the effects of global warming.

Part 3 | Open Ended

17. Renewable resources are not always available in all areas at all times. Water, for example, may be in short supply if there is a drought. Wind may not be plentiful in a sheltered area. Sunlight may be in short supply in certain locations.

18. As a result of global warming, rainfall patterns may change, which could alter ecosystems; other weather patterns may change; polar ice caps might melt, which would raise sea levels. The cause of global warming is unknown. Burning fossil fuels increases the amount of CO_2 in the atmosphere, which traps more of the Sun's heat, which makes Earth warmer.

19. If there was no sunlight, the family might run out of hot water so it might be difficult to take a warm shower or bath, or wash dishes in warm water.

Part 2 | Short Response/Grid In

Record your answers on the answer sheet provided by your teacher or on a sheet of paper.

10. Give one example of a renewable source of energy and one example of a nonrenewable source of energy.

Use the illustration below to answer questions 11 and 12.

11. What type of alternative energy is the girl using in the diagram?

12. Name one benefit and one drawback to using this type of energy for cooking.

13. What are two ways that smog can be reduced?

14. A group of students collects rain outside their classroom, then tests the pH of the collected rain. The pH of the rain is 7.2. Can the students say that their rain is acid rain? Why or why not?

15. Why do we depend on the greenhouse effect for survival?

16. What is the cause of algal blooms in lakes and ponds?

Part 3 | Open Ended

Record your answers on a sheet of paper.

17. Are renewable resources always readily available? Explain.

18. What are the possible worldwide effects of global warming? What causes global warming? Why do some people think that using fossil fuels less will decrease global warming?

19. A family lives in a house that uses solar panels to heat the hot water, a wood-burning stove to heat the house, and a windmill for pumping water from a well into a tower where it is stored and then piped into the house as needed. What would be the result if there was no sunlight for two weeks?

Use the illustration below to answer question 20.

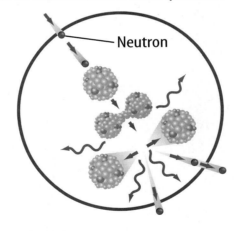

Neutron

20. What does the diagram represent?

21. Explain how different kinds of plastics are recycled.

20. The diagram shows the source of energy for nuclear power. It is what happens inside the fuel rods of a nuclear reactor.

21. Type 1 plastics (soft-drink bottles) are melted and spun into fibers that are used to make other things. Type 2 or 4 plastics (plastic bags) can be reused or recycled. Type 6 and 7 plastics cannot be recycled.

Rubrics

The following rubrics are sample scoring devices for short response and open-ended questions.

Short Response

Points	Description
2	The student demonstrates a thorough understanding of the science of the task. The response may contain minor flaws that do not detract from the demonstration of a thorough understanding.
1	The student has provided a response that is only partially correct.
0	The student has provided a completely incorrect solution or no response at all.

Open Ended

Points	Description
4	The student demonstrates a thorough understanding of the science of the task. The response may contain minor flaws that do not detract from the demonstration of a thorough understanding.
3	The student demonstrates an understanding of the science of the task. The response is essentially correct and demonstrates an essential but less than thorough understanding of the science.
2	The student demonstrates only a partial understanding of the science of the task. Although the student may have used the correct approach to a solution or may have provided a correct solution, the work lacks an essential understanding of the underlying science concepts.
1	The student demonstrates a very limited understanding of the science of the task. The response is incomplete and exhibits many flaws.
0	The student provides a completely incorrect solution or no response at all.

Student Resources

CONTENTS

Scientific Methods

Scientists use an orderly approach called the scientific method to solve problems. This includes organizing and recording data so others can understand them. Scientists use many variations in this method when they solve problems.

Identify a Question

The first step in a scientific investigation or experiment is to identify a question to be answered or a problem to be solved. For example, you might ask which gasoline is the most efficient.

Gather and Organize Information

After you have identified your question, begin gathering and organizing information. There are many ways to gather information, such as researching in a library, interviewing those knowledgeable about the subject, testing and working in the laboratory and field. Fieldwork is investigations and observations done outside of a laboratory.

Researching Information Before moving in a new direction, it is important to gather the information that already is known about the subject. Start by asking yourself questions to determine exactly what you need to know. Then you will look for the information in various reference sources, like the student is doing in **Figure 1.** Some sources may include textbooks, encyclopedias, government documents, professional journals, science magazines, and the Internet. Always list the sources of your information.

Figure 1 The Internet can be a valuable research tool.

Evaluate Sources of Information Not all sources of information are reliable. You should evaluate all of your sources of information, and use only those you know to be dependable. For example, if you are researching ways to make homes more energy efficient, a site written by the U.S. Department of Energy would be more reliable than a site written by a company that is trying to sell a new type of weatherproofing material. Also, remember that research always is changing. Consult the most current resources available to you. For example, a 1985 resource about saving energy would not reflect the most recent findings.

Sometimes scientists use data that they did not collect themselves, or conclusions drawn by other researchers. This data must be evaluated carefully. Ask questions about how the data were obtained, if the investigation was carried out properly, and if it has been duplicated exactly with the same results. Would you reach the same conclusion from the data? Only when you have confidence in the data can you believe it is true and feel comfortable using it.

Interpret Scientific Illustrations As you research a topic in science, you will see drawings, diagrams, and photographs to help you understand what you read. Some illustrations are included to help you understand an idea that you can't see easily by yourself, like the tiny particles in an atom in **Figure 2.** A drawing helps many people to remember details more easily and provides examples that clarify difficult concepts or give additional information about the topic you are studying. Most illustrations have labels or a caption to identify or to provide more information.

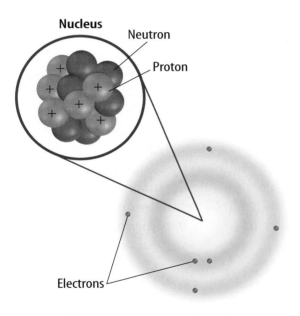

Figure 2 This drawing shows an atom of carbon with its six protons, six neutrons, and six electrons.

Concept Maps One way to organize data is to draw a diagram that shows relationships among ideas (or concepts). A concept map can help make the meanings of ideas and terms more clear, and help you understand and remember what you are studying. Concept maps are useful for breaking large concepts down into smaller parts, making learning easier.

Network Tree A type of concept map that not only shows a relationship, but how the concepts are related is a network tree, shown in **Figure 3.** In a network tree, the words are written in the ovals, while the description of the type of relationship is written across the connecting lines.

When constructing a network tree, write down the topic and all major topics on separate pieces of paper or notecards. Then arrange them in order from general to specific. Branch the related concepts from the major concept and describe the relationship on the connecting line. Continue to more specific concepts until finished.

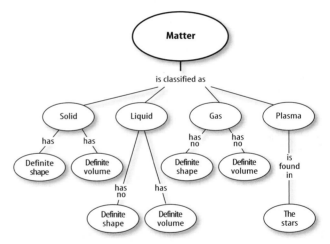

Figure 3 A network tree shows how concepts or objects are related.

Events Chain Another type of concept map is an events chain. Sometimes called a flow chart, it models the order or sequence of items. An events chain can be used to describe a sequence of events, the steps in a procedure, or the stages of a process.

When making an events chain, first find the one event that starts the chain. This event is called the initiating event. Then, find the next event and continue until the outcome is reached, as shown in **Figure 4.**

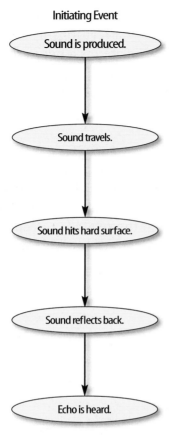

Figure 4 Events-chain concept maps show the order of steps in a process or event. This concept map shows how a sound makes an echo.

Cycle Map A specific type of events chain is a cycle map. It is used when the series of events do not produce a final outcome, but instead relate back to the beginning event, such as in **Figure 5.** Therefore, the cycle repeats itself.

To make a cycle map, first decide what event is the beginning event. This is also called the initiating event. Then list the next events in the order that they occur, with the last event relating back to the initiating event. Words can be written between the events that describe what happens from one event to the next. The number of events in a cycle map can vary, but usually contain three or more events.

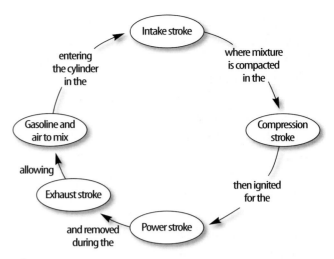

Figure 5 A cycle map shows events that occur in a cycle.

Spider Map A type of concept map that you can use for brainstorming is the spider map. When you have a central idea, you might find that you have a jumble of ideas that relate to it but are not necessarily clearly related to each other. The spider map on sound in **Figure 6** shows that if you write these ideas outside the main concept, then you can begin to separate and group unrelated terms so they become more useful.

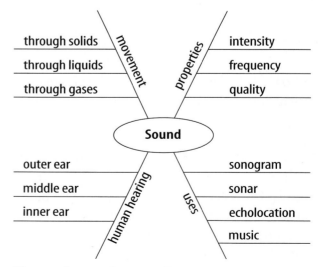

Figure 6 A spider map allows you to list ideas that relate to a central topic but not necessarily to one another.

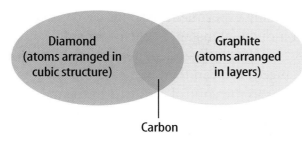

Carbon

Figure 7 This Venn diagram compares and contrasts two substances made from carbon.

Venn Diagram To illustrate how two subjects compare and contrast you can use a Venn diagram. You can see the characteristics that the subjects have in common and those that they do not, shown in **Figure 7.**

To create a Venn diagram, draw two overlapping ovals that that are big enough to write in. List the characteristics unique to one subject in one oval, and the characteristics of the other subject in the other oval. The characteristics in common are listed in the overlapping section.

Make and Use Tables One way to organize information so it is easier to understand is to use a table. Tables can contain numbers, words, or both.

To make a table, list the items to be compared in the first column and the characteristics to be compared in the first row. The title should clearly indicate the content of the table, and the column or row heads should be clear. Notice that in **Table 1** the units are included.

Table 1 Recyclables Collected During Week			
Day of Week	Paper (kg)	Aluminum (kg)	Glass (kg)
Monday	5.0	4.0	12.0
Wednesday	4.0	1.0	10.0
Friday	2.5	2.0	10.0

Make a Model One way to help you better understand the parts of a structure, the way a process works, or to show things too large or small for viewing is to make a model. For example, an atomic model made of a plastic-ball nucleus and pipe-cleaner electron shells can help you visualize how the parts of an atom relate to each other. Other types of models can by devised on a computer or represented by equations.

Form a Hypothesis

A possible explanation based on previous knowledge and observations is called a hypothesis. After researching gasoline types and recalling previous experiences in your family's car you form a hypothesis—our car runs more efficiently because we use premium gasoline. To be valid, a hypothesis has to be something you can test by using an investigation.

Predict When you apply a hypothesis to a specific situation, you predict something about that situation. A prediction makes a statement in advance, based on prior observation, experience, or scientific reasoning. People use predictions to make everyday decisions. Scientists test predictions by performing investigations. Based on previous observations and experiences, you might form a prediction that cars are more efficient with premium gasoline. The prediction can be tested in an investigation.

Design an Experiment A scientist needs to make many decisions before beginning an investigation. Some of these include: how to carry out the investigation, what steps to follow, how to record the data, and how the investigation will answer the question. It also is important to address any safety concerns.

Test the Hypothesis

Now that you have formed your hypothesis, you need to test it. Using an investigation, you will make observations and collect data, or information. This data might either support or not support your hypothesis. Scientists collect and organize data as numbers and descriptions.

Follow a Procedure In order to know what materials to use, as well as how and in what order to use them, you must follow a procedure. **Figure 8** shows a procedure you might follow to test your hypothesis.

Procedure
1. Use regular gasoline for two weeks.
2. Record the number of kilometers between fill-ups and the amount of gasoline used.
3. Switch to premium gasoline for two weeks.
4. Record the number of kilometers between fill-ups and the amount of gasoline used.

Figure 8 A procedure tells you what to do step by step.

Identify and Manipulate Variables and Controls In any experiment, it is important to keep everything the same except for the item you are testing. The one factor you change is called the independent variable. The change that results is the dependent variable. Make sure you have only one independent variable, to assure yourself of the cause of the changes you observe in the dependent variable. For example, in your gasoline experiment the type of fuel is the independent variable. The dependent variable is the efficiency.

Many experiments also have a control—an individual instance or experimental subject for which the independent variable is not changed. You can then compare the test results to the control results. To design a control you can have two cars of the same type. The control car uses regular gasoline for four weeks. After you are done with the test, you can compare the experimental results to the control results.

Collect Data

Whether you are carrying out an investigation or a short observational experiment, you will collect data, as shown in **Figure 9.** Scientists collect data as numbers and descriptions and organize it in specific ways.

Observe Scientists observe items and events, then record what they see. When they use only words to describe an observation, it is called qualitative data. Scientists' observations also can describe how much there is of something. These observations use numbers, as well as words, in the description and are called quantitative data. For example, if a sample of the element gold is described as being "shiny and very dense" the data are qualitative. Quantitative data on this sample of gold might include "a mass of 30 g and a density of 19.3 g/cm^3."

Figure 9 Collecting data is one way to gather information directly.

Figure 10 Record data neatly and clearly so it is easy to understand.

When you make observations you should examine the entire object or situation first, and then look carefully for details. It is important to record observations accurately and completely. Always record your notes immediately as you make them, so you do not miss details or make a mistake when recording results from memory. Never put unidentified observations on scraps of paper. Instead they should be recorded in a notebook, like the one in **Figure 10.** Write your data neatly so you can easily read it later. At each point in the experiment, record your observations and label them. That way, you will not have to determine what the figures mean when you look at your notes later. Set up any tables that you will need to use ahead of time, so you can record any observations right away. Remember to avoid bias when collecting data by not including personal thoughts when you record observations. Record only what you observe.

Estimate Scientific work also involves estimating. To estimate is to make a judgment about the size or the number of something without measuring or counting. This is important when the number or size of an object or population is too large or too difficult to accurately count or measure.

Sample Scientists may use a sample or a portion of the total number as a type of estimation. To sample is to take a small, representative portion of the objects or organisms of a population for research. By making careful observations or manipulating variables within that portion of the group, information is discovered and conclusions are drawn that might apply to the whole population. A poorly chosen sample can be unrepresentative of the whole. If you were trying to determine the rainfall in an area, it would not be best to take a rainfall sample from under a tree.

Measure You use measurements everyday. Scientists also take measurements when collecting data. When taking measurements, it is important to know how to use measuring tools properly. Accuracy also is important.

Length To measure length, the distance between two points, scientists use meters. Smaller measurements might be measured in centimeters or millimeters.

Length is measured using a metric ruler or meter stick. When using a metric ruler, line up the 0-cm mark with the end of the object being measured and read the number of the unit where the object ends. Look at the metric ruler shown in **Figure 11.** The centimeter lines are the long, numbered lines, and the shorter lines are millimeter lines. In this instance, the length would be 4.50 cm.

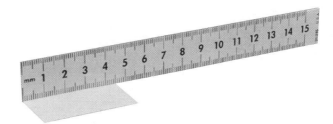

Figure 11 This metric ruler has centimeter and millimeter divisions.

Mass The SI unit for mass is the kilogram (kg). Scientists can measure mass using units formed by adding metric prefixes to the unit gram (g), such as milligram (mg). To measure mass, you might use a triple-beam balance similar to the one shown in **Figure 12.** The balance has a pan on one side and a set of beams on the other side. Each beam has a rider that slides on the beam.

When using a triple-beam balance, place an object on the pan. Slide the largest rider along its beam until the pointer drops below zero. Then move it back one notch. Repeat the process for each rider proceeding from the larger to smaller until the pointer swings an equal distance above and below the zero point. Sum the masses on each beam to find the mass of the object. Move all riders back to zero when finished.

Instead of putting materials directly on the balance, scientists often take a tare of a container. A tare is the mass of a container into which objects or substances are placed for measuring their masses. To mass objects or substances, find the mass of a clean container. Remove the container from the pan, and place the object or substances in the container. Find the mass of the container with the materials in it. Subtract the mass of the empty container from the mass of the filled container to find the mass of the materials you are using.

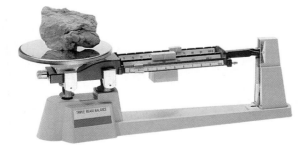

Figure 12 A triple-beam balance is used to determine the mass of an object.

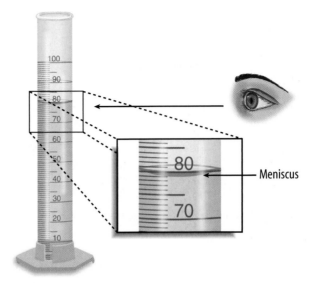

Meniscus

Figure 13 Graduated cylinders measure liquid volume.

Liquid Volume To measure liquids, the unit used is the liter. When a smaller unit is needed, scientists might use a milliliter. Because a milliliter takes up the volume of a cube measuring 1 cm on each side it also can be called a cubic centimeter ($cm^3 = cm \times cm \times cm$).

You can use beakers and graduated cylinders to measure liquid volume. A graduated cylinder, shown in **Figure 13,** is marked from bottom to top in milliliters. In lab, you might use a 10-mL graduated cylinder or a 100-mL graduated cylinder. When measuring liquids, notice that the liquid has a curved surface. Look at the surface at eye level, and measure the bottom of the curve. This is called the meniscus. The graduated cylinder in **Figure 13** contains 79.0 mL, or 79.0 cm^3, of a liquid.

Temperature Scientists often measure temperature using the Celsius scale. Pure water has a freezing point of 0°C and boiling point of 100°C. The unit of measurement is degrees Celsius. Two other scales often used are the Fahrenheit and Kelvin scales.

Figure 14 A thermometer measures the temperature of an object.

Scientists use a thermometer to measure temperature. Most thermometers in a laboratory are glass tubes with a bulb at the bottom end containing a liquid such as colored alcohol. The liquid rises or falls with a change in temperature. To read a glass thermometer like the thermometer in **Figure 14,** rotate it slowly until a red line appears. Read the temperature where the red line ends.

Form Operational Definitions An operational definition defines an object by how it functions, works, or behaves. For example, when you are playing hide and seek and a tree is home base, you have created an operational definition for a tree.

Objects can have more than one operational definition. For example, a ruler can be defined as a tool that measures the length of an object (how it is used). It can also be a tool with a series of marks used as a standard when measuring (how it works).

Analyze the Data

To determine the meaning of your observations and investigation results, you will need to look for patterns in the data. Then you must think critically to determine what the data mean. Scientists use several approaches when they analyze the data they have collected and recorded. Each approach is useful for identifying specific patterns.

Interpret Data The word *interpret* means "to explain the meaning of something." When analyzing data from an experiment, try to find out what the data show. Identify the control group and the test group to see whether or not changes in the independent variable have had an effect. Look for differences in the dependent variable between the control and test groups.

Classify Sorting objects or events into groups based on common features is called classifying. When classifying, first observe the objects or events to be classified. Then select one feature that is shared by some members in the group, but not by all. Place those members that share that feature in a subgroup. You can classify members into smaller and smaller subgroups based on characteristics. Remember that when you classify, you are grouping objects or events for a purpose. Keep your purpose in mind as you select the features to form groups and subgroups.

Compare and Contrast Observations can be analyzed by noting the similarities and differences between two more objects or events that you observe. When you look at objects or events to see how they are similar, you are comparing them. Contrasting is looking for differences in objects or events.

Recognize Cause and Effect A cause is a reason for an action or condition. The effect is that action or condition. When two events happen together, it is not necessarily true that one event caused the other. Scientists must design a controlled investigation to recognize the exact cause and effect.

Draw Conclusions

When scientists have analyzed the data they collected, they proceed to draw conclusions about the data. These conclusions are sometimes stated in words similar to the hypothesis that you formed earlier. They may confirm a hypothesis, or lead you to a new hypothesis.

Infer Scientists often make inferences based on their observations. An inference is an attempt to explain observations or to indicate a cause. An inference is not a fact, but a logical conclusion that needs further investigation. For example, you may infer that a fire has caused smoke. Until you investigate, however, you do not know for sure.

Apply When you draw a conclusion, you must apply those conclusions to determine whether the data supports the hypothesis. If your data do not support your hypothesis, it does not mean that the hypothesis is wrong. It means only that the result of the investigation did not support the hypothesis. Maybe the experiment needs to be redesigned, or some of the initial observations on which the hypothesis was based were incomplete or biased. Perhaps more observation or research is needed to refine your hypothesis. A successful investigation does not always come out the way you originally predicted.

Avoid Bias Sometimes a scientific investigation involves making judgments. When you make a judgment, you form an opinion. It is important to be honest and not to allow any expectations of results to bias your judgments. This is important throughout the entire investigation, from researching to collecting data to drawing conclusions.

Communicate

The communication of ideas is an important part of the work of scientists. A discovery that is not reported will not advance the scientific community's understanding or knowledge. Communication among scientists also is important as a way of improving their investigations.

Scientists communicate in many ways, from writing articles in journals and magazines that explain their investigations and experiments, to announcing important discoveries on television and radio. Scientists also share ideas with colleagues on the Internet or present them as lectures, like the student is doing in **Figure 15.**

Figure 15 A student communicates to his peers about his investigation.

SAFETY SYMBOLS

SAFETY SYMBOLS	HAZARD	EXAMPLES	PRECAUTION	REMEDY
DISPOSAL	Special disposal procedures need to be followed.	certain chemicals, living organisms	Do not dispose of these materials in the sink or trash can.	Dispose of wastes as directed by your teacher.
BIOLOGICAL	Organisms or other biological materials that might be harmful to humans	bacteria, fungi, blood, unpreserved tissues, plant materials	Avoid skin contact with these materials. Wear mask or gloves.	Notify your teacher if you suspect contact with material. Wash hands thoroughly.
EXTREME TEMPERATURE	Objects that can burn skin by being too cold or too hot	boiling liquids, hot plates, dry ice, liquid nitrogen	Use proper protection when handling.	Go to your teacher for first aid.
SHARP OBJECT	Use of tools or glassware that can easily puncture or slice skin	razor blades, pins, scalpels, pointed tools, dissecting probes, broken glass	Practice common-sense behavior and follow guidelines for use of the tool.	Go to your teacher for first aid.
FUME	Possible danger to respiratory tract from fumes	ammonia, acetone, nail polish remover, heated sulfur, moth balls	Make sure there is good ventilation. Never smell fumes directly. Wear a mask.	Leave foul area and notify your teacher immediately.
ELECTRICAL	Possible danger from electrical shock or burn	improper grounding, liquid spills, short circuits, exposed wires	Double-check setup with teacher. Check condition of wires and apparatus.	Do not attempt to fix electrical problems. Notify your teacher immediately.
IRRITANT	Substances that can irritate the skin or mucous membranes of the respiratory tract	pollen, moth balls, steel wool, fiberglass, potassium permanganate	Wear dust mask and gloves. Practice extra care when handling these materials.	Go to your teacher for first aid.
CHEMICAL	Chemicals can react with and destroy tissue and other materials	bleaches such as hydrogen peroxide; acids such as sulfuric acid, hydrochloric acid; bases such as ammonia, sodium hydroxide	Wear goggles, gloves, and an apron.	Immediately flush the affected area with water and notify your teacher.
TOXIC	Substance may be poisonous if touched, inhaled, or swallowed.	mercury, many metal compounds, iodine, poinsettia plant parts	Follow your teacher's instructions.	Always wash hands thoroughly after use. Go to your teacher for first aid.
FLAMMABLE	Flammable chemicals may be ignited by open flame, spark, or exposed heat.	alcohol, kerosene, potassium permanganate	Avoid open flames and heat when using flammable chemicals.	Notify your teacher immediately. Use fire safety equipment if applicable.
OPEN FLAME	Open flame in use, may cause fire.	hair, clothing, paper, synthetic materials	Tie back hair and loose clothing. Follow teacher's instruction on lighting and extinguishing flames.	Notify your teacher immediately. Use fire safety equipment if applicable.

 Eye Safety Proper eye protection should be worn at all times by anyone performing or observing science activities.

 Clothing Protection This symbol appears when substances could stain or burn clothing.

 Animal Safety This symbol appears when safety of animals and students must be ensured.

 Handwashing After the lab, wash hands with soap and water before removing goggles.

Safety in the Science Laboratory

The science laboratory is a safe place to work if you follow standard safety procedures. Being responsible for your own safety helps to make the entire laboratory a safer place for everyone. When performing any lab, read and apply the caution statements and safety symbol listed at the beginning of the lab.

General Safety Rules

1. Obtain your teacher's permission to begin all investigations and use laboratory equipment.

2. Study the procedure. Ask your teacher any questions. Be sure you understand safety symbols shown on the page.

3. Notify your teacher about allergies or other health conditions which can affect your participation in a lab.

4. Learn and follow use and safety procedures for your equipment. If unsure, ask your teacher.

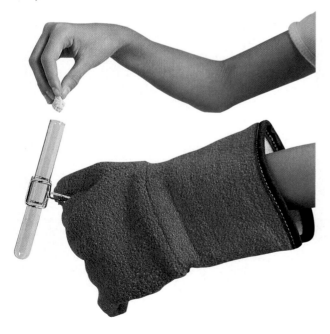

5. Never eat, drink, chew gum, apply cosmetics, or do any personal grooming in the lab. Never use lab glassware as food or drink containers. Keep your hands away from your face and mouth.

6. Know the location and proper use of the safety shower, eye wash, fire blanket, and fire alarm.

Prevent Accidents

1. Use the safety equipment provided to you. Goggles and a safety apron should be worn during investigations.

2. Do NOT use hair spray, mousse, or other flammable hair products. Tie back long hair and tie down loose clothing.

3. Do NOT wear sandals or other open-toed shoes in the lab.

4. Remove jewelry on hands and wrists. Loose jewelry, such as chains and long necklaces, should be removed to prevent them from getting caught in equipment.

5. Do not taste any substances or draw any material into a tube with your mouth.

6. Proper behavior is expected in the lab. Practical jokes and fooling around can lead to accidents and injury.

7. Keep your work area uncluttered.

Laboratory Work

1. Collect and carry all equipment and materials to your work area before beginning a lab.

2. Remain in your own work area unless given permission by your teacher to leave it.

3. Always slant test tubes away from yourself and others when heating them, adding substances to them, or rinsing them.

4. If instructed to smell a substance in a container, hold the container a short distance away and fan vapors towards your nose.

5. Do NOT substitute other chemicals/substances for those in the materials list unless instructed to do so by your teacher.

6. Do NOT take any materials or chemicals outside of the laboratory.

7. Stay out of storage areas unless instructed to be there and supervised by your teacher.

Laboratory Cleanup

1. Turn off all burners, water, and gas, and disconnect all electrical devices.

2. Clean all pieces of equipment and return all materials to their proper places.

3. Dispose of chemicals and other materials as directed by your teacher. Place broken glass and solid substances in the proper containers. Never discard materials in the sink.

4. Clean your work area.

5. Wash your hands with soap and water thoroughly BEFORE removing your goggles.

Emergencies

1. Report any fire, electrical shock, glassware breakage, spill, or injury, no matter how small, to your teacher immediately. Follow his or her instructions.

2. If your clothing should catch fire, STOP, DROP, and ROLL. If possible, smother it with the fire blanket or get under a safety shower. NEVER RUN.

3. If a fire should occur, turn off all gas and leave the room according to established procedures.

4. In most instances, your teacher will clean up spills. Do NOT attempt to clean up spills unless you are given permission and instructions to do so.

5. If chemicals come into contact with your eyes or skin, notify your teacher immediately. Use the eyewash or flush your skin or eyes with large quantities of water.

6. The fire extinguisher and first-aid kit should only be used by your teacher unless it is an extreme emergency and you have been given permission.

7. If someone is injured or becomes ill, only a professional medical provider or someone certified in first aid should perform first-aid procedures.

Time required 1 day (no class time)

Materials

- Purchase inexpensive measuring cups at a discount department store.
- Students can make inexpensive measuring cups by using a new graduated cylinder to fill up a clear plastic cup 50 mL at a time. They can mark the 50 mL increments on the outside of the cup with a permanent marker.

Safety Precaution

Students should make certain their measuring cups are clean and have never contained toxic substances.

Teaching Strategy

Students can convert the number of milliliters of liquid they drank in one day to liters by dividing their total number of milliliters by 1,000.

Conclude and Apply

1. Answers should include the units of milliliters or liters.
2. The mass in grams of individually wrapped foods is printed on the packaging, and a balance could be used to measure the mass of fresh foods or foods poured from a larger container.

Extra Try at Home Labs

EXTRA Labs

From Your Kitchen, Junk Drawer, or Yard

1 Your Daily Drink

Real-World Question
How much do you drink in a day?

Possible Materials
- 500-mL measuring cup
- calculator

Procedure
1. When you drink a bottle or can of juice, soda, water, or other beverage, look on the label of the container to find out the volume of your drink in milliliters.
2. Record the volumes of all the can and bottle drinks you consume at home in one day in your Science Journal.
3. Use a measuring cup to measure the amount of liquids you drink during one day that you pour from a larger container. Record these volumes in your Science Journal.
4. Add up the volumes of all the drinks you consumed during the day.

Conclude and Apply
1. How much liquid did you drink during the day?
2. Infer how you would measure the mass of the foods you ate in one day.

2 Cell Sizes

Real-World Question
How do different cells compare in size?

Possible Materials
- meterstick
- metric ruler
- white paper
- pencil
- pen
- masking tape

Procedure
1. Make a dot on a white sheet of paper with a pencil.
2. Use a metric ruler to make a second dot 1 mm away from the first dot. This distance represents the average length of a bacteria cell.
3. Measure a distance 8 mm away from the first dot and make a third dot. This distance represents the average length of a red blood cell.
4. Mark a spot on the floor with a piece of tape and use the meterstick to measure a distance of 7 meters. Mark this distance with a second piece of tape. This distance represents the average length of an amoeba cell.

Conclude and Apply
1. The distance between the first and second dot is 1,000 times longer than the actual size of a bacterium cell. Calculate the length of an actual bacterium cell.
2. A large chicken egg is just one cell, and it is 100 times longer than an amoeba cell. Calculate the distance you would have to measure to represent the average length of a hen's egg.

Adult supervision required for all labs.

These labs are available at life.msscience.com.

---

2 Cell Sizes

Time required 15 minutes

Materials Students can complete this activity by using only metersticks.

Safety Precaution Caution students to use metersticks with care. Metal metersticks bend easily and can harm others if used carelessly.

Teaching Strategies
- Clear away space on the classroom floor for this activity or have students complete it outside.
- Students can research the length of other types of cells and measure their relative distances on the white sheet of paper or on the floor.

Conclude and Apply
1. 0.001 mm or 1 micrometer
2. 700 meters

3 Expanding Eggs

▶ *Real-World Question*

How can you observe liquids passing through a cell membrane?

Possible Materials 🔲 🔲 🔲 🔲

- glass jar with lid
- white vinegar
- medium chicken egg
- tape measure or string and ruler
- tongs
- measuring cup

▶ *Procedure*

1. Obtain a glass jar with a lid and a medium egg.
2. Make certain your egg easily fits into your jar.
3. Measure the circumference of your egg and then carefully place it in the jar.
4. Pour the white vinegar into the jar until the egg is completely submerged.
5. Place the lid on the jar but do not seal the jar.
6. Observe your egg each day for three days. Measure the circumference of the egg after three days.

▶ *Conclude and Apply*

1. Describe the changes that happened to your egg.
2. Infer why the egg's circumference changed. *HINT: A hen's egg is a single cell.*

4 Putting Down Roots

▶ *Real-World Question*

Can the stem cells of plants reproduce root cells for a new plant?

Possible Materials 🔲 🔲 🔲 🔲

- houseplant
- scissors
- metric ruler
- rooting hormone
- glasses or jars (3)
- water
- magnifying lens

▶ *Procedure*

1. Examine the stems of a houseplant and locate a node on three different stems. A node looks like a small bump.
2. Cut 3 stems off the plant at a 45° angle about 3–4 mm below the node.
3. Remove all flowers and flower buds from the cut stems.
4. Dip the cut end of each stem into rooting hormone solution.
5. Place the end of each stem into a separate glass of water and observe them for a week.

▶ *Conclude and Apply*

1. Describe what happened to the ends of the stems.
2. Infer why flowers and buds should be removed from the stems.
3. Infer how plant stem cells can produce root cells.

Adult supervision required for all labs.

3 Expanding Eggs

Time Required five minutes for set-up; five-minute observation periods for three days

Materials

- Make certain the egg will fit into the jar both before and after the lab is completed. Avoid using large or extra large eggs.
- Spaghetti sauce or pickle jars work well for this lab.
- Students also can measure egg circumferences with lengths of string and metric rulers.

Safety Precaution

Students should wash their hands thoroughly after handling eggs.

Teaching Strategy The eggshell is made of calcium carbonate and has the same chemical composition as limestone. Vinegar dissolves the calcium carbonate, producing bubbles of carbon dioxide during the reaction.

Conclude and Apply

1. The egg's shell will dissolve. The outer membrane of the egg will become rubbery, and the egg will increase in circumference by about 15 percent.
2. The water in the vinegar passes through the membrane of the egg cell expanding the egg's size. The particles inside the egg are too large to move out through the membrane.

4 Putting Down Roots

Time Required several 2–3 minute observation periods for a week

Materials The plant roots will grow more quickly when dipped in rooting hormone, but the hormone is not necessary to complete the activity.

Safety Precaution Students should wash their hands thoroughly after the activity.

Teaching Strategies

- Not all the cuttings will grow roots. Roots will be more easily visible when viewed under a hand lens.
- Consider having students plant their cuttings in soil once roots have grown.

Conclude and Apply

1. Tiny roots should grow on one or more stems.
2. Flowers and buds consume energy for growth. Cuttings can conserve more energy without them.
3. The DNA of each plant cell contains all the information needed to make every type of plant cell.

5 Do Your Ears Hang Low?

Time Required 25 minutes (additional time out of class may be needed)

Material Consider supplying students with clipboards to use when interviewing other classmates.

Safety Precaution Caution students to be polite and respectful when they interview people.

Teaching Strategy To gather a large sample, students can interview friends and family members before class and then interview each other during class.

Conclude and Apply
1. Answers will vary but about 70 to 90 percent of people have free earlobes.
2. Free earlobes is a dominant trait.
3. Since both parents carry a recessive gene for attached earlobes, none of the children will have free earlobes.

Extra Try at Home Labs

5 Do your ears hang low?

Real-World Question
Is ear lobe attachment a dominant or recessive trait?

Possible Materials
- Science Journal
- pencil
- pen
- calculator

Procedure
1. Ask your friends, family members, and other people you know if their ear lobes are attached or free.
2. Try to interview as many people as possible to collect a large sample of data.
3. Record the number of people who have attached ear lobes and the number with free ear lobes in your Science Journal.

Conclude and Apply
1. Calculate the percentage of people who have attached ear lobes and the percentage of people who have free ear lobes.
2. Infer whether or not attached ear lobes is a dominant or recessive trait. Do research to confirm your results.
3. Infer how many children in a family would have free ear lobes if their parents had attached ear lobes.

6 Frozen Fossils

Real-World Question
How can we model the formation of an amber fossil?

Possible Materials
- small glass jar with lid
- honey
- ruler
- dead insect or spider
- small rubber insect or spider
- freezer

Procedure
1. Thoroughly wash and dry a small glass jar and its lid.
2. Pour 3 cm of honey into the jar. Do not pour honey down the sides of the jar.
3. Search for a dead insect or spider around your home or school and drop it into the center of the honey's surface.
4. Pour another 3 cm of honey into the jar to cover the organism.
5. Place the jar in the freezer overnight.

Conclude and Apply
1. Explain how you modeled the formation of an amber fossil.
2. Infer how amber fossils help scientists observe adaptations of organisms over time.

816 STUDENT RESOURCES

Adult supervision required for all labs.

These labs are available at life.msscience.com.

---

6 Frozen Fossils

Time Required 20 minutes

Materials
- Baby food jars work best for this activity.
- Encourage students to search windowsills for dead insects and spiders.
- Clear away space in the classroom freezer for the jars.

Safety Precaution Students should thoroughly wash their hands after handling the insects.

Teaching Strategy Set up a display of the amber fossil models for your class and group the fossils by taxonomic phyla and classes.

Conclude and Apply
1. Amber fossils formed when insects became trapped and covered in tree sap. Over time, the tree sap hardened into amber. The freezing honey modeled the hardening of tree sap.
2. These fossils can be compared with modern day descendents of the organisms.

7 Beating Bacteria

Real-World Question
How do we protect our foods from bacteria?

Possible Materials
- heavy cream or whole milk
- plastic drinking glasses (3)
- refrigerator

Procedure
1. Pour milk into three identical glasses until each glass is three-quarters full.
2. Place one glass in the back of your refrigerator where it will not be disturbed.
3. Place a second glass in a dark, cool place such as inside a kitchen cabinet.
4. Place the third glass on a windowsill in direct sunlight.
5. Observe the milk in each glass every day for several days. In your Science Journal, write down your observations about what is happening to the milk each day.

Conclude and Apply
1. Describe what happened to the milk in each of the glasses.
2. Infer what caused the change in the milk on the windowsill.
3. Infer how a refrigerator protects food from bacteria.

8 Fungus Foods

Real-World Question
How do we protect our foods from mold?

Possible Materials
- unopened jars of baby food or some other type of food such as spaghetti sauce or salsa (4)
- plate
- spoon
- magnifying lens

Procedure
1. Open one of the jars of food and spread the contents out over a plate.
2. Place the plate in a cool place away from direct sunlight where it will not be disturbed for several days.
3. Open a second jar of food and set it next to the plate without the lid on.
4. Break the seal of the third jar of food and set it next to the second jar with the lid on.
5. Do not open the fourth jar but place it next to the other two jars.
6. Observe the food in the jars and on the plate each day for the next several days. Record your observations in your Science Journal.

Conclude and Apply
1. Describe what happened to the food in each container.
2. Explain how food companies protect the foods you buy from fungi such as mold.

Adult supervision required for all labs.

Extra Try at Home Labs

7 Beating Bacteria

Time Required 5-minute observation periods each day for several days

Materials
- Heavy cream or whole milk usually works best for this experiment. Half-and-half also can be used.
- Consider having students measure and record the temperature of the milk samples each day.

Safety Precautions
- Caution students to wash their hands thoroughly after handling the milk.
- Caution students to never drink liquids that have been left out in the open for extended periods of time.

Teaching Strategy Clear away a space in a cabinet and in your classroom refrigerator the day before you complete this experiment.

Conclude and Apply
1. The milk in the refrigerator should look and smell drinkable. After several days, the milk in the cool place will form thick, white lumps in it and smell sour. The milk on the windowsill will form thick, white lumps and smell sour in one or two days.
2. Warm temperatures allowed the bacteria to reproduce rapidly into colonies spoiling the milk.
3. Cold temperatures slow the growth of bacteria reproduction preventing foods from spoiling for longer periods of time.

8 Fungus Foods

Time Required 5-minute observation periods for several days

Materials Banana baby food works well.

Safety Precautions
- Caution students to wash their hands thoroughly after handling the food.
- Caution students to never eat foods that have been left out in the open for extended periods of time.

Teaching Strategy If your room is unusually dry or hot, use an eyedropper to place a few drops of water on the surface of each food sample each day.

Conclude and Apply
1. The food on the plate and on the surface of the food in the second jar will be covered with mold. Some mold will grow in the jar covered by a lid, and no mold will grow in the sealed jar.
2. Foods are cooked and then sealed in airtight containers to prevent growth of mold spores.

9 Prickly Plants

Time Required 30 minutes

Materials
- Instruct students to carefully press the excess air out of the bag before sealing the water inside it.
- Extra tape should be used to secure the toothpicks around the rim of the cardboard tube.

Safety Precaution
Warn students not to try this activity without oven mitts.

Teaching Strategy
Students can save time by laying a strip of tape sticky side up on the table and attaching the ends of several toothpicks on the tape at once.

Conclude and Apply
1. Students should be able to extract the water bag from the roll without the toothpicks without much difficulty, but they will be unable to get past the toothpicks and remove the water from the roll.
2. Water is scarce in the desert. Cacti have developed needles to protect their water rich tissues from birds and other animals.

---

9 Prickly Plants

Real-World Question
Why does a cactus have needles?

Possible Materials
- toilet paper roll or paper towel roll (cut in half)
- transparent tape
- toothpicks (15)
- metric ruler
- oven mitt
- self-sealing bag
- water
- measuring cup

Procedure
1. Pour 50 mL of water into a small self-sealing bag.
2. Stuff the bag of water into the toilet paper roll so that the bag is just inside the roll's rim.
3. Stand the roll on a table and hold it firmly with one hand. Place the oven mitt on your other hand and try to take the bag out of the roll.
4. If needed, place the bag back into the roll.
5. Securely tape toothpicks around the lip of the roll about 1 cm apart. About 4 cm of each toothpick should stick up above the rim.
6. Hold the roll on the table, put the oven mitt on, and try to take the bag out of the roll without breaking the toothpicks.

Conclude and Apply
1. Compare how easy it was to remove the water bag from the toilet paper roll with and without the toothpicks protecting the water.
2. Infer why desert cacti have needles.

10 Feed the Birds

Real-World Question
How can you attract hummingbirds to your yard?

Possible Materials
- plastic water bottle (20 ounce) with bent tube or straw (10 cm length)
- sugar
- water
- pot
- wooden spoon
- red plastic flowers
- red tape or red plastic wrap
- narrow net bag
- strong string or wire

Procedure
1. Wrap red tape or fasten red plastic wrap around the bottle. Fasten red flowers to the bottle.
2. Boil 800 mL of water and gradually stir in 200 mL of sugar until all the sugar is dissolved. Let the solution cool and fill the bottle with the solution.
3. Hang the bottle upside down in the net bag and hang the feeder by a string in a shady location. Hang it above bright red or pink flowers if possible.
4. Observe your feeder daily and watch for hummingbirds.
5. Clean your bottle and refill it with fresh sugar solution every three days.

Conclude and Apply
1. Explain why hummingbirds, bees, bats, and other animals are important to plant reproduction.
2. Infer why flowers are usually brightly colored.

Adult supervision required for all labs.

These labs are available at life.msscience.com.

---

10 Feed The Birds

Time Required 45 minutes and several 5-minute observation periods

Materials
- Use modeling clay to seal any leaks.
- Extra hummingbird solution can be stored in the refrigerator.

Safety Precautions
- Students should wear safety goggles when boiling the water.
- Caution students not to use glass bottles.

Teaching Strategy
Have students work in pairs to prepare the feeder and mix the sugar solution.

Conclude and Apply
1. As these animals gather or eat nectar, they spread the flower's pollen to other plants, and once pollinated, these plants are capable of reproducing.
2. Bright colors attract daytime pollinators.

11 Breathing Plants

● Real-World Question
How do plants breathe?

Possible Materials
- houseplant
- petroleum jelly
- paper towel
- soap
- water

● Procedure
1. Scoop some petroleum jelly out of the jar with your fingertips and coat the top of three or four leaves of the houseplant with jelly. Cover the entire top surface of the leaves only.
2. Coat the bottom of three or four different leaves with a layer of jelly.
3. Choose two or three stems not connected to the leaves you have covered with jelly. Coat these stems from top to bottom with a layer of jelly. Cover the entire stems but not their leaves.
4. Wash your hands with soap and water.
5. Observe the houseplant for three days.

● Conclude and Apply
1. Describe what happened to the leaves and stems covered with jelly.
2. Infer how plants breathe.

12 A Sponge of Water

● Real-World Question
How much water does a sponge hold?

Possible Materials
- large natural sponge
- large artificial sponge (without soap)
- bucket
- shallow basin or pan
- water
- measuring cups (2)
- towel

● Procedure
1. Submerge a large, natural sponge in a bucket of water for about 2 minutes so that it fills up with water. Wait until bubbles stop rising up from the sponge.
2. Place the two measuring cups next to the bucket.

3. Carefully remove the sponge from the water and hold it over a measuring cup. Squeeze all the water out of the sponge into the measuring cup. If you reach the top mark on the measuring cup, use the second measuring cup.
4. Repeat steps 1–3 using the artificial sponge. Compare your results.

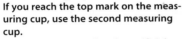

● Conclude and Apply
1. How much water did each sponge hold?
2. Infer how Roman soldiers used sponges as canteens.

Extra Try at Home Labs

11 Breathing Plants

Time Required 20 minutes (plus three 5-minute observation periods)

Materials
- Have soap, water, and paper towels available for clean up.
- Outdoor plants can be used but rain will wash the jelly off the leaves.

Safety Precautions
- Have students wear safety goggles and clothing aprons when handing the petroleum jelly.
- Caution students not to wipe their eyes while handling the jelly.

Teaching Strategy
Explain to students that the jelly on the tops of the leaves does not prevent sunlight from reaching the leaves so the leaves can still photosynthesize.

Conclude and Apply
1. The leaves coated with jelly on their undersides will turn yellow and eventually die and drop off. The other leaves and stems will be unaffected.
2. Plants take in carbon dioxide and give off oxygen through stomata located on the surfaces of their leaves.

12 A Sponge of Water

Time Required 15 minutes

Materials
- Natural sponges will hold more water than artificial sponges.
- Do not purchase artificial sponges sold with soap already added to them.
- Have towels ready for students to use.

Safety Precautions
- Caution students to never drink water taken from their sponges.
- Consider conducting this activity outside to minimize the mess.

Teaching Strategy
Discuss properties of natural and artificial sponges.

Conclude and Apply
1. A large, natural sponge can hold 500–1,000 mL depending on its size. An artificial sponge holds less.
2. Soldiers soaked up stream water with sponges and squeezed the water into their mouths.

13 Invertebrate Groceries

Time Required 30 minutes

Materials Encourage students to visit a local outdoor food market, farmer's market, or ethnic grocery store to find more exotic invertebrates for sale.

Safety Precautions
- An adult should accompany students to the grocery store.
- Caution students to never tap on the glass of a lobster aquarium.

Teaching Strategy Purchase a variety of invertebrates from your local store and bring them in to show your class.

Conclude and Apply
1. Answers will vary but may include lobster, several species of crabs, shrimp, crayfish, several species of clams, mussels, oysters, and scallops. Gourmet stores may sell sea urchins and chocolate covered insects.
2. Grocery stores will probably not sell insects, worms, or echinoderms.
3. Ocean pollution destroys or contaminates populations of marine invertebrates that are important food sources.

Extra Try at Home Labs

13 Invertebrate Groceries

Real-World Question
What types of invertebrates can you find in your local grocery store?

Possible Materials
- access to local grocery store
- guidebook to ocean invertebrates

Procedure
1. Go with an adult to the largest grocery store in your area.
2. Search the seafood section in the store for invertebrates sold as food.
3. Search the grocery aisles selling canned meat for invertebrates sold in cans.
4. Record all the invertebrates you find in the store and identify each invertebrate as a mollusk, worm, arthropod, or echinoderm.
5. If you find more than one type of an organism such as crabs, ask a grocery store employee to identify the different species for you.

Conclude and Apply
1. Identify the types of invertebrates you found.
2. What types of invertebrates were not in your grocery store?
3. Infer why we should be concerned about ocean pollution.

14 Frog Lives

Real-World Question
What do the stages of frog metamorphosis look like?

Possible Materials
- gravel
- small aquarium or bucket
- water
- clean plastic milk jug
- *Anacharis* plants
- tadpole

Procedure
1. Pour a 2-cm layer of aquarium gravel or small pebbles into a small aquarium.
2. Fill the aquarium with water and allow the water to sit for 7 days.
3. Fill a clean, plastic milk jug with tap water and allow it to sit for 7 days.
4. Plant several stalks of *Anacharis* plants in the gravel.
5. Purchase or catch a tadpole and place it in the aquarium along with some of the water from the place where you collected it.
6. Replace 10 percent of the aquarium's water every other day with water from the milk jug.
7. Observe your tadpole each day for 2–3 weeks as it completes its metamorphosis into a frog.

Conclude and Apply
1. Describe the metamorphosis of your frog.
2. Infer why you added the plant *Anacharis* to the aquarium.

Adult supervision required for all labs.

These labs are available at life.msscience.com.

---

14 Frog Lives

Time Required 40 minutes and short observation periods over 2–3 weeks

Materials Purchase extra tadpoles due to mortality rate.

Safety Precautions
- Students should thoroughly wash their hands after handling organisms.
- Students should obtain permission to collect animals on public property.
- Never release nonnative animals into local ecosystems.

Teaching Strategies
- Avoid placing the aquarium outside or in direct sunlight.
- Before the metamorphosis occurs, decide what you will do with the adult frogs.

Conclude and Apply
1. Students should provide both qualitative and quantitative descriptions.
2. to provide oxygen for the gill breathing tadpole

Extra Try at Home Labs

15 Fly Like a Bird

Real-World Question

How does a bird's wings keep it in the air?

Possible Materials
- tennis ball or racquetball
- softball
- flying disc
- stopwatch or watch with second hand

Procedure
1. Throw a ball in a straight line and parallel to the ground as hard as you can.
2. Have a partner use a stopwatch to time how long the ball stays in the air.
3. Throw a flying disc in a straight line and parallel to the ground so that it hovers.
4. Have a partner use a stopwatch to time how long the flying disc stays in the air.
5. Repeat steps 1–4 several times and record your times in your Science Journal.

Conclude and Apply
1. Compare the maximum time the tennis ball stayed in the air to the longest time the flying disc stayed up.
2. Compare the shape of the flying disc when you hold it flat in front of you to the shape of a bird wing. How are they similar?
3. Infer how a bird's wings allow it to fly.

16 Fighting Fish

Real-World Question

How will a Siamese fighting fish react to a mirror?

Possible Materials
- 2 small fish bowls, glass bowls, or small jars
- water (aquarium, purified)
- 1 male Siamese fighting fish (*Betta splendens*)
- 1 female Siamese fighting fish (*Betta splendens*)
- mirror

Procedure
1. Place a male Siamese fighting fish in a small fish bowl with water and a female Siamese fighting fish into a second bowl with water.
2. Place a mirror up to the bowl with the male fish so that he sees his reflection and observe his reaction.
3. Place a mirror up to the bowl with the female fish so that she sees her reflection and observe her reaction.

Conclude and Apply
1. Describe how the male and the female reacted to their reflections.
2. What type of behavior did the male Siamese fighting fish display?
3. Infer why the male fish displays this type of behavior.

Adult supervision required for all labs.

EXTRA TRY AT HOME LABS **821**

Extra Try at Home Labs

15 Fly Like a Bird

Time Required 30 minutes

Materials Brand name flying discs usually fly best.

Safety Precaution Caution students against throwing objects toward people, animals, cars, or buildings.

Teaching Strategies
- This activity works best when students can throw the ball and flying disc from atop a small hill.
- Choose a student who throws a flying disc well to demonstrate the activity for the entire class.

Conclude and Apply
1. Answers will vary, but the flying disc should stay aloft several seconds longer.
2. Both have the shape of an airfoil with a flat bottom and curved top surface.
3. Air moves across the top of the wing faster than the bottom of the wing. The slower air moving underneath the wing has more pressure and provides lift to help keep the bird aloft.

16 Fighting Fish

Time Required 15 minutes

Materials Female Siamese fighting fish are usually sold in a community aquarium. Transfer them to small fish bowls.

Safety Precaution Students should wash their hands after handling fish or water.

Teaching Strategies
- Encourage students to hold the mirror up to the male fish for only a few seconds to avoid overly-aggravating the fish.
- Explain that these fish developed territorial behaviors because they live in small spaces in Asian rice paddies.

Conclude and Apply
1. The female won't react to the mirror. The male will display aggressive behavior such as facing the image, spreading his gill covering extensions and fins, and deepening the color of his scales.
2. territorial behavior
3. Males fight each other for nesting territory and mating rights with females.

EXTRA TRY AT HOME LABS 821

17 Measuring Melanin

Time Required 25 minutes for set-up; 20 minute observation period 2 days later

Materials Collect a range of color swatches for human skin from nearly white to dark brown.

Safety Precaution Students should not leave the plastic bandages on their fingers longer than 2 days.

Teaching Strategy Encourage students to test a wide variety of skin colors.

Conclude and Apply

1. Answers will vary, but darker colored skin will change to a greater degree.
2. Skin responds to light by producing more melanin pigment making the skin darker, but in the absence of light, less melanin is produced creating a lighter color of skin.

Extra Try at Home Labs

Extra Try at Home Labs

17 Measuring Melanin

▶ Real-World Question
How does the amount of melanin vary from person to person?

Possible Materials
- several plastic bandages
- color swatches from a paint or hardware store

▶ Procedure
1. Obtain color swatches from a paint store or hardware store.
2. Identify the color swatch that most closely matches your skin color. Record the color in your Science Journal.
3. Place a plastic bandage around the end of one of your fingers and leave the bandage on for two days.
4. Remove the bandage and observe the change in your skin color. Identify the color swatch that most closely matches the faded skin color. Record the color in your Science Journal.
5. Follow steps 2–4 to measure the amount of melanin in the skin of several other people.

▶ Conclude and Apply
1. Identify how many shades of color your skin and the skin of the other people you tested changed.
2. Infer why your skin color changed.

18 Vitamin Search

▶ Real-World Question
How many vitamins and minerals are in the foods you eat?

Possible Materials
- labels from packaged foods and drinks
- nutrition guidebook or cookbook

▶ Procedure
1. Create a data table to record the "% Daily Value" of important vitamins and minerals for a variety of foods.
2. Collect packages from a variety of packaged foods and check the Nutrition Facts chart for the "% Daily Value" of all the vitamins and minerals it contains. These values are listed at the bottom of the chart.
3. Use cookbooks or nutrition guidebooks to research the "% Daily Value" of vitamins and minerals found in several fresh fruits and vegetables such as strawberries, spinach, oranges, and lentils.

▶ Conclude and Apply
1. Infer why a healthy diet includes fresh fruits and vegetables.
2. Infer why a healthy diet includes a wide variety of healthy foods.

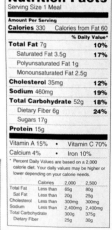

Nutrition Facts
Serving Size 1 Meal

Amount Per Serving

Calories 330	Calories from Fat 60	
		% Daily Value*
Total Fat 7g		**10%**
Saturated Fat 3.5g		**17%**
Polyunsaturated Fat 1g		
Monounsaturated Fat 2.5g		
Cholesterol 35mg		**12%**
Sodium 460mg		**19%**
Total Carbohydrate 52g		**18%**
Dietary Fiber 6g		**24%**
Sugars 17g		
Protein 15g		

Vitamin A 15%	•	Vitamin C 70%
Calcium 4%	•	Iron 10%

* Percent Daily Values are based on a 2,000 calorie diet. Your daily values may be higher or lower depending on your calorie needs.

	Calories	2,000	2,500
Total Fat	Less than	65g	80g
Sat Fat	Less than	20g	25g
Cholesterol	Less than	300mg	300mg
Sodium	Less than	2,400mg	2,400mg
Total Carbohydrate		300g	375g
Dietary Fiber		25g	30g

Adult supervision required for all labs.

These labs are available at life.msscience.com.

---

18 Vitamin Search

Time Required 40 minutes

Materials
- Purchase inexpensive nutrition guidebooks at a local grocery store.
- Many cookbooks contain nutritional information about fresh foods.

Safety Precaution Caution students never to eat or drink anything in science class.

Teaching Strategy Encourage students to evaluate the percentages of vitamins and minerals in their favorite foods and in the foods they eat most frequently.

Conclude and Apply

1. Packaged foods have few vitamins and minerals compared to fresh fruits and vegetables.
2. A single fruit or vegetable will have a high content of one vitamin or mineral but not others. A varied diet will ensure enough of all essential vitamins and minerals are consumed.

19 What's in blood?

Real-World Question
What are the proportions of the components of your blood?

Possible Materials
- bag of brown rice
- white rice
- small bag of wild rice
- measuring cup
- large bowl or large cooking tray

Procedure
1. Measure 1.25 liters of brown rice and pour the rice into a large bowl or on a cooking tray.
2. Measure 100 mL of wild rice and pour it into the bowl or on the tray.
3. Count out 50 grains of white rice and place them in the bowl or on the tray.
4. Mix the three types of rice thoroughly and observe the proportions of the three major components of your blood.

Conclude and Apply
1. Infer what type of rice represents red blood cells.
2. Infer what type of rice represents white blood cells.
3. Infer what type of rice represents platelets.

20 Modeling Glucose

Real-World Question
What does a molecule of glucose used in respiration look like?

Possible Materials
- red polystyrene balls (7)
- blue polystyrene balls (11)
- yellow polystyrene balls (14)
- box of toothpicks

Procedure
1. Use toothpicks to connect the 6 red polystyrene balls together in a line. These balls represent carbon atoms.
2. Attach a blue ball and a yellow ball to the first carbon atom. The blue ball goes to the left and the yellow ball to the right. The blue ball represents an oxygen atom, and the yellow ball represents a hydrogen atom.
3. Attach a hydrogen atom and oxygen atom in a line to the right of the second, fourth and fifth carbon atoms. Attach a hydrogen atom to the left of each of these carbon atoms.
4. Attach a hydrogen atom and oxygen atom in a line to the left of the third carbon atom and a hydrogen atom to the right.
5. Attach two hydrogen atoms and one oxygen atom to the sixth carbon atom. Attach a hydrogen atom to the oxygen atom.

Conclude and Apply
1. Construct models of the other molecules used during respiration.
2. Infer why oxygen is needed during respiration.

Adult supervision required for all labs.

19 What's in blood?

Time Required 15 minutes

Materials
- Purchase a wild rice variety with a black color.
- There are approximately 400 grains of rice in 10 mL.

Safety Precaution Caution students not to eat the rice.

Teaching Strategy
Consider having the class replicate the number of red blood cells, white blood cells, and platelets in 0.1 mL of blood by placing 12.5 L of brown rice, 1 L of wild rice, and 12.5 mL (500 grains) of white rice into a small aquarium or large jar.

Conclude and Apply
1. brown rice
2. wild (black) rice
3. white rice

20 Modeling Glucose

Time required 40 minutes

Materials Polystyrene balls of any three different colors can be used for this activity.

Safety Precautions
- Students should wear safety goggles.
- Caution students to use the toothpicks with care.

Teaching Strategy Have students draw a large arrow on a sheet of paper and use their models to construct the chemical reaction for respiration. Students can also combine their models to construct a balanced chemical reaction.

Conclude and Apply
1. Students should connect two blue balls together to represent an oxygen molecule, a red ball and two blue balls to represent carbon dioxide, and two yellow balls connected to a blue ball to represent a molecule of water.
2. Oxygen burns and breaks down glucose molecules into energy.

21 Pupil Power

Time Required 10 minutes

Materials
- Students can work in pairs using small handheld mirrors.
- Pocket flashlights work best for this activity.

Safety Precautions
- Students should never shine a light directly into their eyes.
- Caution students not to shine the light into the mirror. Reflected light could shine into their eyes.

Teaching Strategy
Students may have to try this activity several times to position the flashlight correctly so that they can clearly see the pupils of their eyes.

Conclude and Apply
1. The eye pupils will abruptly diminish in size.
2. The eye's pupil controls the amount of light entering the eye. In darkness, the pupil opens up wide to gather more light, but it quickly shrinks in size when exposed to light.

Extra Try at Home Labs

21 Pupil Power

Real-World Question
Why do your eyes have pupils?

Possible Materials
- mirror
- flashlight

Procedure
1. Examine your eyes in a mirror in a brightly lit room. Observe the size of the pupil and iris of each eye.
2. Darken the room so that there is no light.
3. Turn on a flashlight and cover its light with the palm of your hand.
4. Hold the flashlight about 10–15 cm in front of your mouth with the beam facing straight up.
5. Quickly remove your hand and immediately observe the pupils of your eyes.

Conclude and Apply
1. Describe what happened to the pupils of your eyes.
2. Infer why your pupils responded to the light in this way.

22 Identifying Iodine

Real-World Question
How many iodine rich foods are in your home?

Possible Materials
- Science Journal
- pen or pencil

Procedure
1. The element iodine is needed in a person's diet for the thyroid gland to work properly. Search your kitchen for the foods richest in iodine including fish, shellfish (clams, oysters, mussels, scallops), seaweed, and kelp.
2. Record all the iodine rich foods you find in your Science Journal.
3. Search your kitchen for foods that may contain iodine if they are grown in rich soil such as onions, mushrooms, lettuce, spinach, green peppers, pineapple, peanuts, and whole wheat bread.
4. Record all of these foods that you find in your Science Journal.

Conclude and Apply
1. Infer whether or not your family eats a diet rich in iodine.
2. Infer why iodine is often added to table salt.
3. Research two diseases caused by a lack of iodine in the diet.

Adult supervision required for all labs.

These labs are available at life.msscience.com.

22 Identifying Iodine

Time Required 20 minutes

Materials Consider bringing several examples of iodine-rich foods to school.

Safety Precautions
- Caution students that consuming too much seafood can lead to toxic levels of heavy metals due to high ocean pollution levels.
- Students should not eat in the lab.

Teaching Strategy Explain that tuna, salmon, and other common canned fish are good sources of iodine, but cod, haddock, and perch are the best sources.

Conclude and Apply
1. Answers will vary.
2. Iodine is added to salt to prevent iodine deficiency in people's diets.
3. goiter and cretinism

Extra Try at Home Labs

23 Acid Defense

▶ Real-World Question
How is stomach acid your internal first line of defense?

Possible Materials 🔲 🔳 🔳
- drinking glasses (2)
- milk
- cola or lemon juice
- masking tape
- marker
- measuring cup

▶ Procedure
1. Pour 100 mL of milk into each glass.
2. Pour 20 mL of cola into the second glass.
3. Using the masking tape and marker, label the first glass *No Acid* and the second glass *Acid*.
4. Place the glasses in direct sunlight and observe the mixture each day for several days.

▶ Conclude and Apply
1. Compare the odor of the mixture in both glasses after one or two days.
2. Infer how this experiment modeled one of your internal defenses against disease.

24 Rock Creatures

▶ Real-World Question
What types of organisms live under stream rocks?

Possible Materials 🔳 🔲 🔳 🔳 🔳 🔲
- waterproof boots
- ice cube tray (white)
- aquarium net
- bucket
- collecting jars
- guidebook to pond life

▶ Procedure
1. Search under the rocks of a local stream. Look for aquatic organisms under the rocks and leaves of the stream. Compare what you find in fast- and slow-moving water.
2. Carefully pull the organisms you find off the rocks and put them into separate compartments of your ice cube tray. Take care not to injure the creatures you find.
3. Use your net and bucket to collect larger organisms.
4. Use your guidebook to pond life to identify the organisms you find.
5. Release the organisms back into the stream once you identify them.

▶ Conclude and Apply
1. Identify and list the organisms you found under the stream rocks.
2. Infer why so many aquatic organisms make their habitats beneath stream rocks.

Adult supervision required for all labs.

23 Disease Fighters

Time Required 40 minutes

Materials For an in-class activity, provide groups with mouthwash, toothpaste, soap, OTC cold medicine, antiseptic, rubbing alcohol, athlete's foot medication, dental floss, OTC allergy medicine, plastic bandages, gauze, disinfectants, and antibiotic ointment.

Safety Precautions
- Students should search their bathroom cabinets with an adult.
- Caution students never to take medication without adult supervision.

Teaching Strategy Have students research the effects of antibacterial soaps on bacterial resistance.

Conclude and Apply
1. Products that fight bacteria include mouthwash, toothpaste, soap, antiseptic, rubbing alcohol, dental floss, plastic bandages, gauze, disinfectant, and antibiotic ointment. Products to fight viruses include a few disinfectant sprays. Allergy medicines fight off allergens. Anti-fungal products include athlete's foot medication and wart medication. Chronic disease medicines include various prescription medications.
2. Answers may include shorter lifespan and frequent suffering from chronic disease symptoms.

24 Rock Creatures

Time Required 45 minutes

Materials Organisms are easier to see in white trays than in trays of other colors.

Safety Precautions
- Students should thoroughly wash their hands after handling organisms.
- Warn students that insects called backswimmers have a painful bite and large crayfish have painful pincers.
- Students should avoid deep water and flooded streams after heavy rains.

Teaching Strategy Conduct your own search of a stream near your school to survey the types of organisms your class will find.

Conclude and Apply
1. Answers may include crayfish, caddisfly larvae, mayfly nymphs, scuds, planaria, leeches, snails, and dragonfly nymphs.
2. Stream rocks provide organisms protection against predators, currents, and ultraviolet sunlight.

Extra Try at Home Labs

25 A Light in the Forest

Time required 30 minutes to test 3 sites

Materials Cutting a paper towel roll in half will make it easier to use.

Safety Precautions

- Caution students to look for poisonous plants such as poison ivy, poison oak, and poison sumac. Students should avoid forest regions with heavy undergrowth.
- Proper clothing includes long pants, long sleeves, light colored clothing, long socks tucked into pants, and hats.

Teaching Strategy
Check out forest sites before the activity and tack colorful sheets of paper to trees to mark the spots where students could take measurements.

Conclude and Apply
1. The percentages of sunlight should be higher near the edge of the forest.
2. Canopies shade the forest floor to prevent the soil from drying out, and they moderate forest temperatures throughout the year.

25 A Light in the Forest

Real-World Question
Does the amount of sunlight vary in a forest?

Possible Materials
- empty toilet paper or paper towel roll
- Science Journal

Procedure:
1. Copy the data table into your Science Journal.
2. Go with an adult to a nearby forest or large patch of trees.
3. Stand near the edge of the forest and look straight up through your cardboard tube. Estimate the percentage of blue sky and clouds you can see in the circle. This percentage is the amount of sunlight reaching the forest floor.
4. Record your location and estimated percentage of sunlight in your data table.
5. Test several other locations in the forest. Choose places where the trees completely cover the forest floor and where sunlight is partially coming through.

Data Table

Location	% of Sunlight

Conclude and Apply
1. Explain how the amount of sunlight reaching the forest floor changed from place to place.
2. Infer why it is important for leaves and branches to stop sunlight from reaching much of the forest floor.

26 Immovable Mollusks

Real-World Question
How do mollusks living in intertidal ecosystems hold on to rocks?

Possible Materials
- plastic suction cup
- water
- paper towel or sponge

Procedure
1. Moisten a paper towel or sponge with water.
2. Press a plastic suction cup on the moist towel or sponge until the entire bottom surface of the cup is wet.

3. Firmly press the suction cup down on a kitchen counter for 10 seconds.
4. Grab the top handle of the suction cup and try removing the cup from the counter by pulling it straight up.

Conclude and Apply
1. Describe what happened when you tried to remove the cup from the counter.
2. Infer how mollusks living in intertidal ecosystems withstand the constant pull of ocean waves and currents.

Adult supervision required for all labs.

These labs are available at life.msscience.com.

26 Immovable Mollusks

Time Required 10 minutes

Materials
- Plastic suction cups measuring 2–3 centimeters in diameter work best for this activity.
- Remove any wire or string from the suction cups' handles.

Safety Precaution Caution students not to place the suction cups on surfaces where they would leave a permanent mark.

Teaching Strategies Students should not place their suction cups on wood surfaces. The cups do not adhere to wood surfaces as firmly as they do to nonporous surfaces.

Conclude and Apply
1. Students will probably not be able to remove the suction cup by pulling it straight up.
2. Mollusks have a muscular, foot-like organ they use to create a powerful suction on rocks to prevent them from being washed away by waves and currents.

27 UV Watch

● Real-World Question
How can you find out about the risks of ultraviolet radiation each day?

Possible Materials
- daily newspaper with weekly weather forecasts
- graph paper

● Procedure
1. Use the local newspaper or another resource to get the weather forecast for the day.
2. Check the UV (ultraviolet light) index for the day. If it provides an hourly UV index level, record the level for 1:00 P.M.
3. Find a legend or do research to discover what the numbers of the UV index mean.
4. Record the UV index everyday for 10 days and graph your results on graph paper.

● Conclude and Apply
1. Explain how the UV index system works.
2. Research several ways you can protect yourself from too much ultraviolet light exposure.

27 UV Watch

Time Required 1–2 minute sessions for 10 consecutive days

Materials
- Students can use online resources to do this activity.
- If you complete this activity in class, supply students with 10 daily newspapers from 10 consecutive days.
- Some local TV news channels also provide daily UV index levels.

Safety Precautions
- Students should use computers only while under adult supervision.
- Warn students not to spend time in the sun unprotected.

Teaching Strategy This activity works best during warm weather seasons.

Conclude and Apply
1. Ultraviolet light levels range from 0–10. Levels of 0–3 are low levels of UV radiation; 4–6 are moderate UV levels, and 7–10 are high levels of UV exposure.
2. When in the sun, wear a wide brim hat, sunscreen with an SPF of 15, long sleeves, and UV protection sunglasses. Time in the sun between 10:00 A.M. and 3:00 P.M. should be limited.

Computer Skills

People who study science rely on computers, like the one in **Figure 16,** to record and store data and to analyze results from investigations. Whether you work in a laboratory or just need to write a lab report with tables, good computer skills are a necessity.

Using the computer comes with responsibility. Issues of ownership, security, and privacy can arise. Remember, if you did not author the information you are using, you must provide a source for your information. Also, anything on a computer can be accessed by others. Do not put anything on the computer that you would not want everyone to know. To add more security to your work, use a password.

Use a Word Processing Program

A computer program that allows you to type your information, change it as many times as you need to, and then print it out is called a word processing program. Word processing programs also can be used to make tables.

Figure 16 A computer will make reports neater and more professional looking.

Learn the Skill To start your word processing program, a blank document, sometimes called "Document 1," appears on the screen. To begin, start typing. To create a new document, click the *New* button on the standard tool bar. These tips will help you format the document.

- The program will automatically move to the next line; press *Enter* if you wish to start a new paragraph.
- Symbols, called non-printing characters, can be hidden by clicking the *Show/Hide* button on your toolbar.
- To insert text, move the cursor to the point where you want the insertion to go, click on the mouse once, and type the text.
- To move several lines of text, select the text and click the *Cut* button on your toolbar. Then position your cursor in the location that you want to move the cut text and click *Paste.* If you move to the wrong place, click *Undo.*
- The spell check feature does not catch words that are misspelled to look like other words, like "cold" instead of "gold." Always reread your document to catch all spelling mistakes.
- To learn about other word processing methods, read the user's manual or click on the *Help* button.
- You can integrate databases, graphics, and spreadsheets into documents by copying from another program and pasting it into your document, or by using desktop publishing (DTP). DTP software allows you to put text and graphics together to finish your document with a professional look. This software varies in how it is used and its capabilities.

Use a Database

A collection of facts stored in a computer and sorted into different fields is called a database. A database can be reorganized in any way that suits your needs.

Learn the Skill A computer program that allows you to create your own database is a database management system (DBMS). It allows you to add, delete, or change information. Take time to get to know the features of your database software.

- Determine what facts you would like to include and research to collect your information.
- Determine how you want to organize the information.
- Follow the instructions for your particular DBMS to set up fields. Then enter each item of data in the appropriate field.
- Follow the instructions to sort the information in order of importance.
- Evaluate the information in your database, and add, delete, or change as necessary.

Use the Internet

The Internet is a global network of computers where information is stored and shared. To use the Internet, like the students in **Figure 17,** you need a modem to connect your computer to a phone line and an Internet Service Provider account.

Learn the Skill To access internet sites and information, use a "Web browser," which lets you view and explore pages on the World Wide Web. Each page is its own site, and each site has its own address, called a URL. Once you have found a Web browser, follow these steps for a search (this also is how you search a database).

Figure 17 The Internet allows you to search a global network for a variety of information.

- Be as specific as possible. If you know you want to research "gold," don't type in "elements." Keep narrowing your search until you find what you want.
- Web sites that end in *.com* are commercial Web sites; *.org, .edu,* and *.gov* are non-profit, educational, or government Web sites.
- Electronic encyclopedias, almanacs, indexes, and catalogs will help locate and select relevant information.
- Develop a "home page" with relative ease. When developing a Web site, NEVER post pictures or disclose personal information such as location, names, or phone numbers. Your school or community usually can host your Web site. A basic understanding of HTML (hypertext mark-up language), the language of Web sites, is necessary. Software that creates HTML code is called authoring software, and can be downloaded free from many Web sites. This software allows text and pictures to be arranged as the software is writing the HTML code.

Use a Spreadsheet

A spreadsheet, shown in **Figure 18,** can perform mathematical functions with any data arranged in columns and rows. By entering a simple equation into a cell, the program can perform operations in specific cells, rows, or columns.

Learn the Skill Each column (vertical) is assigned a letter, and each row (horizontal) is assigned a number. Each point where a row and column intersect is called a cell, and is labeled according to where it is located—Column A, Row 1 (A1).

- Decide how to organize the data, and enter it in the correct row or column.
- Spreadsheets can use standard formulas or formulas can be customized to calculate cells.
- To make a change, click on a cell to make it activate, and enter the edited data or formula.
- Spreadsheets also can display your results in graphs. Choose the style of graph that best represents the data.

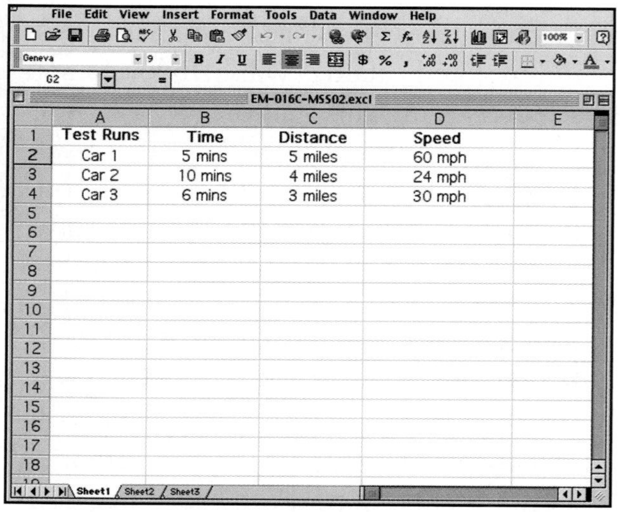

Figure 18 A spreadsheet allows you to perform mathematical operations on your data.

Use Graphics Software

Adding pictures, called graphics, to your documents is one way to make your documents more meaningful and exciting. This software adds, edits, and even constructs graphics. There is a variety of graphics software programs. The tools used for drawing can be a mouse, keyboard, or other specialized devices. Some graphics programs are simple. Others are complicated, called computer-aided design (CAD) software.

Learn the Skill It is important to have an understanding of the graphics software being used before starting. The better the software is understood, the better the results. The graphics can be placed in a word-processing document.

- Clip art can be found on a variety of internet sites, and on CDs. These images can be copied and pasted into your document.
- When beginning, try editing existing drawings, then work up to creating drawings.
- The images are made of tiny rectangles of color called pixels. Each pixel can be altered.
- Digital photography is another way to add images. The photographs in the memory of a digital camera can be downloaded into a computer, then edited and added to the document.
- Graphics software also can allow animation. The software allows drawings to have the appearance of movement by connecting basic drawings automatically. This is called in-betweening, or tweening.
- Remember to save often.

Presentation Skills

Develop Multimedia Presentations

Most presentations are more dynamic if they include diagrams, photographs, videos, or sound recordings, like the one shown in **Figure 19.** A multimedia presentation involves using stereos, overhead projectors, televisions, computers, and more.

Learn the Skill Decide the main points of your presentation, and what types of media would best illustrate those points.

- Make sure you know how to use the equipment you are working with.
- Practice the presentation using the equipment several times.
- Enlist the help of a classmate to push play or turn lights out for you. Be sure to practice your presentation with him or her.
- If possible, set up all of the equipment ahead of time, and make sure everything is working properly.

Figure 19 These students are engaging the audience using a variety of tools.

Computer Presentations

There are many different interactive computer programs that you can use to enhance your presentation. Most computers have a compact disc (CD) drive that can play both CDs and digital video discs (DVDs). Also, there is hardware to connect a regular CD, DVD, or VCR. These tools will enhance your presentation.

Another method of using the computer to aid in your presentation is to develop a slide show using a computer program. This can allow movement of visuals at the presenter's pace, and can allow for visuals to build on one another.

Learn the Skill In order to create multimedia presentations on a computer, you need to have certain tools. These may include traditional graphic tools and drawing programs, animation programs, and authoring systems that tie everything together. Your computer will tell you which tools it supports. The most important step is to learn about the tools that you will be using.

- Often, color and strong images will convey a point better than words alone. Use the best methods available to convey your point.
- As with other presentations, practice many times.
- Practice your presentation with the tools you and any assistants will be using.
- Maintain eye contact with the audience. The purpose of using the computer is not to prompt the presenter, but to help the audience understand the points of the presentation.

Reduce Fractions

$$\frac{66 \div 6}{90 \div 6} = \frac{11}{15}$$

Add and Subtract Fractions

$$\frac{4}{9} + \frac{2}{9} = \frac{6}{9}$$

$$\frac{6 \div 3}{9 \div 3} = \frac{2}{3}$$

Math Review

Use Fractions

A fraction compares a part to a whole. In the fraction $\frac{2}{3}$, the 2 represents the part and is the numerator. The 3 represents the whole and is the denominator.

Reduce Fractions To reduce a fraction, you must find the largest factor that is common to both the numerator and the denominator, the greatest common factor (GCF). Divide both numbers by the GCF. The fraction has then been reduced, or it is in its simplest form.

Example Twelve of the 20 chemicals in the science lab are in powder form. What fraction of the chemicals used in the lab are in powder form?

Step 1 Write the fraction.

$$\frac{\text{part}}{\text{whole}} = \frac{12}{20}$$

Step 2 To find the GCF of the numerator and denominator, list all of the factors of each number.

Factors of 12: 1, 2, 3, 4, 6, 12 (the numbers that divide evenly into 12)

Factors of 20: 1, 2, 4, 5, 10, 20 (the numbers that divide evenly into 20)

Step 3 List the common factors.

1, 2, 4.

Step 4 Choose the greatest factor in the list.

The GCF of 12 and 20 is 4.

Step 5 Divide the numerator and denominator by the GCF.

$$\frac{12 \div 4}{20 \div 4} = \frac{3}{5}$$

In the lab, $\frac{3}{5}$ of the chemicals are in powder form.

Practice Problem At an amusement park, 66 of 90 rides have a height restriction. What fraction of the rides, in its simplest form, has a height restriction?

Add and Subtract Fractions To add or subtract fractions with the same denominator, add or subtract the numerators and write the sum or difference over the denominator. After finding the sum or difference, find the simplest form for your fraction.

Example 1 In the forest outside your house, $\frac{1}{8}$ of the animals are rabbits, $\frac{3}{8}$ are squirrels, and the remainder are birds and insects. How many are mammals?

Step 1 Add the numerators.

$$\frac{1}{8} + \frac{3}{8} = \frac{(1 + 3)}{8} = \frac{4}{8}$$

Step 2 Find the GCF.

$$\frac{4}{8} \quad (\text{GCF, 4})$$

Step 3 Divide the numerator and denominator by the GCF.

$$\frac{4}{4} = 1, \quad \frac{8}{4} = 2$$

$\frac{1}{2}$ of the animals are mammals.

Example 2 If $\frac{7}{16}$ of the Earth is covered by freshwater, and $\frac{1}{16}$ of that is in glaciers, how much freshwater is not frozen?

Step 1 Subtract the numerators.

$$\frac{7}{16} - \frac{1}{16} = \frac{(7 - 1)}{16} = \frac{6}{16}$$

Step 2 Find the GCF.

$$\frac{6}{16} \quad (\text{GCF, 2})$$

Step 3 Divide the numerator and denominator by the GCF.

$$\frac{6}{2} = 3, \quad \frac{16}{2} = 8$$

$\frac{3}{8}$ of the freshwater is not frozen.

Practice Problem A bicycle rider is going 15 km/h for $\frac{4}{9}$ of his ride, 10 km/h for $\frac{2}{9}$ of his ride, and 8 km/h for the remainder of the ride. How much of his ride is he going over 8 km/h?

Unlike Denominators To add or subtract fractions with unlike denominators, first find the least common denominator (LCD). This is the smallest number that is a common multiple of both denominators. Rename each fraction with the LCD, and then add or subtract. Find the simplest form if necessary.

Example 1 A chemist makes a paste that is $\frac{1}{2}$ table salt (NaCl), $\frac{1}{3}$ sugar ($C_6H_{12}O_6$), and the rest water (H_2O). How much of the paste is a solid?

Step 1 Find the LCD of the fractions.

$\frac{1}{2} + \frac{1}{3}$ (LCD, 6)

Step 2 Rename each numerator and each denominator with the LCD.

$1 \times 3 = 3, \ 2 \times 3 = 6$
$1 \times 2 = 2, \ 3 \times 2 = 6$

Step 3 Add the numerators.

$\frac{3}{6} + \frac{2}{6} = \frac{(3 + 2)}{6} = \frac{5}{6}$

$\frac{5}{6}$ of the paste is a solid.

Example 2 The average precipitation in Grand Junction, CO, is $\frac{7}{10}$ inch in November, and $\frac{3}{5}$ inch in December. What is the total average precipitation?

Step 1 Find the LCD of the fractions.

$\frac{7}{10} + \frac{3}{5}$ (LCD, 10)

Step 2 Rename each numerator and each denominator with the LCD.

$7 \times 1 = 7, \ 10 \times 1 = 10$
$3 \times 2 = 6, \ 5 \times 2 = 10$

Step 3 Add the numerators.

$\frac{7}{10} + \frac{6}{10} = \frac{(7 + 6)}{10} = \frac{13}{10}$

$\frac{13}{10}$ inches total precipitation, or $1\frac{3}{10}$ inches.

Practice Problem On an electric bill, about $\frac{1}{8}$ of the energy is from solar energy and about $\frac{1}{10}$ is from wind power. How much of the total bill is from solar energy and wind power combined?

Example 3 In your body, $\frac{7}{10}$ of your muscle contractions are involuntary (cardiac and smooth muscle tissue). Smooth muscle makes up $\frac{3}{15}$ of your muscle contractions. How many of your muscle contractions are made by cardiac muscle?

Step 1 Find the LCD of the fractions.

$\frac{7}{10} - \frac{3}{15}$ (LCD, 30)

Step 2 Rename each numerator and each denominator with the LCD.

$7 \times 3 = 21, \ 10 \times 3 = 30$
$3 \times 2 = 6, \ 15 \times 2 = 30$

Step 3 Add the numerators.

$\frac{21}{30} - \frac{6}{30} = \frac{(21 - 6)}{30} = \frac{15}{30}$

Step 4 Find the GCF.

$\frac{15}{30}$ (GCF, 15)

$\frac{1}{2}$

$\frac{1}{2}$ of all muscle contractions are cardiac muscle.

Example 4 Tony wants to make cookies that call for $\frac{3}{4}$ of a cup of flour, but he only has $\frac{1}{3}$ of a cup. How much more flour does he need?

Step 1 Find the LCD of the fractions.

$\frac{3}{4} - \frac{1}{3}$ (LCD, 12)

Step 2 Rename each numerator and each denominator with the LCD.

$3 \times 3 = 9, \ 4 \times 3 = 12$
$1 \times 4 = 4, \ 3 \times 4 = 12$

Step 3 Add the numerators.

$\frac{9}{12} - \frac{4}{12} = \frac{(9 - 4)}{12} = \frac{5}{12}$

$\frac{5}{12}$ of a cup of flour.

Practice Problem Using the information provided to you in Example 3 above, determine how many muscle contractions are voluntary (skeletal muscle).

Unlike Denominators

Problem 1

$1 \times 5 = 5, 8 \times 5 = 40$

$1 \times 4 = 4, 10 \times 4 = 40$

$\frac{5}{40} + \frac{4}{40} = \frac{9}{40}$

Problem 2

If $\frac{7}{10}$ are involuntary, the remainder are voluntary.

$\frac{10}{10} - \frac{7}{10} = \frac{3}{10}$

Multiply Fractions

$$\frac{3}{14} \times \frac{5}{16} = \frac{(3 \times 5)}{(14 \times 16)} = \frac{15}{224}$$

Find a Reciprocal

$$\frac{9}{4}$$

Divide Fractions

The reciprocal of $\frac{7}{10}$ is $\frac{10}{7}$.

$$\frac{3}{11} \times \frac{10}{7} = \frac{(3 \times 10)}{(11 \times 7)} = \frac{30}{77}$$

Multiply Fractions To multiply with fractions, multiply the numerators and multiply the denominators. Find the simplest form if necessary.

Example Multiply $\frac{3}{5}$ by $\frac{1}{3}$.

Step 1 Multiply the numerators and denominators.

$$\frac{3}{5} \times \frac{1}{3} = \frac{(3 \times 1)}{(5 \times 3)} = \frac{3}{15}$$

Step 2 Find the GCF.

$$\frac{3}{15} \quad (\text{GCF, 3})$$

Step 3 Divide the numerator and denominator by the GCF.

$$\frac{3}{3} = 1, \quad \frac{15}{3} = 5$$

$$\frac{1}{5}$$

$\frac{3}{5}$ multiplied by $\frac{1}{3}$ is $\frac{1}{5}$.

Practice Problem Multiply $\frac{3}{14}$ by $\frac{5}{16}$.

Find a Reciprocal Two numbers whose product is 1 are called multiplicative inverses, or reciprocals.

Example Find the reciprocal of $\frac{3}{8}$.

Step 1 Inverse the fraction by putting the denominator on top and the numerator on the bottom.

$$\frac{8}{3}$$

The reciprocal of $\frac{3}{8}$ is $\frac{8}{3}$.

Practice Problem Find the reciprocal of $\frac{4}{9}$.

Divide Fractions To divide one fraction by another fraction, multiply the dividend by the reciprocal of the divisor. Find the simplest form if necessary.

Example 1 Divide $\frac{1}{9}$ by $\frac{1}{3}$.

Step 1 Find the reciprocal of the divisor.

The reciprocal of $\frac{1}{3}$ is $\frac{3}{1}$.

Step 2 Multiply the dividend by the reciprocal of the divisor.

$$\frac{\frac{1}{9}}{\frac{1}{3}} = \frac{1}{9} \times \frac{3}{1} = \frac{(1 \times 3)}{(9 \times 1)} = \frac{3}{9}$$

Step 3 Find the GCF.

$$\frac{3}{9} \quad (\text{GCF, 3})$$

Step 4 Divide the numerator and denominator by the GCF.

$$\frac{3}{3} = 1, \quad \frac{9}{3} = 3$$

$$\frac{1}{3}$$

$\frac{1}{9}$ divided by $\frac{1}{3}$ is $\frac{1}{3}$.

Example 2 Divide $\frac{3}{5}$ by $\frac{1}{4}$.

Step 1 Find the reciprocal of the divisor.

The reciprocal of $\frac{1}{4}$ is $\frac{4}{1}$.

Step 2 Multiply the dividend by the reciprocal of the divisor.

$$\frac{\frac{3}{5}}{\frac{1}{4}} = \frac{3}{5} \times \frac{4}{1} = \frac{(3 \times 4)}{(5 \times 1)} = \frac{12}{5}$$

$\frac{3}{5}$ divided by $\frac{1}{4}$ is $\frac{12}{5}$ or $2\frac{2}{5}$.

Practice Problem Divide $\frac{3}{11}$ by $\frac{7}{10}$.

Math Skill Handbook

Use Ratios

When you compare two numbers by division, you are using a ratio. Ratios can be written 3 to 5, 3:5, or $\frac{3}{5}$. Ratios, like fractions, also can be written in simplest form.

Ratios can represent probabilities, also called odds. This is a ratio that compares the number of ways a certain outcome occurs to the number of outcomes. For example, if you flip a coin 100 times, what are the odds that it will come up heads? There are two possible outcomes, heads or tails, so the odds of coming up heads are 50:100. Another way to say this is that 50 out of 100 times the coin will come up heads. In its simplest form, the ratio is 1:2.

Example 1 A chemical solution contains 40 g of salt and 64 g of baking soda. What is the ratio of salt to baking soda as a fraction in simplest form?

Step 1 Write the ratio as a fraction.
$$\frac{salt}{baking\ soda} = \frac{40}{64}$$

Step 2 Express the fraction in simplest form.
The GCF of 40 and 64 is 8.
$$\frac{40}{64} = \frac{40 \div 8}{64 \div 8} = \frac{5}{8}$$

The ratio of salt to baking soda in the sample is 5:8.

Example 2 Sean rolls a 6-sided die 6 times. What are the odds that the side with a 3 will show?

Step 1 Write the ratio as a fraction.
$$\frac{number\ of\ sides\ with\ a\ 3}{number\ of\ sides} = \frac{1}{6}$$

Step 2 Multiply by the number of attempts.
$$\frac{1}{6} \times 6\ attempts = \frac{6}{6}\ attempts = 1\ attempt$$

1 attempt out of 6 will show a 3.

Practice Problem Two metal rods measure 100 cm and 144 cm in length. What is the ratio of their lengths in simplest form?

Use Decimals

A fraction with a denominator that is a power of ten can be written as a decimal. For example, 0.27 means $\frac{27}{100}$. The decimal point separates the ones place from the tenths place.

Any fraction can be written as a decimal using division. For example, the fraction $\frac{5}{8}$ can be written as a decimal by dividing 5 by 8. Written as a decimal, it is 0.625.

Add or Subtract Decimals When adding and subtracting decimals, line up the decimal points before carrying out the operation.

Example 1 Find the sum of 47.68 and 7.80.

Step 1 Line up the decimal places when you write the numbers.
$$\begin{array}{r} 47.68 \\ + 7.80 \\ \hline \end{array}$$

Step 2 Add the decimals.
$$\begin{array}{r} 47.68 \\ + 7.80 \\ \hline 55.48 \end{array}$$

The sum of 47.68 and 7.80 is 55.48.

Example 2 Find the difference of 42.17 and 15.85.

Step 1 Line up the decimal places when you write the number.
$$\begin{array}{r} 42.17 \\ - 15.85 \\ \hline \end{array}$$

Step 2 Subtract the decimals.
$$\begin{array}{r} 42.17 \\ - 15.85 \\ \hline 26.32 \end{array}$$

The difference of 42.17 and 15.85 is 26.32.

Practice Problem Find the sum of 1.245 and 3.842.

Use Ratios
$$\frac{100\ cm}{144\ cm} = \frac{100 \div 4}{144 \div 4} = \frac{25}{36}$$
25:36

Add or Subtract Decimals

$$\begin{array}{r} 1 \\ 1.245 \\ + 3.842 \\ \hline 5.087 \end{array}$$

Multiply Decimals

Multiply 4.6 and 2.2 by 10.

$46 \times 22 = 1012$

Each factor had one decimal place.

10.12

Divide Decimals

Multiply both factors by 10.

Divide 756 by 36.

$$\begin{array}{r} 21 \\ 36\overline{)756} \\ 72 \\ \overline{36} \\ 36 \\ \overline{0} \end{array}$$

Use Proportions

$$\frac{3}{18} = \frac{5}{w}$$

$$w \times 3 = 5 \times 18$$

$$\frac{3w}{3} = \frac{90}{3}$$

$$w = 30$$

Multiply Decimals To multiply decimals, multiply the numbers like any other number, ignoring the decimal point. Count the decimal places in each factor. The product will have the same number of decimal places as the sum of the decimal places in the factors.

Example Multiply 2.4 by 5.9.

Step 1 Multiply the factors like two whole numbers.
$24 \times 59 = 1416$

Step 2 Find the sum of the number of decimal places in the factors. Each factor has one decimal place, for a sum of two decimal places.

Step 3 The product will have two decimal places.
14.16

The product of 2.4 and 5.9 is 14.16.

Practice Problem Multiply 4.6 by 2.2.

Divide Decimals When dividing decimals, change the divisor to a whole number. To do this, multiply both the divisor and the dividend by the same power of ten. Then place the decimal point in the quotient directly above the decimal point in the dividend. Then divide as you do with whole numbers.

Example Divide 8.84 by 3.4.

Step 1 Multiply both factors by 10.
$3.4 \times 10 = 34, 8.84 \times 10 = 88.4$

Step 2 Divide 88.4 by 34.

$$\begin{array}{r} 2.6 \\ 34\overline{)88.4} \\ -68 \\ \overline{204} \\ -204 \\ \overline{0} \end{array}$$

8.84 divided by 3.4 is 2.6.

Practice Problem Divide 75.6 by 3.6.

Use Proportions

An equation that shows that two ratios are equivalent is a proportion. The ratios $\frac{2}{4}$ and $\frac{5}{10}$ are equivalent, so they can be written as $\frac{2}{4} = \frac{5}{10}$. This equation is a proportion.

When two ratios form a proportion, the cross products are equal. To find the cross products in the proportion $\frac{2}{4} = \frac{5}{10}$, multiply the 2 and the 10, and the 4 and the 5. Therefore $2 \times 10 = 4 \times 5$, or $20 = 20$.

Because you know that both proportions are equal, you can use cross products to find a missing term in a proportion. This is known as solving the proportion.

Example The heights of a tree and a pole are proportional to the lengths of their shadows. The tree casts a shadow of 24 m when a 6-m pole casts a shadow of 4 m. What is the height of the tree?

Step 1 Write a proportion.
$$\frac{\text{height of tree}}{\text{height of pole}} = \frac{\text{length of tree's shadow}}{\text{length of pole's shadow}}$$

Step 2 Substitute the known values into the proportion. Let h represent the unknown value, the height of the tree.
$$\frac{h}{6} = \frac{24}{4}$$

Step 3 Find the cross products.
$h \times 4 = 6 \times 24$

Step 4 Simplify the equation.
$4h = 144$

Step 5 Divide each side by 4.
$$\frac{4h}{4} = \frac{144}{4}$$
$$h = 36$$

The height of the tree is 36 m.

Practice Problem The ratios of the weights of two objects on the Moon and on Earth are in proportion. A rock weighing 3 N on the Moon weighs 18 N on Earth. How much would a rock that weighs 5 N on the Moon weigh on Earth?

Use Percentages

The word *percent* means "out of one hundred." It is a ratio that compares a number to 100. Suppose you read that 77 percent of the Earth's surface is covered by water. That is the same as reading that the fraction of the Earth's surface covered by water is $\frac{77}{100}$. To express a fraction as a percent, first find the equivalent decimal for the fraction. Then, multiply the decimal by 100 and add the percent symbol.

Example Express $\frac{13}{20}$ as a percent.

Step 1 Find the equivalent decimal for the fraction.

$$
\begin{array}{r}
0.65 \\
20\overline{)13.00} \\
\underline{12\,0} \\
1\,00 \\
\underline{1\,00} \\
0
\end{array}
$$

Step 2 Rewrite the fraction $\frac{13}{20}$ as 0.65.

Step 3 Multiply 0.65 by 100 and add the % sign.
$0.65 \times 100 = 65 = 65\%$

So, $\frac{13}{20} = 65\%$.

This also can be solved as a proportion.

Example Express $\frac{13}{20}$ as a percent.

Step 1 Write a proportion.
$\frac{13}{20} = \frac{x}{100}$

Step 2 Find the cross products.
$1300 = 20x$

Step 3 Divide each side by 20.
$\frac{1300}{20} = \frac{20x}{20}$
$65\% = x$

Practice Problem In one year, 73 of 365 days were rainy in one city. What percent of the days in that city were rainy?

Solve One-Step Equations

A statement that two things are equal is an equation. For example, $A = B$ is an equation that states that A is equal to B.

An equation is solved when a variable is replaced with a value that makes both sides of the equation equal. To make both sides equal the inverse operation is used. Addition and subtraction are inverses, and multiplication and division are inverses.

Example 1 Solve the equation $x - 10 = 35$.

Step 1 Find the solution by adding 10 to each side of the equation.
$x - 10 = 35$
$x - 10 + 10 = 35 + 10$
$x = 45$

Step 2 Check the solution.
$x - 10 = 35$
$45 - 10 = 35$
$35 = 35$

Both sides of the equation are equal, so $x = 45$.

Example 2 In the formula $a = bc$, find the value of c if $a = 20$ and $b = 2$.

Step 1 Rearrange the formula so the unknown value is by itself on one side of the equation by dividing both sides by b.
$a = bc$
$\frac{a}{b} = \frac{bc}{b}$
$\frac{a}{b} = c$

Step 2 Replace the variables a and b with the values that are given.
$\frac{a}{b} = c$
$\frac{20}{2} = c$
$10 = c$

Step 3 Check the solution.
$a = bc$
$20 = 2 \times 10$
$20 = 20$

Both sides of the equation are equal, so $c = 10$ is the solution when $a = 20$ and $b = 2$.

Practice Problem In the formula $h = gd$, find the value of d if $g = 12.3$ and $h = 17.4$.

Use Percentages

$\frac{73}{365} = \frac{x}{100}$

$\frac{7300}{365} = \frac{365x}{365}$

$20\% = x$

Solve One-Step Equations

$h = gd$

$\frac{17.4}{12.3} = \frac{12.3d}{12.3}$

$1.41 = d$

Use Statistics

mean

$8 + 4 + 12 + 8 + 11 + 14 + 16$
$= 73$

$73 \div 7 = 10.4$

median

4, 8, 8, <u>11</u>, 12, 14, 16

mode

4, <u>8</u>, <u>8</u>, 11, 12, 14, 16

range

<u>4</u>, 8, 8, 11, 12, 14, <u>16</u>

$16 - 4 = 12$

Use Statistics

The branch of mathematics that deals with collecting, analyzing, and presenting data is statistics. In statistics, there are three common ways to summarize data with a single number—the mean, the median, and the mode.

The **mean** of a set of data is the arithmetic average. It is found by adding the numbers in the data set and dividing by the number of items in the set.

The **median** is the middle number in a set of data when the data are arranged in numerical order. If there were an even number of data points, the median would be the mean of the two middle numbers.

The **mode** of a set of data is the number or item that appears most often.

Another number that often is used to describe a set of data is the range. The **range** is the difference between the largest number and the smallest number in a set of data.

A **frequency table** shows how many times each piece of data occurs, usually in a survey. **Table 2** below shows the results of a student survey on favorite color.

Table 2 Student Color Choice		
Color	**Tally**	**Frequency**
red	||||	4
blue	＃	5
black	||	2
green	|||	3
purple	＃ ||	7
yellow	＃ |	6

Based on the frequency table data, which color is the favorite?

Example The speeds (in m/s) for a race car during five different time trials are 39, 37, 44, 36, and 44.

To find the mean:

Step 1 Find the sum of the numbers.

$39 + 37 + 44 + 36 + 44 = 200$

Step 2 Divide the sum by the number of items, which is 5.

$200 \div 5 = 40$

The mean is 40 m/s.

To find the median:

Step 1 Arrange the measures from least to greatest.

36, 37, 39, 44, 44

Step 2 Determine the middle measure.

36, 37, <u>39</u>, 44, 44

The median is 39 m/s.

To find the mode:

Step 1 Group the numbers that are the same together.

44, 44, 36, 37, 39

Step 2 Determine the number that occurs most in the set.

<u>44, 44</u>, 36, 37, 39

The mode is 44 m/s.

To find the range:

Step 1 Arrange the measures from largest to smallest.

44, 44, 39, 37, 36

Step 2 Determine the largest and smallest measures in the set.

<u>44</u>, 44, 39, 37, <u>36</u>

Step 3 Find the difference between the largest and smallest measures.

$44 - 36 = 8$

The range is 8 m/s.

Practice Problem Find the mean, median, mode, and range for the data set 8, 4, 12, 8, 11, 14, 16.

Math Skill Handbook

Math Skill Handbook

Use Geometry

The branch of mathematics that deals with the measurement, properties, and relationships of points, lines, angles, surfaces, and solids is called geometry.

Perimeter The **perimeter** (P) is the distance around a geometric figure. To find the perimeter of a rectangle, add the length and width and multiply that sum by two, or $2(l + w)$. Find perimeters of irregular figures by adding the length of the sides.

Example 1 Find the perimeter of a rectangle that is 3 m long and 5 m wide.

Step 1 You know that the perimeter is 2 times the sum of the width and length.
$$P = 2(3\text{ m} + 5\text{ m})$$

Step 2 Find the sum of the width and length.
$$P = 2(8\text{ m})$$

Step 3 Multiply by 2.
$$P = 16\text{ m}$$

The perimeter is 16 m.

Example 2 Find the perimeter of a shape with sides measuring 2 cm, 5 cm, 6 cm, 3 cm.

Step 1 You know that the perimeter is the sum of all the sides.
$$P = 2 + 5 + 6 + 3$$

Step 2 Find the sum of the sides.
$$P = 2 + 5 + 6 + 3$$
$$P = 16$$

The perimeter is 16 cm.

Practice Problem Find the perimeter of a rectangle with a length of 18 m and a width of 7 m.

Practice Problem Find the perimeter of a triangle measuring 1.6 cm by 2.4 cm by 2.4 cm.

Area of a Rectangle The **area** (A) is the number of square units needed to cover a surface. To find the area of a rectangle, multiply the length times the width, or $l \times w$. When finding area, the units also are multiplied. Area is given in square units.

Example Find the area of a rectangle with a length of 1 cm and a width of 10 cm.

Step 1 You know that the area is the length multiplied by the width.
$$A = (1\text{ cm} \times 10\text{ cm})$$

Step 2 Multiply the length by the width. Also multiply the units.
$$A = 10\text{ cm}^2$$

The area is 10 cm².

Practice Problem Find the area of a square whose sides measure 4 m.

Area of a Triangle To find the area of a triangle, use the formula:

$$A = \frac{1}{2}(\text{base} \times \text{height})$$

The base of a triangle can be any of its sides. The height is the perpendicular distance from a base to the opposite endpoint, or vertex.

Example Find the area of a triangle with a base of 18 m and a height of 7 m.

Step 1 You know that the area is $\frac{1}{2}$ the base times the height.
$$A = \frac{1}{2}(18\text{ m} \times 7\text{ m})$$

Step 2 Multiply $\frac{1}{2}$ by the product of 18×7. Multiply the units.
$$A = \frac{1}{2}(126\text{ m}^2)$$
$$A = 63\text{ m}^2$$

The area is 63 m².

Practice Problem Find the area of a triangle with a base of 27 cm and a height of 17 cm.

MATH SKILL HANDBOOK   839

Math Skill Handbook

Perimeter
Problem 1
$$P = 2(18\text{ m} + 7\text{ m})$$
$$P = 2(25\text{ m})$$
$$P = 50\text{ m}$$

Problem 2
$$P = 1.6\text{ cm} + 2.4\text{ cm} + 2.4\text{ cm}$$
$$P = 6.4\text{ cm}$$

Area of a Rectangle
$$A = (4\text{ m} \times 4\text{ m})$$
$$A = 16\text{ m}^2$$

Area of a Triangle
$$A = \frac{1}{2}(27\text{ cm} \times 17\text{ cm})$$
$$A = \frac{1}{2}(459\text{ cm}^2)$$
$$A = 229.5\text{ cm}^2$$

Circumference of a Circle

$C = 2\pi r$

$C = 2\pi(19)$

$C = 38\pi$

$C = 119.3$

Area of a Circle

$A = \pi r^2$

$A = \pi(16\,m)^2$

$A = \pi\,256\,m^2$

$A = 803.8\,m^2$

Circumference of a Circle The **diameter** (*d*) of a circle is the distance across the circle through its center, and the **radius** (*r*) is the distance from the center to any point on the circle. The radius is half of the diameter. The distance around the circle is called the **circumference** (C). The formula for finding the circumference is:

$$C = 2\pi r \ \ or \ \ C = \pi d$$

The circumference divided by the diameter is always equal to 3.1415926... This nonterminating and nonrepeating number is represented by the Greek letter π (pi). An approximation often used for π is 3.14.

Example 1 Find the circumference of a circle with a radius of 3 m.

Step 1 You know the formula for the circumference is 2 times the radius times π.
$C = 2\pi(3)$

Step 2 Multiply 2 times the radius.
$C = 6\pi$

Step 3 Multiply by π.
$C = 19\,m$

The circumference is 19 m.

Example 2 Find the circumference of a circle with a diameter of 24.0 cm.

Step 1 You know the formula for the circumference is the diameter times π.
$C = \pi(24.0)$

Step 2 Multiply the diameter by π.
$C = 75.4\,cm$

The circumference is 75.4 cm.

Practice Problem Find the circumference of a circle with a radius of 19 cm.

Area of a Circle The formula for the area of a circle is:
$A = \pi r^2$

Example 1 Find the area of a circle with a radius of 4.0 cm.

Step 1 $A = \pi(4.0)^2$

Step 2 Find the square of the radius.
$A = 16\pi$

Step 3 Multiply the square of the radius by π.
$A = 50\,cm^2$

The area of the circle is 50 cm².

Example 2 Find the area of a circle with a radius of 225 m.

Step 1 $A = \pi(225)^2$

Step 2 Find the square of the radius.
$A = 50625\pi$

Step 3 Multiply the square of the radius by π.
$A = 158962.5$

The area of the circle is 158,962 m².

Example 3 Find the area of a circle whose diameter is 20.0 mm.

Step 1 You know the formula for the area of a circle is the square of the radius times π, and that the radius is half of the diameter.
$A = \pi\left(\dfrac{20.0}{2}\right)^2$

Step 2 Find the radius.
$A = \pi(10.0)^2$

Step 3 Find the square of the radius.
$A = 100\pi$

Step 4 Multiply the square of the radius by π.
$A = 314\,mm^2$

The area is 314 mm².

Practice Problem Find the area of a circle with a radius of 16 m.

Math Skill Handbook

Math Skill Handbook

Volume The measure of space occupied by a solid is the **volume** (V). To find the volume of a rectangular solid multiply the length times width times height, or $V = l \times w \times h$. It is measured in cubic units, such as cubic centimeters (cm^3).

Example Find the volume of a rectangular solid with a length of 2.0 m, a width of 4.0 m, and a height of 3.0 m.

Step 1 You know the formula for volume is the length times the width times the height.

$V = 2.0\,\text{m} \times 4.0\,\text{m} \times 3.0\,\text{m}$

Step 2 Multiply the length times the width times the height.

$V = 24\,\text{m}^3$

The volume is 24 m^3.

Practice Problem Find the volume of a rectangular solid that is 8 m long, 4 m wide, and 4 m high.

To find the volume of other solids, multiply the area of the base times the height.

Example 1 Find the volume of a solid that has a triangular base with a length of 8.0 m and a height of 7.0 m. The height of the entire solid is 15.0 m.

Step 1 You know that the base is a triangle, and the area of a triangle is $\frac{1}{2}$ the base times the height, and the volume is the area of the base times the height.

$V = \left[\frac{1}{2} (b \times h) \right] \times 15$

Step 2 Find the area of the base.

$V = \left[\frac{1}{2} (8 \times 7) \right] \times 15$

$V = \left(\frac{1}{2} \times 56 \right) \times 15$

Step 3 Multiply the area of the base by the height of the solid.

$V = 28 \times 15$

$V = 420\,\text{m}^3$

The volume is 420 m^3.

Example 2 Find the volume of a cylinder that has a base with a radius of 12.0 cm, and a height of 21.0 cm.

Step 1 You know that the base is a circle, and the area of a circle is the square of the radius times π, and the volume is the area of the base times the height.

$V = (\pi r^2) \times 21$

$V = (\pi 12^2) \times 21$

Step 2 Find the area of the base.

$V = 144\pi \times 21$

$V = 452 \times 21$

Step 3 Multiply the area of the base by the height of the solid.

$V = 9490\,\text{cm}^3$

The volume is 9490 cm^3.

Example 3 Find the volume of a cylinder that has a diameter of 15 mm and a height of 4.8 mm.

Step 1 You know that the base is a circle with an area equal to the square of the radius times π. The radius is one-half the diameter. The volume is the area of the base times the height.

$V = (\pi r^2) \times 4.8$

$V = \left[\pi \left(\frac{1}{2} \times 15 \right)^2 \right] \times 4.8$

$V = (\pi 7.5^2) \times 4.8$

Step 2 Find the area of the base.

$V = 56.25\pi \times 4.8$

$V = 176.63 \times 4.8$

Step 3 Multiply the area of the base by the height of the solid.

$V = 847.8$

The volume is 847.8 mm^3.

Practice Problem Find the volume of a cylinder with a diameter of 7 cm in the base and a height of 16 cm.

Math Skill Handbook

Volume

Problem 1

$V = 8\,\text{m} \times 4\,\text{m} \times 4\,\text{m}$

$V = 128\,\text{m}^3$

Problem 2

$V = \pi r^2 \times \text{height}$

$V = \left[\pi \left(\frac{1}{2} \times 7 \right)^2 \right] \times 16$

$V = [\pi (3.5)^2] \times 16$

$V = [\pi (12.25)] \times 16$

$V = 38.46 \times 16$

$V = 615.36$

Math Skill Handbook

Measure in SI

smaller; 1000; one thousandth

Dimensional Analysis

$x\,\text{mg} = 1\,\cancel{kg} \times \dfrac{1000\,\cancel{g}}{1\,\cancel{kg}} \times \dfrac{1000\,\text{mg}}{1\,\cancel{g}} =$

1,000,000 mg

1,000,000 mg = 1 kg

Science Applications

Measure in SI

The metric system of measurement was developed in 1795. A modern form of the metric system, called the International System (SI), was adopted in 1960 and provides the standard measurements that all scientists around the world can understand.

The SI system is convenient because unit sizes vary by powers of 10. Prefixes are used to name units. Look at **Table 3** for some common metric prefixes and their meanings.

Table 3 Common SI Prefixes			
Prefix	**Symbol**	**Meaning**	
kilo-	k	1,000	thousand
hecto-	h	100	hundred
deka-	da	10	ten
deci-	d	0.1	tenth
centi-	c	0.01	hundredth
milli-	m	0.001	thousandth

Example How many grams equal one kilogram?

Step 1 Find the prefix *kilo* in **Table 3.**

Step 2 Using **Table 3,** determine the meaning of *kilo*. According to the table, it means 1,000. When the prefix *kilo* is added to a unit, it means that there are 1,000 of the units in a "*kilo*unit."

Step 3 Apply the prefix to the units in the question. The units in the question are grams. There are 1,000 grams in a kilogram.

Practice Problem Is a milligram larger or smaller than a gram? How many of the smaller units equal one larger unit? What fraction of the larger unit does one smaller unit represent?

Dimensional Analysis

Convert SI Units In science, quantities such as length, mass, and time sometimes are measured using different units. A process called dimensional analysis can be used to change one unit of measure to another. This process involves multiplying your starting quantity and units by one or more conversion factors. A conversion factor is a ratio equal to one and can be made from any two equal quantities with different units. If 1,000 mL equal 1 L then two ratios can be made.

$$\frac{1,000\ \text{mL}}{1\ \text{L}} = \frac{1\ \text{L}}{1,000\ \text{mL}} = 1$$

One can covert between units in the SI system by using the equivalents in **Table 3** to make conversion factors.

Example 1 How many cm are in 4 m?

Step 1 Write conversion factors for the units given. From **Table 3,** you know that 100 cm = 1 m. The conversion factors are

$$\frac{100\ \text{cm}}{1\ \text{m}} \quad and \quad \frac{1\ \text{m}}{100\ \text{cm}}$$

Step 2 Decide which conversion factor to use. Select the factor that has the units you are converting from (m) in the denominator and the units you are converting to (cm) in the numerator.

$$\frac{100\ \text{cm}}{1\ \text{m}}$$

Step 3 Multiply the starting quantity and units by the conversion factor. Cancel the starting units with the units in the denominator. There are 400 cm in 4 m.

$$4\,\cancel{m} \times \frac{100\ \text{cm}}{1\,\cancel{m}} = 400\ \text{cm}$$

Practice Problem How many milligrams are in one kilogram? (Hint: You will need to use two conversion factors from **Table 3.**)

Math Skill Handbook

Table 4 Unit System Equivalents

Type of Measurement	Equivalent
Length	1 in = 2.54 cm
	1 yd = 0.91 m
	1 mi = 1.61 km
Mass and Weight*	1 oz = 28.35 g
	1 lb = 0.45 kg
	1 ton (short) = 0.91 tonnes (metric tons)
	1 lb = 4.45 N
Volume	$1\ \text{in}^3 = 16.39\ \text{cm}^3$
	1 qt = 0.95 L
	1 gal = 3.78 L
Area	$1\ \text{in}^2 = 6.45\ \text{cm}^2$
	$1\ \text{yd}^2 = 0.83\ \text{m}^2$
	$1\ \text{mi}^2 = 2.59\ \text{km}^2$
	1 acre = 0.40 hectares
Temperature	$°C = \dfrac{(°F - 32)}{1.8}$
	$K = °C + 273$

*Weight is measured in standard Earth gravity.

Convert Between Unit Systems Table 4 gives a list of equivalents that can be used to convert between English and SI units.

Example If a meterstick has a length of 100 cm, how long is the meterstick in inches?

Step 1 Write the conversion factors for the units given. From **Table 4,** 1 in = 2.54 cm.

$$\frac{1\ \text{in}}{2.54\ \text{cm}} \quad and \quad \frac{2.54\ \text{cm}}{1\ \text{in}}$$

Step 2 Determine which conversion factor to use. You are converting from cm to in. Use the conversion factor with cm on the bottom.

$$\frac{1\ \text{in}}{2.54\ \text{cm}}$$

Step 3 Multiply the starting quantity and units by the conversion factor. Cancel the starting units with the units in the denominator. Round your answer based on the number of significant figures in the conversion factor.

$$100\ \cancel{\text{cm}} \times \frac{1\ \text{in}}{2.54\ \cancel{\text{cm}}} = 39.37\ \text{cm}$$

The meterstick is 39.4 in long.

Practice Problem A book has a mass of 5 lbs. What is the mass of the book in kg?

Practice Problem Use the equivalent for in and cm (1 in = 2.54 cm) to show how $1\ \text{in}^3 = 16.39\ \text{cm}^3$.

Convert Between Unit Systems

$$\frac{(1\ \text{in})^3}{(2.54\ \text{cm})^3}$$

$$= \frac{1\ \text{in} \times 1\ \text{in} \times 1\ \text{in}}{2.54\ \text{cm} \times 2.54\ \text{cm} \times 2.54\ \text{cm}}$$

$$= \frac{1\ \text{in}^3}{16.39\ \text{cm}^3}$$

Math Skill Handbook

Math Skill Handbook

Precision and Significant Digits

Problem 1
7; 4

Problem 2
$5.28 \times 5.2 = 27.456$

5.28 has 3 significant digits.

5.2 has 2 significant digits.

When multiplying and dividing, the answer is rounded to the smallest number of significant digits of the numbers being multiplied or divided—in this case, 2.

27.456 is rounded to 27.

Scientific Notation

Problem 1
4; 4

Problem 2
0.000007

Problem 3
5.39×10^2

Precision and Significant Digits

When you make a measurement, the value you record depends on the precision of the measuring instrument. This precision is represented by the number of significant digits recorded in the measurement. When counting the number of significant digits, all digits are counted except zeros at the end of a number with no decimal point such as 2,050, and zeros at the beginning of a decimal such as 0.03020. When adding or subtracting numbers with different precision, round the answer to the smallest number of decimal places of any number in the sum or difference. When multiplying or dividing, the answer is rounded to the smallest number of significant digits of any number being multiplied or divided.

Example The lengths 5.28 and 5.2 are measured in meters. Find the sum of these lengths and record your answer using the correct number of significant digits.

Step 1 Find the sum.

5.28 m	2 digits after the decimal
+ 5.2 m	1 digit after the decimal
10.48 m	

Step 2 Round to one digit after the decimal because the least number of digits after the decimal of the numbers being added is 1.

The sum is 10.5 m.

Practice Problem How many significant digits are in the measurement 7,071,301 m? How many significant digits are in the measurement 0.003010 g?

Practice Problem Multiply 5.28 and 5.2 using the rule for multiplying and dividing. Record the answer using the correct number of significant digits.

Scientific Notation

Many times numbers used in science are very small or very large. Because these numbers are difficult to work with scientists use scientific notation. To write numbers in scientific notation, move the decimal point until only one non-zero digit remains on the left. Then count the number of places you moved the decimal point and use that number as a power of ten. For example, the average distance from the Sun to Mars is 227,800,000,000 m. In scientific notation, this distance is 2.278×10^{11} m. Because you moved the decimal point to the left, the number is a positive power of ten.

The mass of an electron is about 0.000 000 000 000 000 000 000 000 000 000 911 kg. Expressed in scientific notation, this mass is 9.11×10^{-31} kg. Because the decimal point was moved to the right, the number is a negative power of ten.

Example Earth is 149,600,000 km from the Sun. Express this in scientific notation.

Step 1 Move the decimal point until one non-zero digit remains on the left.
1.496 000 00

Step 2 Count the number of decimal places you have moved. In this case, eight.

Step 3 Show that number as a power of ten, 10^8.

The Earth is 1.496×10^8 km from the Sun.

Practice Problem How many significant digits are in 149,600,000 km? How many significant digits are in 1.496×10^8 km?

Practice Problem Parts used in a high performance car must be measured to 7×10^{-6} m. Express this number as a decimal.

Practice Problem A CD is spinning at 539 revolutions per minute. Express this number in scientific notation.

Math Skill Handbook

Make and Use Graphs

Data in tables can be displayed in a graph—a visual representation of data. Common graph types include line graphs, bar graphs, and circle graphs.

Line Graph A line graph shows a relationship between two variables that change continuously. The independent variable is changed and is plotted on the *x*-axis. The dependent variable is observed, and is plotted on the *y*-axis.

Example Draw a line graph of the data below from a cyclist in a long-distance race.

Table 5 Bicycle Race Data	
Time (h)	Distance (km)
0	0
1	8
2	16
3	24
4	32
5	40

Step 1 Determine the *x*-axis and *y*-axis variables. Time varies independently of distance and is plotted on the *x*-axis. Distance is dependent on time and is plotted on the *y*-axis.

Step 2 Determine the scale of each axis. The *x*-axis data ranges from 0 to 5. The *y*-axis data ranges from 0 to 40.

Step 3 Using graph paper, draw and label the axes. Include units in the labels.

Step 4 Draw a point at the intersection of the time value on the *x*-axis and corresponding distance value on the *y*-axis. Connect the points and label the graph with a title, as shown in **Figure 20.**

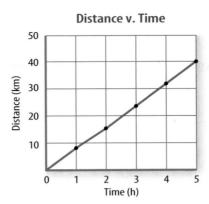

Distance v. Time

Figure 20 This line graph shows the relationship between distance and time during a bicycle ride.

Practice Problem A puppy's shoulder height is measured during the first year of her life. The following measurements were collected: (3 mo, 52 cm), (6 mo, 72 cm), (9 mo, 83 cm), (12 mo, 86 cm). Graph this data.

Find a Slope The slope of a straight line is the ratio of the vertical change, rise, to the horizontal change, run.

$$\text{Slope} = \frac{\text{vertical change (rise)}}{\text{horizontal change (run)}} = \frac{\text{change in } y}{\text{change in } x}$$

Example Find the slope of the graph in **Figure 20.**

Step 1 You know that the slope is the change in *y* divided by the change in *x*.

$$\text{Slope} = \frac{\text{change in } y}{\text{change in } x}$$

Step 2 Determine the data points you will be using. For a straight line, choose the two sets of points that are the farthest apart.

$$\text{Slope} = \frac{(40-0) \text{ km}}{(5-0) \text{ hr}}$$

Step 3 Find the change in *y* and *x*.

$$\text{Slope} = \frac{40 \text{ km}}{5 \text{ h}}$$

Step 4 Divide the change in *y* by the change in *x*.

$$\text{Slope} = \frac{8 \text{ km}}{\text{h}}$$

The slope of the graph is 8 km/h.

Line Graph

x	y
3	52
6	72
9	83
12	86

Puppy Growth

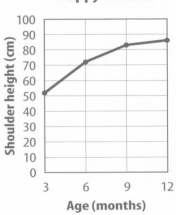

Bar Graph

Composition of Air

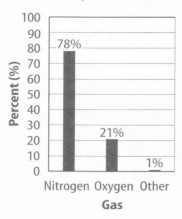

Circle Graph

The total amount of aluminum collected is:

$4.0 \text{ kg} + 1.0 \text{ kg} + 2.0 \text{ kg} = 7.0 \text{ kg}$

$\frac{4.0 \text{ kg}}{7.0 \text{ kg}} = \frac{x}{360°}; \ x = 206°$

$\frac{1.0 \text{ kg}}{7.0 \text{ kg}} = \frac{x}{360°}; \ x = 51°$

$\frac{2.0 \text{ kg}}{7.0 \text{ kg}} = \frac{x}{360°}; \ x = 103°$

Bar Graph To compare data that does not change continuously you might choose a bar graph. A bar graph uses bars to show the relationships between variables. The *x*-axis variable is divided into parts. The parts can be numbers such as years, or a category such as a type of animal. The *y*-axis is a number and increases continuously along the axis.

Example A recycling center collects 4.0 kg of aluminum on Monday, 1.0 kg on Wednesday, and 2.0 kg on Friday. Create a bar graph of this data.

Step 1 Select the *x*-axis and *y*-axis variables. The measured numbers (the masses of aluminum) should be placed on the *y*-axis. The variable divided into parts (collection days) is placed on the *x*-axis.

Step 2 Create a graph grid like you would for a line graph. Include labels and units.

Step 3 For each measured number, draw a vertical bar above the *x*-axis value up to the *y*-axis value. For the first data point, draw a vertical bar above Monday up to 4.0 kg.

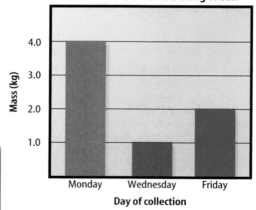

Practice Problem Draw a bar graph of the gases in air: 78% nitrogen, 21% oxygen, 1% other gases.

Circle Graph To display data as parts of a whole, you might use a circle graph. A circle graph is a circle divided into sections that represent the relative size of each piece of data. The entire circle represents 100%, half represents 50%, and so on.

Example Air is made up of 78% nitrogen, 21% oxygen, and 1% other gases. Display the composition of air in a circle graph.

Step 1 Multiply each percent by 360° and divide by 100 to find the angle of each section in the circle.

$78\% \times \frac{360°}{100} = 280.8°$

$21\% \times \frac{360°}{100} = 75.6°$

$1\% \times \frac{360°}{100} = 3.6°$

Step 2 Use a compass to draw a circle and to mark the center of the circle. Draw a straight line from the center to the edge of the circle.

Step 3 Use a protractor and the angles you calculated to divide the circle into parts. Place the center of the protractor over the center of the circle and line the base of the protractor over the straight line.

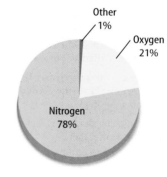

Practice Problem Draw a circle graph to represent the amount of aluminum collected during the week shown in the bar graph to the left.

Math Skill Handbook

Use and Care of a Microscope

Eyepiece Contains magnifying lenses you look through.

Arm Supports the body tube.

Low-power objective Contains the lens with the lowest power magnification.

Stage clips Hold the microscope slide in place.

Coarse adjustment Focuses the image under low power.

Fine adjustment Sharpens the image under high magnification.

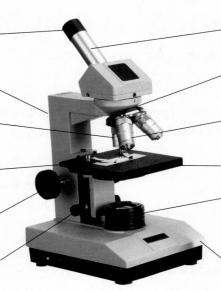

Body tube Connects the eyepiece to the revolving nosepiece.

Revolving nosepiece Holds and turns the objectives into viewing position.

High-power objective Contains the lens with the highest magnification.

Stage Supports the microscope slide.

Light source Provides light that passes upward through the diaphragm, the specimen, and the lenses.

Base Provides support for the microscope.

Caring for a Microscope

1. Always carry the microscope holding the arm with one hand and supporting the base with the other hand.

2. Don't touch the lenses with your fingers.

3. The coarse adjustment knob is used only when looking through the lowest-power objective lens. The fine adjustment knob is used when the high-power objective is in place.

4. Cover the microscope when you store it.

Using a Microscope

1. Place the microscope on a flat surface that is clear of objects. The arm should be toward you.

2. Look through the eyepiece. Adjust the diaphragm so light comes through the opening in the stage.

3. Place a slide on the stage so the specimen is in the field of view. Hold it firmly in place by using the stage clips.

4. Always focus with the coarse adjustment and the low-power objective lens first. After the object is in focus on low power, turn the nosepiece until the high-power objective is in place. Use ONLY the fine adjustment to focus with the high-power objective lens.

Making a Wet-Mount Slide

1. Carefully place the item you want to look at in the center of a clean, glass slide. Make sure the sample is thin enough for light to pass through.

2. Use a dropper to place one or two drops of water on the sample.

3. Hold a clean coverslip by the edges and place it at one edge of the water. Slowly lower the coverslip onto the water until it lies flat.

4. If you have too much water or a lot of air bubbles, touch the edge of a paper towel to the edge of the coverslip to draw off extra water and draw out unwanted air.

Diversity of Life: Classification of Living Organisms

A six-kingdom system of classification of organisms is used today. Two kingdoms—Kingdom Archaebacteria and Kingdom Eubacteria—contain organisms that do not have a nucleus and that lack membrane-bound structures in the cytoplasm of their cells. The members of the other four kingdoms have a cell or cells that contain a nucleus and structures in the cytoplasm, some of which are surrounded by membranes. These kingdoms are Kingdom Protista, Kingdom Fungi, Kingdom Plantae, and Kingdom Animalia.

Kingdom Archaebacteria

one-celled; some absorb food from their surroundings; some are photosynthetic; some are chemosynthetic; many are found in extremely harsh environments including salt ponds, hot springs, swamps, and deep-sea hydrothermal vents

Kingdom Eubacteria

one-celled; most absorb food from their surroundings; some are photosynthetic; some are chemosynthetic; many are parasites; many are round, spiral, or rod-shaped; some form colonies

Kingdom Protista

Phylum Euglenophyta one-celled; photosynthetic or take in food; most have one flagellum; euglenoids

Phylum Bacillariophyta one-celled; photosynthetic; have unique double shells made of silica; diatoms

Phylum Dinoflagellata one-celled; photosynthetic; contain red pigments; have two flagella; dinoflagellates

Phylum Chlorophyta one-celled, many-celled, or colonies; photosynthetic; contain chlorophyll; live on land, in freshwater, or salt water; green algae

Phylum Rhodophyta most are many-celled; photosynthetic; contain red pigments; most live in deep, saltwater environments; red algae

Phylum Phaeophyta most are many-celled; photosynthetic; contain brown pigments; most live in saltwater environments; brown algae

Phylum Rhizopoda one-celled; take in food; are free-living or parasitic; move by means of pseudopods; amoebas

Kingdom Eubacteria
Bacillus anthracis

Phylum Chlorophyta
Desmids

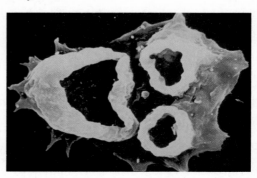

Amoeba

Phylum Zoomastigina one-celled; take in food; free-living or parasitic; have one or more flagella; zoomastigotes

Phylum Ciliophora one-celled; take in food; have large numbers of cilia; ciliates

Phylum Sporozoa one-celled; take in food; have no means of movement; are parasites in animals; sporozoans

Phylum Myxomycota
Slime mold

Phylum Oomycota
Phytophthora infestans

Phyla Myxomycota and Acrasiomycota one- or many-celled; absorb food; change form during life cycle; cellular and plasmodial slime molds

Phylum Oomycota many-celled; are either parasites or decomposers; live in freshwater or salt water; water molds, rusts and downy mildews

Kingdom Fungi

Phylum Zygomycota many-celled; absorb food; spores are produced in sporangia; zygote fungi; bread mold

Phylum Ascomycota one- and many-celled; absorb food; spores produced in asci; sac fungi; yeast

Phylum Basidiomycota many-celled; absorb food; spores produced in basidia; club fungi; mushrooms

Phylum Deuteromycota members with unknown reproductive structures; imperfect fungi; *Penicillium*

Phylum Mycophycota organisms formed by symbiotic relationship between an ascomycote or a basidiomycote and green alga or cyanobacterium; lichens

Lichens

Kingdom Plantae

Divisions Bryophyta (mosses), **Anthocerophyta** (hornworts), **Hepaticophyta** (liverworts), **Psilophyta** (whisk ferns) many-celled nonvascular plants; reproduce by spores produced in capsules; green; grow in moist, land environments

Division Lycophyta many-celled vascular plants; spores are produced in conelike structures; live on land; are photosynthetic; club mosses

Division Arthrophyta vascular plants; ribbed and jointed stems; scalelike leaves; spores produced in conelike structures; horsetails

Division Pterophyta vascular plants; leaves called fronds; spores produced in clusters of sporangia called sori; live on land or in water; ferns

Division Ginkgophyta deciduous trees; only one living species; have fan-shaped leaves with branching veins and fleshy cones with seeds; ginkgoes

Division Cycadophyta palmlike plants; have large, featherlike leaves; produces seeds in cones; cycads

Division Coniferophyta deciduous or evergreen; trees or shrubs; have needlelike or scalelike leaves; seeds produced in cones; conifers

Division Gnetophyta shrubs or woody vines; seeds are produced in cones; division contains only three genera; gnetum

Division Anthophyta dominant group of plants; flowering plants; have fruits with seeds

Kingdom Animalia

Phylum Porifera aquatic organisms that lack true tissues and organs; are asymmetrical and sessile; sponges

Phylum Cnidaria radially symmetrical organisms; have a digestive cavity with one opening; most have tentacles armed with stinging cells; live in aquatic environments singly or in colonies; includes jellyfish, corals, hydra, and sea anemones

Phylum Platyhelminthes bilaterally symmetrical worms; have flattened bodies; digestive system has one opening; parasitic and free-living species; flatworms

Division Bryophyta
Liverwort

Division Anthophyta
Tomato plant

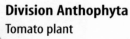

Phylum Platyhelminthes
Flatworm

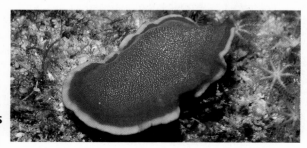

Phylum Chordata

Phylum Nematoda round, bilaterally symmetrical body; have digestive system with two openings; free-living forms and parasitic forms; roundworms

Phylum Mollusca soft-bodied animals, many with a hard shell and soft foot or footlike appendage; a mantle covers the soft body; aquatic and terrestrial species; includes clams, snails, squid, and octopuses

Phylum Annelida bilaterally symmetrical worms; have round, segmented bodies; terrestrial and aquatic species; includes earthworms, leeches, and marine polychaetes

Phylum Arthropoda largest animal group; have hard exoskeletons, segmented bodies, and pairs of jointed appendages; land and aquatic species; includes insects, crustaceans, and spiders

Phylum Echinodermata marine organisms; have spiny or leathery skin and a water-vascular system with tube feet; are radially symmetrical; includes sea stars, sand dollars, and sea urchins

Phylum Chordata organisms with internal skeletons and specialized body systems; most have paired appendages; all at some time have a notochord, nerve cord, gill slits, and a post-anal tail; include fish, amphibians, reptiles, birds, and mammals

PERIODIC TABLE OF THE ELEMENTS

Columns of elements are called groups. Elements in the same group have similar chemical properties.

- Gas
- Liquid
- Solid
- Synthetic

Element — Hydrogen
Atomic number — 1
Symbol — H
Atomic mass — 1.008
State of matter

The first three symbols tell you the state of matter of the element at room temperature. The fourth symbol identifies elements that are not present in significant amounts on Earth. Useful amounts are made synthetically.

1								
1 Hydrogen 1 **H** 1.008								
2 Lithium 3 **Li** 6.941	**2** Beryllium 4 **Be** 9.012							
3 Sodium 11 **Na** 22.990	Magnesium 12 **Mg** 24.305	**3**	**4**	**5**	**6**	**7**	**8**	**9**
4 Potassium 19 **K** 39.098	Calcium 20 **Ca** 40.078	Scandium 21 **Sc** 44.956	Titanium 22 **Ti** 47.867	Vanadium 23 **V** 50.942	Chromium 24 **Cr** 51.996	Manganese 25 **Mn** 54.938	Iron 26 **Fe** 55.845	Cobalt 27 **Co** 58.933
5 Rubidium 37 **Rb** 85.468	Strontium 38 **Sr** 87.62	Yttrium 39 **Y** 88.906	Zirconium 40 **Zr** 91.224	Niobium 41 **Nb** 92.906	Molybdenum 42 **Mo** 95.94	Technetium 43 **Tc** (98)	Ruthenium 44 **Ru** 101.07	Rhodium 45 **Rh** 102.906
6 Cesium 55 **Cs** 132.905	Barium 56 **Ba** 137.327	Lanthanum 57 **La** 138.906	Hafnium 72 **Hf** 178.49	Tantalum 73 **Ta** 180.948	Tungsten 74 **W** 183.84	Rhenium 75 **Re** 186.207	Osmium 76 **Os** 190.23	Iridium 77 **Ir** 192.217
7 Francium 87 **Fr** (223)	Radium 88 **Ra** (226)	Actinium 89 **Ac** (227)	Rutherfordium 104 **Rf** (261)	Dubnium 105 **Db** (262)	Seaborgium 106 **Sg** (266)	Bohrium 107 **Bh** (264)	Hassium 108 **Hs** (277)	Meitnerium 109 **Mt** (268)

The number in parentheses is the mass number of the longest-lived isotope for that element.

Rows of elements are called periods. Atomic number increases across a period.

The arrow shows where these elements would fit into the periodic table. They are moved to the bottom of the table to save space.

Lanthanide series	Cerium 58 **Ce** 140.116	Praseodymium 59 **Pr** 140.908	Neodymium 60 **Nd** 144.24	Promethium 61 **Pm** (145)	Samarium 62 **Sm** 150.36
Actinide series	Thorium 90 **Th** 232.038	Protactinium 91 **Pa** 231.036	Uranium 92 **U** 238.029	Neptunium 93 **Np** (237)	Plutonium 94 **Pu** (244)

Metal
Metalloid
Nonmetal

The color of an element's block tells you if the element is a metal, nonmetal, or metalloid.

Science Online
Visit life.msscience.com for updates to the periodic table.

18
Helium
2
He
4.003

13	14	15	16	17	
Boron	Carbon	Nitrogen	Oxygen	Fluorine	Neon
5	6	7	8	9	10
B	**C**	**N**	**O**	**F**	**Ne**
10.811	12.011	14.007	15.999	18.998	20.180
Aluminum	Silicon	Phosphorus	Sulfur	Chlorine	Argon
13	14	15	16	17	18
Al	**Si**	**P**	**S**	**Cl**	**Ar**
26.982	28.086	30.974	32.065	35.453	39.948

10	11	12					
Nickel	Copper	Zinc	Gallium	Germanium	Arsenic	Selenium	Bromine	Krypton
28	29	30	31	32	33	34	35	36
Ni	**Cu**	**Zn**	**Ga**	**Ge**	**As**	**Se**	**Br**	**Kr**
58.693	63.546	65.409	69.723	72.64	74.922	78.96	79.904	83.798
Palladium	Silver	Cadmium	Indium	Tin	Antimony	Tellurium	Iodine	Xenon
46	47	48	49	50	51	52	53	54
Pd	**Ag**	**Cd**	**In**	**Sn**	**Sb**	**Te**	**I**	**Xe**
106.42	107.868	112.411	114.818	118.710	121.760	127.60	126.904	131.293
Platinum	Gold	Mercury	Thallium	Lead	Bismuth	Polonium	Astatine	Radon
78	79	80	81	82	83	84	85	86
Pt	**Au**	**Hg**	**Tl**	**Pb**	**Bi**	**Po**	**At**	**Rn**
195.078	196.967	200.59	204.383	207.2	208.980	(209)	(210)	(222)
Darmstadtium	Roentgenium	Ununbium		Ununquadium				
110	111	* 112		* 114				
Ds	**Rg**	**Uub**		**Uuq**				
(281)	(272)	(285)		(289)				

* The names and symbols for elements 112 and 114 are temporary. Final names will be selected when the elements' discoveries are verified.

Europium	Gadolinium	Terbium	Dysprosium	Holmium	Erbium	Thulium	Ytterbium	Lutetium
63	64	65	66	67	68	69	70	71
Eu	**Gd**	**Tb**	**Dy**	**Ho**	**Er**	**Tm**	**Yb**	**Lu**
151.964	157.25	158.925	162.500	164.930	167.259	168.934	173.04	174.967
Americium	Curium	Berkelium	Californium	Einsteinium	Fermium	Mendelevium	Nobelium	Lawrencium
95	96	97	98	99	100	101	102	103
Am	**Cm**	**Bk**	**Cf**	**Es**	**Fm**	**Md**	**No**	**Lr**
(243)	(247)	(247)	(251)	(252)	(257)	(258)	(259)	(262)

Glossary/Glosario

Cómo usar el glosario en español:
1. Busca el término en inglés que desees encontrar.
2. El término en español, junto con la definición, se encuentran en la columna de la derecha.

Pronunciation Key

Use the following key to help you sound out words in the glossary.

a	back (BAK)	**ew**	food (FEWD)
ay	day (DAY)	**yoo**	pure (PYOOR)
ah	father (FAH thur)	**yew**	few (FYEW)
ow	flower (FLOW ur)	**uh**	comma (CAH muh)
ar	car (CAR)	**u (+ con)**	rub (RUB)
e	less (LES)	**sh**	shelf (SHELF)
ee	leaf (LEEF)	**ch**	nature (NAY chur)
ih	trip (TRIHP)	**g**	gift (GIHFT)
i (i + con + e)	idea (i DEE uh)	**j**	gem (JEM)
oh	go (GOH)	**ing**	sing (SING)
aw	soft (SAWFT)	**zh**	vision (VIH zhun)
or	orbit (OR buht)	**k**	cake (KAYK)
oy	coin (COYN)	**s**	seed, cent (SEED, SENT)
oo	foot (FOOT)	**z**	zone, raise (ZOHN, RAYZ)

English — A — Español

abiotic: nonliving, physical features of the environment, including air, water, sunlight, soil, temperature, and climate. (p. 712)

acid precipitation: precipitation with a pH below 5.6—which occurs when air pollutants from the burning of fossil fuels react with water in the atmosphere to form strong acids—that can pollute water, kill fish and plants, and damage soils. (p. 779)

active immunity: long-lasting immunity that results when the body makes its own antibodies in response to a specific antigen. (p. 655)

active transport: energy-requiring process in which transport proteins bind with particles and move them through a cell membrane. (p. 77)

adaptation: any variation that makes an organism better suited to its environment. (p. 158)

aerobe (AY rohb): any organism that uses oxygen for respiration. (p. 188)

aggression: forceful behavior, such as fighting, used by an animal to control or dominate another animal in order to protect their young, defend territory, or get food. (p. 464)

algae (AL jee): chlorophyll-containing, plantlike protists that produce oxygen as a result of photosynthesis. (p. 211)

abiótico: características inertes y físicas del medio ambiente, incluyendo el aire, el agua, la luz solar, el suelo, la temperatura y el clima. (p. 712)

lluvia ácida: precipitación con un pH menor de 5.6—lo cual ocurre cuando los contaminantes del aire provenientes de la quema de combustibles fósiles reaccionan con el agua en la atmósfera para formar ácidos fuertes—que puede contaminar el agua, matar peces y plantas, y dañar los suelos. (p. 779)

inmunidad activa: inmunidad duradera que resulta cuando el cuerpo produce sus propios anticuerpos en respuesta a un antígeno específico. (p. 655)

transporte activo: proceso que requiere energía y en el cual las proteínas de transporte se unen con partículas y las trasladan a través de la membrana celular. (p. 77)

adaptación: cualquier variación que haga que un organismo se adapte mejor a su medio ambiente. (p. 158)

aerobio: cualquier organismo que utiliza oxígeno para respirar. (p. 188)

agresión: comportamiento violento, como la lucha, manifestado por un animal para controlar o dominar a otro animal con el fin de proteger a sus crías, defender su territorio o conseguir alimento. (p. 464)

algas: protistas parecidos a las plantas; contienen clorofila y producen oxígeno como resultado de la fotosíntesis. (p. 211)

allele (uh LEEL): an alternate form that a gene may have for a single trait; can be dominant or recessive. (p. 126)

allergen: substance that causes an allergic reaction. (p. 667)

allergy: overly strong reaction of the immune system to a foreign substance. (p. 666)

alveoli (al VEE uh li): tiny, thin-walled, grapelike clusters at the end of each bronchiole that are surrounded by capillaries; carbon dioxide and oxygen exchange takes place. (p. 571)

amino acid: building block of protein. (p. 513)

amniotic egg: egg covered with a shell that provides a complete environment for the embryo's development; for reptiles, a major adaptation for living on land. (p. 413)

amniotic (am nee AH tihk) sac: thin, liquid-filled, protective membrane that forms around the embryo. (p. 635)

anaerobe (AN uh rohb): any organism that is able to live without oxygen. (p. 188)

angiosperms: flowering vascular plants that produce fruits containing one or more seeds; monocots and dicots. (p. 257)

antibiotics: chemicals produced by some bacteria that are used to limit the growth of other bacteria. (p. 193)

antibody: a protein made in response to a specific antigen that can attach to the antigen and cause it to be useless. (p. 654)

antigen (AN tih jun): any complex molecule that is foreign to your body. (p. 654)

anus: opening at the end of the digestive tract through which wastes leave the body. (p. 347)

appendages: jointed structures of arthropods, such as legs, wings, or antennae. (p. 370)

artery: blood vessel that carries blood away from the heart, and has thick, elastic walls made of connective tissue and smooth muscle tissue. (p. 544)

ascus (AS kus): saclike, spore-producing structure of sac fungi. (p. 224)

asexual reproduction: a type of reproduction—fission, budding, and regeneration—in which a new organism is produced from one organism and has DNA identical to the parent organism. (p. 101)

asthma: lung disorder in which the bronchial tubes contract quickly and cause shortness of breath, wheezing, or coughing; may occur as an allergic reaction. (p. 576)

alelo: forma alternativa que un gen puede tener para un rasgo único; puede ser dominante o recesivo. (p. 126)

alergeno: sustancia que causa una reacción alérgica. (p. 667)

alergia: reacción exagerada del sistema inmune a una sustancia extraña. (p. 666)

alvéolos: pequeños racimos de pared delgada que se encuentran al final de cada bronquíolo y que están rodeados por capilares; aquí tiene lugar el intercambio de oxígeno y dióxido de carbono. (p. 571)

aminoácido: bloque de construcción de las proteínas. (p. 513)

huevo amniótico: huevo cubierto por un cascarón coriáceo que proporciona un ambiente completo para el desarrollo del embrión; para los reptiles, una gran adaptación para vivir en la tierra. (p. 413)

saco amniótico: membrana protectora delgada y llena de líquido que se forma alrededor del embrión. (p. 635)

anaerobio: cualquier organismo capaz de vivir sin oxígeno. (p. 188)

angiospermas: plantas vasculares que producen flores y frutos que contienen una o más semillas; pueden ser monocotiledóneas o dicotiledóneas. (p. 257)

antibióticos: químicos producidos por algunas bacterias, utilizados para limitar el crecimiento de otras bacterias. (p. 193)

anticuerpo: proteína formada en respuesta a un antígeno específico y que puede unirse al antígeno para provocar que éste sea inutilizado. (p. 654)

antígeno: molécula compleja que es extraña para el cuerpo. (p. 654)

ano: apertura al final del tracto digestivo a través de la cual los desechos salen del cuerpo. (p. 347)

apéndices: estructuras articuladas de los artrópodos, como las patas, alas o antenas. (p. 370)

arteria: vaso sanguíneo que transporta sangre desde el corazón y tiene paredes gruesas y elásticas hechas de tejido conectivo y tejido muscular liso. (p. 544)

asca: estructura en forma de saco en donde los ascomicetos producen esporas. (p. 224)

reproducción asexual: tipo de reproducción—fisión, gemación y regeneración—en el que un organismo da origen a uno nuevo de ADN idéntico al organismo progenitor. (p. 101)

asma: desorden pulmonar en el que los tubos bronquiales se contraen rápidamente y causan dificultad para respirar, silbido o tos; puede ocurrir como una reacción alérgica. (p. 576)

Glossary/Glosario

atmosphere: air surrounding Earth; is made up of gases, including 78 percent nitrogen, 21 percent oxygen, and 0.03 percent carbon dioxide. (p. 713)

atriums (AY tree umz): two upper chambers of the heart that contract at the same time during a heartbeat. (p. 541)

auxin (AWK sun): plant hormone that causes plant leaves and stems to exhibit positive phototropisms. (p. 314)

axon (AK sahn): neuron structure that carries messages away from the cell body. (p. 595)

atmósfera: aire que rodea a la Tierra; está compuesta de gases, incluyendo 78% de nitrógeno, 21% de oxígeno y 0.03% de dióxido de carbono. (p. 713)

aurículas: las dos cámaras superiores del corazón que se contraen al mismo tiempo durante el latido cardiaco. (p. 541)

auxina: hormona vegetal que causa que las hojas y tallos de las plantas desarrollen un fototropismo positivo. (p. 314)

axón: estructura de la neurona que transmite los mensajes desde el cuerpo de la célula. (p. 595)

B

basidium (buh SIH dee uhm): club-shaped, reproductive structure in which club fungi produce spores. (p. 224)

behavior: the way in which an organism interacts with other organisms and its environment; can be innate or learned. (p. 456)

bilateral symmetry: body parts arranged in a similar way on both sides of the body, with each half being nearly a mirror image of the other half. (p. 335)

binomial nomenclature (bi NOH mee ul • NOH mun klay chur): two-word naming system that gives all organisms their scientific name. (p. 24)

biogenesis (bi oh JEH nuh sus): theory that living things come only from other living things. (p. 19)

biological vector: disease-carrying organism, such as a rat, mosquito, or fly, that spreads infectious disease. (p. 661)

biomes (BI ohmz): large geographic areas with similar climates and ecosystems; includes tundra, taiga, desert, temperate deciduous forest, temperate rain forest, tropical rain forest, and grassland. (p. 744)

biosphere: part of Earth that supports life, including the top portion of Earth's crust, the atmosphere, and all the water on Earth's surface. (p. 684)

biotic (bi AH tihk): features of the environment that are alive or were once alive. (p. 712)

bladder: elastic, muscular organ that holds urine until it leaves the body through the urethra. (p. 580)

brain stem: connects the brain to the spinal cord and is made up of the midbrain, the pons, and the medulla. (p. 598)

bronchi (BRAHN ki): two short tubes that branch off the lower end of the trachea and carry air into the lungs. (p. 571)

budding: form of asexual reproduction in which a new, genetically-identical organism forms on the side of its parent. (p. 224)

basidio: estructura reproductora en forma de mazo en la que los basidiomicetos producen esporas. (p. 224)

comportamiento: forma en la que un organismo interactúa con otros organismos y su entorno; puede ser innato o aprendido. (p. 456)

simetría bilateral: disposición de las partes del cuerpo de manera similar a ambos lados de éste, de tal forma que cada mitad es una imagen especular de la otra. (p. 335)

nomenclatura binomial: sistema de denominación de dos palabras que da a todos los organismos su nombre científico. (p. 24)

biogénesis: teoría que sostiene que los seres vivos sólo provienen de otros seres vivos. (p. 19)

vector biológico: organismo portador de enfermedades, como las ratas, mosquitos y moscas, que propagan enfermedades infecciosas. (p. 661)

biomas: grandes áreas geográficas con climas y ecosistemas similares; incluyen la tundra, la taiga, el desierto, el bosque caducifolio templado, el bosque lluvioso templado, la selva húmeda tropical y los pastizales. (p. 744)

biosfera: capa de la Tierra que alberga la vida, incluyendo la porción superior de la corteza terrestre, la atmósfera y toda el agua de la superficie terrestre. (p. 684)

biótico: características del ambiente que tienen o alguna vez tuvieron vida. (p. 712)

vejiga: órgano muscular elástico que retiene la orina hasta que ésta sale del cuerpo por la uretra. (p. 580)

tronco cerebral: conecta al cerebro con la médula espinal y está compuesto por el mesencéfalo, el puente de Varolio y la médula. (p. 598)

bronquios: dos tubos cortos que se ramifican en la parte inferior de la tráquea y llevan el aire a los pulmones. (p. 571)

gemación: forma de reproducción asexual en la que se forma un organismo nuevo y genéticamente idéntico al lado de su progenitor. (p. 224)

Glossary/Glosario

cambium (KAM bee um): vascular tissue that produces xylem and phloem cells as a plant grows. (p. 255)

capillary: microscopic blood vessel that connects arteries and veins; has walls one cell thick, through which nutrients and oxygen diffuse into body cells, and waste materials and carbon dioxide diffuse out of body cells. (p. 545)

carbohydrate (kar boh HI drayt): nutrient that usually is the body's main source of energy. (p. 514)

carbon cycle: model describing how carbon molecules move between the living and nonliving world. (p. 725)

cardiac muscle: striated, involuntary muscle found only in the heart. (p. 493)

carnivore: animal that eats only other animals or the remains of other animals; mammals having large, sharp canine teeth and strong jaw muscles for eating flesh. (pp. 331, 437)

carrying capacity: largest number of individuals of a particular species that an ecosystem can support over time. (p. 691)

cartilage: tough, flexible tissue that joins vertebrae and makes up all or part of the vertebrate endoskeleton; in humans, thick, smooth, flexible, and slippery tissue layer that covers the ends of bones, makes movement easier by reducing friction, and absorbs shocks. (pp. 395, 486)

cell: smallest unit of an organism that can carry on life functions. (p. 14)

cell membrane: protective outer covering of all cells that regulates the interaction between the cell and the environment. (p. 38)

cell theory: states that all organisms are made up of one or more cells, the cell is the basic unit of life, and all cells come from other cells. (p. 51)

cellulose (SEL yuh lohs): chemical compound made out of sugar; forms tangled fibers in the cell walls of many plants and provides structure and support. (p. 242)

cell wall: rigid structure that encloses, supports, and protects the cells of plants, algae, fungi, and most bacteria. (p. 39)

central nervous system: division of the nervous system, made up of the brain and spinal cord. (p. 597)

cerebellum (sur uh BEH lum): part of the brain that controls voluntary muscle movements, maintains muscle tone, and helps maintain balance. (p. 598)

cámbium: tejido vascular que produce las células del xilema y floema conforme crece la planta. (p. 255)

capilar: vaso sanguíneo microscópico que conecta las arterias con las venas; su pared tiene el grosor de una célula y los nutrientes y el oxígeno se difunden a través de ella hacia las células del cuerpo y los materiales de desecho y el dióxido de carbono hacia afuera de éstas. (p. 545)

carbohidrato: nutriente que generalmente es la principal fuente de energía para el cuerpo. (p. 514)

ciclo del carbono: modelo que describe cómo se mueven las moléculas de carbono entre el mundo vivo y el mundo inerte. (p. 725)

músculo cardiaco: músculo estriado involuntario que sólo se encuentra en el corazón. (p. 493)

carnívoro: animal que se alimenta exclusivamente de otros animales o de los restos de otros animales; mamífero con caninos largos y afilados y músculos fuertes en la mandíbula que le sirven para alimentarse de carne. (pp. 331, 437)

capacidad de carga: el mayor número de individuos de una especie en particular que un ecosistema puede albergar en un periodo de tiempo. (p. 691)

cartílago: tejido resistente y flexible que conecta a las vértebras y constituye todo o parte del endoesqueleto de los vertebrados; en los humanos, capa gruesa y lisa de tejido resbaladizo y flexible que cubre los extremos de los huesos, facilita el movimiento reduciendo la fricción y absorbe los impactos. (pp. 395, 486)

célula: la unidad más pequeña de un organismo que puede continuar con sus funciones vitales. (p. 14)

membrana celular: capa externa protectora de todas las células y reguladora de la interacción entre la célula y su entorno. (p. 38)

teoría celular: establece que todos los organismos están formados por una o más células, que la célula es la unidad básica de la vida y que las células provienen de otras células. (p. 51)

celulosa: compuesto químico formado por azúcares y que forma fibras intrincadas en la pared celular de muchas plantas proporcionando estructura y soporte. (p. 242)

pared celular: estructura rígida que envuelve, sostiene y protege a las células de las plantas, algas, hongos y de la mayoría de las bacterias. (p. 39)

sistema nervioso central: parte del sistema nervioso, compuesto por el cerebro y la médula espinal. (p. 597)

cerebelo: parte del cerebro que controla los movimientos de los músculos voluntarios, mantiene el tono muscular y ayuda a mantener el equilibrio. (p. 598)

Glossary/Glosario

cerebrum (suh REE brum): largest part of the brain, where memory is stored, movements are controlled, and impulses from the senses are interpreted. (p. 598)

chemical digestion: occurs when enzymes and other chemicals break down large food molecules into smaller ones. (p. 523)

chemosynthesis (kee moh SIN thuh sus): process in which producers make energy-rich nutrient molecules from chemicals. (p. 727)

chemotherapy (kee moh THAYR uh pee): use of chemicals to destroy cancer cells. (p. 670)

chlorophyll (KLOR uh fihl): green, light-trapping pigment in plant chloroplasts that is important in photosynthesis. (p. 304)

chloroplast: green, chlorophyll-containing, plant-cell organelle that uses light energy to produce sugar from carbon dioxide and water. (p. 42)

chordate: animal that has a notochord, a nerve cord, pharyngeal pouches, and a postanal tail present at some stage in its development. (p. 394)

chromosome: structure in a cell's nucleus that contains hereditary material. (p. 98)

chyme (KIME): liquid product of digestion. (p. 527)

cilia (SIH lee uh): in protists, short, threadlike structures that extend from the cell membrane of a ciliate and enable the organism to move quickly. (p. 215)

climate: average weather conditions of an area over time, including wind, temperature, and rainfall or other types of precipitation such as snow or sleet. (p. 717)

climax community: stable, end stage of ecological succession in which balance is in the absence of disturbance. (p. 743)

closed circulatory system: blood circulation system in which blood moves through the body in closed vessels. (p. 362)

cochlea (KOH klee uh): fluid-filled structure in the inner ear in which sound vibrations are converted into nerve impulses that are sent to the brain. (p. 608)

commensalism: a type of symbiotic relationship in which one organism benefits and the other organism is not affected. (p. 698)

community: all the populations of different species that live in an ecosystem. (p. 686)

condensation: process that takes place when a gas changes to a liquid. (p. 721)

conditioning: occurs when the response to a stimulus becomes associated with another stimulus. (p. 460)

cerebro: la parte más grande del encéfalo, donde se almacena la memoria, se controlan los movimientos y se interpretan los impulsos provenientes de los sentidos. (p. 598)

digestión química: ocurre cuando las enzimas y otros químicos desintegran las moléculas grandes de los alimentos en otras más pequeñas. (p. 523)

quimiosíntesis: proceso a través del cual los productores fabrican moléculas ricas en energía a partir de agentes químicos. (p. 727)

quimioterapia: uso de sustancias químicas para destruir las células cancerosas. (p. 670)

clorofila: pigmento verde que absorbe luz y que se encuentra en los cloroplastos de las plantas; es importante para la fotosíntesis. (p. 304)

cloroplasto: organelo de las células vegetales, de color verde, que contiene clorofila y que usa la luz solar para convertir el dióxido de carbono y el agua en azúcar. (p. 42)

cordado: animal que posee notocordio, un cordón nervioso, bolsas faríngeas y que presenta cola postnatal en alguna etapa de su desarrollo. (p. 394)

cromosoma: estructura en el núcleo celular que contiene el material hereditario. (p. 98)

quimo: producto líquido de la digestión. (p. 527)

cilio: en los protistas, estructuras cortas en forma de hilo que se extienden desde la membrana celular de un ciliado y permiten al organismo moverse rápidamente. (p. 215)

clima: condiciones meteorológicas promedio de un área durante un periodo de tiempo; incluye viento, temperatura y precipitación pluvial u otros tipos de precipitación como la nieve o el granizo. (p. 717)

clímax comunitario: etapa final estable de la sucesión ecológica en la cual se da un equilibrio en ausencia de alteraciones. (p. 743)

sistema circulatorio cerrado: sistema circulatorio sanguíneo en el cual la sangre se mueve a través del cuerpo en vasos cerrados. (p. 362)

cóclea: estructura del oído interno llena de líquido en la que las vibraciones sonoras se convierten en impulsos nerviosos que son enviados al cerebro. (p. 608)

comensalismo: tipo de relación simbiótica en la que un organismo se beneficia sin afectar al otro. (p. 698)

comunidad: todas las poblaciones de diferentes especies que viven en un mismo ecosistema. (p. 686)

condensación: proceso que tiene lugar cuando un gas cambia a estado líquido. (p. 721)

condicionamiento: ocurre cuando la respuesta a un estímulo llega a estar asociada con otro estímulo. (p. 460)

Glossary/Glosario

consumer: organism that cannot create energy-rich molecules but obtains its food by eating other organisms. (p. 697)

contour feathers: strong, lightweight feathers that give birds their coloring and shape and that are used for flight. (p. 430)

control: standard to which the outcome of a test is compared. (p. 9)

coral reef: diverse ecosystem formed from the calcium carbonate shells secreted by corals. (p. 757)

coronary (KOR uh ner ee) circulation: flow of blood to and from the tissues of the heart. (p. 541)

courtship behavior: behavior that allows males and females of the same species to recognize each other and prepare to mate. (p. 465)

crop: digestive system sac in which earthworms store ingested soil. (p. 366)

cuticle (KYEW tih kul): waxy, protective layer that covers the stems, leaves, and flowers of many plants and helps prevent water loss. (p. 242)

cyclic behavior: behavior that occurs in repeated patterns. (p. 468)

cytoplasm: constantly moving gel-like mixture inside the cell membrane that contains heredity material and is the location of most of a cell's life processes. (p. 38)

consumidor: organismo que no puede fabricar moléculas ricas en energía por lo que debe obtener su alimento ingiriendo otros organismos. (p. 697)

plumas de contorno: plumas fuertes y ligeras que dan a las aves su colorido y forma y que son usadas para volar. (p. 430)

control: estándar contra el que se compara el resultado de una prueba. (p. 9)

arrecife de coral: ecosistema diverso conformado de caparazones de carbonato de calcio secretados por los corales. (p. 757)

circulación coronaria: flujo sanguíneo desde y hacia los tejidos del corazón. (p. 541)

comportamiento de cortejo: comportamiento que permite que los machos y hembras de la misma especie se reconozcan entre sí y se preparen para el apareamiento. (p. 465)

buche: saco del sistema digestivo en el que los gusanos de tierra almacenan el suelo ingerido. (p. 366)

cutícula: capa cerosa protectora que recubre el tronco, hojas y flores de muchas plantas y ayuda a prevenir la pérdida de agua. (p. 242)

comportamiento cíclico: comportamiento que ocurre en patrones repetidos. (p. 468)

citoplasma: mezcla parecida al gel y que está en constante movimiento dentro de la membrana celular, contiene material hereditario y es en donde tiene lugar la mayor parte de los procesos vitales de la célula. (p. 38)

D

day-neutral plant: plant that doesn't require a specific photoperiod and can begin the flowering process over a range of night lengths. (p. 316)

dendrite: neuron structure that receives messages and sends them to the cell body. (p. 595)

dermis: skin layer below the epidermis that contains blood vessels, nerves, oil and sweat glands, and other structures. (p. 497)

desert: driest biome on Earth with less than 25 cm of rain each year; has dunes or thin soil with little organic matter, where plants and animals are adapted to survive extreme conditions. (p. 750)

diaphragm (DI uh fram): muscle beneath the lungs that contracts and relaxes to move gases in and out of the body. (p. 572)

planta de día neutro: planta que no requiere de un fotoperiodo específico y que puede comenzar su periodo de floración basándose en un rango de duración de las noches. (p. 316)

dendrita: estructura de la neurona que recibe mensajes y los envía al cuerpo de la célula. (p. 595)

dermis: capa de la piel debajo de la epidermis que contiene vasos sanguíneos, nervios, glándulas sudoríparas, glándulas sebáceas y otras estructuras. (p. 497)

desierto: el bioma más seco sobre la Tierra con menos de 25 centímetros cúbicos de lluvia al año; tiene dunas o un suelo delgado con muy poca materia orgánica y aquí las plantas y animales están adaptados para sobrevivir en condiciones extremosas. (p. 750)

diafragma: músculo que está debajo de los pulmones y que se contrae y relaja para mover gases hacia dentro y fuera del cuerpo. (p. 572)

Glossary/Glosario

dicot: angiosperm with two cotyledons inside its seed, flower parts in multiples of four or five, and vascular bundles in rings. (p. 258)

diffusion: a type of passive transport in cells in which molecules move from areas where there are more of them to areas where there are fewer of them. (p. 75)

digestion: mechanical and chemical breakdown of food into small molecules that cells can absorb and use. (p. 523)

diploid (DIHP loyd): cell whose similar chromosomes occur in pairs. (p. 104)

DNA: deoxyribonucleic acid; the genetic material of all organisms; made up of two twisted strands of sugar-phosphate molecules and nitrogen bases. (p. 110)

dominant (DAH muh nunt): describes a trait that covers over, or dominates, another form of that trait. (p. 128)

down feathers: soft, fluffy feathers that provide an insulating layer next to the skin of adult birds and that cover the bodies of young birds. (p. 430)

dicotiledónea: angiosperma con dos cotiledones dentro de su semilla, partes florales en múltiplos de cuatro o cinco y haces vasculares distribuidos en anillos. (p. 258)

difusión: tipo de transporte pasivo en las células en el que las moléculas se mueven de áreas de mayor concentración de éstas hacia áreas de menor concentración. (p. 75)

digestión: desintegración mecánica y química de los alimentos en moléculas pequeñas que las células pueden absorber y utilizar. (p. 523)

diploide: célula cuyos cromosomas similares están en pares. (p. 104)

ADN: ácido desoxirribonucleico; material genético de todos los organismos constituido por dos cadenas trenzadas de moléculas de azúcar-fosfato y bases de nitrógeno (p. 110)

dominante: describe un rasgo que encubre o domina a otra forma de ese rasgo. (p. 128)

plumón: plumas suaves y esponjadas que proporcionan una capa aislante junto a la piel de las aves adultas y que cubren los cuerpos de las aves jóvenes. (p. 430)

E

ecology: study of the interactions that take place among organisms and their environment. (p. 685)

ecosystem: all the living organisms that live in an area and the nonliving features of their environment. (p. 685)

ectotherm: vertebrate animal whose internal temperature changes when the temperature of its environment changes. (p. 397)

egg: haploid sex cell formed in the female reproductive organs. (p. 104)

embryo: fertilized egg that has attached to the wall of the uterus. (p. 635)

embryology (em bree AH luh jee): study of embryos and their development. (p. 167)

emphysema (em fuh SEE muh): lung disease in which the alveoli enlarge. (p. 575)

endocytosis (en duh si TOH sus): process by which a cell takes in a substance by surrounding it with the cell membrane. (p. 78)

endoplasmic reticulum (ER): cytoplasmic organelle that moves materials around in a cell and is made up of a complex series of folded membranes; can be rough (with attached ribosomes) or smooth (without attached ribosomes). (p. 43)

ecología: estudio de las interacciones que se dan entre los organismos y su medio ambiente. (p. 685)

ecosistema: conjunto de organismos vivos que habitan en un área y las características de su medio ambiente. (p. 685)

ectotérmico: animal vertebrado cuya temperatura interna cambia cuando cambia la temperatura de su ambiente. (p. 397)

óvulo: célula sexual haploide que se forma en los órganos reproductivos femeninos. (p. 104)

embrión: óvulo fertilizado que se ha adherido a la pared del útero. (p. 635)

embriología: el estudio de los embriones y su desarrollo. (p. 167)

enfisema: enfermedad pulmonar en la cual se dilatan los alvéolos. (p. 575)

endocitosis: proceso mediante el cual una célula capta una sustancia rodeándola con su membrana celular. (p. 78)

retículo endoplásmático (RE): organelo citoplasmático que transporta materiales dentro de una célula y está formado por una serie compleja de membranas plegadas; puede ser rugoso (con ribosomas adosados) o liso (sin ribosomas adosados). (p. 43)

Glossary/Glosario

endoskeleton: supportive framework of bone and/or cartilage that provides an internal place for muscle attachment and protects a vertebrate's internal organs. (p. 395)

endospore: thick-walled, protective structure produced by some bacteria when conditions are unfavorable for survival. (p. 197)

endotherm: vertebrate animal with a nearly constant internal temperature. (pp. 397, 430)

energy pyramid: model that shows the amount of energy available at each feeding level in an ecosystem. (p. 729)

enzyme: a type of protein that regulates nearly all chemical reactions in cells; a type of protein that speeds up chemical reactions in the body without being changed or used up itself. (pp. 71, 524)

epidermis: outer, thinnest skin layer that constantly produces new cells to replace the dead cells rubbed off its surface. (p. 496)

equilibrium: occurs when molecules of one substance are spread evenly throughout another substance. (p. 75)

erosion: movement of soil from one place to another. (p. 785)

estivation: inactivity in hot, dry months. (p. 407)

estuary: extremely fertile area where a river meets an ocean; contains a mixture of freshwater and saltwater and serves as a nursery for many species of fish. (p. 758)

evaporation: process that takes place when a liquid changes to a gas. (p. 720)

evolution: change in inherited characteristics over time. (p. 154)

exocytosis (ek soh si TOH sus): process by which vesicles release their contents outside the cell. (p. 78)

exoskeleton: thick, hard, outer covering that protects and supports arthropod bodies and provides places for muscles to attach. (p. 370)

endoesqueleto: estructura ósea y/o cartilaginosa de soporte que proporciona un medio interno para la fijación de los músculos y que protege a los órganos internos de los vertebrados. (p. 395)

endospora: estructura protectora de pared gruesa que es producida por algunas bacterias cuando las condiciones son desfavorables para su supervivencia. (p. 197)

endotérmico: animal vertebrado con una temperatura interna casi constante. (pp. 397, 430)

pirámide de energía: modelo que muestra la cantidad de energía disponible en cada nivel alimenticio de un ecosistema. (p. 729)

enzima: tipo de proteína que regula casi todas las clases de reacciones químicas en las células; tipo de proteína que acelera las reacciones químicas en el cuerpo sin ser utilizada o consumida. (pp. 71, 524)

epidermis: la capa más delgada y externa de la piel que produce constantemente células nuevas para reemplazar las células muertas que se pierden por fricción de su superficie. (p. 496)

equilibrio: ocurre cuando las moléculas de una sustancia están diseminadas completa y uniformemente a lo largo de otra sustancia. (p. 75)

erosión: movimiento del suelo de un lugar a otro. (p. 785)

estivación: inactividad durante los meses cálidos y secos. (p. 407)

estuario: área extremadamente fértil donde un río desemboca en el océano; contiene una mezcla de agua dulce y salada y sirve como vivero para muchas especies de peces. (p. 758)

evaporación: proceso que tiene lugar cuando un líquido cambia a estado gaseoso. (p. 720)

evolución: cambio en las características heredadas a través del tiempo. (p. 154)

exocitosis: proceso mediante el cual las vesículas liberan su contenido fuera de la célula. (p. 78)

exoesqueleto: cubierta externa, dura y gruesa que protege y soporta el cuerpo de los artrópodos y proporciona lugares para que los músculos se fijen. (p. 370)

F

fat: nutrient that stores energy, cushions organs, and helps the body absorb vitamins. (p. 515)

grasa: nutriente que almacena energía, amortigua a los órganos y ayuda al cuerpo a absorber vitaminas. (p. 515)

fermentation: process by which oxygen-lacking cells and some one-celled organisms release small amounts of energy from glucose molecules and produce wastes such as alcohol, carbon dioxide, and lactic acid. (p. 84)

fertilization: in sexual reproduction, the joining of a sperm and egg. (p. 104)

fetal stress: can occur during the birth process or after birth as an infant adjusts from a watery, dark, constant-temperature environment to its new environment. (p. 638)

fetus: in humans, a developing baby after the first two months of pregnancy until birth. (p. 636)

fin: structure used by fish for steering, balancing, and movement. (p. 399)

fission: simplest form of asexual reproduction in which two new cells are produced with genetic material identical to each other and identical to the previous cell. (p. 188)

flagellum: long, thin whiplike structure that helps organisms move through moist or wet surroundings. (pp. 187, 212)

food group: group of foods—such as bread, cereal, rice, and pasta—containing the same type of nutrients. (p. 520)

food web: model that shows the complex feeding relationships among organisms in a community. (p. 728)

fossil fuels: nonrenewable energy resources—coal, oil, and natural gas—that formed in Earth's crust over hundreds of millions of years. (p. 772)

free-living organism: organism that does not depend on another organism for food or a place to live. (p. 344)

frond: leaf of a fern that grows from the rhizome. (p. 278)

fermentación: proceso mediante el cual las células carentes de oxígeno y algunos organismos unicelulares liberan pequeñas cantidades de energía a partir de moléculas de glucosa y producen desechos como alcohol, dióxido de carbono y ácido láctico. (p. 84)

fertilización: en la reproducción sexual, la unión de un óvulo y un espermatozoide. (p. 104)

estrés fetal: puede ocurrir durante el proceso del nacimiento o luego del mismo mientras un nuevo ser humano se adapta de un ambiente acuoso, oscuro y de temperatura constante a su nuevo ambiente. (p. 638)

feto: en los humanos, bebé en desarrollo desde los primeros dos meses de embarazo hasta el nacimiento. (p. 636)

aleta: estructura parecida a un abanico usada por los peces para mantener la dirección, equilibrio y movimiento. (p. 399)

fisión: la forma más simple de reproducción asexual en la que se producen dos nuevas células cuyo material genético es idéntico entre sí y al de la célula antecesora. (p. 188)

flagelo: estructura alargada en forma de látigo que ayuda a algunos organismos a desplazarse de un lugar a otro en medios acuosos. (pp. 187, 212)

grupo alimenticio: grupo de alimentos—como el pan, el cereal, el arroz y la pasta—que contiene el mismo tipo de nutrientes. (p. 520)

cadena alimenticia: modelo que muestra las complejas relaciones alimenticias entre los organismos de una comunidad. (p. 728)

combustibles fósiles: recursos energéticos no renovables—carbón, petróleo y gas natural—que se formaron en la corteza terrestre durante cientos de millones de años. (p. 772)

organismo de vida libre: organismo que no depende de otro para alimentarse o para tener un lugar en donde vivir. (p. 344)

fronda: hoja de un helecho que crece a partir del rizoma. (p. 278)

G

gametophyte (guh MEE tuh fite) stage: plant life cycle stage that begins when cells in reproductive organs undergo meiosis and produce haploid cells (spores). (p. 275)

etapa de gametofito: etapa del ciclo de vida de las plantas que comienza cuando las células en los órganos reproductores, a través de la meiosis, producen células haploides (esporas). (p. 275)

gene: section of DNA on a chromosome that contains instructions for making specific proteins. (p. 112)

genetic engineering: biological and chemical methods to change the arrangement of a gene's DNA to improve crop production, produce large volumes of medicine, and change how cells perform their normal functions. (p. 141)

genetics (juh NEH tihks): the study of how traits are inherited through the actions of alleles. (p. 126)

genotype (JEE nuh tipe): the genetic makeup of an organism. (p. 130)

genus: first word of the two-word scientific name used to identify a group of similar species. (p. 24)

geothermal energy: heat energy within Earth's crust, available only where natural geysers or volcanoes are located. (p. 775)

germination: series of events that results in the growth of a plant from a seed. (p. 290)

gestation period: period during which an embryo develops in the uterus; the length of time varies among species. (p. 441)

gills: organs that exchange carbon dioxide for oxygen in the water. (p. 360)

gizzard: muscular digestive system structure in which earthworms grind soil and organic matter. (p. 366)

Golgi bodies: organelles that package cellular materials and transport them within the cell or out of the cell. (p. 43)

gradualism: model describing evolution as a slow process by which one species changes into a new species through a continuing series of mutations and variations over time. (p. 160)

grasslands: temperate and tropical regions with 25 cm to 75 cm of precipitation each year that are dominated by climax communities of grasses; ideal for growing crops and raising cattle and sheep. (p. 751)

greenhouse effect: heat-trapping feature of the atmosphere that keeps Earth warm enough to support life. (p. 780)

guard cells: pairs of cells that surround stomata and control their opening and closing. (p. 253)

gymnosperms: vascular plants that do not flower, generally have needlelike or scalelike leaves, and produce seeds that are not protected by fruit; conifers, cycads, ginkgoes, and gnetophytes. (p. 256)

gen: sección de ADN en un cromosoma, el cual contiene instrucciones para la formación de proteínas específicas. (p. 112)

ingeniería genética: métodos biológicos y químicos para cambiar la disposición del ADN de un gen y así mejorar la producción de cosechas, producir grandes volúmenes de un medicamento, o cambiar la forma en que las células realizan sus funciones normales. (p. 141)

genética: estudio de la forma como se heredan los rasgos a través de las acciones de los alelos. (p. 126)

genotipo: composición genética de un organismo. (p. 130)

género: primera palabra, de las dos palabras del nombre científico, que se usa para identificar a un grupo de especies similares. (p. 24)

energía geotérmica: energía calórica en el interior de la corteza terrestre disponible sólo donde existen géiseres o volcanes. (p. 775)

germinación: serie de eventos que resultan en el crecimiento de una planta a partir de una semilla. (p. 290)

periodo de gestación: periodo durante el cual un embrión se desarrolla en el útero; este periodo varía de una especie a otra. (p. 441)

agallas: órganos que intercambian dióxido de carbono y oxígeno en el agua. (p. 360)

molleja: estructura muscular del sistema digestivo en la que los gusanos de tierra muelen el suelo y materia orgánica. (p. 366)

aparato de Golgi: organelo que concentra los materiales celulares y los transporta hacia adentro o afuera de la célula. (p. 43)

gradualismo: modelo que describe la evolución como un proceso lento mediante el cual una especie existente se convierte en una especie nueva a través de series continuas de mutaciones y variaciones a través del tiempo. (p. 160)

pastizales: regiones tropicales y templadas con 25 a 75 centímetros cúbicos de lluvia al año; son dominadas por el clímax comunitario de los pastos e ideales para la cría de ganado y ovejas. (p. 751)

efecto de invernadero: característica de la atmósfera que le permite atrapar calor y mantener la Tierra lo suficientemente caliente para favorecer la vida. (p. 780)

células oclusoras: pares de células que rodean al estoma y que controlan su cierre y apertura. (p. 253)

gimnospermas: plantas vasculares que no florecen, generalmente tienen hojas en forma de aguja o de escama y producen semillas que no están protegidas por el fruto; se clasifican en coníferas, cicadáceas, ginkgoales y gnetofitas. (p. 256)

Glossary/Glosario

H

habitat: place where an organism lives and that provides the types of food, shelter, moisture, and temperature needed for survival. (p. 687)

haploid (HAP loyd): cell that has half the number of chromosomes as body cells. (p. 105)

hazardous wastes: waste materials, such as pesticides and leftover paints, that are harmful to human health or poisonous to living organisms. (p. 786)

hemoglobin (HEE muh gloh bun): chemical in red blood cells that carries oxygen from the lungs to body cells, and carries some carbon dioxide from body cells back to the lungs. (p. 551)

herbivore: animal that eats only plants or parts of plants; mammals with large premolars and molars for eating only plants. (pp. 331, 437)

heredity (huh REH duh tee): the passing of traits from parent to offspring. (p. 126)

hermaphrodite (hur MA fruh dite): animal that produces both sperm and eggs in the same body. (p. 338)

heterozygous (heh tuh roh ZI gus): describes an organism with two different alleles for a trait. (p. 130)

hibernation: inactivity in cold weather; cyclic response of inactivity and slowed metabolism that occurs during periods of cold temperatures and limited food supplies. (pp. 407, 469)

homeostasis: regulation of an organism's internal, life-maintaining conditions. (pp. 15, 595)

hominid: humanlike primate that appeared about 4 million to 6 million years ago, ate both plants and meat, and walked upright on two legs. (p. 171)

homologous (huh MAH luh gus): body parts that are similar in structure and origin and can be similar in function. (p. 168)

homozygous (hoh muh ZI gus): describes an organism with two alleles that are the same for a trait. (p. 130)

Homo sapiens: early humans that likely evolved from Cro-Magnons. (p. 173)

hormone (HOR mohn): in humans, chemical produced by the endocrine system, released directly into the bloodstream by ductless glands; affects specific target tissues, and can speed up or slow down cellular activities. (p. 622)

hábitat: lugar donde vive un organismo y que le proporciona los tipos de alimento, refugio, humedad y temperatura necesarios para su supervivencia. (p. 687)

haploide: célula que posee la mitad del número de cromosomas que tienen las células somáticas. (p. 105)

desperdicios peligrosos: materiales de desecho como los pesticidas y residuos de pintura nocivos para la salud humana o dañinos para los organismos vivos. (p. 786)

hemoglobina: sustancia química de los glóbulos rojos que transporta oxígeno de los pulmones a las células del cuerpo y parte del dióxido de carbono de las células del cuerpo a los pulmones. (p. 551)

herbívoro: animal que se alimenta exclusivamente de plantas o de partes de las plantas; mamífero con premolares y molares grandes que se alimenta exclusivamente de plantas. (pp. 331, 437)

herencia: transferencia de rasgos de un progenitor a su descendencia. (p. 126)

hermafrodita: animal que produce óvulos y espermatozoides en el mismo cuerpo. (p. 338)

heterocigoto: describe a un organismo con dos alelos diferentes para un rasgo. (p. 130)

hibernación: inactividad durante periodos de clima frío; respuesta cíclica de inactividad y disminución del metabolismo que ocurre durante periodos de bajas temperaturas y suministro limitado de alimento. (pp. 407, 469)

homeostasis: control de las condiciones internas que mantienen la vida de un organismo. (pp. 15, 595)

homínido: primate con forma de humano que apareció entre 4 y 6 millones de años atrás, se alimentaba de plantas y carne, y caminaba erguido sobre sus dos pies. (p. 171)

homólogos: partes del cuerpo que son similares en estructura y origen y que pueden tener funciones similares. (p. 168)

homocigoto: describe a un organismo con dos alelos iguales para un rasgo. (p. 130)

Homo sapiens: humanos primitivos que probablemente evolucionaron a partir de los CroMagnon. (p. 173)

hormona: en los humanos, sustancia química producida por el sistema endocrino, liberada directamente al torrente sanguíneo mediante glándulas sin conductos; afecta a tejidos que constituyen blancos específicos y puede acelerar o frenar actividades celulares. (p. 622)

host cell: living cell in which a virus can actively multiply or in which a virus can hide until activated by environmental stimuli. (p. 52)

hybrid (HI brud): an offspring that was given different genetic information for a trait from each parent. (p. 128)

hydroelectric power: electricity produced when the energy of falling water turns the blades of a generator turbine. (p. 773)

hyphae (HI fee): mass of many-celled, threadlike tubes forming the body of a fungus. (p. 222)

hypothesis: prediction that can be tested. (p. 8)

célula huésped: célula viva en la que un virus puede reproducirse activamente o en la que un virus puede ocultarse hasta que es activado por estímulos del medio ambiente. (p. 52)

híbrido: un descendiente que recibe de cada progenitor información genética diferente para un rasgo. (p. 128)

energía hidroeléctrica: electricidad producida cuando la energía generada por la caída del agua hace girar las aspas de una turbina generadora. (p. 773)

hifa: masa de tubos multicelulares en forma de hilos formando el cuerpo de los hongos. (p. 222)

hipótesis: predicción que puede probarse. (p. 8)

I

immune system: complex group of defenses that protects the body against pathogens—includes the skin and respiratory, digestive, and circulatory systems. (p. 652)

imprinting: occurs when an animal forms a social attachment to another organism during a specific period following birth or hatching. (p. 459)

incomplete dominance: production of a phenotype that is intermediate between the two homozygous parents. (p. 134)

infectious disease: disease caused by a virus, bacterium, fungus, or protist that is spread from an infected organism or the environment to another organism. (p. 661)

innate behavior: behavior that an organism is born with and does not have to be learned, such as a reflex or instinct. (p. 457)

inorganic compound: compound, such as H_2O, that is made from elements other than carbon and whose atoms usually can be arranged in only one structure. (p. 71)

insight: form of reasoning that allows animals to use past experiences to solve new problems. (p. 461)

instinct: complex pattern of innate behavior, such as spinning a web, that can take weeks to complete. (p. 458)

intertidal zone: part of the shoreline that is under water at high tide and exposed to the air at low tide. (p. 758)

invertebrate: animal without a backbone. (p. 334)

involuntary muscle: muscle, such as heart muscle, that cannot be consciously controlled. (p. 491)

sistema inmune: grupo complejo de defensas que protege al cuerpo contra agentes patógenos –incluye la piel y los sistemas respiratorio, digestivo y circulatorio. (p. 652)

impronta: ocurre cuando un animal forma un vínculo social con otro organismo durante un periodo específico después del nacimiento o eclosión. (p. 459)

dominancia incompleta: producción de un fenotipo intermedio entre dos progenitores homocigotos. (p. 134)

enfermedad infecciosa: enfermedad causada por virus, bacterias, hongos o protistas, propagada por un organismo infectado o del medio ambiente hacia otro organismo. (p. 661)

comportamiento innato: comportamiento con el que nace un organismo y que no necesita ser aprendido, tal como los reflejos o los instintos. (p. 457)

compuesto inorgánico: compuesto, como H2O, formado por elementos distintos al carbono y cuyos átomos generalmente pueden estar organizados en sólo una estructura. (p. 71)

comprensión: forma de razonamiento que permite a los animales usar experiencias pasadas para solucionar problemas nuevos. (p. 461)

instinto: patrón complejo de comportamiento innato, como tejer una telaraña, que puede durar semanas para completarse. (p. 458)

zona litoral: parte de la línea costera que está bajo el agua durante la marea alta y expuesta al aire durante la marea baja. (p. 758)

invertebrado: animal que no posee columna vertebral. (p. 334)

músculo involuntario: músculo, como el músculo cardiaco, que no puede controlarse conscientemente. (p. 491)

Glossary/Glosario

J

joint: any place where two or more bones come together; can be movable or immovable. (p. 487)

articulación: cualquier lugar en donde se unen dos o más huesos, pudiendo ser fija o flexible. (p. 487)

K

kidney: bean-shaped urinary system organ that is made up of about 1 million nephrons and filters blood, producing urine. (p. 578)

kingdom: first and largest category used to classify organisms. (p. 23)

riñón: órgano del sistema urinario en forma de fríjol, compuesto por cerca de un millón de nefronas; filtra la sangre y produce la orina. (p. 578)

reino: la primera y más grande categoría utilizada para clasificar a los organismos. (p. 23)

L

larynx: airway to which the vocal cords are attached. (p. 571)

law: statement about how things work in nature that seems to be true consistently. (p. 10)

lichen (LI kun): organism made up of a fungus and a green alga or a cyanobacterium. (p. 226)

ligament: tough band of tissue that holds bones together at joints. (p. 487)

limiting factor: anything that can restrict the size of a population, including living and nonliving features of an ecosystem, such as predators or drought. (p. 690)

long-day plant: plant that generally requires short nights—less than ten to 12 hours of darkness—to begin the flowering process. (p. 316)

lymph (LIHMF): tissue fluid that has diffused into lymphatic capillaries. (p. 556)

lymphatic system: carries lymph through a network of lymph capillaries and vessels, and drains it into large veins near the heart; helps fight infections and diseases. (p. 556)

lymph nodes: bean-shaped organs found throughout the body that filter out microorganisms and foreign materials taken up by the lymphocytes. (p. 556)

lymphocyte (LIHM fuh site): a type of white blood cell that fights infection. (p. 556)

laringe: vía respiratoria que contiene las cuerdas vocales. (p. 571)

ley: enunciado acerca de cómo funciona todo en la naturaleza y que constantemente parece ser verdadero. (p. 10)

liquen: organismo formado por un hongo y un alga verde o una cianobacteria. (p. 226)

ligamento: banda de tejido resistente que mantiene unidos a los huesos de las articulaciones. (p. 487)

factor limitante: cualquier factor que pueda restringir el tamaño de una población, incluyendo las características biológicas y no biológicas de un ecosistema, tales como los depredadores o las sequías. (p. 690)

planta de día largo: planta que generalmente requiere de noches cortas—menos de 12 horas de oscuridad—para comenzar su proceso de floración. (p. 316)

linfa: fluido tisular que se ha difundido hacia los capilares linfáticos. (p. 556)

sistema linfático: sistema que transporta la linfa a través de una red de vasos y capilares linfáticos y la vierte en venas grandes cerca del corazón; ayuda a combatir enfermedades e infecciones. (p. 556)

ganglio linfático: órganos en forma de fríjol que se encuentran en todo el cuerpo; filtran y extraen microorganismos y materiales extraños captados por los linfocitos. (p. 556)

linfocito: tipo de glóbulo blanco que combate las infecciones. (p. 556)

mammals: endothermic vertebrates that have hair, teeth specialized for eating certain foods, and mammary glands; in females, mammary glands produce milk for feeding their young. (p. 436)

mammary glands: glands of mammals; in females, produce milk to feed their young. (p. 436)

mantle: thin layer of tissue that covers a mollusk's body organs; secretes the shell or protects the body of mollusks without shells. (p. 360)

marsupial: a mammal with an external pouch for the development of its immature young. (p. 440)

mechanical digestion: breakdown of food through chewing, mixing, and churning. (p. 523)

medusa (mih DEW suh): cnidarian body type that is bell-shaped and free-swimming. (p. 339)

meiosis (mi OH sus): reproductive process that produces four haploid sex cells from one diploid cell and ensures offspring will have the same number of chromosomes as the parent organisms. (p. 105)

melanin: pigment produced by the epidermis that protects skin from sun damage and gives skin and eyes their color. (p. 497)

menstrual cycle: hormone-controlled monthly cycle of changes in the female reproductive system that includes the maturation of an egg and preparation of the uterus for possible pregnancy. (p. 630)

menstruation (men STRAY shun): monthly flow of blood and tissue cells that occurs when the lining of the uterus breaks down and is shed. (p. 630)

metabolism: the total of all chemical reactions in an organism. (p. 81)

metamorphosis: process in which many insect species change their body form to become adults; can be complete (egg, larva, pupa, adult) or incomplete (egg, nymph, adult). (p. 372)

migration: instinctive seasonal movement of animals to find food or to reproduce in better conditions. (p. 470)

mineral: inorganic nutrient that regulates many chemical reactions in the body. (p. 518)

mamíferos: vertebrados endotérmicos que poseen pelo y dientes especializados para comer cierto tipo de alimentos y cuyas hembras tienen glándulas mamarias que producen leche para alimentar a sus crías. (p. 436)

glándulas mamarias: glándulas productoras de leche que las hembras de los mamíferos usan para alimentar a sus crías. (p. 436)

manto: capa delgada de tejido que recubre los órganos corporales de los moluscos; secreta el caparazón o protege el cuerpo de los moluscos sin caparazón. (p. 360)

marsupial: mamífero con una bolsa externa para el desarrollo de sus crías inmaduras. (p. 440)

digestión mecánica: desdoblamiento del alimento a través de la masticación, mezcla y agitación. (p. 523)

medusa: tipo corporal de los cnidarios con forma de campana y nado libre. (p. 339)

meiosis: proceso reproductivo que produce cuatro células sexuales haploides a partir de una célula diploide y asegura que la descendencia tendrá el mismo número de cromosomas que los organismos progenitores. (p. 105)

melanina: pigmento producido por la epidermis que protege a la piel del daño producido por la luz solar y le da a la piel y a los ojos su color. (p. 497)

ciclo menstrual: ciclo mensual de cambios en el sistema reproductor femenino, el cual es controlado por hormonas e incluye la maduración de un óvulo y la preparación del útero para un posible embarazo. (p. 630)

menstruación: flujo mensual de sangre y células tisulares que ocurre cuando el endometrio uterino se rompe y se desprende. (p. 630)

metabolismo: el conjunto de todas las reacciones químicas en un organismo. (p. 81)

metamorfosis: proceso a través del cual muchas especies de insectos cambian su forma corporal para convertirse en adultos; puede ser completa (huevo, larva, pupa, adulto) o incompleta (huevo, ninfa, adulto). (p. 372)

migración: movimiento estacional instintivo de los animales para encontrar alimento o para reproducirse en mejores condiciones. (p. 470)

mineral: nutriente inorgánico que regula una gran cantidad de reacciones químicas en el cuerpo. (p. 518)

Glossary/Glosario

mitochondrion: cell organelle that breaks down food and releases energy. (p. 42)

mitosis (mi TOH sus): cell process in which the nucleus divides to form two nuclei identical to each other, and identical to the original nucleus, in a series of steps (prophase, metaphase, anaphase, and telophase). (p. 98)

mixture: a combination of substances in which the individual substances do not change or combine chemically but instead retain their own individual properties; can be gases, solids, liquids, or any combination of them. (p. 69)

molting: shedding and replacing of an arthropod's exoskeleton. (p. 370)

monocot: angiosperm with one cotyledon inside its seed, flower parts in multiples of three, and vascular tissues in bundles scattered throughout the stem. (p. 258)

monotreme: a mammal that lays eggs with tough, leathery shells and whose mammary glands do not have nipples. (p. 440)

muscle: organ that can relax, contract, and provide the force to move bones and body parts. (p. 490)

mutation: any permanent change in a gene or chromosome of a cell; may be beneficial, harmful, or have little effect on an organism. (p. 114)

mutualism: a type of symbiotic relationship in which both organisms benefit. (p. 698)

mycorrhizae (mi kuh RI zee): network of hyphae and plant roots that helps plants absorb water and minerals from soil. (p. 226)

mitocondria: organelo celular que degrada nutrientes y libera energía. (p. 42)

mitosis: proceso celular en el que el núcleo se divide para formar dos núcleos idénticos entre sí e idénticos al núcleo original, a través de varias etapas (profase, metafase, anafase y telofase). (p. 98)

mezcla: una combinación de sustancias en la que las sustancias individuales no cambian ni se combinan químicamente pero mantienen sus propiedades individuales; pueden ser gases, sólidos, líquidos o una combinación de ellos. (p. 69)

muda: muda y reemplazo del exoesqueleto de un artrópodo. (p. 370)

monocotiledóneas: angiospermas con un solo cotiledón dentro de la semilla, partes florales dispuestas en múltiplos de tres y tejidos vasculares distribuidos en haces diseminados por todo el tallo. (p. 258)

monotrema: mamífero que pone huevos con cascarón coriáceo y resistente y cuyas glándulas mamarias carecen de pezones. (p. 440)

músculo: órgano que puede relajarse, contraerse y proporcionar la fuerza para mover los huesos y las partes del cuerpo. (p. 490)

mutación: cualquier cambio permanente en un gen o cromosoma de una célula; puede ser benéfica, perjudicial o tener un pequeño efecto sobre un organismo. (p. 114)

mutualismo: tipo de relación simbiótica en la que ambos organismos se benefician. (p. 698)

micorriza: estructura formada por una hifa y las raíces de una planta y que ayuda a las plantas a absorber agua y minerales del suelo. (p. 226)

N

natural resources: parts of Earth's environment that supply materials useful or necessary for the survival of living organisms. (p. 770)

natural selection: a process by which organisms with traits best suited to their environment are more likely to survive and reproduce; includes concepts of variation, overproduction, and competition. (p. 156)

nephron (NEF rahn): tiny filtering unit of the kidney. (p. 579)

nerve cord: tubelike structure above the notochord that in most chordates develops into the brain and spinal cord. (p. 395)

recursos naturales: partes del medio ambiente terrestre que proporcionan materiales útiles o necesarios para la supervivencia de los organismos vivos. (p. 770)

selección natural: proceso mediante el cual los organismos con rasgos mejor adaptados a su ambiente tienen mayor probabilidad de sobrevivir y reproducirse; incluye los conceptos de variación, sobreproducción y competencia. (p. 156)

nefrona: pequeña unidad de filtrado del riñón. (p. 579)

cordón nervioso: estructura en forma de tubo sobre el notocordio que en la mayoría de los cordados se desarrolla en el cerebro y en la médula espinal. (p. 395)

neuron (NOO rahn): basic functioning unit of the nervous system, made up of a cell body, dendrites, and axons. (p. 595)

niche: in an ecosystem, refers to the unique ways an organism survives, obtains food and shelter, and avoids danger. (p. 699)

nitrogen cycle: model describing how nitrogen moves from the atmosphere to the soil, to living organisms, and then back to the atmosphere. (p. 722)

nitrogen fixation: process in which some types of bacteria in the soil change nitrogen gas into a form of nitrogen that plants can use. (p. 722)

nitrogen-fixing bacteria: bacteria that convert nitrogen in the air into forms that can be used by plants and animals. (p. 194)

noninfectious disease: disease, such as cancer, diabetes, or asthma, that is not spread from one person to another. (p. 666)

nonrenewable resources: natural resources, such as petroleum, minerals, and metals, that are used more quickly than they can be replaced by natural processes. (p. 771)

nonvascular plant: plant that absorbs water and other substances directly through its cell walls instead of through tubelike structures. (p. 245)

notochord: firm but flexible structure that extends along the upper part of a chordate's body. (p. 394)

nuclear energy: energy produced from the splitting apart of billions of uranium nuclei by a nuclear fission reaction. (p. 774)

nucleus: organelle that controls all the activities of a cell and contains hereditary material made of proteins and DNA. (p. 40)

nutrients (NEW tree unts): substances in foods—proteins, carbohydrates, fats, vitamins, minerals, and water—that provide energy and materials for cell development, growth, and repair. (p. 512)

neurona: unidad básica de funcionamiento del sistema nervioso, formada por un cuerpo celular, dendritas y axones. (p. 595)

nicho: en un ecosistema, se refiere a las formas únicas en las que un organismo sobrevive, obtiene alimento, refugio y evita el peligro. (p. 699)

ciclo del nitrógeno: modelo que describe cómo se mueve el nitrógeno de la atmósfera al suelo, a los organismos vivos y de nuevo a la atmósfera. (p. 722)

fijación del nitrógeno: proceso en el cual algunos tipos de bacterias en el suelo transforman el nitrógeno gaseoso en una forma de nitrógeno que las plantas pueden usar. (p. 722)

bacterias fijadoras de nitrógeno: bacterias que convierten el nitrógeno presente en el aire en formas que pueden ser usadas por plantas y animales. (p. 194)

enfermedad no infecciosa: enfermedad que no se trasmite de una persona a otra, como el cáncer, la diabetes o el asma. (p. 666)

recursos no renovables: recursos naturales, como el petróleo, los minerales y los metales, que son utilizados más rápidamente de lo que pueden ser reemplazados mediante procesos naturales. (p. 771)

planta no vascular: planta que absorbe agua y otras sustancias directamente a través de sus paredes celulares en vez de utilizar estructuras tubulares. (p. 245)

notocordio: estructura firme pero flexible que se extiende a lo largo de la parte superior del cuerpo de un cordado. (p. 394)

energía nuclear: energía producida a partir del fraccionamiento de billones de núcleos de uranio mediante una reacción de fisión nuclear. (p. 774)

núcleo: organelo que controla todas las actividades de una célula y que contiene el material hereditario formado por proteínas y ADN. (p. 40)

nutrientes: sustancias de los alimentos—proteínas, carbohidratos, grasas, vitaminas, minerales y agua—que proporcionan energía y materiales para el desarrollo, crecimiento y reparación de las células. (p. 512)

O

olfactory (ohl FAK tree) cell: nasal nerve cell that becomes stimulated by molecules in the air and sends impulses to the brain for interpretation of odors. (p. 609)

omnivore: animal that eats plants and animals or animal flesh; mammals with incisors, canine teeth, and flat molars for eating plants and other animals. (pp. 331, 437)

célula olfatoria: célula nerviosa nasal que al ser estimulada por moléculas del aire envía impulsos al cerebro para la interpretación de los olores. (p. 609)

omnívoro: animal que se alimenta de plantas y animales; mamífero con incisivos, caninos y molares planos que se alimenta de plantas y otros animales. (pp. 331, 437)

open circulatory system: blood circulation system in which blood moves through vessels and into open spaces around the body organs. (p. 360)

organ: structure, such as the heart, made up of different types of tissues that all work together. (p. 45)

organelle: structure in the cytoplasm of a eukaryotic cell that can act as a storage site, process energy, move materials, or manufacture substances. (p. 40)

organic compounds: compounds that always contain hydrogen and carbon; carbohydrates, lipids, proteins, and nucleic acids are organic compounds found in living things. (p. 70)

organism: any living thing. (p. 14)

osmosis: a type of passive transport that occurs when water diffuses through a cell membrane. (p. 76)

ovary: in plants, swollen base of an angiosperm's pistil, where egg-producing ovules are found; in humans, female reproductive organ that produces eggs and is located in the lower part of the body. (pp. 285, 629)

ovulation (ahv yuh LAY shun): monthly process in which an egg is released from an ovary and enters the oviduct, where it can become fertilized by sperm. (p. 629)

ovule: in seed plants, the female reproductive part that produces eggs. (p. 283)

ozone depletion: thinning of Earth's ozone layer caused by chlorofluorocarbons (CFCs) leaking into the air and reacting chemically with ozone, breaking the ozone molecules apart. (p. 781)

sistema circulatorio abierto: sistema circulatorio sanguíneo en el que la sangre se mueve a través de vasos y entra en espacios abiertos alrededor de los órganos corporales. (p. 360)

órgano: estructura, como el corazón, que consiste en diferentes tipos de tejidos que trabajan conjuntamente. (p. 45)

organelo: estructura del citoplasma de una célula eucariota que puede actuar como sitio de almacenamiento, procesamiento de energía, movimiento de materiales o elaboración de sustancias. (p. 40)

compuestos orgánicos: compuestos que siempre contienen hidrógeno y carbono; los carbohidratos, lípidos, proteínas y ácidos nucleicos son compuestos orgánicos que se encuentran en los seres vivos. (p. 70)

organismo: cualquier ser vivo. (p. 14)

ósmosis: tipo de transporte pasivo que ocurre cuando el agua se difunde a través de una membrana celular. (p. 76)

ovario: en las plantas, base abultada del pistilo de una angiosperma donde se encuentran los óvulos productores de huevos; en los humanos, órgano reproductor femenino que produce óvulos y está localizado en la parte inferior del cuerpo. (pp. 285, 629)

ovulación: proceso mensual en el que un óvulo es liberado de un ovario y entra al oviducto, donde puede ser fertilizado por los espermatozoides. (p. 629)

óvulo: en las gimnospermas, la parte reproductiva femenina que produce huevos. (p. 283)

agotamiento del ozono: adelgazamiento de la capa de ozono de la Tierra causado por los clorofluorocarbonos (CFCs) que escapan al aire y reaccionan químicamente con el ozono rompiendo sus moléculas. (p. 781)

P

parasitism: a type of symbiotic relationship in which one organism benefits and the other organism is harmed. (p. 698)

passive immunity: immunity that results when antibodies produced in one animal are introduced into another's body; does not last as long as active immunity. (p. 655)

passive transport: movement of substances through a cell membrane without the use of cellular energy; includes diffusion, osmosis, and facilitated diffusion. (p. 74)

parasitismo: tipo de relación simbiótica en la que un organismo se beneficia y el otro es perjudicado. (p. 698)

inmunidad pasiva: inmunidad que resulta cuando los anticuerpos producidos en un animal son introducidos en el cuerpo de otro; no es tan duradera como la inmunidad activa. (p. 655)

transporte pasivo: movimiento de sustancias a través de la membrana celular sin usar energía celular; incluye difusión, ósmosis y difusión facilitada. (p. 74)

pasteurization (pas chur ruh ZAY shun): process in which a liquid is heated to a temperature that kills most bacteria. (p. 658)

pathogen: disease-producing organism. (p. 197)

periosteum (pur ee AHS tee um): tough, tight-fitting membrane that covers a bone's surface and contains blood vessels that transport nutrients into the bone. (p. 485)

peripheral nervous system: division of the nervous system, made up of all the nerves outside the CNS; connects the brain and spinal cord to other body parts. (p. 597)

peristalsis (per uh STAHL sus): waves of muscular contractions that move food through the digestive tract. (p. 526)

petroleum: nonrenewable resource formed over hundreds of millions of years mostly from the remains of microscopic marine organisms buried in Earth's crust. (p. 771)

pharyngeal pouches: in developing chordates, the paired openings found in the area between the mouth and digestive tube. (p. 395)

pharynx (FER ingks): tubelike passageway for food, liquid, and air. (p. 570)

phenotype (FEE nuh tipe): outward physical appearance and behavior of an organism as a result of its genotype. (p. 130)

pheromone (FER uh mohn): powerful chemical produced by an animal to influence the behavior of another animal of the same species. (p. 465)

phloem (FLOH em): vascular tissue that forms tubes that transport dissolved sugar throughout a plant. (p. 255)

photoperiodism: a plant's response to the lengths of daylight and darkness each day. (p. 316)

photosynthesis (foh toh SIHN thuh sihs): process by which plants and many other producers use light energy to produce a simple sugar from carbon dioxide and water and give off oxygen. (pp. 82, 305)

phylogeny (fi LAH juh nee): evolutionary history of an organism; used today to group organisms into six kingdoms. (p. 23)

pioneer species: species that break down rock and build up decaying plant material so that other plants can grow; first organisms to grow in new or disturbed areas. (pp. 247, 740)

pistil: female reproductive organ inside the flower of an angiosperm; consists of a sticky stigma, where pollen grains land, and an ovary. (p. 285)

pasterización: proceso mediante el cual un líquido es calentado a una temperatura que mata a la mayoría de las bacterias. (p. 658)

patógeno: organismo que produce enfermedades. (p. 197)

periostio: membrana fuertemente adherida y resistente que cubre la superficie de los huesos, contiene vasos sanguíneos y transporta nutrientes al interior del hueso. (p. 485)

sistema nervioso periférico: parte del sistema nervioso, compuesto por todos los nervios fuera del sistema nervioso central; conecta al cerebro y a la médula espinal con las otras partes del cuerpo. (p. 597)

peristalsis: contracciones musculares ondulantes que mueven el alimento a través del tracto digestivo. (p. 526)

petróleo: recurso no renovable formado durante cientos de millones de años, en su mayoría a partir de los restos de organismos marinos microscópicos sepultados en la corteza terrestre. (p. 771)

bolsas faríngeas: en los cordados en desarrollo, las aperturas pareadas que se encuentran en el área entre la boca y el tubo digestivo. (p. 395)

faringe: pasaje en forma de tubo por donde circulan alimentos, líquidos y aire. (p. 570)

fenotipo: apariencia física externa y comportamiento de un organismo como resultado de su genotipo. (p. 130)

feromona: químico potente producido por un animal para influir en el comportamiento de otro animal de la misma especie. (p. 465)

floema: tejido vascular que forma tubos que transportan azúcares disueltos a toda la planta. (p. 255)

fotoperiodicidad: la respuesta de una planta a la duración de la luz y de la oscuridad cada día. (p. 316)

fotosíntesis: proceso mediante el cual las plantas y muchos otros organismos productores utilizan la energía luminosa para producir azúcares simples a partir de dióxido de carbono y agua y desprender oxígeno. (pp. 82, 305)

filogenia: historia evolutiva de un organismo; usada hoy para agrupar a los organismos en seis reinos. (p. 23)

especies pioneras: especies que descomponen la roca y acumulan material vegetal en descomposición para que otras plantas puedan crecer; los primeros organismos que crecen en áreas nuevas o alteradas. (pp. 247, 740)

pistilo: órgano reproductivo femenino en la flor de una angiosperma; consiste en un ovario y un estigma pegajoso donde caen los granos de polen. (p. 285)

Glossary/Glosario

placenta: an organ that develops from tissues of the embryo and tissues that line the inside of the uterus and that absorbs oxygen and food from the mother's blood. (p. 441)

placental: a mammal whose offspring develop inside the female's uterus. (p. 441)

platelet: irregularly shaped cell fragment that helps clot blood and releases chemicals, that help form fibrin. (p. 551)

plasma: liquid part of blood, made mostly of water, in which oxygen, nutrients, and minerals are dissolved. (p. 550)

pollen grain: small structure produced by the male reproductive organs of a seed plant; has a water-resistant coat, can develop from a spore, and contains gametophyte parts that will produce sperm. (p. 281)

pollination: transfer of pollen grains to the female part of a seed plant by agents such as gravity, water, wind, and animals. (p. 281)

pollutant: substance that contaminates any part of the environment. (p. 778)

polygenic (pah lih JEH nihk) inheritance: occurs when a group of gene pairs acts together and produces a specific trait, such as human eye color, skin color, or height. (p. 136)

polyp (PAH lup): cnidarian body type that is vase-shaped and is usually sessile. (p. 339)

population: all the organisms that belong to the same species living in a community. (p. 686)

postanal tail: muscular structure at the end of a developing chordate. (p. 394)

preening: process in which a bird rubs oil from an oil gland over its feathers to condition them. (p. 430)

pregnancy: period of development—usually about 38 or 39 weeks in female humans—from fertilized egg until birth. (p. 634)

primates: group of mammals including humans, monkeys, and apes that share characteristics such as opposable thumbs, binocular vision, and flexible shoulders. (p. 170)

producer: organism, such as a green plant or alga, that uses an outside source of energy like the Sun to create energy-rich food molecules. (p. 696)

placenta: órgano que se desarrolla a partir de tejido embrionario y de los tejidos que cubren la pared interna del útero y que absorbe oxígeno y alimentos de la sangre de la madre. (p. 441)

placentario: mamífero cuyas crías se desarrollan en el útero de la hembra. (p. 441)

plaqueta: fragmento celular de forma irregular que ayuda a coagular la sangre y libera químicos que ayudan a formar fibrina. (p. 551)

plasma: parte líquida de la sangre compuesta principalmente por agua y en la que se encuentran disueltos oxígeno, nutrientes y minerales. (p. 550)

grano de polen: estructura pequeña producida por los órganos reproductivos masculinos de los espermatófitos; tiene una cubierta resistente al agua, puede desarrollarse a partir de una espora y contiene partes del gametofito que producirán esperma. (p. 281)

polinización: transferencia de los granos de polen a la parte femenina de un espermatófito a través de agentes como la gravedad, el agua, el viento y los animales. (p. 281)

contaminante: sustancia que contamina cualquier parte del medio ambiente. (p. 778)

herencia poligénica: ocurre cuando un grupo de pares de genes actúa conjuntamente y produce un rasgo específico, tal como el color de los ojos, el color de la piel, o la estatura en los humanos. (p. 136)

pólipo: tipo corporal de los cnidarios con forma de jarro y usualmente sésil. (p. 339)

población: todos los organismos que pertenecen a la misma especie dentro de una comunidad. (p. 686)

cola postnatal: estructura muscular en el extremo de un cordado en desarrollo. (p. 394)

acicalamiento: proceso mediante el cual las aves acondicionan sus alas frotándoles grasa producida por una glándula sebácea. (p. 430)

embarazo: período del desarrollo—generalmente unas 38 o 39 semanas en las hembras humanas—que va desde el óvulo fertilizado hasta el nacimiento. (p. 634)

primates: grupo de mamíferos que incluye a los humanos, monos y simios, los cuales comparten características como pulgares opuestos, visión binocular y hombros flexibles. (p. 170)

productor: organismo, como una planta o un alga verde, que utiliza una fuente externa de energía, como la luz solar, para producir moléculas de nutrientes ricas en energía. (p. 696)

protein: large molecule that contains carbon, hydrogen, oxygen, nitrogen, and sometimes sulfur and is made up of amino acids; used by the body for growth and for replacement and repair of body cells. (p. 513)

prothallus (proh THA lus): small, green, heart-shaped gametophyte plant form of a fern that can make its own food and absorb water and nutrients from the soil. (p. 278)

protist: one- or many-celled eukaryotic organism that can be plantlike, animal-like, or funguslike. (p. 210)

protozoan: one-celled, animal-like protist that can live in water, soil, and living and dead organisms. (p. 215)

pseudopods (SEW duh pahdz): temporary cytoplasmic extensions used by some protists to move about and trap food. (p. 216)

pulmonary circulation: flow of blood through the heart to the lungs and back to the heart. (p. 542)

punctuated equilibrium: model describing the rapid evolution that occurs when mutation of a few genes results in a species suddenly changing into a new species. (p. 160)

Punnett (PUN ut) square: a tool to predict the probability of certain traits in offspring that shows the different ways alleles can combine. (p. 130)

proteína: molécula grande que contiene carbono, hidrógeno, oxígeno, nitrógeno y algunas veces azufre, constituida por aminoácidos y usada por el cuerpo para el crecimiento y reemplazo o reparación de las células del cuerpo. (p. 513)

prótalo: gametofito pequeño de color verde en forma de corazón, de un helecho, que puede producir su propio alimento y absorber agua y nutrientes del suelo. (p. 278)

protista: organismo eucariota unicelular o pluricelular que puede parecerse a las plantas, a los animales o a los hongos. (p. 210)

protozoario: protista unicelular similar a los animales y que puede vivir en el agua, en el suelo y en los organismos vivos o muertos. (p. 215)

pseudópodos: extensiones citoplasmáticas temporales usadas por algunos protistas para moverse y atrapar alimento. (p. 216)

circulación pulmonar: flujo sanguíneo del corazón hacia los pulmones y de regreso al corazón. (p. 542)

equilibrio punteado: modelo que describe la evolución rápida que ocurre cuando la mutación de unos pocos genes resulta en que una especie cambie rápidamente para convertirse en otra especie. (p. 160)

Cuadrado de Punnett: herramienta para predecir la probabilidad de ciertos rasgos en la descendencia mostrando las diferentes formas en que los alelos pueden combinarse. (p. 130)

R

radial symmetry: body parts arranged in a circle around a central point. (p. 335)

radioactive element: element that gives off a steady amount of radiation as it slowly changes to a nonradioactive element. (p. 165)

radula (RA juh luh): in gastropods, the tonguelike organ with rows of teeth used to scrape and tear food. (p. 361)

recessive (rih SE sihv): describes a trait that is covered over, or dominated, by another form of that trait and seems to disappear. (p. 128)

recycling: conservation method that is a form of reuse and requires changing or reprocessing an item or natural resource. (p. 789)

reflex: simple innate behavior, such as yawning or blinking, that is an automatic response and does not involve a message to the brain; automatic, involuntary response to a stimulus; controlled by the spinal cord. (pp. 475, 601)

simetría radial: disposición de las partes del cuerpo circularmente alrededor de un punto central. (p. 335)

elemento radiactivo: elemento que emite una cantidad estable de radiación mientras se convierte lentamente en un elemento no radiactivo. (p. 165)

rádula: órgano de los gasterópodos en forma de lengua con filas de dientecillos usado para raspar y desgarrar alimentos. (p. 361)

recesivo: describe un rasgo que está encubierto, o que es dominado, por otra forma del mismo rasgo y que parece no estar presente. (p. 128)

reciclaje: método de conservación como una forma de reutilización y que requiere del cambio o reprocesamiento del producto o recurso natural. (p. 789)

reflejo: comportamiento innato simple, como bostezar o parpadear, que constituye una respuesta automática y no requiere el envío de un mensaje al cerebro; respuesta automática e involuntaria a un estímulo controlada por la médula espinal. (pp. 475, 601)

Glossary/Glosario

renewable resources: natural resources, such as water, sunlight, and crops, that are constantly being recycled or replaced by nature. (p. 771)

respiration: process by which producers and consumers release stored energy from food molecules; series of chemical reactions used to release energy stored in food molecules. (pp. 83, 307)

retina: light-sensitive tissue at the back of the eye; contains rods and cones. (p. 605)

rhizoids (RI zoydz): threadlike structures that anchor nonvascular plants to the ground. (p. 246)

rhizome: underground stem. (p. 278)

ribosome: small cytoplasmic structure on which cells make their own proteins. (p. 42)

RNA: ribonucleic acid; a type of nucleic acid that carries codes for making proteins from the nucleus to the ribosomes. (p. 112)

recursos renovables: recursos naturales, como el agua, la luz solar y los cultivos, que son reciclados o reemplazados constantemente por la naturaleza. (p. 771)

respiración: proceso mediante el cual los organismos productores y consumidores liberan la energía almacenada en las moléculas de los alimentos; serie de reacciones químicas usadas para liberar la energía almacenada en las moléculas de los alimentos. (pp. 83, 307)

retina: tejido sensible a la luz situado en la parte posterior del ojo; contiene conos y bastones. (p. 605)

rizoides: estructuras en forma de hilos que anclan las plantas no vasculares al suelo. (p. 246)

rizoma: tallo subterráneo. (p. 278)

ribosoma: estructura citoplasmática pequeña en la que las células producen sus propias proteínas. (p. 42)

ARN: ácido ribonucleico; tipo de ácido nucleico que transporta los códigos para la formación de proteínas del núcleo a los ribosomas. (p. 112)

S

saprophyte: organism that uses dead organisms as a food source and helps recycle nutrients so they are available for use by other organisms. (pp. 194, 222)

scales: thin, hard plates that cover a fish's skin and protect its body. (p. 399)

scientific methods: procedures used to solve problems and answer questions that can include stating the problem, gathering information, forming a hypothesis, testing the hypothesis with an experiment, analyzing data, and drawing conclusions. (p. 7)

sedimentary rock: a type of rock, such as limestone, that is most likely to contain fossils and is formed when layers of sand, silt, clay, or mud are cemented and compacted together or when minerals are deposited from a solution. (p. 164)

semen (SEE mun): mixture of sperm and a fluid that helps sperm move and supplies them with an energy source. (p. 628)

sessile (SE sile): describes an organism that remains attached to one place during most of its lifetime. (p. 337)

setae (SEE tee): bristlelike structures on the outside of each body segment that helps segmented worms move. (p. 365)

saprófito: organismo que usa a los organismos muertos como una fuente de alimento y ayuda a reciclar los nutrientes de tal forma que estén disponibles para ser usados por otros organismos. (pp. 194, 222)

escamas: placas duras y delgadas que cubren la piel de los peces y protegen su cuerpo. (p. 399)

métodos científicos: procedimientos utilizados para solucionar problemas y responder a preguntas; puede incluir el establecimiento de un problema, recopilación de información, formulación de una hipótesis, comprobación de la hipótesis con un experimento, análisis de la información y presentación de conclusiones. (p. 7)

roca sedimentaria: tipo de roca, como la piedra caliza, con alta probabilidad de contener fósiles y que se forma cuando las capas de arena, sedimento, arcilla o lodo son cementadas y compactadas o cuando los minerales de una solución son depositados. (p. 164)

semen: mezcla de espermatozoides y un fluido que ayuda a la movilización de los espermatozoides y les suministra una fuente de energía. (p. 628)

sésil: organismo que permanece adherido a un lugar durante la mayor parte de su vida. (p. 337)

cerdas: estructuras en forma de cilios presentes en la parte externa de cada segmento corporal y que ayudan a los gusanos segmentados a moverse. (p. 365)

sex-linked gene: an allele inherited on a sex chromosome and that can cause human genetic disorders such as color blindness and hemophilia. (p. 139)

sexual reproduction: a type of reproduction in which two sex cells, usually an egg and a sperm, join to form a zygote, which will develop into a new organism with a unique identity. (p. 104)

sexually transmitted disease (STD): infectious disease, such as chlamydia, AIDS, or genital herpes, that is passed from one person to another during sexual contact. (p. 662)

short-day plant: plant that generally requires long nights—12 or more hours of darkness—to begin the flowering process. (p. 316)

skeletal muscle: voluntary, striated muscle that moves bones, works in pairs, and is attached to bones by tendons. (p. 493)

skeletal system: all the bones in the body; forms an internal, living framework that provides shape and support, protects internal organs, moves bones, forms blood cells, and stores calcium and phosphorus compounds for later use. (p. 484)

smooth muscle: involuntary, nonstriated muscle that controls movement of internal organs. (p. 493)

social behavior: interactions among members of the same species, including courtship and mating, getting food, caring for young, and protecting each other. (p. 462)

society: a group of animals of the same species that live and work together in an organized way, with each member doing a specific job. (p. 463)

soil: mixture of mineral and rock particles, the remains of dead organisms, air, and water that forms the topmost layer of Earth's crust and supports plant growth. (p. 714)

sori: fern structures in which spores are produced. (p. 278)

species: group of organisms that share similar characteristics and can reproduce among themselves producing fertile offspring. (p. 154)

sperm: haploid sex cell formed in the male reproductive organs; in humans, male reproductive cells produced in the testes. (pp. 104, 628)

spiracles (SPIHR ih kulz): openings in the abdomen and thorax of insects through which air enters and waste gases leave. (p. 371)

spontaneous generation: idea that living things come from nonliving things. (p. 19)

gen ligado al sexo: un alelo heredado en un cromosoma sexual y que puede causar desórdenes genéticos humanos como daltonismo y hemofilia. (p. 139)

reproducción sexual: tipo de reproducción en la que dos células sexuales, generalmente un óvulo y un espermatozoide, se unen para formar un zigoto, el cual se desarrollará para formar un nuevo organismo con identidad única. (p. 104)

enfermedad de transmisión sexual (ETS): enfermedad infecciosa como la clamidiasis, SIDA y herpes genital, transmitida de una persona a otra mediante contacto sexual. (p. 662)

planta de día corto: planta que generalmente requiere de noches largas—12 horas o más de oscuridad—para comenzar su proceso de floración. (p. 316)

músculo esquelético: músculo estriado voluntario que mueve los huesos, trabaja en pares y se fija a los huesos por medio de los tendones. (p. 493)

sistema esquelético: todos los huesos en el cuerpo forman una estructura viva interna que proporciona forma y soporte, protege a los órganos internos, mueve a los huesos, forma células sanguíneas y almacena compuestos de calcio y fósforo para uso posterior. (p. 484)

músculo liso: músculo no estriado involuntario que controla el movimiento de los órganos internos. (p. 493)

comportamiento social: interacciones entre los miembros de la misma especie, incluyendo el cortejo y el apareamiento, la obtención de alimento, el cuidado de las crías y la protección de unos a otros. (p. 462)

sociedad: grupo de animales de la misma especie que vive y trabaja conjuntamente de forma organizada, con cada miembro realizando una tarea específica. (p. 463)

suelo: mezcla de partículas minerales y rocas, restos de organismos muertos, aire y del agua que forma la capa superior de la corteza terrestre y favorece el crecimiento de las plantas. (p. 714)

soros: estructuras de los helechos en donde se producen las esporas. (p. 278)

especie: grupo de organismos que comparten características similares entre sí y que pueden reproducirse entre ellos dando lugar a una descendencia fértil. (p. 154)

espermatozoides: células sexuales haploides que se forman en los órganos reproductores masculinos; en los humanos, células reproductoras masculinas producidas por los testículos. (pp. 104, 628)

espiráculos: aperturas del abdomen y tórax de los insectos a través de las cuales entra aire y salen gases de desecho. (p. 371)

generación espontánea: idea que sostiene que los seres vivos proceden de seres inertes. (p. 19)

Glossary/Glosario

sporangium / taste bud

sporangium (spuh RAN jee uhm): round spore case of a zygote fungus. (p. 225)

spores: waterproof reproductive cell of a fungus that can grow into a new organism; in plants, haploid cells produced in the gametophyte stage that can divide by mitosis to form plant structures or an entire new plant or can develop into sex cells. (pp. 223, 275)

sporophyte (SPOR uh fite) stage: plant life-cycle stage that begins when an egg is fertilized by a sperm. (p. 275)

stamen: male reproductive organ inside the flower of an angiosperm; consists of an anther, where pollen grains form, and a filament. (p. 285)

stinging cells: capsules with coiled triggerlike structures that help cnidarians capture food. (p. 340)

stomata (STOH muh tuh): tiny openings in a plant's epidermis through which carbon dioxide, water vapor, and oxygen enter and exit. (pp. 253, 303)

succession: natural, gradual changes in the types of species that live in an area; can be primary or secondary. (p. 740)

symbiosis: any close relationship between species, including mutualism, commensalism, and parasitism. (p. 698)

synapse (SIHN aps): small space across which an impulse moves from an axon to the dendrites or cell body of another neuron. (p. 597)

systemic circulation: largest part of the circulatory system, in which oxygen-rich blood flows to all the organs and body tissues, except the heart and lungs, and oxygen-poor blood is returned to the heart. (p. 543)

esporangio / papila gustativa

esporangio: estructura redondeada que contiene las esporas de un zigomiceto. (p. 225)

esporas: célula reproductora impermeable de un hongo, la cual puede convertirse en un nuevo organismo; en las plantas, las células haploides producidas en la etapa de gametofito que pueden dividirse por mitosis para formar las estructuras de la planta o una planta nueva, o que pueden convertirse en células sexuales. (pp. 223, 275)

etapa de esporofito: etapa del ciclo de vida de una planta que comienza cuando un huevo es fertilizado por un esperma. (p. 275)

estambre: órgano reproductor masculino dentro de la flor de una angiosperma, que consiste en un filamento y una antera donde se forman los granos de polen. (p. 285)

cnidocitos: cápsulas con estructuras enrolladas en forma de gatillo y que ayudan a los cnidarios a capturar su alimento. (p. 340)

estomas: aperturas pequeñas en la superficie de la mayoría de las hojas de las plantas, las cuales permiten que entre y salga dióxido de carbono, agua y oxígeno. (pp. 253, 303)

sucesión: cambios graduales y naturales en los tipos de especies que viven en un área; puede ser primaria o secundaria. (p. 740)

simbiosis: cualquier relación estrecha entre especies, incluyendo mutualismo, comensalismo y parasitismo. (p. 698)

sinapsis: espacio pequeño a través del cual un impulso se mueve del axón a las dendritas o al cuerpo celular de otra neurona. (p. 597)

circulación sistémica: la parte más grande del sistema circulatorio en la que la sangre rica en oxígeno fluye hacia todos los órganos y tejidos corporales excepto el corazón y los pulmones, y la sangre pobre en oxígeno regresa al corazón. (p. 543)

taiga (TI guh): world's largest biome, located south of the tundra between 50°N and 60°N latitude; has long, cold winters, precipitation between 35 cm and 100 cm each year, cone-bearing evergreen trees, and dense forests. (p. 746)

taste bud: major sensory receptor on the tongue; contains taste hairs that send impulses to the brain for interpretation of tastes. (p. 610)

taiga: el bioma más grande del mundo, localizado al sur de la tundra entre 50° y 60° de latitud norte; tiene inviernos prolongados y fríos, una precipitación que alcanza entre 35 y 100 centímetros cúbicos al año, coníferas perennifolias y bosques espesos. (p. 746)

papila gustativa: receptor sensorial principal de la lengua que contiene cilios gustativos que envían impulsos al cerebro para interpretación de los sabores. (p. 610)

temperate deciduous forest: biome usually having four distinct seasons, annual precipitation between 75 cm and 150 cm, and climax communities of deciduous trees. (p. 747)

temperate rain forest: biome with 200 cm to 400 cm of precipitation each year, average temperatures between 9°C and 12°C, and forests dominated by trees with needlelike leaves. (p. 747)

tendon: thick band of tissue that attaches bones to muscles. (p. 493)

tentacles (TEN tih kulz): armlike structures that have stinging cells and surround the mouths of most cnidarians. (p. 340)

testis: male organ that produces sperm and testosterone. (p. 628)

theory: explanation of things or events based on scientific knowledge resulting from many observations and experiments. (p. 10)

tissue: group of similar cells that work together to do one job. (p. 45)

toxin: poisonous substance produced by some pathogens. (p. 197)

trachea (TRAY kee uh): air-conducting tube that connects the larynx with the bronchi; is lined with mucous membranes and cilia, and contains strong cartilage rings. (p. 571)

tropical rain forest: most biologically diverse biome; has an average temperature of 25°C and receives between 200 cm and 600 cm of precipitation each year. (p. 748)

tropism: positive or negative plant response to an external stimulus such as touch, light, or gravity. (p. 312)

tube feet: hydraulic, hollow, thin-walled tubes that end in suction cups and enable echinoderms to move. (p. 380)

tundra: cold, dry, treeless biome with less than 25 cm of precipitation each year, a short growing season, permafrost, and winters that can be six to nine months long. Tundra is separated into two types: arctic tundra and alpine tundra. (p. 745)

bosque caducifolio templado: bioma que generalmente tiene cuatro estaciones distintas, con una precipitación anual entre 75 y 150 centímetros cúbicos y un clímax comunitario de árboles caducifolios. (p. 747)

bosque lluvioso templado: bioma con 200 a 400 centímetros cúbicos de precipitación al año; tiene una temperatura promedio entre 9 y 12°C y bosques dominados por árboles de hojas aciculares. (p. 747)

tendón: banda gruesa de tejido que une los músculos a los huesos. (p. 493)

tentáculos: estructuras en forma de brazo, que poseen cnidocitos y rodean la boca de la mayoría de los cnidarios. (p. 340)

testículos: órganos masculinos que producen espermatozoides y testosterona. (p. 628)

teoría: explicación de cosas o eventos basándose en el conocimiento científico resultante de muchas observaciones y experimentos. (p. 10)

tejido: grupo de células similares que trabajan conjuntamente para hacer una tarea. (p. 45)

toxina: sustancia venenosa producida por algunos patógenos. (p. 197)

tráquea: tubo conductor de aire que conecta a la laringe con los bronquios y que está recubierta por una membrana mucosa y cilios; está formada por anillos cartilaginosos resistentes. (p. 571)

selva húmeda tropical: el bioma más diverso biológicamente; tiene una temperatura promedio de 25°C y recibe entre 200 y 600 centímetros cúbicos de precipitación al año. (p. 748)

tropismo: respuesta positiva o negativa de una planta a un estímulo externo como el rozamiento, la luz o la gravedad. (p. 312)

pie tubular: tubos hidráulicos de pared delgada que terminan en copas de succión y que permiten moverse a los equinodermos. (p. 380)

tundra: bioma sin árboles, frío y seco, con menos de 25 centímetros cúbicos de precipitación al año; tiene una estación corta de crecimiento y permafrost e inviernos que pueden durar entre 6 y 9 meses. La tundra se divide en dos tipos: tundra ártica y tundra alpina. (p. 745)

U

umbilical cord: connects the embryo to the placenta; moves food and oxygen from the placenta to the embryo and removes the embryo's waste products. (p. 441)

cordón umbilical: conecta al embrión con la placenta, lleva nutrientes y oxígeno de la placenta al embrión y retira los productos de desecho de éste. (p. 441)

Glossary/Glosario

ureter: tube that carries urine from each kidney to the bladder. (p. 580)

urethra (yoo REE thruh): tube that carries urine from the bladder to the outside of the body. (p. 580)

uterus: in female humans, hollow, muscular, pear-shaped organ where a fertilized egg develops into a baby. (p. 629)

urinary system: system of excretory organs that rids the blood of wastes, controls blood volume by removing excess water, and balances concentrations of salts and water. (p. 577)

urine: wastewater that contains excess water, salts, and other wastes that are not reabsorbed by the body. (p. 578)

uréter: tubo que conduce a la orina de cada riñón hacia la vejiga. (p. 580)

uretra: tubo que conduce a la orina de la vejiga al exterior del cuerpo. (p. 580)

útero: en seres hermanos femeninos, órgano en forma de pera, hueco y musculoso, en el que un óvulo fertilizado se desarrolla en bebé. (p. 629)

sistema urinario: sistema de órganos excretores que elimina los desechos de la sangre, controla el volumen de sangre eliminando el exceso de agua y balancea las concentraciones de sales y agua. (p. 577)

orina: líquido de desecho que contiene el exceso de agua, sales y otros desechos que no son reabsorbidos por el cuerpo. (p. 578)

vaccination: process of giving a vaccine by mouth or by injection to provide active immunity against a disease. (p. 655)

vaccine: preparation made from killed bacteria or damaged particles from bacterial cell walls or viruses that can prevent some bacterial and viral diseases. (p. 199)

vagina (vuh JI nuh): muscular tube that connects the lower end of a female's uterus to the outside of the body; the birth canal through which a baby travels when being born. (p. 629)

variable: something in an experiment that can change. (p. 9)

variation: inherited trait that makes an individual different from other members of the same species and results from a mutation in the organism's genes. (p. 158)

vascular plant: plant with tubelike structures that move minerals, water, and other substances throughout the plant. (p. 245)

vein: blood vessel that carries blood back to the heart, and has one-way valves that keep blood moving toward the heart. (p. 544)

ventricles (VEN trih kulz): two lower chambers of the heart, that contract at the same time, during a heartbeat. (p. 542)

vertebrae: backbones that are joined by flexible cartilage and protect a vertebrate's spinal nerve cord. (p. 395)

vertebrate: animal with a backbone. (p. 334)

vacunación: proceso de aplicar una vacuna por vía oral o mediante una inyección para proporcionar inmunidad activa contra una enfermedad. (p. 655)

vacuna: preparación fabricada a partir de bacterias muertas o partículas dañadas de las paredes celulares bacterianas o virus y que puede prevenir algunas enfermedades bacterianas y virales. (p. 199)

vagina: tubo musculoso que conecta el extremo inferior del útero de una hembra con el exterior del cuerpo; el canal del nacimiento a través del cual sale un bebé al nacer. (p. 629)

variable: condición que puede cambiar en un experimento. (p. 9)

variación: rasgo heredado que hace que un individuo sea diferente a otros miembros de su misma especie como resultado de una mutación de sus genes. (p. 158)

planta vascular: planta con estructuras semejantes a tubos, las cuales sirven para movilizar minerales, agua y otras sustancias a toda la planta. (p. 245)

vena: vaso sanguíneo que lleva sangre de regreso al corazón y tiene válvulas unidireccionales que mantienen a la sangre en movimiento hacia el corazón. (p. 544)

ventrículos: las dos cámaras inferiores del corazón que se contraen al mismo tiempo durante el latido cardiaco. (p. 542)

vértebra: huesos de la espalda unidos por cartílago flexible y que protegen la médula espinal de los vertebrados. (p. 395)

vertebrado: animal que posee columna vertebral. (p. 334)

vestigial (veh STIHJ ee ul) structure: structure, such as the human appendix, that doesn't seem to have a function and may once have functioned in the body of an ancestor. (p. 168)

villi (VIH li): fingerlike projections covering the wall of the small intestine that increase the surface area for food absorption. (p. 528)

virus: a strand of hereditary material surrounded by a protein coating that can infect and multiply in a host cell. (pp. 52, 658)

vitamin: water-soluble or fat-soluble organic nutrient needed in small quantities for growth, for preventing some diseases, and for regulating body functions. (p. 516)

voluntary muscle: muscle, such as a leg or arm muscle, that can be consciously controlled. (p. 491)

estructura vestigial: estructura, como el apéndice humano, que no parece tener alguna función pero que pudo haber funcionado en el cuerpo de un antepasado. (p. 168)

vellosidades: proyecciones en forma de dedos que cubren la pared del intestino delgado y que incrementan la superficie de absorción de nutrientes. (p. 528)

virus: pieza de material hereditario rodeado de una capa de proteína que infecta y se multiplica en las células huéspedes. (pp. 52, 658)

vitamina: nutriente orgánico soluble al agua y al aceite, necesario en pequeñas cantidades para el crecimiento, prevención de algunas enfermedades y regulación de las funciones del cuerpo. (p. 516)

músculo voluntario: músculo, como el músculo de una pierna o un brazo, que puede controlarse conscientemente. (p. 491)

water cycle: model describing how water moves from Earth's surface to the atmosphere and back to the surface again through evaporation, condensation, and precipitation. (p. 721)

water-vascular system: network of water-filled canals that allows echinoderms to move, capture food, give off wastes, and exchange carbon dioxide and oxygen. (p. 380)

wetland: a land region that is wet most or all of the year. (p. 755)

ciclo del agua: modelo que describe cómo se mueve el agua de la superficie de la Tierra hacia la atmósfera y nuevamente hacia la superficie terrestre a través de la evaporación, la condensación y la precipitación. (p. 721)

sistema vascular acuoso: red de canales llenos de agua que permiten a los equinodermos moverse, capturar alimento, eliminar sustancias de desecho e intercambiar dióxido de carbono y oxígeno. (p. 380)

zona húmeda: región lluviosa la mayor parte del año. (p. 755)

X

xylem (ZI lum): vascular tissue that forms hollow vessels that transport substances, other than sugar, throughout a plant. (p. 256)

xilema: tejido vascular que forma vasos ahuecados que trasportan todo tipo de sustancias, excepto azúcares, en toda la planta. (p. 256)

zygote: new diploid cell formed when a sperm fertilizes an egg; will divide by mitosis and develop into a new organism. (p. 104)

zigoto: célula diploide nueva formada cuando un espermatozoide fertiliza a un óvulo; se dividirá por mitosis y se desarrollará para formar un nuevo organismo. (p. 104)

Index

Italic numbers = illustration/photo   **Bold numbers = vocabulary term**
lab = indicates a page on which the entry is used in a lab
act = indicates a page on which the entry is used in an activity

Index

Index

Index

Index

Index

Magnification Key:
Magnifications listed are the magnifications at which images were originally photographed.
LM—Light Microscope
SEM—Scanning Electron Microscope
TEM—Transmission Electron Microscope

Acknowledgments: Glencoe would like to acknowledge the artists and agencies who participated in illustrating this program: Absolute Science Illustration; Andrew Evansen; Argosy; Articulate Graphics; Craig Attebery represented by Frank & Jeff Lavaty; CHK America; John Edwards and Associates; Gagliano Graphics; Pedro Julio Gonzalez represented by Melissa Turk & The Artist Network; Robert Hynes represented by Mendola Ltd.; Morgan Cain & Associates; JTH Illustration; Laurie O'Keefe; Matthew Pippin represented by Beranbaum Artist's Representative; Precision Graphics; Publisher's Art; Rolin Graphics, Inc.; Wendy Smith represented by Melissa Turk & The Artist Network; Kevin Torline represented by Berendsen and Associates, Inc.; WILDlife ART; Phil Wilson represented by Cliff Knecht Artist Representative; Zoo Botanica.

Photo Credits

Cover Andy Rouse/DRK Photo; **i ii** Andy Rouse/DRK Photo; **vii** Aaron Haupt; **viii** John Evans; **ix** (t)PhotoDisc, (b)John Evans; **x** (l)John Evans, (r)Geoff Butler; **xi** (l)John Evans, (r)PhotoDisc; **xii** PhotoDisc; **xiii** Doug Perrine/Innerspace Visions; **xiv** (t)Mark Burnett, (b)Frans Lanting/Minden Pictures; **xvi** Dr. Jeremy Burgess/Science Photo Library/Photo Researchers; **xvii** Fateh Singh Rathore/Peter Arnold, Inc.; **xix** Ariel Skelley/The Stock Market/CORBIS; **xx** Richard Thatcher/David R. Frazier Photolibrary; **xxi** Mark E. Gibson/Visuals Unlimited; **xxii** Rod Planck/Photo Researchers; **xxvi** Geoff Butler; **xxvii** Matt Meadows; **xxviii** M. Schliwa/Visuals Unlimited; **1** CORBIS; **2–3** Diane Scullion Littler; **3** (l)Jonathan Eisenback/PhotoTake, NYC/PictureQuest, (r)Janice M. Sheldon/Picture 20-20/PictureQuest; **4–5** A. Witte/C. Mahaney/Getty Images; **6** Kjell B. Sandved/Visuals Unlimited; **8 9** Mark Burnett; **11** Tek Image/Science Photo Library/Photo Researchers; **12** Mark Burnett, (label)no credit needed; **13** Mark Burnett; **14** (t)Michael Abbey/Science Source/Photo Researchers, (bl)Aaron Haupt, (br)Michael Delannoy/Visuals Unlimited; **15** Mark Burnett; **16** (tr)Mark Burnett, (tcr)A. Glauberman/Photo Researchers, (bl bcl br)Runk/Schoenberger from Grant Heilman, (others)Dwight Kuhn; **17** (t)Bill Beaty/Animals Animals, (bl)Tom & Therisa Stack/Tom Stack & Assoc., (br)Michael Fogden/Earth Scenes; **18** Aaron Haupt; **19** Geoff Butler; **22** (t)Arthur C. Smith III From Grant Heilman, (bl)Hal Beral/Visuals Unlimited, (br)Larry L. Miller/Photo Researchers; **23** Doug Perrine/Innerspace Visions; **24** (l)Brandon D. Cole, (r)Gregory Ochocki/Photo Researchers; **25** (l)Zig Leszczynski/Animals Animals, (r)R. Andrew Odum/Peter Arnold, Inc.; **26** Alvin E. Staffan; **27** Geoff Butler; **28** (t)Jan Hinsch/Science Photo Library/Photo Researchers, (b)Mark Burnett; **29** Mark Burnett; **30** Marc Von Roosmalen/AP; **31** (l)Mark Burnett, (r)Will & Deni McIntyre/Photo Researchers; **32** KS Studios/Mullenix; **33** Jeff Greenberg/Rainbow; **34** Dwight Kuhn; **35** Dave Spier/Visuals Unlimited; **36–37** Nancy Kedersha/Science Photo Library/Photo Researchers; **39** David M. Phillips/Visuals Unlimited; **40** (t)Don Fawcett/Photo Researchers,

(b)M. Schliwa/Visuals Unlimited; **42** (t)George B. hapman/Visuals Unlimited, (b)P. Motta & T. Naguro/Science Photo Library/Photo Researchers; **43** (t)Don Fawcett/Photo Researchers, (b)Biophoto Associates/Photo Researchers; **47** (l)Biophoto Associates/Photo Researchers, (r)Matt Meadows; **48** (bkgd)David M. Phillips/Visuals Unlimited, (cw from top)courtesy Nikon Instruments Inc., David M. Phillips/Visuals Unlimited, Kathy Talaro/Visuals Unlimited, Michael Abbey/Visuals Unlimited, Michael Gabridge/Visuals Unlimited; **49** (tl)James W. Evarts, (tr)Bob Krist/CORBIS, (cl)courtesy Olympus Corporation, (cr)Michael Abbey/Visuals Unlimited, (bl)Karl Aufderheide/Visuals Unlimited, (br)Lawrence Migdale/Stock Boston/PictureQuest; **52** (l)Richard J. Green/Photo Researchers, (c)Dr. J.F.J.M. van der Heuvel, (r)Gelderblom/Eye of Science/Photo Researchers; **55** Pam Wilson/Texas Dept. of Health; **56 57** Matt Meadows; **58** (t)Quest/Science Photo Library/Photo Researchers, (b)courtesy California University; **59** (l)Keith Porter/Photo Researchers, (r)NIBSC/Science Photo Library/Photo Researchers; **61** Biophoto Associates/Science Source/Photo Researchers; **62** P. Motta & T. Naguro/Science Photo Library/Photo Researchers; **64–65** Jane Grushow/Grant Heilman Photography; **67** Bob Daemmrich; **69** (t)Runk/Schoenberger from Grant Heilman, (b)Klaus Guldbrandsen/Science Photo Library/Photo Researchers; **74** (l)John Fowler, (r)Richard Hamilton Smith/CORBIS; **75** KS Studios; **76** Aaron Haupt; **77** Visuals Unlimited; **78** Biophoto Associates/Science Source/Photo Researchers; **80** Matt Meadows; **82** Craig Lovell/CORBIS; **83** John Fowler; **84** David M. Phillips/Visuals Unlimited; **85** (l)Grant Heilman Photography, (r)Bios (Klein/Hubert)/Peter Arnold; **86** (t)Runk/Schoenberger from Grant Heilman, (b)Matt Meadows; **87** Matt Meadows; **88** Lappa/Marquart; **89** CNRI/Science Photo Library/Photo Researchers; **90** Biophoto Associates/Science Source/Photo Researchers; **94–95** Zig Leszcynski/Animals Animals; **96** (l)Dave B. Fleetham/Tom Stack & Assoc., (r)Cabisco/Visuals Unlimited; **98** Cabisco/Visuals Unlimited; **99** (tl)Michael Abbey/Visuals Unlimited, (others)John D. Cunningham/Visuals Unlimited; **100** (l)Matt Meadows, (r)Nigel Cattlin/Photo Researchers; **101** (l)Barry L. Runk from Grant Heilman, (r)Runk/Schoenberger from Grant Heilman; **102** (l)Walker England/Photo Researchers, (r)Tom Stack & Assoc.; **103** Runk/Schoenberger from Grant Heilman; **104** Dr. Dennis Kunkel/PhotoTake NYC; **105** (tl)Gerald & Buff Corsi/Visuals Unlimited, (r)Fred Bruenner/Peter Arnold, Inc., (bl)Susan McCartney/Photo Researchers; **107** (l)John D. Cunningham/Visuals Unlimited, (c)Jen & Des Bartlett/Bruce Coleman, Inc., (r)Breck P. Kent; **108** (tl)Artville, (tr)Tim Fehr, (c)Bob Daemmrich/Stock Boston/PictureQuest, (bl)Troy Mary Parlee/Index Stock/PictureQuest, (br)Jeffery Myers/Southern Stock/PictureQuest; **114** Stewart Cohen/Stone/Getty Images; **116** (t)Tom McHugh/Photo Researchers, (b)file photo; **117** Monica Dalmasso/Stone/Getty Images; **118** (t)Philip Lee Harvey/Stone, (b)Lester V. Bergman/CORBIS; **120** Walker England/Photo Researchers; **122** Barry L. Runk from Grant Heilman; **123** Cabisco/Visuals Unlimited; **124–125** Ron Chapple/Getty Images; **125** (l r)Geoff Butler; **126** Stewart Cohen/Stone/Getty Images; **129** (bkgd)Jane Grushow from Grant Heilman, (others)Special Collections, National Agriculture Library; **130** Barry L. Runk From Grant Heilman; **132** Richard Hutchings/Photo Researchers; **134** (l)Robert Maier/Animals Animals, (r)Gemma Giannini from Grant Heilman; **135** Raymond Gehman/CORBIS; **136** Dan McCoy from Rainbow; **137** (l)Phil Roach/Ipol, Inc., (r)CNRI/Science

Photo Library/Photo Researchers; **138** Gopal Murti/PhotoTake, NYC; **139** Tim Davis/Photo Researchers; **140** (t)Renee Stockdale/Animals Animals, (b)Alan & Sandy Carey/Photo Researchers; **143** Tom Meyers/Photo Researchers; **144** (t)Runk/Schoenberger from Grant Heilman, (b)Mark Burnett; **145** Richard Hutchings; **146** KS Studios; **151** CNRI/Science Photo Library/Photo Researchers; **152–153** B.G. Thomson/Photo Researchers; **155** Barbera Cushman/DRK Photo; **156** (l c)Tui De Roy/Minden Pictures, (r)Tim Davis/Photo Researchers; **158** (l)Gregory G. Dimijian, M.D./Photo Researchers, (r)Patti Murray/Animals Animals; **159** (l)Darek Karp/Animals Animals, (r)Vonorla Photography; **160** (l)Joe McDonald/Animals Animals, (c)Tom McHugh/Photo Researchers, (r)Tim Davis/Photo Researchers; **161** James Richardson/Visuals Unlimited; **162** Frans Lanting/Minden Pictures; **163** (l)Dominique Braud/Earth Scenes, (c)Carr Clifton/Minden Pictures, (r)John Cancalosi/DRK Photo; **164** (cw from top)Ken Lucas/Visuals Unlimited, John Cancalosi/DRK Photo, Larry Ulrich/DRK Photo, John Cancalosi/Peter Arnold, Inc., Sinclair Stammers/Science Photo Library/Photo Researchers; **165** John Kieffer/Peter Arnold, Inc.; **168** (l)Kees Van Den Berg/Photo Researchers, (r)Doug Martin; **169** Peter Veit/DRK Photo; **170** (l)Mark E. Gibson, (r)Gerard Lacz/Animals Animals; **171** (l)Michael Dick/Animals Animals, (r)Carolyn A. McKeone/Photo Researchers; **172** (l)John Reader/Science Photo Library/Photo Researchers, (r)Archivo Iconografico, S.A./CORBIS; **173** Francois Ducasse/Rapho/Photo Researchers; **174** (b)Kenneth W. Fink/Photo Researchers; **174–175** Aaron Haupt; **176** (t)Oliver Meckes/E.O.S/Gelderblom/Photo Researchers, (b)Lara Jo Regan/Saba; **177** (l)Koster-Survival/Animals Animals, (r)Stephen J. Keasemann/DRK Photo; **179** Tom Tietz/Stone/Getty Images; **180** Gregory G. Dimijian, M.D./Photo Researchers; **181** Patti Murray/Animals Animals; **182–183** Richard Hamilton Smith/CORBIS; **183** (l)Courtesy Broan-NuTone, (r)CORBIS; **184–185** Scimat/Photo Researchers; **186** (l)Oliver Meckes/Photo Researchers, (c r)CNRI/Science Photo Library/Photo Researchers; **188** Dr. L. Caro/Science Photo Library/Photo Researchers; **189** (l to r)Dr. Dennis Kunkel/PhotoTake NYC, David M. Phillips/Visuals Unlimited, R. Kessel/G. Shih/Visuals Unlimited, Ann Siegleman/Visuals Unlimited, SCIMAT/Photo Researchers; **190** (t)T.E. Adams/Visuals Unlimited, (b)Frederick Skavara/Visuals Unlimited; **191** R. Kessel/G. Shih/Visuals Unlimited; **192** T.E. Adams/Visuals Unlimited; **193** (tl)M. Abbey Photo/Photo Researchers, (tr)Oliver Meckes/Eye of Science/Photo Researchers, (bl)S. Lowry/University of Ulster/Stone/Getty Images, (br)A.B. Dowsett/Science Photo Library/Photo Researchers; **194** Ray Pfortner/Peter Arnold, Inc.; **195** (bkgd tl)Jeremy Burgess/Science Photo Library/Photo Researchers, (tr)Ann M. Hirsch/UCLA, (bl)John D. Cunningham/Visuals Unlimited, (br)Astrid & Hanns-Frieder Michler/Science Photo Library/Photo Researchers; **196** (l)Paul Almasy/CORBIS, (r)Joe Munroe/Photo Researchers; **197** (t)Terry Wild Studio, (b)George Wilder/Visuals Unlimited; **198** Amanita Pictures; **199** John Durham/Science Photo Library/Photo Researchers; **200** (t)KS Studios, (b)John Evans; **201** John Evans; **202** (t)P. Canumette/Visuals Unlimited, (c)Dr. Philippa Uwins, The University of Queensland, (bl)Dan Hoh/AP/Wide World Photos, (br)Reuters NewMedia Inc./CORBIS; **204** Carolina Biological /Visuals Unlimited; **206** (l)R. Kessel/G. Shih/Visuals Unlimited, (r)A. B. Dowsett/Science Photo Library/Photo Researchers; **207** (l)Breck P. Kent/Earth Scenes, (r)Ray Pfortner/Peter Arnold, Inc.;

208–209 Steve Austin; Papilio/CORBIS; **211** (l)Jean Claude Revy/PhotoTake, NYC, (r)Anne Hubbard/Photo Researchers; **212** (tl)NHMPL/Stone/Getty Images, (tr)Microfield Scienctific Ltd/Science Photo Library/Photo Researchers, (bl)David M. Phillips/Photo Researchers, (br)Dr. David Phillips/Visuals Unlimited; **213** (l)Pat & Tom Leeson/Photo Researchers, (r)Jeffrey L. Rotman/Peter Arnold, Inc.; **214** Walter H. Hodge/Peter Arnold, Inc.; **215** Eric V. Grave/Photo Researchers; **216** (t)Kerry B. Clark, (b)Astrid & Hanns-Frieder Michler/Science Photo Library/Photo Researchers; **217** Lennart Nilsson/Albert Bonniers Forlag AB; **218** (l)Ray Simons/Photo Researchers, (c)Matt Meadows/Peter Arnold, Inc., (r)Gregory G. Dimijian/Photo Researchers; **219** (t)Dwight Kuhn, (b)Mark Steinmetz; **220** Richard Calentine/Visuals Unlimited; **221** Biophoto Associates/Science Source/Photo Researchers; **222** James W. Richardson/Visuals Unlimited; **223** Carolina Biological Supply/Phototake, NYC; **224** (tl)Mark Steinmetz, (tr)Ken Wagner/Visuals Unlimited, (b)Dennis Kunkel; **225** (l)Science VU/Visuals Unlimited, (r)J.W. Richardson/Visuals Unlimited; **226** (tl)Bill Bachman/Photo Researchers, (tc)Frank Orel/Stone/Getty Images, (tr)Charles Kingery/PhotoTake, NYC, (b)Nancy Rotenberg/Earth Scenes; **227** (tl tc)Stephen Sharnoff, (tr)Biophoto Associates/Photo Researchers, (bl)L. West/Photo Researchers, (br)Larry Lee Photography/CORBIS; **228** (l)Nigel Cattlin/Holt Studios International/Photo Researchers, (r)Michael Fogden/Earth Scenes; **229** Ray Elliott; **230** Mark Steinmetz; **231** (tr)Mark Steinmetz, (b)Ken Wagner/Visuals Unlimited; **232** (t)Alvarode Leiva/Liaison, (b)courtesy Beltsville Agricultural Research Center-West/USDA; **233** (l)Michael Delaney/Visuals Unlimited, (r)Mark Steinmetz; **237** Mark Thayer Photography, Inc., Robert Calentine/Visuals Unlimited, Henry C. Wolcott III/Getty Images; **238–239** Peter Adams /Getty Images; **240** Tom Stack & Assoc.; **241** Laat-Siluur; **242** (t)Kim Taylor/Bruce Coleman, Inc., (b)William E. Ferguson; **243** (tl)Amanita Pictures, (tr)Ken Eward/Photo Researchers, (bl)Photo Researchers, (br)Amanita Pictures; **244** (cw from top)Dan McCoy from Rainbow, Philip Dowell/DK Images, Kevin & Betty Collins/Visuals Unlimited, David Sieren/Visuals Unlimited, Steve Callaham/Visuals Unlimited, Gerald & Buff Corsi/Visuals Unlimited, Mack Henley/Visuals Unlimited, Edward S. Ross, Douglas Peebles/CORBIS, Gerald & Buff Corsi/Visuals Unlimited, Martha McBride/Unicorn Stock Photos; **245** (t)Gail Jankus/Photo Researchers, (b)Michael P. Fogden/Bruce Coleman, Inc.; **246** (l)Larry West/Bruce Coleman, Inc., (c)Scott Camazine/Photo Researchers, (r)Kathy Merrifield/Photo Researchers; **247** Michael P. Gadomski/Photo Researchers; **249** (t)Farrell Grehan/Photo Researchers, (bl)Steve Solum/Bruce Coleman, Inc., (bc)R. Van Nostrand/Photo Researchers, (br)Inga Spence/Visuals Unlimited; **250** (t)Joy Spurr/Bruce Coleman, Inc., (b)W.H. Black/Bruce Coleman, Inc.; **251** Farrell Grehan/Photo Researchers; **252** Amanita Pictures; **253** (l)Nigel Cattlin/Photo Researchers, Inc., (c)Doug Sokel/Tom Stack & Assoc., (r)Charles D. Winters/Photo Researchers; **254** Bill Beatty/Visuals Unlimited; **256** (l)Doug Sokell/Tom Stack & Assoc., (tc)Robert C. Hermes/Photo Researchers, (r)Bill Beatty/Visuals Unlimited, (bc)David M. Schleser/Photo Researchers; **257** (cw from top)E. Valentin/Photo Researchers, Dia Lein/Photo Researchers, Eva Wallander, Tom Stack & Assoc., Joy Spurr/Photo Researchers; **259** (l)Dwight Kuhn, (c)Joy Spurr/Bruce Coleman, Inc., (r)John D. Cunningham/Visuals Unlimited; **260** (l)J. Lotter/Tom Stack & Assoc., (r)J.C. Carton/Bruce Coleman, Inc.; **262** (t)Inga Spence/Visuals Unlimited, (b)David Sieren/Visuals Unlimited; **263** Jim Steinberg/Photo Researchers; **264** (t)Michael Rose/Frank Lane Picture Agency/CORBIS, (b)Dr. Jeremy Burgess/Science Photo Library/Photo Researchers; **266** Stephen P. Parker/Photo Researchers; **270–271** Massimo Mastrorillo/CORBIS; **272** (l)Stephen Dalton/Photo Researchers, (r)Matt Meadows; **273** (l)Holt Studios/Nigel Cattlin/Photo Researchers, (r)Inga Spence/Visuals Unlimited; **274** (l)H. Reinhard/OKAPIA/Photo Researchers, (c)John W. Bova/Photo Researchers, (r)John D. Cunningham/Visuals Unlimited; **276** (l)Biology Media/Photo Researchers, (c)Andrew Syred/Science Photo Library/Photo Researchers, (r)Runk/Schoenberger from Grant Heilman; **278 279** Kathy Merrifield 2000/Photo Researchers; **280** Matt Meadows; **281** (l)John Kaprielian/Photo Researchers, (r)Scott Camazine/Sue Trainor/Photo Researchers; **282** Dr. WM. H. Harlow/Photo Researchers; **283** Christian Grzimek/OKAPIA/Photo Researchers; **284** (l)Stephen P. Parker/Photo Researchers, (c)M. J. Griffith/Photo Researchers, (r)Dan Suzio/Photo Researchers; **285** (tl)Gustav Verderber/Visuals Unlimited, (tr)Rob Simpson/Visuals Unlimited, (b)Alvin E. Staffan/Photo Researchers; **286** (tl)C. Nuridsany & M. Perennou/Science Photo Library/Photo Researchers, (tr)Merlin D. Tuttle/Photo Researchers, (bl)Anthony Mercreca Photo/Photo Researchers, (bc)Kjell B. Sandved/Photo Researchers, (br)Holt Studios LTD/Photo Researchers; **287** William J. Weber/Visuals Unlimited; **289** (tl)Kevin Shafer/CORBIS, (bcl)Tom & Pat Leeson, (bcr)Darryl Torckler/Stone/Getty Images, (others)Dwight Kuhn; **290 292** Doug Martin; **293** Matt Meadows; **294** (t)Kevin Laubacher/FPG., (b)Michael Black/Bruce Coleman, Inc.; **295** Oliver Meckes/Photo Researchers; **296** Ed Reschke/Peter Arnold, Inc.; **298** Andrew Syred/Science Photo Library/Photo Researchers; **299** (l)Dan Suzio/Photo Researchers, (r)Alvin E. Staffan/Photo Researchers; **300–301** Terry Thompson/Panoramic Images; **301** Matt Meadows; **303** Dr. Jeremy Burgess/Science Photo Library/Photo Researchers; **304** (l)John Kieffer/Peter Arnold, Inc., (r)Runk/Schoenberger from Grant Heilman; **305** M. Eichelberger/Visuals Unlimited; **307** (t)Jacques Jangoux/Peter Arnold, Inc., (b)Jeff Lepore/Photo Researchers; **308** Michael P. Gadomski/Photo Researchers; **312** (l)Scott Camazine/Photo Researchers, (c r)Matt Meadows; **315** (t)Artville, (cl)Runk/Schoenberger from Grant Heilman, (c cr)Prof. Malcolm B. Wilkins/University of Glasgow, (bl)Eric Brennan, (br)John Sohlden/Visuals Unlimited; **316** Jim Metzger; **318** (t)Ed Reschke/Peter Arnold, Inc., (b)Matt Meadows; **319** Matt Meadows; **320** Greg Vaughn/Getty Images; **321** (l)Norm Thomas/Photo Researchers, (r)S.R. Maglione/Photo Researchers; **322** Runk/Schoenberger from Grant Heilman; **324** Matt Meadows; **325** Scott Camazine/Photo Researchers; **326–327** Glenn W. Elison; **326** (inset)Stephen St. John/National Geographic Image Collection; **328–329** N. Sefton/Photo Researchers; **329** Icon Images; **330** Zig Leszczynski/Animals Animals; **331** (l)Jeff Foott/DRK Photo, (c)Leonard Lee Rue III/DRK Photo, (r)Hal Beral/Visuals Unlimited; **332** (t)Ken Lucas/Visuals Unlimited, (bl)Joe McDonald/Visuals Unlimited, (br)Zig Leszczynski/Animals Animals; **333** (tl)Tom J. Ulrich/Visuals Unlimited, (tc)Peter & Beverly Pickford/DRK Photo, (tr)Fred McConnaughey/Photo Researchers, (b)Stuart Westmoreland/Mo Yung Productions/Norbert Wu Productions; **335** (l)Stephen J. Krasemann/DRK Photo, (r)Ford Kristo/DRK Photo; **336** (l)Glenn Oliver/Visuals Unlimited, (r)Andrew J. Martinez/Photo Researchers; **339** (t)Norbert WU/DRK Photo, (bl)Fred Bavendam/Minden Pictures, (br)H. Hall/OSF/Animals Animals;

340 Gerry Ellis/GLOBIO.org; **342** David B. Fleetham/Visuals Unlimited; **343** Larry Stepanowicz/Visuals Unlimited; **345** (tl)T.E. Adams/Visuals Unlimited, (tr)Science VU/Visuals Unlimited, (b)Oliver Meckes/Eye of Science/Photo Researchers; **346** Triarch/Visuals Unlimited; **347** Oliver Meckes/Ottawa/Photo Researchers; **348** (tr)NIBSC/Science Photo Library/Photo Researchers, (cl)Sinclair Stammers/Science Photo Library/Photo Researchers, (cr)Arthur M. Siegelman/Visuals Unlimited, (bl)Oliver Meckes/Photo Researchers, (bcl)Andrew Syred/Science Photo Library/Photo Researchers, (bcr)Eric V. Grave/Photo Researchers, (br)Cabisco/Visuals Unlimited; **349** R. Calentine/Visuals Unlimited; **350** (t)T.E. Adams/Visuals Unlimited, (b)Bob Daemmrich; **351** Matt Meadows; **352** (t)PhotoDisc, (b)Shirley Vanderbilt/Index Stock; **353** James H. Robinson/Animals Animals; **354** R. Calentine/Visuals Unlimited; **355** Donald Specker/Animals Animals; **356** (l)Fred McConnaughey/Photo Researchers, (r)Fred Bavendam/Minden Pictures; **357** (l)Stephen J. Krasemann/DRK Photo, (r)Glenn Oliver/Visuals Unlimited; **358–359** Michael & Patricia Fogden/CORBIS; **360** Wayne Lynch/DRK Photo; **361** (l)Jeff Rotman Photography, (r)James H. Robinson/Animals Animals; **362** (t)David S. Addison/Visuals Unlimited, (b)Joyce & Frank Burek/Animals Animals; **363** Clay Wiseman/Animals Animals; **364** Bates Littlehales/Animals Animals; **365** Beverly Van Pragh/Museum Victoria; **366** Donald Specker/Animals Animals; **367** (t)Charles Fisher, Penn State University, (bl)Mary Beth Angelo/Photo Researchers, (br)Kjell B Sandved/Visuals Unlimited; **368** St. Bartholomew's Hospital/Science Photo Library/Photo Researchers; **370** Tom McHugh/Photo Researchers; **371** (t)Ted Clutter/Photo Researchers, (b)Kjell B. Sandved/Visuals Unlimited; **374** Lynn Stone; **375** (l)Bill Beatty/Animals Animals, (r)Patti Murray/Animals Animals; **376** (tl)Bill Beatty/Wild & Natural, (tc)Robert F. Sisson, (tr)Index Stock, (cl)Brian Gordon Green, (c)Joseph H. Bailey/National Geographic Image Collection, (cr)Jeffrey L. Rotman/CORBIS, (b)Timothy G. Laman/National Geographic Image Collection; **377** (t)James P. Rowan/DRK Photo, (b)Leonard Lee Rue/Photo Researchers; **378** Ken Lucas/Visuals Unlimited; **379** Tom Stack & Assoc.; **380** Scott Smith/Animals Animals; **381** Clay Wiseman/Animals Animals; **382** (tl)Andrew J. Martinez/Photo Researchers, (tr)David Wrobel/Visuals Unlimited, (b)Gerald & Buff Corsi/Visuals Unlimited; **383** Ken Lucas/Visuals Unlimited; **384 385** Matt Meadows; **386** (t)David M. Dennis, (b)Harry Rogers/Photo Researchers; **387** (l)Charles McRae/Visuals Unlimited, (r)Mark Moffet/Minden Pictures; **388** Leroy Simon/Visuals Unlimited; **389** William Leonard/DRK Photo; **390** Joyce & Frank Burek/Animals Animals; **391** (l)Clay Wiseman/Animals Animals, (r)Scott Smith/Animals Animals; **392–393** Robert Lubeck/Animals Animals; **394** Fred Bavendam/Minden Pictures; **395** Omni-Photo Communications; **396** (t to b)H. W. Robison/Visuals Unlimited, Flip Nicklin/Minden Pictures, John M. Burnley/Photo Researchers, George Grall/National Geographic Image Collection, M. P. Kahl/DRK Photo, Grace Davies/Omni-Photo Communications; **397** T. A. Wiewandt/DRK Photo; **398** Icon Images; **399** (l to r)Meckes/Ottawa/Photo Researchers, Rick Gillis/University of Wisconsin-La Crosse, Runk/Schoenberger from Grant Heilman; **400** Ken Lucas/Visuals Unlimited; **401** (tl)James Watt/Animals Animals, (tc)Norbert Wu/DRK Photo, (tr)Fred Bavendam/Minden Pictures, (br)Richard T. Nowitz/Photo Researchers; **402 404** Tom McHugh/Photo Researchers; **405** (t)Tom McHugh/Steinhart Aquarium/Photo Researchers, (bl)Bill

Credits

Kamin/Visuals Unlimited, (bc)Norbert Wu/DRK Photo, (br)Michael Durham/GLOBIO.org; **406** Runk/Schoenberger from Grant Heilman; **407** Fred Habegger/Grant Heilman; **408** (t)David Northcott/DRK Photo, (bl br)Runk/Schoenberger from Grant Heilman; **409** (l)Runk/Schoenberger from Grant Heilman, (r)George H. Harrison from Grant Heilman; **410** (l)Mark Moffett/Minden Pictures, (r)Michael Fogden/DRK Photo; **411** Rob and Ann Simpson/Visuals Unlimited; **412** Joe McDonald/Visuals Unlimited; **414** (tl)Klaus Uhlenhut/Animals Animals, (tr)Rob & Ann Simpson/Visuals Unlimited, (b)G and C Merker/Visuals Unlimited; **415** (t)Mitsuaki Iwago/Minden Pictures, (b)Belinda Wright/DRK Photo; **416** (tl)John Sibbick, (tr)Karen Carr, (c)Chris Butler/Science Photo Library/Photo Researchers, (bl)Jerome Connolly, courtesy The Science Museum of Minnesota, (br)Chris Butler; **418** (t)Steve Maslowski/Visuals Unlimited, (b)Michael Newman/PhotoEdit, Inc.; **419** KS Studios; **420** (tl)Hemera Technologies, Inc., (tc)Michael Fogden/Animals Animals, (tr)Tim Flach/Stone/Getty Images, (b)R. Rotolo/Liaison Agency; **422** John Cancalosi/DRK Photo; **424** (tl tr)Runk/Schoenberger from Grant Heilman, (b)Tom McHugh/Photo Researchers; **426–427** Theo Allofs/CORBIS; **428** Michael Habicht/Animals Animals; **430** (l)Crown Studios, (r)KS Studios; **431** (l)Lynn Stone/Animals Animals, (r)Arthur R. Hill/Visuals Unlimited; **433** (l)Zefa Germany/The Stock Market/CORBIS, (r)Sid & Shirley Rucker/DRK Photo; **434** (l)Kennan Ward/CORBIS, (t to b)Wayne Lankinen/DRK Photo, Ron Spomer/Visuals Unlimited, M. Philip Kahl/Gallo Images/CORBIS, Rod Planck/Photo Researchers, (bkgd)Steve Maslowski; **436** Stephen J. Krasemann/DRK Photo; **437** (t)Gerard Lacz/Animals Animals, (bl)Tom Brakefield/DRK Photo, (br)John David Fleck/Liaison Agency/Getty Images; **438** Bob Gurr/DRK Photo; **439** Amos Nachoum/The Stock Market/CORBIS; **440** (t)Jean-Paul Ferrero/AUSCAPE, (bl)Phyllis Greenberg/Animals Animals, (br)John Cancalosi/DRK Photo; **441** (t)Carolina Biological Supply/PhotoTake, NYC, (b)Doug Perine/DRK Photo; **442** (t to b)Stephen J. Krasemann/DRK Photo, David Northcott/DRK Photo, Zig Leszczynski/Animals Animals, Ralph Reinhold/Animals Animals, Anup Shah/Animals Animals, Mickey Gibson/Animals Animals; **443** (t to b)Fred Felleman/Stone/Getty Images, Robert Maier/Animals Animals, Tom Bledsoe/DRK Photo, Wayne Lynch/DRK Photo, Joe McDonald/Animals Animals, Kim Heacox/DRK Photo; **446** (t)David Welling/Animals Animals, (b)Wayne Lankinen/DRK Photo; **447** (t)Richard Day/Animals Animals, (b)Maslowski Photo; **448** (tr)Mark Burnett, (bl)Jeff Fott/DRK Photo, (br)Joe McDonald/Animals Animals; **449** (l r)Tom & Pat Leeson/DRK Photo, (b)Tom Brakefield/DRK Photo; **450** Hans & Judy Beste/Animals Animals; **452** Bob Gurr/DRK Photo; **453** (l)Crown Studios, (r)KS Studios; **454–455** D. Robert & Lorri Franz/CORBIS; **456** (l)Michel Denis-Huot/Jacana/Photo Researchers, (r)Zig Lesczynski/Animals Animals; **457** (l)Jack Ballard/Visuals Unlimited, (c)Anthony Mercieca/Photo Researchers, (r)Joe McDonald/Visuals Unlimited; **458** (t)Stephen J. Krasemann/Peter Arnold, Inc., (b)Leonard Lee Rue/Photo Researchers; **459** (t)The Zoological Society of San Diego, (b)Margret Miller/Photo Researchers; **462** Michael Fairchild/Peter Arnold, Inc.; **463** (t)Bill Bachman/Photo Researchers, (b)Fateh Singh Rathore/Peter Arnold, Inc.; **464** Jim Brandenburg/Minden Pictures; **465** Michael Dick/Animals Animals; **466** (l)Richard Thorn/Visuals Unlimited, (c)Arthur Morris/Visuals Unlimited, (r)Jacana/Photo

Researchers; **467** (starfish)Peter J. Herring, (krill)T. Frank/Harbor Branch Oceanographic Institution, (others) Edith Widder/Harbor Branch Oceanographic Institution; **468** Stephen Dalton/Animals Animals; **469** Richard Packwood/Animals Animals; **470** Ken Lucas/Visuals Unlimited; **472** (t)The Zoological Society of San Diego, (b)Gary Carter/Visuals Unlimited; **473** Dave B. Fleetham/Tom Stack & Assoc.; **474** (t)Walter Smith/CORBIS, (b)Bios (Klein/Hubert)/Peter Arnold, Inc.; **475** (l)Valerie Giles/Photo Researchers, (r)J & B Photographers/Animals Animals; **476** not available; **478** Jim Brandenburg/Minden Pictures; **479** PhotoDisc; **480–481** Birgid Allig/Stone/Getty Images; **481** (inset)Don Mason/The Stock Market/CORBIS; **482–483** Charles O' Rear/CORBIS; **483** Matt Meadows; **484** John Serro/Visuals Unlimited; **488** Geoff Butler; **489** Photo Researchers; **490** Digital Stock; **491** Aaron Haupt; **492** M. McCarron, (t)C Squared Studios/PhotoDisc; **493** (l)Breck P. Kent, (c)Runk/Schoenberger from Grant Heilman, (r)PhotoTake, NYC/Carolina Biological Supply Company; **497** (tl)Clyde H. Smith/Peter Arnold, Inc., (tcl)Erik Sampers/Photo Researchers, (tcr)Dean Conger/CORBIS, (tr)Michael A. Keller/The Stock Market/CORBIS, (bl)Ed Bock/The Stock Market/CORBIS, (bcl)Joe McDonald/Visuals Unlimited, (bcr)Art Stein/Photo Researchers, (br)Peter Turnley/CORBIS; **499** Jim Grace/Photo Researchers; **500** Photo Researchers; **501** Mark Burnett; **504** Sara Davis/The Herald-Sun; **506** Breck P. Kent; **509** (l)Royalty-Free/CORBIS, (r)Jim Grace/Photo Researchers; **510–511** Meckes/Ottawa/Photo Researchers; **512 513 514** KS Studios; **515** (l)KS Studios, (r)Visuals Unlimited; **517** (cabbages, avocado) Artville, (liver)DK Images, (doctor)Michael W. Thomas, (girls)Digital Vision/PictureQuest, (Blood Cells, Blood Clot)David M. Philips/Visuals Unlimited, (others)Digital Stock; **518** Gary Kreyer from Grant Heilman; **519** Larry Stepanowicz/Visuals Unlimited; **520 521** KS Studios; **523** (l)KS Studios, (r)Tom McHugh/Photo Researchers; **525** Geoff Butler; **527** (l)Benjamin/Custom Medical Stock Photo, (r)Dr. K.F.R. Schiller/Photo Researchers; **528** Biophoto Associates/Photo Researchers; **530** KS Studios; **531** Matt Meadows; **532** Goldwater/Network/Saba Press Photos; **533 535** KS Studios; **537** (l)Jose Luis Pelaez, Inc./CORBIS, (r)Dean Berry/Index Stock Imagery; **538–539** Steve Allen/Getty Images; **540 543** Aaron Haupt; **545** Matt Meadows; **546** Martin M. Rotker; **547** (t)StudiOhio, (b)Matt Meadows; **549** First Image; **551** National Cancer Institute/Science Photo Library/Photo Researchers; **555** Meckes/Ottawa/Photo Researchers; **557** Aaron Haupt; **558** (t)Matt Meadows/Peter Arnold, Inc., (b)Matt Meadows; **560** no credit; **561** (l)Manfred Kage/Peter Arnold, Inc., (r)K.G. Murti/Visuals Unlimited; **566–567** The Image Bank/Getty Images; **568** Randy Lincks/CORBIS; **569** Dominic Oldershaw; **570** Bob Daemmrich; **573** Richard T. Nowitz; **575** (l c)SIU/Photo Researchers, (r)Geoff Butler; **576** Renee Lynn/Photo Researchers; **578** (l)Science Pictures Ltd./Science Photo Library/Photo Researchers, (r)SIU/Photo Researchers; **580** Paul Barton/The Stock Market/CORBIS; **581** (bkgd)Gunther/Explorer/Photo Researchers, (l r)Mark Burnett; **582** Richard Hutchings/Photo Researchers; **583** Biophoto Associates/Science Source/Photo Researchers; **584** (t)Larry Mulvehill/Photo Researchers, (b)Matt Meadows; **585** Matt Meadows; **587** (bkgd)Science Photo Library/CORBIS, (l)Ed Beck/The Stock Market/CORBIS, (t)Lane Medical Library, (tr)Gregg Ozzo/Visuals Unlimited, (b)Custom Medical Stock Photo, (br)Tom & DeeAnn McCarthy/The Stock Market/CORBIS;

592–593 John Terrance Turner/FPG/Getty Images; **594** KS Studios; **601** KS Studios; **602** Michael Newman/PhotoEdit, Inc.; **603** KS Studios; **607** Aaron Haupt; **611** Mark Burnett; **612** (t)Jeff Greenberg/PhotoEdit, Inc., (b)Amanita Pictures; **613** Amanita Pictures; **614** Toni Morrison; **615** (l)David R. Frazier/Photo Researchers, (r)Michael Brennan/CORBIS; **619** Eamonn McNulty/Science Photo Library/Photo Researchers; **620–621** Lawerence Manning/CORBIS; **621** John Evans; **622** David Young-Wolff/PhotoEdit, Inc.; **631** Ariel Skelley/The Stock Market/CORBIS; **633** David M. Phillips/ Photo Researchers; **634** (l)Tim Davis/Photo Researchers, (r)Chris Sorensen/The Stock Market/CORBIS; **635** Science Pictures Ltd/Science Photo Library/Photo Researchers; **636** Petit Format/Nestle/Science Source/Photo Researchers; **638** (l)Jeffery W. Myers/Stock Boston, (r)Ruth Dixon; **639** (tl b)Mark Burnett, (tr)Aaron Haupt; **640** KS Studios; **641** (l)NASA/Roger Ressmeyer/CORBIS, (r)AFP/CORBIS; **642** (t)Chris Carroll/CORBIS, (b)Richard Hutchings; **643** Matt Meadows; **644** (l)Ron Kimball Photography, (r)SuperStock, (b)Martin B. Withers/Frank Lane Picture Agency/CORBIS; **645** (l)Bob Daemmrich, (r)Maria Taglienti/The Image Bank/Getty Images; **650–651** S. Lowry/University of Ulster/Stone/Getty Images; **652** Dr. P. Marazzi/Science Photo Library/Photo Researchers; **653** (l)Michael A. Keller/The Stock Market/CORBIS, (r)Runk/ Schoenberger from Grant Heilman, (b)NIBSC/Science Photo Library/Photo Researchers; **656** CC Studio/Science Photo Library/Photo Researchers; **659** (t)Jack Bostrack/Visuals Unlimited, (cl)Cytographics Inc./Visuals Unlimited, (cr)Cabisco/Visuals Unlimited, (b)Visuals Unlimited; **660** MM/Michelle Del Guercio/Photo Researchers; **661** Holt Studios International/Nigel Cattlin/Photo Researchers; **662** (t)Oliver Meckes/Eye of Science/Photo Researchers, (b)Visuals Unlimited; **663** Oliver Meckes/Eye Of Science/ Gelderblom/Photo Researchers; **664** Mark Burnett; **666** (l)Caliendo/Custom Medical Stock Photo, (r)Amanita Pictures; **667** (t)Andrew Syred/Science Photo Library/Photo Researchers, (b)Custom Medical Stock Photo; **668** (l)Jan Stromme/Bruce Coleman, Inc., (c)Mug Shots/The Stock Market/CORBIS, (r)J.Chiasson-Liats/Liaison Agency/Getty Images; **670** KS Studios; **672** (t)Tim Courlas, (b)Matt Meadows; **673** Matt Meadows; **674** Layne Kennedy/CORBIS; **675** (l)Gelderblom/Eye of Science/Photo Researchers, (r)Garry T. Cole/BPS/Stone/Getty Images; **680–681** (bkgd)Jodi Jacobson, Andrew A. Wagner; **681** (inset)L. Fritz/H. Armstrong Roberts; **682–683** Joe McDonald/Visuals Unlimited; **684** (l)Adam Jones/Photo Researchers, (tr)Richard Kolar/Animals Animals, (c)Tom Van Sant/Geosphere Project, Santa Monica/Science Photo Library/Photo Researchers, (br)G. Carleton Ray/Photo Researchers; **685** (t)John W. Bova/Photo Researchers, (b)David Young/Tom Stack & Assoc.; **687** (l)Zig Leszczynski/Animals Animals, (r)Gary W. Carter/ Visuals Unlimited; **690** Mitsuaki Iwago/Minden Pictures; **691** Joel Sartore from Grant Heilman; **693** (t)Norm Thomas/ Photo Researchers, (b)Maresa Pryor/Earth Scenes; **694** (r)Bud Neilson/Words & Pictures/PictureQuest, (others)Wyman P. Meinzer; **696** (l)Michael Abbey/Photo Researchers, (r)OSF/ Animals Animals, (b)Michael P. Gadomski/Photo Researchers; **697** (tcr)Lynn M. Stone, (bl)Larry Kimball/Visuals Unlimited, (bcl)George D. Lepp/Photo Researchers, (bcr)Stephen J. Krasemann/Peter Arnold, Inc., (br)Mark Steinmetz, (others) William J. Weber; **698** (t)Milton Rand/Tom Stack & Assoc., (c)Marian Bacon/Animals Animals, (b)Sinclair Stammers/ Science Photo Library/Photo Researchers; **699** (tl)Raymond A.

Mendez/Animals Animals, (bl)Donald Specker/Animals Animals, (br)Joe McDonald/Animals Animals; **700** Ted Levin/ Animals Animals; **701** Richard L. Carlton/Photo Researchers; **702** (t)Jean Claude Revy/PhotoTake, NYC, (b)OSF/Animals Animals; **703** Runk/Schoenberger from Grant Heilman; **704** Eric Larravadieu/Stone/Getty Images; **705** (l)C.K. Lorenz/ Photo Researchers, (r)Hans Pfletschinger/Peter Arnold, Inc.; **706** CORBIS; **708** (l)Michael P. Gadomski/Photo Researchers, (r)William J. Weber; **710–711** Ron Thomas/Getty Images; **712** Kenneth Murray/Photo Researchers; **713** (t)Jerry L. Ferrara/Photo Researchers, (b)Art Wolfe/Photo Researchers; **714** (t)Telegraph Colour Library/FPG/Getty Images, (b)Hal Beral/Visuals Unlimited; **715** (l)Fritz Polking/Visuals Unlimited, (r)R. Arndt/Visuals Unlimited; **716** Tom Uhlman/ Visuals Unlimited; **720** Jim Grattan; **723** (l)Runk/ Schoenberger from Grant Heilman, (r)Rob & Ann Simpson/ Visuals Unlimited, Runk/Schoenberger from Grant Heilman; **726** WHOI/Visuals Unlimited; **730** Gerald and Buff Corsi/ Visuals Unlimited; **731** Jeff J. Daly/Visuals Unlimited; **732** Gordon Wiltsie/Peter Arnold, Inc.; **733** (l)Soames Summerhay/Photo Researchers, (r)Tom Uhlman/Visuals Unlimited; **738–739** William Campbell/CORBIS Sygma; **740** Jeff Greenberg/Visuals Unlimited; **741** Larry Ulrich/DRK Photo; **742** (bkgd)Craig Fujii/Seattle Times, (l)Kevin R. Morris/CORBIS, (tr br)Jeff Henry; **743** Rod Planck/Photo Researchers; **745** (t)Steve McCutcheon/Visuals Unlimited, (bl)Pat O'Hara/DRK Photo, (br)Erwin & Peggy Bauer/Tom Stack & Assoc.; **746** (tl)Peter Ziminski/Visuals Unlimited, (c)Leonard Rue III/Visuals Unlimited, (bl)C.C. Lockwood/ DRK Photo, (br)Larry Ulrich/DRK Photo; **747** (t)Fritz Polking/Visuals Unlimited, (b)William Grenfell/Visuals Unlimited; **748** Lynn M. Stone/DRK Photo; **750** (l) McDonald Wildlife Photography, Inc./DRK Photo, (r)Steve Solum/Bruce Coleman, Inc.; **751** Kevin Schafer; **753** W. Banaszewski/Visuals Unlimited; **754** (l)Dwight Kuhn, (r)Mark E. Gibson/Visuals Unlimited; **755** James R. Fisher/DRK Photo; **756** D. Foster/ WHOI/Visuals Unlimited; **757** (l)C.C. Lockwood/Bruce Coleman, Inc., (r)Steve Wolper/DRK Photo; **758** (tl)Dwight Kuhn, (tr)Glenn Oliver/Visuals Unlimited, (b)Stephen J. Krasemann/DRK Photo; **759** (l)John Kaprielian/Photo Researchers, (r)Jerry Sarapochiello/Bruce Coleman, Inc.; **760** (t)Dwight Kuhn, (b)John Gerlach/DRK Photo; **761** Fritz Polking/Bruce Coleman, Inc.; **762** courtesy Albuquerque Public Schools; **763** (l)James P. Rowan/DRK Photo, (r)John Shaw/Tom Stack & Assoc.; **767** (l)Leonard Rue III/Visuals Unlimited, (r)Joe McDonald/DRK Photo; **768–769** Grant Heilman Photography; **770** (l)Keith Lanpher/Liaison Agency/Getty Images, (r)Richard Thatcher/David R. Frazier Photolibrary; **771** (t)Solar Cookers International, (bl)Brian F. Peterson/The Stock Market/CORBIS, (br)Ron Kimball Photography; **772** Larry Mayer/Liaison Agency/Getty Images; **775** (tr)Torleif Svenson/The Stock Market/CORBIS, (bl)Rob Williamson, (br)Les Gibbon/Cordaiy Photo Library Ltd./CORBIS; **776** Sean Justice; **777** (t)Lowell Georgia/Science Source/Photo Researchers, (cl)NASA, (c)CORBIS, (cr)Sean Sprague/Impact Visuals/PictureQuest, (bl)Lee Foster/Bruce Coleman, Inc., (br)Robert Perron; **778** Philippe Renault/Liaison Agency/Getty Images; **779** (l)NYC Parks Photo Archive/Fundamental Photographs, (r)Kristen Brochmann/Fundamental Photographs; **783** (l)Jeremy Walker/Science Photo Library/Photo Researchers, (c)John Colwell from Grant Heilman, (r)Telegraph Colour Library/FPG/Getty Images; **784** Wilford Haven/Liaison Agency/Getty Images; **785** (tl)Larry Mayer/

PERIODIC TABLE OF THE ELEMENTS

Columns of elements are called groups. Elements in the same group have similar chemical properties.

Gas
Liquid
Solid
Synthetic

Element —— Hydrogen
Atomic number —— 1
Symbol —— H
Atomic mass —— 1.008

State of matter

The first three symbols tell you the state of matter of the element at room temperature. The fourth symbol identifies elements that are not present in significant amounts on Earth. Useful amounts are made synthetically.

1	2	3	4	5	6	7	8	9
1 Hydrogen 1 H 1.008								
2 Lithium 3 Li 6.941	Beryllium 4 Be 9.012							
3 Sodium 11 Na 22.990	Magnesium 12 Mg 24.305							
4 Potassium 19 K 39.098	Calcium 20 Ca 40.078	Scandium 21 Sc 44.956	Titanium 22 Ti 47.867	Vanadium 23 V 50.942	Chromium 24 Cr 51.996	Manganese 25 Mn 54.938	Iron 26 Fe 55.845	Cobalt 27 Co 58.933
5 Rubidium 37 Rb 85.468	Strontium 38 Sr 87.62	Yttrium 39 Y 88.906	Zirconium 40 Zr 91.224	Niobium 41 Nb 92.906	Molybdenum 42 Mo 95.94	Technetium 43 Tc (98)	Ruthenium 44 Ru 101.07	Rhodium 45 Rh 102.906
6 Cesium 55 Cs 132.905	Barium 56 Ba 137.327	Lanthanum 57 La 138.906	Hafnium 72 Hf 178.49	Tantalum 73 Ta 180.948	Tungsten 74 W 183.84	Rhenium 75 Re 186.207	Osmium 76 Os 190.23	Iridium 77 Ir 192.217
7 Francium 87 Fr (223)	Radium 88 Ra (226)	Actinium 89 Ac (227)	Rutherfordium 104 Rf (261)	Dubnium 105 Db (262)	Seaborgium 106 Sg (266)	Bohrium 107 Bh (264)	Hassium 108 Hs (277)	Meitnerium 109 Mt (268)

The number in parentheses is the mass number of the longest-lived isotope for that element.

Rows of elements are called periods. Atomic number increases across a period.

The arrow shows where these elements would fit into the periodic table. They are moved to the bottom of the table to save space.

Lanthanide series

Cerium 58 Ce 140.116	Praseodymium 59 Pr 140.908	Neodymium 60 Nd 144.24	Promethium 61 Pm (145)	Samarium 62 Sm 150.36

Actinide series

Thorium 90 Th 232.038	Protactinium 91 Pa 231.036	Uranium 92 U 238.029	Neptunium 93 Np (237)	Plutonium 94 Pu (244)